Atomic Mass Values

Name of element	*Symbol*	*Atomic mass*
Actinium	Ac	(227)
Aluminum	Al	26.9815
Americium	Am	(243)
Antimony	Sb	121.75
Argon	Ar	39.948
Arsenic	As	74.9216
Astatine	At	(210)
Barium	Ba	137.34
Berkelium	Bk	(247)
Beryllium	Be	9.0122
Bismuth	Bi	208.980
Boron	B	10.811
Bromine	Br	79.904
Cadmium	Cd	112.40
Calcium	Ca	40.08
Californium	Cf	(254)
Carbon	C	12.01115
Cerium	Ce	140.12
Cesium	Cs	132.905
Chlorine	Cl	35.453
Chromium	Cr	51.996
Cobalt	Co	58.9332
Copper	Cu	63.546
Curium	Cm	(247)
Dysprosium	Dy	162.50
Einsteinium	Es	(254)
Erbium	Er	167.26
Europium	Eu	151.96
Fermium	Fm	(257)
Fluorine	F	18.9984
Francium	Fr	(223)
Gadolinium	Gd	157.25
Gallium	Ga	69.72
Germanium	Ge	72.59
Gold	Au	196.967
Hafnium	Hf	178.49
Helium	He	4.0026
Holmium	Ho	164.930
Hydrogen	H	1.00797
Indium	In	114.82
Iodine	I	126.9044
Iridium	Ir	192.2
Iron	Fe	55.847
Krypton	Kr	83.80
Kurchatovium[*]	Ku	
Lanthanum	La	138.91
Lawrencium	Lr	(257)
Lead	Pb	207.19
Lithium	Li	6.939
Lutetium	Lu	174.97
Magnesium	Mg	24.312
Manganese	Mn	54.9380
Mendelevium	Md	(256)
Mercury	Hg	200.59
Molybdenum	Mo	95.94
Neodymium	Nd	144.24
Neon	Ne	20.183
Neptunium	Np	(237)
Nickel	Ni	58.71
Niobium	Nb	92.906
Nitrogen	N	14.0067
Nobelium	No	(254)
Osmium	Os	190.2
Oxygen	O	15.9994
Palladium	Pd	106.4[1]
Phosphorus	P	30.9738
Platinum	Pt	195.09
Plutonium	Pu	(244)
Polonium	Po	(209)
Potassium	K	39.102
Praseodymium	Pr	140.907
Promethium	Pm	(145)
Protactinium	Pa	(231)
Radium	Ra	(226)
Radon	Rn	(222)
Rhenium	Re	186.2
Rhodium	Rh	102.905
Rubidium	Rb	85.47
Ruthenium	Ru	101.07
Samarium	Sm	150.35
Scandium	Sc	44.956
Selenium	Se	78.96
Silicon	Si	28.086
Silver	Ag	107.868
Sodium	Na	22.9898
Strontium	Sr	87.62
Sulfur	S	32.064
Tantalum	Ta	180.948
Technetium	Tc	(97)
Tellurium	Te	127.60
Terbium	Tb	158.924
Thallium	Tl	204.37
Thorium	Th	232.038
Thulium	Tm	168.934
Tin	Sn	118.69
Titanium	Ti	47.90
Tungsten	W	183.85
Uranium	U	238.03
Vanadium	V	50.942
Xenon	Xe	131.30
Ytterbium	Yb	173.04
Yttriu	Y	88.905
Zinc		65.37
Zirc		91.22

All known elements are included in the list. The value in parentheses in the atomic mass column is, in each case, the mass of the most stable isotope, based on O = 16.000. All other atomic masses are based on C = 12.000.

[*] This na … e name proposed i …

TEACHER'S GUIDE FOR

CHEMISTRY

Patterns and Properties

TEACHER'S GUIDE FOR

CHEMISTRY

Patterns and Properties

Charles L. Bickel

John C. Hogg

W. Thomas Lippincott

Margaret Nicholson

AMERICAN BOOK COMPANY

THE AUTHORS

Charles L. Bickel. Authority on the Physical Sciences, Dr. Bickel is presently Harlan Page Amen Professor at the Phillips Exeter Academy. Former chairman of the Science Department at Phillips Exeter, he has been on the faculties of Lafayette College and Harvard University and is the author of numerous articles in the *Journal of the American Chemical Society* and about 30 science textbooks.

John Clarence Hogg. Scientist and Specialist in Science Education, is presently Harlan Page Amen Professor Emeritus of Phillips Exeter Academy. Professor Hogg has been chairman of the Science Department at Phillips Exeter, Professor of Chemistry at the University of St. John's in Newfoundland, and principal of the United Church College at St. John's. He is an alumnus of Cambridge and Harvard Universities and holder of the Military Cross of Britain.

William T. Lippincott. Expert on Chemical Education, Dr. Lippincott is presently Professor of Chemistry and Head of the Division of General Chemistry at The Ohio State University, Columbus. He is also Editor of The Journal of Chemical Education, and has served the cause of chemical education in many other capacities. Dr. Lippincott is the coauthor of various chemistry textbooks, a member of many scientific and social organizations, and recipient of numerous honors, including the Distinguished Teaching Award of the College of Arts and Sciences of The Ohio State University.

Margaret Nicholson. Expert on Modern Chemistry Curriculum, Miss Nicholson is currently the Chairman of the Science Department of Acalanes High School, Lafayette, California. Because of a long-standing interest in chemical education, she has served on the staff of the CHEMStudy Institute and is an associate editor of the original CHEMStudy text. Miss Nicholson is a member of many distinguished societies and a recipient of the Manufacturing Chemists Association Outstanding Teacher Award.

AMERICAN BOOK COMPANY

New York Cincinnati Atlanta Dallas Millbrae

Published simultaneously in Canada by Van Nostrand Reinhold, Ltd.

1 3 5 7 9 11 13 14 12 10 8 6 4 2

PREFACE

As you look through this Teacher's Edition of *Chemistry: Patterns and Processes*, you are probably anticipating the interests, needs and abilities of each new group of chemistry students. Usually, teachers must adapt the science program to their own situation. Chemistry classes present varying needs because of differing student and teacher capabilities and variations in laboratory facilities and equipment. For these reasons, a suggested time schedule for teaching the units and chapters in the textbook has been omitted. However, other aids that have proved most effective in the authors' teaching experiences have been included.

This Guide provides the following teaching aids for the basic textbook.

1. Overview and introduction for each unit
2. Lesson plan the topic headings in each chapter
3. Learning objectives for each basis for lesson planning and the lesson or topic heading.
4. Suggested teacher commentary. This commentary indicates the emphasis intended by the authors; there are also suggestions for enriching the students' learning experiences.
5. Demonstrations. Demonstrations are provided with a listing of the materials needed to perform the demonstration. Some types of experiments are better performed as demonstrations than as student laboratory work. This is generally true of experiments that do not involve measurements, as in the preparation of gases such as hydrogen or carbon dioxide. Classroom, demonstration also serve another purpose: they help the teacher to teach and the student to observe.

   In general, before a demonstration is performed, there should be some discussion of the underlying principles and the students should at least answer the questions. What do you expect will happen? Why do you expect this to happen? The demonstration should be performed slowly and deliberately so that there is time to observe and comment upon the various phrases as they unfold. When the demonstration is finished, there should be a recapitulation and further questioning. Were there any unexpected happenings? How can the unexpected happenings be accounted for?

6. Answers to questions and exercises at the ends of chapters.
7. Additional questions and problems. These supplementary problems are included for individualizing instruction in the classroom. Some students may need backup or extra work in certain areas of the basic course. The teacher can choose those problems for students who need review and reinforcement.
8. Books, films, filmstrips, and overhead transparencies listed for each unit. Recent books, periodicals, and visual aids are listed at the end of guide for teachers and students who wish to explore certain topics in greater detail.

CONTENTS

TEACHER'S GUIDE FOR

CHEMISTRY

Patterns and Properties

CHAPTER 1

WHAT IS CHEMISTRY?

HENRY CAVENDISH (1731-1810)
(pp. 2-5)

Learning Objectives

1. To name the gas Cavendish obtained by dropping metals into acids.
2. To state the percentage of oxygen Cavendish found in air.
3. To describe the experiments in which Cavendish showed water to be a compound of hydrogen and oxygen.
4. To state the proportions of hydrogen and oxygen in water as determined by Cavendish.
5. To state the difference between a compound and an element in terms of their decomposability.
6. To state the difference between a compound and a mixture in terms of their decomposability.
7. To state the quantitative results of the experiment in which Cavendish combined nitrogen with oxygen.

Suggested Teacher Commentary

This historically oriented section acquaints, or re-acquaints, the students with some elementary physical science. A given class may or may not be well-grounded in this material.

The discovery by Cavendish of argon is a typical example of the way scientific knowledge in a given area gets started. Cavendish was the first scientist to observe that about one percent of air was chemically inactive, but this inactive residue was not definitely recognized as a new element (or rather as a mixture of new elements) for many years, for about 100 years in fact.

THE DISCOVERY OF HELIUM
(pp. 6-8)

Learning Objectives

1. To state the source of the first observed spectral lines of helium.
2. To state the qualitative results of Hillebrand's study of uraninites.
3. To state the difference in density between chemical and atmospheric nitrogen as determined by Rayleigh.
4. To state Rayleigh's tentative hypothesis to explain the results of his experiment.
5. To describe the various steps in the Ramsay-Rayleigh experiment.
6. To state the results of the Ramsay-Rayleigh experiment.
7. To describe the chemical activity of argon.

Suggested Teacher Commentary

A significant milestone on the way to this discovery was Rayleigh's experiment in which he found that the density of atmospheric nitrogen is a little bit greater than the density of chemical nitrogen. This experiment led him to suspect that atmospheric nitrogen is not pure nitrogen. Class demonstrations on the preparation of atmospheric and pure nitrogen will inform students on the nature of Rayleigh's problem and, at the same time, review some chemical techniques such as the collection of gases by displacing water.

Demonstration I To Prepare Nitrogen From Air

Materials recommended: copper gauze, combustion tube, rubber tubing, trough, collecting bottle, beehive shelf.

The first step in preparing atmospheric nitrogen is to remove oxygen from air. This can be done by passing air over hot copper and one way to do this is as follows: Wrap a clean piece of copper gauze into a tight roll and insert the roll into a combustion tube. Then assemble the apparatus as shown in Fig. 1–4. (It is assumed that a compressed air supply is available on the laboratory bench and that the apparatus can be connected with the air supply by a piece of rubber tubing.) Strongly heat the copper gauze and, when it is quite hot, turn the air cock slightly so that a slow stream of air flows through the combustion tube. The stopcock controlling the air flow should be adjusted until air bubbles escape through the water at a rate of only about two per second. When this has been done (and not until), the inverted bottle of water in the trough should be lifted onto the beehive shelf. A gas is now collected by displacing water and presumably this gas is nitrogen. There is no specific chemical test for nitrogen but at least we know that, unlike air, it will not support combustion. When all the water in the bottle is displaced, lift the bottle off the shelf and immediately plunge a lighted match into it. Notice that the flame is immediately extinguished. This is convincing proof that the gas is not air and is reasonable evidence that the gas in the bottle is nitrogen. Notice also that the bright red gauze is now covered with a black deposit of copper oxide. Thus the reaction is

$$2Cu + O_2 \rightarrow 2CuO$$

In this experiment the copper has merely removed the oxygen from air. Although we call the gas atmospheric nitrogen we must remember that it contains a trace of carbon dioxide originally present in air. Clearly all traces of carbon dioxide would have to be removed if we wished to find the density of atmospheric nitrogen. This could be done by passing the gas through a solution of potassium hydroxide before it entered the combustion tube, which is precisely what Rayleigh did. The reaction is

$$2KOH + CO_2 \rightarrow K_2CO_3 + H_2O.$$

A gas picks up moisture if it is bubbled through water or through a water solution. Rayleigh dried the atmospheric nitrogen by passing it over a drying agent such as anhydrous calcium chloride ($CaCl_2$) or phosphoric oxide (P_4O_{10}).

Demonstration II To Prepare Pure Nitrogen

Materials recommended: 500-ml flask, rubber tubing, trough, collecting bottle, beehive shelf, ammonium chloride, sodium nitrite.

Pure nitrogen can also be prepared as a class demonstration. As is stated in the text, pure nitrogen can be obtained from the compound ammonium nitrite (NH_4NO_2). However, ammonium nitrite is a very unstable compound and cannot be stored in a bottle as is the case with ordinary reagents. So in practice two substances are selected which will interact and produce the unstable NH_4NO_2. These substances are ammonium chloride (NH_4Cl) and sodium nitrite ($NaNO_2$). When solutions of these salts are mixed and slightly warmed, they react to form NH_4NO_2.

$$NH_4Cl + NaNO_2 \rightarrow NH_4NO_2 + NaCl$$

The NH_4NO_2 decomposes as soon as it is formed to yield pure nitrogen.

$$NH_4NO_2 \rightarrow N_2 + 2H_2O$$

To prepare pure nitrogen as a class demonstration proceed as follows: Place a mixture of about 15 g of sodium nitrite and 10 g of ammonium chloride in a flask. Pour about 100 ml of water into the flask and stir until the salts have dissolved. Then arrange the apparatus as shown in Fig. TG1–1. Heat the flask *very* gently and collect the nitrogen by displacing water in the bottle. When all the water is displaced, show that the collected gas will extinguish a flame. *Precaution:* Gentle heating is a necessary precaution. If the temperature of the mixture gets too high, nitrogen is

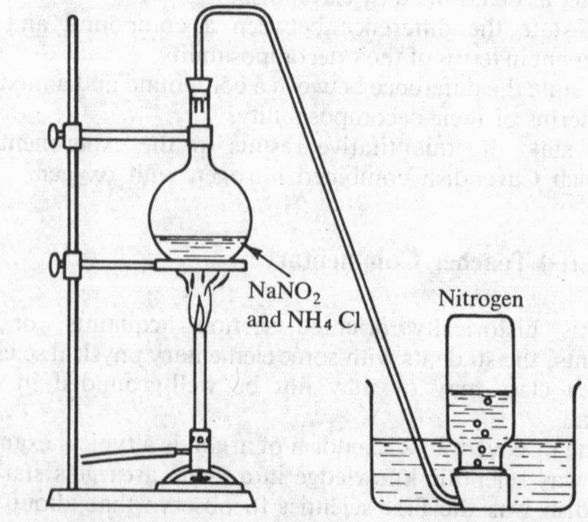

FIG. TG1–1.

evolved very rapidly and the reaction may be out of hand. Indeed, it is advisable to have a pan of cold water available so that, if necessary, the flask can be immersed in the cold water and the rate of reaction slowed down.

RAMSAY'S DISCOVERY OF THE INERT ELEMENTS (pp. 9-15)

Learning Objectives

1. To describe the sequence of steps in Ramsay's method for separating the constituents of air.
2. To name the members of the noble gas family.
3. To describe the chemical activity of the noble gases.
4. To state how the relatively high chemical activity of fluorine might apply to xenon-fluorine compounds.
5. To list some of the uses of the noble gases.
6. To list the various steps that led to the discovery of the noble gases — from Cavendish's early observation to Ramsay's final identification.

Suggested Teacher Commentary

One could point out to the class how often it is the very small anomalous result from an experiment that leads to the big discovery. Cavendish's inexplicable residue was only one part in 120. Another factor that might be pointed out is that many discoveries must await the development of new instrumentation, such as the spectroscope in the case of the inert gases. Finally, there must always be curious scientists to follow up the inconclusive results of earlier research.

Answers to Questions and Exercises

Text page references are provided for those questions which do not require computations. The student's answers will be individually stated, but should focus on the concepts developed in these text pages.

Factual Recall

1. 8–9
2. The two favorable properties of helium are (1) it is lighter than air and therefore buoyant, and (2) it is not flammable. Actually, hydrogen has a greater lifting power than helium but it is highly flammable. The densities of the three gases in g/l are:

   Air = 1.293; helium = 0.177; hydrogen = 0.090.

$$\frac{\text{Buoyancy of helium}}{\text{Buoyancy of hydrogen}} = \frac{(1.293 - 0.177)\text{ g/l}}{(1.293 - 0.090)\text{ g/l}} = \frac{1.116\text{ g/l}}{1.203\text{ g/l}} = 0.93$$

   That is, the lifting power of helium is 93 percent as much as the lifting power of hydrogen.

3. 3–4, Fig. 1-2
4. 4–5, Fig. 1-3(*a*)
5. 5
6. 5, 8–10
7. 6–7
8. 10
9. 7–8
10. 7–8
11. 8
12. 9–10
13. 10–12
14. 15

Apply Your Knowledge!

1. 5
2. 4–5
3. 14–15

UNIT I

ATOMS AND THEIR STRUCTURE

OPENING UNIT I

Leucippus (c. 450 B.C.) and his student Democritus (c. 470-380 B.C.) are usually credited with the development of the idea that matter could not be subdivided indefinitely. Somewhere this process must end with a smallest possible particle. Democritus called these particles *atomos* and believed that their sizes and shapes and mixtures accounted for the material properties observable in his time. However, the idea that matter could *not* be divided indefinitely sounded as silly to their contemporaries and successors as quantum jumps sounded to many scientists of Planck's time. Indeed, the whole idea might have perished had it not been immortalized by the writings of Epicurus, (c. 342–270 B.C.) and by the famous *De Rerum Natura*, by Lucretius (c. 95–55 B.C.)

However, it is Dalton's quantitative atomic theory that has the most significance for modern chemistry, and it may be said to be the real ancestor of the modern atomic theories to be discussed in the next four chapters.

CHAPTER 2

ORGANIZING PRINCIPLES

A SEARCH FOR AN EXPLANATION OF MATTER (pp. 23-25)

Learning Objectives

1. To define the term *reactant*.
2. To define the term *product*.
3. To state Lavoisier's law of conservation of mass.
4. To describe the experiment shown in Fig. 2-2 that demonstrates the law of conservation of mass.
5. To state the percentages of oxygen and copper in copper (II) oxide.
6. To state Proust's law of constant proportions.

Suggested Teacher Commentary

The law of conservation of mass, discovered by Lavoisier in 1789, is probably the most basic law in chemistry. At least it marked the beginning of chemistry as a quantitative science, and even today the whole theory of quantitative analysis is based upon its validity. The law has been tested many times by experiments, particularly as more sensitive weighing devices have become available, but no exception to the law has ever been found. The law can be demonstrated by using the apparatus and chemicals as shown in Fig. 2–2 of the text. In this reaction the reactants are in solution and since no gas is evolved in the reaction only the simplest kind of equipment is needed.

Demonstration I To Verify the Law of Conservation of Mass

Materials recommended: 125-ml Erlenmeyer flask, 75-mm test tube, rubber stopper, thread, balance, silver nitrate solution, dilute hydrochloric acid.

Pour about 25 ml of a solution of silver nitrate into an Erlenmeyer flask. Attach a piece of cotton thread to a small test tube and then almost fill the tube with dilute hydrochloric acid. Lower the tube into the flask and hold it in place by a rubber stopper which prevents the thread from slipping. Weigh the flask and contents on a chemical balance. Lift the flask from the pan of the balance but leave the balancing weights on the other pan. Then tilt the flask so that some of the acid mixes with the silver nitrate solution. As soon as the solutions mix a white precipitate is formed which shows that the substances have reacted chemically. Replace the flask on the pan of the balance to prove that the total mass of the two reactants has not changed, or rather to prove that the mass of the reactants is the same as the mass of the products.

Actually, the white precipitate is due to the formation of silver chloride which is an insoluble substance. And the equation for the reaction is

$$AgNO_3 + HCl \rightarrow AgCl \downarrow + HNO_3$$

DALTON'S ATOMIC THEORY
(pp. 25-30)

Learning Objectives

1. To derive Dalton's atomic theory from the laws of conservation of mass and constant proportions.
2. To state the four major postulates of Dalton's atomic theory as outlined in the text.
3. To describe the physical properties of a Dalton atomic model.
4. Given that atoms of different elements combine in simple proportions to form compounds, to predict the law of multiple proportions.
5. To state the law of multiple proportions as verified by analysis of copper (I) oxide and copper (II) oxide.
6. To describe how atomic masses of elements can be estimated from their relative masses.
7. To name the isotope of the element that is currently used as the atomic mass standard.

Suggested Teacher Commentary

Although Dalton's concept of a spherical, indivisible atom is no longer tenable, it accomplished a great deal in its day. Dalton believed that a chemical reaction was due simply to a rearrangement of atoms, but that the atoms themselves remained intact. We now know that these ideas were quite wrong yet his atomic theory offered a satisfactory explanation of the known laws of conservation of mass and constant proportions. Indeed, it even predicted an unknown law — the law of multiple proportions. However, Dalton's most significant contribution to scientific knowledge concerned the relative masses of the atoms of elements. It is now generally conceded that the greatest achievement in chemistry and physics in the 19th century was the determination of the relative atomic masses of the elements.

Since hydrogen atoms are the lightest of all atoms, Dalton arbitrarily, and sensibly, assigned a value of unity (1.0000) to the relative mass of a hydrogen atom. On this scale the relative mass of an oxygen atom was 15.9000. However, when it was realized that there are far more compounds of oxygen than hydrogen it was logical to change the basis of comparison from hydrogen to oxygen. On the new scale the atomic mass of oxygen was fixed at 16.0000 and the atomic mass of hydrogen became 1.0080.

In the early part of the present century the mass spectrograph was invented and with this instrument the atomic masses of the elements can be found more accurately than by chemical analysis. The mass spectrograph showed that ordinary oxygen is a mixture of three isotopes of oxygen whose atomic masses are 16.0000, 17.0045 and 18.0049 respectively. It is true that atoms of oxygen-17 and oxygen-18 are relatively rare and account for only 0.25 percent of the atoms of ordinary oxygen. Nonetheless, since ordinary oxygen is a mixture of three isotopes (one of which has an atomic mass of 16.0000) its atomic mass ought to have a slightly higher value than 16.0000; in fact, it ought to be 16.0044. In other words, the atomic mass scale ought to be based upon the atomic mass of one of the isotopes of the element rather than upon a mixture of isotopes. This change has now been made. In 1961 the standard was changed from 16.0000 amu for oxygen to 12.0000 for the atomic mass of a specific isotope of carbon. (The isotopes of carbon and oxygen are discussed in Chapter 3 of the text.) However, if atomic masses are expressed to only 4 figures there is no significant difference between the oxygen 16.0000 scale and the carbon 12.0000 scale. For this reason the list of atomic masses in the Appendix is based upon the value of ordinary oxygen as 16.0000. The change in the standard of reference from hydrogen as 1.0000 to oxygen as 16.0000, and then to carbon as 12.0000 is yet another example of basic change made in response to the advancing front of knowledge.

SYMBOLS FOR ELEMENTS OR ATOMS
(pp. 30-31)

Learning Objectives

1. To write the letter symbols for hydrogen, oxygen, sulfur, nitrogen, carbon, calcium, chlorine, aluminum, magnesium, copper, iron, lead, silver, sodium, and potassium.

A CLASSIFICATION OF THE ELEMENTS
(pp. 31-36)

Learning Objectives

1. To define the term *row*.
2. To define the term *group*.
3. To state Mendeleev's Periodic Law.
4. To name the element discovered to fill the gap in Group IV.
5. To define the term *combining capacity*.
6. To state the numerical variation of combining capacity from group to group.
7. To write the formula for aluminum bromide, given the combining capacities of aluminum and bromine.
8. To name the two periodic "misfits" described in the text.

Suggested Teacher Commentary

Mendeleev's arrangement of the elements in order of their atomic masses led to a grouping of elements in chemical families and this in turn led Mendeleev to state that the properties of the elements are a periodic function of their atomic masses. This statement became known as the periodic law, and it turned out to be one of the most significant statements in scientific history, even though it was later proved to be false or, at best, only partly true.

In Mendeleev's time there were only 60 known elements and the empty spaces in the periodic table were rightly interpreted as indicating the positions of undiscovered elements. This conclusion led a number of chemists to search for the missing elements. The chemists were greatly aided in their work by the Mendeleev periodic table. From the known properties of elements in the same family, the properties of the undiscovered elements were largely predictable. That is, chemists knew what to look for and, equally important, they knew when all the natural elements had been discovered.

The misfits in the Mendeleev table were of great significance. Clearly the misfits proved that the periodic "law" of Mendeleev was not an immutable law like the law of conservation of mass. Indeed, some scientists began to doubt that properties of elements depended upon their atomic mass. And towards the end of the 19th century it was suggested that the recurring properties of elements in natural families might, in some way, be due to a common parentage in the structure of their atoms. Strangely enough, Mendeleev ridiculed this idea He maintained that the periodic law was the outcome of experimental research and was in no way connected with the unity of matter.

We now know that there *is* a common parentage. In 1912 a British scientist named Moseley discovered that the properties of elements are a periodic function of the number of protons in the nuclei of their atoms or, as we now say, a periodic function of their atomic number. If elements are arranged according to atomic number, there are no misfits in the periodic table. So again we have still another example of the changing front of scientific knowledge — from the misstated periodic law of Mendeleev in 1870 to the correctly stated periodic law of Moseley in 1912.

Finally, it should be stated that, as a scientist, Mendeleev was ahead of his time when he asserted that every gap in the table represented an undiscovered element. But he showed a lack of vision in failing to see a possible connection between properties of elements and the structure of their atoms. Indeed, he failed to grasp the significance of problems that he himself had raised when he arranged the elements in a periodic table.

Additional Questions and Problems

1. The group number and combining capacity of a few elements are given below:

Group Number	I	II	III	IV	V	VI	VII	VIII
Combining Capacity	1	2	3	4	3	2	1	0
	Li	Ca	Al	C	N	O	Br	

Write formulas for compounds made up of the elements: (*a*) Li and O (*b*) Al and O (*c*) C and O (*d*) Li and Br (*e*) Ca and Br (*f*) Al and Br (*g*) Li and N (*h*) Al and N (*i*) Ca and N

Answer

1. (*a*) Li_2O (*b*) Al_2O_3 (*c*) CO_2 (*d*) LiBr (*e*) $CaBr_2$ (*f*) $AlBr_3$ (*g*) Li_3N (*h*) AlN (*i*) Ca_3N_2

Answers to Questions and Exercises

Text page references are provided for those questions which do not require computations. The student's answers will be individually stated, but should focus on the concepts developed in these text pages.

Factual Recall

1. 24–25
2. 23
3. 25–28
4. 25
5. 29
6. 29–30
7. 32, 35
8. 33–37
9. 35

Apply Your Knowledge!

1. 24
2. 32
3. 34
4. 27–30
5. 30–31

CHAPTER 3

INSIDE THE ATOM

CATHODE RAYS
(pp. 40-45)

Learning Objectives

1. To list the major parts of a gas discharge tube.
2. To describe the operation of a gas discharge tube.
3. To define the term *cathode ray*.
4. To describe the results of Perrin's experiment on the interaction of cathode rays with magnetic fields.
5. To state the reasoning behind Perrin's conclusion that cathode rays are negative particles.
6. To list the major parts of Thomson's experimental apparatus.
7. To state the data Thomson obtained from his experiments.
8. To state the value of the charge-to-mass ratio of the particles as calculated by Thomson.
9. To state Thomson's deduction as to the source of the charged particles.
10. To list the parts of Millikan's oil-drop apparatus.
11. To describe the operation of Millikan's apparatus.
12. To write the equation for determining the electron charge.
13. To state the value and sign of the electron charge.
14. To write the equation for electron mass.
15. To state the value for the electron mass.

Suggested Teacher Commentary

We know that a spark jumps the gap of a spark plug in the ignition system of an automobile. But the terminals of the spark plug are very close together, and if the distance between them were increased to a centimeter or so the spark would not be able to jump the gap. Thus we conclude that air is a poor conductor and that is why most of it must be removed in a discharge tube when the length of the gap is almost a meter.

Demonstration I The Nature of the Charge on Cathode Ray Particles

Materials Recommended: 3 dry cells, horseshoe magnet, copper wire, switch, 2 one-hole rubber stoppers, 2 pencils with erasers.

The following demonstration will help students to understand the mysterious force that acts upon cathode ray particles. A flexible copper wire is connected to a switch and suspended from supports as shown in Fig. TG3–1a&b. The other terminal on the switch is connected to the negative terminal of a battery of three dry cells. Hold a U-shaped magnet so that it straddles the wire and then close the switch so that the current flows. Note the direction to which the wire moves. Clearly the flow of electrons and the magnetic field are at

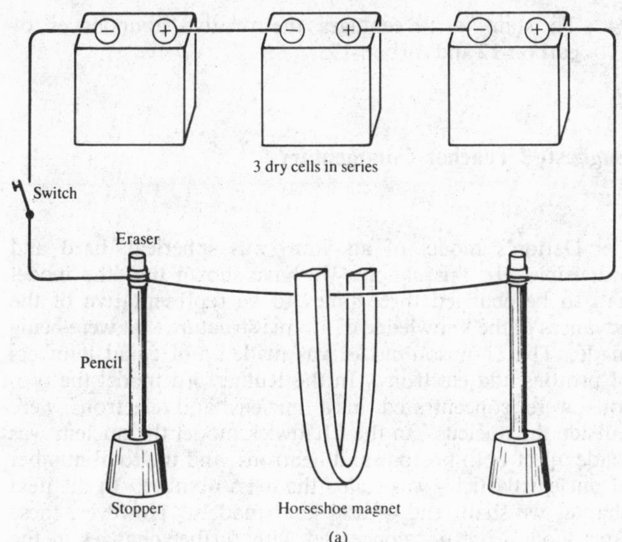

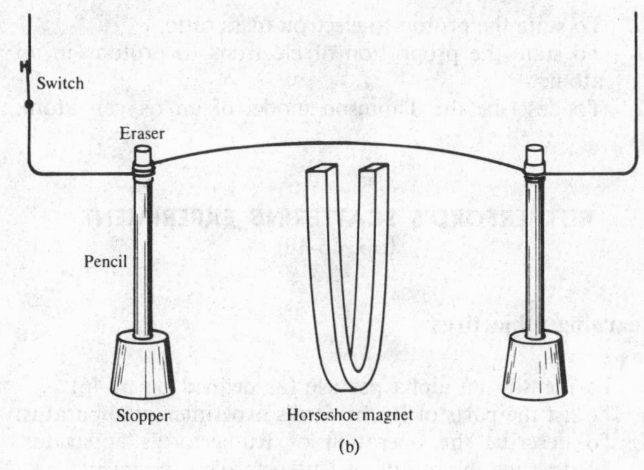

FIG. TG3–1

right angles to each other, and the two fields interact with each other to produce a mechanical force which is exerted on the electrons and causes the wire to move. The direction of this force is perpendicular to both the direction of the magnetic field and the moving electrons; that is, all three directions are at right angles to each other. The three directions can be illustrated by holding the thumb, forefinger and middle finger of the right hand mutually at right angles. If the forefinger points in the direction of the magnetic field, and the middle finger in the direction of the electron flow, the thumb points in the direction of the force as shown in Fig. TG3–2.

If we apply this rule to the way cathode rays are deflected in a magnetic field (as shown in Fig. 3–3 of the text), we must conclude that the cathode ray particles are subject to the same mechanical force and behave in exactly the same way as electrons moving in a wire. In other words, cathode rays are a stream of electrons.

Where do the cathode rays come from in Fig. 3–3 when the current is turned on? Some electrons escape from the cathode and ionize some of the air particles (atoms of oxygen and nitrogen) in the tube. The positive ions are then attracted to the cathode with such force that they knock electrons out of the atoms that make up the cathode. These released electrons then flow towards the positive electrode as a stream of cathode rays.

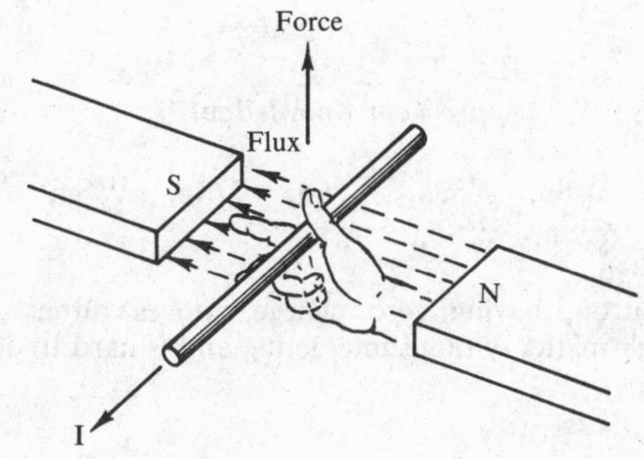

FIG. TG3–2

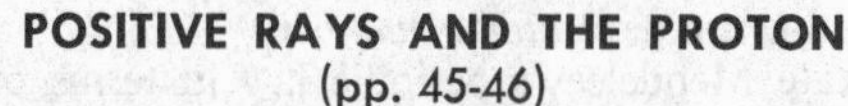

POSITIVE RAYS AND THE PROTON (pp. 45-46)

Learning Objectives

1. To list the parts of a positive-ray tube.
2. To describe how a positive-ray tube operates.
3. To state the physical nature of the positive rays.
4. To state the name given to an atom that has lost one or more electrons.
5. To state the charge sign on an ion that has lost electrons.
6. To write a symbolic equation for the ionization of hydrogen.
7. To state the reasoning that led to Thomson's assumption that positive hydrogen ions are constituents of all atoms.
8. To state the name given to a positive hydrogen ion.
9. To state the value for the mass of a proton.

10. To state the proton-to-electron mass ratio.
11. To state the proportion of electrons to protons in an atom.
12. To describe the Thomson model of an oxygen atom.

RUTHERFORD'S SCATTERING EXPERIMENT
(pp. 46-48)

Learning Objectives

1. To identify an alpha particle (as defined on p. 46).
2. To list the parts of Rutherford's experimental apparatus.
3. To describe the operation of Rutherford's apparatus.
4. To describe the results of Rutherford's experiment.
5. To write the equation that expresses Coulomb's law.
6. To describe a Rutherford atom.
7. To locate the relative positions of protons and electrons in a Rutherford atom.
8. To describe the distribution of mass in a Rutherford atom.

NEUTRONS
(pp. 49-55)

Learning Objectives

1. To state the mass and charge of a neutron.
2. To locate a neutron within an atom.
3. To define the term *mass number*.
4. To define the term *nuclear force*.
5. To define the term *atomic number*.
6. To state Mendeleev's periodic law in terms of atomic number.
7. To state the number of groups in the revised periodic table.
8. To locate the transition elements on the revised periodic table.
9. To list the parts of a mass spectrograph.
10. To describe the operation of a mass spectrograph.
11. To define the term *isotope* in terms of ratio of neutrons to protons and electrons.
12. To write the letter symbol for atomic number.
13. To write the symbols for carbon-12 and carbon-13, including mass and atomic numbers.
14. To state in percentages the relative abundances of carbon-12 and carbon-13.

Suggested Teacher Commentary

Dalton's model of an atom was spherical, hard and indivisible. In this chapter we have shown that the model had to be changed three times to be representative of the advances in the knowledge of atomic structure that were being made. The Thomson model was made up of equal numbers of protons and electrons. In the Rutherford model the protons were concentrated in a nucleus and electrons were outside the nucleus. In the Chadwick model the nucleus was made up of both protons and neutrons, and the total number of nuclear particles was called the mass number. In the next chapter we shall read of still later models. However, these later models are not concerned with further changes in the nucleus, but rather with the way electrons are arranged outside the nucleus.

Answers to Questions and Exercises

Text page references are provided for those questions which do not require computations. The student's answers will be individually stated, but should focus on the concepts developed in these text pages.

Factual Recall

1. 39, Fig. 3–1
2. 40–41
3. 41–42
4. 42–45
5. 45–46
6. 47–49
7. 48
8. 46, 49–50
9. 50
10. 50–51
11. 51

Apply Your Knowledge!

1. ${}^{112}_{50}Sn$, ${}^{114}_{50}Sn$, ${}^{115}_{50}Sn$, ${}^{116}_{50}Sn$, ${}^{117}_{50}Sn$, ${}^{118}_{50}Sn$, ${}^{119}_{50}Sn$, ${}^{120}_{50}Sn$, ${}^{122}_{50}Sn$, ${}^{124}_{50}Sn$,
2. 51, 54–56
3. A neutron, having zero charge, moves rather easily through matter without interacting and is hard to detect.

CHAPTER 4

A THEORY FOR THE ARRANGEMENT OF ELECTRONS IN ATOMS

A CONTINUOUS SPECTRUM
(pp. 59–60)

Learning Objectives

1. To describe the appearance of a continuous spectrum.
2. To describe the continuous spectrum in terms of the relative degree of refraction of the wavelengths that make up white light.

Demonstration I A Continuous Spectrum from an Incandescent Light Source

Materials Recommended: slide projector, black paper, prism, projection screen.

It is instructive to do a class demonstration that shows how white light can be split into a continuous spectrum. Proceed as follows: Cut a slit (about 1/16 inch wide) in a piece of black paper and then mount the paper in a projection lantern slide as shown in Fig. TG4–1. Darken the room and focus the projector so that a sharp image of the slit appears on a white screen in front of the projector. Place a prism of glass or plastic near the lens of the projector, and notice that a spectrum appears off to one side where the refracted light hits the wall of the room. Now move the screen until the spectrum falls upon it and observe that the spectrum colors change gradually from deep red to orange to yellow to green to blue to violet.

LINE SPECTRA
(pp. 60–62)

Learning Objectives

1. To describe the appearance of a line spectrum.
2. To state the luminous source of a line spectrum.
3. To list the parts of a spectroscope.

Demonstration II Line Spectra from Flame Tests

Materials Recommended: platinum wire, sodium chloride solution, strontium salt solution, Bunsen burner, spectroscope.

Hold a platinum wire in a Bunsen flame until it becomes white hot; that is, until it emits white light. Now look at the white-hot wire through a spectroscope and notice that a continuous spectrum is formed.

Dip the platinum wire into a solution of common salt and again hold the wire in the flame. The whole flame is now colored yellow. The yellow flame is characteristic of vaporized atoms of sodium. Now observe the flame through a spectroscope and all you now see is a single yellow line as shown in Fig. 4–2 of the text. This is the bright line spectrum for sodium.

Now dip another platinum wire in a solution of a salt of strontium and again hold the wire in the Bunsen flame. This time the flame is colored red, the red flame being character-

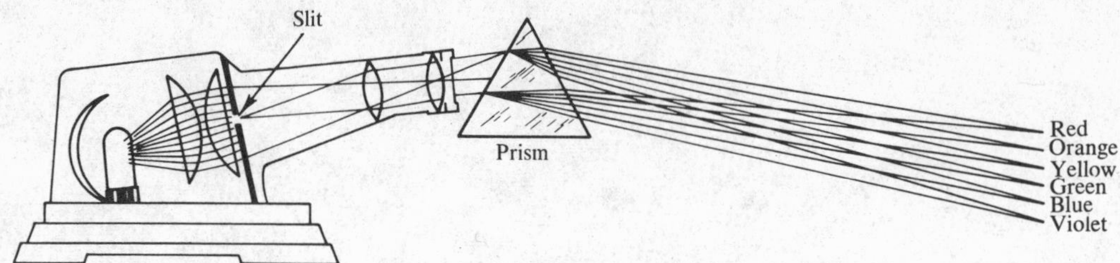

FIG. TG4–1

istic of vaporized atoms of strontium. However, if this flame is observed through a spectroscope the bright line spectrum of strontium is found to consist of 9 lines or so — 3 in the red, 2 in the green, 2 in the blue, and 2 in the violet. The color seen by the unaided eye is really a combination of these colors. However, red is the dominant color so red is the color that is seen. But a spectroscope analyzes the light — it splits the light into its constituent wavelengths and that is why the bright line spectrum of strontium is quite different from the combined color of these wavelengths in a strontium flame.

The yellow and red colors imparted to a Bunsen flame are tests by which sodium and strontium atoms in a compound can be readily identified.

THE WAVE THEORY OF LIGHT
(pp. 62–65)

Learning Objectives

1. To name the two extremes of a transverse wave.
2. To define *wavelength*.
3. To describe the method for measuring wavelength.
4. To define *frequency*.
5. To state the method for measuring frequency.
6. To convert centimeters to angstroms.
7. To state the letter symbol for the angstrom.
8. To state the approximate wavelengths of red and violet light in angstroms.
9. To state letter symbols for wavelength, frequency, and velocity of light.
10. To write the equation relating the velocity, wavelength, and frequency of light.
11. Given the frequency of a light wave, and the constant *c*, to calculate its wavelength.
12. Given the wavelength of a lightwave, and the constant *c*, to calculate its frequency.

THE ELECTROMAGNETIC SPECTRUM
(pp. 65–66)

Learning Objectives

1. To name the major parts of the electromagnetic spectrum.
2. To state the order, from highest to lowest frequencies, of the major parts of the electromagnetic spectrum.
3. To name the regions in the electromagnetic spectrum where the hydrogen lines are found.
4. To state the fact that each element, in its incandescent state, emits its own unique spectrum.

ENERGY
(pp. 66–68)

Learning Objectives

1. To name the forms of energy listed in the text.
2. To state the difference between potential and kinetic energy.
3. To describe several examples of the transformation of one form of energy to another.
4. To describe the series of energy transformations that take place when an atom is excited.

THE QUANTUM THEORY
(pp. 68–69)

Learning Objectives

1. To define the term *quanta*.
2. To state the letter symbol for Planck's constant.
3. To state the value in erg-sec of Planck's constant.
4. To write the equation that expresses a quantum of energy.
5. To state the general features that distinguish quantum theory from wave theory.

6. To describe the photoelectric effect.
7. To define the term *photon*.
8. To relate photons to quanta.
9. To state generally the reasons for the present existence of the wave-particle "duality".

THE LAW OF MOTION AND ROTATING BODIES
(pp. 69–72)

Learning Objectives

1. To state the meaning of the term *planetary electrons*.
2. To state the role played by an applied force in governing the motion of bodies according to classical mechanics.
3. To describe the difference between Bohr's hypothesis on the motion of orbiting electrons and the laws of classical mechanics.
4. To describe the Bohr model of the hydrogen atom.
5. To describe the energy transformations that take place when a hydrogen atom is excited.
6. To write the equation for the energy emitted when a hydrogen atom is excited.
7. To describe what Bohr meant by the ground state — by stationary states.
8. To describe the level to which the excited electron jumps in terms of the quanta it has absorbed.
9. To describe the energy the electron emits in terms of the energy level to which it rises and falls.

ENERGY EMITTED BY ELECTRONS EXPRESSED IN KILOCALORIES
(pp. 72–75)

Learning Objectives

1. To define a *mole*.
2. To state the number of photons in a mole.
3. To calculate the energy, in kilocalories, in a mole of photons that have a frequency of 5×10^{14} Hz.
4. To define the term *ionization energy*.
5. To state the value in kilocalories for ionization energy of hydrogen.
6. To state what range of electron jumps produces visible light — infrared — ultraviolet.

THE LIMITATIONS OF THE BOHR MODEL OF THE ATOM
(pp. 75–76)

Learning Objectives

1. To summarize the successes of the Bohr model in explaining the observations of excited hydrogen.
2. To state what the Bohr model fails to account for.

Suggested Teacher Commentary

Bohr's study of the bright line spectrum of hydrogen led to a new atomic model, model number five. In contradiction to the laws of classical physics, Bohr assumed that the electron of a hydrogen atom could move indefinitely in a circular orbit without absorbing or losing energy. If it did absorb energy, the amount absorbed was a definite package of energy or a quantum. Then, according to Bohr, the electron jumped to a higher level so that the diameter of its circular orbit was increased. Conversely, if it fell to a lower orbit the electron emitted a quantum of energy, a photon, which caused a spectral line. Bohr measured the wavelengths of the five lines in the visible spectrum. Then, from his theoretical assumptions he computed the wavelengths of the five lines. (That is, he used Planck's equation $E = \nu \times h$, and also the wave equation $c = \nu \times \lambda$.) The two sets of wavelengths (the experimental and the theoretical) were identical. In other words, Bohr had discovered a theory which explained the experimental facts as far as a hydrogen atom is concerned. However, for elements heavier than hydrogen (that is, for all elements except hydrogen) the energy emitted when electrons jump to lower levels did not agree with the energy indicated by their bright line spectra. It therefore looked as though circular electronic orbits around an atomic nucleus was a mistaken idea. So scientists looked for still another model that would account for the bright line spectra of all elements. And they found one — a model based on quantum mechanics. It is discussed in the next chapter.

Answers to Questions and Exercises

Text page references are provided for those questions which do not require computations. The student's answers will be individually stated, but should focus on the concepts developed in these text pages.

Factual Recall

1. 59–60
2. 60–62
3. 62–63
4. 63–65
5. 65
6. 66
7. 66–68
8. 68
9. 62–63, 69
10. 70–75
11. 70–75
12. 74
13. 74–75
14. 75, Fig. 4–13

Apply Your Knowledge!

1. 70–76
2. $\lambda = 4.6 \times 10^3 \text{Å} = 4.6 \times 10^{-5}$ cm

$$\nu = \frac{c}{\lambda} = \frac{3 \times 10^{10} \text{ cm/sec}}{4.6 \times 10^{-5} \text{ cm}} = 6.5 \times 10^{14} \text{ Hz}$$

3. $\lambda = 1.216 \times 10^3 \text{Å} = 1.216 \times 10^{-5}$ cm
$\lambda = 0.95 \times 10^3 \text{Å} = 0.95 \times 10^{-5}$ cm

$$\nu = \frac{c}{\lambda} = \frac{3 \times 10^{10} \text{ cm/sec}}{1.22 \times 10^{-5} \text{ cm}} = 2.45 \times 10^{15} \text{ Hz}$$

$$\nu = \frac{c}{\lambda} = \frac{3 \times 10^{10} \text{ cm/sec}}{0.95 \times 10^{-5} \text{ cm}} = 3.16 \times 10^{15} \text{ Hz}$$

4. 1 erg $= 2.39 \times 10^{-11}$ kcal

$$\frac{1 \text{ erg}}{2.39 \times 10^{-11} \text{ kcal}} = 4.18 \times 10^{10} \text{ ergs/kcal}$$

5. $\lambda = 4.86 \times 10^{-5}$ cm

$$\nu = \frac{c}{\lambda} = \frac{3.0 \times 10^{10} \text{ cm/sec}}{4.86 \times 10^{-5} \text{ cm}} = 6.17 \times 10^{14} \text{ Hz}$$

Energy of photon $= \nu \times h = 6.17 \times 10^{14}$ Hz $\times 6.6 \times 10^{-27}$ ergs $= 40.7 \times 10^{-13}$ ergs
Energy per mole of photons $= 40.7 \times 10^{-13}$ ergs $\times 6.02 \times 10^{23}$ photons/mole $= 245 \times 10^{10}$ ergs/mole $= 245 \times 10^{10}$ ergs/mole $\times 2.3 \times 10^{-8}$ cal/erg $= 560 \times 10^2$ cal/mole $= 56$ kcal/mole

6. 4000 Å $= 4 \times 10^{-5}$ cm
6800 Å $= 6.8 \times 10^{-5}$ cm

$$\nu_R = \frac{c}{\lambda} = \frac{3 \times 10^{10} \text{ cm/sec}}{6.8 \times 10^{-5} \text{ cm}} = 4.42 \times 10^{14} \text{ Hz}$$

$$\nu_V = \frac{c}{\lambda} = \frac{3 \times 10^{10} \text{ cm/sec}}{4 \times 10^{-5} \text{ cm}} = 7.5 \times 10^{14} \text{ Hz}$$

$$\frac{E_R}{E_V} = \frac{\nu_R \times h}{\nu_V \times h}$$

$$= \frac{4.42 \times 10^{14} \text{ Hz} \times 6.62 \times 10^{-27} \text{ erg-sec}}{7.5 \times 10^{14} \text{ Hz} \times 6.62 \times 10^{-27} \text{ erg-sec}}$$

$$= \frac{29.26 \times 10^{-13}}{49.65 \times 10^{-13}} = .59$$

7. $$\frac{\nu_1}{\nu_2} = \frac{\dfrac{E_3 - E_2}{h}}{\dfrac{E_6 - E_5}{h}} = \frac{43 \text{ kcal/mole}}{5 \text{ kcal/mole}} = 8.6$$

8. Energy per mole of photons $= 278$ kcal/mole $=$

$$\frac{278 \times 10^3 \text{ cal/mole}}{2.3 \times 10^{-8} \text{ cal/erg}} = 120 \times 10^{11} \text{ ergs/mole}$$

$$\text{Energy of photon} = \frac{120 \times 10^{11} \text{ ergs/mole}}{6.02 \times 10^{23} \text{ photons/mole}} = 20 \times 10^{-12} \text{ ergs/photon}$$

(*b*) $$\nu = \frac{E}{h} = \frac{20 \times 10^{-12} \text{ ergs/photon}}{6.6 \times 10^{-27} \text{ ergs-sec}} = 3.03 \times 10^{15} \text{ Hz}$$

(*a*) $$\lambda = \frac{c}{\nu} = \frac{3.0 \times 10^{10} \text{ cm/sec}}{3.03 \times 10^{15} \text{ Hz}} = 10^{-5} \text{ cm} = 1000 \text{ Å}$$

CHAPTER 5

THE QUANTUM MECHANICAL ATOM

SCHRÖDINGER'S WAVE MECHANICS
(pp. 80–82)

Learning Objectives

1. To summarize Heisenberg's *uncertainty principle.*
2. To state the consequences of applying the uncertainty principle to Bohr's clearly defined electron orbits.
3. To state why three mutually perpendicular axes are required to locate a point in three-dimensional space.
4. To state qualitatively the probability distributions for electrons with respect to distance from the nucleus.
5. To describe, qualitatively, an electron cloud.
6. To state whether or not the boundary surface of an electron cloud is "real" or arbitrary.

Suggested Teacher Commentary

The chapter deals with the latest model of the atom — model number six. It is based upon laws of quantum mechanics as opposed to the laws of classical (or ordinary) mechanics that describe the way ordinary objects behave in space. If we know the mass of an object and the force that acts upon it, the laws of classical mechanics enable us to compute the velocity of the object and to predict the path it will follow. But if we consider a particle as small as an electron classical mechanics no longer apply. That is, it is impossible to foretell the way a single particle will behave, but we can foretell the *probability* of its behaving in a certain manner. Or, to be more specific, it is not possible to compute either the positions or velocities of single particles and therefore the paths of single electrons cannot be predicted. However, quantum mechanics does predict the position of greatest chance for an electron or, stated another way, it predicts the probability of finding an electron in a certain spot.

Scientists first realized that the laws of classical mechanics could not be applied to moving electrons after Rutherford had discovered that an atom consists of a positively charged nucleus plus outside electrons. According to the known laws, electrons travelling at high speed around a nucleus were bound to lose energy and, in consequence, they would be expected to fall into the nucleus. But if this happened atoms would cease to exist.

Bohr found a partial way out of the dilemma by making a revolutionary assertion that contradicted the known laws of classical mechanics. He proposed that an electron can move in a circular orbit around a nucleus without losing energy. He also said that for every atom there are a number of stationary stable states of which the most stable is the ground state. He represented these stationary states pictorially by a series of concentric circles. These stationary states could not be explained in terms of classical physics and Bohr himself introduced the quantum energy concept to account for them. Indeed he proved that bright line spectra reveal differences of energy between the stationary states.

We now know that the stationary states are energy states. According to the modern theory an electron does not move in an orbit round the nucleus but instead it occupies space near the nucleus. The space it occupies is called an orbital. Thus, in effect Bohr's circular orbits are replaced by 7 energy levels called principal quantum numbers 1, 2, 3, 4, 5, 6 and 7. And the motion of an electron is described in terms of its principal quantum number and its orbital.

QUANTUM NUMBERS
(pp. 82–84)

Learning Objectives

1. To describe an electron orbital in terms of its geometry and the energy it represents.
2. To state the meaning of the term *principal quantum number*.
3. To state the meaning of the term *orbital quantum number*.
4. To state the meaning of the term *magnetic quantum number*.
5. To state the meaning of the term *spin quantum number*.

ELECTRON ENERGY LEVELS IN ATOMS
(pp. 85–86)

Learning Objectives

1. To state the relationship of line spectra to electron energy levels.
2. To state the relationships between shell, subshell, and orbital.
3. Given the general equation that the number of orbitals is equal to the square of the principal quantum number, to calculate the number of orbitals in the first four main energy shells.
4. To state the numbers of *s*, *p*, *d*, and *f* orbitals for principal quantum number 4.

THE ARRANGEMENT OF ELECTRONS IN ATOMS
(pp. 86–89)

Learning Objectives

1. To state Pauli's exclusion principle.
2. To state how Pauli's exclusion principle makes it possible to predict the electron arrangements of all atoms.
3. Given the general formula $2n^2$, to state the maximum number of electrons for shells designated by the first three principal quantum numbers.
4. To draw electronic diagrams of the ground-states of the first five elements — hydrogen through boron.
5. To convey the information in Objective 4 in the spectroscopist's notation.

Answers to Questions and Exercises

Text page references are provided for those questions which do not require computations. The student's answers will be individually stated, but should focus on the concepts developed in these text pages.

Factual Recall

1. 79–80
2. 82
3. (*a*) $n = 2$
   (*b*) $n = 3$
   (c) $n = 4, 5, 6,$ or 7
4. (*a*) $2p_x$ refers to the *p* orbital along the *x* axis at the second energy level.
   (*b*) $3p_y$ refers to the *p* orbital along the *y* axis at the third energy level.
   (*c*) $4p_z$ refers to the *p* orbital along the *z* axis at the fourth energy level.
5. Fig. 5–9
6. 86–88

Apply Your Knowledge!

1. N: $1s^2\ 2s^2\ 2p^3$. Ne: $1s^2\ 2s^2\ 2p^6$
   Table 5–2
2. Maximum number of electrons = $2n^2$
   (*a*) 8
   (*b*) 32
3. Figs. 5–8 snd 5–11
4. 82

UNIT 

ORBITAL CLASSIFICATION AND BONDING OF ATOMS

OPENING UNIT II

The spade work that led to the formulation of the quantum mechanical atom was done mostly by the famous team of quantum physicists led by Niels Bohr in Copenhagen. It has been notably successful in explaining the structure of individual atoms and even for predicting the structures of atoms whose existence was unknown at that time. Their work was physics whose applicability to the sister science of chemistry was immediately apparent.

In the next four chapters the discussion will center on the ways in which the structure of the quantum mechanical atom explains the observed properties of elements and compounds.

CHAPTER 6

PERIODIC CLASSIFICATION AND ELECTRON CONFIGURATION

ELECTRON CONFIGURATION OF ELEMENTS IN THE SECOND PERIOD
(pp. 95–97)

Learning Objectives

1. To write the spectroscopic notation for each of the elements in the second period.
2. To draw the electron configuration diagrams for carbon, oxygen, and nitrogen.

CONFIGURATIONS OF ELEMENTS IN THE THIRD PERIOD
(pp. 97–98)

Learning Objectives

1. To write the spectroscopic notation for the outer orbitals of elements in the third period.
2. To draw the electron configuration diagrams for phosphorus and argon.
3. To state why the 3*d* orbitals are empty for elements in the third period.

Suggested Teacher Commentary

This chapter deals with electronic configuration as the basis for the arrangement of elements in the periodic table. In this arrangement elements whose outer orbitals have about the same energy (for example, two 2*s* electrons and six 2*p* electrons) are placed in the same horizontal row. On this basis the order of the elements and the vertical columns (the families) are precisely the same as the order and family arrangement based on atomic numbers.

Row 1 contains elements with electrons in the 1*s* orbital. The energy level of the 2*s* orbital is considerably higher than the level of the 1*s* orbital, and row 2 contains elements whose outer electrons are in the 2*s* and 2*p* orbitals. Similarly, in row 3 there are four orbitals with about the same energy, one 3*s* orbital and three 3*p* orbitals.

CONFIGURATIONS OF ELEMENTS IN THE FOURTH PERIOD
(pp. 99–101)

Learning Objectives

1. To state why the 4*s* orbital is filled before the 3*d* orbital for potassium and calcium.

2. To state the classification of elements that are formed by adding electrons to the *d* and *f* orbitals.

CONFIGURATIONS OF ELEMENTS IN THE FIFTH PERIOD
(pp. 101)

Learning Objectives

1. To state why the 5*s* orbital is filled before the 4*d* orbital for rubidium and strontium.
2. To state why the elements with 4*f* orbitals are in the sixth row rather than the fifth.

Suggested Teacher Commentary

In row 4 there is a break in the *s–p* sequence. Here there are three groups of nine orbitals with about the same energy, one 4*s* orbital, five 3*d* orbitals and three 4*p* orbitals. Notice that when the energy of an orbital is considered, the 3*d* elements are in the fourth row, not in the third. In other words, elements in the fourth row have two principal quantum numbers, 3 and 4. Elements in row 4 with a principal quantum number 3 or 4 are called transition elements.

Transition elements belong to an orbital (or orbitals) interposed between the *s* and *p* orbitals of higher principal quantum number. In row 4 the five 3*d* orbitals, representing 10 elements, are between the 4*s* and 4*p* orbitals. These 10 elements constitute the first group of transition elements. In row 5 the 4*d* orbitals are between the 5*s* and 5*p* orbitals. The 10 elements represented by the five 4*d* orbitals constitute the second group of transition elements.

ELEMENTS IN THE SIXTH PERIOD
(pp. 101–02)

Learning Objectives

1. To name the group of elements that are formed by adding electrons to the 5*d* and to the 4*f* orbitals.

Suggested Teacher Commentary

In row 6 orbitals 4*f* and 5*d* are between orbitals 6*s* and 6*p*. Here there are four kinds of orbitals and two series of transition elements — 4*f* and 5*d*. The inner group consists of 14 elements formed as 14 electrons enter the seven 4*f* orbitals. This group of 14 elements make up the so-called lanthanide series or rare-earth elements.

ELEMENTS IN THE SEVENTH PERIOD
(pp. 102–03)

Suggested Teacher Commentary

The energy levels of the orbitals in the seventh row are shown in Fig. TG6-1. This is clearly an incomplete series since it contains only 17 known elements. The 14 elements in the 5*f* orbitals constitute a transition series called the actinide series. Most of these elements are highly unstable due to the fact that the nuclei of the atoms are unstable. Most of them are synthetic elements which are highly radioactive and exist only for a very short time.

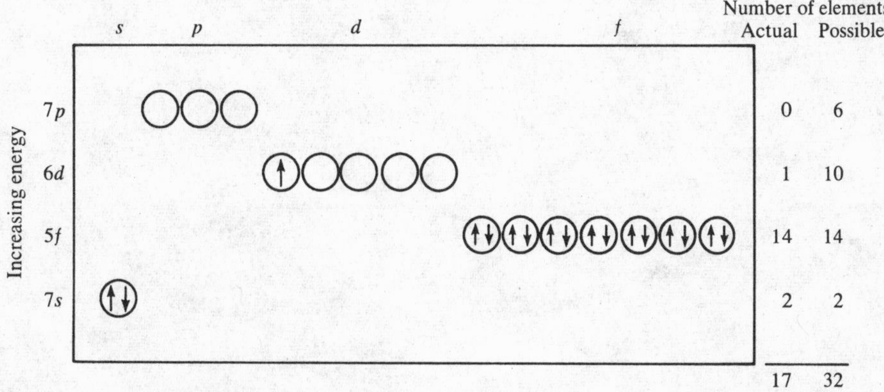

FIG. TG6–1

Answers to Questions and Exercises

Text page references are provided for those questions which do not require computations. The student's answers will be individually stated, but should focus on the concepts developed in these text pages.

Factual Recall

1. (*a*) Transition elements are elements whose d orbitals have a principal quantum number that is one less than the principal quantum numbers of the s and p orbitals in the same energy level.
   (*b*) Scandium has a $3d$ electron in the same energy level as the $4s$ electrons.
   (*c*) $1s^2\ 2s^2\ 2p^6\ 3s^2\ 3p^6\ 4s^2$
2. (*a*) Elements in $6s$ orbital $= 2 \times 1 = 2$
   Elements in $4f$ orbital $= 2 \times 7 = 14$
   Elements in $5d$ orbital $= 2 \times 5 = 10$
   Elements in $6p$ orbital $= 2 \times 3 = \underline{6}$
   32

   (*b*) Total transition elements $= 14$ in $4f + 10$ in $5d = 24$

Apply Your Knowledge!

1. 100, 420
2. 104–05
3. Element 104 falls just below hafnium on the periodic table and thus would share some of its properties. Elements 104 through 112 will form transition elements of the seventh row by filling the $6d$ subshell. They will have chemical properties homologous to the hafnium through mercury series in the row above.
4. Table 6–5, 104–05

CHAPTER 7

RELATION OF ELECTRON CONFIGURATION TO PROPERTIES

Suggested Teacher Commentary

In this chapter we consider the recurring similar electronic configurations of elements in the same column. In column III the recurring configuration is p^1. For example, the configurations of the adjacent elements Al ($Z = 13$) and Ga ($Z = 31$) are $1s^2\ 2s^2\ 2p^6\ 3s^2\ 3p^1$ and $1s^2\ 2s^2\ 2p^6\ 3s^2\ 3p^6\ 4s^2\ 3d^{10}\ 4p^1$. (It should be noted that the symbol Z stands for atomic number.) In column VI the configurations of the adjacent elements O ($Z = 8$), S ($Z = 16$) and Se ($Z = 34$) are $1s^2\ 2s^2\ 2p^4$, $1s^2\ 2s^2\ 2p^6\ 3s^2\ 3p^4$ and $1s^2\ 2s^2\ 2p^6\ 3s^2\ 3p^6\ 4s^2\ 3d^{10}\ 4p^4$. Thus the characteristic recurring configuration is p^4.

THE FAMILY OF NOBLE GASES
(pp. 108–10)

Learning Objectives

1. To define a valence shell.
2. To define a valence electron.
3. To state the identity of valence electron number and group number.
4. To write the electron dot notation for neon, argon, and krypton.
5. To write the electron dot notation for three of the most reactive metals.
6. To write the electron dot notation for three of the most reactive nonmetals.
7. To relate the stability of fluoride and sodium ions to the stability of the noble gases.

THE ALKALI METALS
(pp. 110–11)

Learning Objectives

1. To locate the alkali metals on the periodic table with respect to the noble gases.
2. To state the number of valence electrons possessed by the alkali metals.
3. To describe the more obvious physical properties of the alkali metals.
4. To describe the role played by the valence electron in causing the extreme chemical reactivity of the alkali metals.
5. To write a simple equation expressing the ionization of an alkali metal.
6. To define a metal in terms of the position of its outermost electron with respect to its nucleus.

Demonstration I The Chemical Activity of Sodium and Potassium

Materials recommended: glass plate, knife, metallic sodium, metallic potassium.

The chemical activity of sodium and potassium can readily be shown in a simple demonstration experiment. Both metals readily react with oxygen, water vapor and even carbon dioxide in the air, and so as a protection they are stored in kerosene which does not react with the metals. But even when immersed in kerosene they become coated with a hard whitish crust. The crust is a mixture of Na_2O, NaOH and Na_2CO_3 due to reactions with the small amounts of O_2, H_2O and CO_2 that are dissolved in the kerosene.

Take a piece of sodium out of the bottle, place it upon a glass plate and cut it through with a knife. Notice that the exposed surface is silvery in color but it at once begins to react with air and tarnishes. Now do the same with potassium. The potassium surface is bluish in color and it too begins to tarnish as soon as it is exposed to air.

THE HALOGEN FAMILY
(pp. 111–12)

Learning Objectives

1. To locate the halogens on the periodic table with respect to the noble gases.
2. To state the number of valence electrons possessed by the halogens.
3. To describe the role played by the nuclear charge in causing the chemical activity of the halogens.
4. To write a simple equation expressing the negative ionization of a halogen.
5. To define a nonmetal in terms of the position of its outermost electrons with respect to the nucleus.

Demonstration II The Chemical Activity of Chlorine, Bromine, and Iodine

Materials recommended: combustion spoon, Bunsen burner, bromine, iodine, chlorine, sodium.

Put on display a bottle of chlorine (a greenish gas), a bottle of bromine (a dark red liquid) and some iodine (a black shiny solid). The chemical activity of chlorine can be demonstrated in class in a simple way.

Place a small piece of freshly cut sodium in a combustion spoon. Warm the spoon in the flame of a burner and then lower it into a bottle of chlorine. The sodium burns with a brilliant flame leaving behind a white residue of sodium chloride. The reaction is

$$2Na + Cl_2 \rightarrow 2NaCl + \text{heat}$$

In this reaction the chlorine atoms have filled their outer shells by pulling the single electron out of the outer shells of the sodium atoms. That is, sodium chloride is made up of sodium ions and chloride ions.

THE POSITION OF HYDROGEN IN THE PERIODIC TABLE
(pp. 112–13)

Learning Objectives

1. To state the number of valence electrons possessed by hydrogen.
2. To write a simple equation expressing the ionization of hydrogen.
3. To state the reason for the unusual instability of the H^+ ion.
4. To write a simple equation expressing the ionization of hydrogen to give hydride ion.
5. To state the more usual ionization of hydrogen.

STRUCTURE AND PROPERTIES OF ELEMENTS IN A PERIOD (OR ROW)
(pp. 113–15)

Learning Objectives

1. To state which orbitals are successively filled in passing from left to right along the third row.
2. To state the number of electrons in the 3*s* orbital of sodium.
3. To state the relative activity of magnesium in terms of its nuclear charge and outer electron configuration.
4. To state the relative activity of aluminum in terms of its nuclear charge and outer electron configuration.
5. To describe why silicon may be considered an intermediate between a metal and a nonmetal.
6. To state why phosphorus is a nonmetal in terms of its outer electron configuration.
7. To state the valence of sulfur and why it is a more active nonmetal than phosphorus.
8. To state why chlorine is the most active of the nonmetals in row 3.
9. To state the basis on which argon is classed as a metal or nonmetal.

STRUCTURE AND PROPERTIES OF ELEMENTS IN A COLUMN (OR GROUP)
(p. 115)

Learning Objectives

1. To state the relationship between the activity of a metal in group I in terms of the distance between the outer electrons and the nucleus.
2. To state the relationship between the activity of a halogen in terms of its atomic number.

Answers to Questions and Exercises

Text page references are provided for those questions which do not require computations. The student's answers will be individually stated, but should focus on the concepts developed in these text pages.

Factual Recall

1. (*a*) $1s^2\ 2s^2\ 2p^6\ 3s^2\ 3p^6\ 4s^2\ 3d^{10}\ 4p^4$
   (*b*) Oxygen, sulfur and selenium have 4 electrons in the outer *p* orbitals.
2. 110–11

Apply Your Knowledge!

1. In the seventh row in the group beginning with iron. It will form a transition element in the seventh row by filling the 6*d* subshell.
2. 99–100, 111.

CHAPTER 8

CHEMICAL BONDS

IONIC BONDS
(pp. 117–20)

Learning Objectives

1. To state the respective ionization modes of sodium and chlorine.
2. Using electron dot notation, to summarize the reaction $Na + Cl \rightarrow NaCl$.
3. To state the definition of an ionic bond that appears on p. 118 of the text.
4. To draw a simple diagram of a sodium chloride lattice.
5. Using ordinary symbols and charge signs, to write the equation for combining silver and chlorine.

Suggested Teacher Commentary

Students should realize that both ionic and covalent bonds are electrical forces of attraction. Actually covalent compounds are far more numerous than ionic compounds; that is, covalent bonds are far more numerous than ionic bonds.

The concept of an ionic bond is much easier to understand than the covalent concept. Even the old Bohr atomic model adequately accounts for ionic bonds. If an electron is transferred from one atom to another it is apparent that one atom becomes negatively charged and the other positively, and that there is an electrical force of attraction between the charged atoms (or ions). However, the concept of a covalent bond based on the Bohr model is quite incomprehensible to intelligent students who ask: How is it possible for atoms to share electrons that move in circular orbits? What is the actual path traced by a shared pair of electrons? Only the quantum atomic model can account for covalent bonds.

COVALENT BONDS
(pp. 120–24)

Learning Objectives

1. To state the difference between the electrostatic forces an alkali metal atom and a halogen atom exert on each other and the electrostatic forces two hydrogen atoms exert on each other.
2. To diagram the electrostatic forces between two hydrogen atoms.
3. To write the electron dot notation for a diatomic hydrogen molecule.
4. To diagram the overlapping *s* orbitals of a hydrogen molecule.
5. To state the resemblance of the shared pair of electrons in a hydrogen molecule to the filled shell of a helium atom.
6. To define a nonpolar covalent bond.

7. Using electron dot notation, to write the reaction for the formation of hydrogen fluoride from its elements.
8. To define a polar covalent bond.

Suggested Teacher Commentary

In the quantum model the region occupied by an electron is called an electron cloud. Therefore an electron cloud has a negative charge. Moreover, it is three dimensional and is usually thought of as spherical in shape.

A molecule of hydrogen is diatomic, held together by a covalent bond. A hydrogen molecule consists of two protons and a 2-electron cloud. That part of the cloud between the two nuclei (or protons) is the significant part. There is a mutual attraction between the two protons and that part of the cloud that lies between them. It is this force of attraction that constitutes the covalent bond; it holds the diatomic molecule together. As stated in the text, the net force of repulsion between the nuclei of atoms is reduced if the electron clouds of the atoms overlap, and a covalent bond is always represented by overlapping electron clouds.

WATER, A POLAR MOLECULE
(pp. 125–28)

Learning Objectives

1. To write the electron dot notation for water.
2. To draw the orbital model of water as shown in Fig. 8–9.
3. To state the relative strengths of attraction for electrons of the hydrogen nucleus and the oxygen nucleus.
4. To state the relative probability of an electron pair being nearer the oxygen or the hydrogen nucleus.
5. To state why the oxygen part of the molecule acts as a negative pole while the two hydrogens act as a positive pole.
6. To state the reason for the calculated bond angle in water.
7. To state the reason for the experimentally determined bond angle in water.
8. To relate the polarity of the water molecule to its tendency to form associations with other molecules.
9. To state why the molecules formed of hydrogen and the other group VIA atoms do not cluster as readily as do water molecules.
10. To relate the association of water molecules to its high boiling point.
11. To relate the polarity of water molecules to its dissolving power.

THE SHAPES OF MOLECULES
(pp. 128–31)

Learning Objectives

1. To state the general rule for predicting the shapes of molecules that appears on p. 129 of the text.
2. To state the minimum number of electron pairs in a compound that will require the molecule to have a three-dimensional rather than a planar shape.

Suggested Teacher Commentary

The electron dot formula for methane $\begin{matrix} & H & \\ & \cdot\cdot & \\ H: & C & :H \\ & \cdot\cdot & \\ & H & \end{matrix}$ shows that there are four pairs of electrons around the central atom of carbon. Moreover, this formula picture of methane seems to suggest that the electron pairs are at the corners of a square, in which case the molecule would be uniplanar or flat. However, since these electron pairs repel each other they will be pushed as far apart as possible; that is, the carbon-hydrogen distance will be a maximum. Geometry proves that for the same distance between hydrogen atoms the C–H distance is greater for a tetrahedron than for a square. Thus it is believed that the electron pairs have a tetrahedral orientation; that is, that the carbon atom is at the center of a tetrahedron and the hydrogen atoms are at the four corners. This idea is confirmed by actual geometric measurement of the bond angle (the angle between the central carbon atom and two neighboring hydrogen atoms), and the experimental determination by x-ray diffraction. By geometrical measurement each of the four bond angles is 109°. And the bond angle as found experimentally is precisely the same, namely 109°. Hence the inevitable conclusion is that a molecule of methane is three dimensional, tetrahedral in shape, not flat.

This tetrahedral orientation can be applied to other molecules with four pairs of electrons around a central atom, as for example in ammonia and water. In a molecule of ammonia a nitrogen atom is at the center of the tetrahedron and hydrogen atoms occupy three of the corners as in Fig. TG8-1. That is, all four electron pairs are oriented tetrahedrally. However, since only three of the pairs are bonded to hydrogen atoms there is one lone pair so the shape of the molecule is a pyramid. By geometry the bond angle should be 109°, the same as for methane, and as found by X-ray diffraction it is 107° which is very close.

Similarly, in a water molecule the four electron pairs are oriented tetrahedrally with the oxygen atom at the center of the tetrahedron. However, there are two bonded pairs forming O—H bonds and two lone pairs. Hence a water

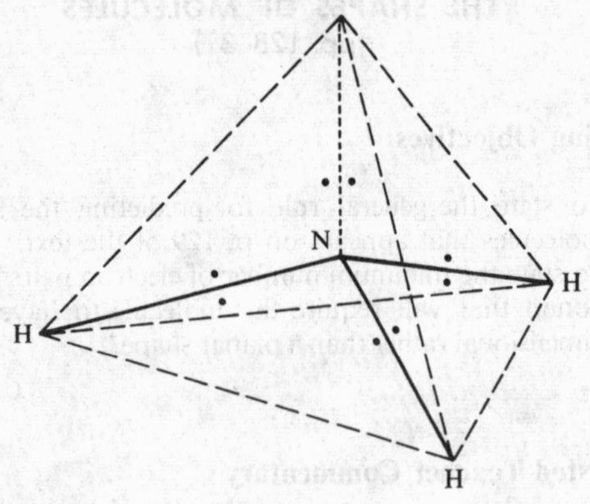

FIG. TG8-1

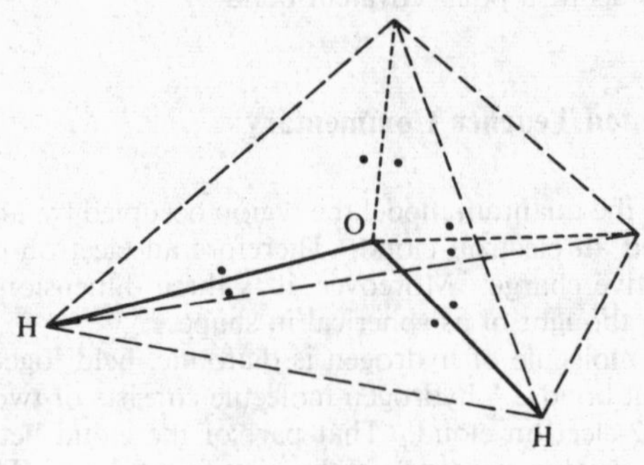

FIG. TG8–2

molecule is angular in shape and all the atoms are in the same plane. By geometry the bond angle between the central atom oxygen and the two hydrogen atoms should be 109°, the same as for H—C—H and for H—N—H. And experimentally by x-ray diffraction it is found to be 104°.

METALLIC BONDS
(pp. 131–32)

Learning Objectives

1. To state that metals by definition have loosely held valence electrons that are free to move readily from atom to atom.
2. To define the term *kernel*.
3. To state why the close packing of the lattice prevents effective covalent bonding in metals.
4. To state that the free electrons exert the attractive force that overcomes the mutually repulsive force of the positively charged kernels.

Answers to Questions and Exercises

Text page references are provided for those questions which do not require computations. The student's answers will be individually stated, but should focus on the concepts developed in these text pages.

Factual Recall

1. 117–20
2. 118–19
3. 120–23
4. 121–24
5. 125–27
6. 125–27
7. 125–27
8. 127–28
9. 131–32

Apply Your Knowledge!

1. 117–18
2. 128–31
3. 131–32
4. 117–120
5. 99–100, 111
6. S_8: covalent, $CaCO_3$: ionic, SiF_4: polar covalent, CsBr: ionic, NH_4Cl: ionic, Mg: metallic

CHAPTER 9

ATOMS AND IONS

SIZES OF ATOMS AND IONS
(pp. 135–37)

Learning Objectives

1. To define *covalent radius*.
2. To state the covalent radius of a hydrogen atom.
3. To state the variation in atomic radii along a row.
4. To state the reason for the variation of atomic radii along a row
5. To state the variation in atomic radii from row to row.
6. To state the reason for the variation of atomic radii from row to row.
7. To state why a sodium atom has a larger radius than a sodium ion.
8. To state why a chloride ion has a larger radius than a chlorine atom.

IONIZATION ENERGY
(pp. 137–43)

Learning Objectives

1. To state the meaning of the term *ionization energy*.
2. To write a simple equation summarizing positive ionization.
3. To describe the gas-discharge tube method for determining ionization energy.
4. To define the term *ionization potential*.
5. To define the term *electron-volt*.
6. To convert electron-volts to kilocalories per mole.
7. To explain the periodicity of ionization numbers when plotted against atomic number.
8. To state the role of the shielding effect in determining ionization energies.
9. To define second, third, fourth, etc, ionization energies.
10. To explain why second third, and fourth ionization energies are greater than the first ionization energies for helium, lithium, and magnesium.

ELECTRON AFFINITY
(pp. 141–43)

Learning Objectives

1. To write a simple equation summarizing negative ionization.
2. To define the term *electron affinity*.
3. To relate electron affinity to chemical activity.
4. To define the term *electronegativity*.
5. To explain the role of electronegativity in determining the type of bond that forms between two atoms.

Answers to Questions and Exercises

Text page references are provided for those questions which do not require computations. The student's answers will be individually stated, but should focus on the concepts developed in these text pages.

Factual Recall

		Electrons per outer shell	
1. Element	Z	$3s$	$3p$
Na	+11	1	—
Si	+14	2	2
Cl	+17	2	5

Distances of electrons from outer shell to nucleus is the same for all three elements. But nuclear charge for Si > charge for Na. Therefore outer shell electrons for Si are pulled closer to the nucleus and, as a result, the atomic volume of Si is less than the atomic volume of Na.

Nuclear charge for Si < charge for Cl but outer electron distances are the same. Therefore, the distances of $3s$ and $3p$ electrons are less for Si than Cl. Hence, atomic volume of Si < volume of Cl.

2. (*a*) Ionization potential of an element is the voltage needed to dislodge an electron from the outer orbital of an atom of the element.
   (*b*) Ionization energy is the energy needed to completely detach the outer electron from an atom.
   (*c*) An electron volt (eV) is the energy needed to move an electron through a potential difference of 1 V.
3. K: $Z = +19$; $1s^2\ 2s^2\ 2p^6\ 3s^2\ 3p^6\ 4s^1$
   Li: $Z = +3$; $1s^2\ 2s^1$
   The $4s$ electron of potassium is farther from its nucleus than is the $2s$ electron of lithium. Therefore, one mole of $4s$ electrons of K are more easily dislodged than one mole of $2s$ electrons of Li, even though the nuclear charge on K is the greater. Hence the ionization energy of K is less than that of Li.
4. In atoms of the noble gases the s and p orbitals are completely filled with 8 electrons. This is the most stable structure of all the atoms in the row. In consequence, it is more difficult to detach an electron from a noble gas atom than from atoms of all other elements in the row.
5. (*a*) The first ionization energy (1st IE) is the energy needed to remove an electron from the highest energy level of a gaseous atom (M). Or,

$$M \rightarrow M^{+1} + e^-$$

The second ionization energy (2nd IE) is the energy needed to remove an electron from a gaseous unipositive ion (M^{+1}). Or,

$$M^{+1} \rightarrow M^{+2} + e^-$$

The third ionization energy is the energy needed to remove an electron from a dipositive ion (M^{+2}). Or,

$$M^{+2} \rightarrow M^{+3} + e^-$$

(*b*) $Mg^{+1} + 350\ \text{kcal} \rightarrow Mg^{+2} + e^-$
$Mg^{+2} + 1850\ \text{kcal} \rightarrow Mg^{+3} + e^-$

Orbital Configuration

Mg: $1s^2\ 2s^2\ 2p^6\ 3s^2$
Mg^{+1}: $1s^2\ 2s^2\ 2p^6\ 3s^1$
Mg^{+2}: $1s^2\ 2s^2\ 2p^6$

The configuration of Mg^{+2} is the same as for a neon atom. That is, the outer orbitals are completely filled. Therefore, it is more difficult to remove an electron from Mg^{+2} than from Mg^{+1}.

6. Ionization energy measures the energy required to release an electron from an *atom;* that is, it measures the power of an atom to hold the electron. Electronegativity measures the power of an atom to attract an electron from another atom to form a chemical bond.
7. (*a*) Na: $1s^2\ 2s^2\ 2p^6\ 3s^1$
   Mg: $1s^2\ 2s^2\ 2p^6\ 3s^2$
   (*b*) Na: 1st ionization energy in kcal/mole = 120
   Mg: 1st ionization energy in kcal/mole = 180
   The removal of the $3s$ electron from a sodium atom requires little energy because it results in a filled electron shell, which is not the case for Mg.
   (*c*) Na^+: $1s^2\ 2s^2\ 2p^6$; 2nd IE in kcal/mole = 1090
   Mg^+: $1s^2\ 2s^2\ 2p^6\ 3s^1$; 2nd IE in kcal/mole = 350
   The removal of the $3s$ electron from the unfilled shell of a unipositive Mg ion results in a filled electron shell and therefore needs little energy. Much more energy is needed to remove an electron from Na^+ since the shell is already full.

Apply Your Knowledge!

1. Calcium atom: $Z = +20$; $1s^2\ 2s^2\ 2p^6\ 3s^2\ 3p^6\ 4s^2$
   Calcium ion: $Z = +20$; $1s^2\ 2s^2\ 2p^6\ 3s^2\ 3p^6$
   In a calcium ion the $4s$ orbital is unoccupied. Therefore the atomic volume of the calcium ion is less than the volume of the calcium atom.

2. Sulfur atom: $Z = +16$; $1s^2\ 2s^2\ 2p^6\ 3s^2\ 3p^4$
Sulfur ion: $Z = +16$; $1s^2\ 2s^2\ 2p^6\ 3s^2\ 3p^6$
A sulfur ion has six electrons in its $3p$ orbitals, but a sulfur atom has only four. The extra electrons in the outer shell of the ion repel the four electrons in the same orbitals. Therefore the atómic volume of the ion is greater than the volume of the atom.
3. 137–42
4. NaF: Difference in electronegativity = 4.0(F) − 0.9(Na) = 3.1
NaCl: Difference in electronegativity = 3.0(Cl) − 0.9(Na) = 2.1
The larger the difference in electronegativity, the more easily are electrons transferred from one atom to another. Na transfers electrons more readily to F than to Cl.
5. Table 9–4
6. 137–42

UNIT III

THE BEHAVIOR OF GASES

Chapter 10 Avogadro's Hypothesis
Chapter 11 The Gas Laws
Chapter 12 Kinetic Molecular Theory
Chapter 13 Formulas, Equations, and Chemical Calculations

OPENING UNIT III

No one who has studied the early history of chemistry can fail to be struck by the prominent role of gases. We recall that Chapter 1 was largely concerned with Cavendish's work on gases. Priestley, Lavoisier, and Dalton also did a great deal of their work with gases. Chapter 10 discusses Cannizzaro's reinterpretation of Avogadro's hypothesis of gas combinations which finally resolved the difficulties that stood in the way of accepting Dalton's atoms. Chapter 11 covers the laws governing the physical properties of gases that led to the kinetic molecular theory of Chapter 12. The quantitative treatment of chemical reactions is dealt with in Chapter 13.

CHAPTER 10

AVOGADRO'S HYPOTHESIS

GAY-LUSSAC'S LAW OF VOLUMES
(pp. 149–50)

Learning Objectives

1. To state Gay-Lussac's law of volumes.
2. To replace *n* with a numerical value in the following reactions:
   n vol hydrogen + *n* vol chlorine → *n* vol hydrogen chloride
   n vol hydrogen + *n* vol oxygen → *n* vol water vapor
   n vol nitrogen + *n* vol hydrogen → *n* vol ammonia

EXPLANATIONS OF GAY-LUSSAC'S LAW
(pp. 150–52)

Learning Objectives

1. Given Dalton's theoretical formula for water as HO, and Gay-Lussac's experimental determination that 1 volume of oxygen and 2 volumes of hydrogen combine to form 2 volumes of water vapor, to state the apparent discrepancy between the theory and the experimental data.
2. To state the difference between an atom and a molecule.
3. To state Avogadro's hypothesis.
4. Given that a molecule of nitric oxide (NO) consists of one atom of nitrogen and one atom of oxygen, and that both nitrogen and oxygen are diatomic, to use Avogadro's hypothesis to substitute for *n* in the following reaction:

$$N_2 + O_2 \rightarrow nNO$$

5. To draw a simple diagram illustrating the reaction in Learning Objective 4.

Suggested Teacher Commentary

Both Dalton's atomic theory and Avogadro's hypothesis were propounded to account for scientific laws that were based on experimental facts. Dalton's theory was accepted without hesitation yet there was a long period of 50 years before scientists as a whole would accept Avogadro's hypothesis as a scientific law. There were several reasons for this delay and one, strangely enough, was due to Dalton's rigid interpretation of his own theory.

Gay-Lussac's law was discovered in the same year (1808) that Dalton stated his atomic theory. Since Gay-Lussac's law was based on experimental data it was indisputable, yet it could not be explained by the new atomic theory. In his theory Dalton stated that compounds are formed by the combination of *atoms*. That is, Dalton believed that atoms of elements combine to form molecules of compounds. And after the discovery of Gay-Lussac's law it was natural to believe that equal volumes of gases contain equal numbers of atoms. Let us apply this idea to the reaction between oxygen and nitrogen to form the gas nitric oxide. Or,

$$\text{nitrogen} + \text{oxygen} \rightarrow \text{nitric oxide (NO)}$$

According to Dalton one atom of N combines with one atom of O to form one molecule of NO. Or, in symbols, $N + O \rightarrow NO$. And since the number of atoms of nitrogen is the same as the number of compound atoms or molecules of nitric oxide, their volumes, according to Dalton, should also be the same. However, Gay-Lussac had discovered by experiment that the volume of nitric oxide was twice the volume of nitrogen. Or, that one volume of N + one volume of O give two volumes of NO.

To solve this problem Avogadro, in 1811, proposed that there are two kinds of ultimate particles, not one — a chemical particle or unit (an atom) and a physical particle or unit (a molecule). And he suggested that molecules of nitrogen and oxygen are both made up of two atoms each. That is, according to Avogadro the reaction is $N_2 + O_2 \rightarrow 2NO$.

Hence the volume of nitrogen is one half the volume of nitric oxide so that Avogadro's argument agreed with the experimental facts. However, at that time there was a generally accepted theory that atoms of the same element possess similar electric charges. So, according to this theory atoms of the same element would repel each other and the formation of a molecule like N_2 was impossible. This idea was a stumbling block to the general acceptance of Avogadro's theory for a period of almost 50 years, until 1858 to be exact. In the period between 1811 and 1858 there had been at least two significant developments in chemical research: (1) Berzelius, a Swedish chemist, had improved the methods of chemical analysis for both solids and gases and had analyzed more than 1000 compounds; (2) Dumas, a French chemist, determined the densities of a large number of gases. In 1858 Cannizzaro, an Italian scientist, discovered a new way to compute atomic masses and also the number of atoms in any molecule of a gaseous element or compound. And in doing so he used analytical data of compounds supplied by Berzelius, gas densities supplied by Dumas, and he assumed the validity of Avogadro's hypothesis. That is, he assumed that the molecular mass of a gaseous compound is the mass of 22.4 liters of the gas measured at STP. Cannizzaro's method was by far the most reliable method of computing atomic masses known at that time. And with this achievement scientists were finally convinced that there are two kinds of unit particles (atoms and molecules), and they accepted without reservation the validity of Avogadro's hypothesis.

GAS DENSITIES AND MOLECULAR MASSES
(pp. 152–55)

Learning Objectives

1. To write in letter symbols the equation for density.
2. Given the density of carbon dioxide as 1.81 g/l at 25°C under a pressure of 1 atm, to compute its molecular mass.

AVOGADRO'S NUMBER
(pp. 155–56)

Learning Objectives

1. To define the term *gram-molecular mass*.
2. To state the gram-molecular mass of carbon monoxide.
3. To state the value of Avogadro's number.
4. Given the gram-molecular mass of chlorine as 71 g, to compute its atomic mass.

THE MOLE
(pp. 156–58)

Learning Objectives

1. To define the term *mole* in terms of Avogadro's number.
2. To state the volume occupied by one mole of gas at 1 atm and 0°C.
3. Given that the density of nitrogen at STP is 1.25 g/l, and its molar mass as 28.0 g/mole, to compute its molar volume at STP.

CANNIZZARO'S METHOD OF FINDING ATOMIC MASSES
(pp. 158–61)

Learning Objectives

1. To derive the masses of elements in a compound, given the compound's molecular mass and its percentage composition.
2. To derive the number of atoms per molecule of elements in compounds, given their masses in grams per mole.
3. To write the formula for a compound, given the number of atoms per molecule of its constituents.
4. To define the term *coefficient*.
5. To write the correct coefficients for the reaction

$$H_2 + O_2 \rightarrow H_2O$$

Additional Questions and Problems

1. What is the mass of one atom of zinc?

Answer

$$\frac{\text{atomic mass}}{\text{Avogadro's number}} = \frac{65.4 \text{ g}}{6.02 \times 10^{23} \text{ atoms}} = 1.08 \times 10^{-22} \text{ g/atom}$$

2. How many atoms are there in 10.8 g of silver?

Answer

$$\frac{\text{Avogadro's number} \times \text{mass of Ag}}{\text{atomic mass}} = \frac{6.02 \times 10^{23} \text{ atoms} \times 10.8 \text{ g}}{108 \text{ g}} = 6.02 \times 10^{22} \text{ atoms}$$

3. How many atoms are there in 10^{-5} g of calcium?

Answer

$$\frac{6.02 \times 10^{23} \text{ atoms} \times 10^{-5} \text{ g}}{40.0} = 1.5 \times 10^{17} \text{ atoms}$$

4. What is the mass of one mole of hydrogen?

Answer

$$6.02 \times 10^{23} \text{ molecules} = 2.0 \text{ g}$$

5. What is the mass of one molecule of helium?

Answer

$$\frac{4.0 \text{ g/mole}}{6.02 \times 10^{23} \text{ molecules/mole}} = 6.7 \times 10^{-24} \text{ g/molecule}$$

6. How many molecules are there in 4.5 g of water?

Answer

$$\frac{6.02 \times 10^{23} \text{ molecules/mole} \times 4.5 \text{ g}}{18 \text{ g/mole}} = 1.5 \times 10^{23} \text{ molecules}$$

7. A pencil mark 1.000 cm long, 0.50 cm wide, and 0.010 thick is made with a soft lead. Assuming that the pencil mark is pure carbon, and that the density of carbon is 2.0 g/cm^3, how many carbon atoms are there in the pencil mark?

Answer

$$V \times D = (1.00 \times 0.05 \times 0.01) \text{ cm}^3 \times 2.0 \text{ g/cm}^3 = 10^{-3} \text{ g}$$

$$IV = \frac{10^{-3} \text{ g} \times 6.02 \times 10^{23} \text{ atoms/mole}}{12\text{g/mole}} = 5 \times 10^{19} \text{ atoms}$$

Answers to Questions and Exercises

Text page references are provided for those questions which do not require computations. The student's answers will be individually stated, but should focus on the concepts developed in these text pages.

Factual Recall

1. 150
2. 151–52
3. 155–56
4. 156–57
5. 156–61

Apply Your Knowledge!

1. $\frac{Cl_2(\text{amu})}{O_2(\text{amu})} = \frac{Cl_2(\text{g/l})}{O_2(\text{g/l})}$

$\frac{Cl_2(\text{amu})}{32.00} = \frac{3.17 \text{ g/l}}{1.43 \text{ g/l}} = 32.00 \text{ amu} \times 2.2 = 71.00 \text{ amu}$

2. N_2 (molar mass) $= \frac{0.313 \text{ g}}{0.250 \text{ l}} \times 22.4 \text{ l} =$

$1.25 \text{ g/l} \times 22.4 \text{ l} = 28.000 \text{ g}$

3. Ethane (C_2H_6) = 30 amu, percent of C = 80
30 amu × 0.80 = 24 amu
Ethanol (C_2H_5OH) = 46 amu, percent of C = 52
46 amu × 0.52 = 24 amu
Methane (CH_4) = 16 amu, percent of C = 75
16 amu × 0.75 = 12 amu
Carbon dioxide (CO_2) = 44 amu, percent of C = 27
44 amu × 0.27 = 11.88 amu
C = 12 amu

CHAPTER **11**

THE GAS LAWS

GAS PRESSURE
(pp. 163–65)

Learning Objectives

1. To define the term *gas pressure*.
2. To describe the operation of a Torricelli barometer.
3. To state an atmosphere in terms of mm of mercury.
4. To define the term *torr*.
5. To describe the operation of a manometer.

THE RELATIONSHIP BETWEEN THE VOLUME AND PRESSURE OF A GAS
(pp. 166–70)

Learning Objectives

1. Given that the levels of an amount of mercury in both arms of a J-tube are equal, to explain why they become unequal as more mercury is added.
2. Given that the levels of an amount of mercury in both arms of a J-tube are equal, to explain why they are equal.
3. To explain why adding 760 mm of mercury to the open end of a J-tube, in which the two levels were initially equal, halves the volume of the gas in the closed end.
4. To state Boyle's law.
5. To write the equation for Boyle's law.
6. To plot pressure against volume from the data in Table 11–1.
7. To plot volume against 1/pressure from the data in Table 11–1

Demonstration I To Demonstrate Boyle's Law

Materials recommended: ring stand, clamp, J-tube, funnel.

The experiment with the J-tube is well worth doing as a class demonstration. (J-tubes are available at supply houses.) Support the J-tube in a vertical position by a stand and clamp. Place a small funnel in the top of the J-tube and pour just enough mercury into the tube to enclose the air in the left arm. The mercury in the two arms should be at the same level. Measure the length of this air column, represented by V in Fig. 11–3. Suppose this length is 18 cm. Since the mercury levels are the same, the pressure upon each surface is also the same. But the right arm is open to the air. Therefore the pressure on the mercury surface in the right arm is one atmosphere or 76 cm. Hence the pressure exerted by the enclosed air in the left arm is also 1 atm or 76 cm.

Now place a red pencil mark at the 9-cm level on the left arm and pour mercury through the funnel until the mercury surface in the left arm reaches this mark. Remove the funnel and, using a meter stick, measure the height of the mercury column above the level of the mercury in the left arm. By measurement the height is 76 cm. Therefore the pressure exerted upon mercury layer at level B is 2 atm (1 atm due to air pressure plus 1 atm due to the mercury column). Hence the pressure exerted by the enclosed air in the left arm is also 2 atm. Thus the pressure of the air was doubled when its volume was halved.

THE RELATIONSHIP BETWEEN THE VOLUME AND TEMPERATURE OF A GAS
(pp. 170–74)

Learning Objectives

1. To state Charles' law.
2. To state absolute zero in Celsius degrees.
3. To state absolute zero in Kelvin degrees.
4. To state the numerical factor for conversion from Celsius to Kelvin degrees.
5. To state the numerical factor for conversion from Kelvin to Celsius degrees.
6. To write the equation for Charles' law.

Demonstration II To Demonstrate Charles' Law

Materials recommended: 30-cm capillary tube, dish, metric ruler, copper wire, thermometer (Celsius), beaker, icewater, mercury, Bunsen burner, hot plate.

Charles' law can be verified by the simple apparatus shown in Fig. 11–7. Seal one end of a capillary tube (about 30 cm long) by holding it in a Bunsen flame. Warm the length of tube slightly to drive out some of the air and then hold the open end below the surface of mercury in a dish. As the air cools and contracts mercury enters the capillary tube. When the length of the mercury pellet is about 1 cm, remove the capillary tube from the dish of mercury and support it in a beaker while it cools to room temperature. At this temperature the length of the enclosed air column should be about 20 cm. Now attach the capillary tube to a ruler by copper wire. Record the reading of the closed end of the tube.

Place the tube in a tall beaker that contains a mixture of ice and water. Stir the mixture with a thermometer and when the temperature is 0°C read the level of the lower end of the pellet. The length of the air column is of course the difference between the two readings on the ruler.

Pour away the mixture of ice and water and fill the beaker with tap water. Again record the pellet reading and the temperature. Now place the beaker on an electric hot plate and stir the water. Record the pellet reading and the temperature at 20° intervals until the water begins to boil. Compute the length of the air column for each of the temperatures and plot a graph of length versus temperature.

THE COMBINED GAS LAW
(pp. 174–75)

Learning Objectives

1. To write the combined gas law equation.

THE GAS CONSTANT
(pp. 176–78)

Learning Objectives

1. To write the equation that incorporates the gas constant.
2. To write the value for the gas constant.

Demonstration III To Find the Density and Molecular Mass of Ether Vapor

Materials recommended: 2.5-l bottle, 2-hole stopper, pressure tubing, 4-mm glass tubing, 75-mm test tube, ether.

The determination of the molecular mass of ether vapor combines the vapor density method discussed in the last chapter and also employs the gas law equation. Ether is a low boiling liquid (B.P. 35°C) and we must find the volume, temperature and pressure of ether as a vapor. The apparatus suitable as a demonstration is shown in the diagram, Fig. TG11–1. The volume of the large bottle (it should be about 2.5 l) is found beforehand by filling it with water and measuring the volume of water with a 1000-ml graduate. The bottle must then be thoroughly dried (by a stream of air) before assembling the apparatus.

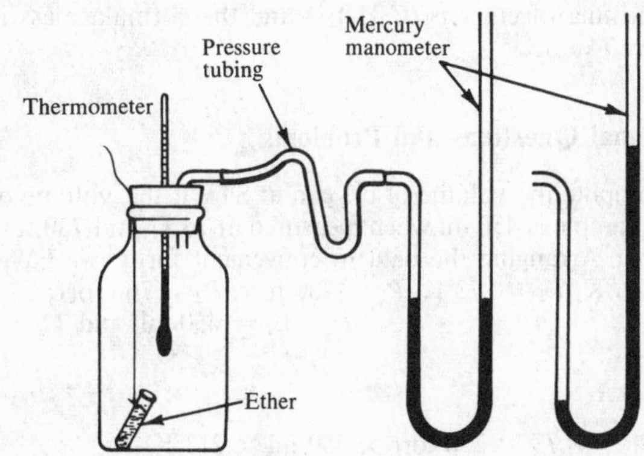

FIG. TG11–1

The bottle is closed by a tightly fitting two-hole rubber stopper which supports a thermometer and a right-angle bend. The bend is connected to the short arm of a manometer by a piece of pressure tubing, about two feet in length. The manometer is made out of 4-mm glass tubing; the short arm should be about 20 cm in length and the long arm about 30 cm.

Attach a piece of thread to a small test tube and then weigh the tube. Nearly fill the tube with ether and weigh again. The mass of ether is the difference between these two weights. (The mass of ether should be about two grams and it should be weighed to the nearest 0.01g) The tube and contents should now be lowered into the bottle and the thread held securely by the stopper in the position shown in the diagram.

Now tilt the bottle so that the ether falls out of the tube and into the bottle. The ether evaporates rapidly and the pressure of the vapor forces mercury down the short arm and up the long arm of the manometer. When the manometer mercury level is steady, measure the vertical distance between the mercury levels in the two arms. Also read the temperature of the ether vapor.

The following data were obtained in one of these experiments:

Volume of bottle = 2.56 l
Mass of ether = 1.96 g
Difference between mercury levels in manometer = 18.0 cm
Temperature of ether vapor = 23°C or 296°K

$$\text{Volume of ether vapor at STP} = 2.56\ \text{l} \times \frac{18.0\ \text{cm}}{76.0\ \text{cm}} \times \frac{273^\circ\text{K}}{296^\circ\text{K}} = 0.56\ \text{l}$$

$$\text{Density of ether vapor at STP} = \frac{M}{V} = \frac{1.96\ \text{g}}{0.56\ \text{l}} = 3.50\ \text{g/l}$$

$$\text{Molecular mass of ether in grams} = \text{mass of } 22.4\ \text{l at STP} = 3.50\ \text{g/l} \times 22.4\ \text{l} = 78\ \text{g}$$

(The formula of ether is $(C_2H_5)_2O$ and the formula mass is therefore 74 amu.)

Additional Questions and Problems

Compute the volume of oxygen at STP if the volume of the gas sample is 450 ml when measured at 23°C and 730 torr pressure. Arranging the data in convenient form, we have: $T_1 = 296^\circ\text{K}$, $T_2 = 273^\circ\text{K}$, $P_1 = 730$ torr, $P_2 = 760$ torr, $V_1 = 450$ ml, and $V_2 = ?$

Solution 1

$$V_2 = \frac{P_1V_1}{T_1} \times \frac{T_2}{P_2} = \frac{730\ \text{torr} \times 450\ \text{ml} \times 273^\circ\text{K}}{760\ \text{torr} \times 296^\circ\text{K}} = 400\ \text{ml}$$

Solution 2

As in earlier examples, this problem can also be solved by common sense by considering the effects of Boyle's and Charles' laws separately, instead of using the gas law equation in a stereotyped manner. Since the absolute temperature drops from 296°K to 273°K, the original volume (450 ml) is decreased by a factor of 273/296. And since the gas pressure increases from 730 mm to 760 mm, the original volume is decreased by a factor of 730/760. Therefore, the final volume is

$$450\ \text{ml} \times \frac{273}{296} \times \frac{730}{760} = 400\ \text{ml}$$

1. The volume of a gas is 50.0 ml when the pressure is 1520 torr and the temperature is 0°C, and becomes 25 ml when the temperature is raised to 546°C. Calculate the final pressure.

Answer

$$P_2 = \frac{P_1V_1T_2}{T_1V_2} = \frac{1520\ \text{torr} \times 50.0\ \text{ml} \times 819^\circ\text{K}}{273^\circ\text{K} \times 25.0\ \text{ml}} = 9120\ \text{torr}$$

2. A gas has a volume of 500 ml at 27°C and 600 torr. (a) Find the volume if the temperature is raised to 127°C. (b) Find the increase in pressure if the gas is in a sealed flask under the above conditions of temperature and pressure and if the temperature is raised to 127°C.

Answer

$$(a)\quad V_2 = \frac{V_1T_2}{T_1} = \frac{500\ \text{ml} \times 400^\circ\text{K}}{300^\circ\text{K}} = 667\ \text{ml}$$

$$(b)\quad P_2 = \frac{P_1T_2}{T_1} = \frac{60\ \text{cm} \times 400^\circ\text{K}}{300^\circ\text{K}} = 800\ \text{torr}$$

$$P_2 - P_1 = 800\ \text{torr} - 600\ \text{torr} = 200\ \text{torr}$$

3. A mass of 0.71 g of chlorine occupies 0.245 l at a temperature of 20°C and a pressure of 745 torr. Using the perfect gas law, compute the molecular mass of chlorine.

Answer

$$n = \frac{PV}{RT} = \frac{0.982\ \text{atm} \times 0.245\ \text{l}}{0.0821\ \text{l-atm/mole} \times 293^\circ\text{K}} = 0.0100\ \text{mole}$$

Hence, 0.0100 mole = 0.71 g and 1.00 mole = 71 g. Therefore the molecular mass of chlorine is 71 amu.

Answers to Questions and Exercises

Text page references are provided for those questions which do not require computations. The student's answers will be individually stated, but should focus on the concepts developed in those text pages.

Factual Recall

1. 164–65
2. 165, Fig. 11–2
3. 165, Fig. 11–2
4. 166–70
5. 170
6. Fig. 11–8
7. 170–71
8. 171–72
9. 176–78

Apply Your Knowledge!

1. He: 273°C − 269°C = 4°K
   H: 273°C − 253°C = 20°K
   O: 273°C − 183°C = 90°K
   CO: 273°C − 192°C = 81°K
   Ne: 273°C − 246°C = 27°K
   Cl: 273°C − 35°C = 238°K
2. H: 14°K − 273°C = −259°C
   N: 63°K − 273°C = −210°C
   Cl: 166°K − 273°C = −107°C
   NH_3: 240°K − 273°C = −33°C

3. $V_2 = \frac{P_1V_1T_2}{T_1P_2} = \frac{380 \text{ torr} \times 2.24 \text{ l} \times 273°\text{K}}{546°\text{K} \times 760 \text{ torr}} = 0.56 \text{ l}$

4. $V_2 = \frac{V_1P_1}{P_2} = \frac{2.00 \text{ l} \times 760 \text{ torr}}{1520 \text{ torr}} = 1.00 \text{ l}$

5. $P_2 = \frac{P_1V_1T_2}{T_1V_2} = \frac{760 \text{ torr} \times 500 \text{ ml} \times 283°\text{K}}{298°\text{K} \times 500 \text{ ml}}$
   $= 722 \text{ torr}$

6. $V_2 = \frac{V_1T_2}{T_1} = \frac{900 \text{ ml} \times 350°\text{K}}{300°\text{K}} = 1050 \text{ ml}$

7. $T_2 = \frac{T_1P_2V_2}{P_1V_1} = \frac{293°\text{K} \times 1000 \text{ torr} \times 200 \text{ l}}{760 \text{ torr} \times 150 \text{ l}}$
   $= 514°\text{K}$ or $241°\text{C}$

8. $T_2 = \frac{T_1P_2}{P_1} = \frac{293°\text{K} \times 1000 \text{ torr}}{700 \text{ torr}}$
   $= 418°\text{K}$ or $145°\text{C}$

9. $V_2 = \frac{P_1V_1T_2}{T_1P_2} = \frac{760 \text{ torr} \times 100 \text{ ml} \times 409.5°\text{K}}{273°\text{K} \times 570 \text{ torr}}$
   $= 200 \text{ ml}$

10. $V_2 = \frac{V_1T_2}{T_1} = \frac{100 \text{ ml} \times 409.5°\text{K}}{136.5°\text{K}} = 300 \text{ ml}$

11. $V_2 = \frac{V_1T_2P_1}{T_1P_2} = \frac{3.65 \text{ l} \times 546°\text{K} \times 760 \text{ torr}}{273°\text{K} \times 1520 \text{ torr}}$
    $= 3.65 \text{ l}$

CHAPTER 12

THE KINETIC MOLECULAR THEORY

Learning Objectives

1. To summarize the postulates of the kinetic molecular theory.
2. To derive Boyle's law from the kinetic theory.
3. To derive Charles' law from the kinetic theory.
4. To derive Avogadro's law from the kinetic theory.

GAS DIFFUSION
(pp. 184–85)

Learning Objectives

1. To define gas diffusion.
2. To define rate of diffusion.
3. To write the equation that applies kinetic theory to gas diffusion.
4. To state Graham's law of diffusion.

Demonstration I The Diffusion of Ammonia and Hydrogen Chloride

Materials recommended: ring stand, clamp, 1 meter glass tube (about 25mm o.d.), 2 one-hole rubber stoppers, glass rods, concentrated ammonia water, concentrated hydrochloric acid.

This experiment should be done as a demonstration to verify Graham's law of diffusion. Let symbols R_{NH_3} and R_{HCl} represent the rates of diffusion of ammonia and hydrogen chloride molecules.

Then,

$$\frac{R_{NH_3}}{R_{HCl}} = \frac{\sqrt{\text{molecular mass of HCl}}}{\sqrt{\text{molecular mass of NH}_3}} = \sqrt{\frac{36.5}{17}} = \sqrt{2.14}$$
$$= 1.46$$

Therefore,

$$\frac{\text{distance traveled by NH}_3\text{ molecules}}{\text{distance traveled by HCl molecules}} = \frac{1.46}{1}$$

Suppose the length of the tube is 100 cm and that the leading molecules of NH_3 travel d cm. Then, leading molecules of HCl travel $(100 - d)$ cm. Hence,

$$\frac{d\text{ cm}}{(100 - d)\text{ cm}} = 1.46 \quad \text{and} \quad d = 59.5\text{ cm}$$

Thus the white ring should appear about 60 cm from the ammonia end of the tube.

Measure the length of the tube and compute the spot where the white ring should appear. Mark a ring around the tube with a colored grease pencil at the computed position.

The glass tube should be about one meter long and one inch in diameter. Select two one-hole rubber stoppers that fit snugly into the tube. Half fill the hole in each of the stoppers by inserting a short piece of glass rod about half way into the opening. Put two drops of concentrated ammonia water into the hole of one of the stoppers and two drops of concentrated hydrochloric acid into the other hole. Then push the two stoppers into the ends of the tube at the same moment. Gas molecules escape from the solutions and a white ring of smoke is formed where the molecules meet and react. It usually takes about 10 minutes for the smoke to appear. Does the position of the ring coincide, or nearly coincide, with the predicted position?

Demonstration II The Diffusion of Hydrogen

Materials recommended: Ring stand, clamp, 2-l beaker, porous cup, 2-l glass bottle, 2-hole rubber stopper, 1-hole rubber stopper, glass tubing.

Since rates of diffusion of gases are inversely proportional to their molecular masses, they must also be inversely proportional to their densities. The density of air is 1.293 g/l and the density of hydrogen is 0.090 g/l. Hence,

$$\frac{\text{diffusion rate of hydrogen}}{\text{diffusion rate of air}} = \sqrt{\frac{1.293}{0.090}}$$

$$= \sqrt{143}$$

$$= 12$$

That is, hydrogen diffuses about 12 times as fast as air. The big difference between these diffusion rates can be shown by the following spectacular demonstration.

Set up the apparatus as shown in TG12–1.

A glass tube (1/2 inch in diameter) connects a porous cup to a bottle containing water. The end of the bent outlet from the bottle is constricted into a nozzle or jet. First displace the air in a 2-l beaker by hydrogen. This is done by inverting the beaker and leading hydrogen from a cylinder through a glass tube that reaches the top of the beaker. Then place the beaker of hydrogen over the porous cup and notice that a stream of water is forced out of the bottle through the outlet tube.

Hydrogen from the beaker diffuses into the cup and, at the same time, air from the cup diffuses into the beaker. But the stream of water proves that the pressure on the water surface has been increased. Therefore the rate of diffusion of hydrogen molecules into the cup must be greater than the rate of diffusion of air molecules out of it.

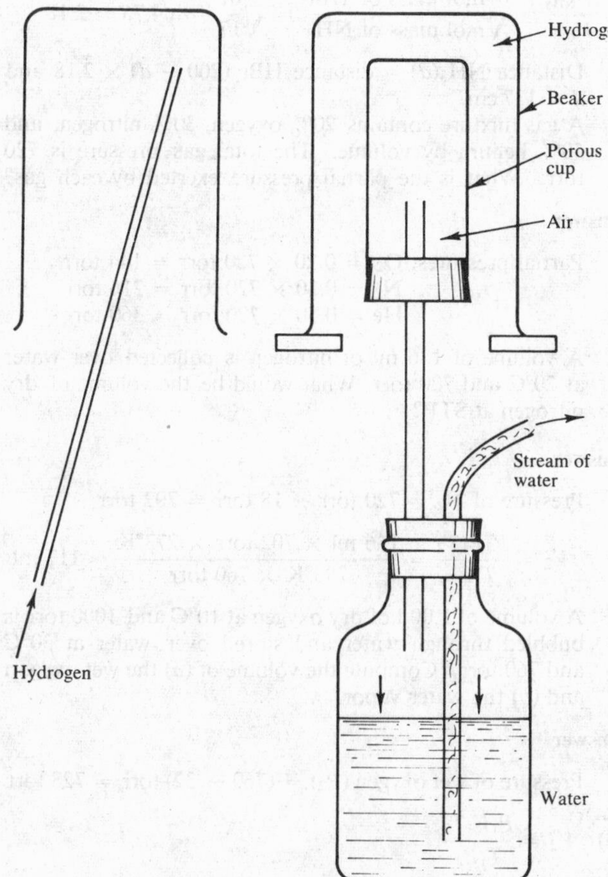

FIG. TG12–1

THE LAW OF PARTIAL PRESSURES
(pp. 185–88)

Learning Objectives

1. To define partial pressure.
2. To state the law of partial pressures.
3. To apply kinetic theory to the law of partial pressures.
4. To define the term *saturation* as applied to vapor pressure.
5. To define the term *equilibrium* as applied to vapor pressure.
6. To define vapor pressure.
7. To state the vapor pressure of water at 20°C.
8. To write the equation for the vapor pressure of hydrogen collected over water.

Demonstration III To Demonstrate the Vapor Pressures of Different Liquids

Materials recommended: Battery jar, glass tubing, medicine dropper, mercury, water, alcohol, ether.

Figure 12–7 in the text shows four mercury barometers and the demonstration allows us to compare the vapor pressures of water, alcohol, and ether. First, water. Half fill the stem of a medicine dropper with water. Hold the opening of the dropper below the end of the barometer tube and squeeze the bulb so that a drop or two of water is released. Since water is less dense than mercury it rises to the top of the mercury column where it instantly evaporates and creates a vapor pressure. If necessary, repeat the operation until a layer of liquid water rests upon the surface of the mercury. When this happens the space above the mercury must be saturated with water vapor. Notice that the mercury column falls about 2 cm (or 20 mm). Therefore the pressure of water vapor at room temperature is about 20 mm. The pressure exerted by the layer of liquid water is so small that it cannot be measured with this apparatus. (Remember that the pressure of a 34-foot column of water is equal to the pressure of a 76-cm column of mercury.)

Alcohol. Use a dry medicine dropper and repeat the above operation using alcohol in the second barometer tube. Observe that the depression of the mercury column (and therefore the vapor pressure of alcohol) is about 4.5 cm or 45 mm.

Ether. Repeat the operation, forcing ether into the third barometer tube. This time the mercury column falls about 43 cm or 430 mm.

DEVIATIONS FOR THE GAS LAWS
(pp. 188–89)

Learning Objectives

1. To define a *real* gas.
2. To define an *ideal* gas.
3. To state the approximate pressures at which the constant *PV* breaks down.

Additional Questions and Problems

1. Compute the average velocity of molecules of carbon dioxide at 0°C, given the average velocity of oxygen molecules at the same temperature is 1000 miles per hour.

Answer

$$\text{Velocity of } CO_2 = \sqrt{\frac{\text{mol mass of } O_2}{\text{mol mass of } CO_2}} \times \text{velocity of } O_2$$

$$= \sqrt{\frac{32 \text{ amu}}{44 \text{ amu}}} \times 1000 \text{ miles/hour}$$

$$= \sqrt{0.73} \times 1000 \text{ miles/hour}$$

$$= 850 \text{ miles/hour}$$

2. If methane (CH_4) diffuses the length of a 100-cm tube in 10 sec, how far would ethane gas (C_2H_6) diffuse in the same time?

Answer

$$\frac{V_{C_2H_6}}{V_{CH_4}} = \sqrt{\frac{\text{mol mass of } CH_4}{\text{mol mass of } C_2H_6}} = \sqrt{\frac{16}{30}}$$

$$= \sqrt{0.53} = 0.73$$

Distance C_2H_6 = distance $CH_4 \times 0.73 = 73$ cm.

3. Ammonia and hydrogen bromide gas are introduced into the opposite ends of a 200-cm tube at the same instant. On contact, the gases react to form the white solid ammonium bromide. Where will the ring of ammonium bromide be formed?

Answer

$$\frac{V_{NH_3}}{V_{HBr}} = \sqrt{\frac{\text{mol mass of HBr}}{\text{mol mass of } NH_3}} = \sqrt{\frac{81}{17}} = \sqrt{4.75} = 2.18$$

Distance $NH_3(d)$ = distance HBr $(200 - d) \times 2.18$ and $d = 137$ cm.

4. A gas mixture contains 20% oxygen, 30% nitrogen, and 50% helium by volume. The total gas pressure is 720 torr. What is the partial pressure exerted by each gas?

Answer

Partial pressures: $O_2 = 0.20 \times 720$ torr $= 144$ torr
$N_2 = 0.30 \times 720$ torr $= 216$ torr
$He = 0.50 \times 720$ torr $= 360$ torr

5. A volume of 136 ml of nitrogen is collected over water at 20°C and 720 torr. What would be the volume of dry nitrogen at STP?

Answer

Pressure of N_2 = 720 torr − 18 torr = 702 torr

$$V_2 = \frac{V_1P_1T_2}{T_1P_2} = \frac{136 \text{ ml} \times 702 \text{ torr} \times 273°\text{K}}{293°\text{K} \times 760 \text{ torr}} = 117 \text{ ml}$$

6. A volume of 1.00 l of dry oxygen at 10°C and 1000 torr is bubbled through water and stored over water at 30°C and 760 torr. Compute the volume of (*a*) the wet oxygen and (*b*) the water vapor.

Answer

Pressure of wet oxygen (P_2) = (760 − 32) torr = 728 torr

$$(a) \quad V_2 = \frac{P_1V_1T_2}{T_1P_2}$$

$$= \frac{1000 \text{ torr} \times 1.00 \text{ l} \times 303°\text{K}}{283°\text{K} \times 728 \text{ torr}} = 1.47 \text{ l}$$

(*b*) Volume of water vapor = 1.47 l

7. The volume of a gas collected over water is 298 ml at 25°C and 754 torr. Compute the volume of this same amount of gas at 210 torr and −63°C if it is dried.

Answer

$$P_1 = 754 \text{ torr} - 24 \text{ torr} = 730 \text{ torr}$$

$$V_2 = \frac{P_1V_1T_2}{T_1P_2} = \frac{730 \text{ torr} \times 298 \text{ ml} \times 210°\text{K}}{298°\text{K} \times 210 \text{ torr}} = 730 \text{ ml}$$

Answers to Questions and Exercises

Text page references are provided for those questions which do not require computations. The student's answers will be individually stated, but should focus on the concepts developed in these text pages.

Factual Recall

1. 181–82
2. 182
3. 182–84
4. 184
5. 185–87

Apply Your Knowledge!

1. $$\text{Moles of } CO_2 = \frac{0.60 \times 44 \text{ g}}{44 \text{ g/mole}} = 0.60 \text{ mole}$$

$$\text{Moles of CO} = \frac{0.40 \times 28 \text{ g}}{28 \text{ g/mole}} = 0.40 \text{ mole}$$

2. (*a*) Vapor pressure = 18 torr
(*b*) Partial pressure of H_2 = (720 − 18) = 702 torr
(*c*) Pressure of dry H_2 = 702 torr

CHAPTER 13

FORMULAS, EQUATIONS, AND CHEMICAL CALCULATIONS

EMPIRICAL FORMULAS
(pp. 191–93)

Learning Objectives

1. To define the term *empirical formula.*
2. To state the basis for the derivation of an empirical formula.
3. To calculate the formula for tin oxide as in Example 13–1.

MOLECULAR FORMULAS
(pp. 193–95)

Learning Objectives

1. To define the term *molecular formula.*
2. To state that molecular formulas are applicable only to substances composed of molecules.
3. To state the empirical formulas of acetylene and benzene.
4. To state the molecular formulas of acetylene and benzene.
5. To state the difference between atomic mass and molecular mass.

Suggested Teacher Commentary

In this chapter we are concerned with stoichiometry which is the quantitative relationships (such as mass, moles, or volumes) of reactants and products in chemical reactions If we know the composition of a compound (either the percentage composition of the constituent elements or the weights of the constituent elements in a known weight of the compound) we can derive the empirical formula of the compound.

Empirical Formulas

An empirical formula indicates the ratio of the various *atoms* in a compound. On the other hand, a molecular formula indicates the actual number of atoms of each element in one molecule of the compound.

It is important to distinguish between the meaning of the terms *empirical* and *molecular* formula. As formulas they are usually different but they may be the same, and in some cases the term molecular formula has no meaning at all.

The empirical formula of any compound can always be determined, but the molecular formula of a compound can be found only if the compound exists in molecular form. For example, we know that gases are made up of molecules. The compounds acetylene and benzene have the same empirical formula, namely CH. And since they exist as gases we can compute their molecular masses and derive their molecular formulas. The molecular formula for benzene is C_6H_6 and for acetylene it is C_2H_2. On the other hand there are no molecules in crystalline solids, and the empirical formula is the only kind of formula applicable to such compounds. For instance, sodium chloride has an empirical formula (NaCl) but no molecular formula.

In computing empirical formulas we first compute the moles of the constituent atoms. For example, one mole of oxygen atoms is the mass of 6.0×10^{23} atoms of oxygen which is 16.0 g, not 32.0 g. One mole of oxygen molecules is, of course, 32.0 g. But we are concerned only with ratios of atoms in an empirical formula, not with molecules.

FORMULA MASSES
(p. 195)

Learning Objectives

1. To define the term *formula mass*.
2. To state the difference between formula mass and molecular mass.
3. To state why formula mass can be applied where molecular mass cannot.
4. To compute the formula mass of sodium chloride.

VALENCE AND FORMULAS
(pp. 195–97)

Learning Objectives

1. To define the term *valence*.
2. To define valence for ionic bonds.
3. To define valence for polar covalent bonds.
4. To state the conditions that determine whether valence is negative or positive.
5. To state the rule for the order of elements in a compound formula.
6. To state the rule for the algebraic sum of valences in a compound formula.
7. To state the valences of calcium and chlorine.
8. To balance the valences in calcium chloride.
9. To write the formula for calcium chloride.
10. To define the term *multivalence*.
11. To state which groups of elements possess multivalence.
12. To state the reason for the multivalence of the transition elements in terms of electron configuration.
13. To balance the valences for copper (I) oxide and copper (II) oxide.
14. Given the valences of copper and oxygen, to write the formulas for copper (I) oxide and copper (II) oxide.
15. To state the meaning of the roman numerals in compounds of multivalent elements.

TO CALCULATE THE PERCENTAGE COMPOSITION OF A COMPOUND FROM ITS FORMULA
(pp. 197–98)

Learning Objectives

1. To state the quantitative meaning of the symbol of an element in a formula.
2. To calculate the percentage composition by mass of glucose, as in Example 13–3.

EQUATIONS
(pp. 198–200)

Learning Objectives

1. To define a chemical equation.
2. To define the term *coefficient*.
3. To define the term *reaction*.
4. To state the purpose of the coefficient in chemical equation.

CALCULATIONS OF MASS AND VOLUMES USING EQUATIONS
(pp. 200–05)

Learning Objectives

1. To define the term *stoichiometry*.
2. To state the three types of stoichiometric problems.
3. To describe a mass-mass problem.
4. To describe a mass-volume problem.
5. To describe a volume-volume problem.

Additional Questions and Problems

1. By analysis, a compound contains 2.22% hydrogen, 26.7% carbon, and 71.1% oxygen. What is its simplest formula?

Answer

$$\text{Moles of H atoms} = \frac{2.22\text{ g}}{1.00\text{ g/mole}} = 2.22\text{ moles} \qquad \text{one}$$

$$\text{Moles of C atoms} = \frac{26.7\text{ g}}{12.0\text{ g/mole}} = 2.22\text{ moles} \quad \text{or} \quad \text{one}$$

$$\text{Moles of O atoms} = \frac{71.1\text{ g}}{16.0\text{ g/mole}} = 4.45\text{ moles} \qquad \text{two}$$

The empirical formula is therefore HCO_2.

2. If 20.0 *g* of tin combines with oxygen to give 22.7 g of tin oxide, find the simplest formula of the oxide and give its name.

Answer

$$\text{Moles of Sn} = \frac{20.0\text{ g}}{119\text{ g/mole}} = 0.167\text{ mole}$$

$$\text{Moles of O} = \frac{2.7\text{ g}}{16.0\text{ g/mole}} = 0.167\text{ mole}$$

The empirical formula is therefore SnO, and the name is tin (II) oxide or stannous oxide.

3. The simplest formula for butane is C_2H_5. Its molecular mass is 58. Find its molecular formula.

Answer C_4H_{10}

4. A sample of a compound contains 0.16 g hydrogen, 1.28 g oxygen, and 1.12 g nitrogen. (*a*) Find the simplest formula. (*b*) Find the molecular formula if the molecular mass is 64.

Answer

$$(a)\quad \text{Moles of H} = \frac{0.16\text{ g}}{1.00\text{ g/mole}} = 0.16\text{ mole} \qquad \text{two}$$

$$\text{Moles of O} = \frac{1.28\text{ g}}{16.0\text{ g/mole}} = 0.08\text{ mole} \quad \text{or} \quad \text{one}$$

$$\text{Moles of N} = \frac{1.12\text{ g}}{14.0\text{ g/mole}} = 0.08\text{ mole} \qquad \text{one}$$

The empirical formula is H_2ON.

$$(b)\quad (H_2ON)_n = 64$$

$$(2 + 16 + 14)_n = 64$$

$$n = \frac{64}{32} = 2$$

The molecular formula is therefore $H_4O_2N_2$.

5. Find the molecular formula of a compound, given the following data: phosphorus, 20.2%; oxygen, 10.43%; chlorine, 69.34%; molecular mass, 154.

Answer $POCl_3$

6. Hydrated sodium carbonate contains 37.2% Na_2CO_3 and 62.8% water. Find the formula of the hydrate.

Answer

$$\text{Moles of } Na_2CO_3 = \frac{37.2\text{ g}}{106\text{ g/mole}} = 0.35\text{ mole} \qquad \text{one}$$

or

$$\text{Moles of } H_2O = \frac{62.8\text{ g}}{18.0\text{ g/mole}} = 3.5\text{ moles} \qquad \text{ten}$$

The empirical formula is therefore $Na_2CO_3 \cdot 10H_2O$.

7. Find the number of molecules of water of hydration if 8.00 g of a salt hydrate lose 4.00 g when strongly heated and if the formula mass of the anhydrous salt is 108.

Answer

$$\text{Moles of salt} = \frac{4.00\text{ g}}{108\text{ g/mole}} = 0.0371\text{ mole}$$

$$\text{Moles of } H_2O = \frac{4.00\text{ g}}{18.0\text{ g/mole}} = 0.223\text{ mole}$$

$$\frac{\text{Moles of } H_2O}{\text{Moles of salt}} = \frac{0.223}{0.0371} = \frac{6}{1}$$

Six molecules of water of hydration.

8. Calculate the percentage of oxygen in (*a*) CO, (*b*) CO_2, (*c*) CaO, (*d*) $MgCO_3$, (*e*) $Ca_3(PO_4)_2$, (*f*) $Na_2CO_3 \cdot H_2O$.

Answer

(*a*) 57.1%, (*b*) 72.7%, (*c*) 28.6%, (*d*) 57.1%, (*e*) 41.3% (*f*) 51.6%

9. Find the percentage composition of (*a*) HCl (*b*) NH_4OH (*c*) NaCl (*d*) H_2SO_4 (*e*) $Ca(OH)_2$.

Answer

(*a*) 2.7% H, 97.3% Cl, (*b*) 14.3% H, 40% N, 45.7% O (*c*) 39.3% Na, 60.7% Cl, (*d*) 2.0% H, 32.7% S, 65.3% O, (*e*) 2.7% H, 43.3% O, 54.0% Ca

10. Calculate the percentage of water in hydrated barium chloride, $BaCl_2 \cdot 2H_2O$.

Answer 14.8% H_2O

11. Calculate the percentage of (*a*) water, (*b*) oxygen, (*c*) hydrogen in $CaCl_2 \cdot 6H_2O$.

Answer

(*a*) 49.3% H_2O, (*b*) 43.8% O, (*c*) 5.5% H

12. Calculate the percentage of nitrogen in NH_4NO_2.

Answer 43.7% N

13. A sample of ammonia, occupying 300 ml at STP, has a mass of 0.228 g. Compute (*a*) the density of the gas, (*b*) the molecular mass of the gas.

Answer

(*a*) $\text{Density} = \dfrac{0.228\ \text{g}}{0.300\ \text{l}} = 0.76\ \text{g/l}$

(*b*) $\text{Molecular mass} = 0.76\ \text{g/l} \times 22.4\ \text{l/mole} = 17.0\ \text{g/mole}$

14. Calculate the volume at standard pressure of 20 g of chlorine at (*a*) 0°C, (*b*) 27°C.

Answer

(*a*) 6.3 l, (*b*) 6.9 l

15. Find the molecular mass of a gas if 150 ml of it at STP have a mass of 0.1875 g.

Answer

$$\text{Molecular mass in } g = \frac{0.1875\ \text{g} \times 22.4\ \text{l/mole}}{0.150\ \text{l}} = 28.0\ \text{g/mole}$$

16. The volume of 1.96 g of a gas is 1.19 l at 27°C and 700 torr pressure. Find the correct formula of the gas if its composition is 81.8% carbon and 18.2% hydrogen.

Answer

$$\text{Volume at STP} = \frac{1.19\ \text{l} \times 273°\text{K} \times 700\ \text{torr}}{300°\text{K} \times 760\ \text{torr}} = 1.00\ \text{l}$$

$$\text{Molar mass} = 1.96\ \text{g/l} \times 22.4\ \text{l/mole} = 44\ \text{g/mole}$$

$$\text{Moles of C} = \frac{0.818 \times 44\ \text{g}}{12.0\ \text{g/mole}} = 3.0\ \text{moles}$$

$$\text{Moles of H} = \frac{0.182 \times 44\ \text{g}}{1.00\ \text{g/mole}} = 8.0\ \text{moles}$$

The empirical formula is C_3H_8. Since $(C_3H_8)_n = 44n$, = 1, the molecular formula is C_3H_8.

17. Find the molecular mass of a gas if 0.0500 mole of it weighs 3.00 *g* and occupies 1140 ml at 20°C and 800 torr pressure.

Answer

$$\text{Mass of one mole} = \frac{3.00\ \text{g}}{0.050\ \text{mole}} = 60.0\ \text{g/mole}$$

$$\text{Molecular mass} = 60.0\ \text{amu}$$

18. Compute the mass of phosphoric oxide formed by burning 117 g of phosphorus.

Answer 268 g of P_4O_{10}

19. Steam reacts with hot iron, giving hydrogen and the magnetic oxide of iron, Fe_3O_4. How much iron must react to liberate 1.00 g of hydrogen?

Answer 21.0 g of Fe

20. An excess of sulfur is added to 0.50 mole of iron and the mixture is strongly heated. (*a*) How much sulfur reacts with the iron? (*b*) How many moles of iron (II) sulfide are formed?

Answer

Fe	+	S	→	FeS
1 mole		1 mole		1 mole

(*a*) 0.50 mole of S = 16.0 g
(*b*) 0.50 mole of FeS

21. Zinc reacts with chlorine to give zinc chloride. If 0.500 mole of zinc reacts, calculate the (*a*) mass of zinc chloride formed, (*b*) moles of chlorine consumed.

Answer

Zn	+	Cl_2	→	$ZnCl_2$
1 mole 65 g		1 mole		1 mole 136 g

(*a*) Mass $ZnCl_2$ = 0.500 mole × 136 g/mole = 68 g
(*b*) 0.50 mole of chlorine consumed.

22. Sodium reacts with water to give sodium hydroxide (NaOH) and hydrogen. If 9.2 g of sodium react, calculate the (*a*) mass of water consumed, (*b*) moles of NaOH formed, (*c*) moles of hydrogen liberated.

Answer

2Na	+	$2H_2O$	→	2NaOH	+	H_2
2 moles 46 g		2 moles 36 g		2 moles 80 g		1 mole 2 g

(*a*) $\text{Moles of Na} = \dfrac{9.2\ \text{g}}{23\ \text{g/mole}} = 0.400\ \text{mole}$

Mass of water = 0.400 mole × 18 g/mole = 7.2 g

(*b*) Moles of NaOH = 0.400 mole
(*c*) Moles of H_2 = 0.200 mole

23. If 0.250 mole of aluminum reacts with oxygen to give aluminum oxide, calculate the (*a*) moles of product, (*b*) mass of oxygen consumed.

Answer

4Al	+	$3O_2$	→	$2Al_2O_3$
4 moles 108 g		3 moles 96 g		2 moles 204 g

(*a*) 0.125 mole of Al_2O_3

(*b*) Moles of O_2 = 0.250 mole × 3/4 = 0.188 mole
Mass of oxygen = 0.188 mole × 32 g/mole = 6.02 g

24. A mixture of 50.0 g of aluminum and 2.00 moles of oxygen is strongly heated. (*a*) Compute the mass of product. (*b*) Compute the moles of reactant in excess.

Answer

(*a*) $4Al + 3O_2 \rightarrow 2Al_2O_3$
4 moles 3 moles 2 moles

$$\text{Moles of Al} = \frac{50.0 \text{ g}}{27 \text{ g/mole}} = 1.86 \text{ moles}$$

1.86 moles of Al reacts with $1.86 \times 3/4 = 1.40$ moles of oxygen, and the oxygen is in excess.

$$\text{Mass of } Al_2O_3 = 0.93 \text{ mole} \times 204 \text{ g/mole} = 190 \text{ g}$$

(*b*) Moles of O_2 in excess $= 2.00 - 1.40 = 0.60$ mole.

25. Zinc reacts with NaOH according to the equation,

$$Zn + 2NaOH = Na_2ZnO_2 + H_2$$

Compute the moles of hydrogen liberated when 4.0 g NaOH are added to 3.25 g zinc.

Answer

$Zn + 2NaOH \rightarrow Na_2ZnO_2 + H_2$
1 mole 65 g 2 moles 80 g 1 mole

$$3.25 \text{ g Zn} = \frac{3.25 \text{ g}}{65 \text{ g/mole}} = 0.0500 \text{ mole Zn}$$

$$4.0 \text{ g NaOH} = \frac{4.0 \text{ g}}{40 \text{ g/mole}} = 0.100 \text{ mole NaOH}$$

Therefore, neither is in excess.

$$\text{Moles of } H_2 \text{ released} = \text{moles of Zn used up} = 0.0500 \text{ mole}$$

26. Find the moles of magnesium needed to produce 20.0 l of hydrogen at STP by passing steam over hot magnesium.

Answer

$Mg + H_2O \rightarrow MgO + H_2$
1 mole 24.3 g 1 mole 22.4 l

(*a*) $\text{Moles of Mg} = \text{moles of } H_2 = \dfrac{20.0 \text{ l}}{22.4 \text{ l/mole}} = 0.89 \text{ mole.}$

(*b*) Mass of Mg $= 0.89$ mole $\times$ 24.3 g/mole $= 21.7$ g.

27. The equation for the complete combustion of methane is

$$CH_4 + 2O_2 = CO_2 + 2H_2O$$

If 8.0 g of methane are burned, compute (*a*) the volume of oxygen at STP consumed, (*b*) the volume of carbon dioxide produced at 546°C, (*c*) the moles of water formed.

Answer

(*a*) $CH_4 + 2O_2 \rightarrow CO_2 + 2H_2O$
1 mole 16.0 g 2 moles 44.8 l 1 mole 22.4 l 2 moles

$$\text{Moles of } O_2 = 2 \times \text{moles of } CH_4 = 2 \times \frac{8.0 \text{ g}}{16 \text{ g/mole}} = 1.00 \text{ mole}$$

$$\text{Volume of } O_2 \text{ at STP} = 1.00 \text{ mole} \times 22.4 \text{ l/mole} = 22.4 \text{ l}$$

(*b*) $\text{Volume } CO_2 = \dfrac{\text{Volume } O_2}{2} = \dfrac{22.4 \text{ l}}{2} \times \dfrac{819°\text{K}}{273°\text{K}} = 33.6 \text{ l}$

(*c*) Moles of H_2O = moles of O_2 = 1.00 mole.

28. How many grams of carbon will combine with 4400 ml of oxygen measured at 800°C if the product is (*a*) carbon dioxide, (*b*) carbon monoxide?

Answer

$$\text{Volume } O_2 \text{ at } 273°\text{K} = \frac{4.4 \text{ l} \times 273°\text{K}}{1073°\text{K}} = 1.12 \text{ l}$$

(*a*) $C + O_2 \rightarrow CO_2$
1 mole 12 g 1 mole 22.4 l

$$\text{Moles of C} = \text{moles of } O_2 = \frac{1.12 \ l}{22.4 \ l\text{/mole}} = 0.0500 \text{ mole}$$

$$\text{Mass of C} = 0.0500 \text{ mole} \times 12 \text{ g/mole} = 0.60 \text{ g}$$

(*b*) $2C + O_2 \rightarrow 2CO$
Mass of C = twice mass of C in (*a*) = 1.20 *g*

29. Calculate the mass of zinc needed to produce 20.0 *l* of hydrogen at 27°C and 770 torr pressure by passing steam over hot zinc.

Answer

$Zn + H_2O \rightarrow ZnO + H_2$
1 mole 65.4 g 1 mole 22.4 l

$$\text{Volume of } H_2 \text{ at STP} = 20.0 \text{ l} \times \frac{273°\text{K}}{300°\text{K}} \times \frac{770 \text{ torr}}{760 \text{ torr}} = 18.5 \text{ l}$$

$$\text{Moles of Zn} = \text{moles of } H_2 = \frac{18.5 \text{ l}}{22.4 \text{ l/mole}} = 0.826 \text{ mole}$$

$$\text{Mass of Zn} = 0.826 \text{ mole} \times 65.4 \text{ g/mole} = 54.3 \text{ g}$$

30. One volume of methane is consumed in the reaction,

$$CH_4 + 2O_2 = CO_2 + 2H_2O$$

all gas volumes being measured at 500°C and one atm pressure. (*a*) How many volumes of oxygen must be used? (*b*) How many volumes of carbon dioxide are produced?

Answer

(*a*) 2 volumes O_2, (*b*) one volume CO_2

31. Compute the volume of (*a*) hydrogen, (*b*) nitrogen formed at STP if 600 ml of ammonia at STP are completely decomposed.

Answer

$$\underset{2\text{ moles}}{2NH_3} \rightarrow \underset{1\text{ mole}}{N_2} + \underset{3\text{ moles}}{3H_2}$$

(*a*) $$\text{Volume } H_2 = 600 \text{ ml} \times \frac{3 \text{ moles}}{2 \text{ moles}} = 900 \text{ ml}$$

(*b*) $$\text{Volume } N_2 = \text{volume } NH_3/2 = 300 \text{ ml}$$

32. A gas mixture, prepared from 3.36 l of oxygen at STP and 4.48 l of carbon monoxide at 273°C and 380 torr pressure, is heated until the reaction to give carbon dioxide is complete. Compute (*a*) the volume of carbon dioxide produced at 546°C and 760 torr pressure, (*b*) the volume of gas reactant in excess at 546°C and 760 torr pressure.

Answer

$$\underset{2\text{ moles}}{2CO} + \underset{1\text{ mole}}{O_2} \rightarrow \underset{2\text{ moles}}{2CO_2}$$

$$\text{Volume of CO at STP} = \frac{4.48 \text{ l} \times 273°\text{K} \times 380 \text{ torr}}{546°\text{K} \times 760 \text{ torr}} = 1.12 \text{ l}$$

$$\frac{\text{Volume CO}}{\text{Volume } O_2} = \frac{1.12 \text{ l}}{3.36 \text{ l}} = \frac{1}{3}$$

The oxygen is in excess.

(*a*) $$\text{Moles of CO} = \frac{1.12 \text{ l}}{22.4 \text{ l/mole}} = 0.0500 \text{ mole}$$

$$\text{Moles of } CO_2 = 0.0500 \text{ mole}$$

$$\text{Volume of } CO_2 = \frac{0.0500 \text{ mole} \times 22.4 \text{ l/mole} \times 819°\text{K}}{273°\text{K}} = 3.36 \text{ l}$$

(*b*) $$\text{Volume of } O_2 \text{ in excess} = (3.36 \text{ l} - 0.56 \text{ l}) \times \frac{819°\text{K}}{273°\text{K}} = 2.80 \text{ l} \times 3 = 8.40 \text{ l}$$

33. Three l of the gas propane are consumed in the reaction,

$$C_3H_8 + 5O_2 \rightarrow 3CO_2 + 4H_2O$$

all gas volumes being measured at 300°C. (*a*) What volume of oxygen must be used? (*b*) What volume of carbon dioxide is produced?

Answer

(*a*) Volume O_2 = 15.0 l (*b*) Volume CO_2 = 9.0 l

34. 0.100 mole of carbon monoxide is burned. (*a*) Compute the volume of oxygen at 273°C required for the combustion. (*b*) Compute the volume of carbon dioxide produced at 819°C.

Answer

(*a*) $$\underset{2\text{ moles}}{2CO} + \underset{1\text{ mole}}{O_2} \rightarrow \underset{2\text{ moles}}{2CO_2}$$

$$\text{Moles of } O_2 = 0.0500 \text{ mole}$$

$$\text{Volume of } O_2 = \frac{0.0500 \text{ mole} \times 22.4 \text{ l/mole} \times 546°\text{K}}{273°\text{K}} = 2.24 \text{ l}$$

(*b*) $$\text{Volume } CO_2 = 0.100 \text{ mole} \times 22.4 \text{ l/mole} \times \frac{1092°\text{K}}{273°\text{K}} = 8.96 \text{ l}$$

35. In the reaction, $CaC_2 + 2H_2O = Ca(OH)_2 + C_2H_2$, calculate the moles of calcium carbide needed to give 13.35 l of acetylene at 27°C and 70 torr pressure.

Answer

$$\text{Volume of } C_2H_2 \text{ at STP} = \frac{13.35 \text{ l} \times 273°\text{K} \times 70 \text{ torr}}{300°\text{K} \times 760 \text{ torr}} = 1.12 \text{ l}$$

$$\overset{n}{\underset{1\text{ mole}}{CaC_2}} + 2H_2O = Ca(OH)_2 + \overset{1.12\text{ l}}{\underset{22.4\text{ l}}{C_2H_2}} \qquad n = 0.0500 \text{ mole}$$

36. Compute the volume of gas product at STP when 0.125 mole of sodium reacts with water.

Answer

$$\overset{0.125\text{ mole}}{\underset{2\text{ moles}}{2Na}} + 2H_2O = 2NaOH + \overset{V}{\underset{22.4\text{ l}}{H_2}} \qquad V = 1.40 \text{ l}$$

Answers to Questions and Exercises

Text page references are provided for those questions which do not require computations. The student's answers will be individually stated, but should focus on the concepts developed in these text pages.

Factual Recall

1. 191–93
2. 193–95
3. 193
4. 195
5. 192–93

Apply Your Knowledge!

1. (*a*) K_2O (*b*) $MgCl_2$ (*c*) Na_2S (*d*) Ca_3N_2 (*e*) $PbBr_2$ (*f*) AlN (*g*) MnF_2
2. (*a*) Cu_2S (*b*) Fe_2O_3 (*c*) Sn_3N_4 (*d*) HgO (*e*) $FeCl_2$ (*f*) CuI_2 (*g*) HgBr
3. (*a*) 20 (*b*) 38 (*c*) 48 (*d*) 36.5 (*e*) 127
4. (*a*) 101 (*b*) 150 (*c*) 110 (*d*) 78 (*e*) 68
5. (*a*) $2H_2 + O_2 \rightarrow 2H_2O$
   (*b*) $2Sn + O_2 \rightarrow 2SnO$
   (*c*) $2Cu + S \rightarrow Cu_2S$
   (*d*) $2CuCl + Cl_2 \rightarrow 2CuCl_2$
   (*e*) $4FeO + O_2 \rightarrow 2Fe_2O_3$
   (*f*) $2AlBr_3 + 3Cl_2 \rightarrow AlCl_3 + 3Br_2$
6. $$\text{Moles of S atoms} = \frac{40.0\text{ g}}{32.0\text{ g/mole}} = 1.25\text{ moles}$$
   $$\text{Moles of O atoms} = \frac{60.0\text{ g}}{16.0\text{ g/mole}} = 3.75\text{ moles}$$
   $$\frac{\text{Moles of S atoms}}{\text{Moles of O atoms}} = \frac{1.25\text{ moles}}{3.75\text{ moles}} = \frac{1}{3}$$
   The empirical formula is therefore SO_3.
7. FeO
8. The empirical formula is Hg_2O, and the name is mercury (I) oxide or mercurous oxide.
9. (*a*) 5.9% (*b*) 5% (*c*) 1.2% (*d*) 14.3% (*e*) 6.1% (*f*) 5.5%
10. 1.53 g
11. $$\text{Volume at STP} = \frac{10.0\text{ l} \times 380\text{ torr} \times 273°\text{K}}{760\text{ torr} \times 546°\text{K}}$$
    $$\text{Moles of CO} = \frac{2.50\text{ l}}{22.4\text{ l/mole}} = 0.111\text{ mole}$$
12. (*a*) 11.1 g of H_2 (*b*) 88.9 g of O_2
13. $$\underset{\substack{2\text{ moles}\\68\text{ g}}}{2H_2O_2} \rightarrow 2H_2O + \underset{\substack{1\text{ mole}\\32\text{ g}}}{O_2}$$
    $$\text{Moles of } H_2O_2 = \frac{102\text{ g}}{34\text{ g/mole}} = 3.0\text{ moles}$$
    $$\text{Moles of oxygen} = \frac{3.0}{2} = 1.50\text{ moles}$$

UNIT 

SOLUTIONS AND IONIZATION

OPENING UNIT IV

At this point the student has already learned a good bit about ions, as the term has turned up in the discussion of chemical combinations and other topics. Unit IV will be more concerned with dissociation of compounds into constituent ions than with combination although recombination and equilibrium are also discussed. Ions are the units recurrent theme. Although Arrhenius' detailed explanation of what Faraday's enigmatic ions really were does not appear until Chapter 15, it is important that the student have a clear idea of the role played by ions in the material of Chapter 14.

CHAPTER 14

SOLUTIONS

WHAT IS A SOLUTION
(pp. 211–12)

Learning Objectives

1. To define a solution.
2. To define a solute.
3. To define a solvent.
4. To state which is the solute and which is the solvent in a water-sugar solution.
5. To name the most common solvent.

HOW IONIC SOLIDS DISSOLVE
(p. 212)

Learning Objectives

1. To describe the dipolar nature of water molecules.
2. To describe the crystalline structure of sodium chloride.
3. To describe the electrical orientation of the water molecules to the sodium and chloride ions.
4. To describe the mechanism by which water molecules break down the crystal structure of sodium chloride.
5. To define the term *hydrated ion.*
6. To draw a simple diagram of a hydrated ion.

HOW MOLECULAR COMPOUNDS DISSOLVE
(pp. 212–13)

Learning Objectives

1. To name the two types of forces that hold a molecular substance together.
2. To state why a nonpolar molecule does not readily go into solution.
3. To state why a polar molecule goes into solution more readily than a nonpolar molecule.
4. To compare the bond strengths of sugar and common salt.
5. To state the mechanism by which a sugar molecule goes into a water solution.

SATURATED SOLUTIONS
(p. 214)

Learning Objectives

1. To describe the mechanism by which potassium nitrate ions go into solution.
2. To define the term *precipitation.*
3. To state the process that is the reverse of dissolution.
4. To describe the process by which a solution becomes saturated.

5. To state the meaning of the term a *condition of equilibrium*.
6. To state the conditions in a solution required for a state of equilibrium to exist.
7. To write a qualitative equation expressing an equilibrium state in a solution.
8. To describe the temperature dependence of solubility and of the rate of recrystallization.
9. To describe the temperature dependence of the equilibrium state in a solution.

LE CHÂTELIER'S PRINCIPLE
(p. 215)

Learning Objectives

1. To state Le Châtelier's principle.
2. To define the term *stress.*

SOLUBILITY
(pp. 215–16)

Learning Objectives

1. To state the definition of solubility as given in the text.
2. To describe the temperature dependence of the solubility of several of the substances in Fig. 14-7.

TEMPERATURE CHANGES DURING SOLUTION
(pp. 216–17)

Learning Objectives

1. To define the term *endothermic*.
2. To define the term *exothermic*.
3. To describe an endothermic change in a solution.
4. To describe an exothermic change in solution.
5. To state the meaning of the term *net change* with respect to endothermic and exothermic changes in a solution.
6. To define the term *heat of solution*.
7. To state the meaning of the plus and minus signs as applied to heats of solution.
8. To state the units used to specify heats of solution.
9. To apply Le Châtelier's principle to the temperature-solubility relationships of solutions.

Demonstration I To Demonstrate the Heat of Solution of an Aqueous Potassium Nitrate Solution.

Materials recommended: 100 mm test tubes, thermometer, tap water, powdered potassium nitrate.

This chapter on solutions is an important one, and the concepts of solubility and concentrations of solutions are frequently referred to in later chapters. In the laboratory manual there are two experiments on solubility and it is strongly urged that students do both of them.

In the text it states that the heat of solution of potassium nitrate is $+8.5$ kcal/mole. The positive sign means that more energy is stored in the ingredients (KNO_3 and H_2O) than the solution. Therefore the change is endothermic and takes place with a drop in temperature. The absorption of heat is due to the fact that the ionic bonds in the crystal are very strong and the energy needed to break the bonds is taken from the ingredients as heat energy. This endothermic change can be demonstrated with very simple apparatus as follows.

Half fill a test tube with tap water, place a thermometer in the water and read the temperature. Remove the thermometer and pour about 6 grams of powdered KNO_3 into the test tube. Close the tube with the thumb and shake the tube. Notice that on standing some KNO_3 remains undissolved; that is, the solution is now saturated. Again place the thermometer in the solution and observe that there has been a drop in temperature of about 10 degrees. Now half fill another test tube with tap water. Let a few students hold the tubes, one in each hand, and they will realize that the "solution" tube feels colder than the "water" tube.

THE SOLUBILITY OF GASES
(p. 217)

Learning Objectives

1. To describe the temperature dependence of the solubility of gases.
2. To state that in the solution of gases the change is always exothermic.
3. To apply Le Châtelier's principle to solutions of gases.

Demonstration II To Demonstrate the Temperature Dependence of the Solubility of Gases.

Materials recommended: Bottle of soda water, flask, 1-hole stopper, glass tubing, ring stand, Bunsen burner, shelf, pneumatic trough, collecting bottle.

Carbon dioxide gas is fairly soluble in water. The solubility of this gas can be greatly increased by applying pressure to the gas while it is being dissolved. Such a solution is called soda water — it is used as a beverage.

Remove the cap from a bottle of soda water and observe that numerous bubbles of CO_2 escape. However, even after all the bubbles have escaped, there is a good deal of gas still in solution. The dissolved gas can be expelled by heating the solution as in the following demonstration. Pour some soda water into a flask and support the flask on a stand. Rest an inverted bottle of water on a shelf in a pneumatic trough and connect the flask and bottle of water by a delivery tube. The arrangement is shown in Fig. TG14–1. Heat the flask and observe that bubbles of carbon dioxide escape rapidly and are collected by displacing water in the bottle. Clearly, the higher the temperature the less is the solubility of carbon dioxide in water.

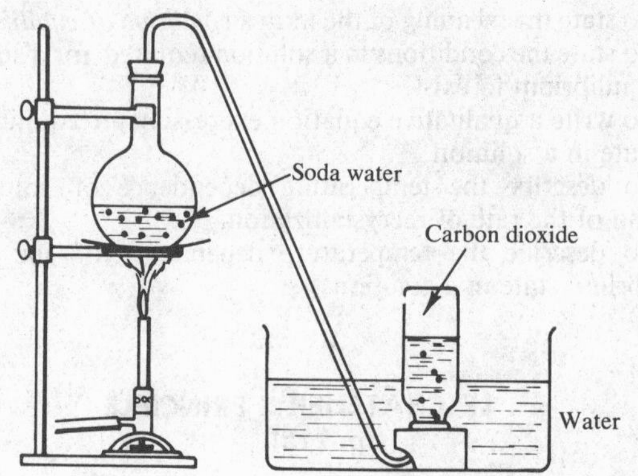

FIG. TG14–1

CONCENTRATION OF SOLUTIONS
(pp. 217–21)

Learning Objectives

1. To define the term *dilute*.
2. To define the term *concentrated*.
3. To define the term *molarity*.
4. To state the units used to express molarity.
5. To write the equation that expresses molarity.
6. To define the term *molality*.
7. To state the units used to express molality.

FREEZING AND BOILING POINTS OF SOLUTIONS
(pp. 221–27)

Learning Objectives

1. To state that the freezing point of an aqueous solution of a substance is below that of pure water.
2. To list the three sets of equilibria that exist in a beaker of ice water.
3. To describe the role of vapor pressure in determining the freezing points of solutions.
4. To state the effect of progressive freezing on the concentration of a solution.
5. To state the dependence of the freezing points of solutions on their concentrations.
6. To state Raoult's law.
7. To write the equation that expresses Raoult's law.
8. To state that the boiling point of a solution is higher than the boiling point of its solvent.
9. To state Raoult's law as it applies to boiling points of solutions.
10. To state the boiling point constant in terms of moles per kilogram of water.
11. To state why the freezing points of solutions of ionic compounds cannot be predicted by Raoult's law.

Suggested Teacher Commentary

In experiments dealing with Raoult's law we must read only the *initial* freezing point of a solution. This is an important point to remember. Suppose we wish to find the molality of a solution of urea and suppose that, as the solution is cooled, ice crystals first appear when the temperature is −1.86°C. This is the initial freezing point of the solution and therefore the depression of the freezing point is 1.86 C°. If we continue to cool the solution, more ice crystals form and the temperature (the freezing point) drops below −1.86°C. Moreover, as more ice crystallizes the remaining solution becomes more concentrated; that is, its molality increases. With still further cooling, still more ice crystallizes out and the molality of the residual solution increases still further. This process continues until the solution is saturated. If the saturated solution is cooled, both ice and urea (solid) separate from solution so that the molality of the solution no longer increases. However, we must bear in mind that what we want to know is the molality of the *original* solution, and for this reason we must read only the *initial* freezing point of the solution.

Additional Questions and Problems

1. The solubility of a salt is 24.0 g at 20°C and 46.0 g at 30°C. (*a*) What mass of the salt can be dissolved in 60.0

g of water at 30°C? (*b*) What mass of salt will be precipitated if the saturated solution in (*a*) is cooled to 20°C? (*c*) Compute the density of the saturated solution in (*a*) if the volume of the solution is 64.0 ml. (*d*) Compute the density of the saturated solution in (*b*) if the volume of the solution is 62.5 ml.

Answer

(*a*) $\text{Mass dissolved at 30°C} = \dfrac{46.0 \text{ g}}{100 \text{ g water}} \times 60.0 \text{ g water} = 27.6 \text{ g}$

(*b*) $\text{Mass dissolved at 20°C} = \dfrac{24.0 \text{ g}}{100 \text{ g water}} \times 60.0 \text{ g water} = 14.4 \text{ g}$

$\text{Mass precipitated} = 27.6 \text{ g} - 14.4 \text{ g} = 13.2 \text{ g}$

(*c*) $\text{Density} = \dfrac{\text{mass}}{\text{volume}} = \dfrac{60.0 \text{ g} + 27.6 \text{ g}}{64.0 \text{ ml}} = 1.37 \text{ g/ml}$

(*d*) $\text{Density} = \dfrac{\text{mass}}{\text{volume}} = \dfrac{60.0 \text{ g} + 14.4 \text{ g}}{62.5 \text{ ml}} = 1.19 \text{ g/ml}$

2. The solubility values of sodium chlorate at different temperatures are 79 g at 0°C, 89 g at 10°C, 101 g at 20°C, 113 g at 30°C, 126 g at 40°C, 140 g at 50°C, 155 g at 60°C, 172 g at 70°C, 189 g at 80°C, and 230 g at 100°C. (*a*) Draw the solubility curve for sodium chlorate from these data. (*b*) Estimate the solubility of sodium chlorate at 90°C from the solubility curve. (*c*) What mass of sodium chlorate could be dissolved in 40 g of water at 75°C? (*d*) Twenty-four g of sodium chlorate are shaken with 20 g of water at 25°C. How much sodium chlorate remains undissolved? (*e*) At what temperature would the excess solid in (*d*) just go into solution?

Answer

(*b*) 208 g $NaClO_3$/100 g water (*c*) 73 g $NaClO_3$ (*d*) 3.0 g $NaClO_3$ (*e*) 35°C

3. Calculate the molarity of the following: (*a*) 9.8 g of sulfuric acid (H_2SO_4) in 100 ml of solution, (*b*) 0.062 g of carbonic acid (H_2CO_3) in two l of solution, (*c*) 1.00 g of sodium hydroxide (NaOH) in 500 ml of solution, (*d*) 2.08 g of barium chloride ($BaCl_2$) in 2.50 l of solution, (*e*) 3.42 g of aluminum sulfate [$Al_2(SO_4)_3$] in 500 ml of solution.

Answer

(*a*) 1.00 molar

(*b*) $\text{Moles of } H_2CO_3(n) = \dfrac{6.2 \times 10^{-2} \text{ g}}{62 \text{ g/mole}} = 1.00 \times 10^{-3} \text{ mole}$

$\text{Molarity of } H_2CO_3 = \dfrac{n}{V} = \dfrac{1.00 \times 10^{-3} \text{ mole}}{2.0 \text{ l}} = 5.0 \times 10^{-4}\, M$

(*c*) $5.0 \times 10^{-2}\, M$ (*d*) $4.0 \times 10^{-3}\, M$

(*e*) $\text{Moles of } Al_2(SO_4)_3 = n = \dfrac{3.42 \text{ g}}{342 \text{ g/mole}} = 10^{-2} \text{ mole}$

$\text{Molarity} = \dfrac{10^{-2} \text{ mole}}{0.5 \text{ l}} = 2.0 \times 10^{-2}\, M$

4. How many grams of the solute are required to prepare (*a*) 100 ml of 0.15 *M* sodium hydroxide (NaOH), (*b*) 300 ml of 0.56 *M* hydrochloric acid (HCl), (*c*) 500 ml of 0.200 *M* sulfuric acid (H_2SO_4), (*d*) 200 ml of 0.100 *M* calcium chloride ($CaCl_2$), (*e*) 2.50 l of 0.0200 *M* iron (III) sulfate?

Answer

(*a*) $\text{Moles of NaOH} = M \times V = 0.15 \text{ mole/l} \times 0.100 \text{ l} = 0.015 \text{ mole}$

$\text{Mass} = 0.015 \text{ mole} \times 40 \text{ g/mole} = 0.60 \text{ g}$

(*b*) 6.1 g

(*c*) $\text{Moles of } H_2SO_4 = M \times V = 0.200 \text{ mole/l} \times 0.500 \text{ l} = 0.100 \text{ mole}$

$\text{Mass} = 0.100 \text{ mole} \times 98 \text{ g/mole} = 9.8 \text{ g}$

(*d*) 2.22 g (*e*) 20.0 g

5. Fifty ml of 12 *M* sulfuric acid are diluted to 500 ml of solution. Compute the molarity of the diluted acid.

Answer

$\text{Moles of } H_2SO_4(n) = 12 \text{ moles/l} \times 0.0500 \text{ l} = 0.600 \text{ mole}$

$\text{Molarity} = \dfrac{n}{V} = 0.600 \text{ mole}/0.500 \text{ l} = 1.2 \text{ mole/l} = 1.2\, M$

6. Calculate the molality of a solution which contains 1.60 g of methyl alcohol (CH_3OH) and 100 g of water.

Answer

$\text{Moles of } CH_3OH = \dfrac{1.60 \text{ g}}{32 \text{ g/mole}} = 0.0500 \text{ mole}$

$\text{Molality} = \dfrac{0.0500 \text{ mole}}{0.100 \text{ kg water}} = 0.500 \text{ molal}$

7. A solution of glucose ($C_6H_{12}O_6$) in 200 g of water is 0.500 molal. What is the mass of glucose in the solution?

Answer

0.500 molal glucose = 180/2 g glucose per kg water

$\text{Mass of glucose in 200 g water} = \dfrac{90 \text{ g glucose}}{1 \text{ kg water}} (0.200 \text{ kg water}) = 18.0 \text{ g}$

8. A solution of 17.1 g of sucrose ($C_{12}H_{22}O_{11}$) in water freezes at $-0.93°C$. What is the mass of water in the solution?

Answer

$$\text{Molality of solution} = \frac{t}{k_f} = \frac{0.93\ C°}{1.86\ C°/\text{mole/kg water}} = 0.500\ \text{mole/kg}$$

$$\text{Moles of sucrose} = \frac{17.1\ g}{342\ g/\text{mole}} = 0.0500\ \text{mole}$$

$$\text{Molality: } \frac{0.0500\ \text{mole}}{x\ \text{kg water}} = \frac{0.500\ \text{mole}}{1\ \text{kg water}}$$

$$x = 1/10\ \text{kg water} = 100\ \text{g of water}$$

9. A solution contains 3.10 g of ethylene glycol ($C_2H_6O_2$) and 20.0 g of water. Compute the (*a*) molality of the solution, (*b*) freezing point of the solution.

Answer

$$\text{Moles of ethylene glycol} = \frac{3.10\ g}{62\ g/\text{mole}} = 0.0500\ \text{mole}$$

$$\text{Molality} = \frac{0.0500\ \text{mole}}{0.0200\ \text{kg}} = 2.50\ \text{molal}$$

$$\Delta t = \text{molality} \times k_f = 2.50 \times 1.86\ C° = 4.65\ C°$$

Therefore the freezing point $= -4.65°C$.

10. A solution contains 2.30 g of glycerol ($C_3H_8O_3$) and 20.0 g of water. Compute the (*a*) molality of the solution, (*b*) boiling point of the solution.

Answer

(*a*) $$\text{Molality of glycerol} = \frac{2.30\ g}{92\ g/\text{mole} \times 0.0200\ \text{kg}} = 1.25\ \text{molal}$$

(*b*) $$\Delta t = \text{molality} \times k_b = 1.25 \times 0.51\ C° = 0.64\ C°$$

Therefore the boiling point is 100.64°C

11. A solution containing 50.0 g of water and 13.5 g of solute freezes at $-2.79°C$. (*a*) What is the molality of the solution? (*b*) Find the molecular mass of the solute. (*c*) Compute the boiling point of the solution if the solute is non-volatile.

Answer

(*a*) $$\text{Molality} = \frac{\Delta t}{k_f} = \frac{2.79\ C°}{1.86\ C°\ \text{kg/mole}} = 1.50\ \text{molal}$$

(*b*) $$\text{Molecular mass} = \frac{13.5\ g \times 1.86\ C°\ \text{kg/mole}}{2.79\ C° \times 0.0500\ \text{kg}} = 180\ g/\text{mole}$$

(*c*) Boiling point = 100.77°C

12. A solution of glucose ($C_6H_{12}O_6$) in water freezes at $-9.3°C$. Compute the mass of glucose in 50.0 g of the solution.

Answer

$$\text{Molality of solution} = \frac{9.3\ C°}{1.86\ C°} = 5.00\ \text{molal}$$

A 5.00 molal solution of glucose contains 5.00 × 180 g or 900 g of glucose per kilogram of water.

$$\frac{900\ \text{g glucose}}{1000\ \text{g water}} = \frac{m\ \text{grams glucose}}{50.0 - m\ \text{g water}}$$

$$m = 23.7\ \text{g of glucose}$$

13. Enough glycerol ($C_3H_8O_3$) is added to 8.0 kg of water in a car radiator to prevent freezing down to $-8.6°C$. What mass of glycerol must be added?

Answer

$$\text{Mass of glycerol} = \frac{8.6\ C° \times 92\ g/\text{mole} \times 8.0\ \text{kg}}{1.86\ C°\ \text{kg/mole}} = 3400\ g\ \text{or}\ 3.40\ \text{kg}$$

14. A solution prepared by dissolving 1.50 g of benzophenone ($C_{13}H_{10}O$) in 20.0 g of benzene (C_6H_6, freezing point 5.50°C) freezes at 3.48°C. What is the freezing point depression constant for benzene as a solvent?

Answer

F.P. depression constant

$$= \frac{2.02\ C° \times 182\ g/\text{mole} \times 0.0200\ \text{kg}}{1.50\ g} = 4.90\ C°\ \text{kg/mole}$$

Answers to Questions and Exercises

Text page references are provided for those questions which do not require computations. The student's answers will be individually stated, but should focus on the concepts developed in these text pages.

Factual Recall

1. 209–14 2. 212 3. 212–13
4. 212–13 5. 215–17 6. 215–17
7. 217–221

Apply Your Knowledge!

1. Mass of water = 44.9 g − 17.5 g = 27.4 g

(*a*) $\text{Solubility} = \dfrac{17.5 \text{ g salt}}{27.4 \text{ g water}} \times 100 \text{ g water} = 63.8 \text{ g}$

(*b*) $\text{Solubility in moles} = \dfrac{63.9 \text{ g}}{101 \text{ g/mole}} = 0.634 \text{ mole}$

Find Out!

(*a*)
$$\text{Molecular mass} = \frac{0.150\, g \times 1.86 \text{ C}^\circ \text{ kg/mole}}{0.43 \text{ C}^\circ \times 0.0100 \text{ kg}} = 65 \text{ g/mole}$$

(*b*) CH_3O

(*c*) $(CH_3O)n = 65 \quad n = 2$, therefore the molecular formula is $C_2H_6O_2$.

(*d*)
$$\text{Molecular mass} = (12.01 \times 2) + (1.008 \times 6) + (16.00 \times 2) = 62.07 \text{ amu}$$

CHAPTER 15

IONIZATION

ELECTROLYTES AND NONELECTROLYTES
(pp. 229–30)

Learning Objectives

1. To describe Faraday's apparatus for measuring the electrical conductivity of solutions.
2. To define an electrolyte.
3. To define a nonelectrolyte.
4. To state that acids, bases, and salts are electrolytes.

Suggested Teacher Commentary

The development of the modern atomic theory is still another example of the way scientific knowledge advances. Earlier theories that are propounded to account for experimental evidence become untenable in the light of later discoveries. As explained in Chapter 18, the earliest ionization theory was proposed by Faraday about 1830. When he passed a direct current through solutions of salts, the metallic component was deposited on the negative electrode (the cathode). To account for his observations Faraday stated that molecules of an electrolyte are decomposed into ions when a potential difference is applied to the electrodes, and the ions then flow to the electrodes — the positive ion to the negatively charged electrode and vice versa. In other words, according to Faraday, two conditions are essential for ion formation: (1) The electrolyte must be dissolved in water, and (2) a potential difference must be applied to the solution. These ideas persisted until 1887 when Arrhenius partially rejected Faraday's theory.

ARRHENIUS' THEORY OF IONIZATION
(pp. 230–34)

Learning Objectives

1. To state the main postulates of the Arrhenius theory.
2. To write the equation for the ionic dissociation of sodium chloride in water.
3. To define a precipitate.
4. To define the term *spectator ion*.
5. To relate the change of freezing point with molality to Arrhenius' theory.
6. To state the main postulates of the Debye-Hückel theory.

Suggested Teacher Commentary

Arrhenius' theory was intended to explain certain known experimental facts concerning solutions of electrolytes. For example, these solutions conduct an electric current and they give an abnormal depression of the freezing point as computed from Raoult's law. Since the depression of the freezing point does not depend upon an applied potential, Arrhenius discarded this postulate in the Faraday theory. And instead he maintained that molecules are changed to ions when the electrolyte is dissolved in water. Moreover, he maintained that in the solution there was a mixture of both molecules and ions. This latter assumption turned out to be false. But let us examine Arrhenius' reasoning which at that time justified the validity of this assumption.

Arrhenius knew that the conductivity of a solution of an electrolyte is increased if the solution is diluted with water. He argued that this would not be possible if the electrolyte were already completely ionized. In other words, he maintained that if a salt as a solid is made up of ions, the total number of ions in solution would be constant, in which case the conductivity (which depends upon the flow of ions) could not change no matter how much water was added. This argument seemed to be reasonable.

His idea that an electrolyte in solution is a mixture of molecules and ions was also supported (or appeared to be supported) by experimental evidence. It was known, for example, that the depression of the freezing point of a solution of a salt, such as KCl, is *almost* (but not quite) twice as large as the depression as computed from Raoult's law. Moreover, as the solution is further diluted with water, the abnormality increases until eventually the depression of the freezing point becomes *exactly* twice as much as for a nonelectrolyte.

Arrhenius assumed that ions, like molecules, diminish the vapor pressure of a water solution and, in consequence, depress its freezing point. But ionization increases the number of particles in solution, so Arrhenius argued that the only way to account for the increasing depression of the freezing point was to assume that molecules dissociate into ions when a solution is diluted by the addition of water, and that this process will continue until all the molecules are ionized.

The idea that a solution contains both molecules and ions was generally accepted until the early part of the present century when X-ray analysis proved beyond all doubt that strong electrolytes are completely ionized in the solid state. In other words, it was evident that, for strong electrolytes, addition of water did not cause ions to be formed and indeed that the term *molecule* could not be applied to strong electrolytes.

How then could the abnormality of the freezing point depression of a strong electrolyte be explained? As stated in the text, the Debye-Hückel theory offered a satisfactory explanation. This theory assumes that strong electrolytes are completely ionized and it maintains that the abnormal depression of the freezing point is attributable to attractions between oppositely charged ions.

Thus, in summary, according to the modern theory there are two kinds of electrolytes, strong and weak. Strong electrolytes are completely ionized. Some (for example, practically all salts) consist only of ions in the solid state; others (for example, hydrogen chloride) are completely ionized when dissolved in water. On the other hand, weak electrolytes are only partially ionized when dissolved in water. For example, a solution of acetic acid is a mixture of molecules of acetic acid and of hydrogen ions and acetate ions.

Demonstration I To Show that Ion Formation in Salts Does Not Depend on the Addition of Water

Materials recommended: Ring stand, evaporating dish, Bunsen burner, vertical stand, clamp, light bulb, socket, copper wire, sodium nitrate.

As already stated, X-ray analysis proves that salts as solids are made up of ions. This same idea can be verified as a class demonstration by testing the electrical conductivity of a molten salt. The procedure is as follows:

Put some sodium nitrate into an evaporating dish, place the dish on a stand and insert two stout copper wires (which are connected to a source of current through a light bulb) into the sodium nitrate. The arrangement is shown in Fig. TG15–1.

Heat the dish. When the sodium nitrate melts (melting point of $NaNO_3$ is 308°C) the bulb lights up. Now turn off the Bunsen burner and, after cooling for a few minutes, the light goes out.

The only explanation is that, as a solid, sodium nitrate is a lattice of ions (Na^+ and NO_3^-) held together by strong electrostatic forces. At 308°C the lattice bonds are broken, the sodium nitrate melts, and the ions are free to move and conduct the current. As a result the bulb lights up. As the molten salt cools, the ions attract each other and again form a solid lattice so that the current can no longer flow through the circuit and the light bulb goes out.

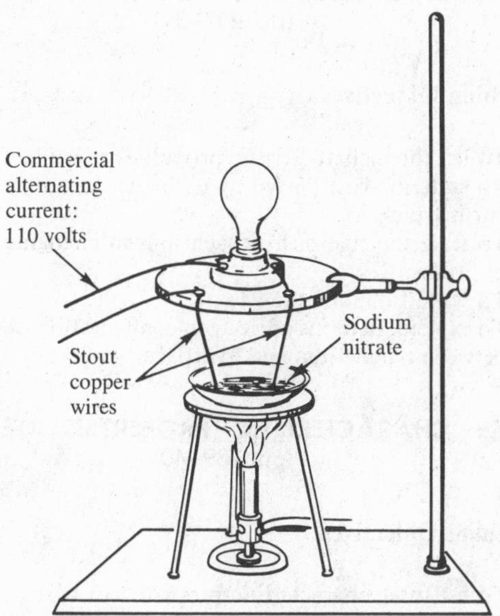

FIG. TG15–1

THE IONIZATION OF COVALENT MOLECULES
(pp. 234–35)

Learning Objectives

1. To state why a molecule of hydrogen chloride is polar.
2. To write the electron dot notation for hydrogen chloride.
3. To state that a water molecule is polar.
4. To write the electron dot notation for a doubly hydrated hydrogen chloride molecule.
5. To define a hydronium ion.
6. To write in chemical symbols the equation that expresses the hydration of hydrogen chloride.

STRONG AND WEAK ELECTROLYTES
(pp. 236–37)

Learning Objectives

1. To distinguish between strong and weak electrolytes in terms of degree of ionization.
2. To write the electron dot formula for acetic acid.
3. To state that the O—H bond in acetic acid is less easily broken than the H—Cl bond.
4. To state what is meant by the statement *the reaction is mostly to the left*.

SOME CHARACTERISTIC PROPERTIES OF ACIDS
(pp. 237–39)

Learning Objectives

1. To list three characteristic properties of acids.
2. To state the role played by hydrogen ions in the taste of citrus fruits.
3. To state the role of hydrogen ions in changing the color of litmus.
4. To write Equation (15-24).
5. To explain, in terms of electron configuration, the reaction between magnesium and hydrogen.

SOME CHARACTERISTIC PROPERTIES OF BASES
(pp. 239–40)

Learning Objectives

1. To list three characteristic properties of bases.
2. To state the role played by hydroxide ions in the taste of soap.
3. To state the role played by hydroxide ions in changing the color of litmus.
4. To write the equation for the reaction between sodium hydroxide and water.
5. To state the definition of the neutralization of an acid by a base.
6. To write the ionic equation for the neutralization of hydrochloric acid by sodium hydroxide.
7. To define a salt.

TERNARY ACIDS AND THEIR SALTS
(pp. 240–41)

Learning Objectives

1. To define a ternary acid.
2. To state the conditions under which a ternary acid's name may end in *-ic*.
3. To state the conditions under which the salt of a ternary acid's name may end in *-ate*.
4. To state the conditions under which a ternary acid's name may end in *-ous*.
5. To state the conditions under which the salt of a ternary acid's name may end in *-ite*.

COMPLEX IONS
(pp. 241–44)

Learning Objectives

1. To define a complex ion.
2. To state the normal degree of stability of complex ions in solution.
3. To state the usual charge of a complex ion.
4. To write the electron dot notation for a chlorate ion.
5. To state, in terms of electron configuration, how it becomes stable.
6. To write the formula for ammonium sulfate.
7. To write the equation that expresses the reaction between sodium carbonate and iron (III) nitrate.

SLIGHTLY SOLUBLE BASES
(pp. 244–45)

Learning Objectives

1. To state why most bases are only slightly soluble.

Additional Questions and Problems

1. If 0.110 mole of aluminum chloride (Al_2Cl_6) is added to a solution containing 0.340 mole of silver nitrate, (*a*) how many moles of silver chloride are precipitated? (*b*) What mass in g of silver chloride is precipitated?

Answer

$$\underset{1\ \text{mole}}{AlCl_3} + \underset{3\ \text{moles}}{3AgNO_3} \rightarrow \underset{1\ \text{mole}}{Al(NO_3)_3} + \underset{3\ \text{moles}}{3AgCl}$$

(*a*) $$\frac{\text{Moles } AgNO_3}{\text{Moles } AlCl_3} = \frac{0.340}{0.110}$$

Therefore $AgNO_3$ is in excess.

Moles of AgCl = 3 × moles of $AlCl_3$ = 0.330 mole

(*b*) Mass of AgCl = 0.330 mole × 143.5 g/mole = 47.4 g.

2. Compute the volume of hydrogen liberated at STP if 3.6 g of calcium are dropped into 4.0 g of water.

Answer

$$\underset{1\ \text{mole}}{Ca} + \underset{2\ \text{moles}}{2H_2O} \rightarrow Ca(OH)_2 + \underset{1\ \text{mole}}{H_2}$$

$$\frac{\text{Moles Ca}}{\text{Moles } H_2O} = \frac{3.6\ \text{g}/40\ \text{g/mole}}{4.0\ \text{g}/18\ \text{g/mole}} = \frac{0.090\ \text{mole}}{0.222\ \text{mole}}$$

Water is in excess.

Volume of H_2 = 0.090 mole × 22.4 l/mole = 2.02 l

3. In the reaction between magnesium and dilute sulfuric acid, 0.56 l of gas product is liberated at STP. Compute the (*a*) moles of magnesium consumed, (*b*) moles of acid consumed, (*c*) mass in g of salt produced.

Answer

$$\underset{1\ \text{mole}}{Mg} + \underset{1\ \text{mole}}{H_2SO_4} \rightarrow \underset{1\ \text{mole}}{MgSO_4} + \underset{1\ \text{mole}}{H_2}$$

(*a*) $$\text{Moles of } H_2 = \frac{0.56\ \text{l}}{22.4\ \text{l/mole}} = 0.0250\ \text{mole}$$

Moles of Mg = 0.0250 mole

(*b*) Moles of acid = 0.0250 mole.

(*c*) Mass of salt = 0.0250 mole × 120 g/mole = 3.00 g.

4. A hydrochloric acid solution containing 0.200 g of hydrogen ion is added to an excess of magnesium metal. (*a*) Compute the volume of gas product at 20°C and 740 torr pressure. (*b*) Compute the mass of magnesium ion formed.

Answer

$$\underset{1\ \text{mole}}{Mg} + \underset{2\ \text{moles}}{2H^+} \rightarrow \underset{1\ \text{mole}}{Mg^{+2}} + \underset{1\ \text{mole}}{H_2}$$

(*a*) $$\text{Moles of } H^+ = \frac{0.200\ \text{g}}{1.00\ \text{g/mole}} = 0.200\ \text{mole}$$

$$\text{Volume of } H_2 = 0.100\ \text{mole} \times 22.4\ \text{l/mole} \times \frac{293°\text{K} \times 760\ \text{torr}}{273°\text{K} \times 740\ \text{torr}} = 2.47\ \text{l}$$

(*b*) Mass of Mg^{+2} = 0.100 mole × 24.3 g/mole = 2.43 g.

5. A solution of a strong base containing 0.500 mole of hydroxide ion is added to a solution of a strong acid containing 0.250 mole of hydrogen ion. How many moles of water are formed?

Answer

$$\underset{1\ \text{mole}}{OH^-} + \underset{1\ \text{mole}}{H^+} \rightarrow \underset{1\ \text{mole}}{H_2O}$$

The hydroxide ion is in excess. Moles of water = 0.250 mole.

6. A solution containing 0.150 mole of hydroxide ion is added to a solution containing 0.150 mole of cupric ion. Compute the moles of cupric hydroxide precipitated.

Answer

$$\underset{1\ \text{mole}}{Cu^{+2}} + \underset{2\ \text{moles}}{2OH^-} \rightarrow \underset{1\ \text{mole}}{Cu(OH)_2}$$

The cupric ion is in excess. Moles of $Cu(OH)_2$ = 0.0750 mole.

7. A 0.100 molal solution of a substance in water freezes at −0.300°C. Is the substance an electrolyte or a nonelectrolyte? Justify your answer by means of calculations.

Answer

The freezing point of a 0.100 molal solution of a nonelectrolyte = 0.100 × 1.86 = −0.186°C. The substance is therefore dissociated and is an electrolyte.

8. In this problem assume that the electrolytes are completely dissociated in solution and in each case show by calculation whether the statement is true or false.
   (*a*) A solution of 17.1 g of sucrose in 100 g of water boils at 100.51°C.
   (*b*) A solution of 29.25 g of sodium chloride in 100 g of water boils at 100.51°C.
   (*c*) A solution of 20.0 g of ferric sulfate in 100 g of water freezes at −0.93°C.
   (*d*) A solution of 2.8 g of potassium hydroxide in 100 g of water freezes at −1.86°C.
   (*e*) A solution of 4.9 g of sulfuric acid in 100 g of water freezes below −1.50°C.

Answer

(a) $\Delta t = \dfrac{17.1 \text{ g} \times 0.51 \text{ C° kg/mole}}{342 \text{ g/mole} \times 0.100 \text{ kg}} = 0.26 \text{ C°}$

B.P. = 100.26°C False

(b) $\Delta t = \dfrac{29.25 \text{ g} \times 0.51 \text{ C° kg/mole}}{58.5 \text{ g/mole} \times 0.100 \text{ kg}} \times 2 = 5.1 \text{ C°}$

B.P. = 105.1°C False

(c) $\Delta t = \dfrac{20.0 \text{ g} \times 1.86 \text{ C° kg/mole}}{400 \text{ g/mole} \times 0.100 \text{ kg}} \times 5 = 4.65 \text{ C°}$

F.P. = −4.65°C False

(d) $\Delta t = \dfrac{2.8 \text{ g} \times 1.86 \text{ C° kg/mole}}{56 \text{ g/mole} \times 0.100 \text{ kg}} \times 2 = 1.86 \text{ C°}$

F.P. = −1.86°C True

(e) $\Delta t = \dfrac{4.9 \text{ g} \times 1.86 \text{ C° kg/mole}}{98 \text{ g/mole} \times 0.100 \text{ kg}} \times 3 = 2.79 \text{ C°}$

F.P. = −2.79°C True

9. Fifty ml of 0.80 *M* silver nitrate react completely with 1.60 *M* aluminum chloride. Compute the (*a*) volume of aluminum chloride solution used up, (*b*) mass of the precipitate.

Answer

$3Ag^+ + AlCl_3 \rightarrow Al^{+3} + 3AgCl$

3 moles 1 mole 3 moles

(*a*) Moles Ag^+ = 0.80 mole/l × 0.050 l = 0.040 mole

Moles $AlCl_3 = \dfrac{0.040 \text{ mole}}{3} = 0.0133$ mole

Volume $AlCl_3 = \dfrac{0.0133 \text{ mole}}{1.60 \text{ mole/l}} = 0.0083$ l or 8.3 ml

(*b*) Mass = 0.040 mole × 143.5 g/mole = 5.7 g.

10. Calculate the moles of gas product if 100 ml of 6.0 *M* nitric acid are added to 10.6 g of sodium carbonate.

Answer

$Na_2CO_3 + 2HNO_3 \rightarrow 2NaNO_3 + CO_2 + H_2O$

1 mole 2 moles 1 mole

Moles $Na_2CO_3 = \dfrac{10.6 \text{ g}}{106 \text{ g/mole}} = 0.100$ mole

Moles HNO_3 = 0.100 l × 6.0 moles/l = 0.600 mole

The nitric acid is in excess.

Moles CO_2 = 0.100 mole

11. Calculate the mass of the precipitate formed by adding 500 ml of 1.50 *M* barium chloride to 200 ml of 4.00 *M* sodium sulfate.

Answer

$Na_2SO_4 + BaCl_2 \rightarrow BaSO_4 + 2NaCl$

1 mole 1 mole 1 mole

Moles Na_2SO_4 = 0.200 l × 4.00 moles/l = 0.800 mole

Moles $BaCl_2$ = 0.500 l × 1.50 moles/l = 0.750 mole

The sodium sulfate is in excess.

Mass = 0.750 mole × 233 g/mole = 175 g

Answers to Questions and Exercises

Text page references are provided for those questions which do not require computations. The student's answers will be individually stated, but should focus on the concepts developed in these text pages.

Factual Recall

1. 230
2. (*a*) $Al_2(SO_4)_3 + 3Ca(OH)_2 \rightarrow 2Al(OH)_3 \downarrow + 3CaSO_4 \downarrow$
   (*b*) $AgNO_3 + NaCl \rightarrow AgCl \downarrow + NaNO_3$
   (*c*) $3MgCl_2 + 2H_3PO_4 \rightarrow Mg_3(PO_4)_2 \downarrow + 6HCl$
3. (*a*) $Fe^{+2} + 2Cl^- + 2Na^+ + 2OH^- \rightarrow Fe(OH)_2 \downarrow + 2Na^+ + 2Cl^-$
   (*b*) $Ba^{+2} + 2Cl^- + 2H^+ + SO_4^{-2} \rightarrow BaSO_4 \downarrow + 2H^+ + 2Cl^-$
   (*c*) $Zn^{+2} + SO_4^{-2} + 2H^+ + S^{-2} \rightarrow ZnS \downarrow + 2H^+ + SO_4^{-2}$
4. (*a*) $2Al + 3H_2SO_4 \rightarrow Al_2(SO_4)_3 + 3H_2 \uparrow$
   (*b*) $Zn + 2HCl \rightarrow ZnCl_2 + H_2 \uparrow$
   (*c*) $Ca(OH)_2 + 2HNO_3 \rightarrow Ca(NO_3)_2 + 2H_2O$

Apply Your Knowledge!

1. Molten KNO_3 consists of K^+ and NO_3^- ions and may be compared to a water solution.
2. $2Al + 3H_2SO_4 \rightarrow Al_2(SO_4)_3 + 3H_2$

   2 moles 3 moles 1 mole 3 moles

   (*a*) Moles of Al $= \dfrac{5.4 \text{ g}}{27.0 \text{ g/mole}} = 0.200$ mole

   Mass of acid = 0.300 mole × 98 g/mole = 29.3 g

   (*b*) Moles of salt = 0.100 mole.

   (*c*) Volume of hydrogen = 0.300 mole × 22.4 l/mole = 6.72 l

3. $$2KClO_3 \rightarrow 2KCl + 3O_2$$
2 moles 2 moles 3 moles

(*a*) $$\text{Moles of } O_2 = \frac{22.4 \text{ l}}{22.4 \text{ l/mole}} = 1.00 \text{ mole}$$

$$\text{Moles of chlorate used} = 2/3 \text{ mole}$$
$$\text{Mass of chlorate} = 2/3 \text{ mole} \times 122.5 \text{ g/mole} = 81.6 \text{ g}$$

(*b*) Moles of KCl = 0.667 mole.

4. $$CaCl_2 + K_2CO_3 \rightarrow 2KCl + CaCO_3$$
1 mole 1 mole 2 moles 1 mole

$$\text{Moles of } CaCl_2 = \frac{11.1 \text{ g}}{111 \text{ g/mole}} = 0.100 \text{ mole}$$

$$\text{Moles of } K_2CO_3 = \frac{6.90 \text{ g}}{138 \text{ g/mole}} = 0.0500 \text{ mole}$$

The $CaCl_2$ is in excess.

$$\text{Moles of } CaCO_3 \text{ formed} = \text{moles of } K_2CO_3 \text{ used} = 0.0500 \text{ mole}$$

5. $$2Al + 6HCl \rightarrow 2AlCl_3 + 3H_2$$
2 moles 6 moles 2 moles 3 moles

$$\text{Moles of Al} = \frac{5.0 \text{ g}}{27 \text{ g/mole}} = 0.185 \text{ mole}$$

$$\frac{\text{Moles HCl}}{\text{Moles Al}} = \frac{0.50}{0.185} = \frac{2.7}{1}$$

Therefore Al is in excess.

(*a*) Moles of salt = 0.50/3 = 0.167 mole.

(*b*) $$\text{Moles of } H_2 = 0.50/2 = 0.250 \text{ mole}$$
$$\text{Volume of } H_2 \text{ at STP} = 0.250 \text{ mole} \times 22.4 \text{ l/mole} = 5.60 \text{ l}$$

(*c*) $$\text{Corrected volume} = \frac{5.60 \text{ l} \times 298°\text{K} \times 760 \text{ torr}}{273°\text{K} \times 700 \text{ torr}} = 6.62 \text{ l}$$

6. $$2Al + 3H_2SO_4 \rightarrow Al_2(SO_4)_3 + 3H_2$$
2 moles 3 moles

$$\text{Moles of gas at STP} = 0.250 \text{ mole} \times 3/2 = 0.375 \text{ mole}$$

$$\text{Volume of gas} = 0.375 \text{ mole} \times 22.4 \text{ l/mole} \times \frac{293°\text{K}}{273°\text{K}} = 9.00 \text{ l}$$

7. $$2KClO_3 \rightarrow 2KCl + 3O_2$$
2 moles 2 moles 3 moles

(*a*) $$\text{Volume of } O_2 = 3/2 \times 0.0100 \text{ mole} \times 22.4 \text{ l/mole} \times \frac{546°\text{K}}{273°\text{K}} = 0.672 \text{ l}$$

(*b*) Moles of KCl = 0.0100 mole.

CHAPTER 16

ACIDS AND BASES

WATER AS A WEAK ELECTROLYTE (pp. 248–50)

Learning Objectives

1. To write the electron dot notation for water, indicating dipolarity.
2. To write the equation showing the break down of associated water molecules into hydronium and hydroxide ions.
3. To state that this reaction involves the transfer of a proton from one water molecule to another.
4. To write the conventional notation for hydrogen ion concentration.
5. To state the meaning of the $[H^+]$ and $[OH^-]$ notations in units.
6. To write the equation for the ion product for water.
7. To state the value for the ion product for water.
8. To state the relative numbers of hydrogen and hydroxide ions in water.
9. To derive the molarity of water from the constant K_w.
10. To state the number of moles per l of hydrogen and hydroxide ions in water.
11. To state the value of K_w for all aqueous solutions at room temperature.
12. Given that the addition of a strong acid to water must increase the concentration of hydrogen ion, to apply Le Chatelier's principle to show how the value of K_w is restored.

Demonstration I To Demonstrate the Slight Degree of Ionization of Pure Water.

Materials recommended: Beaker, copper terminals, copper wire, vertical stand, clamp and mount, 25-watt light bulb, socket, neon light tube, tap water, distilled water.

The exceedingly small degree of ionization of water is one of its most important properties, and this fact should be impressed upon the students by a suitable demonstration. This can be done by comparing the electrical conductivities of tap water and pure water (distilled water). For this purpose the conductivity apparatus described in Fig. 15–2 is satisfactory, except that the light bulb should be a 25-watt bulb.

First dip the copper terminals into a beaker of tap water, close the switch and notice that the light bulb glows faintly. Clearly, tap water conducts a current although not as well as dilute HCl. Now remove all traces of tap water from the terminals by rinsing them with distilled water, and then immerse them in a beaker of distilled water. This time the bulb does not glow at all which seems to indicate that pure water is not ionized even slightly. However, a neon bulb is much more sensitive to small currents than an ordinary bulb. So, replace the 25-watt bulb with a neon light bulb. This time when the switch is closed the bulb lights up with a red glow. Therefore pure water is slightly ionized; it is a weak electrolyte. (The conductivity of tap water is due to the ions of the various impurities that are always present in tap water.)

A neon bulb contains only neon gas at low pressure. Within the bulb there are two D-shaped terminals or electrodes called "dees." Under an applied potential neon atoms lose an electron

$$n \text{ Ne} \rightarrow n \text{ Ne}^+ + n \text{ e}^{-1}$$

That is, the gas becomes ionized and the electrons move to the anode (and from the anode they flow out of the bulb and along the wire). At the same time, neon ions move to the cathode. At the cathode the neon ions combine with electrons (supplied by the current) to re-form neon atoms. Or, $n \text{ Ne}^+ + n \text{ e}^{-1} \rightarrow n \text{ Ne}$. That is, neon gas is re-formed at the cathode.

The moving neon ions emit a characteristic red color and, since an alternating current is used in this experiment, the red glow appears on both D-shaped electrodes.

DEFINITIONS OF ACIDS AND BASES

(pp. 250–54)

Learning Objectives

1. To define an acid in terms of its hydrogen-ion-to-hydroxide-ion ratio.
2. To define a base in terms of its hydrogen-ion-to-hydroxide-ion ratio.
3. To write Equation (16-9).
4. To state the definition of *p*H as given on p. 251.
5. Given the hydrogen-ion concentration, to calculate the *p*H of a substance.
6. Given its *p*H, to calculate the hydrogen-ion concentration of a substance.
7. To describe several acid-base indicators.

ACID-BASE NEUTRALIZATION

(pp. 254–58)

Learning Objectives

1. To write the ionic equation for the neutralization of hydrochloric acid by sodium hydroxide.
2. To state why there is no reaction between the sodium and chloride ions, in terms of their electron configurations.
3. To state why the hydrogen ions and hydroxide ions react to form water.
4. To describe the titration process.
5. To define the term *end point*.
6. To define a *standard* solution.
7. Given the molarity of the standard solution, and the quantity required to neutralize a given quantity of an acid, to calculate the molarity of the acid.

Demonstration II To Demonstrate the Use of Acid-Base Indicators.

Materials recommended: Vertical stand, double clamp, 2 burets, 125-ml Erlenmeyer flask, 0.1 molar hydrochloric acid, 0.1 molar sodium hydroxide, methyl orange, phenolphthalein.

As stated in the text, various indicators can be used to mark the end point of a strong base-strong acid titration even though the indicators change color over different *p*H ranges. Ideally an indicator should change color when the *p*H of the solution is 7. But this is unnecessary. Indeed, phenolphthalein (with a *p*H range of about 8.0 to 9.8) and methyl orange (with a range of about 3.1 to 4.4) give the same end point as would an "ideal" indicator. This important fact can easily be demonstrated as in the following experiment.

Fill one buret with dilute HCl (about 0.1 molar) and fill another buret with dilute NaOH (about 0.1 molar). Run exactly 20.0 ml of HCl into an Erlenmeyer flask and then add 2 drops of methyl orange. Read the volume of NaOH in the other buret and then run NaOH into the Erlenmeyer flask until the methyl orange changes color from red to yellow. Again read the base buret and compute the volume of NaOH used in the titration.

Now repeat the operation, except that in the second run 2 drops of phenolphthalein are used as indicator. Again measure the volume of base used when the phenolphthalein changes color, this time from colorless to permanent pink. If reasonable care is taken (that is, if you avoid overshooting the end point) the volumes of NaOH are the same for each titration. In other words, methyl orange and phenolphthalein show precisely the same end point.

However, it should be added that these two indicators would not give the same end point if a strong base is titrated with a weak acid (for example, NaOH and CH_3COOH), nor if a strong acid is titrated with a weak base (for example, HCl and $NH_{3(aq)}$). In the first example, phenolphthalein would be a suitable indicator, but not methyl orange. In the second example, methyl orange would be a suitable indicator, but not phenolphthalein.

STRONG AND WEAK ACIDS

(pp. 259–63)

Learning Objectives

1. To define a *strong* acid.
2. To define a *weak* acid.
3. To write the ionic equation for the decomposition of carbonic acid.
4. To write the equation that expresses decomposition of carbonic acid into water and carbon dioxide.

5. To write the equation for the decomposition of the bicarbonate ion into hydrogen and carbonate ions.
6. To write the general equation expressing the ionization constant for acids.
7. To state the value for K_A at 25°C.
8. To state why the ionization constant for hydrochloric acid is infinitely large.
9. To calculate the value of K_A for water.
10. To define a polybasic acid.
11. To write the equations for both steps of the ionization of sulfuric acid.
12. To write the equations for the determination of K_A for both steps.

HYDROLYSIS OF SALTS
(pp. 263–64)

Learning Objectives

1. To state the ionic structure of solid salts.
2. To write the equation for the break down of sodium acetate in water.
3. To write the equation for the reaction of the acetate ion with water.
4. To define the term *hydrolysis*.
5. To state why the *p*H of a sodium chloride solution is 7.

Suggested Teacher Commentary

The hydrolysis of the salt of a strong acid and a weak base is not discussed in the text. Such a salt is ammonium chloride (NH_4Cl).

In solution, free ions are formed. Or

$$NH_4{}^+Cl^- \xrightarrow{\text{water}} NH_4{}^+ + Cl^-$$

Thus the four ions in water solution are

$$\begin{array}{ccc} & & NH_4{}^+ + Cl^- \\ H_2O & \rightleftharpoons & OH^- + H^+ \\ & & \updownarrow \\ & & NH_4OH \end{array}$$

Hydrogen ion and chloride ion do not react because HCl is a strong acid. However, ammonium ion combines with hydroxide ion because NH_4OH is a weak base. Hence OH^- is removed from solution, and $[H^+] \times [OH^-] < 10^{-14}$. Therefore more water dissociates to make $[H^+] \times [OH^-] = 10^{-14}$. As a result, $[H^+] > [OH^-]$ and the solution is acidic.

THE BRÖNSTED-LOWRY THEORY OF ACIDS AND BASES
(pp. 264–67)

Learning Objectives

1. To state that in the ionization process, water reacts chemically with acids and bases.
2. To state the Brönsted-Lowry theory.
3. To write the formula for the hydronium ion.
4. To write the equation for the reaction of hydrogen chloride with water.
5. To state why water is a base, and HCl an acid, according to the Brönsted-Lowry theory.
6. To write the equation for the reaction of ammonia with water.
7. To state that water can be either an acid or a base.
8. To write the general equation for a reversible acid-base reaction.
9. To define a conjugate acid-base pair.

Suggested Teacher Commentary

Before Brönsted's time an acid was defined as a substance that increases the concentration of hydronium ion in a solution, and a base was defined as a substance that decreases the concentration of the hydronium ion, or increases the concentration of the hydroxide ion. In 1923, Brönsted and Lowry proposed much more comprehensive definitions of acids and bases, definitions that not only extended the acid-base concept of water solutions but which also applied to non-aqueous solutions.

As stated in the text, an acid is defined as a donor of protons, whereas a base is an acceptor of protons. In the reaction,

$$\underset{\text{acid}}{HCl} + \underset{\text{base}}{H_2O} \rightleftharpoons \underset{\text{acid}}{H_3O^+} + \underset{\text{base}}{Cl^-}$$

HCl is an acid because it donates a proton to H_2O, thereby forming H_3O^+, and H_2O is a base because it accepts a proton from HCl, thereby forming Cl^-. H_3O^+ is also an acid because it donates a proton to Cl^- to form HCl, and Cl^- is also a base because it accepts a proton from H_3O^+ to form HCl.

Now let us consider a non-aqueous solution. In liquid ammonia (which is the solvent) NH_4Cl reacts with KNH_2 (potassium amide). Both these substances ionize in ammonia solution.

$$NH_4{}^+Cl^- \xrightarrow{NH_3} NH_4{}^+ + Cl^-$$

$$K^+NH_2{}^- \xrightarrow{NH_3} K^+ + \underset{\text{amide ion}}{NH_2{}^-}$$

The following reaction then takes place,

$$\underset{\text{acid}}{NH_4^+} + \underset{\text{base}}{NH_2^-} \rightleftharpoons 2NH_3$$

In this reaction NH_4^+ donates a proton to NH_2^- and, as a result, both ions are changed to molecular NH_3. Thus, according to the Brönsted definition, NH_4^+ is an acid and NH_2^- is a base. Notice that this non-aqueous reaction is similar to the neutralization reaction in water solution,

$$\underset{\text{acid}}{H_3O^+} + \underset{\text{base}}{OH^-} \rightleftharpoons 2H_2O$$

Additional Questions and Problems

1. A solution contains 0.000365 g of hydrogen chloride per l. (*a*) What is the *p*H of the solution? (*b*) What would be the color of (*i*) methyl orange, (*ii*) phenolphthalein, (*iii*) thymol blue in this solution?

Answer

(*a*) $[H^+] = \dfrac{0.000365 \text{ g}}{36.5 \text{ g/mole} \times 1 \text{ l}} = 10^{-5} \quad pH = 5.0$

(*b*) (*i*) yellow (*ii*) colorless (*iii*) yellow

2. How many g of the solute are required to prepare (*a*) 100 ml of hydrochloric acid with a *p*H of 1.0, (*b*) 500 ml of sulfuric acid with a *p*H of 3.0, (*c*) 10.0 l of nitric acid with a *p*H of 0.5, (*d*) 250 ml of sodium hydroxide solution with a *p*H of 13.0, (*e*) 100 ml of barium hydroxide solution with a *p*H of 11.0?

Answer

(*a*) $[H^+] = 10^{-1}$ Mass $= M \times \text{molecular mass} \times \text{volume}$
$= 10^{-1} \text{ mole/l} \times 36.5 \text{ g/mole} \times 0.100 \text{ l} = 0.365 \text{ g}$

(*b*) $[H^+] = 10^{-3}$ and M of $H_2SO_4 = 5 \times 10^{-4}$ since one H_2SO_4 provides two H^+.

$$\text{Mass} = 5 \times 10^{-4} \text{ mole/l} \times 98 \text{ g/mole} \times 0.500 \text{ l} = 0.0245 \text{ g}$$

(*c*) $[H^+] = 0.3$ Mass $= 0.3 \text{ mole/l} \times 63 \text{ g/mole} \times 10.0 \text{ l} = 189 \text{ g}$

(*d*) $[OH^-] = 0.1$ Mass $= 0.1 \text{ mole/l} \times 40 \text{ g/mole} \times 0.250 \text{ l} = 1.00 \text{ g}$

(*e*) $[OH^-] = 10^{-3}$ and M of $Ba(OH)_2 = 5 \times 10^{-4}$ since one $Ba(OH)_2$ provides two OH^-.

$$\text{Mass} = 5 \times 10^{-4} \text{ mole/l} \times 171 \text{ g/mole} \times 0.100 \text{ l} = 0.00855 \text{ g}$$

3. Twenty ml of 0.450 M sodium hydroxide neutralize 50.0 ml of a sulfuric acid solution. Compute the (*a*) molarity of the acid, (*b*) *p*H of the acid, (*c*) *p*H of the base.

Answer

$$\underset{\text{2 moles}}{2NaOH} + \underset{\text{1 mole}}{H_2SO_4} \rightarrow Na_2SO_4 + 2H_2O$$

(*a*) Moles NaOH $= 0.450 \text{ mole/l} \times 0.0200 \text{ l} = 0.00900 \text{ mole}$

$$\text{Moles acid} = \frac{0.00900 \text{ mole}}{2} = 0.00450 \text{ mole}$$

$$\text{Molarity of acid} = \frac{0.00450 \text{ mole}}{0.0500 \text{ l}} = 0.0900\ M$$

(*b*) $[H^+] = 2 \times 0.0900 \text{ mole/l} = 0.180\ M \quad pH = 0.74$

(*c*) $[H^+] = \dfrac{10^{-14}}{0.450} = 2.2 \times 10^{-14} \quad pH = 13.65$

4. Compute the volume of 0.100 M sulfuric acid needed to neutralize 10.0 ml of 0.200 M potassium hydroxide.

Answer

$$\underset{\text{2 moles}}{2KOH} + \underset{\text{1 mole}}{H_2SO_4} \rightarrow K_2SO_4 + 2H_2O$$

$$\text{Moles base} = 0.200 \text{ mole/l} \times 0.0100 \text{ l} = 0.002000 \text{ mole}$$

$$\text{Moles acid} = \frac{0.00200 \text{ mole}}{2} = 0.00100 \text{ mole}$$

$$\text{Volume acid} = \frac{0.00100 \text{ mole}}{0.100 \text{ mole/l}} = 0.0100 \text{ l or } 10.0 \text{ ml}$$

5. Fifty ml of 5.0 M sulfuric acid are diluted to 250 ml. Calculate the (*a*) molarity of the diluted acid, (*b*) *p*H of the diluted acid.

Answer

(*a*) $\text{Molarity} = \dfrac{50 \text{ ml} \times 5.0\ M}{250 \text{ ml}} = 1.00\ M$

(*b*) $[H^+] = 1.00\ M \times 2 = 2.00\ M \quad pH = -0.30$

6. A sample of solid sodium hydroxide is dissolved in water to give 250 ml of solution. Thirty-five ml of this solution neutralize 50.0 ml of 0.100 M hydrochloric acid. Compute the mass of the sample of sodium hydroxide.

Answer

$$\underset{\text{1 mole}}{NaOH} + \underset{\text{1 mole}}{HCl} \rightarrow NaCl + H_2O$$

$$\text{Moles HCl} = 0.100 \text{ mole/l} \times 0.0500 \text{ l} = 0.00500 \text{ mole}$$

$$\text{Moles NaOH} = 0.00500 \text{ mole}$$

Mass of NaOH in titration sample $= 0.00500 \text{ mole} \times 40 \text{ g/mole} = 0.200 \text{ g}$

$$\text{Total mass of NaOH} = \frac{250 \text{ ml} \times 0.200\text{g}}{35.0 \text{ ml}} = 1.43 \text{ g}$$

7. Dilute sulfuric acid is prepared by making 9.8 g of H_2SO_4 up to 500 ml of solution with water. Enough 0.100 *M* barium hydroxide is added to 50.0 ml of the diluted acid to give a faint pink color with phenolphthalein. (*a*) What volume of base must be added? (*b*) What is the mass of the precipitate? (*c*) How many moles of water are formed?

Answer

$$\underset{1\text{ mole}}{Ba(OH)_2} + \underset{1\text{ mole}}{H_2SO_4} \rightarrow \underset{1\text{ mole}}{BaSO_4} + \underset{2\text{ moles}}{2H_2O}$$

$$\text{Molarity of acid} = \frac{9.8\text{ g}}{98\text{ g/mole} \times 0.500\text{ l}} = 0.200\ M$$

(*a*) Moles of acid used = 0.200 mole/l × 0.0500 l = 0.0100 mole

Moles of base used = 0.0100 mole

$$\text{Volume of base} = \frac{0.0100\text{ mole}}{0.100\text{ mole/l}} = 0.100\text{ l or }100\text{ ml}$$

(*b*) Mass = 0.0100 mole × 233 g/mole = 2.33 g.

(*c*) Moles = 0.0100 mole × 2 = 0.0200 mole.

8. In the titration of 0.100 *M* HCl and 0.100 *M* NaOH, the base is slowly added to 20.0 ml of the acid. Compute the *p*H of the solution after the following volumes of NaOH have been added: (*a*) 5.0 ml, (*b*) 10.0 ml, (*c*) 15.0 ml, (*d*) 16.0 ml, (*e*) 17.0 ml, (*f*) 18.0 ml, (*g*) 19.0 ml, (*h*) 19.5 ml, (*i*) 20.0 ml, (*j*) 20.5 ml, (*k*) 21.0 ml, (*l*) 22.0 ml, (*m*) 25.0 ml, (*n*) 30.0 ml. Finally, plot the *p*H values against the volumes of 0.100 *M* NaOH and explain the meaning of the graph.

Answer

The method which applies to (*a*) through (*h*) is

$$[H^+] = \frac{\text{volume of HCl in excess} \times M \text{ of HCl}}{\text{volume of mixture}}$$

(*a*) $[H^+] = \dfrac{15.0\text{ ml} \times 0.100\ M}{25.0\text{ ml}} = 6.0 \times 10^{-2}$ $pH = 1.22$

(*b*) $[H^+] = 3.3 \times 10^{-2}$ $pH = 1.48$

(*c*) $[H^+] = 1.43 \times 10^{-2}$ $pH = 1.85$

(*d*) $[H^+] = 1.11 \times 10^{-2}$ $pH = 1.95$

(*e*) $[H^+] = 8.1 \times 10^{-3}$ $pH = 2.09$

(*f*) $[H^+] = 5.3 \times 10^{-3}$ $pH = 2.28$

(*g*) $[H^+] = 2.6 \times 10^{-3}$ $pH = 2.59$

(*h*) $[H^+] = 1.3 \times 10^{-3}$ $pH = 2.90$

(*i*) An equivalent quantity of base has been added and the *p*H of the salt solution is therefore 7.0.

The method which applies to (*j*) through (*n*) is

$$[OH^-] = \frac{\text{volume of NaOH in excess} \times M \text{ of NaOH}}{\text{volume of mixture}}$$

(*j*) $[OH^-] = \dfrac{0.5\text{ ml} \times 0.100\ M}{40.5\text{ ml}} = 1.23 \times 10^{-3}$

$[H^+] = \dfrac{10^{-14}}{1.23 \times 10^{-3}} = 8.1 \times 10^{-12}$ $pH = 11.09$

(*k*) $[OH^-] = 2.4 \times 10^{-3}$ $[H^+] = 4.1 \times 10^{-12}$ $pH = 11.38$

(*l*) $[OH^-] = 4.8 \times 10^{-3}$ $[H^+] = 2.1 \times 10^{-12}$ $pH = 11.68$

(*m*) $[OH^-] = 1.11 \times 10^{-2}$ $[H^+] = 9.0 \times 10^{-13}$ $pH = 12.05$

(*n*) $[OH^-] = 2.0 \times 10^{-2}$ $[H^+] = 5.0 \times 10^{-13}$ $pH = 12.30$

9. Compute (*a*) the *p*H, and (*b*) the percentage ionization of 0.50 *M* acetic acid.

Answer

(*a*) Assume that $[H^+] = [CH_3COO^-]$.

$$[H^+] = \sqrt{K_A \times M \text{ of acid}} = \sqrt{1.8 \times 10^{-5} \times 0.50} = \sqrt{9 \times 10^{-6}} = 3 \times 10^{-3}$$

$pH = 2.52$

(*b*)

$$\%\text{ ionization} = \frac{[H^+]}{[CH_3COOH]} \times 100 = \frac{3 \times 10^{-3} \times 10^2}{0.50} = 0.6\%$$

Answers to Questions and Exercises

Text page references are provided for those questions which do not require computations. The student's answers will be individually stated, but should focus on the concepts developed in these text pages.

Factual Recall

1. 247–50
2. 250–51
3. 251–52
4. 253–54, Fig. 16-7
5. 254–55
6. 260
7. 261–62
8. 263–64
9. 264

Apply Your Knowledge!

1. $[H^+] = \dfrac{\text{mass of acid (g)}}{\text{molecular mass of acid} \times \text{volume of solution (l)}}$

(*a*) $[H^+] = \dfrac{1.825\text{ g}}{36.5\text{ g/mole} \times 0.100\text{ l}} = 0.500\ M$

(*b*) $[H^+] = \dfrac{4.9\text{ g}}{98\text{ g/mole} \times 0.250\text{ l}} \times 2 = 0.400\ M$

(*c*) $[H^+] = \dfrac{0.00063\ \text{g}}{63\ \text{g/mole} \times 0.500\ \text{l}} = 2.00 \times 10^{-5}\ M$

(*d*) $[H^+] = \dfrac{8.1\ \text{g}}{81\ \text{g/mole} \times 0.500\ \text{l}} = 0.200\ M$

(*e*) $[H^+] = \dfrac{1.28\ \text{g}}{128\ \text{g/mole} \times 0.100\ \text{l}} = 0.100\ M$

2. $p\text{H} = -\log [H^+]$.

(*a*) $[H^+] = 5 \times 10^{-1}$ $p\text{H} = 0.30$
(*b*) $[H^+] = 4 \times 10^{-1}$ $p\text{H} = 0.40$
(*c*) $[H^+] = 2 \times 10^{-5}$ $p\text{H} = 4.70$
(*d*) $[H^+] = 2 \times 10^{-1}$ $p\text{H} = 0.70$
(*e*) $[H^+] = 10^{-1}$ $p\text{H} = 1.00$

3. $[OH^-] = \dfrac{\text{mass of base (g)}}{\text{molecular mass of base} \times \text{volume of solution (l)}}$

(*a*) $[OH^-] = \dfrac{4.0\ \text{g}}{40\ \text{g/mole} \times 0.250\ \text{l}} = 0.400\ M$

(*b*) $[OH^-] = \dfrac{1.85\ \text{g}}{74\ \text{g/mole} \times 0.100\ \text{l}} = 0.250\ M$

(*c*) $[OH^-] = \dfrac{11.2\ \text{g}}{56\ \text{g/mole} \times 5.0\ \text{l}} = 0.0400\ M$

4. (*a*) $[H^+] = \dfrac{10^{-14}}{0.400} = 2.5 \times 10^{-14}$ $p\text{H} = 13.60$

(*b*) $[H^+] = \dfrac{10^{-14}}{0.250} = 4 \times 10^{-14}$ $p\text{H} = 13.40$

(*c*) $[H^+] = \dfrac{10^{-14}}{0.0400} = 2.5 \times 10^{-13}$ $p\text{H} = 12.60$

5. (*a*) $[H^+] = 1.0$
(*b*) $[H^+] = 10^{-4}$
(*c*) $[H^+] = 10^{-10}$
(*d*) $[H^+] = 5 \times 10^{-3}$
(*e*) $[H^+] = 4 \times 10^{-5}$
(*f*) $[H^+] = 3.2 \times 10^{-13}$
(*g*) $[H^+] = 3.2 \times 10^{-2}$
(*h*) $[H^+] = 3.2$

6. (*a*) $[H^+] = 10^{-10}$ $[OH^-] = \dfrac{K_w}{10^{-10}} = 10^{-4}$

(*b*) (*i*) red (*ii*) yellow (*iii*) yellow

UNIT V

ELECTROCHEMISTRY

Chapter 17 Oxidation-Reduction
Chapter 18 Chemical Effects of an Electric Current

OPENING UNIT V

Alessandro Volta's announcement in 1800 that an electric current could be produced by two different metals separated by a conducting solution of salt caused a sensation in the scientific community. Other scientists began to experiment with the implications of his discovery with a speed that has a modern flavor about it. Only a few weeks after his announcement, Nicholson and Carlisle electrolyzed water. That same year, Davy began his study of the chemical effects of electricity. By 1806, he was able to assert with some confidence that electrical forces determined the combining capacities of the elements. Two years later, he had isolated from their compounds potassium, sodium, magnesium, strontium, barium, and calcium. It had become clear that electricity not only could come from chemical reactions but could also produce them. Chapter 17 of this unit deals with oxidation-reduction reactions. In Chapter 18, the quantitative work of Davy's assistant, Michael Faraday, is covered.

CHAPTER 17

OXIDATION-REDUCTION

OXIDATION-REDUCTION IN IONIC EQUATIONS (pp. 274–76)

Learning Objectives

1. To write the electron dot notation for the oxidation of sodium.
2. To define an oxidizing agent in terms of electron transfer.
3. To write the equation for the reduction of iron ore to iron.
4. To define a reducing agent in terms of electron transfer.
5. Given the reaction $Zn + 2H^+ \rightarrow Zn + H_2$, to state which is the oxidizing agent and which is the reducing agent.
6. To define the term *redox* reaction.
7. To define the term chemical activity in terms of electron transfer.
8. To name a very active metal and a very inactive metal.
9. To state the meaning of the fact that heat is released in the Zn-Cu^{+2} reaction.

Demonstration I To Show the Relative Activities of Zinc, Copper, and Mercury.

Materials recommended: test tube, 150-ml beaker, mossy zinc, copper penny, copper (II) sulfate solution, mercury (I) nitrate solution.

It is easy to demonstrate by simple experiments that copper is less active than zinc but more active than mercury.

To show that zinc is more active than copper

Pour some copper (II) sulfate solution into a test tube, add a few pieces of mossy zinc, then close the tube with the thumb and shake gently. Notice that the zinc becomes coated with a dark red deposit of copper and, at the same time, the blue color of the solution becomes fainter and eventually disappears. The blue color is the color of hydrated Cu^{+2} and the Zn^{+2} is colorless. So the reaction is $Zn + Cu^{+2} \rightarrow Zn^{+2} + Cu$. That is, zinc metal displaces copper from a solution of cupric ion.

To show that copper is more active than mercury

A penny is about 90% copper and so a penny is a convenient source of copper. Clean a penny with vinegar and salt and then place it in a beaker which contains a solution of mercury (I) nitrate. Observe that after about 10 seconds the penny becomes covered with a "silvery" coating of mercury. The reaction is $Cu + 2Hg^+ \rightarrow Cu^{+2} + 2Hg$. That is, copper displaces mercury from a solution of Hg^+ ion. Therefore copper is more active than mercury.

A GALVANIC CELL (pp. 276–82)

Learning Objectives

1. To describe a galvanic cell.
2. To describe a half-cell.
3. To describe a salt bridge.

4. To write the equations for the half-reactions that take place in zinc and copper half-cells.
5. To write the equation for the net reaction that takes place in two half-cells.
6. To define the term *electrode*.
7. To define the term *anode*.
8. To define the term *cathode*.
9. To state at which electrode oxidation takes place.
10. To state at which electrode reduction takes place.
11. To define the term *current*.
12. To define the term *potential*.
13. To state the units (and their symbols) used to measure current and potential.
14. To define the term *electrode potential*.
15. To describe a hydrogen half-cell.
16. To write the equation for the half-reaction in the hydrogen half-cell.
17. To describe the measurement of electrode potential using a hydrogen half-cell.
18. To define and write the symbol for standard electrode potential.
19. To compute the voltage of the combination of a copper half-cell with a zinc half-cell.
20. To describe the operation of a Daniell cell.

Demonstration II A Zinc-Copper Electrochemical Cell.

Materials recommended: 1 × 5 inch copper strip, 1 × 5 inch zinc strip, ammeter, 2 1-l beakers, switch, copper wire, U-tube, cotton, dilute sulfuric acid, saturated potassium chloride solution.

A zinc-copper cell can be prepared as follows: Cut a strip of thin sheet copper about one inch by five inches and a strip of sheet zinc about the same size. Attach a clip (which acts as a terminal) to each of the metal strips. Connect the copper terminal to a switch by a copper wire and attach the other end of the switch to the positive terminal of an ammeter. (The positive terminal of an ammeter must be connected to the positive terminal of the cell, and vice versa. That is, electrons enter the ammeter at the negative terminal and leave the ammeter at the positive terminal.) Then connect the other terminal of the ammeter to the zinc strip. Half fill a beaker with very dilute sulfuric acid and immerse the metal strips in the acid as shown in Fig. TG17–1.

Notice that bubbles of hydrogen escape from the zinc metal but not from the copper.

$$Zn + 2H^+ \rightarrow Zn^{+2} + H_2$$

Now close the switch and observe (1) that the needle of the ammeter is deflected and (2) that bubbles of hydrogen escape from the strip of copper. The ammeter deflection proves that a current is flowing through the circuit. The release of hydrogen on the surface of the copper strip is due to the reaction between hydrogen ions and electrons that enter the Cu electrode, $2H^+ + 2e^- \rightarrow H_2$.

Now replace the ammeter by a voltmeter, again connecting the positive terminal of the cell to the positive terminal of the voltmeter. Notice that the reading of the voltmeter (which is the voltage or potential of the cell) is about 1.1 V.

The cell is made up of two parts, (1) the Zn part plus the electrolyte and (2) the Cu part plus the electrolyte. And, as stated in the text, these two parts can be separated into *half-cells* and the reactions in them are then *half-reactions* (Fig. 17–3). However, before a current can flow through the two half-cells they must be connected by a salt bridge which allows ions to move freely from one half-cell to the other. A suitable salt bridge is an inverted U-tube filled with a saturated solution of a suitable electrolyte such as potassium chloride. If the ends of the tube are closed with cotton plugs, as shown in Fig. TG17–2, the tube is more easily manipulated and the ions can flow through the barrier of cotton.

We must remember that an anode is the electrode where oxidation takes place. Conversely, the cathode accepts

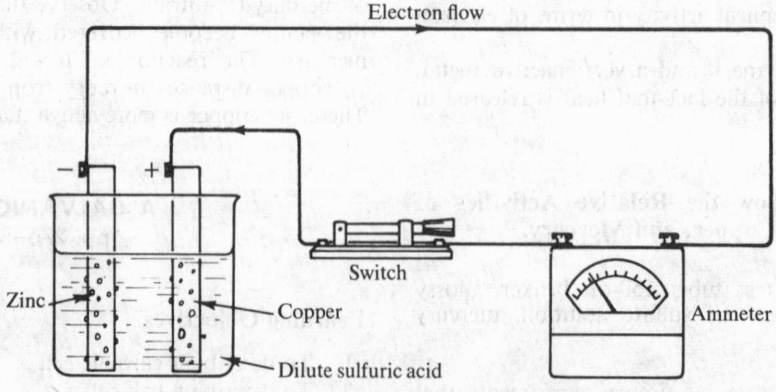

FIG. TG17–1

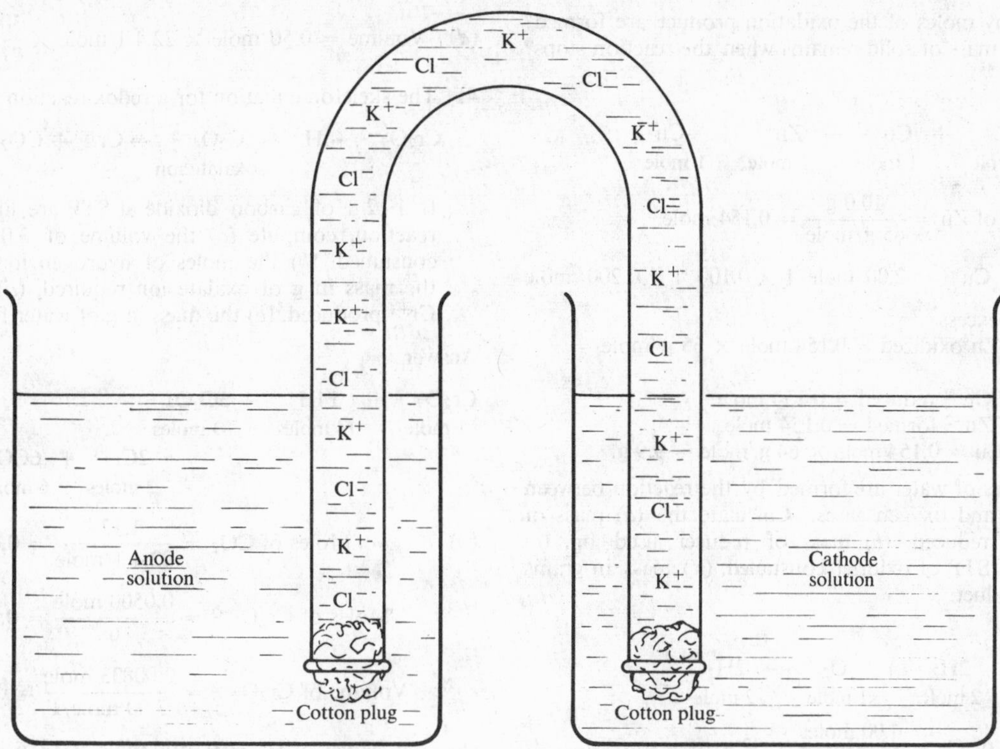

FIG. TG17–2

electrons. Hence we associate the terms cathode and reduction. Thus electrons flow from the negative to the positive terminal.

STANDARD OXIDATION POTENTIALS
(pp. 283)

Learning Objectives

1. To define a standard oxidation potential.
2. To state the meaning of the plus and minus signs associated with E^0.

OXIDATION NUMBERS
(p. 283–89)

Learning Objectives

1. To state the oxidation number of an atom.
2. To state that oxidation involves loss of electrons, with a consequent increase in oxidation number.
3. To state that reduction involves a gain of electrons, with a consequent reduction in oxidation number.
4. To state that an oxidizing agent is reduced in a reaction and decreases its oxidation number.
5. To state that a reducing agent is oxidized in a reaction and increases its oxidation number.
6. To state the oxidation number of a covalent molecule composed of identical elements.
7. To state the rule for applying the electronegativity scale to assigning oxidation numbers to dissimilar elements in covalent compounds.
8. To state the rules for computing oxidation numbers listed on p. 286 of the text.
9. To state the rules for balancing redox equations by oxidation numbers listed on p. 287 of the text.
10. To describe the ion-electron method for balancing redox reactions.

Additional Questions and Problems

1. One hundred ml of 2.00 *M* copper (II) sulfate are added to 10.0 g of zinc metal. (*a*) What mass of reducer is used up? (*b*) How many moles of oxidizer are used up? (*c*)

How many moles of the oxidation product are formed? (*d*) What mass of solid remains when the reaction stops?

Answer

$$Zn + Cu^{+2} \rightarrow Zn^{+2} + Cu$$
1 mole 1 mole 1 mole 1 mole

$$\text{Moles of Zn} = \frac{10.0\ g}{65\ g/mole} = 0.154\ mole$$

$$\text{Moles of } Cu^{+2} = 2.00\ mole/l \times 0.100\ l = 0.200\ mole$$

Cu^{+2} is in excess.

(*a*) Mass of Zn oxidized = 0.154 mole × 65 g/mole = 10.0 g.
(*b*) Moles of Cu^{+2} reduced = 0.154 mole.
(*c*) Moles of Zn^{+2} formed = 0.154 mole.
(*d*) Mass of Cu = 0.154 mole × 64 g/mole = 9.9 g.

2. Four moles of water are formed by the reaction between hydrogen and oxygen gases. Calculate the (*a*) mass of substance reduced, (*b*) mass of reducer used up, (*c*) volume at STP of oxidizer consumed, (*d*) mass in grams of the product.

Answer

$$2H_2 + O_2 \rightarrow 2H_2O$$
2 moles 1 mole 2 moles

(*a*) $$\text{Mass of } O_2 = \frac{4.00\ moles}{2} \times 32\ g/mole = 64\ g$$

(*b*) $$\text{Mass of } H_2 = 4.00\ moles \times 2.02\ g/mole = 8.08\ g$$

(*c*) $$\text{Volume of } O_2 = \frac{64\ g \times 22.4\ l/mole}{32\ g/mole} = 44.8\ l$$

(*d*) $$\text{Mass of } H_2O = 4.00\ moles \times 18\ g/mole = 72\ g$$

3. The skeleton equation for a reaction of iron with dilute nitric acid is

$$Fe + H^+ + NO_3^- \rightarrow Fe^{+3} + NO \uparrow + H_2O$$

If 0.50 mole of iron is consumed in this reaction, find (*a*) the mass in g of oxidation product, (*b*) the moles of oxidizer consumed, (*c*) the moles of water formed, (*d*) the volume of gas product at 27°C and 760 torr pressure.

Answer

$$Fe + 4H^+ + NO_3^- \rightarrow$$
1 mole 1 mole

$$Fe^{+3} + NO\ (g) + 2H_2O$$
1 mole 1 mole 2 moles

(*a*) Mass of Fe^{+3} = 0.50 mole × 56 g/mole = 28 g.
(*b*) Moles of NO_3^- = 0.50 mole.
(*c*) Moles of H_2O = 2 × 0.50 mole = 1.00 mole.

(*d*) $$\text{Volume} = 0.50\ mole \times 22.4\ l/mole \times \frac{300°K}{273°K} = 12.3\ l.$$

4. The skeleton equation for a redox reaction is

$$Cr_2O_7^{-2} + H^+ + C_2O_4^{-2} \rightarrow Cr^{+3} + CO_2 \uparrow + H_2O$$
oxalate ion

If 1.12 l of carbon dioxide at STP are liberated in this reaction, compute (*a*) the volume of 3.00 *M* $Cr_2O_7^{-2}$ consumed, (*b*) the moles of hydrogen ion used up, (*c*) the mass in g of oxalate ion required, (*d*) the moles of Cr^{+3} produced, (*e*) the mass in g of water formed.

Answer

$$Cr_2O_7^{-2} + 14H^+ + 3C_2O_4^{-2} \rightarrow$$
1 mole 14 moles 3 moles

$$2Cr^{+3} + 6CO_2 + 7H_2O$$
2 moles 6 moles 7 moles

(*a*) $$\text{Moles of } CO_2 = \frac{1.12\ l}{22.4\ l/mole} = 0.0500\ mole$$

$$\text{Moles of } Cr_2O_7^{-2} = \frac{0.0500\ mole}{6} = 0.00833\ mole$$

$$\text{Volume of } Cr_2O_7^{-2} = \frac{0.00833\ mole}{3.00\ mole/l} = 0.00278\ l$$

(*b*) $$\text{Moles of } H^+ = 0.0500\ mole \times 14/6 = 0.117\ mole$$

(*c*) $$\text{Mass of } C_2O_4^{-2} = \frac{0.0500\ mole}{2} \times 88\ g/mole = 2.20\ g$$

(*d*) $$\text{Moles of } Cr^{+3} = \frac{0.0500\ mole}{3} = 0.0167\ mole$$

(*e*) $$\text{Mass of } H_2O = 0.0500\ mole \times 7/6 \times 18\ g/mole = 1.05\ g$$

Answers to Questions and Exercises

Text page references are provided for those questions which do not require computations. The student's answers will be individually stated, but should focus on the concepts developed in those text pages.

Factual Recall

1. 273–76 2. 275, 283 3. 279–81
4. 280, Fig. 17–5
5. (*a*) Glossary, 562; (*b*) Glossary, 562; (*c*) Glossary, 562; (*d*) Glossary, 562

6. 283–88 7. 285–88

8. $KMnO_4 + H_2S + H_2SO_4 \rightarrow K_2SO_4 + MnSO_4 + H_2O + S$

Change in oxidation number of Mn is 5, and the change in oxidation number of S is 2. Least common multiple is 10. Hence,

$2KMnO_4 + 5H_2S + H_2SO_4 \rightarrow K_2SO_4 + 2MnSO_4 + 8H_2O + 5S$

9. $Cr_2O_7^{-2} + H^+ + Br^- \rightarrow Cr^{+3} + H_2O + Br_2$

(*a*) Reduction of $Cr_2O_7^{-2}$ to Cr^{+3},

$Cr_2O_7^{-2} + 14H^+ + 6e^{-1} \rightarrow 2Cr^{+3} + 7H_2O$
Oxidation of Br^- to Br_2, $6Br^- - 6e^{-1} \rightarrow 3Br_2$.
Balanced equation is

$Cr_2O_7^{-2} + 14H^+ + 6Br^- \rightarrow 2Cr^{+3} + 7H_2O + 3Br_2$

(*b*) Charges in reactants $= -2 + 14 - 6 = +6$
Charge in product $= 2 \times 3 = +6$

Apply Your Knowledge!

1.

Half-reaction	E^0 in V
$Mg \rightarrow Mg^{+2} + 2e^{-1}$	+2.34
$Cu^{+2} + 2e^{-1} \rightarrow Cu$	+.34

E^0 of cell = 2.68 V

2. (*a*)

Half-reaction	E^0 in V
$Fe \rightarrow Fe^{+2} + 2e^{-1}$	+0.44
$Cu^{+2} + 2e^{-1} \rightarrow Cu$	+0.34

E^0 of cell = 0.78 V

(*b*) Cations (Cu^{+2}) are reduced at the copper strip (the cathode).

3. $Zn + 2H^+ \rightarrow Zn^{+2} + H_2$
1 mole, 2 moles, 1 mole, 1 mole

(*a*) $\text{Moles of } H_2 = \dfrac{1.12\ l}{22.4\ l/\text{mole}} = 0.0500 \text{ mole}$

Moles of H^+ used up $= 0.0500$ mole $\times 2 = 0.100$ mole

(*b*) Moles of Zn = 0.0500 mole.
(*c*) Moles of Zn^{+2} = 0.0500 mole.

(*d*) $\text{Volume of } H^+ = \dfrac{0.100 \text{ mole}}{6.00 \text{ moles}/l} = 0.0167\ l \text{ or } 16.7 \text{ ml}$

4. $2H_2 + O_2 \rightarrow 2H_2O$
2 moles, 1 mole, 2 moles

(*a*) Moles of H_2 = 1 mole
Moles of O_2 = 1 mole
Moles of H_2O formed = 1 mole

(*b*) Mass of O_2 used up = 0.500 mole × 32 g/mole = 16 g.
(*c*) Mass of O_2 reduced = 16 g.

5. $2MnO_4^- + 16H^+ + 10I^- \rightarrow 2Mn^{+2} + 5I_2 + 8H_2O$
2 moles, 16 moles, 10 moles; 2 moles, 5 moles

(*a*) $\text{Moles of } I_2 = \dfrac{2.54 \text{ g}}{254 \text{ g/mole}} = 0.0100 \text{ mole}$

Moles of MnO_4^- = 0.0100 mole × 2/5
= 0.00400 mole

$\text{Volume of } MnO_4^- = \dfrac{0.00400 \text{ mole}}{0.500 \text{ mole}/l} = 0.00800\ l$

(*b*) Moles of Mn^{+2} = 0.0100 mole × 2/5 = 0.00400 mole.
(*c*) Mass of H^+ = 0.0100 mole × 16/5 × 1.01 g/mole = 0.0322 g.
(*d*) Moles of I^- = 0.0100 mole × 2 = 0.0200 mole.

6. $10Al + 36H^+ + 6NO_3^- \rightarrow 10Al^{+3} + 18H_2O + 3N_2$
10 moles, 6 moles; 10 moles, 3 moles

(*a*) Moles of NO_3^- consumed
= 0.0150 mole = 1.50 moles/l × 0.0100 l
Moles of Al = 0.0150 mole × 10/6 = 0.0250 mole

(*b*) $\text{Volume of } N_2 = \dfrac{0.0150 \text{ mole} \times 22.4\ l/\text{mole} \times 293°\text{K} \times 760 \text{ torr}}{2 \times 273°\text{K} \times 700 \text{ torr}}$
= 0.196 l

(*c*) Mass of Al^{+3} = 0.0250 mole × 27 g/mole = 0.675 g

CHAPTER 18

CHEMICAL EFFECTS OF AN ELECTRIC CURRENT

AN ELECTROLYTIC CELL
(pp. 295–300)

Learning Objectives

1. To state the difference between an electrolytic and an electrochemical cell.
2. To state that the source of electrons is external to the electrolytic cell.
3. To state which electrode in an electrolytic cell receives the electrons.
4. To state that electrons flow from the negative terminal of the external electrochemical cell.
5. To state that oxidation takes place at the positive terminal of an electrolytic cell.
6. To state that reduction takes place at the negative terminal of an electrolytic cell.
7. To list the parts of a common dry cell.
8. To draw the diagram for a battery of two dry cells.
9. To state the source of electrons within an electrolytic cell.
10. To define the term *anion*.
11. To define the term *cation*.
12. To state to which electrode anions and cations are attracted.
13. To write the equation for the net reaction of the electrolysis of hydrochloric acid.
14. To write the equation for the electrolysis of dilute sulfuric acid.
15. To write the equations, including oxidation potentials, for the half-reactions in the electrolysis of dilute sulfuric acid.
16. To write the equations, including oxidation potentials, for the half-reactions in the electrolysis of sodium chloride.

Suggested Teacher Commentary

In the electrolysis of sodium chloride solution there are two possible anode reactions,

$$2Cl^- - 2e^- \rightarrow Cl_2 \qquad E^0 = -1.36 \text{ volts}$$
$$2H_2O - 4e^- \rightarrow 4H^+ + O_2 \qquad E^0 = -1.23 \text{ volts}$$

In a one molar solution it is much easier to discharge chloride ions than to decompose water molecules so that, as is stated in the text, the only anode reaction is the release of chlorine. However, as chlorine gas escapes, the concentration of chloride ion in solution decreases and it become increasingly difficult to discharge chloride ions. As electrolysis proceeds the decomposition of water molecules occurs so that oxygen as well as chlorine is released at the anode. Indeed, when the concentration of chloride ion is reduced to a very small value, the anode product is chiefly oxygen. And this is what we would expect from an examination of the two oxidation potentials, namely -1.23 volts and -1.36 volts.

Precisely the same argument applies to the electrolysis of hydrochloric acid. At first only chlorine is released at the anode. But as the concentration of chloride ion steadily diminishes, oxygen as well as chlorine is released until eventually the anode product is oxygen only. And when this occurs the electrolysis of $HCl_{(aq)}$ yields the same products as the electrolysis of $H_2SO_{4(aq)}$.

ELECTROPLATING
(pp. 300–02)

Learning Objectives

1. To state the essential conditions for electroplating.
2. To write the equation for the cathode reaction in the electroplating of copper.
3. To write the equation for the anode reaction in the electroplating of copper.

ELECTROLYTIC REFINING OF COPPER
(pp. 302–03)

Learning Objectives

1. To describe the electrolytic refining of copper.

FARADAY'S LAWS OF ELECTROLYSIS
(pp. 303–08)

Learning Objectives

1. To describe the apparatus for the electrolytic deposition of silver.
2. To state Faraday's first law of electrolysis.
3. To write the value for the faraday.
4. To state Faraday's second law of electrolysis.
5. To define the term *equivalent mass*.

Suggested Teacher Commentary

The experimental data collected in the experiment described on page 304 can be used to establish the charge on a silver ion and also on an iron (III) ion. In one experiment, the volume of wet hydrogen collected at 22°C and 755 torr pressure was 250 ml and at the same time the masses of Ag and Fe deposited on the electrodes were 2.16 g and 0.37 g respectively.

By a gas law computation the volume of dry hydrogen at STP is 0.224 l and therefore the mass of hydrogen is 0.020 g. By experiment,

$$\frac{\text{Mass of H}}{\text{Mass of Ag}} = \frac{0.020\text{g}}{2.16\text{g}} = \frac{1}{108} = \frac{\text{atomic mass of H}}{\text{atomic mass of Ag}}$$

Hence the number of H atoms released equals the number of Ag atoms released. Therefore the charge on a silver ion must be the same as the charge on a hydrogen ion. And, assuming a hydrogen ion is H^+, a silver ion is Ag^+. By experiment,

$$\frac{\text{Mass of H}}{\text{Mass of Fe}} = \frac{0.020\text{g}}{0.37\text{g}} = \frac{3}{56} = \frac{3 \times \text{atomic mass of H}}{1 \times \text{atomic mass of Fe}}$$

Hence for every atom of Fe deposited there must be 3 atoms of H released. Therefore the charge on an iron (III) ion must be three times as great as the charge on a hydrogen ion. That is, an iron (III) ion is Fe^{+3}.

THE LEAD STORAGE CELL
(pp. 308–11)

Learning Objectives

1. To describe the operation of a lead storage cell.
2. To write the equation for the net anode reaction of a discharging lead cell.
3. To write the equation for the net cathode reaction of a discharging lead cell.
4. To calculate the oxidation potential of a discharging lead cell.
5. To write the equation for the net reaction of the charging process of a lead cell.

Additional Questions and Problems

1. A sodium hydroxide solution is electrolyzed for exactly one hour by a current of 5.00 amperes. (*a*) What is the volume of anode product at 273°C and 1520 torr pressure? (*b*) How many moles of gas are liberated at the cathode? (*c*) How many grams of water are decomposed?

Answer

$$Q = \frac{5.00 \text{ coulombs/sec} \times 3600 \text{ sec}}{96{,}500 \text{ coulombs/F}} = 0.187 \text{ F}$$

(*a*) Mass of oxygen = 0.187 F × 8.00 g/F = 1.50 g.

Volume of oxygen

$$= \frac{1.50 \text{ g} \times 22.4 \text{ l/mole} \times 546°\text{K} \times 760 \text{ torr}}{32 \text{ g/mole} \times 273°\text{K} \times 1520 \text{ torr}}$$

$$= 1.05 \text{ l}$$

(*b*) Mass of hydrogen = 0.187F × 1.008 g/**F** = 0.189 g

$$\text{Moles of hydrogen} = \frac{0.189\text{ g}}{2.016\text{ g/mole}} = 0.094\text{ mole}$$

(*c*) $2H_2O \rightarrow 2H_2 + O_2$

2 moles 2 moles

Moles of water = 0.094 mole

2. The electrolysis of dilute sulfuric acid for 20.0 hours by a current of 2.68 A gives 44.8 l of cathode gas product at 273°C. (*a*) Calculate the value of **F** in coulombs. (*b*) How many moles of anode product are produced?

Answer

(*a*) $$\text{Volume of hydrogen at STP} = \frac{44.8\text{ l} \times 273°\text{K}}{546°\text{K}} = 22.4\text{ l}$$

$$\text{Faradays} = \frac{22.4\text{ l}}{11.2\text{ l}/\mathbf{F}} = 2.00\text{ F}$$

$$\text{Coulombs}/\mathbf{F} = \frac{2.68\text{ C/sec} \times 2.00\text{ hr} \times 3600\text{ sec/hr}}{2.00\mathbf{F}}$$

$$= 96{,}500\text{ coulombs}/\mathbf{F}$$

(*b*) $$\text{Moles of cathode product} = \frac{22.4\text{ l}}{22.4\text{ l/mole}} = 1.000\text{ mole}$$

$$\text{Moles of anode product} = \frac{1.000\text{ mole}}{2} = 0.500\text{ mole}$$

3. If a current of 0.500 A is maintained for 10.0 minutes in the electrolysis of a salt of an inactive metal, the cathode gains 0.336 g. What is the valence of the metal if the atomic mass is 108?

Answer

$$Q = \frac{0.500\text{ C/sec} \times 600\text{ sec}}{96{,}500\text{ C/F}} = 0.00311\text{ F}$$

$$\text{Equivalent mass of metal} = \frac{0.336}{0.00311\text{ F}} = 108\text{ g/F}$$

$$\text{Valence} = \frac{\text{atomic mass}}{\text{equivalent mass}} = \frac{108\text{ g}}{108\text{ g}} = 1$$

4. A Daniell cell delivers 0.100 A to an external circuit for 60 minutes. (*a*) What is the change in mass of the anode? (*b*) What is the change in mass of the cathode? (*c*) How many moles of zinc ion are formed?

Answer

$$Q = \frac{0.100\text{ C/sec} \times 3600\text{ sec}}{96{,}500\text{ C/F}} = 0.00373\text{ F}$$

(*a*) Mass of Zn oxidized = 0.00373 **F** × 32.5 g/**F** = 0.121 g.
(*b*) Mass of Cu deposited = 0.00373 **F** × 32g /**F** = 0.119 g.

(*c*) $$\text{Moles of } Zn^{+2} = \frac{0.121\text{ g}}{65\text{ g/mole}} = 0.00186\text{ mole}$$

5. The cathode gains 2.07 g in mass per hour during the electrolysis of a salt of an inactive metal, using a current of 0.512 A. Calculate the equivalent mass of the metal.

Answer

$$Q = \frac{0.512\text{ C/sec} \times 3600\text{ sec}}{96500\text{ C/F}} = 0.0191\text{ F}$$

$$\text{Mass}/\mathbf{F} = \frac{2.07\text{ g}}{0.0191\text{ F}} = 108\text{ g}$$

Equivalent mass = 108 g

6. A lead cell provides a current of 1.00 A for 2.00 hours to an electrolytic cell filled with copper (II) sulfate solution. Compute (*a*) the mass of lead metal converted at the anode of the lead cell, (*b*) the moles of lead sulfate formed at the cathode of the lead cell, (*c*) the mass in g of product deposited on the cathode of the electrolytic cell.

Answer

$$Q = \frac{1.00\text{ C/sec} \times 7200\text{ sec}}{96{,}500\text{ C/F}} = 0.0746\text{ F}$$

(*a*) $$\text{Mass} = 0.0746\text{ faraday} \times \frac{207\text{ g/F}}{2} = 7.72\text{ g}$$

(*b*) $$\text{Mass of } PbSO_4 = \frac{7.72\text{ g} \times 303\text{ g/mole}}{207\text{ g/mole}} = 11.3\text{ g}$$

$$\text{Moles of } PbSO_4 = \frac{11.3\text{ g}}{303\text{ g/mole}} = 0.0373\text{ mole}$$

(*c*) Mass of Cu = 0.0746 **F** × 32 g/**F** = 2.39 g.

7. In rechargng a discharged lead cell, a current of 5.00 A is maintained for 2.00 hours. Compute (*a*) the mass in g of lead formed at the cathode of the cell, (*b*) the moles of lead dioxide formed at the anode of the cell.

Answer

$$Q = \frac{5.00\text{ C/sec} \times 7200\text{ sec}}{96{,}500\text{ C/F}} = 0.374\text{ F}$$

(*a*) $$\text{Mass of lead} = 0.374\text{ F} \times \frac{207\text{ g/F}}{2} = 38.6\text{ g}$$

(*b*) $$\text{Mass of } PbO_2 = 0.374\text{ F} \times \frac{239\text{ g/F}}{2} = 44.7\text{ g}$$

$$\text{Moles of } PbO_2 = \frac{44.7\text{ g}}{239\text{ g/mole}} = 0.187\text{ mole}$$

8. An electrolytic cell is used to electroplate silver on the surface of a steel salad fork. If the current is 0.500 A, how long will it take to deposit 2.00 g of silver?

Answer

$$\text{Faradays needed} = \frac{2.00\text{ g}}{108\text{ g/F}} = 0.0185\text{ F}$$

$$t = \frac{96{,}500\text{ C/F} \times 0.0185\text{ F}}{0.500\text{ C/sec}} = 3570\text{ sec or}$$

59 min and 30 sec

Answers to Questions and Exercises

Text page references are provided for those questions which do not require computations. The student's answers will be individually stated, but should focus on the concepts developed in those text pages.

Factual Recall

1. 296–97
2. 303
3. 303–04
4. 304–05
5. 306–07

Apply Your Knowledge!

1. $$\text{Volume of oxygen at STP} = \frac{33.6\text{ l} \times 273°\text{K} \times 380\text{ torr}}{546°\text{K} \times 760\text{ torr}} = 8.40\text{ l}$$

$$\text{Mass of oxygen} = \frac{8.40\text{ l} \times 32\text{ g/mole}}{22.4\text{ l/mole}} = 12.0\text{ g}$$

$$\text{Faradays} = \frac{12.0\text{ g}}{8.00\text{ g/F}} = 1.50\text{ F}$$

$$I = \frac{96{,}500\text{ C/F} \times 1.50\text{ F}}{8.00\text{ hr} \times 3600\text{ sec/hr}} = 5.03\text{ C/sec or } 5.03\text{ A}$$

2. $$Q = \frac{20.0\text{ C/sec} \times 3600\text{ sec}}{96{,}500\text{ C/F}} = 0.746\text{ F}$$

$$\text{Mass/F} = \frac{23.9\text{ g}}{0.746\text{ F}} = 32.0\text{ g/F}$$

Equivalent mass of Cu = 32.0 g

3. $$Q = \frac{4.00\text{ C/sec} \times 7200\text{ sec}}{96{,}500\text{ C/F}} = 0.299\text{ F}$$

(*a*) $$\text{Mass/F} = \frac{19.7\text{ g}}{0.299\text{ F}} = 65.7\text{ g/F}$$

Equivalent mass = 65.7 g

(*b*) Atomic mass = 65.7g × 3 = 197 g.
(*c*) Gold

4. $$Q = \frac{1.50\text{ C/sec} \times 3000\text{ sec}}{96{,}500\text{ C/F}} = 0.0466\text{ F}$$

(*a*) Mass = 0.0466 *F* × 32 g/F = 1.49 g.
(*b*) Mass lost = 1.49 g.

5. $$Q = \frac{2.68\text{ C/sec} \times 3600\text{ sec}}{96{,}500\text{ C/F}} = 0.100\text{ F}$$

(*a*) Number of electrons = 0.100 F × 6.02 × 10^{23} e^-/F = 6.02 × 10^{22} electrons

(*b*) Mass of chlorine = 0.100 F × 35.5 g/F = 3.55 g

$$\text{Moles of chlorine} = \frac{3.55\text{ g}}{71\text{ g/mole}} = 0.0500\text{ mole}$$

(*c*) Volume of hydrogen = 0.0500 mole × 22.4 l/mole = 1.12 l

(*d*) Moles of OH^- formed = 0.0500 mole × 2 = 0.100 mole

$$OH^- = \frac{0.100\text{ mole}}{1\text{ l}} = 0.1$$

$$H^+ = \frac{10^{-14}}{10^{-1}} = 10^{-13} \quad pH = 13.0$$

6. $$Q = \frac{1.34\text{ C/sec} \times 7200\text{ sec}}{96{,}500\text{ C/F}} = 0.100\text{ F}$$

(*a*) $$\text{Mass/F} = \frac{1.74\text{ g}}{0.100\text{ F}} = 17.4\text{ g/F}$$

Equivalent mass = 17.4 g

7. $$Q = \frac{0.100\text{ C/sec} \times 600\text{ sec}}{96{,}500\text{ C/F}} = 0.000622\text{ F}$$

(*a*) Number of electrons = 0.000622 F × 6.02 × 10^{23} e^-/F = 3.75 × 10^{20} electrons

(*b*) Q = 0.100 C/sec × 600 sec = 60 C.
(*c*) Mass of Zn^{+2} = 0.00622 F × 32.5 g/F = 0.0202 g.

UNIT VI

CHEMICAL DYNAMICS

OPENING UNIT VI

By this time the student has been introduced to the fact that some reactions are reversible. For example, hydrogen and iodine may combine to form hydrogen iodide. Conversely, hydrogen iodide may break up into its constituent elements. Further, within a given sample, the two opposing processes go on simultaneously. The rate at which the two processes take place depends on the substances reacting, their concentrations, and the temperature. At first, the two reaction rates are different, but eventually they reach equilibrium (in a closed system). To upset the equilibrium, a stress must be applied to the system (Le Châtelier's principle). Chapter 19 discusses reaction rates and the heats involved in them. Chapter 20 deals with the equilibrium of reactions in a closed system.

CHAPTER 19

RATES AND HEATS OF CHEMICAL REACTIONS

TEMPERATURE AND RATE OF REACTION
(pp. 317–19)

Learning Objectives

1. To state the general rule for the temperature dependence of chemical reaction rates.
2. To relate the temperature dependence of reaction rates to the kinetic theory.
3. To define activation energy.
4. To state, qualitatively, the probability of a given molecule having activation energy.

HEAT OF REACTION
(pp. 319–22)

Learning Objectives

1. To define the term *heat of reaction.*
2. To define ΔH.
3. To describe an exothermic reaction.
4. To describe an endothermic reaction.

CONCENTRATION AND REACTION RATE
(pp. 322–25)

Learning Objectives

1. To state that the rate of reaction is proportional to the product of the concentrations of the reactants.
2. To state the law of mass action.
3. To relate the concentration of gas reactants to gas pressure.
4. To write the equation for the relation between reaction rate and reactant concentration.
5. To define heat of combustion.
6. To write the equation for the combustion of carbon monoxide.

AN ENDOTHERMIC REACTION
(p. 326)

Learning Objectives

1. To write the equation for the reaction that produces water gas.

2. To compute the value of ΔH for the water gas reaction from the heats of reaction in Equations (19-13), (19-2), and (19-14B).

EFFECT OF CATALYSTS ON RATE OF REACTION (pp. 326–28)

Learning Objectives

1. To state the purpose of a catalyst.
2. To name the catalyst often used in the production of oxygen.
3. To state the adsorption theory to explain catalysis.
4. To describe the activated complex theory of catalysis.
5. To state the role played by surface area in chemical reaction rates.

Demonstration I To Show the Effect of Changing Temperature and Concentration on the Rate of Reaction.

Materials recommended: 150-ml beaker, Bunsen burner, potassium iodate solution, sodium sulfite, 0.10 *M* hydrochloric acid, starch.

As stated in the text, the rate of reaction between reactants depends upon a number of factors such as temperature, concentration, a catalyst, and the state of division of the reacting substances. Demonstration experiments should be performed to show the influence of each of these factors.

The effects of temperature change and change in concentration can be shown by doing the so-called iodine-clock experiment, which depends upon the fact that free iodine reacts with starch to form a dark blue compound. The term *clock* refers to the timing device used to measure the time it takes for the blue color to appear.

The chemistry of the reaction is somewhat complicated and the reagents must be prepared with care. Nonetheless, the observations are striking and convincing, and time spent on the preparation of these demonstrations is well worthwhile.

Iodate ion (IO_3^-) and sulfite ion (SO_3^{-2}) are the reactants. Actually the reaction takes place in two steps: (1) iodate ion is reduced to iodide ion by sulfite ion, or $IO_3^- + 3SO_3^{-2} \rightarrow I^- + 3SO_4^{-2}$; (2) when all the sulfite ion has been oxidized, the excess iodate ion oxidizes the iodide ion (formed in the first step) in the presence of hydrogen ion to free iodine, or $IO_3^- + 5I^- + 6H^+ \rightarrow 3I_2 + 3H_2O$. The free iodine then reacts with starch and a blue color is seen in the solution. This is a very sensitive test for iodine; that is, only a minute amount of iodine is needed to give an intense blue color with starch.

In the first demonstration the potassium iodate solution is 0.010 *M* (2.14 g KIO_3/1 of solution). In the second demonstration three KIO_3 solutions of different molarities are used, namely 0.020 *M* (4.28 g/l), 0.015 *M* (3.21 g/l), and 0.010 *M*. Needless to say these solutions must be made up beforehand. To make the sulfite solution, add 1.26 g of Na_2SO_3 to 160 ml of 0.10 *M* HCl, and then add enough water to this solution to make the volume 750 ml. Then dissolve 2.5 g of soluble starch in 250 ml of boiling water. The starch solution is allowed to cool and then added to the Na_2SO_3 solution, making a total volume of one l of solution.

A. *To show the effect of a rise in temperature on the rate of reaction*

Pour 25 ml of 0.010 *M* KIO_3 into a 150-ml beaker. Add 25 ml of the sulfite-starch solution and note the time in seconds it takes for a dark blue color to appear.

Now pour another 25 ml of the same 0.010 *M* KIO_3 into another beaker and gently heat it until the temperature is about 20° above room temperature. Add 25 ml of the sulfite-starch solution to the warmed KIO_3 solution, and again record the time in seconds for the dark blue color to appear. As you might expect, the reaction time is reduced when the temperature is raised.

B. *To show the effect of change in concentration on the rate of reaction*

This experiment consists of three different runs. The sulfite solution is the same for each run but the concentration of the iodate solution varies, diminishing from 0.020 *M* to 0.015 *M* to 0.010 *M* in successive runs.

Pour 25 ml of 0.020 *M* KIO_3 into a 150-ml beaker. Add 25 ml of the sulfite-starch solution and record the time taken for the blue color to appear.

Now substitute 0.015 *M* KIO_3 for the 0.020 *M* KIO_3 and repeat the above procedure. Again record the time for the blue color to appear.

Again repeat the procedure except that the 0.010 *M* KIO_3 is used. Again record the reaction time.

A comparison of the three time periods clearly shows that, as the concentration of the iodate solution is diminished, the time of reaction is increased, and therefore the rate of reaction is reduced.

Demonstration II To Show That a Suitable Catalyst Can Increase the Rate of Reaction

Materials recommended: Platinum foil, copper wire, 6 × 6 inch square of cardboard, 1-l beaker, Bunsen burner, methanol.

Methanol (methyl alcohol) is oxidized to CO_2 and H_2O, very slowly at ordinary temperatures and much more rapidly at high temperatures.

$$2CH_3OH + 3O_2 \rightarrow 2CO_2 + 4H_2O$$

The reaction rate can be greatly accelerated in the presence of platinum which acts as a catalyst. It is supposed that methanol vapor and oxygen are adsorbed by the surface layer of the platinum, thereby bringing the reactants into close contact and, as a result, speeding up the rate at which they react. Proceed as follows:

Attach a piece of platinum foil to a short length of copper wire. Have a piece of cardboard (about 6 inches by 6 inches) at hand in case it is needed. Pour about 25 ml of methanol into a tall one-l beaker and then warm the beaker. Heat the platinum foil to redness and lower it at once into the beaker, just above the liquid surface. Notice that the platinum glows, and continues to glow, at a bright red heat. This effect is due to the heat released when methanol vapor is oxidized on the surface of the platinum. The heat released in the reaction may ignite the methanol vapor. If this happens, cover the beaker with the cardboard and the flame will be extinguished.

Demonstration III To Show That the Rate of Burning of a Combustible Material Depends on its State of Division.

Materials recommended: Stand, ring burner, clamp, calcium chloride tube, rubber tubing, lycopodium or starch powder.

If a block of wood is lowered onto a Bunsen flame for a minute or so the wood chars but does not burn. If a splinter of wood from the same block is lowered onto the flame it burns at once. The reason is that the splinter has a much larger surface of wood exposed to the air than has the block. The surface can be still further increased by grinding wood to a powder, and wood powder burns much more rapidly than a splinter. In practice, it is more convenient to use lycopodium powder which can be purchased from a supply house. Lycopodium powder consists of the spores of club moss. It has about the same composition as wood but the particles of lycopodium powder are exceedingly fine.

Rig up the apparatus as shown in Fig. TG19-1. Attach a piece of rubber tubing to a calcium chloride tube, place 3 or 4 grams of lycopodium powder (or starch powder) in the tube and fasten the tube to a stand, five or six inches below a ring burner. Light the ring burner, then blow with a strong quick puff through the rubber tube. The powder rises through the flame and, as it does so, it burns with a spectacular flash.

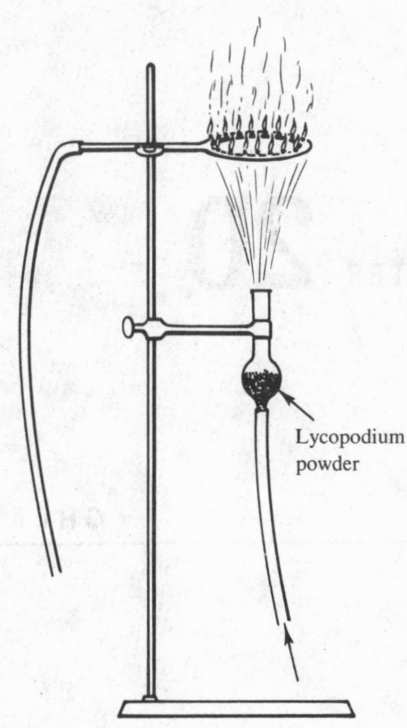

FIG TG19–1

Answers to Questions and Exercises

Text page references are provided for those questions which do not require computations. The student's answers will be individually stated, but should focus on the concepts developed in these text pages.

Factual Recall

1. 318–19
2. 318–19
3. 320
4. 318–19
5. 323, 332–34
6. 326–28
7. 328

Apply Your Knowledge!

1. (*a*)

$$\begin{array}{ll} N_2 + O_2 \rightarrow 2NO & \Delta H = +21.6 \text{ kcal/mole} \\ 2NO + O_2 \rightarrow 2NO_2 & \Delta H = -13.5 \text{ kcal/mole} \\ \hline N_2 + 2O_2 \rightarrow 2NO_2 & \Delta H = +\ 8.1 \text{ kcal/mole} \end{array}$$

(*b*) Endothermic, because heat is absorbed; that is, ΔH is positive.

2. (*a*)

$$\begin{array}{ll} C_{(graphite)} + O_2(g) \rightarrow & \Delta H = -94.05 \text{ kcal} \\ CO_2(g) \rightarrow C_{(diamond)} & \Delta H = +94.5 \text{ kcal} \\ \hline & \Delta H = \ \ 0.45 \text{ kcal} \end{array}$$

(*b*) The necessity for great pressure.

CHAPTER 20

CHEMICAL EQUILIBRIUM

THE EQUILIBRIUM CONSTANT
(pp. 332–37)

Learning Objectives

1. To write Equation (20-4).
2. To state the difference between a forward reaction and a reverse reaction.
3. To state that the two reaction rates are equal at equilibrium.
4. To state that the rate to the right is proportional to the product of the concentrations of *A* and *B*.
5. To state that the rate to the left is proportional to the product of the concentrations of *C* and *D*.
6. To define the equilibrium constant.
7. To write the equation for the equilibrium constant.
8. To state that all chemical reactions in closed containers can be expected to proceed to equilibrium.
9. To write the general equation for the equilibrium constant using varying coefficients.
10. To state the meaning of the value of *K* in terms of reaction to the right or left.
11. To calculate the value of *K*, given a set of molar concentration values.

FACTORS THAT AFFECT EQUILIBRIUM
(pp. 337–38)

Learning Objectives

1. To state two factors that, when changed, affect the equilibrium of a reaction.
2. To describe the effects of a change in concentration on the equilibrium of a reaction.
3. To explain why the value of *K* is not changed by a change in reactant concentration.

THE EFFECT OF A CHANGE IN PRESSURE
(pp. 338–39)

Learning Objectives

1. To state how increasing the pressure of a gas increases its concentration.

2. To state under what conditions a change in pressure favors a reaction to the right or the left.

THE EFFECT OF CHANGING TEMPERATURE
(pp. 339–40)

Learning Objectives

1. To state the effect of temperature change on an exothermic reaction.
2. To state the effect of a temperature change on an endothermic reaction.

APPLICATIONS OF LE CHÂTELIER'S PRINCIPLE
(pp. 340–42)

Learning Objectives

1. To describe the effects of a pressure change on the reaction for the formation of ammonia in terms of Le Châtelier's principle.
2. To describe the effects of a temperature change on the reaction for the formation of ammonia in terms of Le Châtelier's principle.

Suggested Teacher Commentary

$$N_2 + 3H_2 \rightleftharpoons 2NH_3$$

In the text it states that at a temperature of 200°C and a pressure of 200 atm the yield of ammonia is 86%. Although this is a very high yield of ammonia yet, in the Haber process itself, the temperature is about 500°C and the pressure about 1000 atm, and the yield of ammonia is only about 40%. Why accept an apparently lower yield than is attainable? The answer concerns the time required to reach equilibrium. At 200°C the rate of reaction is very slow so, as a practical matter, the time it takes to reach equilibrium would be far too long to make the process economically profitable. At 500°C equilibrium is reached more rapidly but still not fast enough. However, the rate of reaction is greatly accelerated (and the time to reach equilibrium correspondingly diminished) by using a suitable catalyst which in this process is finely divided iron. The significant item in the industrial process is the yield of ammonia per hour of operation.

The ammonia is cooled and some of it liquefies. Hence the liquefied ammonia is automatically removed from the gas mixture. The residual nitrogen and hydrogen then joins the oncoming stream of gas and it is again circulated through the catalyst chamber. Thus, although the yield at equilibrium is only 40% ammonia, yet the yield of ammonia per hour of operation is considerably higher than if the operating temperature were 200°C.

IONIC EQUILIBRIA
(pp. 342–45)

Learning Objectives

1. To state, quantitatively, the ionization constant for a strong electrolyte.
2. To state, quantitatively, the ionization constant for a weak electrolyte.
3. To state, quantitatively, the ionization constant for a strong base.
4. To state, quantitatively, the ionization constant for a weak base.
5. To define the ionization constant for water.
6. To state the value for K_w.

SOLUBILITY PRODUCT
(pp. 345–47)

Learning Objectives

1. To define the term *solubility product*.
2. To write the equation for K_{sp}.

THE COMMON ION EFFECT
(pp. 348–49)

Learning Objectives

1. To describe the common ion effect.

Suggested Teacher Commentary

As stated in the text the common ion effect is the effect produced when one of the ions of a weak electrolyte is added to a solution of the electrolyte. Thus, if sodium acetate is added to a solution of acetic acid, $CH_3COOH \rightleftharpoons CH_3COO^- + H^+$, the concentration of acetate ion (the common ion) is increased and therefore the concentration of hydrogen ion is decreased. This effect can be demonstrated as follows:

Add 18 ml of water to 2 ml of dilute (6 *M*) acetic acid. Add about four drops of methyl orange and observe the red color of the indicator. Divide the solution into two parts and keep one for reference. Add about 1 g of solid sodium acetate to the other part and notice the change in color of the indicator. The methyl orange changes color from deep red to almost yellow which, you recall, is its color in a neutral solution. In other words, the addition of acetate ion has had the effect of reducing the concentration of hydrogen ion.

Additional Questions and Problems

1. Find the hydrogen ion concentration in a 2.0 *M* solution of acetic acid, given the ionization constant of 1.8×10^{-5} for the acid.

Answer

$$[H^+] = [CH_3COO^-]$$

$$[H^+] = \sqrt{1.8 \times 10^{-5} \times 2.0} = \sqrt{36 \times 10^{-6}} = 6 \times 10^{-3}$$

2. Compute $[H^+]$ and $[OH^-]$ in a 10^{-4} *M* solution of HCl.

Answer

$$[H^+] = 10^{-4} \quad \text{assuming complete dissociation}$$

$$[OH^-] = \frac{10^{-14}}{10^{-4}} = 10^{-10}$$

3. Find the solubility product constant of silver bromide at 20°C, given its solubility at 20°C is 8.4×10^{-5} g/l of saturated solution.

Answer

$$\text{Solubility in moles/l} = \frac{8.4 \times 10^{-5}\ \text{g/l}}{188\ \text{g/mole}} = 4.46 \times 10^{-7}\ \text{mole/l}$$

$$[Ag^+] = [Br^-] = 4.46 \times 10^{-7}$$

$$K_{sp}{}^{20°C} = [Ag^+][Br^-] = (4.46 \times 10^{-7})^2 = 1.99 \times 10^{-13}$$

4. What is the molarity of a saturated solution of calcium carbonate at 25°C, given its K_{sp} at 25°C is 4.8×10^{-9}.

Answer

$$\text{Solubility in moles/l} = \sqrt{K_{sp}} = \sqrt{48 \times 10^{-10}} = 6.95 \times 10^{-5}$$

$$\text{Molarity of } Ca^{+2} = \text{molarity of } CO_3{}^{-2} = 6.95 \times 10^{-5}$$

5. Compute the solubility product value for zinc sulfide at 20°C, given its solubility at 20°C is 3.3×10^{-9} g/l of saturated solution.

Answer

$$\text{Solubility in moles/l} = \frac{3.3 \times 10^{-9}\ \text{g/l}}{97\ \text{g/mole}} = 3.4 \times 10^{-11}\ \text{mole/l}$$

$$[Zn^{+2}] = [S^{-2}] = 3.4 \times 10^{-11}$$

$$K_{sp}{}^{20°C} = [Zn^{+2}][S^{-2}] = (3.4 \times 10^{-11})^2 = 1.16 \times 10^{-21}$$

6. The solubility of barium sulfate at 50°C is 9.1×10^{-3} g/l of saturated solution. Compute its solubility product value at 50°C.

Answer

$$\text{Solubility in moles/l} = \frac{9.1 \times 10^{-3}\ \text{g/l}}{233\ \text{g/mole}} = 3.9 \times 10^{-5}$$

$$[Ba^{+2}] = [SO_4{}^{-2}] = 3.9 \times 10^{-5}$$

$$K_{sp}{}^{50°C} = [Ba^{+2}][SO_4{}^{-2}] = (3.9 \times 10^{-5})^2 = 1.52 \times 10^{-9}\ \text{mole/l}$$

7. Compute the solubility of silver iodide in g/l of saturated solution, given its K_{sp} is 1.40×10^{-16} at 20°C.

Answer

$$\text{Solubility in moles/l} = \sqrt{K_{sp}} = \sqrt{1.40 \times 10^{-16}} = 1.19 \times 10^{-8}$$

$$\text{Solubility in g/l} = 1.19 \times 10^{-8}\ \text{mole/l} \times 235\ \text{g/mole} = 2.80 \times 10^{-6}\ \text{g/l}$$

8. Solid silver nitrate is added to a 0.0100 *M* solution of sodium chloride. What quantity (in grams) of silver nitrate can be dissolved in 100 ml of the sodium chloride solution to just saturate the solution with respect to silver chloride? The K_{sp} of silver chloride is 1.7×10^{-10}.

Answer

$$[Cl^-] = 10^{-2} \qquad [Ag^+] = \frac{1.7 \times 10^{-10}}{10^{-2}} = 1.7 \times 10^{-8}$$

$$\text{Mass of } AgNO_3 = 1.7 \times 10^{-8}\ \text{mole/l} \times 170\ \text{g/mole} \times 0.100\ \text{l} = 2.9 \times 10^{-7}\ \text{g}$$

Answers to Questions and Exercises

Text page references are provided for those questions which do not require computations. The student's answers will be individually stated, but should focus on the concepts developed in these text pages.

Factual Recall

1. $$R_1 = k_1[A] \times [B]^3 \quad \text{and} \quad R_2 = [C]^2 \times [D]^2$$

At equilibrium $R_1 = R_2$ and therefore

$$k_1[A] \times [B]^3 = k_2[C]^2 \times [D]^2$$

$$\text{Equilibrium constant} = K = \frac{k_1}{k_2} = \frac{[C]^2 \times [D]^2}{[A] \times [B]^3}$$

2. $$N_2 + 3H_2 \leftrightharpoons 2NH_3$$
$4\,n$ molecules $2\,n$ molecules

$$K = \frac{[NH_3]^2}{[N_2] \times [H_2]^3} = 0.027 \text{ at } 350°C$$

By Le Châtelier's principle, if the pressure on the gases is increased a reaction takes place to oppose the stress; that is, to reduce the pressure. Hence the point of equilibrium is shifted to the right and the yield of ammonia increased. However, an increase would increase the concentration of all three gases in such a way that the value of the equilibrium constant remains unchanged at 350°C; that is, $K = 2.7 \times 10^{-2}$, whatever the pressure.

3. $$N_2 + 3H_2 \rightleftharpoons 2NH_3$$

$$K = \frac{[NH_3]^2}{[N_2] \times [H_2]^3} = 0.0066 \text{ at } 450°C$$

If either the concentration of N_2 or H_2 is increased, these gases will be used up at a faster rate so that more NH_3 will be formed. That is, the point of equilibrium would be shifted to the right. However, the concentration values of N_2 and H_2 and NH_3 are changed in such a way that, when equilibrium is restored, the computation of the equilibrium constant gives the same numerical value. That is, the equilibrium constant is not affected by a change in the concentration of either of the reactants or of the product. At 450°C, $K = 6.6 \times 10^{-3}$ whatever the change in concentrations.

4. 340
5. 341–42
6. 339–40
7. 343–44

Apply Your Knowledge!

1. $$[H^+] = [A^-] = 0.100 \text{ mole/l} \times 0.04 = 4 \times 10^{-3}$$

$$K_A = \frac{[H^+][A^-]}{[HA]} = \frac{(4 \times 10^{-3})^2}{0.096} = \frac{16 \times 10^{-6}}{9.6 \times 10^{-2}}$$
$$= 1.7 \times 10^{-4}$$

2. $$[OH^-] = [M^+] = 2.0 \text{ moles/l} \times 0.01 = 2.0 \times 10^{-2}$$

$$K_B = \frac{[M^+][OH^-]}{[MOH]} = \frac{(2.0 \times 10^{-2})^2}{2.0} = 2.0 \times 10^{-4}$$

3. $[H^+] = [A^-]$

$$[H^+] = \sqrt{K_A \times M \text{ of acid}} = \sqrt{10^{-7} \times 1} = \sqrt{10 \times 10^{-8}}$$
$$= 3.2 \times 10^{-4}$$

$$\text{Percent of ionization} = \frac{3.2 \times 10^{-4}}{1} \times 100 = 0.032\%$$

4. $[OH^-] = [NH_4^+]$

$$[OH^-] = \sqrt{K_B \times M \text{ of base}} = \sqrt{1.8 \times 10^{-5} \times 5 \times 10^{-2}}$$
$$= \sqrt{90 \times 10^{-8}} = 9.5 \times 10^{-4}$$

$$\text{Percent of ionization} = \frac{9.5 \times 10^{-4}}{5 \times 10^{-2}} \times 100 = 1.9\%$$

UNIT VII

VERTICAL COLUMNS OF ELEMENTS (CHEMICAL FAMILIES) AND HORIZONTAL ROWS OF ELEMENTS

OPENING UNIT VII

Unit VII considers in more detail than previously the recurrent patterns of outer *s* and *p* orbitals as they relate to the chemical properties of the elements. Two vertical columns (families) of elements are considered — the alkali metals and the halogens (Chapters 21 and 22). Columns of elements have similar, though not identical, chemical properties.

Chapters 23 and 24 are concerned with two rows of elements, in which a gradual change in atomic structure occurs as you go from left to right along the row. This change in atomic structure is accompanied by changes in chemica properties of the elements in the row.

For example, in the third row there is an active metal (sodium) at the extreme left and an inert gas (argon) on the extreme right. Similarly the transition elements begin with active potassium on the left and end with inert krypton on the right.

These electronic pattern changes, as they affect chemical properties, may be said to be the "hard core" of this unit.

CHAPTER 21

THE ALKALI METALS

THE ALKALI METALS (pp. 355–56)

Learning Objectives

1. To name the alkali metals.
2. To locate the alkali metals on the periodic table.
3. To list the properties of the alkali metals.

Suggested Teacher Commentary

The Alkali Metals

This group of elements has the lowest known ionization energies. As a consequence of their readiness to lose the outer valence electron, they are never found free in nature. Of course this also means that they are very active — they easily form ionic bonds with other elements. The fact that their valence is always +1, makes their properties highly predictable.

The structure of the metals is crystalline, made up of ions with a +1 charge. The valence electrons constitute a "gas" of free electrons that accounts for their high heat and electrical conductivity. The valence electrons also account for the lustrous appearance of the pure metal. When light falls on them, they vibrate and re-radiate the energy. The crystal lattice is loosely packed, causing their softness, ductility, and malleability.

PROPERTIES AND ATOMIC STRUCTURE (pp. 356–62)

Learning Objectives

1. To relate the properties of the alkali metals to their electronic structures.
2. To describe the dependence of the activities of the alkali metals on their ionization energies.
3. To contrast the ionization energies of the alkali metals with neighboring elements in the same row.
4. To write the equation for the reaction of sodium with chlorine.
5. To state the type of bonding in compounds formed with alkali metals.
6. To write the equations for reactions between the alkali metals and water.
7. To state the reason for the strong alkalinity of water solutions of alkali metals.
8. To state the colors of the flame tests of sodium, lithium, and potassium.
9. To describe the appearance of the spectra of lithium, sodium, potassium, rubidium, and cesium.
10. To describe the natural occurrence of alkali metals.
11. To list the steps in the operation of the Downs cell.
12. To state the uses of the alkali metals as listed in the text.

Suggested Teacher Commentary

Each alkali metal consists of a noble-gas core with a single outer electron. When the outer electron is removed, a very stable ion is formed. For example, the sodium ion has the configuration of neon (2-8), and the potassium ion has the configuration of argon (2-8-8).

Demonstration I Flame Tests for Sodium and Potassium.

Materials recommended: platinum wire, Bunsen burner, KOH solution, NaOH solution.

As already stated, the colors of the hot vapors of sodium and potassium are yellow and lilac respectively. Actually, these colors can be seen even if there is only a trace of metal and so the color of the flame is a sensitive test for the presence of sodium or potassium ion. As stated in an earlier chapter, the color is due to the light energy emitted when outer electrons fall from higher to lower energy levels. Thus the test applies to the vapor of the ions as well as to the metal.

A. *The test for potassium ion*

Hold a piece of platinum wire in a Bunsen flame until it imparts no color to the flame. The wire is then clean. Dip the end of the clean wire into the solution of KOH. Again hold the wire in the Bunsen flame and observe the lilac color. This flame test is clearly sensitive enough to reveal a mere trace of potassium ion on the wire.

B. *The test for sodium ion*

Heat the platinum wire in the Bunsen flame until all traces of lilac color have disappeared. Then dip the wire in the solution of NaOH. Heat the wire in the Bunsen flame and observe the intense yellow color imparted to the flame. Moreover, the color persists for some time and, indeed, it only finally disappears after long heating.

Demonstration II Comparative Activities of Sodium and Potassium With water.

Materials recommended: 100 ml beaker, forceps, pea-sized pellets of sodium and potassium, litmus paper, taper.

As stated in the text, sodium and potassium react vigorously with water, forming a metallic hydroxide and releasing hydrogen. The reactions are highly exothermic and enough heat is generated to melt the metals. In addition, the temperature is high enough to ignite the hydrogen in the potassium reaction but not in the sodium reaction.

Care must be exercised in this demonstration since the escaping hydrogen may cause the hot molten metal to spatter, particularly the molten potassium. As a precaution, the beaker should not be more than half-filled with water — the dry wall of the beaker is then tall enough to prevent spattered metal from escaping. Now proceed as follows: Remove the crust from metallic sodium and then cut off a piece about the size of a small pea. Pick up the piece of sodium with forceps and drop it into water in a beaker. The sodium floats on the water and reacts vigorously with it. The heat of reaction melts the sodium and the escaping hydrogen causes the globule to follow an erratic path. Using a long taper, ignite the escaping hydrogen. Notice that the gas burns with a yellow flame, the yellow color being due to the sodium vapor in the burning hydrogen. When the reaction has stopped, dip a piece of litmus paper into the solution. The litmus turns blue, proving that the solution is alkaline.

Now, using another beaker of water, repeat the above procedure with a small "pea" of potassium. The potassium melts, the escaping hydrogen bursts into flame, and the molten globule moves rapidly over the water surface. This time the flame has a lilac color, and because the hydrogen is escaping rapidly the molten globule will probably explode with a crack. Again do the litmus test to prove that the residual solution is alkaline.

Additional Questions and Problems

1. The reaction of lithium with water liberates 3.36 l of gas at 27°C and 0.500 atm pressure. Compute (*a*) the moles of metal consumed, (*b*) the quantity in g of water used up, (*c*) the moles of base produced, (*d*) the *p*H of the solution if its volume is 1 l.

Answer

$$\underset{2\text{ moles}}{2\text{Li}} + \underset{2\text{ moles}}{2\text{H}_2\text{O}} \rightarrow \underset{2\text{ moles}}{2\text{LiOH}} + \underset{1\text{ mole}}{\text{H}_2}$$

$$\text{Volume of H}_2\text{ at STP} = \frac{3.36\text{ l} \times 273°\text{K} \times 0.500\text{ atm}}{300°\text{K} \times 1.00\text{ atm}} = 1.53\text{ l}$$

$$\text{Moles of H}_2 = \frac{1.53\text{ l}}{22.4\text{ l/mole}} = 0.0683\text{ mole}$$

(*a*) Moles of Li = 0.0683 mole × 2 = 0.1366 mole.
(*b*) Mass of H_2O = 0.1366 mole × 18 g/mole = 2.46 g.
(*c*) Moles of base = 0.1366 mole.

(*d*) $[OH^-] = 0.1366 \qquad [H^+] = \frac{10^{-14}}{0.1366} = 7.37 \times 10^{-14}$

$pH = 13.13$

Answers to Questions and Exercises

Text page references are provided for those questions which do not require computations. The student's answers will be individually stated, but should focus on the concepts developed in those text pages.

Factual Recall

1. Na: $1s^2\ 2s^2\ 2p^6\ 3s^1$
   K: $1s^2\ 2s^2\ 2p^6\ 3s^2\ 3p^6\ 4s^1$
2. 356–58
3. Table 21–1
4. 357–58
5. 359
6. 360
7. 361–62
8. 363–65

Apply Your Knowledge!

1. $$\text{Faradays needed} = \frac{10^6\ \text{g}}{23\ \text{g}/F} = 4.35 \times 10^4\ F$$

$$\text{Time in seconds} = \frac{96{,}500\ \text{C}/F}{5000\ \text{C/sec}} \times 4.35 \times 10^4\ F$$

$$= 8.4 \times 10^5\ \text{sec (9 days, 17 hours)}$$

2. (*a*) $2Li + Cl_2 \rightarrow 2LiCl + 195\ \text{kcal}$ (1 mole Cl_2)

$$\text{Heat liberated} = \frac{0.250\ \text{mole} \times 195\ \text{kcal}}{1.00\ \text{mole}}$$

$$= 48.8\ \text{kcal}$$

(*b*) $2Na + Cl_2 \rightarrow 2NaCl + 197\ \text{kcal}$ (1 mole Cl_2)

$$\text{Heat liberated} = \frac{0.250\ \text{mole} \times 197\ \text{kcal}}{1.00\ \text{mole}}$$

$$= 49.3\ \text{kcal}$$

(*c*) $2K + Cl_2 \rightarrow 2KCl + 209\ \text{kcal}$ (1 mole Cl_2)

$$\text{Heat liberated} = \frac{0.250\ \text{mole} \times 209\ \text{kcal}}{1.00\ \text{mole}}$$

$$= 52.3\ \text{kcal}$$

CHAPTER 22

THE HALOGENS

THE HALOGENS
(pp. 367–68)

Learning Objectives

1. To name the halogens.
2. To state which group they occupy in the periodic table.

Demonstration I To Prepare Chlorine.

Materials recommended: Stand, clamps, ring, asbestos-centered gauze, bunsen Burner, flask, 1-hole stopper, glass and rubber tubing, collecting bottles, glass cover plates.

There should be numerous class demonstrations to illustrate some of the typical properties of the halogens, particularly the properties of chlorine. In preparing chlorine, remember that it is a poisonous gas so that the room should be well ventilated, or better still, the experiment should be done under a hood.

Arrange the apparatus as shown in Fig. TG22–1. Pour about 5 g of manganese dioxide and about 10 ml of concentrated hydrochloric acid into the flask. A reaction begins at once and yellowish-green chlorine gas can be seen in the flask. Heat the flask gently to speed up the reaction. When the bottle is filled with the yellow-green gas, replace it with another dry bottle. Close the bottle of chlorine with a glass cover, and collect two more bottles of gas in the same way.

BONDING IN FLUORINE MOLECULES
(pp. 368–69)

Learning Objectives

1. To write the spectroscopic notation for fluorine.
2. To write the electron dot notation for a fluorine molecule.

VAN DER WAALS FORCES
(pp. 369–71)

Learning Objectives

1. To describe the van der Waals forces.

SOME PROPERTIES OF THE HALOGENS
(pp. 371–76)

Learning Objectives

1. To state that all of the halogens are good oxidizing agents.
2. To write Equation (22-5).
3. To state the type of bonding shown by Equation (22-5).
4. To state the name of binary halogen compounds.
5. To define a replacement reaction.

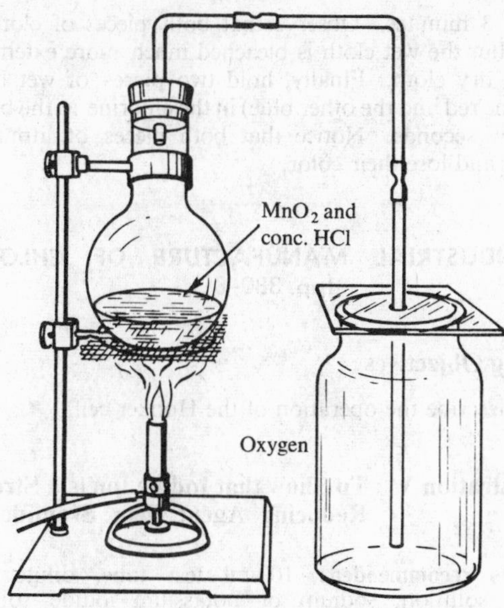

FIG. TG22-1

6. To write Equation (22-9).
7. To write the electron dot notation for hydrogen fluoride.
8. To write Equation (22-14).
9. To explain the high boiling point of hydrogen fluoride.
10. To name the acids formed in reactions between the hydrogen halides and water.
11. To write Equation (22-21).
12. To define a halogen oxyacid.
13. To explain why the oxidation number of chlorine in hypochlorous acid is +1.
14. To explain why the halogen oxyacids become progressively stronger as oxygen atoms are added.
15. To state the name endings of the salts of halogen oxyacids.

Demonstration II To Show the Reactions Between Chlorine and Copper and Chlorine and Iron.

Materials recommended: Copper foil, iron filings, tongs, combustion spoon, Bunsen burner, 2 bottles of chlorine.

Although copper is one of the relatively inactive metals, it readily reacts with chlorine, particularly when heated, to form copper (II) chloride. To demonstrate this reaction proceed as follows: Hold a piece of copper foil (or a coil of fine copper wire) by a pair of tongs. Heat the copper in a Bunsen flame and then lower it into a bottle of chlorine. Observe the vigorous reaction in which the copper becomes red hot.

To show the reaction with iron, fill a combustion spoon with iron filings, heat the filings in a Bunsen flame, and then lower the spoon into a bottle of chlorine. The heat of reaction is sufficient to make the iron red hot. Notice also the brown colored solid ($FeCl_3$) in the spoon. The equations for the reactions are

$$Cu + Cl_2 \rightarrow CuCl_2$$
$$2Fe + 3Cl_2 \rightarrow 2FeCl_3$$

Demonstration III To Show that Chlorine is more Active than Bromine or Iodine.

Materials recommended: Test tubes, chlorine water, dilute potassium bromide solution, dilute potassium iodide solution, carbon tetrachloride.

Chlorine will displace bromine from a bromide and iodine from an iodide. The equations for these reactions are

$$Cl_2 + 2Br^- \rightarrow 2Cl^- + Br_2$$
$$Cl_2 + 2I^- \rightarrow 2Cl^- + I_2$$

These are oxidation reactions; chlorine oxidizes both bromide ion and iodide ion. To demonstrate these oxidation reactions proceed as follows: Pour about 50 ml of water into bottle of chlorine, close the bottle with the hand, and shake. Chlorine dissolves in the water and some of it reacts with water. The equation for the reaction is

$$Cl_2 + H_2O \rightleftharpoons HCl + HOCl$$

The solution is called chlorine water.

Make a dilute solution of potassium bromide in one test tube (about 10 ml of it) and a dilute solution of potassium iodide in another. Pour a few drops of chlorine water into each test tube and shake. A yellowish color (of bromine) appears in one tube and a brownish color (of iodine) in the other. As a confirmatory test for bromine, add about 5 ml of carbon tetrachloride. Close the tube with the thumb, shake the tube, and let the mixture settle. The bromine dissolves in the CCl_4 and, since CCl_4 is insoluble in water, it collects as a layer below the water. Notice that the CCl_4 layer is red in color which is the characteristic color of free bromine. Now repeat this procedure for iodine. That is, add CCl_4 to the other tube and shake. Upon standing, the CCl_4 sinks to the bottom of the tube and it is colored violet. Violet is the characteristic color of free iodine and clearly the iodine has dissolved in the CCl_4.

PREPARATION OF THE HALOGENS
(pp. 377–78)

Learning Objectives

1. To write the general equation for the preparation of a halogen.
2. To state that the general equation is an oxidation reaction.
3. To write Equation (22-27).
4. To explain why fluorine must be prepared by electrolysis of the molten salt.

SOME USES OF THE HALOGENS
(pp. 378–79)

Learning Objectives

1. To name two well-known fluorocarbons and state their uses.
2. To explain how hypochlorous acid acts as a bleach.
3. To describe briefly the photographic process.

Demonstration IV To Show the Bleaching Action of Chlorine.

Materials recommended: Two pieces of colored cotton cloth, 250-ml beaker, red and blue litmus paper, dilute hydrochloric acid, bleaching powder.

Chlorine is used to bleach paper and cloth on a wide scale. Actually, the bleaching action is due to released oxygen rather than to chlorine itself. The oxygen oxidizes dyes to form products that are colorless. In other words, the chlorine must be wet so that oxygen can be liberated, as in the reactions,

$$Cl_2 + H_2O \rightleftharpoons HCl + HOCl$$
$$2HOCl \rightleftharpoons 2HCl + O_2$$

A simple way to prepare small amounts of chlorine is to pour dilute hydrochloric acid upon bleaching powder ($CaOCl_2$). The reaction is

$$CaOCl_2 + 2HCl \rightarrow CaCl_2 + H_2O + Cl_2$$

Now proceed as follows: Support two pieces of colored cotton cloth (one wet and one dry) on the lip of a beaker. Sprinkle 2 or 3 g of bleaching powder into the beaker and then pour about 10 ml of dilute HCl onto the bleaching powder. Close the beaker with a glass cover. Notice that a yellow gas is released during the vigorous reaction that takes place. Examine the cloth after it has been exposed to the chlorine for 2 or 3 minutes. Observe that both pieces of cloth are affected but the wet cloth is bleached much more extensively than the dry cloth. Finally, hold two pieces of wet litmus paper (one red and the other blue) in the chlorine in the beaker for a few seconds. Notice that both pieces of litmus are bleached and lose their color.

THE INDUSTRIAL MANUFACTURE OF CHLORINE
(pp. 380–81)

Learning Objectives

1. To describe the operation of the Hooker cell.

Demonstration V To Show that Iodide Ion is a Stronger Reducing Agent than Bromide Ion.

Materials recommended: 100-ml test tube, dilute ferric chloride solution, sodium or potassium iodide solution, carbon tetrachloride, sodium or potassium bromide.

All the halogens are oxidizers; fluorine is the strongest oxidizer and iodine the weakest. Bromine is a stronger oxidizer than iodine, or, $Br_2 + 2e^- \rightarrow 2Br^-$ takes place more readily than $I_2 + 2e^- \rightarrow 2I^-$. Conversely, iodide ion is a more powerful reducer than bromide ion, or, $2I^- - 2e^- \rightarrow I_2$ takes place more readily than $2Br^- - 2e^- \rightarrow Br_2$. The difference in reducing power can be demonstrated by using ferric ion (Fe^{+3}) as the oxidizer. Proceed as follows: Pour about 5 ml of dilute ferric chloride solution into a test tube and add about one ml of sodium iodide or potassium iodide solution. Pour about 2 or 3 ml of CCl_4 into the test tube. Stopper the tube, shake it vigorously, and then let the tube stand for a minute or so. The CCl_4 layer sinks to the bottom and its color is deep violet, indicating the presence of free iodine. The reaction is

$$2Fe^{+3} + 2I^- \rightarrow 2Fe^{+2} + I_2$$

That is, Fe^{+3} is the oxidizer and I^- is the reducer.

Now repeat the experiment but use a solution of sodium bromide (or potassium bromide) instead of sodium iodide. In this case the CCl_4 layer remains colorless. Therefore no bromine is released; that is, bromide ions do not reduce ferric ions.

Demonstration VI To Prepare Hydrogen Chloride.

Materials recommended: Stand, clamps, ring, dropping funnel, flask, 2-hole stopper, Bunsen burner, glass and rubber tubing, collecting bottle, cardboard, pan of water, blue litmus, sodium chloride, concentrated sulfuric acid.

Hydrogen chloride is by far the most important of the hydrogen halides. As a class demonstration it can be prepared by the reaction between common salt and concentrated sulfuric acid. The equation for the reaction is

$$NaCl + H_2SO_4 \rightarrow NaHSO_4 + HCl$$

Proceed as follows: Arrange the apparatus as shown in Fig. TG22–2. Place about 10 g of NaCl in the flask and pour about 10 ml of concentrated sulfuric acid into the funnel. Turn the stopcock and allow the acid to drop slowly into the flask. Heat gently to speed up the reaction. Hydrogen chloride gas flows into the dry bottle which has a cardboard cover. To tell when the bottle is filled with HCl gas, hold a piece of wet blue litmus paper near the mouth of the bottle. When the litmus turns red, HCl gas must be escaping from the bottle.

When this happens remove the tube and cardboard cover and close the bottle with a glass cover. Now invert the bottle in a pan of water and remove the cover. Water rushes into the bottle, proving that the gas is very soluble. The reaction is

$$HCl(g) \xrightarrow{H_2O} HCl(aq) \rightarrow H^+ + Cl^-$$

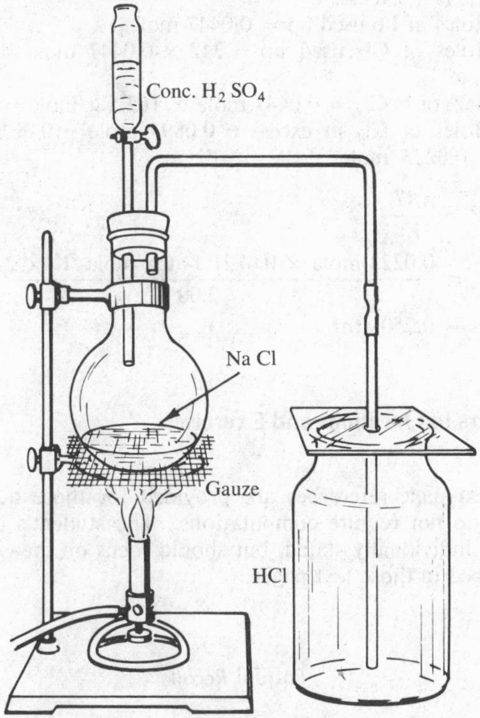

FIG. TG22–2

To test for hydrogen ion, show that the solution turns blue litmus red. To test for chloride ion, pour about 5 ml of dilute silver nitrate into the solution. The white precipitate indicates the formation of insoluble silver chloride. Or,

$$Ag^+ + Cl^- \rightarrow AgCl(s)$$

Additional Questions and Problems

1. The hydrogen fluoride liberated by the reaction of 3.9 g of calcium fluoride with concentrated sulfuric acid reacts with silicon dioxide according to the equation, $4HF + SiO_2 = SiF_4 + 2H_2O$. (*a*) What volume of hydrogen fluoride is liberated at 20°C? (*b*) How many moles of SiO_2 are consumed?

Answer

$$\underset{2\text{ moles}}{2CaF_2} + 2H_2SO_4 \rightarrow 2CaSO_4 + \underset{4\text{ moles}}{4HF}$$

$$\underset{4\text{ moles}}{4HF} + \underset{1\text{ mole}}{SiO_2} \rightarrow SiF_4 + 2H_2O$$

$$\text{Moles of } CaF_2 = \frac{3.9\text{ g}}{78\text{ g/mole}} = 0.050\text{ mole}$$

(*a*) $$\text{Volume of HF} = 0.100\text{ mole} \times 22.4\text{ l/mole} \times \frac{293°K}{273°K} = 2.41\text{ l}$$

(*b*) $$\text{Moles of } SiO_2 = \frac{0.050\text{ mole}}{2} = 0.0250\text{ mole}$$

2. Compute the weight in grams of concentrated sulfuric acid needed to react with 0.100 mole of sodium chloride.

Answer

$$\underset{1\text{ mole}}{NaCl} + \underset{1\text{ mole}}{H_2SO_4} \rightarrow NaHSO_4 + HCl$$

Mass of H_2SO_4 = 0.100 mole × 98 g/mole = 9.8 g.

3. What weight of silver bromide is precipitated by the addition of 40 ml of 0.500 *M* bromide ion solution to 25 ml of 0.750 *M* silver ion solution?

Answer

$$\underset{1\text{ mole}}{Ag^+} + \underset{1\text{ mole}}{Br^-} \rightarrow \underset{1\text{ mole}}{AgBr}$$

Moles of Ag^+ = 0.025 l × 0.75 mole/l = 0.0187 mole
Moles of Br^- = 0.040 l × 0.50 mole/l = 0.0200 mole

The bromide ion is in excess.

Mass of AgBr = 0.0187 mole × 188 g/mole = 3.52 g

4. At standard pressure a 2.54-g sample of iodine occupies 0.470 l at 300°C, 0.798 l at 700°C, 1.9 l at 1275°C, and

3.23 l at 1700°C. (*a*) Calculate the molecular-weight value for iodine vapor at (*i*) 300°C, (*ii*) 700°C, (*iii*) 1275°C, (*iv*) 1700°C. (*b*) Write the molecular formula for iodine vapor at (*i*) 300°C, (*ii*) 700°C, (*iii*) 1700°C. (*c*) Indicate, as an equilibrium, the situation at 1275°C.

Answer

$$\text{Molecular mass} = \frac{\text{mass} \times R \times T}{P \times V}$$

(*a*) (*i*) Mol. mass

$$= \frac{2.54 \text{ g} \times 0.0821 \text{ l-atm/mole-°K} \times 573\text{°K}}{1 \text{ atm} \times 0.470 \text{ l}}$$

$$= 255 \text{ g/mole}$$

(*ii*) Molecular mass = 255 g/mole. (*iii*) Molecular mass = 169 g/mole. (*iv*) Molecular mass = 127 g/mole.

(*b*) (*i*) I_2. (*ii*) I_2. (*iii*) Mixture of I_2 and I. (*iv*) I.

(*c*) $I_2 \rightleftharpoons 2I$.

5. Enough 6.0 *M* hydrochloric acid is added to 17.4 g of manganese dioxide for complete reaction. (*a*) What volume of acid must be used? (*b*) What volume of gas product is liberated at 60°C? (*c*) How many moles of salt product are formed? (*d*) What is the molarity of the salt solution which is produced? Assume that the volume of the salt solution is the same as the volume of the acid used.

Answer

$$\underset{1 \text{ mole}}{MnO_2} + \underset{4 \text{ moles}}{4HCl} \rightarrow \underset{1 \text{ mole}}{MnCl_2} + 2H_2O + \underset{1 \text{ mole}}{Cl_2}$$

(*a*)

$$\text{Moles } MnO_2 = \frac{17.4 \text{ g}}{87 \text{ g/mole}} = 0.200 \text{ mole}$$

$$\text{Moles HCl} = 0.200 \text{ mole} \times 4 = 0.800 \text{ mole}$$

$$\text{Volume of HCl} = \frac{0.800 \text{ mole}}{6.0 \text{ moles/l}} = 0.133 \text{ l}$$

(*b*)

$$\text{Volume of } Cl_2 = 0.200 \text{ mole} \times 22.4 \text{ l/mole} \times \frac{333\text{°K}}{273\text{°K}}$$

$$= 5.47 \text{ l}$$

(*c*)

$$\text{Moles of salt} = 0.200 \text{ mole}$$

(*d*)

$$\text{Molarity of salt solution} = \frac{0.200 \text{ mole}}{0.133 \text{ l}} = 1.50\ M$$

6. One hundred ml of chlorine gas at STP are absorbed by a sodium bromide solution. How many moles of bromine are set free?

Answer

$$\underset{1 \text{ mole}}{Cl_2} + 2NaBr \rightarrow 2NaCl + \underset{1 \text{ mole}}{Br_2}$$

$$\text{Moles of } Cl_2 = \frac{0.100 \text{ l}}{22.4 \text{ l/mole}} = 0.00447 \text{ mole}$$

$$\text{Moles of } Br_2 = 0.00447 \text{ mole}$$

7. The bromine liberated in Problem 9 is led into a potassium iodide solution. How many moles of iodine are set free?

Answer

$$\underset{1 \text{ mole}}{Br_2} + 2KI \rightarrow 2KBr + \underset{1 \text{ mole}}{I_2}$$

Moles of I_2 = moles of Br_2 = 0.00447 mole.

8. A 2.50-g sample of iron powder is dropped into a 2.00-l container filled with chlorine at STP. The container is sealed, then heated until a reaction occurs, and finally cooled to 0°C. Calculate the (*a*) moles of iron used up, (*b*) moles of chlorine used up, (*c*) weight in g of reaction product, (*d*) final gas pressure in the container.

Answer

$$\underset{2 \text{ moles}}{2Fe} + \underset{3 \text{ moles}}{3Cl_2} \rightarrow \underset{2 \text{ moles}}{2FeCl_3}$$

$$\text{Moles Fe} = \frac{2.50 \text{ g}}{56 \text{ g/mole}} = 0.0447 \text{ mole}$$

$$\text{Moles } Cl_2 = \frac{2.00 \text{ l}}{22.4 \text{ l/mole}} = 0.0893 \text{ mole}$$

Chlorine is in excess.

(*a*) Moles of Fe used up = 0.0447 mole.

(*b*) Moles of Cl_2 used up = 3/2 × 0.0447 mole = 0.0670 mole.

(*c*) Mass of $FeCl_3$ = 0.0447 mole × 162.5 g/mole = 7.25 g.

(*d*) Moles of Cl_2 in excess = 0.0893 mole − 0.0670 mole = 0.0223 mole.

$$P = \frac{nRT}{V}$$

$$= \frac{0.0223 \text{ mole} \times 0.0821 \text{ l-atm/mole-°K} \times 273\text{°K}}{2.00\ l}$$

$$= 0.250 \text{ atm}$$

Answers to Questions and Exercises

Text page references are provided for those questions which do not require computations. The student's answers will be individually stated, but should focus on the concepts developed in those text pages.

Factual Recall

1. 369–71
2. 372
3. 368–69
4. 372–73
5. 373–74
6. Table 22-8, 377

Apply Your Knowledge!

1. $MnO_2 + 4HCl \rightarrow MnCl_2 + 2H_2O + Cl_2$
   1 mole 4 moles 1 mole

$$\text{Moles of } MnO_2 = \frac{0.87 \text{ g}}{87 \text{ g/mole}} = 10^{-2} \text{ mole}$$

$$\text{Moles of HCl} = 0.0075 \text{ l} \times 6.0 \text{ moles/l} = 0.0450 \text{ mole}$$

The HCl is in excess.

$$\text{Volume of chlorine} = 10^{-2} \text{ mole} \times 22.4 \text{ l/mole} \times \frac{300°\text{K}}{273°\text{K}}$$

$$= 0.246\ l$$

2. $NaCl + H_2SO_4 \rightarrow NaHSO_4 + HCl$
   1 mole 1 mole 1 mole

(*a*) $$\text{Moles of NaCl} = \frac{11.7 \text{ g}}{58.5 \text{ g/mole}} = 0.200 \text{ mole}$$

$$\text{Mass of } H_2SO_4 = 0.200 \text{ mole} \times 98 \text{ g/mole} = 19.6 \text{ g}$$

(*b*) Moles of HCl = 0.200 mole
Moles of KOH = 0.200 mole

$$\text{Volume of KOH} = \frac{0.200 \text{ mole}}{0.100 \text{ mole/l}} = 2.00 \text{ l}$$

3. (*a*) The anode gas product is oxygen.

$$Q = \frac{0.50 \text{ C/sec} \times 1800 \text{ sec}}{96{,}500 \text{ C}/F} = 9.3 \times 10^{-3}F$$

$$\text{Volume of } O_2 = 9.3 \times 10^{-3}F \times 5.6 \text{ l}/F = 0.052 \text{ l}$$

(*b*) $$\text{Volume of } Cl_2 = 9.3 \times 10^{-3}F \times 11.2 \text{ l}/F = 0.104 \text{ l}$$

CHAPTER 23

ELEMENTS IN THE THIRD ROW OF THE PERIODIC TABLE

ELECTRON CONFIGURATION OF ELEMENTS OF THE THIRD ROW
(pp. 385–89)

Learning Objectives

1. To draw the electron orbital diagrams for sodium and argon as in Fig. 23–1.
2. To write the spectroscopic notation for the electron configurations of sodium and argon.
3. To state the meaning of the following variation on the spectroscopic notation for sodium: (Ne)$3s^1$; for argon: (Ne)$3s^2\ 3p^6$.
4. To state the general direction of increase in ionization energy along the third row.
5. To explain the increase of ionization energy with increasing Z along the third row.
6. To state what determines whether an element is a reducing or oxidizing agent.
7. To state the type of bonds formed by sodium and chlorine.
8. To state why aluminum has less tendency to form ionic bonds than magnesium.
9. To state why silicon forms covalent bonds.
10. To state why sulfur may form either ionic or covalent bonds.
11. To state why the melting points of the metals in the third row increase with increasing Z.
12. To state why silicon has such a high melting point.

Demonstration II To Show the Reaction of Aluminum with Strong Acids and Strong Bases.

Materials recommended: Test tube, Bunsen burner, small pieces of aluminum, dilute hydrochloric acid, dilute sodium hydroxide.

Both aluminum oxide and aluminum hydroxide are amphoteric compounds; that is, they are able to neutralize both acids and bases. To show the amphoteric nature of $Al(OH)_3$ proceed as follows: Dissolve about 0.5 g of aluminum sulfate in about 10 ml of water. Add about 2 ml of ammonia water and a gelatinous precipitate of $Al(OH)_3$ is formed,

$$Al_2(SO_4)_3(aq) + 6NH_4OH(aq) \rightarrow 2Al(OH)_3(s) + 3(NH_4)_2SO_4\,(aq)$$

Divide the gelatinous mixture into two parts. To one part add dilute HCl and to the other a dilute solution of NaOH. Notice that, in both cases, the precipitate is dissolved. Hence, $Al(OH)_3$ reacts with both a strong acid and a strong base. In the first case $Al(OH)_3$ behaves as a weak base, and in the second case it behaves as a weak acid. Therefore $Al(OH)_3$ is amphoteric.

Since $Al(OH)_3$ and also Al_2O_3 react with both acid and basisolutions to form water, we would consequently expect aluminum metal to react with strong acids and strong bases to liberate hydrogen. Such reactions do actually occur and the equations for the reactions are $2Al(s) + 6H^+ \rightarrow 2Al^{+3} + 3H_2(g)$ and $2Al(s) + 6OH^- \rightarrow 2AlO_3^{-3} + 3H_2(g)$.

To demonstrate these reactions, proceed as follows: Pour about 10 ml of dilute HCl into a test tube and add a few pieces of aluminum. If the reaction is slow to start, warm the test tube. When bubbles of gas begin to escape rapidly, close the tube with the thumb until you feel the pressure of the confined gas. Then place the end of the tube near a Bunsen flame and remove the thumb. The slight explosion that occurs inside the tube is a characteristic test for hydrogen. Now repeat the procedure, except that 10 ml of dilute NaOH solution is used instead of the dilute HCl.

CHEMICAL PROPERTIES
(pp. 389–98)

Demonstration I To Show the Thermite Reaction.

Materials recommended: Stand, ring, filter paper, Bunsen burner, metal dish, sand, asbestos sheets, fuse powder, magnesium ribbon, powdered aluminum, iron (III) oxide.

As stated in the text, a mixture of aluminum powder and iron (III) oxide is called thermite. If the mixture is heated sufficiently, aluminum reduces Fe^{+3} to metallic iron. The reaction is highly exothermic and the amount of heat released is enough to melt the iron formed in the reaction. To demonstrate this reaction, proceed as follows: Support a folded double-walled filter paper in a ring attached to a stand as in Fig. 23-7 of text. Place a metal dish containing a thick layer of sand below the paper cone and protect the bench with several sheets of asbestos placed under the dish. Half fill the cone with thermite. Make a depression near the middle of the thermite surface and fill the depression with about 5 g of fuse powder (a mixture of aluminum powder and barium peroxide). Dip a piece of magnesium ribbon into the fuse powder (the ribbon should extend at least three inches above the thermite surface). Using a burner, ignite the Mg ribbon. The burning magnesium ignites the fuse powder which, in turn, starts the thermite reaction, and molten iron can be seen falling into the sand.

Learning Objectives

1. To state why aluminum is a good reducing agent.
2. To state why aluminum oxide is stable.
3. To define the term amphoteric.
4. To state why aluminum hydroxide can act as an acid.
5. To describe the Hall process for refining aluminum.
6. To state why sulfur is an oxidizing agent.
7. To state the type of bonding between sulfur and metals.
8. To state why sulfur acts as a reducing agent in its reactions with oxygen.
9. To describe the Frasch process.
10. To name the two most common oxyacids of sulfur.
11. To state why sulfurous acid is a weak acid.
12. To state why sulfuric acid is a strong acid.
13. To describe the contact process for manufacturing sulfuric acid.

Demonstration III To Show the Contact Process of Preparing Sulfur Trioxide.

Materials recommended: Triple-neck bottle, 2 Bunsen burners, 4-cm glass tube, 5 one-hole stoppers, 2 solid stoppers, glass U-tube with side arms, glass and rubber tubing, battery jar, glass wool, platinized asbestos, oxygen, sulfur dioxide.

The contact process, $2SO_2 + O_2 \rightleftharpoons 2SO_3$, can be shown as a class demonstration by arranging the apparatus as shown in Fig. TG23-1. Sulfur dioxide and oxygen gases are conveniently obtained from small cylinders of these gases which can be purchased from supply houses. Attach these cylinders by rubber tubes to the glass inlet tubes in the bubble counter bottle. The bottle contains concentrated sulfuric acid to a depth of about 25 mm. The acid dries the gases that pass through it and also serves as a bubble counter; that is, it indicates the speed at which the gases enter the bottle. (The

FIG. TG23–1

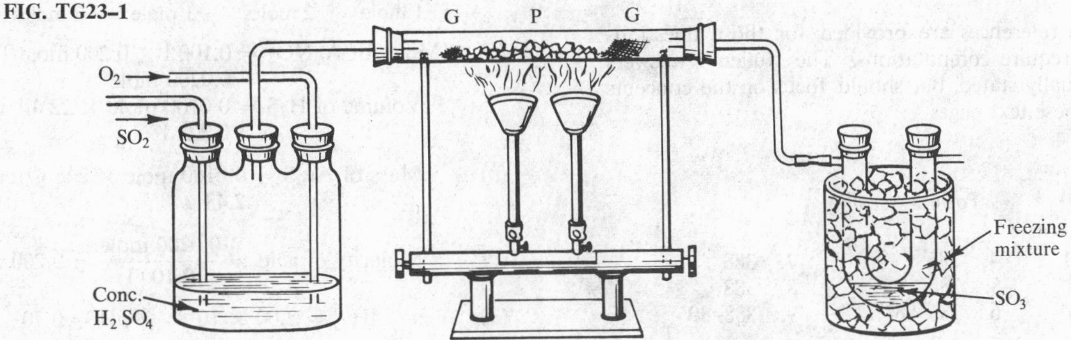

equation shows the speed of sulfur dioxide should be approximately twice the speed of oxygen.) The glass tube, heated by burners, contains platinized asbestos (P) held in place by glass wool (G) on either side of it. The escaping sulfur trioxide passes through a U-shaped tube surrounded by a freezing mixture.

Observe that colorless gases enter the glass tube but that dense white fumes leave it. Moreover, some of the sulfur trioxide condenses to a liquid in the U-tube.

Additional Questions and Problems

1. The electrolysis of a molten cryolite solution of aluminum oxide is carried out for 24 hours with a current of 5000 amperes. Compute (*a*) the quantity of cathode product, (*b*) the volume of anode product at a temperature of 900°C.

Answer

$$Q = \frac{5000\ C/sec \times 24\ hr \times 3600\ sec/hr}{96{,}500\ C/F} = 4470\ F$$

(*a*) Mass of Al = 4470 F × 9.0 g/F = 40,300 g or 40.3 kg

(*b*) $$\text{Volume} = \frac{4470\ F \times 5.6\ l/F \times 1173°K}{273°K} = 1.08 \times 10^5\ l$$

2. A contact process industrial plant produces 1000 tons of 100% sulfuric acid in a 24-hour period. How much Frasch sulfur must be supplied, assuming a 100% conversion in each step of the process?

Answer

$$\underset{2\ moles}{2S} + 3O_2 + 2H_2O \rightarrow \underset{2\ moles}{2H_2SO_4}$$

$$\text{Mass of sulfur} = 1000\ tons \times \frac{32\ g}{98\ g} = 326\ tons$$

Answers to Questions and Exercises

Text page references are provided for those questions which do not require computations. The student's answers will be individually stated, but should focus on the concepts developed in these text pages.

Factual Recall

1. Table 23-1
2. 385
3. 385
4. 386
5. 386
6. 386–88
7. 388
8. 388
9. 388–89
10. 389–90
11. 390–91
12. 390–91
13. 390–91
14. Fig. 23-8, 391–93
15. 393–94
16. 394
17. 394–95, Fig. 23-11
18. Fig. 23-14, 396–98
19. 395–96
20. 396
21. 395–96

Apply Your Knowledge!

1.

$$\underset{1\ mole}{FeS} + \underset{2\ moles}{2HCl} \rightarrow \underset{1\ mole}{FeCl_2} + \underset{1\ mole}{H_2S}$$

(*a*) $$\text{Moles of FeS} = \frac{17.6\ g}{88\ g/mole} = 0.200\ mole$$

$$\text{Moles of HCl} = 2 \times 0.200\ mole = 0.400\ mole$$

(*b*) $$\text{Volume of } H_2S = 0.200\ mole \times 22.4\ l/mole = 4.48\ l$$

(*c*) $$\text{Volume of HCl} = \frac{0.400\ mole}{6.00\ moles/l} = 0.0666\ l$$

$$\text{Molarity of salt} = \frac{0.200\ mole}{0.0666\ l} = 3.00\ M$$

2.

$$\underset{2\ moles}{2H_2S} \rightarrow \underset{3\ moles}{3O_2} \rightarrow \underset{2\ moles}{2H_2O} + \underset{2\ moles}{2SO_2}$$

(*a*) $$\text{Moles of } SO_2 = \frac{1.12\ l \times 273°K}{22.4\ l/mole \times 546°K} = 0.0250\ mole$$

$$\text{Moles of } H_2S = 0.0250\ mole$$

(*b*) $$\text{Volume of } O_2 = 3/2 \times 0.0250\ mole \times 22.4\ l/mole = 0.840\ l$$

$$\text{Volume of air} = 0.840\ l \times 5 = 4.20\ l$$

(*c*) $$\text{Mass of } H_2O = 0.0250\ mole \times 18\ g/mole = 0.45\ g$$

3.

$$\underset{1\ mole}{H_2S} + \underset{2\ moles}{2AgNO_3} \rightarrow \underset{1\ mole}{Ag_2S} + \underset{2\ moles}{2HNO_3}$$

(*a*) $$\text{Moles of } AgNO_3 = 0.100\ l \times 0.200\ mole/l = 0.0200\ mole$$

$$\text{Volume of } H_2S = 0.0100\ mole \times 22.4\ l/mole = 0.224\ l$$

(*b*) $$\text{Mass of } Ag_2S = 0.0100\ mole \times 248\ g/mole = 2.48\ g$$

(*c*) $$\text{Molarity of acid} = \frac{0.0200\ mole}{0.100\ l} = 0.200\ M$$

(*d*) $$[H^+] = 2.00 \times 10^{-1} \qquad pH = 0.70$$

4. $FeS + 2HCl \rightarrow FeCl_2 + H_2S$
1 mole 2 moles 1 mole

$$\text{Moles FeS} = \frac{4.5\text{ g}}{88\text{ g/mole}} = 0.0511\text{ mole}$$

Moles HCl = 0.0167 l × 6.0 moles/l = 0.100 mole

FeS is in excess.

Moles of H_2S formed = 0.0500 mole

$Pb(NO_3)_2 + H_2S \rightarrow PbS + 2HNO_3$
1 mole 1 mole 1 mole

Moles of $Pb(NO_3)_2$ = 0.250 l × 0.500 mole/l
= 0.125 mole

$Pb(NO_3)_2$ is in excess.

Mass of PbS = 0.0500 mole × 239 g/mole = 12.0 g

5. (*a*) $[H^+] = 1 \qquad [S^{-2}] = \dfrac{10^{-23}}{1} = 10^{-23}$

The ion product, $[Zn^{+2}] \times [S^{-2}]$, in the solution is $10^{-1} \times 10^{-23}$, or 10^{-24}, which is less than the K_{sp} of ZnS, so that there is no precipitate of ZnS.

Mass of CuS = 0.100 l × 0.100 mole/l × 96 g/mole
= 0.96 g

(*b*) $[H^+] = 10^{-7} \qquad [S^{-2}] = \dfrac{10^{-23}}{(10^{-7})^2} = 10^{-9}$

The ion product, $[Zn^{+2}] \times [S^{-2}]$, in the solution is $10^{-1} \times 10^{-9}$ or 10^{-10} which is much greater than the K_{sp} of ZnS. Therefore, both CuS and ZnS precipitate.

Mass of ZnS precipitate
= 0.100 l × 0.100 mole/l × 97 g/mole = 0.97 g

Total mass of precipitate = 0.97 g + 0.96 g = 1.93 g

6. $2H_2SO_3 + O_2 \rightarrow 2H_2SO_4$
1 mole 2 moles

$$\text{Moles of } O_2 = \frac{0.56\text{ l}}{22.4\text{ l/mole}} = 0.0250\text{ mole}$$

Moles of H_2SO_4 = 0.0500 mole

$H_2SO_4 + 2NaOH \rightarrow Na_2SO_4 + 2H_2O$
1 mole 2 moles

Moles of NaOH = 0.100 mole

$$\text{Volume of NaOH} = \frac{0.100\text{ mole}}{0.500\text{ mole/l}} = 0.200\text{ l}$$

7. $Cu + 2H_2SO_4 \rightarrow CuSO_4 + 2H_2O + SO_2$
1 mole 2 moles 1 mole

(*a*) $$\text{Moles of Cu} = \frac{3.2\text{ g}}{64\text{ g/mole}} = 0.050\text{ mole}$$

Moles of H_2SO_4 = 0.100 mole

$$\text{Volume of } H_2SO_4 = \frac{0.100\text{ mole} \times 98\text{ g/mole}}{1.85\text{ g/ml}} = 5.3\text{ ml}$$

(*b*) $$\text{Volume of } SO_2 = 0.050\text{ mole} \times 22.4\text{ l/mole} \times \frac{546°K}{273°K} = 2.24\text{ l}$$

8. $NaHSO_3 + HCl \rightarrow NaCl + SO_2 + H_2O$
1 mole 1 mole

$$\text{Moles } NaHSO_3 = \frac{5.2\text{ g}}{104\text{ g/mole}} = 0.0500\text{ mole}$$

$$\text{Volume of HCl} = \frac{0.0500\text{ mole}}{10.0\text{ moles/l}} = 0.0050\text{ l or 5.0 ml}$$

9. $2MnO_4^- + 5SO_3^{-2} + 6H^+ \rightarrow 2Mn^{+2} + 5SO_4^{-2} + 3H_2O$
2 moles 5 moles

Moles of MnO_4^- = 0.100 l × 0.100 mole/l
= 0.0100 mole

Moles of SO_4^{-2} = 5/2 × 0.0100 mole
= 0.0250 mole

10. $SO_4^{-2} + Ba^{+2} \rightarrow BaSO_4$
1 mole 1 mole

Moles of Ba^{+2} = 0.0250 mole

$$\text{Volume of } BaCl_2 = \frac{0.0250\text{ mole}}{1.50\text{ moles/l}} = 0.0167\text{ l}$$

11. $NaCl + H_2SO_4 \rightarrow NaHSO_4 + HCl$
1 mole 1 mole 1 mole

$$\text{Moles of } H_2SO_4 = \frac{4.9\text{ g}}{98\text{ g/mole}} = 0.050\text{ mole}$$

(*a*) Mass of NaCl = .050 mole × 58.5 g/mole
= 2.93 g

(*b*) $$\text{Molarity of HCl} = \frac{0.050\text{ mole}}{0.0100\text{ l}} = 5.0\ M$$

(*c*) Moles of KOH required = 0.050 mole

$$\text{Volume of KOH} = \frac{0.050\text{ mole}}{5.0\text{ moles/l}} = 0.0100\text{ l or 10.0 ml}$$

12. Mass of $BaSO_4 = 2.33$ g
Mass of $BaCO_3 = 4.30 \text{ g} - 2.33 \text{ g} = 1.97$ g

(*a*) Moles of $BaCO_3$ or $CO_3^{-2} = \dfrac{1.97 \text{ g}}{197 \text{ g/mole}}$
$= 0.0100$ mole

Molarity of $CO_3^{-2} = \dfrac{0.0100 \text{ mole}}{0.100 \text{ l}} = 0.100\ M$

(*b*) Moles of $BaSO_4$ or $SO_4^{-2} = \dfrac{2.33 \text{ g}}{233 \text{ g/mole}}$
$= 0.0100$ mole

Molarity of $SO_4^{-2} = \dfrac{0.0100 \text{ mole}}{0.100 \text{ l}} = 0.100\ M$

(*c*) Moles of $BaCl_2$ added $= 0.0100 \text{ mole} + 0.0100 \text{ mole}$
$= 0.0200$ mole

Volume of $BaCl_2 = \dfrac{0.0200 \text{ mole}}{0.500 \text{ mole/l}}$
$= 0.0400$ l or 40 ml

13. (*a*) 100 g of ore contains 45 g of Al or

$$45 \text{ g} \times \frac{Al_2O_3}{2Al} = 45 \text{ g} \times \frac{102}{54}$$
$$= 85 \text{ g of } Al_2O_3$$

Percent of oxygen as $Al_2O_3 = \dfrac{85 \text{ g} - 45 \text{ g}}{100 \text{ g}} \times 100$
$= 40\%$

(*b*) Percent of rocky impurity

$$= \frac{100 \text{ g} - 85 \text{ g}}{100 \text{ g}} \times 100 = 15\%$$

CHAPTER 24

TRANSITION ELEMENTS IN THE FOURTH ROW

PROPERTIES OF THE TRANSITION ELEMENTS IN THE FOURTH ROW
(pp. 405–09)

Learning Objectives

1. To state that electrons are added to the 4*s* orbitals before they are added to the 3*d* orbitals.
2. To state that the sequence of elements that add electrons to their 3*d* orbitals before the group that adds electrons to their 4*p* orbitals constitute the transition elements of row 4.
3. To name the first element to add an electron to one of its 3*d* orbitals.
4. To state why the transition elements have similar properties.
5. To state that all the transition elements are metals.
6. To state why copper and chromium have only one electron in their 4*s* orbital.
7. To state why the melting points of the transition elements are high.
8. To state why the melting point of zinc is lower than that of the other transition elements.
9. To state why the transition elements exhibit a multiplicity of oxidation states.
10. To define the term *paramagnetism*.
11. To define the term *ferromagnetism*.
12. To state why the atomic diameters of the transition elements are similar.
13. To state why the densities of the transition elements increase with increasing Z.
14. To state why the transition elements have only slightly different ionization energies.

THE FIRST SIX TRANSITION ELEMENTS IN THE FOURTH ROW
(pp. 409–18)

Learning Objectives

1. To state, in terms of electron configuration, why scandium has an oxidation number of $+3$.
2. To state the advantageous properties of titanium.
3. To state the major disadvantage of using titanium.
4. Given that titanium has four electrons available for bonding, to state why its oxidation states may be $+2$, $+3$, or $+4$.
5. To describe, in terms of electron configuration, how vanadium can change its oxidation state from $+5$ to $+4$ and back to $+5$ in its reaction with sulfur dioxide.
6. To state why manganese is a constituent of all steels.
7. To write Equation (24-11).
8. To describe the operation of a blast furnace.
9. To describe the operation of a basic-oxygen furnace.
10. To describe what is believed to be the rusting process of iron.

Demonstration I To Show the Multivalence of Iron.

Materials recommended: Test tubes, iron (II) sulfate, sodium hydroxide, hydrogen peroxide, hydrogen sulfide, iron (III) chloride.

The multivalence states of the transition elements can easily be demonstrated by test tube experiments. Iron is probably the most familiar transition element. The ferric ion is yellow brown in color and the ferrous ion green. The most common ferric compound is $FeCl_3$ and the most common ferrous compound is $FeSO_4$. Ferrous ion can easily be oxidized to ferric ion and, conversely, ferric ion can be reduced to ferrous ion. Or,

$$Fe^{+2} - e^- \xrightarrow{\text{oxidation}} Fe^{+3}$$

and

$$Fe^{+3} + e^- \xrightarrow{\text{reduction}} Fe^{+2}$$

A. *Oxidation of* Fe^{+2} *to* Fe^{+3}

Ferrous ion is slowly oxidized to ferric ion in air or, better still, by adding a little hydrogen peroxide (H_2O_2). A still better way is to oxidize ferrous hydroxide, $Fe(OH)_2$, a greenish gelatinous precipitate.

Make a dilute solution of $FeSO_4$ and add a few ml of NaOH. Observe the green precipitate,

$$Fe^{+2} + 2OH^- \rightarrow Fe(OH)_2(s)$$

On standing, the green ferrous hydroxide is oxidized to reddish brown ferric hydroxide by oxygen of the air,

$$\underset{\text{green}}{4Fe(OH)_2(s)} + O_2 + 2H_2O \rightarrow \underset{\text{brown}}{4Fe(OH)_3(s)}$$

Or, using H_2O_2 as the source of oxygen,

$$2Fe(OH)_2(s) + H_2O_2 \rightarrow 2Fe(OH)_3(s)$$

B. *Reduction of* Fe^{+3} *to* Fe^{+2}

Hydrogen sulfide is a suitable reducing agent. If hydrogen sulfide gas is bubbled into a solution of ferric chloride, the brown color disappears and a white suspension of sulfur is formed. That is,

$$2FeCl_3 + H_2S \rightarrow 2FeCl_2 + S(s) + 2HCl$$

Or, $$2Fe^{+3} + S^{-2} \rightarrow 2Fe^{+2} + S(s)$$

Or, $$2Fe^{+3} + 2e^- \xrightarrow{\text{reduction}} 2Fe^{+2}$$

$$S^{-2} - 2e^- \xrightarrow{\text{oxidation}} S(s)$$

Demonstration II To Show the Multivalence of Chromium and Manganese.

Materials recommended: Test tubes, dilute sodium sulfite solution, dilute sulfuric acid, dilute potassium chro-mate solution, dilute potassium permanganate solution, concentrated potassium hydroxide solution.

Potassium chromate (a yellow solid) and potassium permanganate (a dark purple solid) are convenient sources of chromium and manganese in their highest oxidation states (+6 for chromium and +7 for manganese). The following demonstrations are easily performed and illustrate the oxidizing action of chromate ion (CrO_4^{-2}) and permanganate ion (MnO_4^-).

A. *Reduction of* CrO_4^{-2} *to* Cr^{+3}

Prepare a dilute solution of sodium sulfite. Acidify the solution with dilute sulfuric acid and then add dilute potassium chromate solution. The yellow color of the chromate ion changes to the greenish color of chromic ion by the reducing action of sulfite ion. The equation for the reaction is

$$\underset{\text{yellow}}{2CrO_4^{-2}} + 10H^+ + 3SO_3^{-2} \rightarrow \underset{\text{green}}{2Cr^{+3}} + 5H_2O + 3SO_4^{-2}$$

B. *The Reduction of* MnO_4^- *in Acid, Neutral, and Basic Solution*

Prepare a dilute solution of sodium sulfite as reducing agent and proceed as follows.

In acid solution. Acidify a portion of the sulfite solution with dilute sulfuric acid and then add a few drops of dilute potassium permanganate solution. The purple color of the permanganate ion disappears as sulfite ion reduces the permanganate ion to colorless Mn^{+2}.

$$\underset{\text{purple}}{2MnO_4^-} + 6H^+ + 5SO_3^{-2} \rightarrow \underset{\text{colorless}}{2Mn^{+2}} + 3H_2O + 5SO_4^{-2}$$

In this reaction the oxidation state of manganese changes from +7 to +2.

In neutral solution. Add a few drops of dilute permanganate solution to a second portion of the sulfite solution. The purple color of the permanganate ion is discharged and is replaced by the brownish color of MnO_2 which precipitates from the solution.

$$2MnO_4^- + 2H^+ + 3SO_3^{-2} \rightarrow \underset{\text{brown}}{2MnO_2(s)} + H_2O + 3SO_4^{-2}$$

In this case the oxidation state of manganese changes from +7 to +4.

In basic solution. Add concentrated KOH solution to a third portion of the sulfite solution and then add a few drops of the permanganate solution. The purple color changes to the deep green of manganate ion (MnO_4^{-2}) as sulfite ion reduces the permanganate.

$$2MnO_4^- + 2OH^- + SO_3^{-2} \rightarrow \underset{\text{green}}{2MnO_4^{-2}} + H_2O + SO_4^{-2}$$

In this case the oxidation state of manganese changes from +7 to +6.

In summary, the permanganate ion is reduced by sulfite ion to Mn^{+2} in acid solution, to Mn^{+4} (in MnO_2) in neutral solution, and to Mn^{+6} (in MnO_4^{-2}) in basic solution. That is, the extent of reduction of manganese depends upon the *p*H of the solution.

THE REMAINING TRANSITION ELEMENTS IN THE FOURTH ROW

(pp. 418–21)

Learning Objectives

1. To state the chief use of cobalt.
2. To state, in terms of electron configuration, why copper's oxidation number is +2.
3. To state, in terms of electron configuration, why zinc does not behave like a transition element.

Additional Questions and Problems

1. One mole of iron (II) hydroxide is exposed to moist air until reaction is complete. Calculate (*a*) the moles of product, (*b*) the volume of oxygen which reacts at STP.

Answer

$$\underset{4\text{ moles}}{4Fe(OH)_2} + \underset{1\text{ mole}}{O_2} + xH_2O \rightarrow \underset{2\text{ moles}}{2Fe_2O_3 \cdot nH_2O}$$

(*a*) $\text{Moles of product} = \dfrac{1.00\text{ mole}}{2} = 0.500\text{ mole}$

(*b*) $\text{Volume of } O_2 = \dfrac{1.00\text{ mole}}{4} \times 22.4\text{ l/mole} = 5.6\text{ l}$

2. A hematite ore contains 95% ferric oxide and 5% silica. If 1000 tons of this ore are subjected to the blast furnace process and if it is assumed that the only reaction of the ferric oxide is with carbon monoxide, (*a*) how much coke is required to produce the carbon monoxide, (*b*) how many liters of air (20% oxygen by volume) at 1092°C must be supplied to produce the carbon monoxide, (*c*) how much limestone must be added?

Answer

(*a*)

$$\underset{1\text{ mole}}{Fe_2O_3} + \underset{3\text{ moles}}{3CO} \rightarrow 2Fe + 3CO_2$$

$$\text{Moles } Fe_2O_3 = \frac{1000\text{ tons} \times 0.95 \times 2000\text{ lb/ton} \times 454\text{ g/lb}}{160\text{ g/mole}} = 5.40 \times 10^6\text{ moles}$$

Moles CO $= 3 \times 5.40 \times 10^6\text{ moles} = 1.62 \times 10^7\text{ moles}$

Mass of C $= 1.62 \times 10^7\text{ moles} \times 12\text{ g/mole} = 1.95 \times 10^8\text{ g or 214 tons}$

(*b*)

$$\underset{2\text{ moles}}{2C} + \underset{1\text{ mole}}{O_2} \rightarrow \underset{2\text{ moles}}{2CO}$$

$$\text{Volume of } O_2 = \frac{1.62 \times 10^7\text{ moles}}{2} \times 22.4\text{ l/mole} \times \frac{1365°K}{273°K} = 9.1 \times 10^8\text{ l}$$

Volume of air $= 5 \times 9.1 \times 10^8\text{ l} = 4.55 \times 10^9\text{ l}$

(*c*)

$$\underset{\substack{1\text{ mole}\\60}}{SiO_2} + \underset{\substack{1\text{ mole}\\100}}{CaCO_3} \rightarrow CaSiO_3 + CO_2$$

$$\text{Tons of } CaCO_3 = 50\text{ tons} \times \frac{100}{60} = 83\text{ tons}$$

3. One hundred tons of zinc oxide ore are reduced by carbon (coke). (*a*) How many tons of carbon are consumed? (*b*) How many liters of carbon monoxide are formed at 819°C? (*c*) How much energy in kilocalories is liberated in burning the carbon monoxide?

Answer

$$\underset{\substack{1\text{ mole}\\81}}{ZnO} + \underset{\substack{1\text{ mole}\\12}}{C} \rightarrow Zn + \underset{\substack{1\text{ mole}\\28}}{CO}$$

(*a*) $\text{Tons of C} = 100\text{ tons} \times \dfrac{12}{81} = 14.8\text{ tons}$

(*b*) $\text{Mass of CO in g} = \dfrac{28}{12} \times 14.8\text{ tons} \times 2000\text{ lb/ton} \times 454\text{ g/lb} = 3.14 \times 10^7\text{ g}$

$$\text{Volume of CO} = \frac{3.14 \times 10^7\text{ g}}{28\text{ g/mole}} \times 22.4\text{ l/mole} \times \frac{1092°K}{273°K} = 1.00 \times 10^8\text{ l}$$

(*c*)

$$\underset{1\text{ mole}}{CO} + \tfrac{1}{2}O_2 \rightarrow CO_2 + 68\text{ kcal}$$

$$\text{Moles of CO} = \frac{3.14 \times 10^7\text{ g}}{28\text{ g/mole}} = 1.12 \times 10^6\text{ moles}$$

Energy liberated $= 1.12 \times 10^6\text{ moles} \times 68\text{ kcal/mole} = 7.6 \times 10^7\text{ kcal}$

Answers to Questions and Exercises

Text page references are provided for those questions which do not require computations. The student's answers will be individually stated, but should focus on the concepts in these text pages.

Factual Recall

1. 403–05	4. 405–06	7. 407–08
2. 403–05	5. 406–07	8. 408
3. 403–05	6. 407	

Apply Your Knowledge!

1. $2Cu_2O + O_2 \rightarrow 4CuO$
   2 moles 1 mole

$$\text{Volume of } O_2 = \frac{0.50 \text{ mole}}{2} \times 22.4 \text{ l/mole} = 5.6 \text{ l}$$

$$\text{Volume of air} = 5.6 \text{ l} \times 5 = 28.0 \text{ l}$$

2. $2Sc + 6H_2O \rightarrow 2Sc^{+3} + 6OH^- + 3H_2$
   2 moles 6 moles 2 moles 3 moles

$$\text{Moles of Sc} = \frac{2.25 \text{ g}}{45 \text{ g/mole}} = 0.0500 \text{ mole}$$

(*a*) Moles of H_2O = 0.0500 mole × 3 = 0.150 mole.
(*b*) Mass = 0.0500 mole × 96 g/mole = 4.80 g.
(*c*) $\text{Volume of } H_2 = 0.0500 \text{ mole} \times 3/2 \times 22.4 \text{ l/mole} \times \frac{300°K \times 760 \text{ torr}}{273°K \times 684 \text{ torr}} = 1.37 \text{ l}$

3. $Ti + 2Cl_2 \rightarrow TiCl_4$
   1 mole 2 moles

$$\text{Moles of } Cl_2 = \frac{4.48 \text{ l} \times 273°K}{22.4 \text{ l/mole} \times 546°K} = 0.100 \text{ mole}$$

$$\text{Moles of Ti} = \frac{0.100 \text{ mole}}{2} = 0.0500 \text{ mole}$$

4. $Zn + 2Cr^{+3} \rightarrow Zn^{+2} + 2Cr^{+2}$
   1 mole 2 moles

$$\text{Moles of } Cr^{+3} = \frac{1.30 \text{ g}}{52 \text{ g/mole}} = 0.0250 \text{ mole}$$

$$\text{Moles of Zn} = \frac{0.0250 \text{ mole}}{2} = 0.0125 \text{ mole}$$

5. $Cr_2O_7^{-2} + 6Fe^{+2} + 14H^+ \rightarrow 2Cr^{+3} + 6Fe^{+3} + 7H_2O$
   1 mole 6 moles

$$\text{Moles of } Fe^{+2} = 0.100 \text{ l} \times 0.250 \text{ mole/l} = 0.0250 \text{ mole}$$

$$\text{Volume of } Cr_2O_7^{-2} = \frac{0.0250 \text{ mole}}{6 \times 0.100 \text{ mole/l}} = 0.0417 \text{ l}$$

6. $MnO_2 + 4HCl \rightarrow MnCl_2 + 2H_2O + Cl_2$
   1 mole 4 moles 1 mole 1 mole

$$\text{Moles of } MnO_2 = \frac{4.40 \text{ g}}{87 \text{ g/mole}} = 0.0506 \text{ mole}$$

(*a*) $\text{Volume of acid} = \frac{0.0500 \text{ mole} \times 4}{6.00 \text{ mole/l}} = 0.0337 \text{ l}$

(*b*) $\text{Molarity} = \frac{0.0506 \text{ mole}}{0.0337 \text{ l}} = 1.50\ M$

(*c*) $\text{Volume} = 0.0506 \text{ mole} \times 22.4 \text{ l/mole} \times \frac{323°K}{273°K} = 1.34 \text{ l}$

7. $2MnO_4^- + 5H_2C_2O_4 + 6H^+ \rightarrow 2Mn^{+2} + 10CO_2 + 8H_2O$
   2 moles 5 moles 2 moles 10 moles

$$\text{Moles of } CO_2 = \frac{1.12 \text{ l}}{22.4 \text{ l/mole}} = 0.0500 \text{ mole}$$

(*a*) $\text{Mass} = \frac{0.0500 \text{ mole}}{2} \times 90 \text{ g/mole} = 2.25 \text{ g}$

(*b*) $\text{Volume} = \frac{0.0500 \text{ mole}}{5 \times 0.100 \text{ mole/l}} = 0.100 \text{ l}$

(*c*) $\text{Moles} = \frac{0.0500 \text{ mole}}{5} = 0.0100 \text{ mole}$

8. $2Fe^{+3} + H_2S \rightarrow 2Fe^{+2} + S + 2H^+$
   2 moles 1 mole 2 moles 1 mole

$$\text{Moles of } Fe^{+3} = 0.0100 \text{ l} + 0.200 \text{ mole/l} = 0.00200 \text{ mole}$$

(*a*) $\text{Volume of } H_2S = \frac{0.00200 \text{ mole}}{2} \times 22.4 \text{ l/mole} = 0.0224 \text{ l}$

(*b*) Moles of Fe^{+2} = 0.00200 mole

(*c*) $\text{Mass of S} = \frac{0.00200 \text{ mole}}{2} \times 32 \text{ g/mole} = 0.032 \text{ g}$

UNIT 

ORGANIC CHEMISTRY

OPENING UNIT VIII

Until Wöhler's synthesis of urea from ammonium cyanate in 1828 (see p. 426) the notion that organic compounds possessed some sort of "vital" element forced a dualism on the science of chemistry. Even today, the echoes of this idea can be heard in the terms *organic* and *inorganic*. And, of course, it is true that this distinction can generally be made. But in the early part of the last century, the separatism was not merely taxonomic — the quick and the dead were thought of as two different things to be thought about according to different sets of precepts. This, despite the fact that it was perfectly well known that organic substances consisted mainly of ordinary carbon, hydrogen, oxygen, and in the case of "animal" substances, nitrogen. It was not thought however, that organic substances could be made in a test tube since no one knew how to produce the necessary vital force.

In 1845, Wöhler's student, Kolbe, synthesized acetic acid. In the next decade, Berthelot synthesized organic compounds by the dozens. Today there are more than 2 million known organic compounds.

Chapter 25 is concerned mostly with the variety of carbon and hydrogen compounds. Chapter 26 adds to the discussion a third element — oxygen. The last chapter in this unit considers these compounds as the building blocks of living things.

CHAPTER 25

THE HYDROCARBONS: COMPOUNDS OF CARBON AND HYDROGEN

THE ALKANES
(pp. 428–40)

Learning Objectives

1. To state what is meant by the assertion *the electronic structure of the carbon atom is midway between that of helium and neon.*
2. To state that carbon shows little tendency to lose its 2*s* and 2*p* electrons to form C^{+4} ion or to gain electrons to form a C^{-4} ion.
3. To state that the bonding of carbon is almost always covalent.
4. To state that carbon is tetravalent in most of its compounds.
5. To diagram the covalent bonds of methane.
6. To state that the methane molecule is tetrahedral.
7. To define the term *alkane*.
8. To describe the conditions that determine activities of the alkanes.
9. To write the electron dot formulas for methane, ethane, and propane.
10. To write the structural formulas for methane, ethane, and propane.
11. To state that the alkane molecules are three-dimensional.
12. To write the general formula for the alkanes.
13. To state the relation of the melting and boiling points of the alkanes to their molecular masses.
14. To define the term *structural isomer*.
15. To define the term *straight chain.*
16. To write a straight-chain formula for C_4H_{10}.
17. To define the term *branched chain.*
18. To write the branched-chain formula for C_4H_{10}.
19. To write the formula for a methyl group.
20. To diagram the numbering system for a straight carbon chain.
21. Given the numbering system for a straight carbon chain, to state the names of the isomers of C_6H_{14}.
22. To state the relation between the number of isomers of an alkane to the number of carbon atoms it possesses.
23. To define the term *cycloalkane.*
24. To diagram a six-carbon ring.
25. To state the three types of alkane reactions listed on p. 436 of the text.
26. To define the conditions for the complete combustion of methane.
27. To write the equation for the complete combustion of methane.
28. To define the conditions for the incomplete combustion of methane.
29. To write the equation for the incomplete combustion of methane.
30. To write the equation that expresses the production of carbon black.
31. To state the relation of the amount of heat energy released to the completeness of combustion of a hydrocarbon.
32. To define the term *cracking*.
33. To write equations for two possible crackings of $C_{16}H_{34}$.

34. To define the term *substitution reaction*.
35. To state that all the halogens except iodine can take part in substitution reactions.
36. To write Equation (25-11).
37. To state that, by successive steps, all the hydrogens in methane can be replaced by a halogen.

Suggested Teacher Commentary

As stated in the text, the alkanes (paraffin hydrocarbons) are relatively inactive and stable compounds. This means that an alkane contains less energy than the elements from which it is derived. Let us consider methane, the simplest alkane, and compute the heat of formation of methane from its elements. It is not possible to synthesize methane from carbon and hydrogen according to the equation, $C + 2H_2 \rightarrow CH_4$, so that the energy change in this reaction cannot be measured directly by experiment. We can, however, compute the heat of formation of methane, given the value for its heat of combustion, and the values for the heats of combustion of hydrogen and carbon.

When one mole of methane is burned to give carbon dioxide and water, 211 kcal of heat is liberated. Or,

$$CH_4 + 2O_2 \rightarrow CO_2 + 2H_2O \qquad \Delta H = -211 \text{ kcal}$$

One mole of methane (16 g) contains 12 g of carbon and 4 g of hydrogen. The energy liberated when 12 g of carbon are oxidized to carbon dioxide is 94 kcal,

$$C + O_2 \rightarrow CO_2 \qquad \Delta H = -94 \text{ kcal}$$

And the energy liberated when 4 g of hydrogen are oxidized to water is 136 kcal,

$$2H_2 + O_2 \rightarrow 2H_2O \quad \Delta H = -68 \times 2 \text{ kcal}$$

Therefore the total energy liberated by burning 12 g of carbon and 4 g of hydrogen is 230 kcal. What happens to the "missing" 19 kcal (230 – 211) of energy? This must be the energy required to decompose one mole of methane into its elements. Or,

$$CH_4 \rightarrow C + 2H_2 \qquad \Delta H = +19 \text{ kcal}$$

We can now write the equation for the synthesis of methane as

$$C + 2H_2 \rightarrow CH_4 \qquad \Delta H = -19 \text{ kcal}$$

In other words, the heat of formation of methane is −19 kcal/mole. Methane is therefore an exothermic compound; that is, it contains less energy than the elements from which it is derived and is therefore a relatively stable substance.

THE ALKENES
(pp. 440–46)

Learning Objectives

1. To write the general formula for an alkene.
2. To distinguish between saturated and unsaturated hydrocarbons in terms of their number of hydrogen atoms.
3. To write the electron dot notation for ethene and propene.
4. To write the structural formulas for ethene and propene.
5. To define a double bond in terms of shared electron pairs.
6. To state that this type of bonding is characteristic of the alkenes.
7. To state why a double bond is weaker than a single bond.
8. To write the structural formulas for the three isomers of C_4H_8.
9. To name the three isomers of C_4H_8.
10. To write the two possible structures for 2-butene.
11. To define the term *geometrical isomer*.
12. To define the prefixes *cis* and *trans*.
13. To write the two general structural formulas that indicate the possibility of geometrical isomerism.
14. To write equations for the complete, incomplete, and still less complete combustion of ethene.
15. To state the characteristic reaction of the alkenes.
16. To describe hydrogenation.
17. To write the equation for the addition of bromine to ethene.
18. To write the equation for the addition of hypochlorous acid to ethene.
19. To write the equation for the addition of sulfuric acid to ethene.
20. To write the equation for the conversion of ethylsulfuric acid to ethanol.

THE ALKYNES
(pp. 446–48)

Learning Objectives

1. To state the degree of saturation of the alkynes.
2. To write the electron dot formulas for ethyne and propyne.
3. To write the structural formulas for ethyne and propyne.

4. To write the general formula for the alkynes.
5. To state why geometrical isomerism does not occur in triple-bonded compounds.
6. To write the equations for the two reactions involved in the preparation of acetylene.
7. To write the equations for the combustion of acetylene.
8. To state that addition reactions are characteristic of the alkynes.
9. To relate the triple bond to the amounts of substances with which alkynes will react.
10. To write the equation for the reaction between two molecules of acetylene.
11. To define the term *addition polymerization*.

Suggested Teacher Commentary

Let us now compute the heat of formation of acetylene in the same way as we did the alkanes. The heat of combustion of acetylene is 312 kcal per 26 g (one mole) of acetylene burned,

$$C_2H_2 + 5/2\ O_2 \rightarrow 2CO_2 + H_2O \qquad \Delta H = -312 \text{ kcal}$$

The energy liberated when 24 g of carbon are oxidized is 2 × 94 kcal or 188 kcal, and the energy liberated when 2 g of hydrogen are burned is 68 kcal. The sum of these energy quantities is 256 kcal, whereas the heat of combustion of acetylene is 312 kcal. This means that 312 – 256 kcal, or 56 kcal, are liberated when one mole of acetylene is decomposed. Or,

$$C_2H_2 \rightarrow 2C + H_2 \qquad \Delta H = -56 \text{ kcal}$$

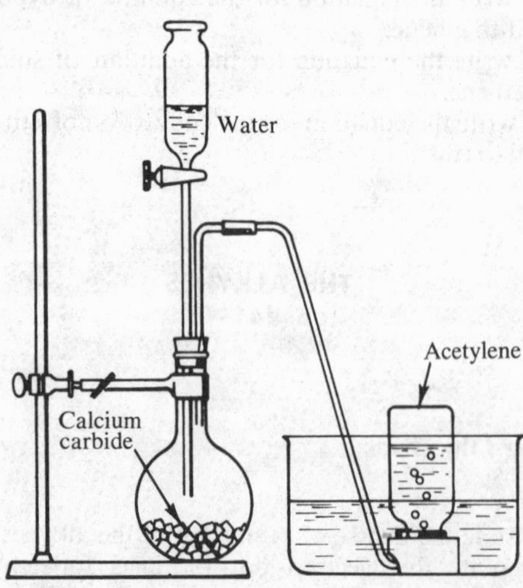

FIG. TG25–1

which can also be expressed as

$$2C + H_2 \rightarrow C_2H_2 \qquad \Delta H = +56 \text{ kcal}$$

This means that the heat of formation of acetylene from its elements is +56 kcal/mole. In other words, acetylene is an endothermic compound, and it follows that it contains more energy than the elements from which it is derived. It also means that acetylene is an unstable substance. Indeed, it is well known that acetylene is potentially explosive and that it is unsafe to store acetylene in a highly compressed state.

From the above examples, we can state the general relationship. Heat of formation of a substance equals sum of the heats of formation of the combustion products minus heat of combustion of the substance.

Demonstration I To Show the Preparation of Acetylene.

Materials recommended: Stand, clamp, flask, dropping funnel, glass and rubber tubing, 2-hole stopper, battery jar, shelf, collecting bottle, calcium carbide, water.

Acetylene (ethyne) occupies a unique position among carbon compounds because it can be prepared from simple inorganic substances, namely calcium carbide and water. The preparation should be carried out as follows. Place some small lumps of calcium carbide in a flask and arrange the apparatus as shown in Fig. TG25–1. Let water in a dropping funnel fall drop by drop onto the carbide. A vigorous, exothermic reaction occurs and acetylene is collected by displacing water. The reaction for the preparation is

$$CaC_2 + 2H_2O \rightarrow C_2H_2 + Ca(OH)_2 + \text{heat energy}$$

Hold a burning match near the mouth of a bottle of acetylene placed upright on the bench. The gas burns with a sooty flame. Indeed, the soot is oily and it soils anything with which it comes into contact. For this reason the combustion of acetylene should be carried out under a hood.

Demonstration II To Show the Addition of Bromine to Acetylene.

Materials recommended: Bottle of acetylene, bromine, glass plate.

Collect a second bottle of acetylene and add a drop of bromine to the gas. Cover the bottle with a glass plate and shake the contents. The reddish color of bromine disappears at once, indicating that acetylene readily reacts with bromine to give an addition product. The equation for the reaction is

$$C_2H_2 + Br_2 \rightarrow C_2H_2Br_2$$

or

$$C_2H_2 + 2Br_2 \rightarrow C_2H_2Br_4$$

THE AROMATIC HYDROCARBONS
(pp. 449–52)

Learning Objectives

1. To name the two major classes of organic compounds.
2. To define the term *aliphatic*.
3. To define the term *aromatic*.
4. To state the structural differences between aliphatic and aromatic compounds.
5. To write the formula for benzene.
6. To write the structural formula for benzene.
7. To state that benzene has none of the typical reactions of the aliphatic compounds.
8. To write the structural formula for cyclohexene.
9. To state the structural differences between benzene and cyclohexene.
10. To diagram a benzene ring.
11. To state what types of reactions are characteristic of benzene.
12. To write the equation for the reaction of benzene with chlorine in the presence of iron.
13. To write the formula for toluene.
14. To write the structural formula for toluene, using a benzene ring diagram.
15. To write the formula for naphthalene.
16. To write the structural formula for napthalene — using both conventional bonds and letter symbols and benzene ring diagrams.

Suggested Teacher Commentary

Carbon compounds occupy three-dimensional space and their structure cannot be satisfactorily presented on the flat surface of a textbook or a chalkboard. Teachers are strongly advised to construct molecular models of carbon compounds so that students can visualize their three-dimensional structure. Carbon atoms are usually represented by black balls, hydrogen atoms by yellow ones, oxygen atoms by red balls, and so on. Wooden pegs or coil springs represent covalent bonds.

The use of models is absolutely essential in the study of isomerism. The differences between structural isomers, geometrical isomers, and optical isomers cannot be visualized by students unless models of typical isomers are constructed.

Answers to Questions and Exercises

Text page references are provided for those questions which do not require computations. The student's answers will be individually stated, but should focus on the concepts developed in these text pages.

Factual Recall

1. 427-28
2. 428
3. Fig. 25-1
4. 442–44
5. Fig. 25-7
6. 431–35
7. Table 25–1, 431
8. 432–33
9. 440
10. 441
11. 446
12. 449–51
13. 449–52
14. 431–35
15. C—C—C—C—C—C—C (heptane); C—C—C—C—C—C with C on the fifth carbon (2-methyl hexane)

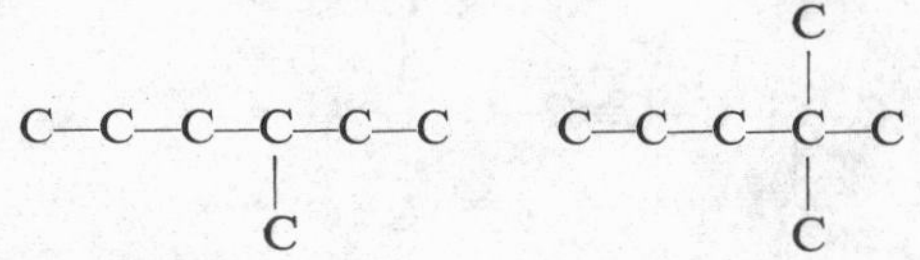

3-methyl hexane   2,2-dimethyl pentane

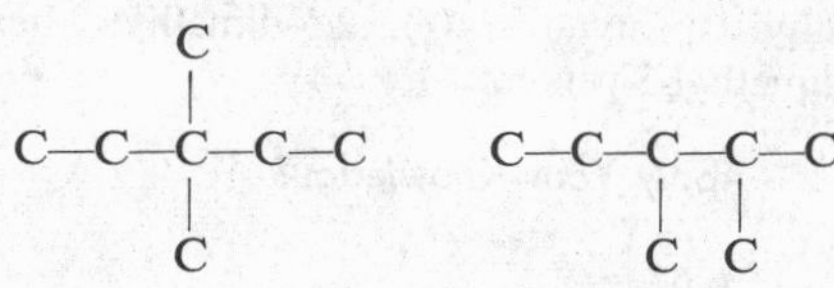

3,3-dimethyl pentane   2,3-dimethyl pentane

C—C—C—C—C with C on the second and fourth carbons: 2,4-dimethyl pentane

C—C—C—C with C—C on the second carbon: 3-ethyl pentane or ethyl pentane

C—C—C—C with C above and below the third carbon and C below the second: 2,2,3-trimethyl butane or trimethyl butane

16. 442–43
17. (*a*) C—C—C with C below the middle carbon (*b*) C—C—C—C with C above and below each of the two middle carbons (*c*) C—C—C—C—C—C with C below the second and fifth carbons
18. (*a*) methyle propane (*b*) 2,2,3,3-tetramethyl butane or tetramethyl butane (*c*) 2,5-dimethyl hexane
19. (*a*) No. One of the carbon atoms that holds the double bond has two hydrogen atoms attached to it. (*b*) and (*c*) Yes. Each of the two carbon atoms that hold the double bond has two unlike groups attached to it.

20. 438 21. 431

22. (*a*) $C_3H_8 + 5O_2 \rightarrow 3CO_2 + 4H_2O$
(*b*) $2C_3H_8 + 7O_2 \rightarrow 6CO + 8H_2O$
(*c*) $C_3H_8 + 2O_2 \rightarrow 3C + 4H_2O$

23. 439 24. 445–46

25. (*a*)
```
C—C—C=C—C—C
        |
        C
```
(*b*)
```
C—C—C—C≡C—C—C
          |
          C
```
(*c*)
```
  C
  |
C—C—C—C—C=C
  | | |
  C C C
```
(*d*)
```
C—C—C—C≡C
  | |
  C C—C
```
(*e*)
```
    C         C
    |         |
C—C—C—C—C≡C—C—C—C—C
    |         | |
    C         C C
```

26. (*a*) 2,2,6,6-tetramethyl-3-heptene
(*b*) 4-methyl-1-pentyne (*c*) 2,5-dimethyl-3-hexyne
(*d*) 2,4-dimethyl-1-pentene

Apply Your Knowledge!

1. (*a*)
$$\left.\begin{array}{l} \text{C: } \dfrac{80}{12} = 6.67 \\[2ex] \text{H: } \dfrac{20}{1} = 20 \end{array}\right\} = \frac{1}{3} \qquad \text{Simplest formula is } CH_3$$

(*b*) Molecular mass
$$= \frac{1.20 \text{ g} \times 0.0821 \text{ l-atm/mole-°K} \times 293\text{°K}}{770 \text{ torr}/760 \text{ torr/atm} \times 0.950 \text{ l}}$$
$$= 30 \text{ g/mole}$$

(*c*) $(CH_3)_n = 30 \qquad n = 2$

Molecular formula is C_2H_6.

(*d*)
```
  H H
  | |
H—C—C—H
  | |
  H H
```

(*e*) The alkanes or paraffin hydrocarbons

2.
$$\underset{1 \text{ mole}}{CaC_2} + H_2O \rightarrow CaO + \underset{1 \text{ mole}}{C_2H_2}$$

$$\text{Moles of } CaC_2 = \frac{3.2 \text{ g}}{64 \text{ g/mole}} = 0.050 \text{ mole}$$

Volume of C_2H_2
$$= \frac{0.050 \text{ mole} \times 22.4 \text{ l/mole} \times 313\text{°K} \times 760 \text{ torr}}{273\text{°K} \times 740 \text{ torr}}$$
$$= 1.32 \text{ l}$$

3. (*a*)
$$\left.\begin{array}{l} \text{C: } \dfrac{85.7}{12} = 7.15 \\[2ex] \text{H: } \dfrac{14.3}{1} = 14.3 \end{array}\right\} = \frac{1}{2} \qquad \text{Simplest formula is } CH_2.$$

(*b*) Molecular mass
$$= \frac{1.40 \text{ g} \times 0.0821 \text{ l-atm/mole°-K} \times 273\text{°K}}{1.00 \text{ atm} \times 0.560 \text{ l}}$$
$$= 56 \text{ g/mole}$$

$(CH_2)_n = 56 \qquad n = 4$

Molecular formula is C_4H_8.

(*c*) Molecular mass
$$= \frac{2.80 \text{ g} \times 0.0821 \text{ l-atm/mole°-K} \times 373\text{°K}}{700 \text{ mm}/760 \text{ torr/atm} \times 1.66 \text{ l}}$$
$$= 56 \text{ g/mole}$$

$(CH_2)_n = 56 \qquad n = 4$

Molecular formula is C_4H_8.

(*d*) The two hydrocarbons are isomers. Their structures might be $CH_3—CH_2—CH{=}CH_2$ and $CH_3—CH{=}CH—CH_3$.

4. (*a*)
$$\left.\begin{array}{l} \text{C: } \dfrac{83.7}{12} = 6.97 \\[2ex] \text{H: } \dfrac{16.3}{1} = 16.3 \end{array}\right\} = \frac{3}{7} \qquad \text{Simplest formula is } C_3H_7.$$

Molecular mass
$$= \frac{1.72 \text{ g} \times 0.0821 \text{ l-atm/mole-°K} \times 373\text{°K}}{1.00 \text{ atm} \times 0.612 \text{ l}}$$
$$= 86 \text{ g/mole}$$

$(C_3H_7)_n = 86 \qquad n = 2$

Molecular formula is C_6H_{14}.

(*b*)
```
C—C—C—C—C—C     C—C—C—C—C
                      |
                      C

    C
    |
C—C—C—C—C       C—C—C—C
    |               |
    C               C

C—C—C—C
  | |
  C C
```

5. (*a*)
$$\underset{1 \text{ mole}}{CH_4} + 2O_2 \rightarrow CO_2 + 2H_2O + 211 \text{ kcal}$$

$$\text{Moles of methane} = \frac{67.2\ l}{22.4\ l/\text{mole}} = 3.00\ \text{moles}$$

$$\text{Energy liberated} = 3.00\ \text{moles} \times 211\ \text{kcal/mole} = 633\ \text{kcal}$$

(*b*) $CH_4 + 3/2\ O_2 \rightarrow CO + 2H_2O + 141\ \text{kcal}$
1 mole

$$\text{Energy liberated} = 3.00\ \text{moles} \times 141\ \text{kcal/mole} = 423\ \text{kcal}$$

(*c*) $CH_4 + O_2 \rightarrow C + 2H_2O + 117\ \text{kcal}$
1 mole

$$\text{Moles of methane} = \frac{48\ g}{16\ g/\text{mole}} = 3.00\ \text{moles}$$

$$\text{Energy liberated} = 3.00\ \text{moles} \times 117\ \text{kcal/mole} = 351\ \text{kcal}$$

6. $CH_4 + 4Cl_2 \rightarrow CCl_4 + 4HCl$
1 mole 4 moles 1 mole 4 moles

(*a*) Moles of Cl_2 = 100 moles × 4 = 400 moles

(*b*) $$\text{Mass} = \frac{100\ \text{moles} \times 154\ g/\text{mole}}{100\ g/kg} = 15.4\ kg$$

(*c*) Moles of HCl = 100 moles × 4 = 400 moles

$$\text{Molarity of acid} = \frac{400\ \text{moles}}{100\ \text{liters}} = 4.00\ M$$

7. $$\text{Moles of } Br_2 = \frac{160\ g}{160\ g/\text{mole}} = 1\ \text{mole}$$

$C_2H_4 + Br_2 \rightarrow C_2H_4Br_2$
1 mole 1 mole

The gas is ethylene. One mole of acetylene would react with two moles of bromine (that is, with 320 g of bromine).

8. (*a*) $CH_2{=}CH_2 + HOCl \rightarrow CH_2OH{-}CH_2Cl$
1 mole 1 mole 1 mole

$$\text{Moles of ethylene} = \frac{11.2\ l}{22.4\ l/\text{mole}} = 0.500\ \text{mole}$$

$$\text{Mass of HOCl} = 0.500\ \text{mole} \times 52.5\ g/\text{mole} = 26.3\ g$$

(*b*) One mole of the chlorohydrin gives one mole of the glycol. Therefore the moles of glycol = 0.500 mole.

9. $C_2H_4 + H_2SO_4 \rightarrow C_2H_5HSO_4$
1 mole 1 mole 1 mole
28 98

$C_2H_5HSO_4 + H_2O \rightarrow C_2H_5OH + H_2SO_4$
1 mole 1 mole
46

(*a*) $$\text{Mass of ethylene} = 100\ \text{tons} \times \frac{28}{46} = 61\ \text{tons}$$

(*b*) $$\text{Mass of } H_2SO_4 = 100\ \text{tons} \times \frac{98}{28} = 350\ \text{tons}$$

10. The number of gas particles is doubled. The pressure is therefore doubled; that is, the pressure becomes 20 atm.

11. $CH_4 + 2O_2 \rightarrow CO_2 + 2H_2O + 211\ \text{kcal}$
1 mole 2 moles 1 mole 2 moles

$$\text{Moles of } CH_4 = \frac{224\ l}{22.4\ l/\text{mole}} = 10.0\ \text{moles}$$

(*a*) $$\text{Energy released} = 10.0\ \text{moles} \times 211\ \text{kcal/mole} \times 1000\ \text{cal/kcal} = 2.11 \times 10^6\ \text{cal}$$

(*b*) $$\text{Volume of } O_2 = 2 \times 10.0\ \text{moles} \times 22.4\ l/\text{mole} = 448\ l$$

(*c*) $$\text{Mass of } H_2O = 2 \times 10.0\ \text{moles} \times 18\ g/\text{mole} = 360\ g$$

(*d*) Moles of CO_2 = 10.0 moles

12. $CaC_2 + H_2O \rightarrow CaO + C_2H_2$
1 mole 1 mole

$$\text{Moles of } CaC_2 = \frac{3.20 \times 10^3\ g}{64\ g/\text{mole}} = 50.0\ \text{moles}$$

$$\text{Volume of } C_2H_2 = 50.0\ \text{moles} \times 22.4\ l/\text{mole} = 1120\ l$$

13. $2C_6H_{14} + 19O_2 \rightarrow 12CO_2 + 14H_2O$
2 moles 12 moles 14 moles = 26 moles

$$\text{Moles of } C_6H_{14} = \frac{760\ g}{86\ g/\text{mole}} = 8.83\ \text{moles}$$

$$\text{Moles of gas products} = 8.83\ \text{moles} \times 13 = 115\ \text{moles}$$
$$\text{Volume of gas products} = 115\ \text{moles} \times 22.4\ l/\text{mole} \times \frac{819°K}{273°K} = 6720\ l$$

14. $C_2H_4 + Br_2 \rightarrow C_2H_4Br_2$
1 mole 1 mole 1 mole

$$\text{Moles of the dibromide} = \frac{500\ g}{188\ g/\text{mole}} = 2.66\ \text{moles}$$

(*a*) $$\text{Volume of } C_2H_4 = 2.66\ \text{moles} \times 22.4\ l/\text{mole} \times \frac{263°K}{273°K} = 57.5\ l$$

(*b*) Moles of Br_2 = 2.66 moles

15. $MgCl_2 \rightarrow Mg + Cl_2$
1 mole 1 mole

$$\text{Moles of } MgCl_2 = \text{Moles of } Cl_2 = \frac{190 \times 10^3 \text{ g}}{95 \text{ g/mole}}$$
$$= 2.00 \times 10^3 \text{ moles}$$

$$\underset{4 \text{ moles}}{4Cl_2} + \underset{1 \text{ mole}}{CH_4} \rightarrow \underset{1 \text{ mole}}{CCl_4} + \underset{4 \text{ moles}}{4HCl}$$

Therefore, one mole of CH_4 is equivalent to four moles of $MgCl_2$.

(*a*) $$\text{Moles of } CH_4 = \frac{2.00 \times 10^3 \text{ moles}}{4}$$
$$= 5.0 \times 10^2 \text{ moles}$$

(*b*) $$\text{Mass of } CCl_4 = \frac{5.0 \times 10^2 \text{ moles} \times 154 \text{ g/mole}}{100 \text{ g/kg}}$$
$$= 77 \text{ kg}$$

(*c*) $$\text{Volume of HCl} = 4 \times 5.0 \times 10^2 \text{ moles} \times 22.4 \text{ l/mole} = 4.48 \times 10^4 \text{ l}$$

(*d*) $$\text{Volume of acid} = \frac{2.00 \times 10^3 \text{ moles}}{6.00 \text{ moles/l}}$$
$$= 3.33 \times 10^2 \text{ l}$$

16. (*a*)
$$\left.\begin{aligned} C&: \frac{88.9}{12} = 7.4 \\ H&: \frac{11.1}{1} = 11.1 \end{aligned}\right\} = \frac{2}{3} \quad \text{Simplest formula is } C_2H_3.$$

Molecular mass
$$= \frac{1.32 \text{ g} \times 0.0821 \text{ l-atm/mole°-K} \times 373°\text{K}}{1.00 \text{ atm} \times 0.765 \text{ l}}$$
$$= 53 \text{ g/mole}$$

$$(C_2H_3)_n = 53 \qquad n = 2$$

Molecular formula is C_4H_6.

(*b*) No. There are isomers of C_4H_6.

(*c*) No. The substance may be an alkyne or it may be a diene. One mole of either of these would add two moles of bromine.

(*d*) Yes. The presence of a bromine atom on each of the four carbon atoms identifies the substance as a diene. The structural formula of the substance is $CH_2{=}CH{-}CH{=}CH_2$ and its name is 1,3-butadiene.

CHAPTER 26

ALCOHOLS, ACIDS, AND THEIR DERIVATIVES

THE ALCOHOLS (pp. 459–63)

Learning Objectives

1. To write the structural formula for methane.
2. To write the structural formula for methanol.
3. To state that all alcohols consist of a parent hydrocarbon plus hydroxyl groups replacing one or more hydrogen atoms.
4. To state the general formula for alcohols with one hydroxyl group.
5. To state the meaning of the hyphenated number in the names of alcohols.
6. To describe the role of the proportion of hydroxyl groups to carbon atoms in determining the solubility of an alcohol in water.
7. To state why alcohols and their water solutions are poor conductors of electricity.
8. To write the equation for the synthesis of methanol.
9. To describe the fermentation of starch into ethanol.
10. To define the term *polyhydric alcohol*.
11. To write the general structural formulas for primary, secondary, and tertiary alcohols.
12. To state that *R* may stand for a number of alkyl groups.

THE CONTROLLED OXIDATION OF ALCOHOLS (pp. 463–66)

Learning Objectives

1. To state that the oxidation of an alkane cannot be controlled.
2. To state that the oxidation of a primary or secondary alcohol can be controlled so that the carbon chain is left intact.
3. To define the term *aldehyde.*
4. To write the structural equation for the oxidation of methanol into formaldehyde (metha*nal*).
5. To write the structural equation for the oxidation of ethanol into acetaldehyde (etha*nal*).
6. To write the structural equation for the oxidation of formaldehyde to formic acid.
7. To write the structural equation for the conversion of acetaldehyde into acetic acid.
8. To state that organic acids are not easily oxidized.
9. To state that an organic acid is the end product of the controlled oxidation of a primary alcohol.
10. To define the term *ketone*.
11. To write the structural equation for the oxidation of 2-propanol to propanone (acetone).

12. To write the general structural formula for a ketone.
13. To write the structural formula for a carbonyl group.
14. To state why tertiary alcohols are not easily oxidized.
15. To state that oxidation of a tertiary alcohol breaks the carbon chain.

Demonstration I To Show the Controlled Oxidation of Methanol by Cupric Oxide.

Materials recommended: 150-ml beaker, copper wire, cork stopper, Bunsen burner, 10 ml of methanol.

The oxidation of methanol to formaldehyde (methanal) can be easily demonstrated. To do this, stick the end of a copper wire into a cork stopper which serves as an insulating handle. Heat the free end of the wire in a Bunsen flame until it is coated with black cupric oxide. Now warm about 10 ml of methanol in a small beaker, reheat the end of the wire, and hold it just above the warm liquid methanol. The black oxide soon disappears and in its place the bright shiny red of metallic copper appears. The equation for the reaction is,

$$\underset{\text{methanol}}{CH_3OH} + CuO \rightarrow Cu + H_2O + \underset{\text{formaldehyde}}{H\text{—}CHO}$$

That is, the methanol is oxidized to formaldehyde and the cupric oxide is reduced to copper.

ORGANIC ACIDS
(pp. 466–69)

Learning Objectives

1. To write the structural formula for a carboxyl group.
2. To write the conventional formula for a carboxyl group.
3. To state the name ending for an organic acid.
4. To write the general formula for a fatty acid.
5. To write the equation for the dissociation of ethanoic acid in water.
6. To write the value of K_A for ethanoic acid.
7. To write the molecular formulas for maleic and fumaric acids.
8. To write the isomeric structural formulas for maleic and fumaric acids.
9. To state which is the *cis* and which is the *trans* isomer.
10. To explain why maleic acid is the *cis* isomer and fumaric acid is the *trans* isomer.
11. To write Equation (26-17).

Suggested Teacher Commentary

The models of maleic and fumaric acids clearly show that maleic acid can easily lose the elements of water to give an anhydride but that fumaric acid cannot. Moreover, the models of the dextro and levo forms of lactic acid should be constructed and then manipulated as follows. Place the two models on the bench so that they face each other as a left hand faces a right hand. The one model is clearly the mirror image of the other. Now attempt to superimpose the one model on the other and show that this cannot be done. Finally, show that if any two groups of one isomer are exchanged, the other isomer is thereby produced; that is, the two models can then be superimposed and they are no longer mirror images.

A THIRD KIND OF ISOMERISM
(pp. 469–71)

Learning Objectives

1. To define the term *optically active.*
2. To define the term *optical isomer.*
3. To define the prefixes *dextro* and *levo*, as applied to optical isomers.
4. To describe the operation of a polarimeter.
5. To write the structural formula for lactic acid.
6. To describe an asymmetric molecule.
7. To state that optical activity is a property of asymmetric molecules.
8. To state why oppositely asymmetric molecules cannot be superimposed upon each other.

ESTERS
(pp. 471–75)

Learning Objectives

1. To define an ester.
2. To write the equation for the formation of ethyl acetate.
3. To write the general equation for the formation of an ester.
4. To define the term *saponification.*
5. To write the structural formula for stearin.
6. To write the equation for the formation of soap.
7. To define an amine.
8. To write the molecular formulas for methylamine and dimethylamine.

9. To describe the properties of amines.
10. To write the equation for the reaction of trimethylamine with hydrochloric acid.

AMINO ACIDS AND PROTEINS
(pp. 474–75)

Learning Objectives

1. To define an amino acid.
2. To write the molecular formula for glycine.
3. To state that the $—NH_2$ end of an amino acid is basic, and that the $—COOH$ end is acidic.
4. To explain how amino acids may possibly link together to form proteins.
5. To define the term *condensation polymerization*.
6. To state the approximate number of known amino acids.
7. To state the range of molecular mass values for proteins.

CARBOHYDRATES
(pp. 475–78)

Learning Objectives

1. To state how "natural" carbohydrates are synthesized.
2. To write the general molecular formula for a carbohydrate.
3. To state that the sugars, starch, and cellulose are carbohydrates.
4. To state the number of carbon atoms in a monosaccharide.
5. To state the number of carbon atoms in a disaccharide.
6. To state the molecular mass value ranges for sugars, starch, and cellulose.
7. To write the equation for the breakdown of sucrose into glucose and fructose.
8. To write the equation for the formation of glucose from cellulose and starch.
9. To write the equation for the oxidation of glucose in body cells.
10. To state how glucose and fructose are structurally joined to form sucrose.
11. To state that glucose and fructose are isomers.
12. To state that starch breaks down into maltose and glucose.
13. To state that cellulose is the chief structural unit of the cell walls of plants.
14. To state the simplest formula for both starch and cellulose.
15. To explain the molecular mass difference between starch and cellulose.

FOODS
(pp. 478–79)

Learning Objectives

1. To state the purposes of the various types of foods in human nutrition.
2. To state that trace quantities of minerals are necessary ingredients in human nutrition.

Demonstration II To Show the Dehydration of a Carbohydrate.

Materials recommended: 100-ml beaker, large pan, glass rod, paper, Bunsen burner, saturated table sugar solution, concentrated sulfuric acid.

As stated in the text, the elements hydrogen and oxygen are present in carbohydrates in the same proportion as in water; that is, the general formula for carbohydrates is $C_x(H_2O)_y$. Although carbohydrates are not hydrates of carbon, they can be dehydrated to give carbon and water as products. The general equation for this reaction is

$$C_x(H_2O)_y \xrightarrow[\text{dehydrating agent}]{} xC + y\,H_2O$$

The dehydration of sucrose (ordinary table sugar) can be easily demonstrated as follows. Pour about 10 ml of a saturated solution of sugar into a tall beaker and set the beaker in a large pan. Add about 10 ml of concentrated sulfuric acid to the beaker and immediately stir the contents with a long glass rod. The heat liberated by the reaction of sulfuric acid with water accelerates the decomposition of the sugar. Notice that the sulfuric acid is the dehydrating agent. The equation for the reaction is

$$C_{12}H_{22}O_{11} + 11H_2SO_4 \rightarrow 12C + 11H_2SO_4\cdot H_2O$$

The black porous mass of carbon can be freed of impurities by washing it thoroughly with water. Carbon produced in this way is one of the purest forms of the element which can be prepared.

The dehydration of cellulose by concentrated sulfuric acid can also be easily demonstrated by writing on a piece of paper with a glass rod dipped in the acid, and then warming the paper in the hot gases above a Bunsen flame. The black lines which appear are carbon, and the equation for the reaction is

$$(C_6H_{10}O_5)_n + 5nH_2SO_4 \rightarrow 6nC + 5nH_2SO_4\cdot H_2O$$

Additional Questions and Problems

1. One mole of sucrose is hydrolyzed. If the volume of the solution is 1.50 l, what is the molarity of the resulting solution?

Answer

$$\underset{1\ \text{mole}}{C_{12}H_{22}O_{11}} + H_2O \rightarrow \underset{2\ \text{moles}}{C_6H_{12}O_6 + C_6H_{12}O_6}$$

$$\text{Molarity of solution} = \frac{2.00\ \text{moles}}{1.50\ \text{l}} = 1.33\ M$$

2. Maleic anhydride is obtained by heating 464 g of fumaric acid. (*a*) How many moles of the anhydride are formed? (*b*) What is the volume of water vapor liberated at 300°C?

Answer

$$\underset{1\ \text{mole}}{C_4H_4O_4} \rightarrow \underset{1\ \text{mole}}{C_4H_2O_3} + \underset{1\ \text{mole}}{H_2O}$$

$$\text{Moles of fumaric acid} = \frac{464\ \text{g}}{116\ \text{g/mole}} = 4.00\ \text{moles}$$

(*a*) Moles of the anhydride = 4.00 moles

(*b*) $$\text{Volume of } H_2O \text{ vapor} = 4.00\ \text{moles} \times 22.4\ \text{l/mole} \times \frac{573°\text{K}}{273°\text{K}} = 188\ \text{l}$$

3. Compute the number of moles of lactic acid in one gallon of sour milk if 18.5 g of slaked lime are required for neutralization.

Answer

$$\underset{2\ \text{moles}}{2CH_3CHOHCOOH} + \underset{1\ \text{mole}}{Ca(OH)_2} \rightarrow \underset{1\ \text{mole}}{(CH_3CHOHCOO)_2Ca} + 2H_2O$$

$$\text{Moles of } Ca(OH)_2 = \frac{18.5\ \text{g}}{74\ \text{g/mole}} = 0.250\ \text{mole}$$

$$\text{Moles of lactic acid} = 2 \times 0.250\ \text{mole} = 0.500\ \text{mole}$$

4. A 92-g sample of ethanol is consumed in the controlled oxidation of the alcohol. Calculate (*a*) the moles of ethanal formed, (*b*) the weight in grams of acetic acid obtained by oxidizing the ethanal, (*c*) the moles of oxygen gas consumed in the conversion of the alcohol to the acid.

Answer

(*a*) $$\underset{1\ \text{mole}}{C_2H_5OH} \rightarrow \underset{1\ \text{mole}}{CH_3CHO}$$

$$\text{Moles of } C_2H_5OH = \frac{92\ \text{g}}{46\ \text{g/mole}} = 2.00\ \text{moles}$$

$$\text{Moles of } CH_3CHO = 2.00\ \text{moles}$$

(*b*) $$\underset{1\ \text{mole}}{CH_3CHO} \rightarrow \underset{1\ \text{mole}}{CH_3COOH}$$

$$\text{Mass of acid} = 2.00\ \text{moles} \times 60\ \text{g/mole} = 120\ \text{g}$$

(*c*) $$\underset{1\ \text{mole}}{C_2H_5OH} + \underset{1\ \text{mole}}{O_2} \rightarrow CH_3COOH + H_2O$$

$$\text{Moles of } O_2 = 2.00\ \text{moles}$$

5. A 4.39-g sample of a vegetable oil (molecular weight of oil = 878) is completely hydrogenated (saturated) by the absorption of 0.448 l of hydrogen at 273°C and standard pressure. How many ethylenic linkages are there in the oil molecule?

Answer

$$\text{Moles of oil} = \frac{4.39\ \text{g}}{878\ \text{g/mole}} = 0.00500\ \text{mole}$$

$$\text{Moles of } H_2 = \frac{0.448\ \text{l} \times 273°\text{K}}{22.4\ \text{l/mole} \times 546°\text{K}} = 0.0100\ \text{mole}$$

One mole of the oil absorbs two moles of H_2. There are therefore two ethylenic linkages per molecule of oil.

6. How much energy (in calories) is released by the oxidation of one pound of glucose in the body?

Answer

$$\underset{1\ \text{mole}}{C_6H_{12}O_6} + 6O_2 \rightarrow 6CO_2 + 6H_2O + 674\ \text{kcal}$$

$$\text{Moles of } C_6H_{12}O_6 = \frac{1\ \text{lb} \times 454\ \text{g/lb}}{180\ \text{g/mole}} = 2.52\ \text{moles}$$

$$\text{Energy} = 2.52\ \text{moles} \times 674\ \text{kcal/mole} \times 1000\ \text{cal/kcal} = 1.70 \times 10^6\ \text{calories}$$

7. An unsaturated acid whose formula is $C_{17}H_{33}COOH$ is hydrogenated to give the saturated acid. (*a*) Calculate the volume of hydrogen at 300°C required to hydrogenate 564 g of the unsaturated acid. (*b*) How many moles of saturated acid are obtained?

Answer

$$C_{17}H_{33}COOH + H_2 \rightarrow C_{17}H_{35}COOH$$

$$\text{Moles of unsaturated acid} = \frac{564\ \text{g}}{282\ \text{g/mole}} = 2.00\ \text{moles}$$

(a) Volume of H_2 = 2.00 moles × 22.4 l/mole × $\frac{573°K}{273°K}$

= 94.0 l

(b) Moles of saturated acid = 2.00 moles

8. One hundred g of glucose are oxidized to give carbon dioxide and water, and the carbon dioxide is absorbed in sodium hydroxide solution to give sodium carbonate. (a) What is the volume of carbon dioxide at 20°C? (b) What volume of oxygen at 20°C is needed for the oxidation? (c) What weight of sodium carbonate is formed?

Answer

$$\underset{1\text{ mole}}{C_6H_{12}O_6} + 6O_2 \rightarrow \underset{6\text{ moles}}{6CO_2} + 6H_2O$$

$$\text{Moles of glucose} = \frac{100\text{ g}}{180\text{ g/mole}} = 0.555\text{ mole}$$

(a) Volume of CO_2 = 0.555 mole × 6 × 22.4 l/mole

$$\times \frac{293°K}{273°K} = 80.3\text{ l}$$

(b) Volume of O_2 = 80.3 l

(c)

$$\underset{1\text{ mole}}{CO_2} + 2NaOH \rightarrow \underset{1\text{ mole}}{Na_2CO_3} + H_2O$$

Mass of Na_2CO_3 = 0.555 mole × 6 × 106 g/mole
= 354 g

9. By analysis, the composition by weight of a compound is 60% carbon, 13.3% hydrogen, and 26.7% oxygen. A 0.300-g sample of the compound, as vapor, occupies 161 ml at 120°C and 760 torr pressure. (a) Find the molecular formula of the substance. (b) Can you name the substance and write its structural formula? Why or why not? (c) The compound is dehydrated by aluminum oxide at a high temperature. Can you now name the substance and write its structural formula? Why or why not? (d) The compound is easily oxidized to a product having the same number of carbon atoms, and the product turns moist blue litmus red. Can you now name the substance and write its structural formula? Explain.

Answer

(a) C: $\frac{60}{12}$ = 5 three
to
H: $\frac{13.3}{1}$ = 13.3 eight Simplest formula is C_3H_8O.
to
O: $\frac{26.7}{16}$ = 1.67 one

$$\text{Molecular mass} = \frac{0.300\text{ g} \times 0.0821\text{ l atm/mole} = °K \times 393°K}{1.00\text{ atm} \times 0.161\text{ l}}$$

= 60 g/mole

$(C_3H_8O)_n = 60 \qquad n = 1$

Molecular formula is C_3H_8O.

(b) No. There are at least three isomers of C_3H_8O.
(c) No. There are at least two isomers of C_3H_8O which can be dehydrated by Al_2O_3.
(d) Yes. $CH_3CH_2CH_2OH$ is easily oxidized to CH_3CH_2COOH (propanoic acid). The name of the substance is 1-propanol.

10. By analysis, the composition by weight of a compound is 58.8% carbon, 9.8% hydrogen, and 31.4% oxygen. A solution of 0.51 g of the compound in 20.0 g of water freezes at −0.47°C and is a very poor conductor of electricity. (a) Find the molecular formula of the compound. (b) Can you name the substance and write its structural formula? Why or why not? (c) One mole of the compound reacts with one mole of sodium hydroxide to give the sodium salt of the compound. Can you now name the substance and write its structural formula? Why or why not? (d) The compound can be separated into one substance which is dextrorotatory and another substance which is levorotatory. Can you now write its structural formula? Explain. (e) Can you name the substance?
[*Hints:* (1) See Chapter 14 for the determination of molecular weights by the depression of the freezing point; (2) $CH_3—\underset{\displaystyle CH_3}{\underset{|}{CH}}—COOH$ is 2-methyl propanoic acid.]

Answer

(a) C: $\frac{58.8}{12}$ = 4.9 five
to
H: $\frac{9.8}{1}$ = 9.8 ten Simplest formula is $C_5H_{10}O_2$.
to
O: $\frac{31.4}{16}$ = 1.97 two

$$\text{Molecular mass} = \frac{0.51\text{ g} \times 1.86\text{ C°-kg/mole}}{0.47\text{ C°} \times 0.0200\text{ kg}}$$

= 101 g/mole

$(C_5H_{10}O_2)_n = 101 \qquad n = 1$

Molecular formula is $C_5H_{10}O_2$.

(b) No. There are several isomers of $C_5H_{10}O_2$.
(c) No. The substance is an acid but there are several isomers of $C_5H_{10}O_2$ which are acids.

(*d*) Yes. Only one isomer of $C_5H_{10}O_2$ has an asymmetric carbon atom. This substance is

$$CH_3CH_2\underset{\displaystyle CH_3}{\underset{|}{CH}}\text{—}COOH.$$

(*e*) The name of the substance is 2-methyl butanoic acid.

Answers to Questions and Exercises

Text page references are provided for those questions which do not require computations. The student's answers will be individually stated, but should focus on the concepts developed in these text pages.

Factual Recall

1. 459
2. 460
3. (*a*) $CH_3CH_2CH_2OH$ (*b*) $CH_3CHOHCH_3$ (*c*) $CH_3CH_2CH_2CH_2CH_2OH$ (*d*) $CH_3CH_2CH_2CHOHCH_3$ (*e*) $CH_3CH_2CHOHCH_2CH_3$
4. (*a*) 1-propanol (*b*) 2-butanol (*c*) 3-pentanol (*d*) 2-hexanol
5. (*a*) 2-butene (*b*) 3-methyl-1-butanol (*c*) 1-butyne (*d*) 4-methyl-2-pentene (*e*) dimethylp ropane (*f*) ethanoic acid (*g*) methyl acetate (*h*) ethanol (*i*) 1,2-dichloroethane (*j*) 1,3-dichlorobutane (*k*) 2-methyl-2-propanol (*l*) methylamine (*m*) sucrose (*n*) 1,2-dibromoethene
6. 466–71
7. 471–73
8. 472

Apply Your Knowledge!

1. (*a*) $O(\%) = \frac{16}{74} \times 100 = 21.6\%$

   (*b*) $O(\%) = \frac{16}{74} \times 100 = 21.6\%$

   (*c*) $O(\%) = \frac{48}{92} \times 100 = 52.2\%$

2. $$\underset{1\text{ mole}}{CO} + \underset{2\text{ moles}}{2H_2} \rightarrow \underset{1\text{ mole}}{CH_3OH}$$

   $$\text{Moles of } CH_3OH = \frac{10^6\text{ g}}{32\text{ g/mole}} = 3.12 \times 10^4\text{ moles}$$

   (*a*) $\text{Volume of CO} = 3.12 \times 10^4\text{ moles} \times 22.4\text{ l/mole} = 7.00 \times 10^5\text{ l}$

   (*b*) $\text{Moles of } H_2 = 2 \times 3.12 \times 10^4\text{ moles} = 6.24 \times 10^4\text{ moles}$

3. $$\underset{1\text{ mole}}{C_6H_{12}O_6} \rightarrow \underset{2\text{ moles}}{2C_2H_5OH} + \underset{2\text{ moles}}{2CO_2}$$

   $$\text{Moles of glucose} = \frac{9.0 \times 10^4\text{ g}}{180\text{ g/mole}} = 5.00 \times 10^2\text{ moles}$$

   (*a*) $\text{Moles of } C_2H_5OH = 2 \times 5.00 \times 10^2\text{ moles} = 1.00 \times 10^3\text{ moles}$

   (*b*) $\text{Volume of } CO_2 = 1.00 \times 10^3\text{ moles} \times 22.4\text{ l/mole} \times \frac{303°K}{273°K} = 2.49 \times 10^4\text{ l}$

4. $$\underset{1\text{ mole}}{C_2H_5OH} + \underset{1\text{ mole}}{O_2} \rightarrow \underset{1\text{ mole}}{CH_3COOH} + H_2O$$

   (*a*) $\text{Mass of acid} = 10.0\text{ moles} \times 60\text{ g/mole} = 600\text{ g}$

   (*b*) $\text{Volume of } O_2 = 10.0\text{ moles} \times 22.4\text{ l/mole} = 224\text{ l}$

   $\text{Volume of air} = 5 \times 224\text{ l} = 1.12 \times 10^3\text{ l}$

5. $$\underset{1\text{ mole}}{CH_3COOH} + NaOH \rightarrow \underset{1\text{ mole}}{CH_3COONa} + H_2O$$

   $\text{Moles of NaOH} = 0.0670\text{ l} \times 0.500\text{ mole/l} = 0.0335\text{ mole}$

   $\text{Moles of } CH_3COOH = 0.0335\text{ mole}$

   $\text{Mass of } CH_3COOH = 0.0335\text{ mole} \times 60\text{ g/mole} = 2.01\text{ g}$

   $\text{Mass of vinegar} = 50.0\text{ ml} \times 10.02\text{ g/ml} = 51.0\text{ g}$

   $$\text{Percent by mass of } CH_3COOH = \frac{2.01\text{ g}}{51.0\text{ g}} \times 100 = 3.95\%$$

6. $$\underset{1\text{ mole}}{(C_{17}H_{35}COO)_3C_3H_5} + 3NaOH \rightarrow \underset{3\text{ moles}}{3C_{17}H_{35}COONa} + \underset{1\text{ mole}}{C_3H_5(OH)_3}$$

   $$\text{Moles of tristearin} = \frac{10.0\text{ tons} \times 2000\text{ lb/ton} \times 454\text{ g/lb}}{890\text{ g/mole}} = 1.02 \times 10^4\text{ moles}$$

   (*a*) $\text{Moles of soap} = 1.02 \times 10^4\text{ moles}$

   $$\text{Mass of soap} = \frac{3.06 \times 10^4\text{ moles} \times 918\text{ g/mole}}{1000\text{ g/kg}} = 2.81 \times 10^4\text{ kg}$$

   (*b*) $\text{Moles of glycerol} = 1.02 \times 10^4\text{ moles}$

7. $$\underset{1\text{ mole}}{(CH_3)_3N} + \underset{1\text{ mole}}{HCl} \rightarrow (CH_3)_3NHCl$$

   $\text{Moles of HCl} = 0.500\text{ mole}$

   $$\text{Volume of HCl} = \frac{0.500\text{ mole}}{6.00\text{ mole/l}} = 0.0833\text{ l}$$

8. $(CH_3)_3NHCl + NaOH \rightarrow (CH_3)_3N + NaCl + H_2O$
1 mole 1 mole

Moles of $(CH_3)_3NHCl = 0.100\ l \times 3.00$ moles/l $= 0.300$ mole

$$\text{Volume of amine} = 0.300 \text{ mole} \times 22.4\ l/\text{mole} \times \frac{333°K}{273°K} = 8.20\ l$$

9. $(C_6H_{10}O_5)_n + nH_2O \rightarrow nC_6H_{12}O_6$
1 mole n mole

$$\text{Moles of starch} = \frac{10^5 \text{ g}}{162n \text{ g/mole}} = \frac{6.12 \times 10^2 \text{ moles}}{n}$$

Moles of glucose $= 6.12 \times 10^2$ moles

10. $C_6H_{12}O_6 + 6O_2 \rightarrow 6CO_2 + 6H_2O + 674$ kcal
1 mole

$$\text{Moles of glucose} = \frac{4 \times 10^3 \text{ kcal}}{674 \text{ kcal/mole}} = 5.95 \text{ moles}$$

CHAPTER 27

SOME CHEMISTRY OF LIFE PROCESSES

CARBOHYDRATES
(pp. 484–85)

Learning Objectives

1. To name the three classes of carbohydrates.
2. To name the three constituent elements of carbohydrates.
3. To state that starches are long chains of glucose molecules.
4. To define carbohydrates as sources of energy.
5. To write the structural formula for a fragment of a starch chain.
6. To write the structural formula for a fragment of a cellulose chain.

LIPIDS
(pp. 486–88)

Learning Objectives

1. To name the two main classes of lipids.
2. To write the general structural formula for a fat.
3. To state that fats are composed of esters of glycerol and long-chain carboxylic acids.
4. To state that most of the common *R* groups associated with fats are composed of 15 to 17 carbon atoms.
5. To state that fat is stored in the human body as an energy source.
6. To state that fats have an energy value more than twice that of carbohydrates or proteins.
7. To describe the digestion of fats.
8. Using benzene rings, to diagram the structural unit for a steroid.
9. To state where steroids are distributed in the human body.

PROTEINS
(pp. 488–92)

Learning Objectives

1. To state what body tissues require protein for synthesis.
2. To name the elements proteins generally contain.
3. To state why proteins are sometimes said to be polymers of α-amino acids.
4. To describe the peptide link.
5. To state that coiling and a variety of bonding arrangements are characteristic of proteins.
6. To state that the sequence of amino acids determines the shapes and many of the properties of proteins.
7. To explain the reason for the very large number of possible proteins.

SOME CHEMISTRY OF LIVING CELLS
(pp. 492–501)

Learning Objectives

1. To give a broad structural description of a human cell.
2. To state, in percentages, the efficiency of a human cell.

3. To state the questions on text page 492 regarding the operation of the human cell.
4. To define an enzyme.
5. To state that enzymes are proteins.
6. To state that enzymes are catalysts.
7. To state that most enzymes catalyze a single reaction.
8. To state the estimated number of different kinds of enzymes present in a cell.
9. To state that enzyme reactions usually take place in a series of steps, with a single enzyme controlling each step.
10. To state that it is believed that the shape of an enzyme determines the specificity of its action.
11. To state that a given enzyme can transform from 10,000 to 5 million reactant molecules to produce molecules in one minute under optimum conditions.
12. To state the ways in which enzymes are activated.
13. To state why cells need a mechanism for storing the energy released in oxidation of fuels.
14. To describe the roles of ATP and ADP in storing and releasing energy.
15. To write Equation (27-5).
16. To state the organ where glycogen is stored.
17. To state under what conditions glycogen will be released into the blood stream.
18. To state that food entering the body cannot be used until broken down by the alimentary system into simpler molecules.
19. To state that amino acids must somehow be assembled in a certain sequence to form the necessary proteins for building new cell material.
20. To state what fraction of amino acid residue in hemoglobin incorrectly placed can cause illness.
21. To state that the ordering of amino acids into various proteins is a function of ribonucleic acids.
22. To write the structural formula for a portion of an RNA molecule.
23. To state that there are many different kinds of RNA molecules.
24. To state what determines the differences among RNA molecules.
25. To state the function of messenger RNA.
26. To state the function of transfer RNA.
27. To describe the function of a gene.
28. To describe the structure of a gene.
29. To name the chemical compound that makes up a gene.
30. To describe the function of DNA with respect to RNA molecules.
31. To state that DNA molecules are the agents that produce new cells that are exact replicas of the parent cells.
32. To locate the DNA molecule within the cell.
33. To describe the shape of a DNA molecule.
34. To describe the chemical structure of a DNA molecule, as in Fig. 27-10.
35. To state that all the genetic information that is needed to make a full-grown adult is stored in the DNA molecule in a fertilized egg and in every other cell in the body.

Demonstration I To Show Enzymatic Reaction.

Materials recommended: Test tubes, corn starch, iodine starch indicator solution, fresh papaya seeds.

The two following demonstrations show two separate types of enzymatic reaction. In the first case, the enzyme, amylase, is secreted in the saliva. In the second, the enzyme, thioglucosidase, is contained within the ingested substance.

A. Prepare a suspension of 10 grams of corn starch in 50 ml of distilled water. Pour about 10 ml of this suspension into a test tube. Add 1 drop of iodine starch indicator solution and shake. Note the color change. Have members of the class chew paraffin until about 10 ml of saliva can be collected in a test tube, then add 5 ml of starch-iodine mixture to the saliva. Note the time required for the color to disappear. This can be explained as the action of the starch-hydrolyzing enzyme amylase, present in the saliva. The reaction is

$$\underset{\text{starch}}{C_6H_{10}O_5} + H_2O \xrightarrow{\text{amylase}} \underset{\text{glucose}}{C_6H_{12}O_6}$$

B. Thioglucosides (glucosinolates) are found in certain plant families, such as the papaya. These substances are hydrolyzed by the enzyme thioglucosidase according to the reaction

$$\underset{\text{thioglucoside}}{\underset{\displaystyle \| \atop N{-}SO_4^-}{R{-}C}{-}S{-}C_6H_{11}O_5} + H_2O \xrightarrow{\text{thioglucosidase}}$$

$$\underset{\text{isothiocyanate}}{R{-}N{=}C{=}S} + \underset{\text{glucose}}{C_6H_{12}O_6} + SO_4^{-2} + H^+$$

Remove the outer gelatinous coating from the papaya seeds and wash thoroughly under running water for 1 min. The seeds are then crushed between the teeth and sensed with the front part of the tongue. The taste is slightly bitter-sweet. After a time a faint taste like that of mustard oil may appear.

After rinsing the mouth with tap water, entire papaya are crushed between the teeth. The gelatinous coating has little taste, but the seed itself has a strong mustard-oil flavor.

The difference between the taste of the seeds with and without the gelatinous coating can be attributed to the fact that the enzyme thioglucosidase is confined to the coating. Crushing the whole seed in the mouth permits the enzyme in the coating and the thioglucoside (glucosinolate) in the embryo and endosperm of the seed to mix forming the mustard-flavored benzyl isothiocyanate. The slight mustard-oil flavor of seeds with the coating removed suggests that some amount of enzyme activity may be present in the embryo and endosperm, but that it is small compared to the activity in the gelatinous coating.

Answers to Questions and Exercises

Text page references are provided for those questions which do not require computations. The student's answers will be individually stated, but should focus on the concepts developed in these text pages.

Factual Recall

1. Biochemistry is the study of chemical processes in living things. Biology, by contrast, covers a wide variety of aspects of life and living things. Virtually all living cells operate on basically the same chemical principles, but a large organism has a great deal of organization above the cellular operation.
2. 484–88
3. 484–85, Fig. 27-1
4. 484
5. 484
6. 484
7. They are all cyclic in structure in their common forms and they all contain several OH groups in addition to carbon and hydrogen. Therefore, they undergo many common chemical reactions and have similar physical properties.
8. 486–88
9. RCO_2Na, where R is a hydrocarbon chain usually containing from 12 to 17 carbon atoms. Soap is made by treating fats with NaOH or a similar base.
10. 487
11. 487
12. 487–88
13. 488
14. 488–92
15. 488
16. 488–92
17. 489–92
18. Table 27-2
19. 492
20. 492–94
21. 494–96
22. 494–96
23. 494–96
24. 496
25. 496–501
26. 500–01

Apply Your Knowledge!

1. In general, they have the cyclic, or ring-like structure, and have numerous OH groups bonded to their carbon atoms.
2. Fig. 27-1
3. Table 27-1
4. In the duodenum fat is broken down into a carboxylic acid and glycerol. The equation that could be written is exactly the reverse of Equation 27-3. See also page 487.
5.

Testosterone
(a male hormone)

Estrone
(a female hormone)

Calciferol
(Vitamin D)

Cholic Acid
(a bile acid)

Cholesterol

Note the similar ring structure in all these compounds

6.

alanine: —NH—C(H)(CH3)—C(=O)—

tyrosine: —NH—C(H)(CH2—C6H4—OH)—C(=O)—

serine: NH—C(H)(HOCH3)—C(=O)—

cysteine: NH—C(H)(CH2—SH)—C(=O)—

aspartic acid: NH—C(H)(HO2CCH2)—C(=O)—

valine: NH—C(H)(CH3—CH—CH3)—C(=O)—

threonine: NH—C(H)(CH—CH3, OH)—C(=O)—

threonine: NH—C(H)(CH3—CH—OH)—C(=O)—

serine: NH—C(H)(CH2—OH)—C(=O)—

H
NH—C—
CH_2
OH

tyrosine

H
NH—C—C—
$HOCH_2$ O

serine

7. Some microorganisms are capable of synthesizing all the amino acids essential for growth. The more complex organisms, such as man, cannot. The necessary amino acids must be provided in food — mostly in proteins. Essential amino acids for the young adult male are: tryptophan, phenylalanine, lysine, threonine, valine, methionine, leucine, and isoleucine.

8. 491–94, Figs. 27-4 and 27-5.
9. 493–94
10. 494
11. 494
12. 494–96
13. 494–96
14. 497
15. 498–501

16. In complex organisms the cells perform specific functions by carrying out only a small number of the reactions they are potentially able to perform in view of the genes present. Apparently the cell can repress the tendency to manufacture certain RNA molecules in enzymes.

NUCLEAR REACTIONS

OPENING UNIT IX

In this unit the significance of the electron configurations of atoms largely disappears, although they are not entirely without effect on nuclear reactions. However, in these two chapters, the nucleus itself dominates the stage. The discussion begins in Chapter 28 with two fortuitous accidents, the discovery of X rays and radioactivity, the isolation and classification of many new elements by the Curies and others, and Rutherford's discovery that one element could be changed into another by bombardment with particles from radioactive elements. Chapter 28 ends with the applications of radioisotopes and the production of the transuranium series of elements.

Chapter 29 covers nuclear fission and the nuclear forces, and their application to the production of power. The chapter ends with a discussion of the nuclear fusion reaction.

CHAPTER **28**

RADIOACTIVITY

RADIATIONS EMITTED BY A SAMPLE OF RADIUM (pp. 510–12)

Learning Objectives

1. To list the parts of the apparatus used by Rutherford to study the radiations of radium.
2. To describe the results of Rutherford's experiment.
3. To state the names and letter symbols of the radiations emitted in Rutherford's experiment.
4. To state the nature of an alpha ray.
5. To state the source in the atom of alpha rays.
6. To state that alpha rays are ionizing radiation.
7. To state the nature of a beta ray.
8. To state the source in the atom of beta rays.
9. To state that beta rays are ionizing radiation.
10. To write the reaction for the proposed production of a beta particle.
11. To state the nature of gamma rays.
12. To describe the penetrating power of gamma radiation.
13. To state the conditions in the nucleus that give rise to gamma ray emission.

Suggested Teacher Commentary

Radium compounds are used to make luminous paint. To do this, a minute amount of a radium salt (only a few cents worth) is added to a paint which contains a fluorescent substance such as zinc sulfide. Radiations from the radium cause the zinc sulfide to scintillate. Watches, compasses, and airplane instruments can be read in the dark if luminous paint is applied to the dials of these devices. A most impressive demonstration is to observe the scintillations from a luminous dial through a microscope. The procedure is as follows: First draw all shades and darken the room as completely as possible. Then examine a luminous dial from a watch or a compass needle through the microscope (a magnification of 40 or 50 diameters is about right).

A flash of light is seen every time an alpha particle strikes a particle of zinc sulfide. Or, expressed another way, the number of alpha particles emitted can be determined by counting the flashes of light. However, 1 g of radium emits millions of alpha particles every minute so that in practice it is impossible to count the flashes from a luminous dial. Indeed, there are so many of them that the whole surface of the dial appears to be "on the boil." Moreover, their boiling effect will continue for many years, indeed for many centuries. You recall that the half-life of radium is about 1600 years.

RADIOACTIVE DISINTEGRATION (pp. 512–17)

Learning Objectives

1. To write the equation for the alpha decay of radium (28-4).
2. To state the proper position of the atomic number with respect to the letter symbol.

3. To state the proper position of the mass number with respect to the letter symbol.
4. To write Equation (28-6).
5. To state that in a nuclear equation the total number of protons and neutrons is conserved.
6. To state that in a nuclear reaction, the total number of atoms is *not* conserved.
7. To explain the general rule for atomic number of the product element resulting from alpha decay.
8. To explain the general rule for the atomic number of the product element resulting from beta decay.
9. To write Equation (28-7).
10. To state that in a nuclear equation the total atomic number is conserved.
11. To state that the fraction of atoms that disintegrate in a radioactive element per second remains constant.
12. To define the term *half-life*.
13. To state the end product of the disintegration series that begins with uranium-238.
14. To state that the lives of individual atoms in a radioactive element cannot be predicted.
15. To state why Rutherford found alpha, beta, and gamma radiation from radium although radium emits only alpha particles.

Suggested Teacher Commentary

The lives of individual atoms of the same radioactive element vary enormously. Indeed, the lives of radioactive atoms of the same element may vary all the way from the vanishingly small to an infinitely long period of time. For this reason it is impossible to predict when a *particular* atom will disintegrate. Nonetheless, since we are dealing with billions of atoms we can predict that a *certain fraction* of the whole will disintegrate in a given time. This is a statistical concept and there are many applications of it in scientific phenomena. For instance, temperature is a measure of the kinetic energy of atoms. However, the kinetic energies of individual atoms vary a great deal even at the same temperature. So, temperature is a measure of the *average* kinetic energies.

Even insurance companies rely upon averages when writing life policies for individuals. From statistical evidence a graph showing the death rate of a large group of human beings is somewhat like Fig TG28-1.

The graph shows that under the age of 40 the chance of dying is very small. But after 40 the chance of dying increases more and more rapidly with the years and, after 85, the probability is exceedingly high. However, there is an *average* expectation of life for all individuals in the group. Suppose this is 70 years of age. This is a statistical figure and it is the basis for the conditions of a life insurance policy. If you take out a life policy you are in effect making a bet with your

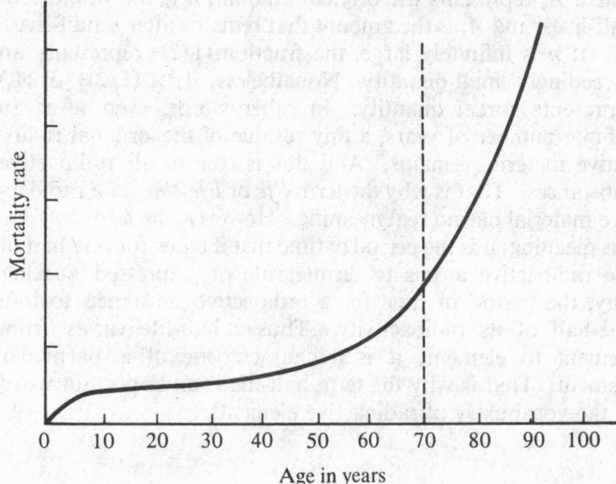

FIG. TG28–1

insurance company. For odds fixed by the annual premiums the insurance company is willing to bet that you will live to the statistically average age. On the other hand, you bet that you will not. And, unfortunately, the only way you can win your bet is to die before the average age.

The average age of human beings (and also the rate of dying) is affected by many factors — biological, physiological, environment, pollution, exposure to various adverse conditions, such as coal mining. But these variable factors do not apply to the rate of disintegration of radioactive atoms. A radioactive change proceeds at a steady rate which never varies. It is the same whatever the temperature or pressure, and in this respect a nuclear reaction is quite unlike a chemical reaction.

The fraction of the number of atoms which disintegrate per second remains constant throughout the life of the sample. For example, if one-half of a sample disintegrates in n years, one-half of the remainder (that is, 1/4 of the whole) will disintegrate in the next n years, and one-half of the remainder (or 1/8 of the whole) will disintegrate in the next n years, and so on.

The amount of radioactive substance that remains after a given number of half-lives can easily be computed. For instance, after 5 half-lives only $(1/2)^5$ or 1/32 of the original amount (1.0) remains intact. This relationship is expressed by the equation,

$$\frac{1}{32} = 1.0 \times \left(\frac{1}{2}\right)^5$$

or in general form,

$$A_n = A_o \times (1/2)^n$$

where A_o represents the original amount, n is the number of half-lives, and A_n is the amount that remains after n half-lives.

If n is infinitely large, the fraction $(1/2)^n$ represents an exceedingly small quantity. Nonetheless, $A_o \times (1/2)^n$ (or A_n) represents a real quantity. In other words, even after an infinite number of years, a tiny residue of the original radioactive material remains. And this is true of all radioactive substances. That is why the term *life* or *life-time* of a radioactive material has no real meaning. However, the term *half-life* has meaning; it is the period of time that it takes for one-half of the radioactive atoms to disintegrate or, expressed another way, the period of time for a radioactive substance to lose one-half of its radioactivity. Thus a half-life varies from element to element; it is a characteristic of a particular element. That is why the term half-life is an important word in the vocabulary of radioactive elements.

TRANSMUTATIONS OF NONRADIOACTIVE ELEMENTS
(pp. 517–19)

Learning Objectives

1. To state why Rutherford chose a relatively low Z element for his transmutation experiment.
2. To list the parts of Rutherford's apparatus for the transmutation of nitrogen.
3. To state the cause of the scintillations on the zinc sulfide screen when the polonium alpha source was placed at a distance of from 30–40 cm.
4. To write Equation (28-8).

BOMBARDMENT OF STABLE NUCEI WITH HIGH-SPEED PARTICLES
(pp. 519–22)

Learning Objectives

1. Given the results of Rutherford's experiment, to state the evidence for the presence of protons in nuclei.
2. To state the type of incident particle that must be used to penetrate the nuclei of elements heavier than potassium.
3. To state how these particles are accelerated.
4. To write Equation (28-9).
5. To state the charge of a neutron.
6. To state why neutrons penetrate nuclei more easily than charged particles.
7. To write Equation (28-10).
8. To define the term *neutron capture*, as exemplified by Equation (28-10).
9. To define the term *artificial radioactivity*.
10. To write Equation (28-13).

RADIOISOTOPES
(pp. 522–24)

Learning Objectives

1. To state that the radioisotopes used in such fields as industry, agriculture, and medicine are typically beta emitters and short half-lived.
2. To describe the operation of a Geiger-Mueller counter.
3. To describe the biological effects of ingested iodine-131.
4. To state the therapeutic uses of cobalt-60.
5. To describe the use of a radioactive tracer.
6. To describe one of the uses of gamma-ray photography in industry.

TRANSURANIUM ELEMENTS
(pp. 524–26)

Learning Objectives

1. To define the term *transuranium element*.
2. To name the bombarding particle used in the production of neptunium-239.
3. To name the bombarding particles used in the synthesis of elements beyond plutonium.
4. To write Equations (28-21) and (28-22).
5. To write Equations (28-26) and (28-27).

Answers to Questions and Exercises

Text page references are provided for those questions which do not require computations. The student's answers will be individually stated, but should focus on the concepts developed in these text pages.

Factual Recall

1.	509–10	6.	517–19	10.	515–17
2.	510	7.	519–20	11.	522–24
3.	511	8.	520–21	12.	522–23
4.	511–12	9.	521–22	13.	524–26
5.	513–15				

Apply Your Knowledge!

1. ${}_{82}^{214}\text{Pb}$
α emission involves the loss of 2 protons, reducing the value of Z by 2, plus 2 neutrons, thereby reducing the total atomic mass by 4.

2. ${}_{84}^{210}\text{Po}$
β emission of an electron is too small a mass loss to significantly affect the total atomic mass. However, it is believed that β emission involves the decay of a neutron into a proton. The net effect is the gain of 1 proton, raising the value of Z by 1.

3. $${}_{84}^{218}\text{Po} \rightarrow {}_{82}^{214}\text{Pb} + {}_{2}^{4}\text{He}$$
$${}_{83}^{210}\text{Bi} \rightarrow {}_{84}^{210}\text{Po} + {}_{-1}^{0}\text{e}$$

4. $${}_{92}^{238}\text{U} \rightarrow {}_{90}^{234}\text{Th} + {}_{2}^{4}\text{He}$$
$${}_{90}^{234}\text{Th} \rightarrow {}_{91}^{234}\text{Pa} + {}_{-1}^{0}\text{e}$$
$${}_{91}^{234}\text{Pa} \rightarrow {}_{92}^{234}\text{U} + {}_{-1}^{0}\text{e}$$
$${}_{92}^{234}\text{U} \rightarrow {}_{90}^{230}\text{Th} + {}_{2}^{4}\text{He}$$

5. (*a*) $${}_{92}^{238}\text{U} + {}_{0}^{1}\text{n} \rightarrow {}_{92}^{239}\text{U}$$
$${}_{92}^{239}\text{U} \rightarrow {}_{93}^{239}\text{Np} + {}_{-1}^{0}\text{e}$$
(*b*) $${}_{93}^{239}\text{Np} \rightarrow {}_{94}^{239}\text{Pu} + {}_{-1}^{0}\text{e}$$

6. (*a*) ${}_{2}^{4}\text{He}$ (*b*) ${}_{1}^{1}\text{H}$ (*c*) ${}_{12}^{24}\text{Mg}$ (*d*) ${}_{1}^{2}\text{H}$ (*e*) ${}_{0}^{1}\text{n}$

CHAPTER 29

NUCLEAR ENERGY

FISSION OF U-235
(pp. 530–32)

Learning Objectives

1. To state that uranium-235 is the fissionable isotope.
2. To state that uranium-235 is the rare isotope of uranium.
3. To write Equation (29-1).
4. To state that a single neutron is used up in the reaction in Equation (29-1), but that three are released.
5. To state in kcal the amount of heat released in the chemical combustion of one mole of carbon.
6. To state in kcal the amount of heat released in the fission of one mole of uranium-235.
7. To write Einstein's equation for the equivalence of mass and energy.
8. To state in kcal the energy released when 1 g of matter is totally converted to energy.
9. To state the law of conservation of mass as propounded by Lavoisier.
10. To state that, according to Einstein's equation, the mass of the combustion products of carbon is less than the mass of the original reactants.
11. To state that the mass loss in ordinary chemical reactions is to small too be measured.
12. To state that the mass loss predictable from Einstein's equation nevertheless applies to ordinary chemical reactions, even though undetectable.
13. To state the law of mass energy.

Suggested Teacher Commentary

The German scientists Hahn and Strassman made an unexpected discovery in 1939 when they bombarded uranium atoms with neutrons. They had expected to produce a heavy isotope of uranium. To their surprise, however, they identified radioactive barium, a relatively light element, among the products of the nuclear reaction. Barium is much lighter than uranium and, to account for its formation, they assumed that some nuclei of uranium atoms had been split into two parts of approximately equal size. This in turn suggested two possibilities:

(1) $_{92}{}^{235}U + {}_0{}^1n \rightarrow {}_{56}{}^{144}Ba + {}_{36}{}^{92}Kr$

(2) $_{92}{}^{238}U + {}_0{}^1n \rightarrow {}_{56}{}^{145}Ba + {}_{36}{}^{94}Kr$

The neutron-proton ratio shows that all four products are highly unstable. Limiting our discussion to the fission of U-235, one way of achieving stability, as stated in the text, is by release of neutrons as in

$$_{92}{}^{235}U + {}_0{}^1n \rightarrow {}_{56}{}^{137}Ba + {}_{36}{}^{84}Kr + 15\ {}_0{}^1n$$

Still another way of achieving stability would be by the formation of stable atoms of other elements with the same atomic masses as $_{56}{}^{144}Ba$ and $_{36}{}^{92}Kr$. For example, unstable $_{56}{}^{144}Ba$ could form stable neodymium ($_{60}{}^{144}Nd$) by the emission of 4 electrons, and unstable $_{36}{}^{92}Kr$ could form stable zirconium ($_{40}{}^{92}Zr$) by the emission of 4 electrons. These nuclear changes can be shown as

$$_{56}{}^{144}Ba \rightarrow {}_{60}{}^{144}Nd + 4e^-$$

and $$_{36}{}^{92}Kr \rightarrow {}_{40}{}^{92}Zr + 4e^-$$

It should now be apparent that the fission of uranium-235 results in a large number of pairs of products.

NUCLEAR FORCES
(pp. 532–36)

Learning Objectives

1. To name the force that holds the nucleus together.
2. To state the distance over which the nuclear force is effective.
3. To state at what atomic number the neutron-proton ratio exceeds 1.00.
4. To state why, when Z is greater than 20, the ratio of neutrons to protons exceeds 1.00.
5. To state at what neutron-to-proton ratio the nucleus becomes unstable.
6. To state how an unstable nucleus stabilizes itself.
7. To write Equation (29-3).
8. To define the term *mass defect*.
9. To state in kcal the amount of heat released in the fusion of 2 protons and 2 neutrons to form an alpha particle.
10. To state in amu the mass loss in the fusion of 2 protons and 2 neutrons to form an alpha particle.
11. To state that the total nucleon number is conserved in the reaction in Objective 10.
12. To define the term *binding energy*.
13. To state in kcal the binding energy per nucleon of helium.
14. To state that the products of a fission reaction have greater binding energies than that of the uranium nucleus.
15. To derive the relative amounts of energy released in the fission and fusion reactions from the slopes of the graph in Fig. 29-4.

Suggested Teacher Commentary

Mass defect is a term used to represent the energy released in binding together the protons and neutrons in the nucleus of an atom. This energy is due to the loss in mass that takes place when protons and neutrons "combine" and it can be computed from the mass-energy relation as expressed in the Einstein equation, $E = mc^2$.

By computing the binding energy per nucleon in one mole of atoms we obtain a measure of the stability of the nuclei of atoms of that particular element. For example, let us consider the binding energy in the nucleus of an atom of oxygen of atomic mass 16.0000 amu. This atom of oxygen consists of a nucleus made up of 8 protons and 8 neutrons, plus 8 outer electrons. The sum of the masses of these particles is

$$\begin{aligned}
8 \text{ protons} &= 8 \times 1.00813 = 8.06504 \text{ amu}\\
8 \text{ neutrons} &= 8 \times 1.00897 = 8.07176 \text{ amu}\\
8 \text{ electrons} &= 8 \times 0.00055 = 0.00440 \text{ amu}\\
\text{Total mass} &= 16.14120 \text{ amu}
\end{aligned}$$

Hence the mass of an oxygen atom is less than the sum of the masses of the constituent parts by 0.14120 amu; that is, the mass defect is 0.14120 amu. Hence the binding energy is 0.1412 g/mole $\times 9 \times 10^{20}$ ergs/g $= 1.2708 \times 10^{20}$ ergs/mole $\times 2.4 \times 10^{-8}$ cal/erg $= 3.6 \times 10^{12}$ cal/mole $= 3.6 \times 10^9$ kcal/mole. And, since there are 16 nucleons per nucleus, the binding energy per nucleon per mole $= (3.6 \times 10^9)/16 = 1.91 \times 10^8$ kcal = 191 million kilocalories. And, since the value for uranium is about 175 calories it is apparent that the nucleus of an oxygen atom is much more stable than the nucleus of a uranium atom.

The mass defects (or binding energies) of the nuclei of atoms of other elements can be computed in the same way. Take ^{56}Fe, for example, which is the most abundant isotope of iron. This atom consists of 26 protons, 30 neutrons, and 26 electrons, and their masses are

$$\begin{aligned}
26 \text{ protons} &= 26 \times 1.00813 = 26.2114 \text{ amu}\\
30 \text{ neutrons} &= 30 \times 1.00897 = 30.2691 \text{ amu}\\
26 \text{ electrons} &= 26 \times 0.00055 = 0.0143 \text{ amu}\\
\text{Total mass} &= 56.4948 \text{ amu}
\end{aligned}$$

The atomic mass for ^{56}Fe is 55.9571, hence the mass defect is $56.4948 - 55.9571 = 0.5377$ amu. The binding energy per mole = 0.5377 g/mole $\times 9 \times 10^{20}$ ergs/g $= 4.839 \times 10^{20}$ ergs/mole $\times 2.4 \times 10^{-8}$ cal/erg $= 11.6 \times 10^9$ kcal/mole. The binding energy per nucleon per mole $= \dfrac{11.6 \times 10^9}{56} = 2.04 \times 10^8$ kcal = 204 million kilocalories. Hence, as shown in Fig. 29-3, iron is even more stable than oxygen.

ENERGY RELEASED IN FISSION
(pp. 537–40)

Learning Objectives

1. To name the products of the fission of uranium-235 that are found in the greatest abundance.
2. To state the algebraic sum of the changes in proton and neutron number in a fission reaction.
3. To state approximately the percentage of mass converted to energy in a fission reaction.
4. To state the amount of coal that must be burned to equal the heat output of the fission of 1 mole of uranium-235.
5. To describe a fission chain reaction.

6. To state how a chain reaction can be controlled.
7. To name the five essential parts of a nuclear reactor.
8. To describe the operation of a power reactor.

NUCLEAR FUSION
(pp. 541–42)

Learning Objectives

1. To state that the energy production in stars is thought to be the result of the fusion of hydrogen into helium.
2. To write Equation (29-9).
3. To state approximately the percentage of mass converted to energy in the fusion reaction.
4. To state the value of the thermonuclear temperature.
5. To state that deuterium and tritium fuse more readily and at lower temperatures than hydrogen.
6. To state that the fusion reaction, once started, is self-sustaining.
7. To state that the oceans can supply an all but unlimited supply of fuel for a fusion reactor.

Answers to Questions and Exercises

Text page references are provided for those questions which do not require computations. The student's answers will be individually stated, but should focus on the concepts developed in these text pages.

Factual Recall

1. 530–31
2. 531–32
3. 532, Fig. 29-3
4. 532–34
5. 534–35
6. 529, 15 $_0{}^1n$
7. 537–38
8. 538–40
9. 538–40

Apply Your Knowledge!

1. Loss of mass $= \dfrac{312 \text{ kcal}}{216 \times 10^8 \text{ kcal/g}} = 1.44 \times 10^{-8}$ g
2. $_{92}{}^{235}U \rightarrow {}_{61}{}^{151}Pm + {}_{35}{}^{82}Br + 2{}_0{}^1n + 4{}_{-1}{}^0e$

APPENDIX

ENRICHMENT MATERIALS
(Chapter 1)

Films

Chemical Changes All About Us. 14 min, c. Coronet Instructional Films.
Chemical Families. 22 min, c. Modern Learning Aids.
Chemistry. 11 min, b/w. Gateway Productions, Inc.
Chemistry in College. 15 min; c, b/w. Indiana University Audio-Visual Center.
Chemistry of Air. 13 min, b/w. McGraw-Hill Films.
Chemists at Work–1. 30 min; c, b/w. Encyclopaedia Britannica Educational Corp.
Chemists at Work–2—Some Special Instruments. 30 min; c, b/w. Encyclopaedia Britannica Educational Corp.
Elements, Compounds, Mixtures. 30 min; c, b/w. Coronet Instructional Films.
Helium. 27½ min, c. U.S. Bureau of Mines.
Introduction to Chemistry. 11 min; c, b/w. Coronet Instructional Films.
Liquid Helium. 39 min, b/w. Michigan State University Instructional Media Center.
Oxygen. 11 min, b/w. Coronet Instructional Films.
Perfection of Matter. 20 min, c. Contemporary Films/McGraw-Hill.
Safety in the Chemistry Laboratory. 15 min, b/w. Indiana University Audio-Visual Center.
Scientific Method in Action. 19 min, c. International Film Bureau, Inc.
Simple Changes in Matter. 11 min, b/w. Coronet Instructional Films.

Filmstrips

Chemistry and the Nobel Prize. 40 frames, c. Popular Science Audio-Visuals, Inc.
Fuel Cells. 40 frames, c. Popular Science Audio-Visuals, Inc.
Hydrogen, Oxygen and Water. 47 frames, c. Society for Visual Education, Inc.
The Noble Gases. 40 frames, c. Popular Science Audio-Visuals, Inc.
Preparing Oxygen—The Life-giving Gas. 40 frames, c. Popular Science Audio-Visuals, Inc.
What Is Chemistry? 40 frames, b/w. McGraw-Hill Films.

Overhead Projectuals

Chemicals: Atoms, Molecules, Elements and Compounds. Eye Gate House, Inc. (014-3).
A Chemical Classification of Matter. Creative Visuals (540.AO-50).
Classification of Substances. Creative Visuals (540.BO-04).
Mixtures and Compounds. Tweedy Transparencies (1104-3).
Physical States of Matter. Creative Visuals (540.AO-49).

Physical vs. Chemical Change. Eye Gate House, Inc. (003-1).
Simple Chemical Reactions. Eye Gate House, Inc. (014-8).
Simple Chemical Tests. Eye Gate House, Inc. (014-7).
Some Types of Chemical Reactions. Tweedy Transparencies (1303-4).
The States of Matter. Tweedy Transparencies (1104-4).

ENRICHMENT MATERIALS
(Unit I)

Films

Atoms and Molecules. 13 min; c, b/w. Encyclopaedia Britannica Educational Corp.
Chemical Instruments. 19 min, c. University of Southern California.
Chemical Lab Safety. 25 min, c. U.S. Public Health Service.
Conquest of the Atom. 22 min, b/w. International Film Bureau, Inc.
Evidence for Molecules and Atoms. 19 min, c. Encyclopaedia Britannica Educational Corp.
Explaining Matter—Atoms and Molecules. 14 min, c. Encyclopaedia Britannica Educational Corp.
Explaining Matter—Chemical Change. 11 min, c. Encyclopaedia Britannica Educational Corp.
Hydrogen. 14 min, c. Coronet Instructional Films.
Interview with Linus Pauling. 60 min, b/w. Contemporary Films/McGraw-Hill.
Matter and Energy. 11 min, c. Coronet Instructional Films.
Particles of Matter. 14 min; c, b/w. Universal Education and Visual Arts.
Philip Morrison: Principle of Uncertainty. 30 min, c. Peter M. Robeck and Co. Inc.
Solids, Liquids and Gases. 9 min; c, b/w. McGraw-Hill Films.
States of Matter. 13 min, b/w. McGraw-Hill Films.

Filmstrips

Atomic and Molecular Weights. 51 frames, c. Society for Visual Education, Inc.
Atoms and Molecules. 46 frames, c. Society for Visual Education, Inc.
Classification of Matter. 49 frames, c. Encyclopaedia Britannica Educational Corp.
The Composition of Atoms. 49 frames, c. Encyclopaedia Britannica Educational Corp.
Elements, Compounds, Mixtures. 53 frames, c. Society for Visual Education, Inc.
Elements—What Are They? 30 frames, c. Filmstrip House, Inc.
Hydrogen—The Fundamental Atom. 40 frames, c. Popular Science Audio-Visuals, Inc.
Introduction to the Chemistry Laboratory, Part I. 30 frames, c. Encyclopaedia Britannica Educational Corp.
Introduction to the Chemistry Laboratory, Part II. 30 frames, c. Encyclopaedia Britannica Educational Corp.
Laboratory Techniques. 40 frames, b/w. McGraw-Hill Films.
Measurement In Chemistry. 30 frames, c. Encyclopaedia Britannica Educational Corp.
Structure of the Atom. 40 frames, b/w. McGraw-Hill Films.
What's in the Atom? 51 frames, c. Popular Science Audio-Visuals, Inc.

Overhead Projectuals

Atomic Orbitals. Creative Visuals (540.AO-04).
Bright-line Spectrum. DCA Transparencies (L-27).
Cathode Rays. Creative Visuals (540.AO-53).
Cathode Ray Tube. Eye Gate House, Inc. (035-93).
Cathode Ray Tube. McGraw-Hill Films.
Coulomb's Law. Eye Gate House, Inc. (035-7).
Deflection of Alpha Particles. DCA Transparencies (M-72).
Effect of a Magnetic Field on Radiation. DCA (M-74).
Electric Field Between Parallel Plates. McGraw-Hill Films.
Electric Field Pattern. McGraw-Hill Films.
Electromagnetic Spectrum. Creative Visuals (540.AO-11).
Electron Distribution Wheel. Creative Visuals (540-AO-13).
Energy Difference of Electron Levels. Creative Visuals (540.AO-15).
Energy Level Diagram. DCA Transparencies (C-11).
Energy Levels of Electrons. Creative Visuals (540.AO-14).
Forces on Charged Particles. McGraw-Hill Films.
History of the Atom. DCA Transparencies (C-3).
Hydrogen Atom Orbitals. DCA Transparencies (C-8).
Hydrogen Spectrum Lines and Electron Energy Levels. Creative Visuals (540.BO-13).
Ionizing Radiation. DCA Transparencies (C-33).
Magnetism and Atomic Structure. Eye Gate House, Inc. (035-29).
Mass Spectrograph. McGraw-Hill Films.
Mass Spectrograph—Animation. Creative Visuals (540.AO-47).
Mass Spectrograph—Schematic. Creative Visuals (540.AO-46).
Millikin's Oil Drop Experiment. DCA Transparencies (M-71).
Proof of Existence of Atoms. DCA Transparencies (C-4).
Quantum Designations for Electrons. Creative Visuals (540. AO-32).
Rutherford's Experiment. DCA Transparencies (C-38).
Rutherford's Scattering Experiment. Creative Visuals (540. AO-54).

Stabilizing Forces of Orbits with 2 Electrons. DCA Transparencies (C-7).
Standing Waves. McGraw-Hill Films.
Structure of a Helium Atom. Tweedy Transparencies (1104-1).
Types of Radiation. DCA Transparencies (C-36).
J. J. Thompson's Experiment. DCA Transparencies (M-70).
Why Atoms Have Remained Invisible. DCA Transparencies (C-5).
Wilson Cloud Chamber. DCA Transparencies (M-75).

ENRICHMENT MATERIALS
(Unit II)

Films

Atomic Models, Valence and the Periodic Table. 44 min, c. University of Iowa.
Atomic Theory of Matter. 30 min; c, b/w. Encyclopaedia Britannica Educational Corp.
Chemical Bond and Atomic Structure. 16 min; c, b/w. Coronet Instructional Films.
Chemical Bonding. 16 min, c. Modern Learning Aids.
Chemical Properties of Water. 14 min; c, b/w. Coronet Instructional Films.
Chemistry of Water. 14 min, c. Sutherland Educational Films, Inc.
Crystals. 25 min; c, b/w. Modern Learning Aids.
Crystals and Their Structures. 22 min, b/w. Modern Learning Aids.
How Big Is an Atom? 30 min, b/w. Indiana University Audio-Visual Center.
Measuring a Molecule. 28 min, b/w. Mr. Wizard, Prism Enterprises, Inc.

Filmstrips

Atomic Structure and Chemistry. 40 frames, c. Popular Science Audio-Visuals, Inc.
Atomic Theory. 40 frames, b/w. McGraw-Hill Films.
Atoms, Molecules and Ions. 48 frames, c. Society for Visual Education, Inc.
The Chemical Bond. 50 frames, b/w. McGraw-Hill Films.
Construction of Molecular Models. 53 frames, c. Encyclopaedia Britannica Educational Corp.
The Coordinate Covalent Bond. 40 frames, c. Popular Science Audio-Visuals, Inc.
The Covalent Bond: Molecular Orbitals. 40 frames, c. Popular Science Audio-Visuals, Inc.
Covalent Bonds—Covalent Structures. 42 frames, c. Popular Science Audio-Visuals, Inc.
Crystallization. 30 frames, c. Encyclopaedia Britannica Educational Corp.
Crystals. 40 frames, b/w. McGraw-Hill Films.
Crystals and Their Properties. 40 frames, c. Popular Science Audio-Visuals, Inc.
The Ionic Bond. 40 frames, c. Popular Science Audio-Visuals, Inc.
Ionic and Covalent Bonds. 48 frames, c. Encyclopaedia Britannica Educational Corp.
Ionization Potential and Electronegativity. 40 frames, c. Popular Science Audio-Visuals, Inc.
Matter and Molecules. 44 frames, c. Eye Gate House, Inc.
Metals and the Metallic Bond. 40 frames, c. Popular Science Audio-Visuals, Inc.
Molecules, Compounds and Elements. 51 frames, c. Herbert M. Elkins Co.
Orbitals — Atomic and Molecular. 40 frames, c. Popular Science Audio-Visuals, Inc.
The Periodic System. 48 frames, c. Society for Visual Education, Inc.
Periodic Table. 40 trames, b/w. McGraw-Hill Films.
Relative Sizes of Atoms. 32 frames, c. Encyclopaedia Britannica Educational Corp.
Relative Sizes of Ions. 27 frames, c. Encyclopaedia Britannica Educational Corp.
Simple Chemical Reactions. 42 frames, c. Popular Science Audio-Visuals, Inc.
The Size of Molecules. 30 frames, c. Encyclopaedia Britannica Educational Corp.

Overhead Projectuals

Atomic and Ionic Diameters. Creative Visuals (540.AO-02).
Atomic and Ionic Radii. Creative Visuals (540.AO-03).
Atomic Planes in a Crystal Model. McGraw-Hill Films.
Atomic Structure. Tweedy Transparencies (1303-1).
Atomic Structure and Elements. Creative Visuals (540.AO-05).
Atoms Combining to Form Molecules. Tweedy Transparencies (1104-2).
Comparative Electronegativities of Elements. Creative Visuals (540.AO-45).
Covalent and Ionic Bonds. DCA Transparencies (C-15).
Covalent Bonding. DCA Transparencies (M-73).
Directed Orbitals. DCA Transparencies (C-9).
Historical Development of the Periodic Law. DCA Transparencies (C-12).
Hydrogen Atom Orbitals. DCA Transparencies (C-8).
Hypothetical Transition of Neon to Other Molecules by Shifting Protons. DCA Transparencies (C-10).
Ion Formation and Chemical Bonding. Creative Visuals (540.AO-17).
Ionization Potentials. Creative Visuals (540.AO-18).
Metallic Bond. DCA Transparencies (C-17).

Molecular Structure of Matter. DCA Transparencies (C-2).
Molecules from Atoms. Tweedy Transparencies (1303-2).
Periodic Functions. DCA Transparencies (C-13).
Periodic Table. Creative Visuals (540.AO-27).
Periodic Table of the Elements. Tweedy Transparencies (1303-5).
Representation of Atoms and Molecules. DCA Transparencies (C-6).
Resonance Bonding (Dash Bond Form). Creative Visuals (540.AO-58).
Resonance Bonding (Electron Dot Form). Creative Visuals (540.AO-57).
Structure of Some Atoms. Tweedy Transparencies (1303-6).

ENRICHMENT MATERIALS
(Unit III)

Films

Atoms and Molecules — Their Symbols and Formulas. 30 min; c, b/w. Encyclopaedia Britannica Educational Corp.
Density. 13 min, b/w. McGraw-Hill Films.
Density Identification. 28 min, b/w. Mr. Wizard, Prism Enterprises, Inc.
Explaining Matter — Molecules in Motion. 11 min, c. Encyclopaedia Britannica Educational Corp.
Gas Law Calculations — How Errors Arise in Experiments. 30 min; c, b/w. Encyclopaedia Britannica Educational Corp.
Gas Laws and Their Application — Boyle, Charles and Gay-Lussac. 13 min, b/w. Encyclopaedia Britannica Educational Corp.
Gas Pressure and Molecular Collisions. 21 min, b/w. Modern Learning Aids.
The Gas Temperature Scale — Absolute Zero. 30 min; c. b/w. Encyclopaedia Britannica Educational Corp.
Gases and How They Combine. 22 min, c. Modern Learning Aids.
Magnetic Fields in Three Directions. 28 min, b/w. Mr. Wizard, Prism Enterprises, Inc.

Filmstrips

The Avogadro Number. 40 frames, c. Popular Science Audio-Visuals, Inc.
Balancing Equations by Electron Transfer. 40 frames; c, b/w. McGraw-Hill Films.
Boyle's Law. 30 frames, c. Encyclopaedia Britannica Educational Corp.
Charles' Law. 30 frames, c. Encyclopaedia Britannica Educational Corp.
The Chemical Formula. 55 frames, b/w. McGraw-Hill Films.
Determination of a Formula. 30 frames, c. Encyclopaedia Britannica Educational Corp.
Equations. 40 frames, b/w. McGraw-Hill Films.
Experiments With Volume and Density. 49 frames, c. Society for Visual Education, Inc.
Gas Laws. 40 frames, c. McGraw-Hill Films.
Kinetic Molecular Theory. 59 frames, b/w. McGraw-Hill Films.
Molar Volume of Gas. 30 frames, c. Encyclopaedia Britannica Educational Corp.
The Mole Concept. 40 frames, c. Popular Science Audio-Visuals, Inc.
Solids, Liquids, Gases and Molecules. 51 frames, c. Herbert M. Elkins Co.
Symbols, Formulas, Equations. 50 frames, c. Society for Visual Education, Inc.

Overhead Projectuals

Balancing Equations by the Inspection Method. DCA Transparencies (C-29).
Boyle-Charles' Combined Gas Law Formula. Creative Visuals (540.BO-12).
Boyle's Law (a). Creative Visuals (540.AO-06).
Boyle's Law (b). Creative Visuals (540.AO-07).
Charles' Law. DCA Transparencies (H-9).
Charles' Law (a). Creative Visuals (540.AO-08).
Charles' Law (b). Creative Visuals (540.AO-09).
Chemical Formulas, the Mole and Avogadro's Number. Creative Visuals (540.BO-10).
Dalton's Law of Partial Pressure. Creative Visuals (540.BO-11).
Effect of Heat on Molecules in Ice, Water and Steam. DCA Transparencies (H-22).
Equilibrium Vapor Pressure. DCA Transparencies (H-19).
Formula Drill. Creative Visuals (540.BO-01).
General Gas Law. Creative Visuals (540.BO-26).
Graham's Law of Diffusion. Creative Visuals (540.BO-14).
Gram-Equivalent. Creative Visuals (540.BO-25).
Heat and Temperature. Creative Visuals (540.BO-24).
Kinetic Molecular Theory. Creative Visuals (540.AO-19).
The Kinetic Theory and the Gas Laws. DCA Transparencies (H-11).
Kinetic Theory of Matter. Eye Gate House, Inc. (005-14).
Stoichiometry. Creative Visuals (540.BO-20).
Temperature Scales. Creative Visuals (540.AO-37).
The Torricellian Barometer. Eye Gate House, Inc. (005-16).
Units of Measurement — Metric-English. Creative Visuals (540.BO-23).

Units, Unit Cancellation. Creative Visuals (540.BO-08).
Valence Drill. Creative Visuals (540.BO-02).
Vapor Pressure of Various Liquids. Creative Visuals (540.AO-42).
Vapor Pressure, Variation with Temperature. Creative Visuals (540.AO-41).

ENRICHMENT MATERIALS
(Unit IV)

Films

Acid-Base Indicators. 19 min, c. Modern Learning Aids.
Acids. 5 min; c, b/w. Association Films, Inc.
Acids and Bases — An Introduction. 30 min, c. Encyclopaedia Britannica Educational Corp.
Acids, Bases and Oxides. 14 min, c. Purdue University Audio-Visual Center.
Acids, Bases and Salts. 21 min, c. Coronet Instructional Films.
An Acid-Base Titration. 30 min; c, b/w. Encyclopaedia Britannica Educational Corp.
Indicators and pH. 28 min; c, b/w. Coronet Instructional Films.
Liquids in Solutions. 11 min; c, b/w. Encyclopaedia Britannica Educational Corp.
Properties of Solutions. 28 min; c, b/w. Coronet Instructional Films.
Selective Solvents. 28 min, b/w. Mr. Wizard, Prism Enterprises, Inc.

Filmstrips

Acid-Base Theories. 40 frames, c. Popular Science Audio-Visuals, Inc.
Acid and Basic Solutions. 40 frames, b/w. McGraw-Hill Films.
Acids, Bases and Salts. 48 frames, c. Society for Visual Education, Inc.
Acids and Bases. 30 frames, c. Encyclopaedia Britannica Educational Corp.
Hydrogen Ion Concentration — pH. 40 frames, c. McGraw-Hill Films.
Hydrolysis. 30 frames, c. Encyclopaedia Britannica Educational Corp.
Hydrolysis of Salts. 40 frames, c. McGraw-Hill Films.
Ionization. 30 frames, c. Encyclopaedia Britannica Educational Corp.
Ionization. 30 frames, b/w. McGraw-Hill Films.
LeChâtelier's Principle. 40 frames, c. Popular Science Audio-Visuals, Inc.
pH. 30 frames, c. Encyclopaedia Britannica Educational Corp.
Phase Rule. 40 frames, c. McGraw-Hill Films.
Solutions of Definite Concentration. 40 frames, c. McGraw-Hill Films.
Some Things Dissolve. 40 frames, c. McGraw-Hill Films.
Sulfuric, King of the Acids. 40 frames, c. McGraw-Hill Films.
Titration. 30 frames, c. Encyclopaedia Britannica Educational Corp.

Overhead Projectuals

Conjugate Acid-Base Pairs — Proton Transfer. Creative Visuals (540.AO-66).
Dissolving of Ionic Salts by Water. Creative Visuals (540.AO-10).
Electronic-Lewis Structures. Creative Visuals (540.BO-22).
Factors Affecting Solubility. Creative Visuals (540.AO-43).
Hydration of Ions in Water Solutions. Creative Visuals (540.AO-16).
Ionization of Acids, Bases and Salts. DCA Transparencies (C-27).
LeChâtelier's Principle. Popular Science Audio-Visuals, Inc. (Set TC-3).
LeChâtelier's Principle — Applications. Creative Visuals (540.AO-20).
Molal and Molar Solutions. DCA Transparencies (C-24).
Molecular Weight Determination from Freezing Point Data. Creative Visuals (540.BO-19).
Naming Acids and Salts. Creative Visuals (540.AO-21).
Normal Solutions. Creative Visuals (540.BO-07).
Normal Solutions. DCA Transparencies (C-23).
Normal Solutions in Titrations. Creative Visuals (540.AO-22).
Normal Solutions — Typical Problems. Creative Visuals (540.AO-23).
pH Indicators. Creative Visuals (540.AO-28).
pH Relations. Creative Visuals (540.AO-29).
Raoult's Law (a). Creative Visuals (540.AO-33).
Raoult's Law (b). Creative Visuals (540.AO-34).
Semi-quantitative Solubilities of Compounds. Creative Visuals (540.AO-44).
Solubilities of Various Substances. Creative Visuals (540.AO-36).
Solubility and Activity Drill. Creative Visuals (540.BO-03).
Solubility Product Principle. Creative Visuals (540.AO-68).
Solutions. Creative Visuals (540.BO-27).
Solutions (General Principles). DCA Transparencies (C-22).
Testing for Acids and Bases. Tweedy Transparencies (1104-5).
Van der Waals' Bond. DCA Transparencies (C-16).

ENRICHMENT MATERIALS
(Unit V)

Films

Electricity from Chemicals. 14 min; c, b/w. Coronet Instructional Films.
Electricity in Motion. 30 min; c, b/w. Encyclopaedia Britannica Educational Corp.
Electrochemical Cells. 22 min, c. Modern Learning Aids.
Electrochemical Reactions. 14 min; c, b/w. Coronet Instructional Films.
Electrochemistry. 11 min, b/w. Encyclopaedia Britannica Educational Corp.
Electrolysis — 1 and 2. 30 min each; c, b/w. Encyclopaedia Britannica Educational Corp.
Indoor Lightning. 28 min, b/w. Mr. Wizard, Prism Enterprises, Inc.
The Lead Storage Battery — The Dry Cell. 30 min; c, b/w. Encyclopaedia Britannica Educational Corp.

Filmstrips

Electrochemical and Electrolytic Cells. 40 frames, c. Popular Science Audio-Visuals, Inc.
Electrochemistry. 30 frames, c. Encyclopaedia Britannica Educational Corp.
Electrochemistry — Linking of Two Sciences. 40 frames, c. Popular Science Audio-Visuals, Inc.
Electrolysis. 40 frames, b/w. McGraw-Hill Films.
Electroplating. 40 frames, c. McGraw-Hill Films.
Equivalent Weight. 30 frames, c. Encyclopaedia Britannica Educational Corp.
Hydrides and Oxides. 40 frames, c. Popular Science Audio-Visuals, Inc.
Oxidation-Reduction. 40 frames, c. Popular Science Audio-Visuals, Inc.
Oxidation-Reduction Reactions. 30 frames, c. Encyclopaedia Britannica Educational Corp.
Oxidation-Reduction Titration. 30 frames, c. Encyclopaedia Britannica Educational Corp.
Voltaic Cells. 40 frames, c. McGraw-Hill Films.

Overhead Projectuals

Activity Series. Creative Visuals (540.AO-01).
Ammeter and Voltmeter. McGraw-Hill Films.
Balancing Equations by the Oxidation-Reduction Method. DCA Transparencies (C-32).
Copper Electroplating. Eye Gate House, Inc. (035-27).
The Dry Cell. Eye Gate House, Inc. (035-19).
Electric Circuit. Eye Gate House, Inc. (035-12).
Electricity by Chemical Action. DCA Transparencies (C-26).
Electrochemical and Electrolytic Cells. Popular Science Audio-Visuals, Inc.
Electrochemistry. Creative Visuals (540.BO-29).
Electrolysis of Cupric Chloride Solution. Creative Visuals (540.AO-64).
Electrolysis of Water. Eye Gate House, Inc. (035-26).
Electrolysis of Water Solutions of Salts. DCA Transparencies (C-25).
Electrolytes. Creative Visuals (540.BO-05).
Electromotive Series. Creative Visuals (540.AO-12).
Equivalent Weight. DCA Transparencies (C-28).
Faraday's Laws of Electrolysis. Eye Gate House, Inc. (035-28).
Local Action in a Voltaic Cell. Eye Gate House, Inc. (035-17).
Oxidation Numbers. DCA Transparencies (C-30).
Oxidation and Reduction. Creative Visuals (540.AO-26).
Oxidation Potentials — Representations and Mechanical Addition to Obtain Cell Voltages. Creative Visuals (540.AO-65).
Principle of Oxidation-Reduction Numbers. DCA Transparencies (C-31).
Reduction of Electropositive Metals by Electrolysis. DCA Transparencies (C-39).
Simple Voltaic Cell. Eye Gate House, Inc. (035-16).

ENRICHMENT MATERIALS
(Unit VI)

Films

Catalysis. 10 min, b/w. Encyclopaedia Britannica Educational Corp.
Catalysis. 17 min, c. Modern Learning Aids.
Catalysis. 16 min, c. Sutherland Educational Films, Inc.
Chemical Equilibrium — A Typical Weak Acid. 30 min, c. Encyclopaedia Britannica Educational Corp.
A Chemical Reaction and Its Equation. 30 min; c, b/w. Encyclopaedia Britannica Educational Corp.
Energy and Reaction. 15 min; c, b/w. McGraw-Hill Films.
Equilibrium. 24 min, c. Modern Learning Aids.
Equilibrium in Saturated Solutions of Salts — Calcium Carbonate. 30 min; c, b/w. Encyclopaedia Britannica Educational Corp.
How To Change a Chemical Reaction. 28 min, b/w. Modern Learning Aids.
Ionic Equilibrium. 16 min; c, b/w. Coronet Instructional Films.
Rates of Chemical Reactions. 30 min; c, b/w. Encyclopaedia Britannica Educational Corp.
Rates of Reaction. 28 min; c, b/w. Coronet Instructional Films.

Thermochemistry Temperature and Reaction Extents. 30 min; c, b/w. Encyclopaedia Britannica Educational Corp.

Filmstrips

Catalysts at Work. 40 frames. c. Popular Science Audio-Visuals, Inc.
Chemical Kinetics. 40 frames, c. Popular Science Audio-Visuals, Inc.
Energy and Entropy: Driving Force of a Chemical Reaction. 40 frames, c. Popular Science Audio-Visuals, Inc.
Energy of Reactions. 30 frames, c. Encyclopaedia Britannica Educational Corp.
Equilibrium. 30 frames, c. Encyclopaedia Britannica Educational Corp.
Equilibrium. 40 frames; c, b/w. McGraw-Hill Films.
The Equilibrium Constant. 40 frames, c. Popular Science Audio-Visuals, Inc.
Equilibrium Constant — K_e. 40 frames, c. McGraw-Hill Films.
Rate of Reactions. 40 frames; c, b/w. McGraw-Hill Films.
Reaction Rates. 30 frames, c. Encyclopaedia Britannica Educational Corp.
Reversible Reactions and Reactions to Completion. 40 frames, c. Popular Science Audio-Visuals, Inc.
Solubility Product Constant — K_{sp}. 40 frames, c. McGraw-Hill Films.
Thermochemistry. 40 frames, c. Popular Science Audio-Visuals, Inc.

Overhead Projectuals

Chemical Equilibrium. DCA Transparencies (C-21).
Chemical Equilibrium. Creative Visuals (540.BO-15).
Chemical Kinetics. Popular Science Audio-Visuals, Inc.
Energy and Chemical Reactions. Creative Visuals (540.AO-51).
Energy of Activation — Chemical Reactions. Creative Visuals (540.AO-52).
Equilibrium Constant. Creative Visuals (540.AO-56).
Equilibrium in Reversible Chemical Reactions. Creative Visuals (540.AO-55).
Factors Affecting the Speed of Reactions. DCA Transparencies (C-19).
Heats of Formation. Creative Visuals (540.BO-09).
Physical Equilibrium. DCA Transparencies (C-20).
Reaction Mechanism. DCA Transparencies (C-18).
Reversible Reactions and Reactions to Completion. Popular Science Audio-Visuals, Inc.
Solubility and Activity Drill. Creative Visuals (540.BO-03).
Thermochemistry. Popular Science Audio-Visuals, Inc.

ENRICHMENT MATERIALS
(Unit VII)

Films

The Alkali Metals. 30 min; c, b/w. Encyclopaedia Britannica Educational Corp.
The Alkaline Earth Metals. 30 min; c, b/w. Encyclopaedia Britannica Educational Corp.
The Chemistry of Lime. 30 min; c, b/w. Encyclopaedia Britannica Educational Corp.
The Chemistry of Photography. 30 min; c, b/w. Encyclopaedia Britannica Educational Corp.
The Chemistry of Sodium Bicarbonate. 30 min c, b/w. Encyclopaedia Britannica Educational Corp.
Melting — Points and Pointers. 28 min, b/w. Mr. Wizard, Prism Enterprises, Inc.
Metals and Nonmetals. 10 min; c, b/w. Coronet Instructional Films.
Phosphorus. 19 min; c, b/w. Coronet Instructional Films.
The Sulfur Family. 30 min; c, b/w. Encyclopaedia Britannica Educational Corp.

Filmstrips

The Behavior and Use of Metals. 42 frames, c. Popular Science Audio-Visuals, Inc.
Boron and Aluminum. 40 frames, c. Popular Science Audio-Visuals, Inc.
Changing Ores Into Metals. 40 frames, c. Popular Science Audio-Visuals, Inc.
The Chemistry of Boron and Aluminum. 30 frames, c. Encyclopaedia Britannica Educational Corp.
Chemistry of Columns I and II. 30 frames, c. Encyclopaedia Britannica Educational Corp.
Chemistry of Group VIA. 40 frames, c. Popular Science Audio-Visuals, Inc.
Chemistry of the Halogens. 30 frames, c. Encyclopaedia Britannica Educational Corp.
Chemistry of Iron. 30 frames, c. Encyclopaedia Britannica Educational Corp.
Chemistry of Sulfur. 30 frames, c. Encyclopaedia Britannica Educational Corp.
Chemistry of Sulfuric Acid. 30 frames, c. Encyclopaedia Britannica Educational Corp.
The Fluorine Story. 40 frames, c. McGraw-Hill Films.
Group VII — The Halogens. 40 frames, c. Popular Science Audio-Visuals, Inc.
The Halogens. 48 frames, c. Society for Visual Education, Inc.

Metals and Their Ores. 48 frames, c. Society for Visual Education, Inc.

Metals of Groups IA and IIA. 40 frames, c. Popular Science Audio-Visuals, Inc.

Nitrogen and Its Compounds. 40 frames, c. Popular Science Audio-Visuals, Inc.

Nitrogen Fixation. 40 frames, c. McGraw-Hill Films.

Putting Sulfur to Work. 40 frames, c. Popular Science Audio-Visuals, Inc.

Sulphur and Nitrogen. 48 frames, c. Society for Visual Education, Inc.

The Transition Elements. 40 frames, c. Popular Science Audio-Visuals, Inc.

Van der Waals Forces. 40 frames, c. Popular Science Audio-Visuals, Inc.

Overhead Projectuals

Alloys. DCA Transparencies (C-41).

The Blast Furnace Process. DCA Transparencies (C-40).

Comparison of Halogens and Alkalies. DCA Transparencies (C-14).

Oxidation States. Creative Visuals (540.AO-24).

Oxidation States of Common Elements. Creative Visuals (540.AO-25).

ENRICHMENT MATERIALS
(Unit VIII)

Films

Alcohols. 30 min; c, b/w. Encyclopaedia Britannica Educational Corp.

Animal, Vegetable, Mineral. 10 min, c. Radim Films, Inc.

Catalytic Reforming: Part 1 — Reforming Reaction. 13 min, c. Radim Films, Inc.

Catalytic Reforming: Part 2 — Reforming Unit. 13 min, c. Radim Films, Inc.

Chemical Conquest. 24 min; c, b/w. National Film Board of Canada.

The Chemical History of the Candle. 24 min, c. Rarig Film Productions.

Chemical Machinery. 28 min; c, b/w. McGraw-Hill Films.

Chemical Organization of the Cell. 28 min; c, b/w. McGraw-Hill Films.

Chemical Reactions in Higher Plants. 30 min; c, b/w. Encyclopaedia Britannica Educational Corp.

Chemical Reactions in the Animal Body. 30 min; c, b/w. Encyclopaedia Britannica Educational Corp.

Chemistry Laboratory Demonstration — Fermentation Products. 14 min, b/w. Purdue University Audio-Visual Center.

The Chemistry of Behavior — Psychopharmacology. 29 min, b/w. Indiana University Audio-Visual Center.

The Chemistry of Life. 19 min, c. National Aeronautics and Space Administration.

Chemistry of Oil. 13 min, c. Radim Films, Inc.

Distillation of Oil: Part 1 — The Bubble Tower. 11 min, c. Radim Films, Inc.

Distillation of Oil: Part 2 — Crude Oil Distillation. 10 min, c. Radim Films, Inc.

Distillation of Oil: Part 3 — The Stabilizer. 18 min, c. Radim Films, Inc.

Distillation of Oil: Part 4 — Vacuum Distillation Unit. 14 min, c. Radim Films, Inc.

Flowing Solids. 15 min, c. Modern Talking Picture Service, Inc.

Fuels — Their Nature and Use. 11 min, b/w. Encyclopaedia Britannica Educational Corp.

Hydrocarbons and Their Structures. 14 min; c, b/w. Coronet Instructional Films.

The Nature of Burning. 16 min; c, b/w. McGraw-Hill Films.

Refinery at Work. 21 min, c. Modern Talking Picture Service, Inc.

The River Must Live. 21 min, c. Shell Oil Company.

Rubber from Oil. 32 min, c. U.S. Bureau of Mines.

The Story of Lubricating Oil. 22 min, c. U. S. Bureau of Mines.

Why Octanes Vary. 11 min, c. Radim Films, Inc.

Filmstrips

The Carbon Compounds. 48 frames, c. Society for Visual Education, Inc.

The Chemical Lab in Your Body. 40 frames, c. Popular Science Audio-Visuals, Inc.

The Chemistry of Carbon and Silicon. 40 frames, c. Popular Science Audio-Visuals, Inc.

Functional Organic Groups. 40 frames, c. Popular Science Audio-Visuals, Inc.

Hydrocarbons. 40 frames; c, b/w. McGraw-Hill Films.

Organic Chemistry. 40 frames, c. Popular Science Audio-Visuals, Inc.

The Story of Plastics. 40 frames, c. Popular Science Audio-Visuals, Inc.

Synthetic Giant Molecules. 40 frames, c. Popular Science Audio-Visuals, Inc.

Overhead Projectuals

Absorption of Digested Food. Tweedy Transparencies (1200-12).
Animated Portrayal of Measurement of Polarized Light Rotation. Creative Visuals (540.AO-61).
Aromatics. DCA Transparencies (C-43).
Compounds of the Primordial Atmosphere. (from Nature and Origin of Science) Milliken Transparencies.
The Digestive System. Tweedy Transparencies (1200-8).
Enzyme Activity I (Destructive). Tweedy Transparencies (1200-10).
Enzyme Activity II (Constructive). Tweedy Transparencies (1200-11).
Evoluation of Organic Molecules. (from Nature and Origin of Science) Milliken Transparencies.
Isomerism. DCA Transparencies (C-44).
Metabolism and Energy Release. Tweedy Transparencies (1200-15).
Nomenclature — Organic Chemistry. DCA Transparencies (C-42).
Organic Catalysts. (from Nature and Origin of Science) Milliken Transparencies.
Organic Chemistry — An Elementary Survey. Creative Visuals (540.AO-59).
Polarimeter — Measurement of Rotation of a Plane of Polarized Light. Creative Visuals (540.AO-60).
Polarization. DCA Transparencies (L-32).
Typical Organic Reactions. DCA Transparencies (C-45).

ENRICHMENT MATERIALS
(Unit IX)

Films

Atom and Agriculture. 12 min, b/w. Encyclopaedia Britannica Educational Corp.
The Atom Alchemist. 13 min, b/w. Handel Film Corp.
Atom and Biological Science. 12 min, b/w. Encyclopaedia Britannica Educational Corp.
Atom and Medicine. 12 min, b/w. Encyclopaedia Britannica Educational Corp.
Atom in Industry. 13 min, b/w. Handel Film Corp.
Atomic Energy. 11 min, b/w. Encyclopaedia Britannica Educational Corp.
Atomic Furnaces. 13 min, b/w. Handel Film Corp.
Elements and Their Isotopes. 30 min; c, b/w. Encyclopaedia Britannica Educational Corp.
Making Elements. 29 min, b/w. Indiana University Audio-Visual Center.
Radioactive Fingerprints. 28 min, b/w. Mr. Wizard, Prism Enterprises, Inc.

Filmstrips

Evolution of the Elements. 40 frames, c. Popular Science Audio-Visuals, Inc.
Experiments with Subatomic Particles. 30 frames, c. Encyclopaedia Britannica Educational Corp.
Nuclear Energy. 40 frames, b/w. McGraw-Hill Films.
What Is a Neutron? 40 frames, c. Popular Science Audio-Visuals, Inc.

Overhead Projectuals

Electricity from Nuclear Fission. Tweedy Transparencies (1303-9).
Fission. DCA Transparencies (M-78).
Fusion Reactions. DCA Transparencies (M-79).
The Geiger Counter. DCA Transparencies (M-76).
Ionizing Radiation. DCA Transparencies (C-33).
Isotopes of Hydrogen. Tweedy Transparencies (1303-3).
Natural Radioactivity. Tweedy Transparencies (1303-7).
Nuclear Binding Energy. DCA Transparencies (C-34).
Nuclear Fission. Tweedy Transparencies (1303-8).
Nuclear Fission and Fusion. DCA Transparencies (C-35).
Nuclear Products of Disintegration of Radioactive Substances. Creative Visuals (540.AO-48).
Radioactive Decay. DCA Transparencies (C-37).
Uranium Series. McGraw-Hill Films.

PRODUCERS AND DISTRIBUTORS OF AUDIOVISUAL AIDS

Association Films, Inc., 600 Madison Ave., New York, N.Y. 10022
Contemporary Films/McGraw-Hill, 330 West 42nd St., New York, N.Y. 10036
Coronet Instructional Films, 65 East Water St., Chicago, Ill. 60601
Creative Visuals, distr. by A-V Communications Inc., 159 Verdi St., Farmingdale, N.Y. 11735

DCA Transparencies, distr. by A-V Communications, Inc., 159 Verdi St., Farmingdale, N.Y. 11735
Herbert M. Elkins Co., 10031 Commerce Ave., Tujunga, Calif. 91042
Encyclopaedia Britannica Educational Corp., 425 North Michigan Ave., Chicago, Ill. 60611
Eye Gate House, Inc., 146-01 Archer Ave., Jamaica, N.Y. 11435
Filmstrip House, Inc., 432 Park Avenue South, New York, N.Y. 10016
Gateway Productions, Inc., 1859 Powell St., San Francisco, Calif. 94133
Handel Film Corp., 6926 Melrose Ave., Hollywood, Calif.
Indiana University Audio-Visual Center, Film Library, Bloomington, Ind. 47401
International Film Bureau, Inc., 332 South Michigan Ave., Chicago, Ill. 60604
McGraw-Hill Films, 330 West 42nd St., New York, N.Y. 10036
Michigan State University Instructional Media Center, East Lansing, Mich. 48823
Milliken, distr. by A-V Communications, Inc., 159 Verdi St., Farmingdale, N.Y. 11735
Modern Learning Aids, 1212 Avenue of the Americas, New York, N.Y. 10036
Modern Talking Picture Service, Inc., 1212 Avenue of the Americas, New York, N.Y. 10036
Mr. Wizard, Prism Enterprises, Inc., 220 East 23rd St., New York, N.Y. 10010
NASA, Code FAD, Washington, D.C. 20546
National Film Board of Canada, Ste. 819, 680 Fifth Ave., New York, N.Y. 10019
Purdue University Audio-Visual Center, Lafayette, Ind. 47907
Radim Films, Inc., 211 East 43rd St., New York, N.Y. 10036
Rarig Film Productions, 5510 University Way, Seattle, Wash. 98105
Peter M. Robeck and Co., Inc., 230 Park Ave., New York, N.Y. 10017
Shell Oil Co., Film Library, 450 North Meridian St., Indianapolis, Ind. 46204
Sutherland Educational Films, Inc., 201 North Occidental Blvd., Los Angeles, Calif.
Tweedy Transparencies, distr. by A-V Communications, Inc., 159 Verdi St., Farmingdale, N.Y. 11735
U.S. Bureau of Mines, Motion Pictures, 4800 Forbes Ave., Pittsburgh, Pa. 15213
U.S. Public Health Service, Department of Health, Education and Welfare, 330 Independence Ave., S.W., Washington, D.C. 20201
Universal Education and Visual Arts, 221 Park Avenue South, New York, N.Y. 10003
University of Iowa, A-V Center, Iowa City, Iowa 52240
University of Southern California, University Park, Los Angeles, Calif. 90007

NOTES

NOTES

NOTES

NOTES

NOTES

NOTES

NOTES

NOTES

CHEMISTRY

Patterns and Properties

AMERICAN BOOK COMPANY

CHEMISTRY

Patterns and Properties

Charles L. Bickel
John C. Hogg
W. Thomas Lippincott
Margaret Nicholson

THE AUTHORS

Charles L. Bickel. Authority on the Physical Sciences, Dr. Bickel is presently Harlan Page Amen Professor at the Phillips Exeter Academy. Former chairman of the Science Department at Phillips Exeter, he has been on the faculties of Lafayette College and Harvard University and is the author of numerous articles in the *Journal of the American Chemical Society* and about 30 science textbooks.

John Clarence Hogg. Scientist and Specialist in Science Education, is presently Harlan Page Amen Professor Emeritus of Phillips Exeter Academy. Professor Hogg has been chairman of the Science Department at Phillips Exeter, Professor of Chemistry at the University of St. John's in Newfoundland, and principal of the United Church College at St. John's. He is an alumnus of Cambridge and Harvard Universities and holder of the Military Cross of Britain.

William T. Lippincott. Expert on Chemical Education, Dr. Lippincott is presently Professor of Chemistry and Head of the Division of General Chemistry at The Ohio State University, Columbus. He is also Editor of The Journal of Chemical Education, and has served the cause of chemical education in many other capacities. Dr. Lippincott is the coauthor of various chemistry textbooks, a member of many scientific and social organizations, and recipient of numerous honors, including the Distinguished Teaching Award of the College of Arts and Sciences of The Ohio State University.

Margaret Nicholson. Expert on Modern Chemistry Curriculum, Miss Nicholson is currently the Chairman of the Science Department of Acalanes High School, Lafayette, California. Because of a long-standing interest in chemical education, she has served on the staff of the CHEMStudy Institute and is an associate editor of the original CHEMStudy text. Miss Nicholson is a member of many distinguished societies and a recipient of the Manufacturing Chemists Association Outstanding Teacher Award.

AMERICAN BOOK COMPANY

New York Cincinnati Atlanta Dallas Millbrae

 Manufactured in the United States of America.
Published simultaneously in Canada by Van Nostrand Reinhold, Ltd.
1 3 5 7 9 11 13 14 12 10 8 6 4 2

ACKNOWLEDGMENTS

Associated Designers—artwork

Ken Martin—historical chemistry portraiture art

Fundamental Photographs—photography

Front Matter Photo Credits

p. *ii* (top) New York City high-school chemistry classroom—Photo Trends;*(r:top)* chlorine burning; *(r: bottom)* Formation of chrome yellow; *(l)* Silver crystals forming on a piece of copper wire immersed in a solution of $AgNO_3$—Lada Simek
p. *vi* (*top*) Aluminum ore and aluminum metal—Hoppock Associates *(bottom: l—r)* Copper sulfate, copper sulfide, copper acetate, with copper wool in background—Lada Simek
p. *vii* (*top*) Molten sulfur cooling—Hoppock Associates; (*bottom*) Magnesium ribbon burning—Lada Simek
p. *x (top: l)* Rocket that uses liquid oxygen—NASA: *(top:r)* Graduate student doing research—courtesy of the United Nations; *(center)* Underwater archeological vessel—Flip Schulke, Black Star Photos; *(bottom: l)* Chemist using a balance—Mobil Oil Co.; *(bottom: r)* Echo I—NASA

Chapter Introduction Photo Credits

p. 1: "L'Alchimista" by Joanes Statensis Flandrus, 1570, House of Francesco I° de Medici (courtesy of the Florence Museum); p. 95: Lawrence Radiation Laboratory; p. 107: Argonne National Laboratory; p. 135: Dr. Ralph Lapp; p. 355: NASA; p. 383: International Harvester Co.; p. 403: "Bird in Space," 1919, by Constantin Brancusi (courtesy of the Museum of Modern Art; p. 427: Standard Oil Co. of New Jersey; p. 483: "Family Group," 1945–49, by George Moore (courtesy of the Museum of Modern Art); p. 510: Brookhaven National Laboratory; p. 529: USAEC, Richland Operations Office.

Text Photo Credits

p. 7, Fig. 1-4: Lada Simek; p. 8, Fig. 1-5: Wide World Photos; p. 9, Fig. 1-7: Allied Chemical Corp,; p. 11, Fig. 1-8: General Electric Co., p. 12, Fig. 1-9: Russe Kinne, Photo Researchers; p. 13, Fig. 1-10: © *Life* Magazine; Fig. 1-11: The Whitney Museum of American Art; pp. 20, and 56, Figs. U-1 and 3-17: Brookhaven National Laboratory; pp. 195 and 197, Figs. 13-1 and 13-2: Perkin & Elmer; p. 251, Fig. 16-3: Sargent-Welch Scientific Co.,; p. 253, Fig. 16-4: Hoppock Associates; p. 257, Fig. 16-8 (*r*): Lada Simek; p. 275, Fig. 17-2: Museum of Primitive Art; p. 278, Fig. 17-4 (*r*): National Bureau of Standards; p. 301, Fig. 18-9: International Silver Co.; p. 303, Fig. 18-12: Ammonia Co.; p. 311, Fig. 18-18: Union Carbide Corp,; p. 357, Fig. 21-1: (*l*) Utah Travel Council, (*r*) International Salt Co.; p. 362, Fig. 21-5: NASA; p. 380, Fig. 22-9: Hooker Chemical Corp.; p. 393, Fig. 23-9: Alcoa; p. 395, Fig. 23-11 (*r*): Freeport Sulphur Co.; p. 397, Fig. 23-13 (*bottom*): Allied Chemical Corp.; p. 410, Fig. 24-3: NASA (Saturn C-1); p. 411, Fig. 24-6: General Motors Corp,; p. 413, Fig. 24-10: "Le Guichet" by Calder, with permission of The Lincoln Center of the Performing Arts—photo by Edith Reichman; p. 416, Fig. 24-13: American Iron and Steel Inst.; p. 417, Fig. 24-15: *Steelways*, American Iron & Steel Inst.; p. 419, Fig. 24-18: Lawrence Williams and Sons; Fig. 24-20: Anaconda Wire & Cable Co., p. 436, Fig. 25-8: General Motors Corp.; p. 439, Fig. 25-11: Getty Oil Co.—Photo Library of American Petroleum Institute; p. 442, Fig. 25-14: Lada Simek; p. 448, Fig. 25-17: Mobil Oil Co.; p. 462, Fig. 26-2: Seagram Distillers Corp.; Fig. 26-3: Hoffritz Corp.; p. 466, Fig. 26-5: Monkmeyer Press Photo; p. 468, Fig. 26-6 (*l*):Rudolph & Sons: p. 493, Fig. 27-5 (*bottom*): courtesy of *Journal of Chemical Education*; pp. 498, 499, 500, Figs. 27-8, 27-9: with permission of Ginn & Co. (Garrett, Verhoek, and Lippincott: *Chemistry, A Study of Matter*); p. 500, Fig. 27-10: Courtesy of John Wiley & Sons, Inc. (Conn & Stumpf: *Outlines of Bio-Chemistry*, 2nd ed.); p. 518, Fig. 28-6: Courtesy of Professor W. Bentner, Max Planck Institut für Kern-Physik; p. 520, Fig. 28-8: Lawrence Radiation Laboratory; p. 530, Fig. 29-1: Coal Institute; p. 531, Fig. 29-2: Connecticut Yankee Power Co.; p. 539, Fig. 29-6: USAEC Richland Operations Office; p. 542, Fig. 29-9: General Electric Co.

CONTENTS

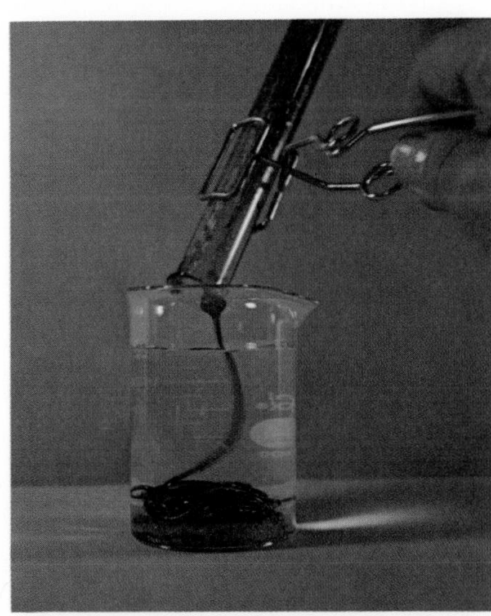

PREFACE

The traditional high school chemistry course of a decade ago has been markedly changed in both content and purpose. The chief aim of such a course was to broaden a student's academic fare by emphasizing the role of chemical processes in his daily life. These courses were informative and descriptive, but there was much emphasis on memorizing chemical facts. Actually, it could scarcely be otherwise since teachers were hesitant to acknowledge the fact that many chemical processes cannot be explained except in terms of physical principles. The new approach does not hesitate to call upon physics when necessary, and in consequence it is both meaningful and logical. It seeks to understand why chemical operations proceed the way they do; it poses the never-ending questions: How? and Why? However, even in spite of this scientific approach, it would be idle to expect that all our questions can be answered.

Scientific knowledge is the sum of the contributions of many scientists through the past 200 years or so. Chemistry is a science that has evolved slowly. Its frontiers are not stationary, but ever advancing. And students should be aware of this characteristic facet of scientific knowledge. That is, a present front should not be presented as a *fait accompli*, but rather as the culmination of a series of advances, often over intellectual ground that has since been discarded. Modern chemistry has a rich heritage of theories that have served their purpose and then been rejected. These belong to history. Therefore, an occasional dip into chemical history gives a student a deeper comprehension of underlying principles as we see them today.

This book reflects this changing philosophy in presenting chemistry as a viable subject to high school students. In contemplating this volume the authors looked for a basic unifying concept that could be applied throughout the book. One indisputable fact is that the chemical properties of elements are determined by the electronic configurations of their atoms. This suggested that atomic structure should be introduced as early as is reasonably possible. And this has been done. Nonetheless this approach was not without its problems. To understand the changing pattern of electronic configurations, a knowledge of energy and its transformations is necessary; the transformation of potential energy to heat energy, to light energy, and even to electrical energy. The physical principles involved in these transformations are discussed in the text when they are needed. Once the electronic structure of atoms is established, chemical bonding follows quite naturally. Moreover, with increasing atomic number the recurrence of certain electronic patterns is apparent, and it is reasonable to place elements with similar electronic patterns in the same chemical family. Indeed, once the pattern is established the properties of the elements are in large measure predictable. The emphasis on atomic structure also provides a dramatic illustration of the startling changes in the front of knowledge, slowly at first, then through a period of 20 years quite rapidly. In brief: From Dalton's spherical indivisible atom in 1808, to Rutherford's nuclear atom in 1910, to Bohr's circular selective electronic orbits in 1914, to the present quantum model with its electron cloud in 1925 or thereabouts.

One final point concerning this book: All chemical knowledge has been derived from experiments and a number of classical experiments are described in detail in the text. But beyond this the student should himself be actively engaged in the experimental method. This can be done by class demonstrations and by individual laboratory work. Both play their part. Demonstrations are usually performed by the instructor and they are a valuable teaching aid. Through them a student acquires keen observation and critical judgment, and if the demonstrations are skillfully performed he picks up helpful manual techniques. However, the scientific attitude of mind cannot be properly developed unless a student wrestles with the problems of individual experimental work in the laboratory. To solve a problem the student collects data, then interprets the data and arrives at a conclusion. Is the conclusion justified by the data he has collected or is still more evidence needed? Laboratory work is a personal and challenging exercise, indeed an indispensable exercise.

The 29 chapters of the text are grouped into 9 units. The chapters within a unit have many features in common. At the end of each chapter there is a wide variety of questions to test the reading comprehension of the student. And at the end of most of the chapters there is also a group of problems graded in difficulty. One of the features of the text is the role of units in problem solving. Both units and numbers are carried throughout the steps, as well as in the answer to the problem. Multiplication, division and root taking are best done by slide rule. The slide rule is described in the Appendix and students are strongly urged to learn how to use this simple, time-saving device.

CHAPTER 1

WHAT IS CHEMISTRY?

THE WORD CHEMISTRY may bring up a mental picture of the many synthetic substances that we see around us. We may think of brightly colored dyes, strong and versatile plastics, synthetic fibers that can be woven into cloth as soft as silk, or of drugs used to combat disease. It is true that dyes, plastics, synthetic fibers, and drugs are manufactured by chemical processes. But a study of these processes would not answer the question: What is Chemistry? Where can we look for the answer? Each new discovery in the field of chemistry depends upon earlier discoveries, sometimes in other fields such as physics and biology. What, then, sets chemistry apart from physics and biology? Arbitrary boundary lines among the various branches of science are gradually disappearing. It is still convenient, however, to associate chemistry primarily with the study of matter—its composition, the changes it undergoes, and the energy exchanges involved in these changes.

Observe and classify . . .

Make a list of 10 very familiar objects or examples of matter around you. How would you group or classify this variety of matter by your senses alone? One of your first observations would be the state, or phase, in which matter exists: solid, liquid, gas. What physical properties of matter are the basis for classifying your examples as solid, liquid, gas?

Probably the best way to seek an answer to the question is to trace the development of some particular chemical discovery. To demonstrate this, we will trace the discovery of the "noble" gases, the best

Research . . .

You know of three phases of matter: solid, liquid, and gas. A fourth phase of matter exists—*plasma.* Find out what plasmas are, where they are usually found, how laboratory plasmas are produced and what applications they may have.

known of which are argon and helium. It is a fascinating story, a kind of jigsaw puzzle that men worked on for more than a century before all the pieces fell into place.

Impure argon was "discovered" in the year 1894 although it had been isolated (but not identified) by accident as early as 1784. Why was there a gap of more than a hundred years between the isolation of argon and its identification? The answer lies in the work of a remarkable English scientist named Henry Cavendish.

Henry Cavendish (1731–1810)

Cavendish made a surprisingly large number of discoveries of fundamental importance. First he studied a gas which he obtained by dropping a metal, such as zinc, iron, or tin, into either dilute sulfuric acid or dilute hydrochloric acid. He noted that this gas had flammable and explosive properties and referred to it as "flammable air," but considered it to be an imaginary substance called "phlogiston" and thought that it came from the metals. After its true nature was determined, it was given its present name *hydrogen* (water former) by Antoine Lavoisier (1743–1794), a French chemist.

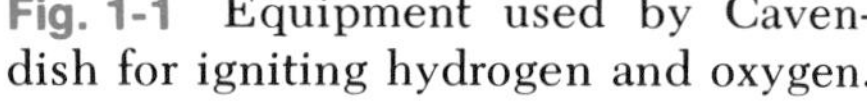

Fig. 1-1 Equipment used by Cavendish for igniting hydrogen and oxygen.

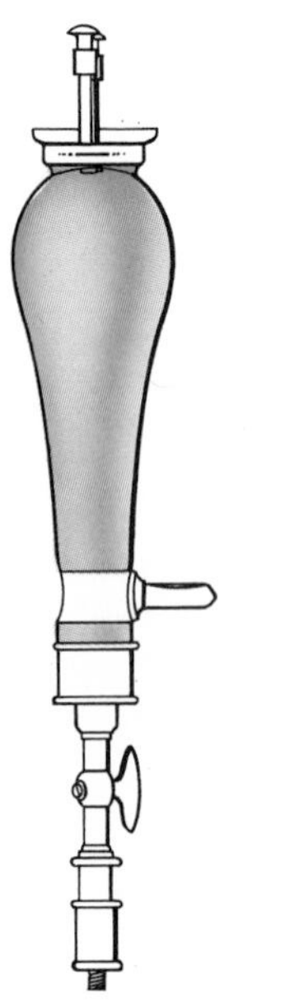

Cavendish worked with great care on each problem that interested him. The apparatus he used was very simple, indeed crude, yet his quantitative results were remarkably accurate when compared with those of contemporary investigations of similar problems made with more elaborate apparatus. He is probably best known for his work on air and water. He analyzed atmospheric air and found that it contained 20.8% of oxygen. Or, to be more exact, he found that 100 volumes of air contain 20.8 volumes of oxygen and 79.2 volumes of nitrogen. (The currently accepted value for the content of oxygen in air is 21.0% by volume.)

In another experiment, Cavendish proved that water is a *compound* of hydrogen and oxygen. To do this he mixed hydrogen and oxygen in a glass globe (see Fig. 1-1) and ignited the mixture with an electric spark. There was a loud explosion, and a dew formed on the walls of the globe. Cavendish proved that this dew was plain water, and thus the chemical reaction can be represented as

$$\text{hydrogen} + \text{oxygen} = \text{water}$$

Moreover, he measured the gas volumes involved in this reaction and found that 2 volumes of hydrogen combine with 1 volume of oxygen. In other words, Cavendish proved that water consists of 2 parts by volume of hydrogen and 1 part by volume of oxygen.

Cavendish's most intriguing contribution was undoubtedly his isolation of a chemically inactive gas from air. Before describing this experiment in some detail, it may be wise to explain some of the terms we must use.

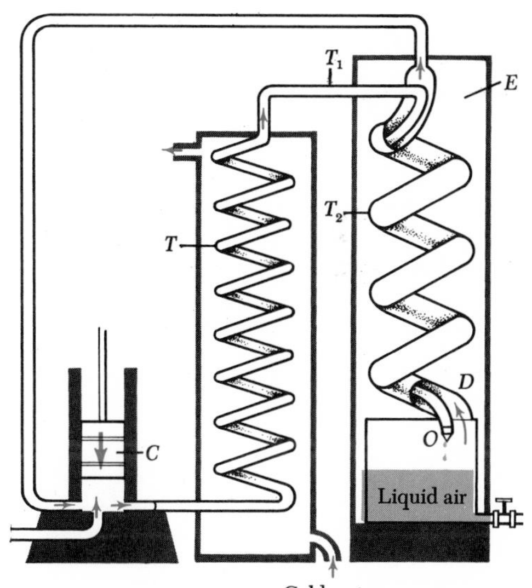

Fig. 1-2 Schematic diagram of apparatus for liquefying air. Atmospheric air (from which CO_2 and moisture have been removed) is compressed by compressor C. To remove the heat of compression, the air is passed through a coiled tube T surrounded by running cold water. The air then flows through the coiled tube T_1 in the expansion chamber E. When it escapes through the fine opening O it suddenly expands and cools. The cooled air then returns through pipe T_2 at D, thereby cooling the oncoming air. Cooled air is repeatedly forced through the circuit of tubes. Every time it expands at O its temperature drops, until eventually it liquefies.

Some Chemical Terms

Hydrogen, oxygen, and nitrogen are *elements*, whereas water is a *compound*. As you probably recall from your elementary science, an element consists of atoms of one kind. Therefore, elements cannot be decomposed (broken down) into simpler substances, at least not in any ordinary chemical reaction. A compound, on the other hand, is formed when two or more elements are linked together as the result of a chemical reaction. Clearly, a compound can be decomposed into simpler substances. Elements are relatively rare; compounds are plentiful. Actually there are fewer than 90 natural elements but there are hundreds of thousands of compounds.

Air, however, is primarily a mixture of oxygen and nitrogen. (It also contains small quantities of other gases.) In a mixture, the ingredients are free—they may be elements and/or compounds—and it is usually easier to separate a mixture into its ingredients than to decompose a compound into its constituents. Thus, air (like any other mixture) can be separated into oxygen and nitrogen by *physical* rather than *chemical* methods. One way of separation starts with liquefying the air and heating the liquid. The chief constituents are collected as they escape at their different boiling points.

The boiling temperatures of liquid oxygen and nitrogen are very low, much lower than the boiling point of water, which is 100 °C at 1 atmosphere of pressure. Indeed, the boiling temperature of oxygen is −183 °C and for nitrogen it is −196 °C. How can such low temperatures be attained?

As you may know from experience with a bicycle pump, air becomes hotter when it is compressed. Conversely, air (or any gas for that matter) becomes cooler if it is suddenly expanded. In fact, if compressed air is expanded repeatedly (as shown in Fig. 1-2), it liquefies at a temperature of about −200 °C. If the temperature of

Speculate . . .
Use of a physical method does *not* result in the formation of a substance not already present. Why not?

Definition . . .
Any change in matter resulting in the formation of a substance not previously present is called a chemical reaction.

liquid air is allowed to rise slowly, it first reaches the boiling point of nitrogen (−196 °C). The temperature then remains steady until the nitrogen has escaped as a gas; the escaping nitrogen can, of course, be collected and stored. When the last of the nitrogen has escaped, the temperature of the remaining liquid (which is liquid oxygen) begins to rise and continues to do so until it reaches −183 °C. At this temperature, the oxygen escapes as a gas and it too can be piped into steel cylinders and stored.

This process, used for separating a mixture of liquids into its constituent parts or fractions, is called *fractional distillation* and will be referred to later in this chapter. And now to return to Cavendish.

Cavendish's Discovery of an Inert Gas

Cavendish had made hydrogen and oxygen combine in the presence of an electric spark. Would an electric spark also cause oxygen and nitrogen to combine? To answer this question he devised a simple apparatus that consisted of two wine glasses and a bent glass tube. Both wine glasses and the tube were filled with mercury and a solution of potash in water. Some air was then introduced into the tube by displacing the fluid. Two metal wires connected to a high-voltage source of electricity (an electrostatic machine) were then inserted through opposite ends of the tube until they nearly touched. The arrangement is shown in Fig. 1-3(*a*).

Fig. 1-3 Cavendish apparatus for combining nitrogen and oxygen: (*a*) Early version. (*b*) Later, more efficient version.

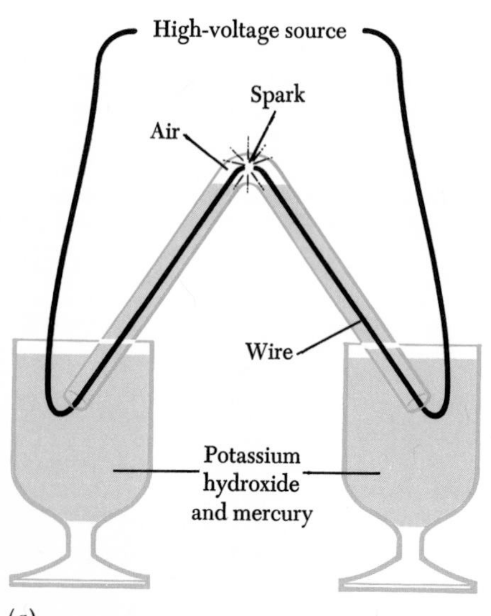

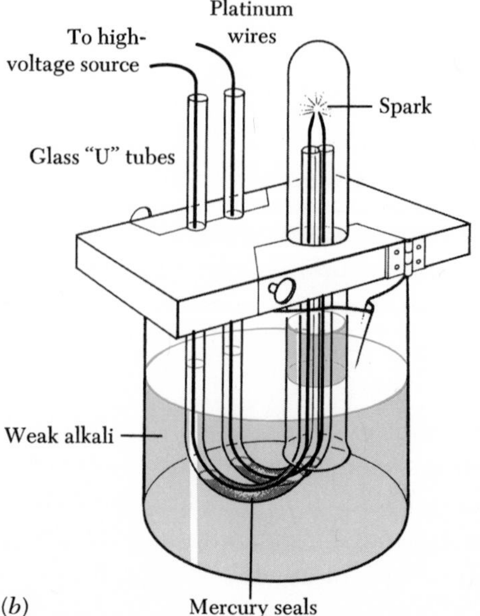

When the voltage was applied, electric sparks jumped across the gap between the wires and, at the same time, a reddish-brown gas was formed. The brown gas then disappeared and the water level rose in the tube. How did Cavendish explain these observations? He assumed that, in the presence of an electric spark, oxygen combined with nitrogen to form an oxide of nitrogen:

oxygen + nitrogen $\longrightarrow$ an oxide of nitrogen (brown gas)

And, since the brown color disappeared and water rose in the tube, he concluded that the brown gas had dissolved in the water. Later he proved that the gas not only dissolves in water but also reacts with it chemically to form nitric acid:

oxide of nitrogen + water $\longrightarrow$ nitric acid

Cavendish then argued that since the ratio of nitrogen to oxygen in air is approximately 4 : 1, the residual gas in the tube must be nitrogen. So he added more *oxygen* to the gas in the tube and started the sparking again. He continued the oxygen addition and sparking until no more brown gas was formed. He then assumed that all the nitrogen had been used up and that the *remaining small volume of gas in the tube was the excess of oxygen that had been added.* Finally, he added a chemical that he knew would absorb the oxygen. However, *a tiny bubble of unabsorbed gas remained.* Cavendish repeated this experiment several times and each time a small bubble of gas remained. What was the residual gas? Was it a new element? Cavendish certainly suggested such a possibility, for in summarizing his experiment he wrote "Having condensed as much of the nitrogen as I could, I then absorbed the oxygen after which only a small bubble of air remained unabsorbed. So if there be any part of our atmosphere which differs from the rest it is not more than 1/120 part of the whole."

This was a cautious statement but a prophetic one. Actually, Cavendish's hint of a new element was ignored for more than a century. Chemists believed that the residual gas was unabsorbed nitrogen. They explained that Cavendish's leftover bubble resulted from inferior apparatus or *experimental error.* In Cavendish's day there was no way of identifying the gas. None existed until about 70 years later, when an optical instrument called a spectroscope was invented.

Observe . . .
An observation you can probably make is that some matter (for example, concrete or cloth) has parts with different physical properties. Other matter such as water, air, or aluminum foil seem to have the same physical properties throughout. How can you classify these examples further? On the basis of sense observation alone you cannot discover that water is a *compound* and that aluminum is an *element.* These chemical differences must be discovered by experimentation using special tools and techniques.

Speculate . . .
Sometimes a discovery must wait until enough technological progress has been made. Why?

The Discovery of Helium

One of the inert gases in the atmosphere is helium; its name is derived from the Greek word *helios* which means *sun*. How did helium get its unusual name? We must first state that if a luminous gas is observed through a spectroscope (an instrument described on page 62), a number of brightly colored lines are seen. As we shall discover in Chapter 4, every element, when heated until it becomes a luminous gas, has its own particular set of bright lines. In this way, the observed pattern of bright lines indicates which elements are present in any particular gas. In the late 1850's, by means of the newly invented spectroscope, scientists examined and recorded the characteristic bright lines of all known elements. Then the scientists became interested in the bright lines emitted by the hot gases that compose the sun. Were the elements making up the sun the same as the elements of earth? However, in making spectroscopic observations they ran into difficulty.

The temperature of the interior of the sun is estimated to be about 20,000,000 °C, the temperature of the sun's surface is about 6000 °C. Above the surface is incandescent gas, the corona, which extends into space for millions of miles. Below the corona is a bright region extending thousands of miles above the surface and called the chromosphere. The elements in the chromosphere are presumably the same as the elements in the sun's core.

Neither the corona nor the chromosphere can be seen in the full glare of the daytime sun. When the central core of the sun is covered, as during an eclipse, the corona shines by its own light. A picture of the corona and photosphere of the sun is shown in Fig. 1-6.

In 1868, a solar eclipse was visible in India and a group of scientists went there to examine the chromosphere through a spectroscope. Among the bright lines observed there was a prominent yellow line which did not correspond with any yellow lines emitted by known elements on earth. They, therefore, assumed that the yellow line was emitted by an element that occurs only in the sun. And for this reason they named the element *helium*. The next piece in the jigsaw puzzle came from an unexpected quarter, a uranium ore from California called uraninite or cleveite.

Research . . .
Read up on the life and discoveries of Lord Rayleigh (1842–1919). You might find him under "S", since he was born John William Strutt.

In 1888, Dr. W. F. Hillebrand (1853–1925) of the U.S. Geological Survey studied the gas which was released when certain uraninites were boiled with dilute sulfuric acid. Chemical examination led him to believe that this gas was nitrogen. However, spectroscopic examination revealed not only the lines characteristic of nitrogen, but some strange ones as well. Moreover, even when he had sparked his sample with oxygen for a long time, there was still some gas remaining. (Cavendish had also found such a residue from atmospheric nitrogen.) The puzzle continues with another odd piece—the determination of the density of nitrogen.

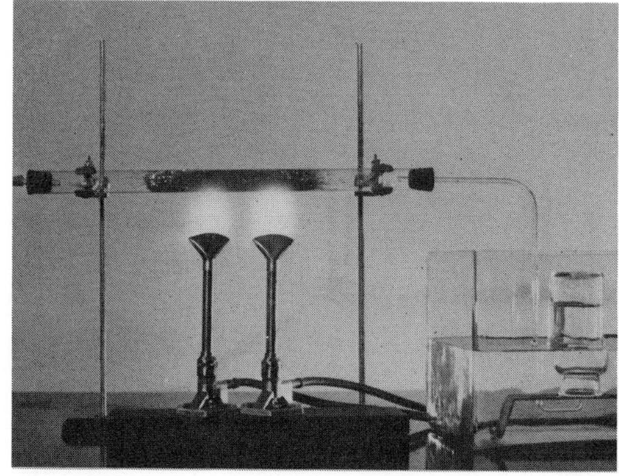

Fig. 1-4 Preparation of nitrogen from the air. What is removed?

Rayleigh's Determination of the Density of Nitrogen

In 1892 the English physicist, Lord Rayleigh, made a series of accurate determinations of the densities of some common gases, including nitrogen. Gas densities are discussed at some length in Chapter 10, but here we can define gas density as *the mass of one liter (l) of a gas at a temperature of 0°C and a pressure of one atmosphere.* For example, the density of oxygen is 1.4290 g/l.

Rayleigh determined the density of both chemical nitrogen and atmospheric nitrogen. Chemical nitrogen can be prepared by decomposing various compounds of nitrogen. For example, if ammonium nitrite is heated, it breaks down into nitrogen and water vapor. Or,

ammonium nitrite $\longrightarrow$ nitrogen + water vapor

The water vapor can easily be condensed to liquid water and the nitrogen is then dried by passing it over a drying agent such as calcium chloride. Rayleigh found that the density of *chemical nitrogen* is 1.2506 g/l.

As you learned earlier (page 3), atmospheric nitrogen can be obtained from liquid air. It can also be obtained by passing a slow current of air over hot copper gauze as shown in Fig. 1-4. Oxygen reacts with hot copper to form copper oxide, a black solid, but nitrogen does not. Nitrogen is less chemically active than oxygen.

copper + oxygen $\longrightarrow$ copper oxide
copper + nitrogen $\longrightarrow$ no reaction

The nitrogen collected in this manner is wet; it is saturated with water vapor. Moreover, as you may know, there is also carbon dioxide in the air. However, the carbon dioxide can be removed by bubbling the nitrogen through a solution of potassium hydroxide,

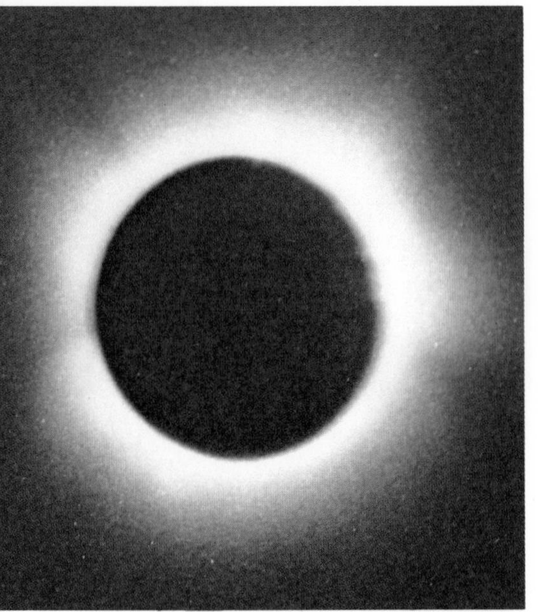

Fig. 1-5 The corona as seen during the total eclipse of March 7, 1970. Explain why this formation is called the "diamond ring."

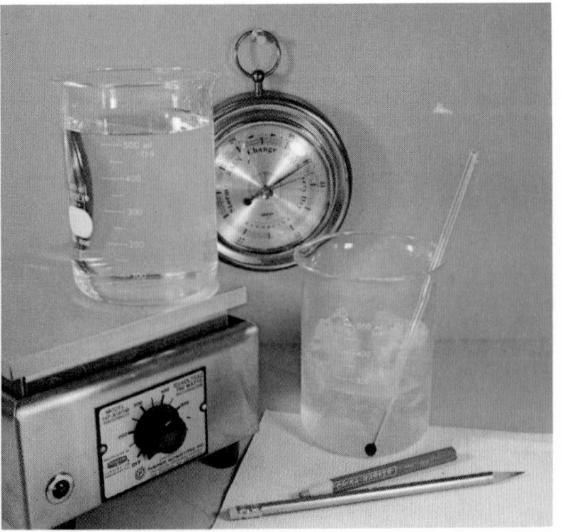

Speculate . .
A scientist frequently must translate his ideas into special equipment in order to perform necessary experiments. Why?

and the moisture can be removed by a drying agent. Rayleigh found that the density of *dry atmospheric nitrogen* is 1.2572 g/l. That is, the density of atmospheric nitrogen is about 0.5% greater than that of chemical nitrogen. The difference between the two values is small. However, it was considerably greater than the limits of error that could be expected in the experiment itself. How could this difference be accounted for? Rayleigh looked up the almost forgotten memoirs of Cavendish and he was particularly interested in the paragraph quoted earlier in the chapter. Was the residual "nitrogen" bubble of Cavendish in some way related to the density of atmospheric nitrogen? Or, to be more specific, did atmospheric nitrogen contain an element, hitherto undiscovered, that is denser than nitrogen? To answer this question, he teamed up with a Scottish chemist named William Ramsay (1852–1916) and together they devised an experiment that led to a memorable discovery.

The Discovery of Argon by Ramsay and Rayleigh

In their classic experiment (in 1894), Ramsay and Rayleigh used specially designed equipment to remove the known constituents of air, one by one, by passing a known volume of air through a series of chemical reagents. (See Fig. 1-6.) First, the carbon dioxide was trapped by bubbling the air through a concentrated solution of potassium hydroxide. Next, the water vapor was removed by passing the air over a drying agent. In the third step, oxygen was removed by passing the dry air through a long glass tube containing a spiral of copper wire heated to a high temperature. How was the nitrogen removed? Nitrogen combines with hot magnesium to form a white solid called magnesium nitride:

$$\text{nitrogen} + \text{magnesium} \longrightarrow \text{magnesium nitride}$$

Hence, in the final step, the remaining gas was passed over hot magnesium. However, as in the Cavendish experiment, a small residue of gas remained unabsorbed.

This final operation was repeated many times to make sure that *all* nitrogen was removed. Nevertheless a small gas residue still remained. Ramsay and Rayleigh concluded that the residual gas was a new element. Since it would not combine with hot magnesium, they gave it the descriptive name *argon,* derived from the Greek word *argos* which means idle or inactive.

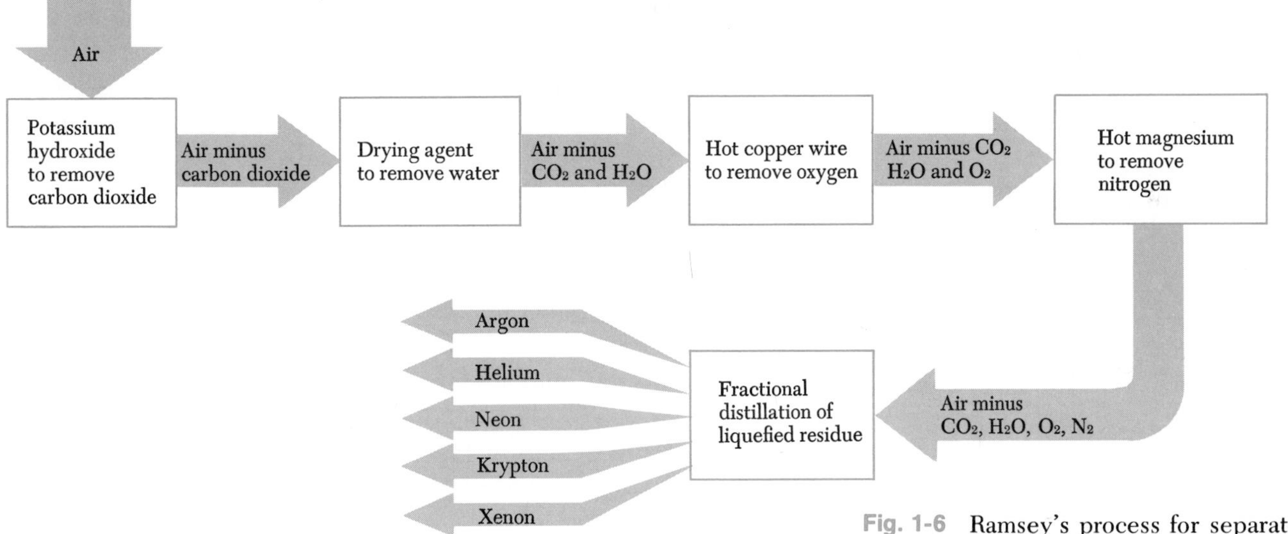

Fig. 1-6 Ramsey's process for separating the constituents of air. By this process he discovered a family of elements—the noble gases.

Ramsay's Discovery of the Inert Elements

Ramsay continued the investigation of "argon" for some years. Was "argon" a single substance or a mixture of substances? Since "argon" is chemically inactive, this question could not be answered by chemical tests. However, there were several physical tests that could be made. He examined the spectrum of "argon" through a spectroscope and found in the unfamiliar pattern the bright yellow line characteristic of helium. Until Ramsay made this observation no one had suspected that helium existed on earth. The amount of helium in crude "argon"(or in the air) is exceedingly small, but Ramsay searched for it in larger amounts.

He learned of Hillebrand's peculiar results on "nitrogen" obtained from uraninites; Ramsay obtained ore samples from Hillebrand and after repeating Hillebrand's experiments, followed them by examining the "nitrogen" with a spectroscope. He found the "extra" lines to include the characteristic yellow line of helium. The proportion of helium in the gas from the ore was much greater than its proportion in ordinary air.

Ramsay applied fractional distillation to his crude liquid "argon." He collected five different fractions that boiled off at different temperatures and thus was convinced that his sample of "argon" ob-

Fig. 1-7 A modern scientist at work in a modern laboratory.

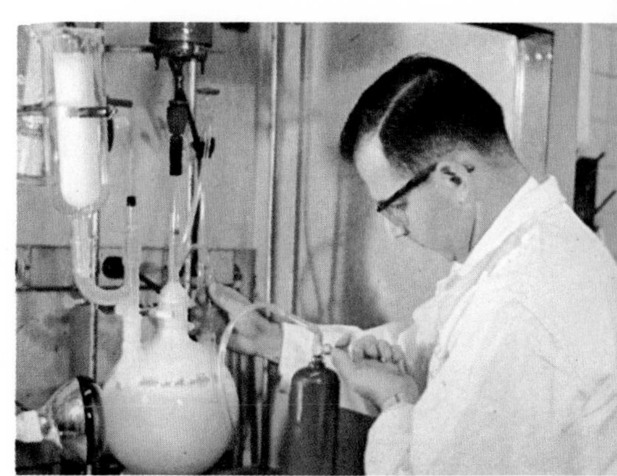

tained from air was really a mixture of five different elements. One of the elements was relatively abundant, but the other four were present only in very small amounts. He kept the name *argon* for the most abundant element, retained *helium* for the gas first detected in the sun, and named the others *neon* (from Greek *neos,* new), *krypton* (from Greek *kryptos,* hidden), and *xenon* (from Greek *xenos,* stranger).

Ramsay examined each of these gases and found their properties to be remarkably similar. They are all colorless, odorless, and tasteless. Moreover, they are so chemically inactive that Ramsay was unable to form any compounds from any of them. For this reason he called them the *inert* elements. However, because of their chemical aloofness and their reluctance to combine with the more common elements they came to be known as the *noble gases.*

Elements with similar properties are said to be in the same *chemical family.* Thus, by the year 1900 Ramsay had discovered five members of the so-called *noble gas family.* (The sixth member of the family, the gas *radon*, was discovered independently a few months later.) The outstanding contributions of Ramsay and Rayleigh won for them the highest of all scientific awards, the Nobel prize: Ramsay's was in chemistry and Rayleigh's in physics. Both awards were made in 1904.

The Chemical Inactivity of the Noble Gases

Since the noble gases are chemically inactive, at first sight this family would appear to be a relatively unimportant one. But this is not the case. The very inactivity of these elements raises such questions as:

Why does chemical inactivity apply only to the noble gas elements?

Why are all other elements chemically active to various degrees?

What determines whether an element is active or inactive?

The answers to these questions depend upon the particular structure of the atoms that comprise an element. And the structure of the atoms of the noble gas elements is of paramount importance when considering the general topic of atomic structure.

For nearly 70 years chemists tried without success to make a compound containing a noble gas element. Then in 1962, it was found that xenon combined with platinum fluoride to form xenon hexafluoroplatinate

$$Xe + PtF_6 \longrightarrow XePtF_6 \quad (1\text{-}1)$$

This was a major discovery and was quickly followed by the preparation of xenon fluorides. See Tables 1-1 and 1-2.

Table 1-1 Conditions used for preparing the xenon fluorides

Compound	Ratio Xe/F_2	Temperature, °C	Time, hours	Pressure, atm
XeF_2	7.5:1	400	16	75
XeF_4	1:5	400	1	6
XeF_6	1:20	250	16	50

Table 1-2 Physical properties of the xenon fluorides

Compound	Color of solid	Color of vapor	Melting point, °C	Vapor pressure at 25°C, mm Hg	Density, g/ml at 25°C
XeF_2	Colorless	Colorless	129	4.6	4.32
XeF_4	Colorless	Colorless	117	2.5	4.04
XeF_6	Colorless	Greenish-yellow	49.5	27	3.41

Why the combination with fluorine? As we shall learn later, fluorine is the most active of all nonmetallic elements—far more active than oxygen. Six compounds of xenon are now known. Krypton fluoride has also been prepared by irradiating a mixture of the gases krypton and fluorine with electrons at a temperature of −150°C. So far, however, all attempts to make compounds of helium, argon, and neon have failed, so that these gases still appear to be completely inert.

Why do the heavier elements of the family (xenon and krypton) combine with fluorine whereas the lighter elements (helium, neon, and argon) do not? Again, the answer concerns the structure of their atoms, a topic that will be discussed in the chapters immediately

Note . . .
Many scientists are called "pure" scientists. They are interested in discovering new knowledge for the sake of the knowledge itself. Others seek to find application of the new discoveries. These are the "practical" or "applied" scientists.

ahead. Has the final episode in the history of the noble gas family now been written? The answer to this question is surely, "Certainly not!" Research will continue. And, with improved techniques and wider knowledge, experiments that have failed today may succeed tomorrow, and there may be completely unexpected discoveries in the field of the noble gases.

Some Uses of the Noble Gases

Fig. 1-8 Helium-filled weather balloons help to predict and study weather.

The uses of the noble gases depend mostly upon their lack of chemical activity. With the exception of helium, the gases are prepared in commercial quantities from liquid air. Strangely enough, helium occurs in concentrations as high as 7 or 8% in natural gas in certain regions in the United States, so natural gas is the industrial source of helium.

Helium is a light gas, only a little denser than hydrogen, which is the lightest of all gases. Unlike hydrogen, it is incombustible and so is an ideal gas for use in blimps and weather balloons (Fig. 1-8). Helium is also used instead of nitrogen in the "air" used by deep-sea divers and astronauts, because it helps to prevent adverse effects (Fig. 1-9).

Argon is chiefly used for filling light bulbs. A bulb filled with a mixture of nitrogen and argon is bright and long lasting. Neon is used extensively in advertising. If an electric discharge is passed through a tube of neon gas, the neon atoms emit a characteristic red glow which makes it suitable for use in decorative signs (Fig. 1-10) and beacon lights for airplanes. Xenon is also used in lights and beacons (Fig. 1-11)

The Answer—What is Chemistry?

We have seen that chemistry is a study of the properties and composition of matter and the changes which matter undergoes. But it is also far more than that. As we shall see later, chemistry is also concerned with the energy exchanges that accompany all changes in matter. Chemical knowledge derived from this study is based on experiments in which very careful observations are made. Usually an experiment is designed to answer a particular question.

Cavendish asked: Will nitrogen combine with oxygen in the presence of an electric spark?

Rayleigh asked: Why is the density of atmospheric nitrogen significantly greater than that of chemical nitrogen?

Fig. 1-9 The diver's "air" tanks contain a mixture of oxygen and helium. Why?

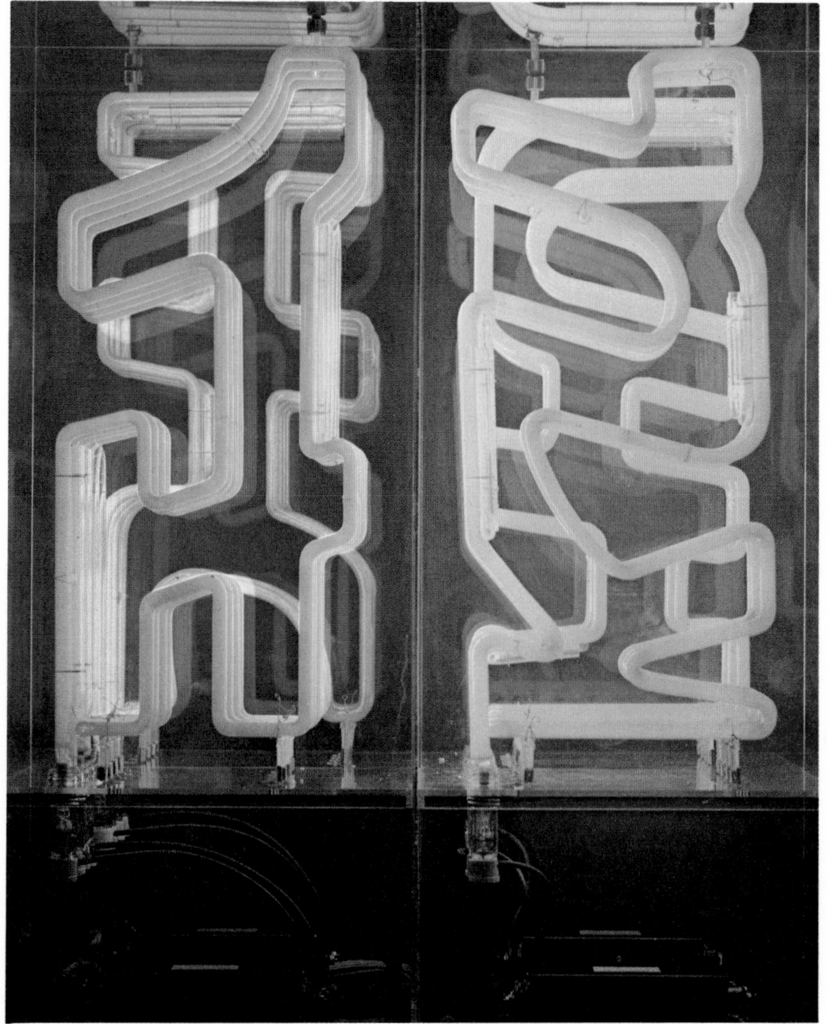

Fig. 1-10 Neon lights are also used as an art form. This composition by Chryssa is called "Fragment of Gates to Times Square II."

Fig. 1-11 This tiny xenon arc lamp gives as much light as 327 ordinary 60-watt bulbs. Why is the engineer wearing goggles?

Ramsay asked: Is the residual inactive gas in atmospheric air a single element or a mixture of elements?

And the new experiments in turn led to further questions and to more experimentation.

In the never-ending questioning the chemist most frequently asks: Why?

Why does a particular substance behave the way it does?

If a question can be answered experimentally, a theory may be proposed to explain the experiment. Sometimes a model serves the same purpose.

A scientific model is some familiar operational system that can be studied and thus helps us to understand how an unfamiliar system operates. A model may be physical or conceptual. Conceptual models may be expressed in words or mathematical symbols. Frequently a model is the most easily understood way of expressing a theory (see Bohr atomic model, p. 71). A model can also be used to explain or predict. The earliest chemical theory (the atomic theory) is discussed in the next chapter and the earliest atomic model is also described.

A chemist is always on the lookout for a regular pattern of behavior. Ramsay, for example, observed that helium, neon, argon, krypton, and xenon are *gases* which must be cooled to very low temperatures before they can be liquefied. He also observed that all seemed to be *chemically inert* and had *unusually low melting points*. These similarities led him to realize that he had discovered five elements and that these elements made up a "family." Sometimes experiments raise questions that cannot be answered by using the equipment and apparatus available at that time. After Ramsay's discovery of the noble gases, it was reasonable to ask: Why are these elements chemically inert? This question was finally answered by the unrelenting efforts of many physicists through a period of at least 20 years. The contributions of some of these physicists are described in Chapters 3, 4, and 5.

Speculate . . .
Scientific knowledge expands as the necessary tools of discovery become available. Why?

The more scientists seek answers to their questions, the more they realize that *absolute* answers are rarely if ever possible. A new point of attack, or improved equipment, may provide evidence to disprove concepts that were previously taken for granted. For instance, it was believed for more than 50 years that the noble gases were completely inert. And then in 1962 this particular belief was shattered. Chemists must ever be ready to modify their theories or even to discard them if new observations make them untenable.

Summary

Air is a mixture of gases, chiefly oxygen and nitrogen, which make up almost 99% of dry air. The determination of the *exact* composition of air involved experimental work spread over more than a century. First, Cavendish discovered a small elusive residue in addition to oxygen, nitrogen, carbon dioxide, and water vapor. What was this residue? The first inkling of the answer to this question came when Rayleigh, more than a century later, found that the density of atmospheric nitrogen is a little bit greater than the density of pure nitrogen obtained by the decomposition of compounds of nitrogen. He suspected that atmospheric nitrogen contained an element denser than nitrogen. Rayleigh and Ramsay confirmed this suspicion after proving in their own experiments that Cavendish's residual gas was a new substance, which they named *argon*. Was "argon" a single element? By fractional distillation Ramsay discovered that "argon" was a mixture of five gaseous elements—helium, neon, argon, krypton, and xenon. All these elements are in the same chemical family, the family of the noble gas elements.

Chemical knowledge is derived from experiments. In doing experiments, scientists follow a logical sequence of steps, usually referred to as the scientific method. These steps include (1) careful observations of all the things that happen, (2) accurate recording of the information gained through observation, (3) organization of the information with a sharp lookout for regularities in behavior, (4) drawing of conclusions from experimental observations, and (5) formulation of an explanation to account for the observations, often with the aid of a theory or a model.

Factual Recall

1. Explain how the chief constituents of air can be separated.
2. What particular properties of helium make it the most suitable gas for use in lighter-than-air craft?
3. (*a*) Explain the terms *distillation* and *fractional distillation*.
   (*b*) How can air be liquefied?
   (*c*) How can oxygen gas be obtained from liquid air?

4. Describe the Cavendish experiment on the combination of atmospheric oxygen and nitrogen.

5. What information did Cavendish acquire from the experiment described in Question 4?

6. In summarizing the experiment in Question 4, Cavendish wrote, "If there be any part of our atmosphere that differs from the rest, it is not more than 1/120 part of the whole."
   (*a*) Why did Cavendish make this statement?
   (*b*) Was the statement justified in the light of subsequent research?

7. Explain how and why helium got its name.

8. (*a*) What is a chemical family?
   (*b*) Name the elements in the noble gas family.
   (*c*) Why do these elements belong in the same family?

9. What led Rayleigh to suspect that nitrogen obtained from air contained another gas?

10. What experimental evidence is there to prove that (*a*) nitrogen is less active than oxygen, (*b*) argon is less active than nitrogen?

11. Describe the Ramsay-Rayleigh experiment by which argon was discovered.

12. (*a*) State the question propounded by Ramsay following the experiment described in Question 10.
    (*b*) How did Ramsay find the answer to this question?

13. (*a*) Are all members of the noble gas family completely inert elements?
    (*b*) Explain.

14. What is the so-called experimental method? That is, what procedure must be followed if experiments are used to acquire scientific knowledge?

Apply Your Knowledge!

1. Why was it stated that argon was "discovered" in 1894 but had been isolated by accident in 1784? Why was the first not a discovery?

2. What characteristics of the scientific or experimental method were involved in Cavendish's experiments on nitrogen and oxygen?

3. Why do regularities in experimental results have special significance to a scientist?

Find Out!

1. How might Cavendish have proved that the "dew" found in the globe after exploding hydrogen and oxygen was water?
2. Are there instances of "fractional distillation" that occur in nature? What are they?

Suggested Readings

Asimov, I., *Noble Gases.* New York: Basic Books, 1966.

Bartlett, N., "Noble Gas Compounds," *International Science and Technology,* **33:** 55–56 (September 1964).

Chernick, C.L., *Chemistry of the Noble Gases* (pamphlet). Washington: U.S. Atomic Energy Commission, Division of Technical Information, 1967.

Chernick, C.L., "The Noble Gas Compounds," *Chemistry,* **37:** 6–12 (January 1964).

Claassen, H.H., *The Noble Gases.* Boston: D.C. Heath 1966.

Jaffe, B., *Crucibles* (Rev. and Abr. Ed.). New York: Fawcett, 1960. (See Chapter IV.)

Moody, G. J. and J. D. R. Thomas, *Noble Gases and their Compounds.* New York: Pergamon, 1964.

Pollack, G.L., "Solid Noble Gases," *Scientific American,* **215:**64 (October 1966).

Ramsay, Sir W., *The Gases of the Atmosphere: The History of their Discovery.* London: Macmillan, 1915.

Selig, H., J. G. Malm, and H.H. Claassen, "The Chemistry of the Noble Gases," *Scientific American,* **210:** 66–77 (May 1964).

Travers, M.W., *Discovery of the Rare Gases,* New York: Longmans, Green, 1928.

Wolfenden, J.H., "The Noble Gases and the Periodic Table: Telling It Like It Was," *Journal of Chemical Education,* **46:** 569 (September 1969).

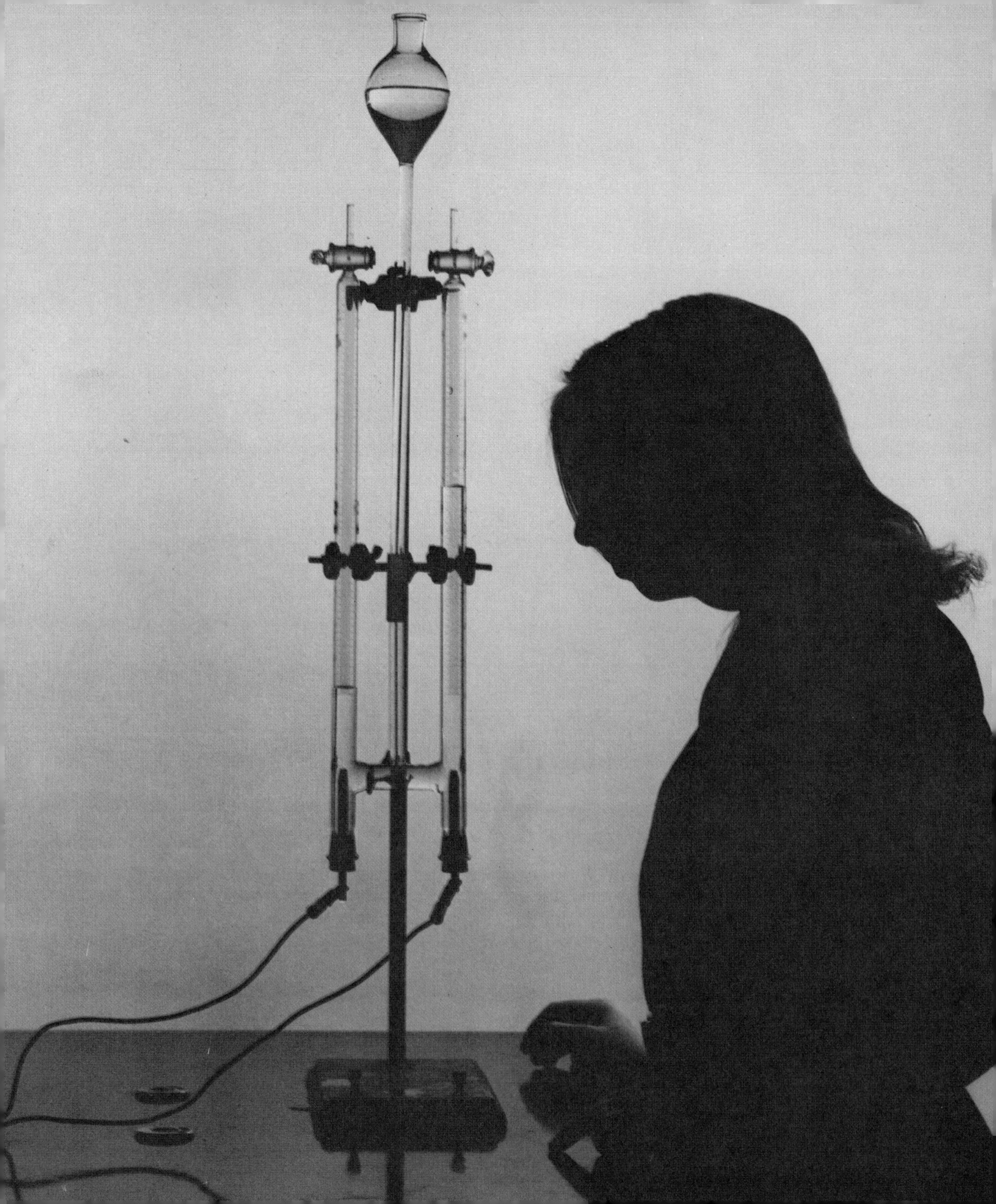

UNIT I

ATOMS AND THEIR STRUCTURE

ATOMS ARE EVERYWHERE. They are the building blocks of elements and compounds. Atoms are much too small to be seen by the eye or even by the most powerful microscopes. Since direct observation of atoms is impossible, scientists resort to theories and models to account for their chemical behavior.

The first atomic theory was proposed by John Dalton in the early part of the 19th Century. Dalton's model of an atom was a spherical, indivisible solid which varied in size from element to element. With his theory and his model Dalton could both account for two known chemical laws (the law of conservation of mass and the law of constant proportions) and predict a new law of multiple proportions.

Accepting Dalton's assumption that all atoms of an element have the same mass, chemists of the 19th Century calculated relative atomic masses for all the known elements. The atomic mass scale turned out to be the most significant contribution to chemical knowledge in the 19th Century. It led to the first periodic classification of elements and the determination of formulas for compounds.

By the end of the 19th Century it became apparent that atoms have parts and are therefore divisible. First, J. J. Thomson and R. A.

Millikan proved that electrons are an essential part of all atoms. Next, Rutherford proved that each atom has a nucleus. Such a nucleus (except for a hydrogen nucleus) is made up of two constituents, *protons* and *neutrons*. The electrons are outside of the nucleus and the positive charge on the nucleus is exactly balanced by the negative charge on the electrons.

In the early part of the present century, after studying the colors in the bright-line spectrum of hydrogen, Niels Bohr suggested still another atomic model. According to Bohr, electrons revolved in a circular orbit around the nucleus. If atoms were excited, the electrons absorbed particles of energy called photons, and jumped to other orbits further from the nucleus. As they fell back toward the nucleus some of their potential energy was transformed into light energy and the photons emitted produced the colored bright lines of the spectrum. Bohr derived an equation from which he was able to compute the energy of an electron at the various orbits or energy levels, and also the wavelengths of the emitted light as the electrons fall from higher to lower orbits. Moreover, his calculated values for the energy levels of hydrogen atoms accounted for the values obtained by various experimenters. As a result, the concept of circular electronic orbits was applied to all atoms and this model provided the generally accepted picture for a number of years. However, doubts were cast upon the Bohr model when it was realized that the Bohr equation applied only to the spectrum of hydrogen. A newer model, based on quantum mechanics, was then devised to account for the line spectra of all atoms.

Fig. U-1 A linear accelerator used in nuclear research.

The quantum model indicates the region in space where the electron is most likely to be found. It can be likened to a closely packed swarm of bees flying around a hive, where the hive represents the nucleus of an atom and the positions of the bees represent the possible positions of a *single* electron. The region traversed by the electron is called an *electron cloud*.

If there is more than one electron around the nucleus, the cloud (or *orbital*) of each electron may have a different shape and different average distance from the nucleus. There are four different orbital shapes, designated by the letters *s*, *p*, *d*, or *f*. The electron orbitals are often called energy levels. Energy levels are designated by quantum numbers.

HISTORICAL CHEMISTRY LABORATORY

This is part of the original work of Robert A. Millikan, *The Elementary Electric Charge,* in which he described his method of determining the charge of electrons.*

Robert A. Millikan (1868–1953)

The only essential modification in the method consists in replacing the droplet of water or alcohol by one of oil, mercury or some other nonvolatile substance, and in introducing it into the observing space in a new way.

Figure 1 shows the apparatus used in the following experiments. By means of a commercial "atomizer" A a cloud of fine droplets of oil is blown with the aid of dust-free air into the dust-free chamber C. One or more of the droplets of this cloud is allowed to fall through a pinhole p into the space between the plates M, N of a horizontal air condenser and the pinhole is then closed by means of an electromagnetically operated cover not shown in the diagram. If the pinhole is left open, air currents are likely to pass through it and produce irregularities. The plates M, N are heavy, circular, ribbed brass castings 22 cm in diameter having surfaces which are ground so nearly to true planes that the error is nowhere more than .02 mm. These planes are held exactly 16 mm apart by means of three small ebonite posts, held firmly in place by ebonite screws. A*

The atomizer method of producing very minute but accurately spherical drops for the purpose of studying their behavior in fluid media, was first conceived and successfully carried out in January 1908 at the Ryerson Laboratory by Mr. J. Y. Lee, while he was engaged in a quantitative investigation of Brownian movements. His spheres were blown from Wood's metal, wax, and other like substances which solidify at ordinary temperatures. Since then the method has been almost continuously in use here, upon this and a number of other problems, and elsewhere upon similar problems.

*From *The Physical Review*, **32** (1911), p. 349.

strip of thin-sheet ebonite C passes entirely around the plates, thus forming a completely enclosed air space. Three glass windows, 1.5 cm square, are placed in this ebonite strip at the angular positions 0°, 165°, and 180°. A narrow parallel beam of light from an arc lamp enters the condenser through the first window and emerges through the last. The other window serves for observing, with the aid of a short focus telescope placed about 2 feet distant, the illuminated oil droplet as it floats in the air between the plates. The appearance of this drop is that of a brilliant star on a black background. It falls, of course under the action of gravity, toward the lower plate; but before it reaches it, an electrical field of strength between 3,000 volts and 8,000 volts per centimeter is created between the plates by means of the battery B, and, if the droplet had received a frictional charge of the proper sign and strength as it was blown out through the atomizer, it is pulled up by this field against gravity, toward the upper plate. Before it strikes it the plates are short-circuited by means of the switch S and the time required by the drop to fall under gravity the distance corresponding to the space between the cross hairs of the observing telescope is accurately determined. Then the rate at which the droplet moves up under the influence of the field is measured by timing it through the same distance when the field is on. This operation is repeated and the speeds checked an indefinite number of times, or until the droplet catches an ion from among those which exist normally in air, or which have been produced in the space between the plates by any of the usual ionizing agents like radium or x-rays. The fact that an ion has been caught and the exact instant at which the event happened is signaled to the observer by the change in the speed of the droplet under the influence of the field. From the sign and magnitude of this change in speed, taken in connection with the constant speed under gravity, the sign and the exact value of the charge carried by the captured ion are determined. The error in a single observation need not exceed one third of one percent. It is from the values of the speeds observed that all of the conclusions above mentioned are directly and simply deduced.

The experiment is particularly striking when, as often happens, the droplet carries but one elementary charge and then by the capture of an ion of opposite sign is completely neutralized so that its speed is altogether unaffected by the field. In this case the computed charge is itself the charge on the captured ion.

The measurement of the distance between the cross hairs, correct to about .01 mm, is made by means of a standard scale placed vertically at exactly the same distance from the telescope as the pinhole p.

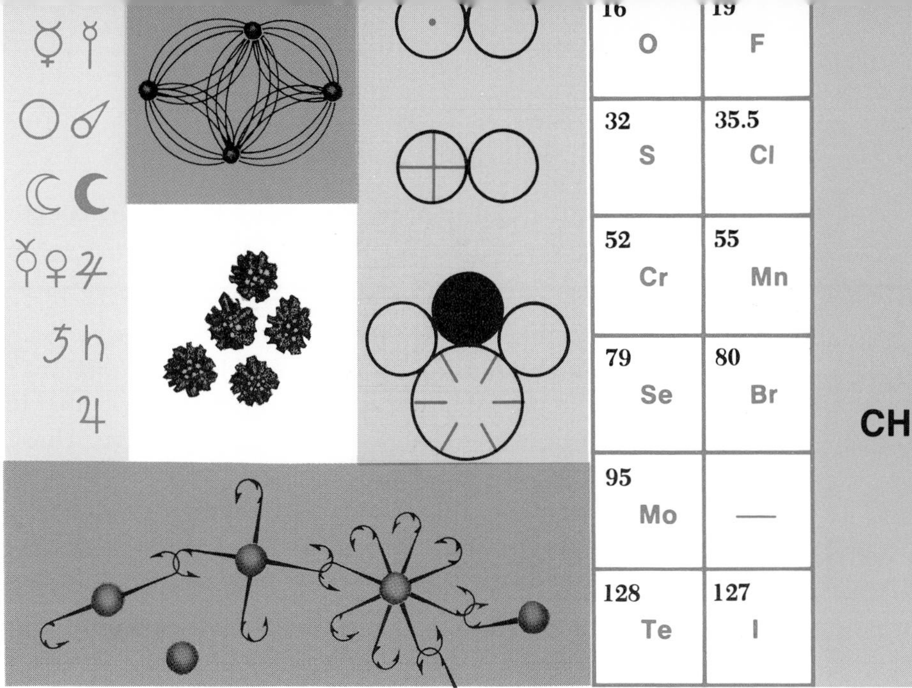

16
O
19
F
32
S
35.5
Cl
52
Cr
55
Mn
79
Se
80
Br
95
Mo
—
128
Te
127
I

CHAPTER 2

ORGANIZING PRINCIPLES

AS YOU LEARNED IN Chapter 1, scientists are ever on the lookout for a pattern of behavior. When such an orderly behavior pattern is found, it is expressed as a broad generalization, which we have defined as a *law*. But a law is only a statement of fact, and scientists seek more than facts. They want a rational explanation of the facts; they want answers to the questions "How?" and "Why?". They want a theory that will offer a plausible explanation of the known facts. An acceptable scientific theory must not only account for the experimental facts available, but it must also be able to predict what will happen under new and untested conditions. Indeed, the predictive value of a theory is probably its most useful asset.

A Search for an Explanation of Matter

Atoms

The word *atom* is probably the most frequently used term in scientific literature. It was used by Greek philosophers more than 2,000 years ago, and, it should not be surprising that the concept of an atom has changed considerably through the ages.

Although Greek philosophers did no experiments to test their ideas, some thought of atoms as nature's building blocks. (See page 23.) Thus, although a lump of copper looked like a continuous piece of matter, they argued that it was made up of a vast number of particles that were much too small to be seen by the eye. These tiny particles were thought to be indivisible and indestructible. Hence they were called atoms, from the Greek *atomos,* meaning *cannot be split* or *indivisible*. Today however, we think of atoms as very complex structures made up of a number of even smaller particles.

The crude atomic concepts of the Greek philosophers languished without experimental support and were almost forgotten until the early part of the 17th Century. At this time they were revived and cultivated by Robert Boyle (1627–1691), whose experiments with gas pressure indicated their value. Isaac Newton (1642–1727) too was an "atomist." About 1800, John Dalton, an English scientist, revised the old atomic theories to account for two laws of chemical combination that had recently been published. One of these laws was discovered by Antoine Lavoisier.

The Law of Conservation of Mass

Fig. 2-1 The analytical balance is the chemist's most important tool.

Lavoisier was the first man to recognize the importance of the analytical balance in experimental work. (See Fig. 2-1.) Through a 20-year period (1775 to 1795) he studied a large number of chemical reactions by weighing the starting substances, called *reactants*, and the substances formed in the reaction, called *products*. In every case he found that the mass of the products was exactly equal to the mass of the reactants. These observations constitute a general statement of experimental data applicable to all the reactions studied and called a *scientific* (or *natural*) *law*. Lavoisier thus had discovered a natural law: *There is no observable gain or loss of mass in a chemical reaction carried out under ordinary conditions*. This statement is called the *Law of Conservation of Mass*.

The validity of this law has been tested many times with improved and more sensitive balances, but no balance has ever revealed the slightest difference between the masses of reactants and products in ordinary chemical reactions. (See Fig. 2-2.)

The Law of Constant Proportions

During the latter part of the 18th Century, chemists concentrated upon the problem of analyzing compounds, particularly upon the analysis of a compound that could be made in several different ways. One such compound is copper (II) oxide, a black powder (referred to in Chapter 1) which can be made in at least four ways. Copper (II) oxide can be prepared by prolonged heating of copper in air or oxygen and by heating copper (II) nitrate. By analysis, it is found that the percentage by mass of copper in every sample of copper (II) oxide is 80.0%, and the percentage of oxygen is 20.0%. In fact, most compounds are found to have a constant percentage composition no matter how they are prepared. Here, then is a concise description of still another law of nature. It was stated by Joseph Proust (1754–1826), a French chemist, and is called the *Law of Constant Proportions* (or the *Law of Definite Proportions*). This law states: *A given compound always contains the same elements in fixed proportions by mass.*

Fig. 2-2 The law of conservation of mass. (*a*) Test tube containing $Pb(NO_3)_2$ suspended in a flask containing K_2CrO_4 solution. (*b*) The flask is inverted and the two liquids have mixed and formed a heavy precipitate. The position of the balance pointer, however, remains unchanged, because the mass in the flask has not changed.

(*a*)

(*b*)

Dalton's Atomic Theory

John Dalton (1766–1834) proposed his theory in 1803 to account for the two known laws of chemical combination. This theory grew out of an attempt to answer the question: What must be the ultimate structure of matter if it is to behave according to our observations on the laws of chemical combination? He answered this question by assuming that all matter is made up of tiny particles called *atoms*, and he assigned certain definite properties to them. He also drew pictures (crude models) symbolizing them (Fig. 2-3). A list of these atomic properties constitutes his atomic theory. The four main postulates or assumptions of this theory are:

1. Atoms are basic particles of matter. They cannot be split into smaller particles nor can they be destroyed.

2. Atoms of the same element are identical; they have the same mass, and the same chemical properties.

3. Atoms of different elements have different masses and different chemical properties.

4. Atoms of different elements combine in simple proportions to form compounds.

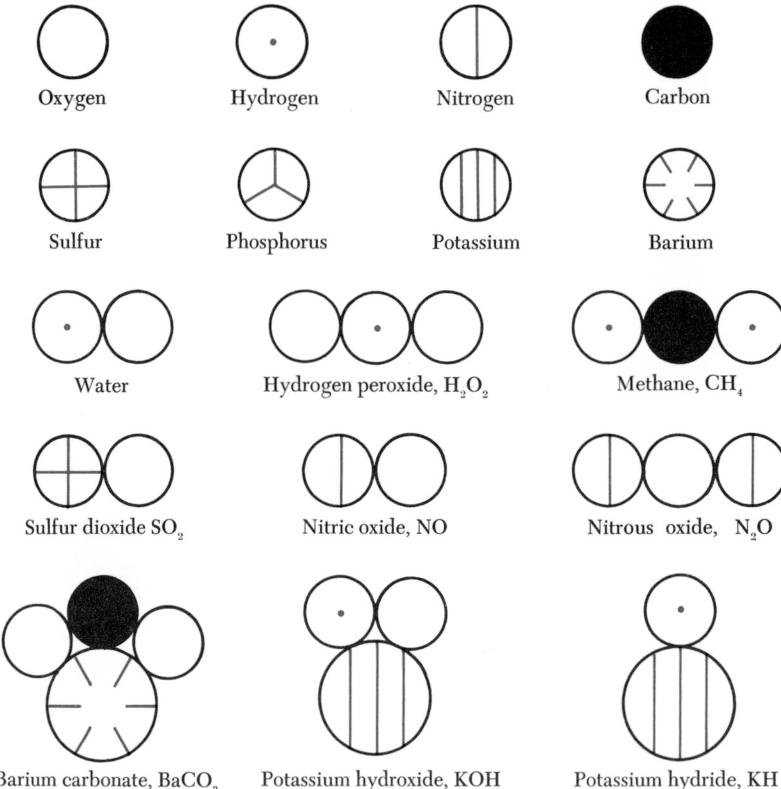

Fig. 2-3 Atomic symbols as used by John Dalton, about 1803.

A model of the Dalton atom is usually represented as a small incompressible sphere. We can think of it as a tiny ball of steel. And, since atoms combine with each other to form compounds, our spherical models must have hooks of some kind to hold them together. Dalton's models had such hooks; atoms have none.

How did Dalton apply his theory to account for the two known laws of chemical combination? The law of conservation of mass was easily explained. The theory states that atoms are indestructible, and therefore matter is also indestructible. In addition, since a given quantity of matter is measured by its mass, any change in mass in a chemical reaction is impossible. The law of conservation of mass states that in a chemical reaction atoms may change their association with other atoms, but no atoms are lost and none are gained.

Investigate . . .

Take a length of fine copper wire-about 25 cm—and cut it in half; divide one half again into halves. Continue cutting the wire into smaller and smaller pieces. Can you now follow the reasoning of the Greek philosophers?

The explanation of the law of constant proportions is a little more complicated. Dalton's reasoning was as follows: If two samples of matter have exactly the same properties, they must be made up of atoms of the same kind in the same numerical proportion and therefore must be samples of the same compound. Moreover, since all atoms of the same kind have the same mass, these two samples must have the same percentage composition by mass. It follows logically from the atomic theory that a compound always contains the same elements in a fixed proportion by mass.

Note . . .
Dalton used the term *weight*, not *mass*. However, mass rather than weight is what he meant and therefore this is the term used. The mass (m) of an object is the quantity of matter in the object. The weight (F_w) of an object is the magnitude of the force of attraction between the mass of the earth and the mass of the object.

The Law of Simple Multiple Proportions

The ultimate test of a theory is its ability to predict what will happen in untried cases and even to predict new laws. Dalton's theory met this test. Let us see how.

The fourth postulate of Dalton's theory states that different atoms combine in simple ratios to form compounds. By this he meant that one atom of element A may combine with one atom of element B to form compound AB; also, that one atom of A may combine with two atoms of B to form compound AB_2; that two atoms of A may combine with three atoms of B to form A_2B_3, and so on. Thus, the theory indicated that if elements A and B combine, compounds with such variations as A_2B, AB, A_2B_3, and AB_2 might be possible. By inspection, you can see that the A to B ratios of the A and B atoms in A_2B, AB, A_2B_3, and AB_2 are the same as those in A_2B, A_2B_2, A_2B_3, and A_2B_4. In the compounds of the latter arrangement, there is a fixed mass of A (namely A_2) but different masses of B which are in the ratio of 1:2:3:4. An example of this is shown in Table 2-1.

Table 2-1 Compounds of nitrogen and oxygen

Compound	Formula	Mass of oxygen (g) combined with 1 g of nitrogen	Relative masses of oxygen combined with 1 g of nitrogen
Nitrogen (I) oxide	N_2O	0.5711	1
Nitrogen (II) oxide	NO	1.1422	2
Nitrogen (III) oxide	N_2O_3	1.7134	3
Nitrogen (IV) oxide	NO_2	2.2845	4
Nitrogen (V) oxide	N_2O_5	2.8557	5

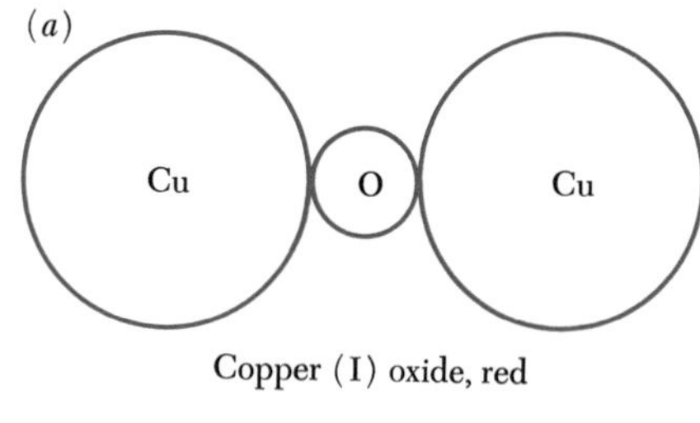

Copper (I) oxide, red

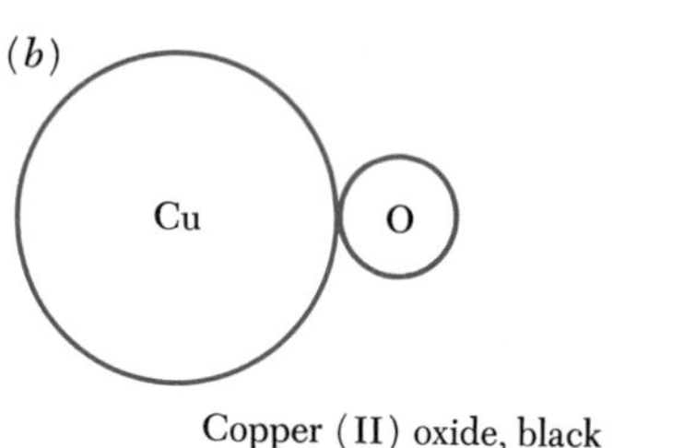

Copper (II) oxide, black

Fig. 2-4 Dalton's symbols for CuO and Cu_2O.

This simple whole-number ratio led Dalton to predict the *Law of Simple Multiple Proportions*, which can be stated as follows: *When two elements combine to form more than one compound, if the mass of one element is fixed, the mass of the other varies in a ratio of whole numbers, usually small.*

Many groups of compounds were found to illustrate the predicted law. For instance, if copper is heated in air or oxygen, one of two possible compounds (oxides) is formed, depending upon such conditions as temperature and the amount of oxygen available. One of the oxides is red and is called copper (I) oxide. (An older name is cuprous oxide.) The other is black and is called copper (II) oxide. (Its older name is cupric oxide.) (See Fig. 2-4.)

An analysis of these compounds shows that in copper (I) oxide

$$\frac{\text{mass of copper}}{\text{mass of oxygen}} = \frac{8}{1}$$

and in copper (II) oxide

$$\frac{\text{mass of copper}}{\text{mass of oxygen}} = \frac{4}{1}$$

The masses of copper that combine with 1 g of oxygen are 8 g and 4 g; therefore, these masses of copper are in the ratio of 2:1, a simple whole-number ratio. This verifies the law. The results above also suggest that the ratio by mass of copper atoms to oxygen atoms is twice as great in the former compound as in the latter but they do not suggest that the formulas are Cu_80 and Cu_40. Why?

Atomic Masses

Probably the most significant statement in Dalton's theory was that all atoms of the same element have the same mass. If this were true, then each element would have a characteristic atomic mass that Dalton could calculate. However, individual atoms are too small to be weighed directly on a balance. In Dalton's time there was no known way of finding the actual or absolute masses of atoms, but their *relative* masses could be determined. That is, the mass of one atom could be compared with the mass of another.

The relative masses of atoms are adequate for all ordinary purposes, and fortunately they can be found by fairly simple methods. For instance, the relative atomic masses of hydrogen and oxygen can be computed by determining the percentage composition by mass of water. This composition is found to be 11.1% hydrogen and 88.9% oxygen. Hence, in water,

$$\frac{\text{mass of oxygen}}{\text{mass of hydrogen}} = \frac{88.9}{11.1} = \frac{7.95}{1}$$

We also know that water can be decomposed electrically. This process, called electrolysis, yields two volumes of hydrogen per volume of oxygen, suggesting that the simplest formula for water is H_2O; that is, water consists of two atoms of hydrogen for each atom of oxygen. (See Fig. 2-5.) Therefore, in one molecule of water,

$$\frac{\text{mass of 1 atom of oxygen}}{\text{mass of 2 atoms of hydrogen}} = \frac{7.95}{1.00}$$

Or, comparing masses of single atoms,

$$\frac{\text{mass of 1 oxygen atom}}{\text{mass of 1 hydrogen atom}} = \frac{7.95}{0.50} = \frac{15.90}{1.00}$$

Notice that the atomic mass of oxygen (15.90) is compared with hydrogen as unity. Dalton also determined the atomic masses of other elements based upon this arbitrary standard.

Dalton selected hydrogen as the element of reference because hydrogen is the lightest of all elements. Thus, by calling the atomic mass of hydrogen 1.000, the atomic masses of all other elements are greater than one. However, far more elements combine with oxygen than hydrogen, and therefore in later years oxygen became the reference element of choice with an atomic mass arbitrarily fixed at 16.000. By international agreement, the atomic masses of all other elements were expressed in terms of this new value. The value for hydrogen was changed from 1.000 to

$$\frac{1.000 \times 16.000}{15.90} = 1.008$$

It soon became convenient to talk about the masses of atoms, but because these masses were so small—much smaller than any of the conventional mass units, such as grams, pounds, etc.—it was necessary to define a new and very tiny unit of mass to be used in discussing atomic masses. This new reference unit was one-sixteenth of the mass of an atom of oxygen and its value was equal to 1 unit on the *atomic mass scale*. The atomic mass of oxygen was 16.000 *atomic mass units* (amu) and that of hydrogen 1.008 amu. On the

Note . . .

The *ous* and *ic* endings are found in older chemical literature. Keep the terms in mind so that you can understand them when you see them again.

Fig. 2-5 The Hoffman apparatus is used for the electrolysis of water.

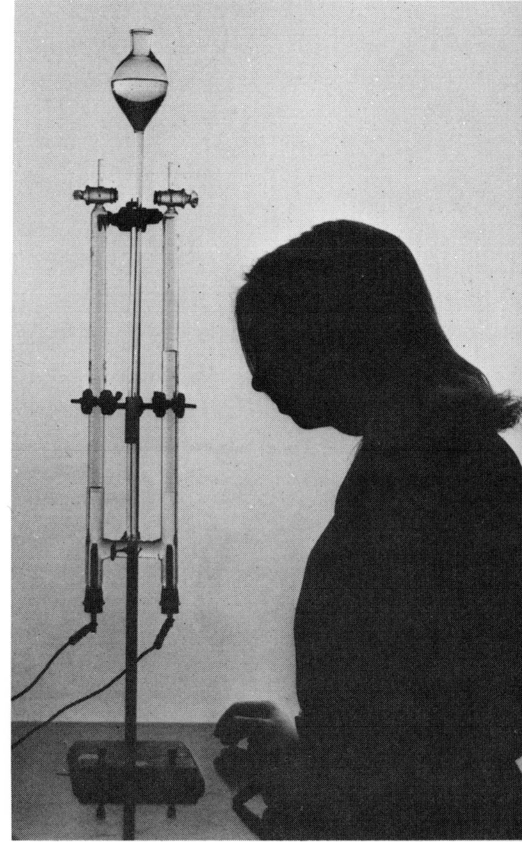

Fig. 2-6 Symbols for familiar substances used by the ancient Greeks and medieval alchemists.

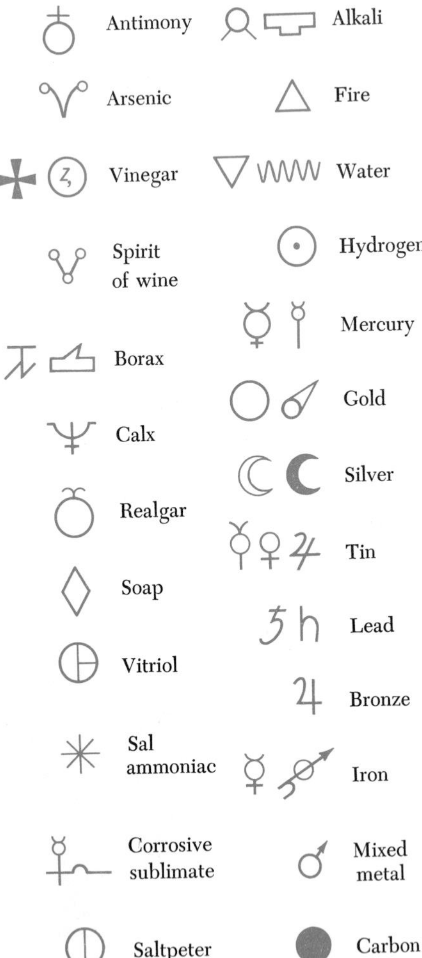

hydrogen scale, the atomic value for chlorine was 35.3 and therefore, on the atomic mass scale, its value was

$$\frac{35.3 \times 16.000}{15.90} = 35.5 \text{ amu}$$

Later, scientists questioned the fact that atomic masses were not whole numbers. Further investigation revealed that many elements actually were mixtures of atoms with the same chemical properties but slightly different masses. When an element consists of such a mixture, each component is known as an *isotope*. Some isotopes are more common than others. Isotopes will be discussed again in Chapter 3.

In 1961, a new atomic mass standard was adopted. This was based on atoms of the most common carbon isotope which has a mass of 12 amu. A list of the atomic masses of all the elements, based on the carbon-12 standard, is in the Appendix. The values found in this table are actually "average" atomic masses calculated for the naturally occurring mixtures of isotopes of the various elements.

Symbols for Elements or Atoms

As one would expect, the names of elements are different in different languages. However, the chemical symbols of the elements are the same, whatever the language. For example, although the French word for iron is *fer* and the German one is *eisen*, yet in both languages the symbol used is Fe. Many strange chemical symbols have been found in old books (see Fig. 2-6). The Swedish chemist Jöns Jaköb Berzelius (1779–1848) was the first one to use letter symbols for the chemical elements and the current system is based on his rules.

Most chemical symbols are derived from the English names of the elements. Whenever possible, the first letter is used and the letter is capitalized. Thus H is the symbol for hydrogen, O for oxygen, S for sulfur, and N for nitrogen. In many instances more than one element begins with the same letter; to avoid confusion, the symbols for these elements are formed by adding a second letter which is not capitalized. Consider, for example, the symbols for elements whose names begin with the letter C. The symbol for carbon is C; for calcium, Ca; for chlorine, Cl; for chromium, Cr; for cadmium,

Cd; for cobalt, Co; for cesium, Cs; and for curium, Cm. Other common elements with two-letter symbols are aluminum, Al; argon, Ar; magnesium, Mg; manganese, Mn; zinc, Zn; and helium, He.

A few symbols, about ten in all, are derived from the Latin names of the elements. These include copper, Cu (cuprum); gold, Au (aurum); iron, Fe (ferrum); lead, Pb (plumbum); mercury, Hg (hydrargyrum); potassium, K (kalium); silver, Ag (argentum); sodium, Na (natrium); antimony, Sb (stibium); and tin, Sn (stannum). The privilege of naming a new element is accorded the discoverer. Interestingly, in the case of lawrencium, element 103, the discoverers suggested the symbol Lw, but, because the letter *w* does not appear in all scientific languages, the symbol now used is Lr.

Investigate . . .
Many common "English" names of elements are derived from words in other languages. You know about the names of the noble gases. See what you can find out about magnesium, chlorine, chromium, and cobalt.

A Classification of the Elements

The analytical chemists of the 19th Century found the atomic masses of all the known elements, which numbered about 60 by the middle of the century. A partial list of these elements arranged in increasing order of their atomic masses was hydrogen (1), lithium (7), beryllium (9), boron (11), carbon (12), nitrogen (14), oxygen (16), fluorine (19), sodium (23), magnesium (24), aluminum (27), silicon (28), phosphorus (31), sulfur (32), chlorine (35.5), potassium (39), calcium (40). It was observed that when hydrogen was omitted and the rest arranged in rows of seven as in Table 2-2, the elements in the vertical columns had remarkably similar properties.

Lithium (Li), sodium (Na), and potassium (K) have similar chemical properties: They are all low-density, highly reactive metals. Similarly, beryllium (Be), magnesium (Mg), and calcium (Ca) have many properties in common. Carbon (C) and silicon (Si) are also similar, as are nitrogen (N) and phosphorus (P); oxygen (O) and sulfur (S); fluorine (F) and chlorine (Cl). The last eight elements mentioned are all nonmetals. Is there really some relationship between the masses of atoms and their chemical properties? Unfortunately, beyond the element calcium there is a break in the rhythm of similarities, and some chemists regarded the other similarities to be mere coincidence and of no particular significance. However, in 1869, a Russian chemist named Dimitri Mendeleev had other ideas.

Table 2-2 Elements arranged in order of atomic mass

Li	**Be**	**B**	**C**	**N**	**O**	**F**
Na	**Mg**	**Al**	**Si**	**P**	**S**	**Cl**
K	**Ca**					

Mendeleev also found there was a recurrence of similar properties for elements up to atomic mass 35.5 when they were arranged

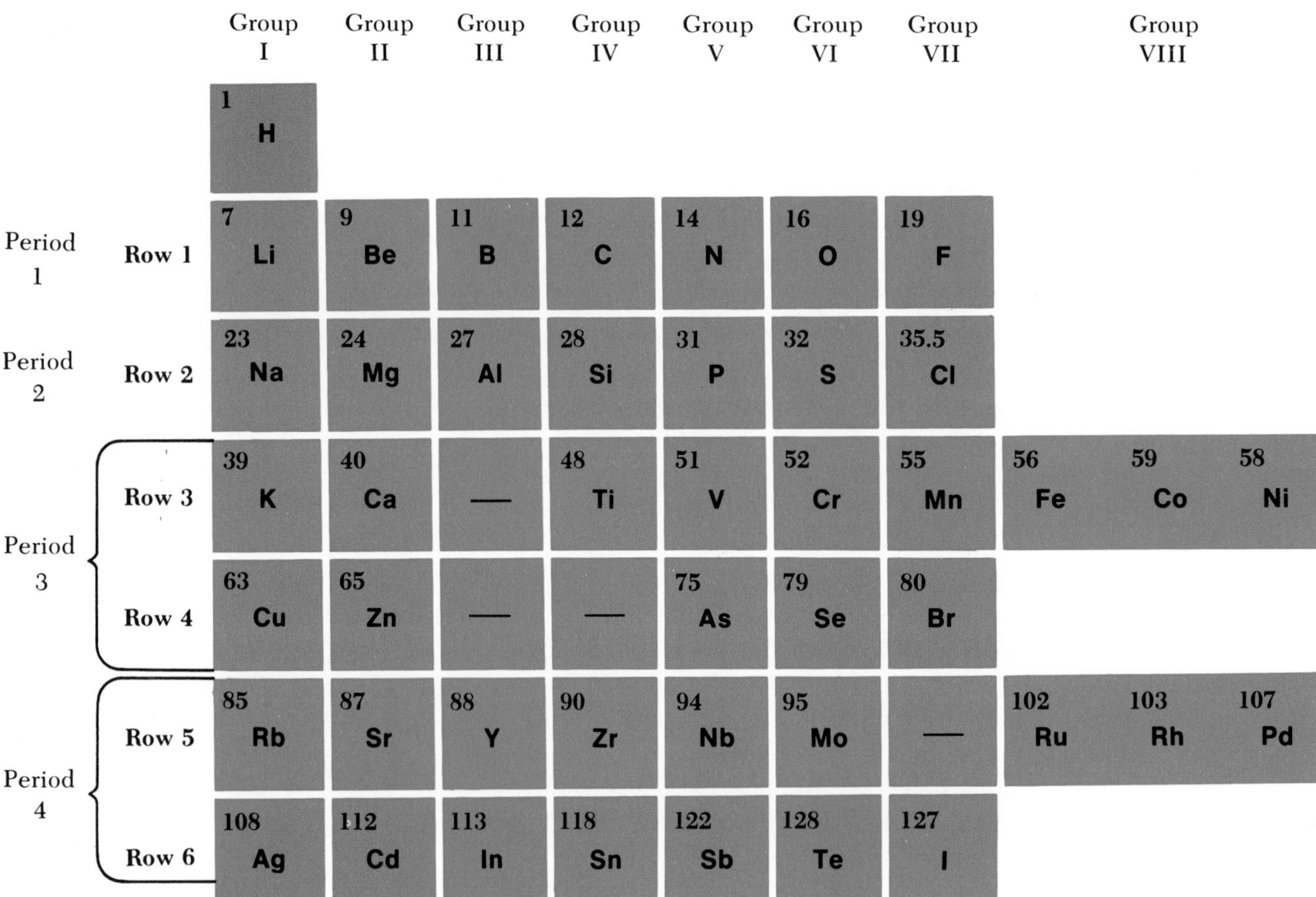

		Group I	Group II	Group III	Group IV	Group V	Group VI	Group VII	Group VIII		
		1 H									
Period 1	Row 1	7 Li	9 Be	11 B	12 C	14 N	16 O	19 F			
Period 2	Row 2	23 Na	24 Mg	27 Al	28 Si	31 P	32 S	35.5 Cl			
Period 3	Row 3	39 K	40 Ca	—	48 Ti	51 V	52 Cr	55 Mn	56 Fe	59 Co	58 Ni
	Row 4	63 Cu	65 Zn	—	—	75 As	79 Se	80 Br			
Period 4	Row 5	85 Rb	87 Sr	88 Y	90 Zr	94 Nb	95 Mo	—	102 Ru	103 Rh	107 Pd
	Row 6	108 Ag	112 Cd	113 In	118 Sn	122 Sb	128 Te	127 I			

Fig. 2-7 The first four periods of Mendeleev's periodic table.

in order of increasing atomic masses. However, a recurrence did not appear until double rows (each containing 14 elements) had been lined up. The horizontal rows of elements with recurring properties were called *periods*. As shown in Fig. 2-7, the first period was made up of row number 1 and the second period was row number 2, but the third period consisted of two rows, and each of the remaining periods also of two rows. Thus, the first two periods were short, and the other periods long.

The short periods contained seven elements and all spaces were filled, but the long periods were not filled. For example, in the third period, the elements calcium (atomic mass 40) and titanium (atomic mass 48) were known. Calcium, in row 3, was similar to magnesium, in row 2, but titanium (Ti), in row 3, was related in no simple way to aluminum, in row 2. Since there was a large difference between the atomic masses of calcium and titanium (a difference of eight), Mendeleev suspected that there might be an element between calcium and titanium, (as yet underscovered) with an atomic mass of approximately 44. Accordingly, he left an empty space between calcium and titanium, a space that hopefully would be filled when the missing element was discovered. Mendeleev left a large number of such spaces, particularly in the later periods, for the so-called undiscovered elements.

Mendeleev called the vertical columns of elements *groups*, and for convenience used Roman numerals in numbering the groups. He observed a similarity in the properties of the elements in the same group, particularly among the first 16 elements, that is, from lithium to calcium. Beyond calcium, however, there is little correlation between adjacent elements. For example, there is little or no chemical similarity between silicon (Si) and titanium (Ti) in Group IV, or between phosphorus (P) and vanadium (V) in Group V. But there is a marked similarity between alternate elements. For instance, the following pairs of elements have similar properties: phosphorus (P) and arsenic (As) in Group V; sulfur (S) and selenium (Se) in Group VI.

For this reason, Mendeleev made the two rows from potassium to bromine, as well as rows 5 and 6, into single long periods: Periods 3 and 4. There are also similarities between the following alternate pairs of elements: potassium and rubidium, calcium and strontium, zinc and cadmium, arsenic and antimony, bromine and iodine. With this proviso, the vertical columns or groups consist of families of elements with closely related physical and chemical properties. Thus, the elements lithium, sodium, potassium, and rubidium comprise a natural family, as do the elements fluorine, chlorine, bromine, and iodine. Mendeleev's observations can be summarized in the following statement: *The properties of the elements vary with their atomic masses in a systematic way*. This statement is now known as the *Periodic Law*. But is it a scientific law?

Uses of the Periodic Table

As stated earlier, one of the greatest uses of a scientific law is its ability to predict what will happen in untested cases. Did the periodic law meet this test? Mendeleev had enough confidence in the validity of the new law to predict the properties of a number of elements that had not been discovered at the time. For example, there were two empty spaces between zinc and arsenic in Period 3, Row 4.

Bearing in mind the similarities between *alternate* elements, he maintained that the space in Group IV would be filled by an element whose properties would be about the average of the properties of silicon (Si) and tin (Sn). He called the unknown element ekasilicon, and from the known properties of silicon and tin he predicted the properties of ekasilicon. Thus, Mendeleev argued that since the atomic masses of silicon and tin were 28 and 118 respectively, the atomic mass of ekasilicon would be about

$$\frac{28 + 118}{2} = 73$$

In 1871 Mendeleev published a table of properties of the undiscovered ekasilicon, and in 1885 a German chemist named Clemens Winkler (1838–1904) discovered the missing element. He called it germanium (Ge) in honor of his native country. In Table 2-3 the actual properties of germanium are compared with those which had been predicted by Mendeleev 14 years earlier.

Note . . .
The prefix *eka* is the Sanskrit word for one and was used by Mendeleev to indicate the unknown element *one* below a known element in a column of the periodic table.

Table 2-3 Actual and predicted properties of germanium

Properties	Properties of ekasilicon (Es), as predicted by Mendeleev in 1871	Actual properties of germanium (Ge), discovered in 1885
State of element	solid, metal	solid, metal
Atomic mass	73	72.59
Density	5.5 g/cm³	5.47 g/cm³
Formula of oxide	EsO_2	GeO_2
Density of oxide	4.7 g/cm³	4.7 g/cm³
Formula of chloride	$EsCl_4$	$GeCl_4$
Density of chloride	1.9 g/ml	1.9 g/ml
Boiling point of chloride	below 100 °C	86 °C

Mendeleev also predicted the properties of other undiscovered elements with the same astonishing degree of accuracy. Thus, the predictive power of the periodic law was established, and chemists had more faith in its validity. But did the law meet all other requirements of reliability?

The Combining Capacity of Elements in Each Group

Another important observation related to Mendeleev's table is that elements in the same group or family have the same chemical combining capacity. This combining capacity has been defined as the number of hydrogen atoms which will unite with or displace one atom of another element. It can be represented by a number which changes from group to group by regular increments, increasing from 1 to 4 and then decreasing from 4 to 1, as shown in Table 2-4. Thus, hydrogen and the Group I (or *alkali*) metals (Li, Na, K, Rb) have a combining capacity of 1 and so do the elements in Group VII (called *halogens*): F, Cl, Br, I. With this information, we can write the *formulas* of such compounds as sodium chloride (NaCl), lithium bromide (LiBr), potassium fluoride (KF), and rubidium iodide (RbI).

Table 2-4 Variation of combining capacity with group number

Group numbers	I	II	III	IV	V	VI	VII
Combining capacity	1	2	3	4	3	2	1

The elements in Groups II and VI have a combining capacity of 2, and thus the formulas for typical compounds are $MgCl_2$, $CaBr_2$, and K_2S. Elements in Groups III and V have a combining capacity of 3. Some formulas of compounds of elements selected from Groups III and V are Al_2S_3, NH_3, PCl_3, and AlN. Finally, carbon (C) and silicon (Si) in Group IV, have a combining capacity of 4, and the formulas of some stable compounds of these elements are CCl_4, SiO_2, and CH_4.

Discovery of the Noble Gas Family

During the 30 years following Mendeleev's arrangement of the periodic table, many new elements were discovered and a corresponding number of empty spaces filled in. Then, in 1900, Ramsay discovered the five elements that constitute the noble gas family. In terms of the Mendeleev table, the discovery of a new family could neither have been predicted nor expected. Did the new family fit into the periodic table?

Note . . .
A chemical formula is a "shorthand" way of indicating which elements are in a compound and in what proportion they occur in that compound; e.g., NaCl is the formula for table salt— its chemical name is sodium (Na) chloride (Cl) and it contains one atomic mass of sodium for each atomic mass of chlorine.

The atomic masses of the new elements were found to be helium (4), neon (20), argon (40), krypton (84), and xenon (131). If these elements are arranged in a vertical column, it is apparent that they fall into place at the right end of the Mendeleev table. Moreover, since these elements were found to be chemically inactive, the combining capacity of the new group was "zero." See Table 3-2.

Some Misfits in the Periodic Table

The fact that the Mendeleev table could accommodate a whole new family of elements was additional evidence in support of the periodic law. Nonetheless, there was also some evidence that did not support it. Previously we stated that the elements in the table were arranged in order of their atomic masses. Although this was true for the majority of elements, in a few cases exceptions had to be made. For example, iodine had to be placed *after* tellurium in the table although the atomic mass of iodine is 127 and the atomic mass of tellurium is 128. If these elements were placed in spaces according to atomic mass, iodine would *not* fall into Group VII, the group in which it clearly belongs on the basis of its chemical properties. When the noble gases were discovered, another glaring misfit came to light—this one involved argon (atomic mass 40) and potassium (atomic mass 39). Argon obviously belongs to the family of noble gases and potassium belongs to the family of alkali (or Group I) metals. However, if these elements were placed in the table according to their atomic masses rather than their chemical properties, argon (a noble gas) would be among the active metals and potassium (an active metal) would be among the noble gases.

Why the misfits? Mendeleev ascribed them to experimental error. He maintained that with more refined methods of finding atomic masses, the elements would fit naturally into place. But this explanation did not satisfy other scientists. There must be a more convincing explanation than this! Was there an idea or a theory which could account for the exceptions in properties?

Even the favorable aspects of the periodic table raised questions in the minds of scientists: What causes the similarity of properties of elements in the same family? Why are elements in one family more chemically active than elements in another? Why are some periods short and others long? Why the remarkable stability (or chemical inactivity) among the members of the noble gas family? Some scientists suggested that the answer to these questions were probably related to some common structural features among atoms of elements in the same family. This, in turn, suggested that atoms have parts, and are therefore *not* indivisible as Dalton had stated. We shall investigate this suggestion in Chapter 3.

Summary

The systematic study of chemistry began with Lavoisier and Dalton about 200 years ago. Lavoisier discovered the Law of Conservation of Mass and Proust's work led to the discovery of the Law of Constant Proportions. Dalton proposed an atomic theory to account for these laws. His theory predicted the Law of Simple Multiple Proportions, which was verified experimentally. This sequence is common scientific procedure. First, a discovery through experiment; next, a theory to account for the discovery; third, a new discovery predicted from the theory; finally, confirmation of the theoretical discovery by experiment.

A natural sequel to Dalton's atomic theory was the determination of the relative masses of atoms. (The actual or absolute masses of atoms were not determined until about 100 years after Dalton's time.) The masses of atoms were first compared with hydrogen, whose relative mass was arbitrarily selected as unity, or 1.000. The atomic mass scale that is used today is based on the value of carbon-12 as 12.000 atomic mass units (amu).

When Mendeleev arranged the elements according to the order of their atomic masses, he observed a recurring sequence of properties—the properties of an element were more or less duplicated in every eighth succeeding element. The relationship between atomic masses and the properties of the corresponding elements were expressed in the Periodic Law. However, the periodic "law" was not an immutable law like the Law of Conservation of Mass; there were exceptions to it. This raised some questions about the validity of the law but not enough to destroy its usefulness. Do the properties of elements really vary according to atomic masses or do they depend upon some other atomic factor, as yet unidentified?

Factual Recall

1. Explain how Lavoisier arrived at the law of constant proportions.
2. (*a*) What is the essential difference between a scientific law and a theory?
   (*b*) A scientific theory must meet certain established criteria. What are they?
3. Outline the reasoning by which Dalton predicted the law of multiple proportions from the atomic theory.
4. What is probably the most significant postulate in Dalton's atomic theory? Why?
5. (*a*) Why was hydrogen originally selected as the standard of mass? (*b*) Why was the standard of mass later changed to oxygen?
6. What is meant by (*a*) the term *atomic mass scale*? (*b*) the term

atomic mass unit? (*c*) the statement that the value of a chlorine atom on the atomic mass scale is 35.5 amu?

7. In the Mendeleev arrangement of elements, (*a*) what is a *period*? (*b*) what is a *group*?
8. (*a*) State the periodic law based on the Mendeleev arrangement.
   (*b*) Cite evidence which supports the law.
   (*c*) Cite evidence which refutes it.
9. Mendeleev arranged the elements by families in 1869. In 1900, Ramsay discovered the noble gas family. Did Ramsay's discovery support or refute the Mendeleev classification? Explain.

Apply Your Knowledge!

1. The law of conservation of mass is sometimes stated: *Nothing is created or destroyed in a chemical reaction.* Is this statement the equivalent of the statement in the text, or are there implied differences? Explain.
2. From the following elements select three in the same group: Na, Ca, Mg, Al, K, Cl, S, F, Li, O.
3. "The discovery of the element germanium gave credence to the Mendeleev classification of the elements." This sentence is taken from a scientific paper. What does it mean?
4. Given the composition of carbon dioxide by mass as 27.3% carbon and 72.7% oxygen and the molecular formular as CO_2, explain how the masses of the oxygen and carbon atoms may be compared.
5. Why was the symbol Cf selected for californium? Do any other symbols use a second letter as far removed from the first as this?

Find Out!

1. How many of the first 92 elements were still undiscovered in 1925? In 1950?
2. Mendeleev predicted properties for gallium. Look up its atomic mass and density; also the formula of the oxide of gallium. Mendeleev predicted these quite accurately. On what do you think his predictions were based?

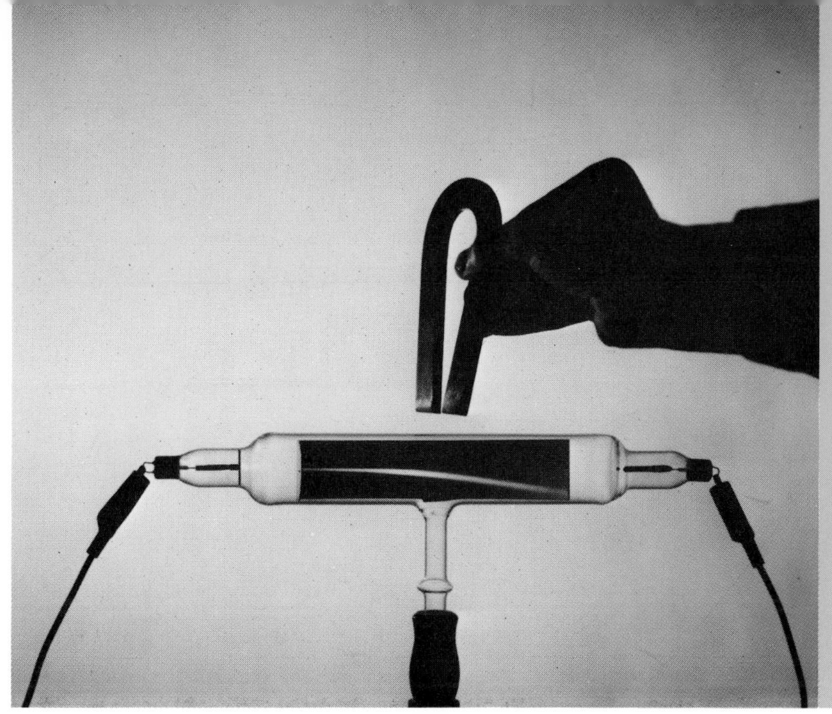

CHAPTER 3

INSIDE THE ATOM

THE GROWING DOUBT THAT MASS determined the periodic order of the elements led to much research in many different fields. Observations of researchers suggested that atoms were divisible.

The first conclusive evidence for the electrical structure of atoms came from repeated experiments with discharge tubes. A diagram of a discharge tube is shown in Fig. 3-1. Metal discs are sealed into each end of the tube and serve as terminals or *electrodes.* These electrodes are attached to a source of electricity of about 10,000 volts that can be applied across the electrodes in the tube. The discharge tube also contains a short outlet attached to a vacuum pump, so that air can be removed from it.

When the voltage is applied, nothing happens. But if the pump is also started, the air in the tube begins to conduct electricity. When the air pressure is reduced to about 1/100 atm, the air glows with a pink color throughout the length of the tube. If the gas pressure is further reduced to about 1/1000 atm, the glow quickly fades out, but a greenish glow, or fluorescence, is seen on the glass wall of the tube near the positive electrode, the *anode.* This fluorescence always has the same greenish color and does not depend upon the kind of gas in the tube or upon the kind of metal in the electrodes.

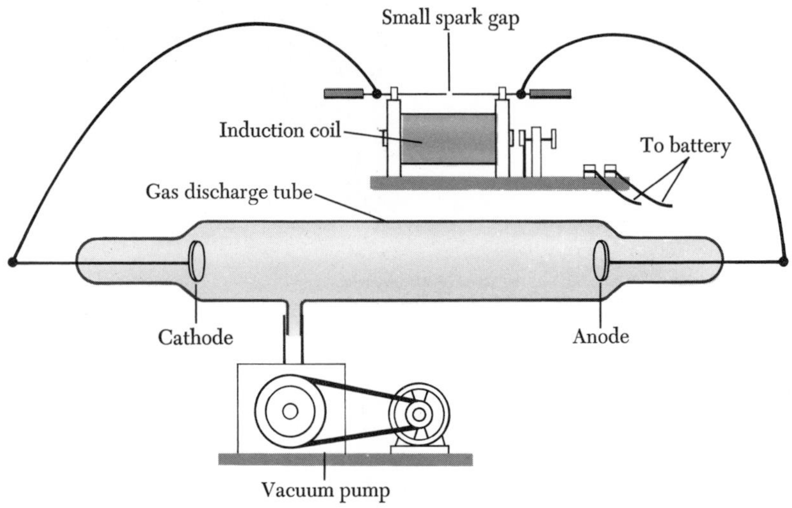

Fig. 3-1 A gas discharge tube. The vacuum pump removes most of the gas in the tube and the induction coil produces a high potential difference between the electrodes. When the pressure in the tube is reduced to about 1/1000 atm, a greenish glow or fluorescence is observed.

Cathode Rays

Glass is not the only substance that fluoresces in a discharge tube. If a metal strip coated with zinc sulfide is placed in a discharge tube, it too fluoresces with a greenish glow when a current flows through the circuit. In 1895, a French scientist named Jean Perrin (1870–1942) designed a discharge tube, like that shown in Fig. 3-2, to investigate the cause of the fluorescence. A metal plate with a narrow slit was placed near the negative terminal (the *cathode*) and a metal strip coated with zinc sulfide was mounted lengthwise in the tube to serve as a screen. When the current was turned on, a straight, narrow greenish beam from slit to anode showed up on the screen. Since this beam appeared to emerge from the cathode, the beam was called a *cathode ray*. Perrin then placed a horseshoe magnet over the tube (Fig. 3-3), and the beam was bent downward. When the positions of the magnetic poles were reversed, the beam was bent upward. From the orientation of the magnetic

Note . . .
Cathode rays were given this name by the German physicist Eugene Goldstein (1850–1930).

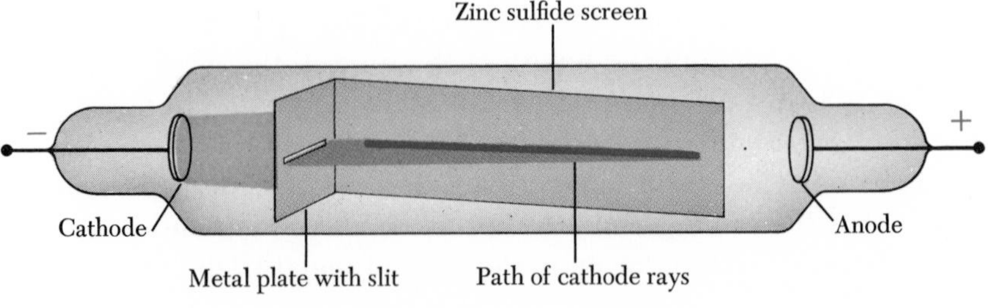

Fig. 3-2 Perrin's cathode-ray tube. The path of particles emitted by the cathode can be observed on the ZnS screen.

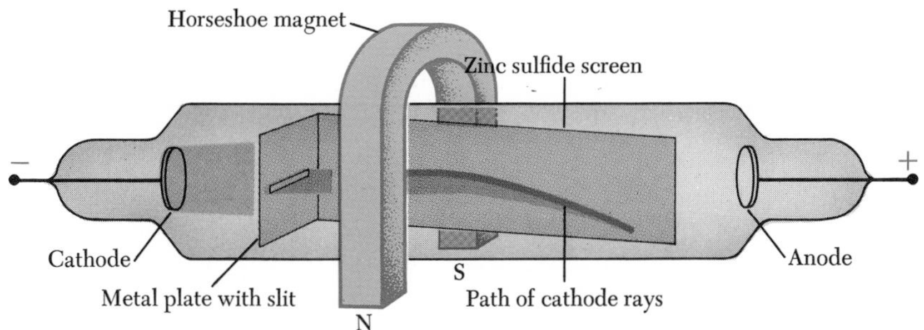

Fig. 3-3 A magnet causes deviation in the path of cathode rays.

field and the direction of deflection of the beam, Perrin concluded that *the beam was made up of negatively charged particles.*

The Discovery of the Electron

The Perrin conclusion gave rise to a number of questions. What is the mass of a negatively charged particle? How much charge does it carry? Where do the particles come from? The first scientist to find even a partial answer to these questions was J. J. Thomson (1856–1940) an English physicist who studied the effects of applying both *electric* and *magnetic* fields to the charged particles. (Fig. 3-4).

Thomson used a modified discharge tube similar to that shown in Fig. 3-5. The tube contained a metal cathode disc near one end of the tube and a metal anode disc, perforated with a small opening, placed near the cathode. The two electrodes were connected to a source of high voltage (10,000 V or more). Two parallel metal

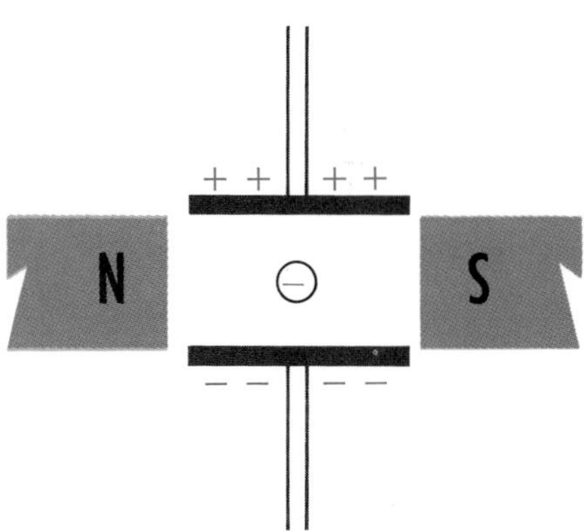

Fig. 3-4 Diagram illustrating Thomson's experiment. Negatively charged particles move out of the plane of the page, toward you; moreover, both electric and magnetic fields are applied to the moving particles, and the two fields are perpendicular to each other. Here, the electric field is vertical and the magnetic field is horizontal. The force in the electric field tends to displace the negative particles *upward*; the force in the electric field tends to displace them *downward*. The strength of the electric field can easily be adjusted so that the forces exerted by the two fields are equal; the particle will then move on a straight path.

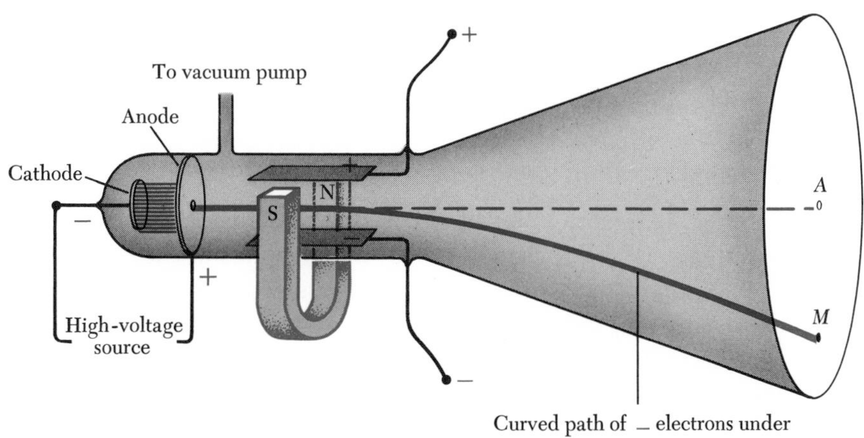

Fig. 3-5 Diagram of apparatus similar to that used by Thomson for determining the e/m ratio for an electron.

plates were placed in the tube in such a position that the cathode beam would pass between them. These plates were connected to an adjustable high-voltage source. The magnetic field was supplied by two external electromagnets; the coils of the electromagnets are represented in the diagram by the poles of a horseshoe magnet. The end wall of the tube was coated with zinc sulfide.

When a high-voltage current was applied between the electrodes, a narrow beam of negatively charged particles passed through the perforated anode and caused a fluorescent spot on the glass wall in position *A*. When the magnetic field was applied, the path of the rays curved downward, and the luminous spot appeared at point *M*. When the electric field was applied between the plates, the spot rose, and with proper adjustment of the strength of the electric field, the spot eventually returned to its original position *A*. Thomson's data included (1) the strength of the magnetic field, (2) the radius of curvature of the path of the particles under the influence of the magnetic field, and (3) the strength of the electric field that produced an equal but opposite effect to that of the magnetic field.

Note . . .
Although Thomson discovered the electron, he did not use this term, although it had been introduced into the literature in 1881 by G.J. Stoney (1826–1911). The term came into general use later.

Thomson used two methods to compute the ratio of the charge to the mass (e/m) of the negatively charged particles, now called *electrons*. The value of e/m was found to be -1.76×10^8 C/g. The negative sign indicates the negative charge on the electron. This value for e/m was found to be the same regardless of the material used as a cathode. From this result, Thomson made the important deduction that *electrons are an essential part of all atoms*. Thomson found only the ratio of the charge to the mass; 12 years later an American scientist, Robert Millikan, used Thomson's e/m value to determine both the charge and the mass of an electron.

Definition . . .
A coulomb (C) is a unit quantity of electric charge; it is the quantity of electricity that passes a given point in a wire if a current of 1 ampere (A) flows through the wire for 1 second.

The Charge of an Electron

A diagram of an apparatus for the Millikan experiment is shown in Fig. 3-6. It consists of a chamber with metal plates at the top and bottom, the upper plate having a small aperture through its center. The plates can be given electric charges, one positive and the other negative, by attaching them to the terminals of an adjustable voltage of several hundred volts supplied by a battery. If minute drops of oil are sprayed from an atomizer onto the upper plate, many of the droplets become charged by friction as they escape

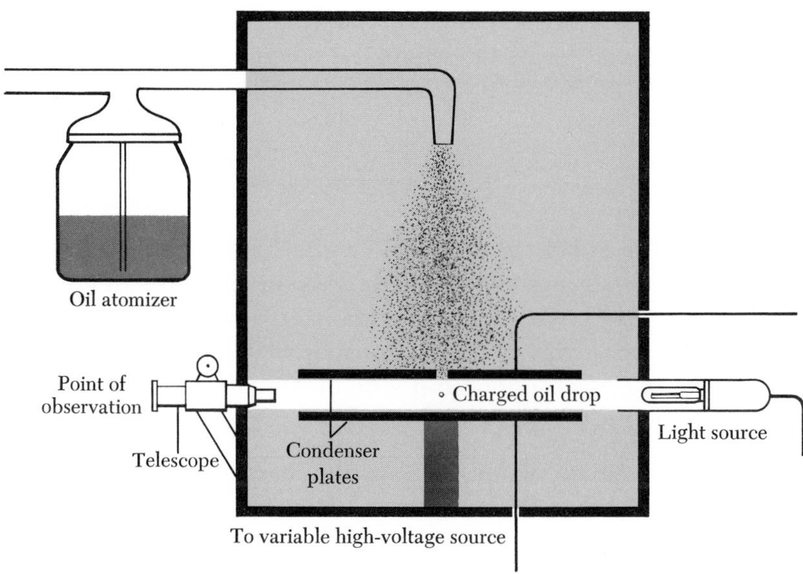

Fig. 3-6 Diagram of apparatus for the Millikan experiment, which determines the charge on an electron.

through the nozzle of the atomizer, and some of them pass through the aperture and into the chamber. A voltage is then applied to the plates.

Let us assume that the droplet under investigation is charged negatively, and let us consider the forces that act upon it. First, there is its weight. The weight (F_W) of the droplet can be expressed as a downward gravitational force:

$$(F_W) = m \times g$$

where m is its mass expressed in grams and g is the acceleration due to gravity (980 cm/sec^2). There is also an electrical force. The negatively charged drop is repelled by the negative charge on the lower plate and attracted by the positive charge on the upper plate. Therefore the net electrical force is upward, opposite in direction to the gravitational force. This situation is shown in Fig. 3-7.

Fig. 3-7 Forces acting on a charged oil droplet in Millikan's experiment. The downward force of gravity just balances the upward electrical force, and so the drop remains stationary.

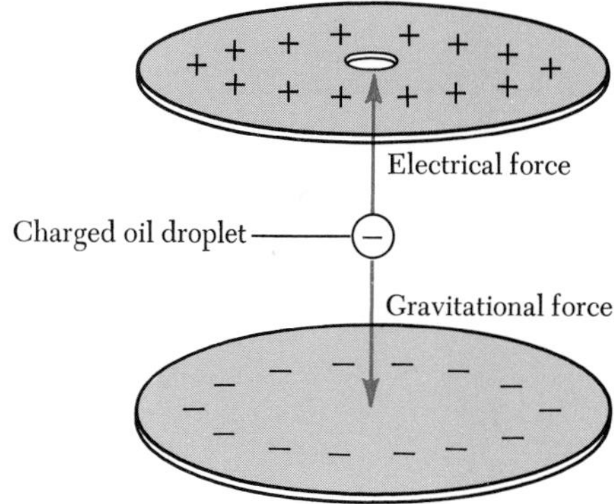

The net electrical force is the product of the strength of the electric field between the plates (E) and the charge on the drop (e). Hence the net electrical force on the drop is $E \times e$. This force can be increased or decreased by changing the voltage applied to the plates. The voltage is adjusted until the charged drop is held steady in the field of view as seen through the telescope. When this happens, the electrical force on the drop is equal and opposite to the gravitational force. Or, expressed in symbols:

$$E \times e = m \times g$$

$$e = \frac{mg}{E} \tag{3-1}$$

The mass of the spherical drop (m) can be found from its volume and density; the strength of the field (E) is the potential difference between the plates, which can be measured with a voltmeter; the acceleration due to gravity (g) is a constant (980 cm/sec^2). Since all the quantities on the right-hand side of the equation are known, the value of e can be computed.

Millikan made hundreds of readings on charged drops of oil and found that the charge (e) was either 1.60×10^{-19} C, or some integral multiple of this quantity, such as 3.20×10^{-19} C or 4.80×10^{-19} C. He never found a charge less than 1.60×10^{-19} C, and he therefore concluded that this particular value is the fundamental unit of charge. That is, the charge of an electron is 1.60×10^{-19} C.

The Mass of an Electron

Once the charge on an electron was found, it was a simple matter to compute the mass. To do this Millikan used the equation

$$m = \frac{e}{e/m} \tag{3-2}$$

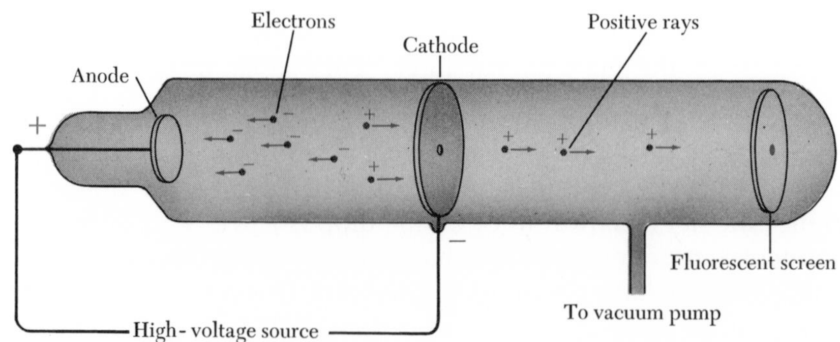

Fig. 3-8 Positive-ray tube. Positively charged particles, the result of the collisions between electrons and atoms, travel through an opening in the cathode and reach the fluorescent screen.

Thus, $m = \dfrac{e}{e/m}$

$$= \frac{1.60 \times 10^{-19}\ \text{C/electron}}{1.76 \times 10^{8}\ \text{C/g}} = 9.1 \times 10^{-28}\ \text{g/electron}$$

Both Thomson and Millikan were awarded Nobel prizes in chemistry for outstanding contributions to knowledge of the electron.

Positive Rays and the Proton

Shortly after Thomson's determination of e/m for an electron, a new set of rays was discovered; these rays traveled in a direction opposite to that taken by cathode rays. [A discharge tube that produces these rays is shown in Fig. 3-8. In this apparatus the cathode is perforated, *not* the anode. Moreover, the tube contains a little gas (for example, hydrogen) in contrast to the high-vacuum condition that existed in the equipment used previously.] When a high voltage was applied between the electrodes, a luminous spot appeared on a zinc sulfide screen placed behind the cathode. Clearly the fluorescence was caused by *positively charged particles*, and Thomson called the beam of these particles *positive rays*. What are positively charged particles?

To answer this question, Thomson found the ratio of charge to mass of these charged particles by deflecting them in electric and magnetic fields. The e/m value varied for each of the different gases that he placed (in very small quantities) in the discharge tube; for example, the value for hydrogen was greater than that for oxygen. How can this be explained? As electrons stream from cathode to anode they collide with atoms and molecules of gas in the nearly evacuated tube, knocking some electrons from these atoms and molecules. Atoms are electrically neutral, and when an atom loses an electron it becomes positively charged. The positively charged atoms, known as *ions*, then move toward the cathode, and the released electrons move toward the anode. The removal of an electron is called *ionization*, and the resultant positively charged particle is called a *positive ion*. Thus, if hydrogen atoms are bombarded by electrons, some hydrogen ions are formed. This change can be represented in abbreviated form as

$$\text{hydrogen atom} \xrightarrow{\text{bombarded}} \text{hydrogen ion} + \text{electron}$$

The Jolly Electron

There was a jolly electron—
alternately bound and free—
Who toiled and spun from morn to night,
no snark so lithe as he,
And this the burden of his song
forever used to be:—
I care for nobody, no, not I, since
nobody cares for me.

Though Crookes at first suspected my
presence on this earth
'Twas J.J. that found me—in spite
of my tiny girth.
He measured first the "*e* by *m*" of my
electric worth:
I love J.J. in a filial way, for he
it was gave me birth.

. . .

'Twas Johnstone Stoney invented my
new electric name,
Then Rutherford, and Bohr too, and
Moseley brought me fame.
They guessed (within the atom) my
inner and outer game.
You'll all agree what they did for me
I'll do it for them, the same.

R.A.S. Paget

Infer . . .
Atoms of different gases have different masses. Would the loss of an electron therefore, produce particles of different e/m values?

Note . . .
In 1920, Thomson's colleague Ernest Rutherford coined the term *proton.*

Or, in symbols,

$$H \longrightarrow H^+ + e^- \tag{3-3}$$

where the symbols for hydrogen ion and electron are H^+ and e^-.

Thomson assumed that the charge on a hydrogen ion was precisely the same as the charge on an electron, but of opposite kind. Since the e/m value for a hydrogen ion was greater than that for other positive ions, the mass of the hydrogen ion was less than that of the other ions. Therefore, he assumed that hydrogen ions are fundamental constituents of all atoms. These ions were later called *protons*. The mass of a proton is found to be 1.67×10^{-24} g, which is 1836 times the mass of an electron. Therefore, the proton accounts for 1836/1837 of the mass of a hydrogen atom.

On the basis of these data, Thomson postulated that all atoms are made up of equal numbers of protons and electrons. You recall that on the atomic mass scale the mass of hydrogen is about 1.0 amu. Moreover, according to Thomson, a hydrogen atom consists of one proton and one electron. By analogy, he argued that since the atomic mass of oxygen is 16.0 amu, the atom is made up of 16 protons and 16 electrons. Following this reasoning, Thomson constructed a model for an atom of oxygen. This model is shown in Fig 3-9. The Thomson model was a far cry from the spherical, indivisible atom proposed by Dalton. However, Thomson said nothing about the arrangement of the parts of an atom nor of their motion.

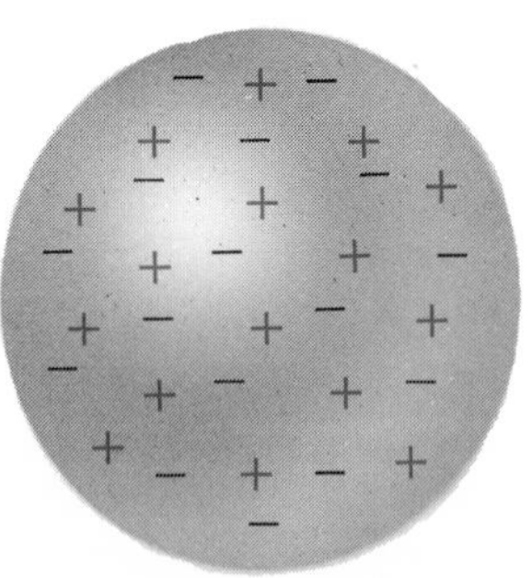

Fig. 3-9 Thomson's model of an oxygen atom. The model is something like a pudding containing 16 large raisins (protons) and 16 small currants (electrons). Both the arrangement of the model and the numbers of protons and electrons are now known to be incorrect.

Are the constituent parts arranged in some particular pattern? In 1911 the New Zealand-born British scientist, Ernest Rutherford (1871–1937), designed an experiment which gave at least a partial answer to this question.

Rutherford's Scattering Experiment

In Rutherford's time it was known that radium, a radioactive element, emits positively charged particles, called alpha (α) particles, which travel in straight lines at high speed. Rutherford investigated the effect of bombarding very thin slivers of metallic foil with α particles. The apparatus he used is shown in Fig. 3-10. A minute amount of radium was placed in a thick-walled block of lead, and α particles escaped through a fine aperture at the end of this block. The particles were directed toward the gold foil, and a screen

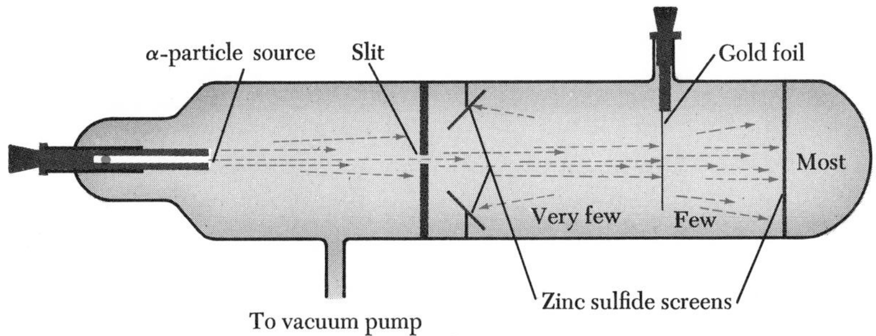

Fig. 3-10 Rutherford's experiment with a thin gold foil.

impregnated with zinc sulfide was placed beyond the foil. Since zinc sulfide emits flashes of light (scintillations) when struck by α particles, these flashes could be observed and counted through a microscope. The screen was mounted upon a supporting arm, which could be rotated through a complete circle. The apparatus (except for the microscope) was enclosed in an evacuated chamber so that α particles would not be deflected by collisions with air molecules.

When Rutherford first placed the screen immediately behind the gold foil, a patch of scintillations appeared on the screen. Clearly α particles had passed right through the metal foil just as machine-gun bullets would pass through a paper target. The screen was then rotated through various angles, and at every stopping place a few scintillations appeared on the screen—even when the screen had been rotated through an angle of almost 180°. Rutherford referred to this phenomenon as a *scattering effect*, and he was particularly puzzled by the scattering of α particles through large angles—that is, angles greater than 90°. In such cases it looked as though the α particles had collided with something head on and then rebounded almost along their own tracks.

The Nucleus of an Atom

The α particles had clearly been disturbed by a large electrical force. This could be explained by assuming that a positive charge is concentrated at the center of an atom, rather than being uniform throughout the atom, as Thomson had suggested. Rutherford postulated a different atomic model, in which he called this central positive charge the *nucleus*. As an α particle approaches a nucleus head on, according to Coulomb's law, the electrical force of repulsion between the positive nucleus and an α particle increases as the

Note . . .
Rutherford's first experiments were with gold foil, so this description refers to gold foil. He also worked with silver, platinum, and other metals.

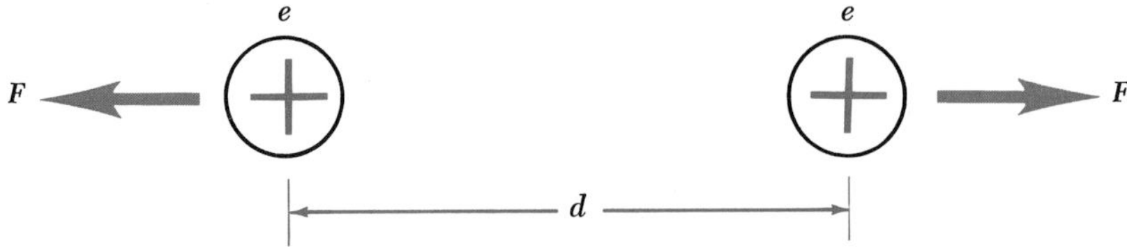

Fig. 3-11 Diagrammatic representation of Coulomb's law.

distance between nucleus and α particle decreases (see Fig. 3-11). Eventually the forward force of the particle is overcome and the particle is deflected through a large angle, almost back along its path of approach.

Note . . .
Coulomb's law can be expressed as

$$F = \frac{e \times e'}{d^2} \tag{3-4}$$

where F is the force of repulsion between two like charges e and e', and d is the distance between the charges. Thus the greater the charges and the shorter the distance of closest approach, the stronger will be the repelling force. (See Fig. 3-11.)

This situation is shown in Fig. 3-12. If the approach is not head on but still within the field of the nuclear charge, then the α particle is deflected through a smaller angle. These experimental results are summarized in Fig. 3-13. Rutherford also argued that the space around the nucleus must be occupied by electrons, and that the positive charge on the nucleus must be balanced by the negative charges on the electrons.

Rutherford's Model of an Atom

Rutherford's experiments showed that a nucleus must contain protons. The number of protons in a nucleus is called its *atomic number* (symbolized as Z). Rutherford estimated the atomic numbers of several metal atoms by measuring the scattering angle of α particles which passed through foils of these metals.

The atomic number of each element is now known; (See Table 3-2.) Since an atom is electrically neutral, the atomic number of an element *is also the number of electrons outside the nucleus of the atom.*

Fig. 3-12 The α particle is deflected through a wide angle by the positive charge on a nucleus.

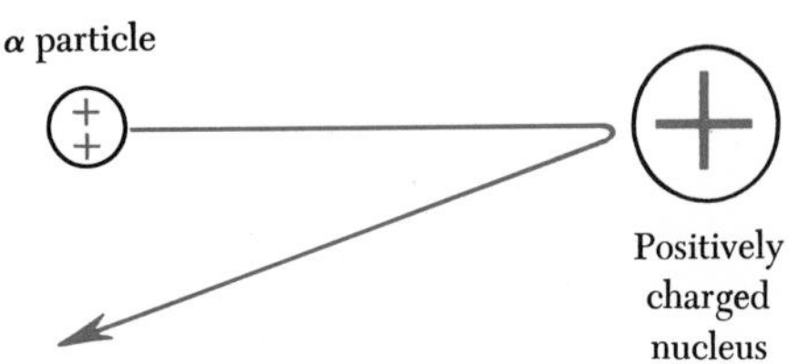

Rutherford's model of an atom was quite different from Thomson's. The Rutherford atom had a positively charged nucleus surrounded by enough electrons to neutralize the positive charge. Rutherford also suggested that electrons move around the nucleus like planets move around the sun. Rutherford's model of a carbon atom is shown in Fig. 3-14. Practically all the mass of the atom is concentrated in the nucleus, and the volume of the nucleus is so small compared with the volume of the whole atom that if the nucleus of an atom were the size of a grain of sand, the entire atom would be the size of a basketball court.

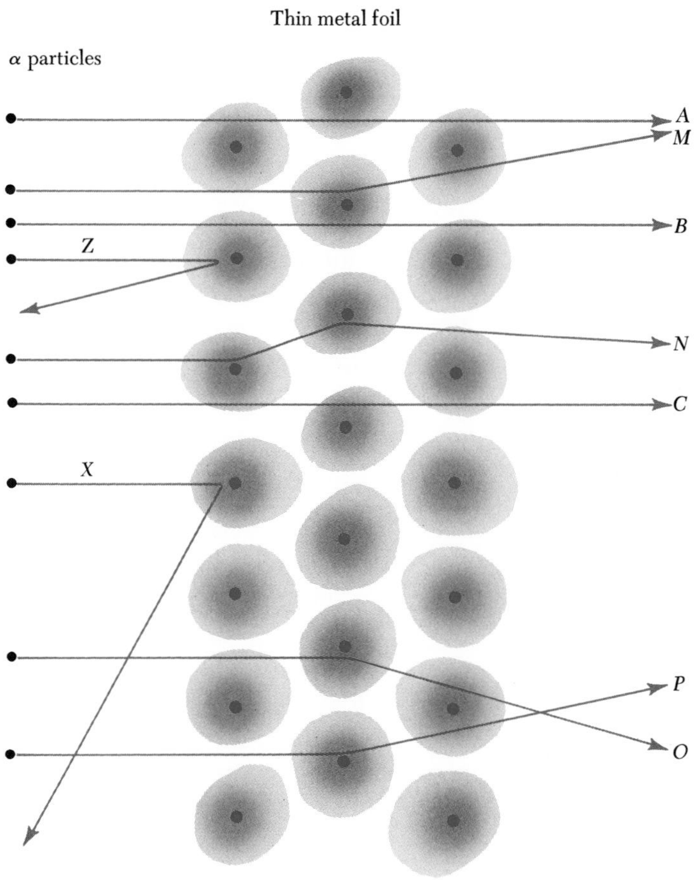

Fig. 3-13 Scattering of α particles by atomic nuclei in a metallic foil.Schematic diagram showing a parallel beam of α particles striking a section of metal foil whose thickness is only three layers of atoms. The nuclei of the atoms are indicated by open circles and the electrons surrounding the nuclei are shown as dots. Most of the α particles (as in *A*, *B*, *C*) go through the foil without deflection, indicating that there must be relatively large spaces between the nuclei. Some α particles (like *M*, *N*, *O*, P) are deflected through small angles. A few (like *X*) are deflected through a large angle, and occasionally (as in Z) there is a head-on collision and the α particle is turned back almost along its own original path.

Neutrons

The masses of atoms were much too high to be accounted for on the basis of the numbers of protons and electrons present. For example, the oxygen atom (atomic mass, about 6 amu) would have a mass of about 8 amu if only protons and electrons were present. This descrepancy confused Thomson, who had then suggested that oxygen atoms might contain 16 protons. It also confused many other scientists. Finally, in 1932, an English scientist named James Chadwick (1891–   ) discovered that the nuclei of all atoms except hydrogen contained uncharged (neutral) particles. which he called *neutrons*. Thus, the nucleus of an atom is essentially an aggregate of protons and neutrons. The mass of a neutron is approximately the same as the mass of a proton. However, their properties are quite different.

Fig. 3-14 Rutherford model of a carbon atom.

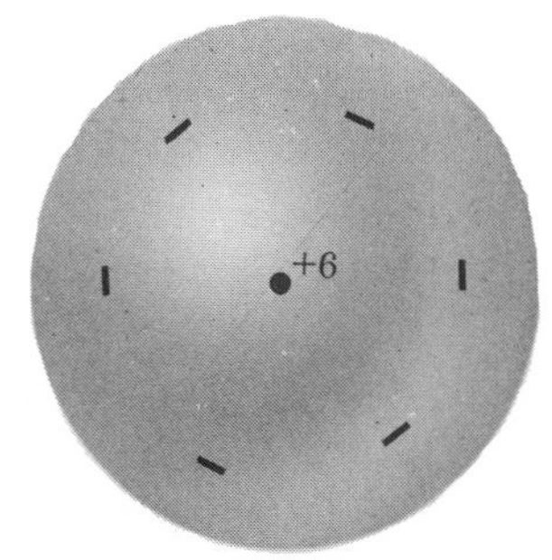

Note . . .
Other, smaller, particles have also been discovered in atoms, but the electron, the proton, and the neutron are the most important.

In summary, the three fundamental particles in the structure of matter are electrons, protons, and neutrons. The charge and mass of each are given in Table 3-1.

The sum of the protons and neutrons of an atom is called its *mass number*. The mass number of the most common atom of hydrogen is one (1) because there is only a single proton in the nucleus of this hydrogen atom. Since the nucleus of the most common helium atom consists of 2 protons and 2 neutrons, the mass number of this helium atom is 4.

Table 3-1 Properties of the fundamental atomic particles

Property	Electron	Proton	Neutron
Charge	Unit negative charge (−1)	Unit positive charge (+1)	No charge (0)
Mass	9.11×10^{-28} g	1.67×10^{-24} g	1.67×10^{-24} g

We have learned that positive charges repel each other. Then why do not the 8 protons in the nucleus of an oxygen atom repel each other and cause the nucleus to disintegrate? Actually, there *is* an electrical force of repulsion acting on the 8 protons. However, when the protons and protons or protons and neutrons are exceedingly close together, another force, called a *nuclear force*, becomes effective. A nuclear force is effective only within a very short range, but within this short range it is a powerful force of attraction, much more powerful than the electrical force of repulsion. Nuclear forces are discussed in Chapter 29.

A Periodic Table Derived from Atomic Numbers

Definition . . .
The mass number of an element is the nearest integer to the actual mass value expressed in atomic mass units: it is symbolized as *A*.

The real significance of atomic numbers becomes apparent when we recall that the total number of electrons in a neutral atom is equal to the atomic number—that is, equal to the number of protons in the nucleus of the atom. It took many years to discover that nearly all physical and chemical properties of atoms depend upon the number and arrangement of their electrons. Thus, it follows that the properties of elements are more closely related to their atomic numbers rather than to their atomic masses. As a result, the Mendeleev periodic law was amended to read: *The properties of the elements are periodic functions of their atomic numbers.*

The Mendeleev periodic table was also amended. In the new table, the elements were arranged in order of increasing atomic numbers. Since all hydrogen atoms have a single proton, hydrogen became element number 1, and since all helium atoms have two protons, it became element number 2, and so on up to the heavier elements like nobelium, and lawrencium, elements 102, and 103 respectively. A periodic table based on atomic numbers is shown in Table 3-2. This table is simpler than the Mendeleev table. It should be observed that there are no misfits in the new table; every element follows its predecessor in natural sequence. The elements are divided into eight main groups labeled with Roman numerals: I, II, III, IV, V, VI, VII, and 0. Thus, the alkali metals are in Group I and the noble gas elements in Group 0. The metals lie on the left, the nonmetals on the right.

Between Groups II and III there are four horizontal rows of elements called *transition elements*, which will be discussed later. Arranging the transition elements in this way eliminates the double rows of elements as well as Group VIII of the Mendeleev table. The periods or rows, like the groups, are numbered in sequence. The significance of the periodic table will be discissed in later chapters, but it is not too early to ask if the arrangement of elements in the periodic table is in any way connected to the number and arrangement of electrons in the atoms of the elements.

Isotopes

The nucleus of the most common atom of hydrogen consists of a single proton, and this atom consists of one proton plus one electron. But, since the mass of an electron is negligibly small compared with the mass of a proton, the mass of this hydrogen atom is determined almost completely by the proton. Similarly, the masses of all other atoms are very nearly the sum of the numbers of neutrons and protons present in their nuclei. If we consider each of these particles (proton and neutron) as a unit of mass, we would expect to find that the atomic masses of all elements are whole numbers, or very nearly whole numbers. Yet a glance at a table of atomic masses shows that this is not so. Although the atomic mass of hydrogen is 1.0, that of neon is 20.2, of chlorine 35.5, of copper 63.5, and of tin 118.7. How can these apparent inconsistencies be explained?

Fig. 3-15 Attractive forces between subatomic particles.

ELECTRON AND PROTON

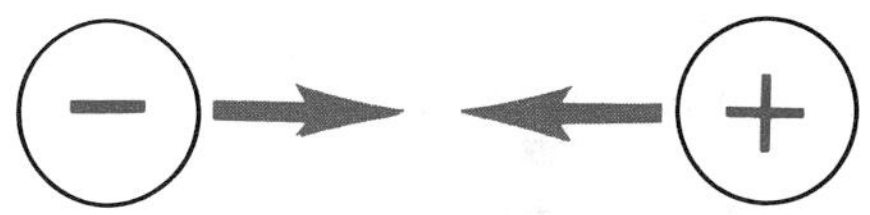

These have equal and opposite charges, and therefore an electrostatic force of attraction.

PROTON AND NEUTRON

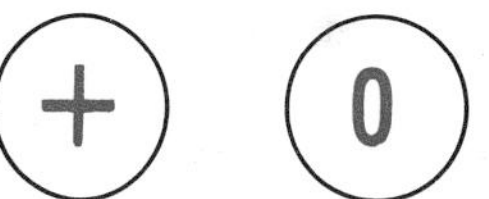

These have no electrostatic force. At very short distances (about 10^{-18} cm), these particles attract one another. This attractive force is what keeps the atomic nucleus intact.

PROTON AND PROTON

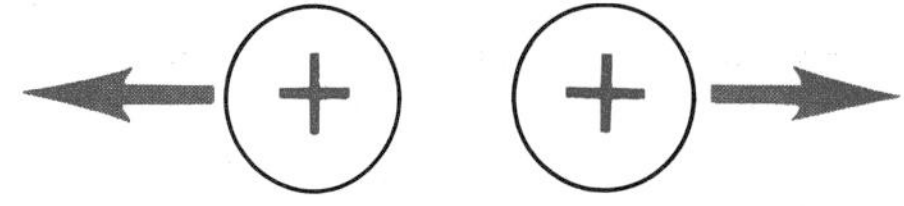

These have like charges, and therefore an electrostatic force of repulsion. At very short distances (about 10^{-18} cm), a nuclear force of attraction is strong enough to overcome the electrostatic force.

Table 3-2 Periodic Table of the Elements

	I	II						Transition elements		
1	1 1.00797 **H** Hydrogen									
2	3 6.939 **Li** Lithium	4 9.0122 **Be** Beryllium								
3	11 22.9898 **Na** Sodium	12 24.312 **Mg** Magnesium								
4	19 39.102 **K** Potassium	20 40.08 **Ca** Calcium	21 44.956 **Sc** Scandium	22 47.90 **Ti** Titanium	23 50.942 **V** Vanadium	24 51.996 **Cr** Chromium	25 54.9380 **Mn** Manganese	26 55.847 **Fe** Iron	27 58.9332 **Co** Cobalt	28 58.71 **Ni** Nickel
5	37 85.47 **Rb** Rubidium	38 87.62 **Sr** Strontium	39 88.905 **Y** Yttrium	40 91.22 **Zr** Zirconium	41 92.906 **Nb** Niobium	42 95.94 **Mo** Molybdenum	43 (99) **Tc** Technetium	44 101.07 **Ru** Ruthenium	45 102.905 **Rh** Rhodium	46 106.4 **Pd** Palladium
6	55 132.905 **Cs** Cesium	56 137.34 **Ba** Barium	57-71 Series of lanthanide elements	72 178.49 **Hf** Hafnium	73 180.948 **Ta** Tantalum	74 183.85 **W** Tungsten	75 186.2 **Re** Rhenium	76 190.2 **Os** Osmium	77 192.2 **Ir** Iridium	78 195.09 **Pt** Platinum
7	87 (223) **Fr** Francium	88 (226) **Ra** Radium	89-103 Series of actinide elements	104 Kurchatovium (?)	105 Hahnium (?)					

Series of lanthanide elements	57 138.91 **La** Lanthanum	58 140.12 **Ce** Cerium	59 140.907 **Pr** Praseodymium	60 144.24 **Nd** Neodymium	61 (145) **Pm** Promethium	62 150.35 **Sm** Samarium	63 151.96 **Eu** Europium
Series of actinide elements	89 (227) **Ac** Actinium	90 232.038 **Th** Thorium	91 (231) **Pa** Protactinium	92 238.03 **U** Uranium	93 (237) **Np** Neptunium	94 (242) **Pu** Plutonium	95 (243) **Am** Americium

		III	IV	V	VI	VII	VIII
							2 4.0026 **He** Helium
		5 10.811 **B** Boron	6 12.01115 **C** Carbon	7 14.0067 **N** Nitrogen	8 15.9994 **O** Oxygen	9 18.9984 **F** Fluorine	10 20.183 **Ne** Neon
		13 26.9815 **Al** Aluminum	14 28.086 **Si** Silicon	15 30.9738 **P** Phosphorus	16 32.064 **S** Sulfur	17 35.453 **Cl** Chlorine	18 39.948 **Ar** Argon
29 63.54 **Cu** Copper	30 65.37 **Zn** Zinc	31 69.72 **Ga** Gallium	32 72.59 **Ge** Germanium	33 74.9216 **As** Arsenic	34 78.96 **Se** Selenium	35 79.909 **Br** Bromine	36 83.80 **Kr** Krypton
47 107.870 **Ag** Silver	48 112.40 **Cd** Cadmium	49 114.82 **In** Indium	50 118.69 **Sn** Tin	51 121.75 **Sb** Antimony	52 127.60 **Te** Tellurium	53 126.9044 **I** Iodine	54 131.30 **Xe** Xenon
79 196.967 **Au** Gold	80 200.59 **Hg** Mercury	81 204.37 **Tl** Thallium	82 207.19 **Pb** Lead	83 208.980 **Bi** Bismuth	84 (210) **Po** Polonium	85 (210) **At** Astatine	86 (222) **Rn** Radon

64 157.25 **Gd** Gadolinium	65 158.924 **Tb** Terbium	66 162.50 **Dy** Dysprosium	67 164.930 **Ho** Holmium	68 167.26 **Er** Erbium	69 168.934 **Tm** Thulium	70 173.04 **Yb** Ytterbium	71 174.97 **Lu** Lutetium
96 (247) **Cm** Curium	97 (249) **Bk** Berkelium	98 (251) **Cf** Californium	99 (254) **Es** Einsteinium	100 (252) **Fm** Fermium	101 (256) **Md** Mendelevium	102 (254) **No** Nobelium	103 (257) **Lr** Lawrencium

Note . . .
Thomson's colleague, F.W. Aston (1877–1945), later improved the mass spectrograph (also called mass spectrometer), confirmed Thomson's results, and made further studies.

Part of the answer to this question was found when Thomson's positive ray apparatus was modified in such a way that the masses of ions could be measured directly. In the new instrument, called a *mass spectrograph* (Fig. 3-16*b*), atoms (or molecules) of gas (or vapor) were bombarded by a beam of electrons; this bombardment caused ionization. The positive ions were then deflected from their original paths by a magnetic field. Ions of the same mass were focused on the same point on a photographic film. And, when the film was developed a dark line appeared at the point of impact, just as though the film had been exposed to light. The amount of deflection depended upon the mass of the ion—the lighter the mass, the greater the deflection. Thus, two ions of different masses would result in two lines on the film.

The first element to be studied in the mass spectrograph was the gas neon. It was already known that the atomic mass of neon is 20.2 amu. However, after a photographic film (calibrated in atomic mass units) had been exposed to neon ions, *no* line appeared at the 20.2 mark. Instead, *two* lines were seen, one at the 20.0 mark

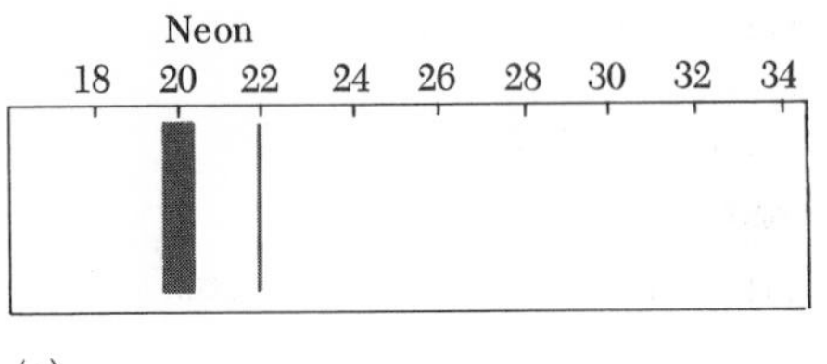

(*a*)

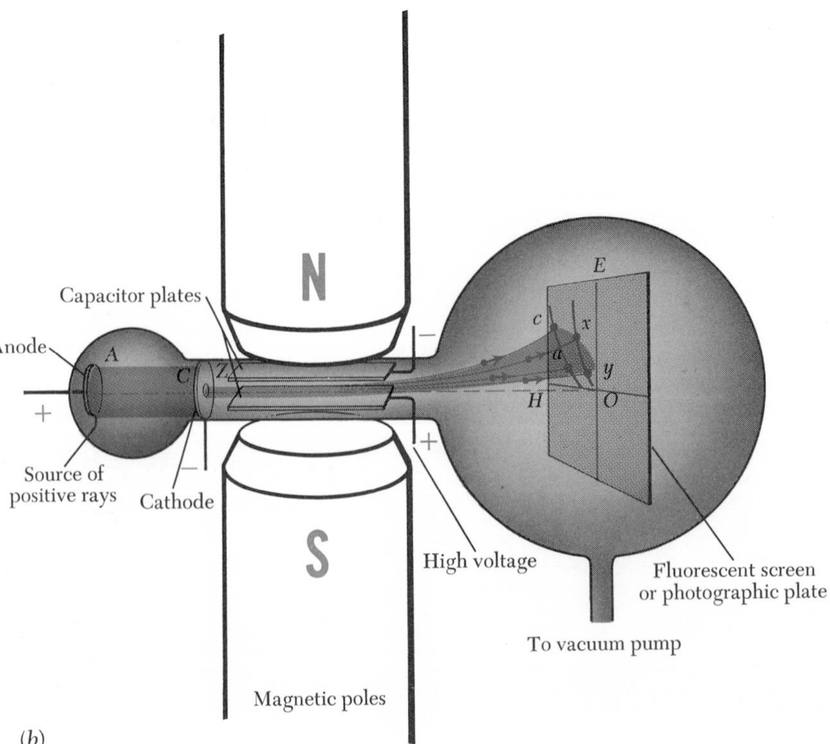

(*b*)

Fig. 3-16 (*a*) Mass spectrum of neon showing lines corresponding to ions of the two common isotopes of neon. (*b*) Diagram of J.J. Thomson's mass spectrograph. If the gas in the apparatus contains two kinds of atoms, the positive ions passing through the cathode will have two different masses. Each ion will contain the same positive charge, and will therefore experience the same electric and magnetic forces when passing through the fields, but the heavier particles will not be deflected as much as the lighter ones. The net result is that the heavier particles form one parabolic curve like xy and the lighter particles another curve like ac.

and the other at the 22.0 mark. (See Fig. 3-16*a*.) How could this observation be interpreted? Clearly, neon gas must be a mixture of two isotopes. *Isotopes are atoms of the same element having different atomic masses.*

A mass spectrograph determines not only the masses of the isotopes but also their relative abundance. For example, the relative intensities of the two neon lines show that atoms of isotope 20.0 are nine times as abundant as atoms of isotope 22.0. In other words, neon is a mixture of 90% of the lighter isotope and 10% of the heavier one. Hence, the "average" atomic mass is

Investigation . . .

Does natural neon contain only neon-20 and neon-22?

$$(0.90 \times 20.0) + (0.10 \times 22.0) = 18.0 + 2.2 = 20.2$$

This value agrees with the value of the atomic mass of neon as determined by standard methods using larger samples of neon gas.

Isotopes can readily be accounted for in terms of protons and neutrons. Since their chemical properties are alike, all isotopes of any element must have the same number of electrons, and therefore an identical number of protons in the nucleus. For chlorine, this number (the atomic number, Z) is shown to be 17. Since the difference between the mass number and the atomic number is the number of neutrons, the nucleus of chlorine-35 contains 17 protons and 18 neutrons, and the nucleus of chlorine-37 contains 17 protons and 20 neutrons. Symbols for these isotopes are $^{35}_{17}Cl$ and $^{37}_{17}Cl$, where the upper number is the mass number (*A*) and the lower number is the atomic number (Z).

Most elements are mixtures of isotopes. Ordinary oxygen, for example, is a mixture of three isotopes: oxygen-16, oxygen-17, and oxygen-18. Since the atomic number of oxygen is 8, the symbols for these isotopes are $^{16}_{8}O$, $^{17}_{8}O$, and $^{18}_{8}O$. Oxygen-16 is by far the most abundant of the isotopes, accounting for 99.76% of all atoms of oxygen; oxygen-17 and oxygen-18 together account for only 0.24%. Ordinary carbon consists of two stable isotopes: carbon-12 and carbon-13. Since the atomic number of carbon is 6, the symbols for these isotopes are $^{12}_{6}C$ and $^{13}_{6}C$, respectively. Carbon-12 is much more abundant than C-13, accounting for 98.9% of ordinary carbon.

Even ordinary hydrogen is a mixture of two stable isotopes: hydrogen-1 and hydrogen-2. The nucleus of hydrogen-1 consists of a single proton, whereas the nucleus of hydrogen-2 consists of 1 proton and 1 neutron. Therefore, the symbols of these isotopes are

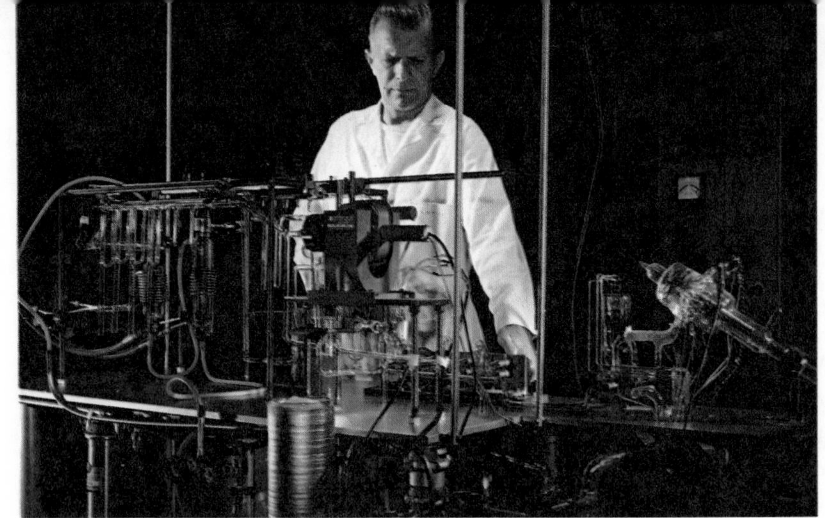

Fig. 3-17 A high-sensitivity rare-gas mass spectrometer used in chemical research. This instrument is capable of detecting as little as one billionth of a cubic millimeter of gas. It is used in studies of the ages of meteorites and investigations of the bombardment of satellites in space by helium atoms.

^1_1H and ^2_1H, respectively. Because the atomic mass of hydrogen-2 is twice that of hydrogen-1, hydrogen-2 is sometimes called heavy hydrogen or, in modern usage, deuterium (symbol D). Actually, deuterium is quite rare, for an ordinary sample of hydrogen is a mixture of 99.98% hydrogen-1 and 0.02% deuterium. Tritium, ^3_1H, third isotope of hydrogen, is present in natural hydrogen in minute amounts. This isotope is radioactive; that is, the nucleus decomposes spontaneously into other nuclei. Many elements have radioactive isotopes. Such isotopes are discussed in Chapter 28.

An Atomic Mass Scale Based on Carbon-12

Atomic masses were based originally upon hydrogen as 1.000, and then upon oxygen as 16.000. At that time it was assumed that all oxygen atoms had the same mass. However, we now know there are three isotopes of oxygen, although two of them, oxygen-17 and oxygen-18, occur in nature only to a very slight extent. Still, for precision work it became obvious that atomic masses should be expressed in terms of the relative mass of some particular isotope. In 1961, therefore, a new standard, adopted by international agreement., was based upon the most common isotope of carbon, carbon-12 ($^{12}_6C$), taken as 12.000 amu. When the various isotopes and their abundances are taken into account, the atomic mass of hydrogen on this new scale is 1.0079 amu; that of ordinary carbon is 12.01 amu; oxygen, 15.99 amu; sodium, 22.99 amu; and sulfur, 32.06 amu. The difference between the oxygen scale and the new carbon scale is very slight indeed, actually about 1 part in 10,000. However, if atomic masses are expressed to five or six significant figures, there is a marked difference between the two scales. In work of high precision, this difference is important.

Summary

Late in the 19th Century, scientists discovered that atoms are made up of three different kinds of particles. Slowly, a "picture" of the inside of an atom began to emerge. First the electron was discovered, then the proton, the neutron, and, later, many others. And, once a new particle was discovered, scientists set about the task of finding both its mass and the amount of charge it carried.

The mass spectrograph uncovered the fact that atoms of the same element could have different masses. Atoms of the same element but different mass are called *isotopes*. Isotopes of the same element have the same number of protons but different numbers of neutrons.

The discovery of isotopes raised the question of the reliability of an atomic mass scale that was based on ordinary oxygen (16.000 amu), an element which was found to be a mixture of three isotopes, oxygen-16, oxygen-17, and oxygen-18. The assignment of a definite value to some specific isotope would be a more accurate base of reference. Thus, scientists base the modern atomic mass scale on the more plentiful of the two natural isotopes of carbon, with a mass value arbitrarily fixed at 12.0000 amu.

Factual Recall

1. (*a*) What are the essential parts of a gas discharge tube?
   (*b*) How does it operate?
2. (*a*) Describe Perrin's experiment on cathode rays.
   (*b*) What were his conclusions?
3. (*a*) Describe Thomson's experiment on cathode rays.
   (*b*) What did he discover?
4. (*a*) Describe the experiment by which Millikan discovered the charge on an electron. (*b*) How did he interpret his results?
5. (*a*) Explain why Thomson concluded that protons are fundamental constituents of all atoms. (*b*) Draw a Thomson model of a helium atom.
6. Discuss the experimental evidence that led Rutherford to state that every atom has a positively charged nucleus.
7. Define the term *atomic number* in terms of (*a*) protons, (*b*) electrons.

8. Given the atomic number of carbon as 6 and its atomic mass as 12 amu, compare the Rutherford model with the Thomson model of a carbon atom.
9. Compare the three fundamental particles with respect to their mass and charge.
10. State the modern periodic law and explain how it differs from the Mendeleev periodic law.
11. If the elements are arranged according to atomic number rather than atomic mass, there are no misfits in the table. Why?

Apply Your Knowledge!

1. If tin vapor is in the chamber of a mass spectrograph, ten lines appear on the photographic film, and the deviations of the lines show that the masses of the isotopes are 112, 114, 115, 116, 117, 118, 119, 120, 122, and 124 amu. Given the atomic number of tin as 50, write the symbols for each of these isotopes.
2. A mass spectrograph for a sample of chlorine shows two lines for chlorine ions. Account for the two lines and make a prediction as to their relative abundance. (The greater the abundance the more intense the line on the spectrograph.)
3. Why was the neutron discovered so many years later than the electron and proton?

Find Out!

1. The experiments that Rutherford performed could not have been carried out before 1900. Why is this true?
2. Look up more details in the works of Thomson, Rutherford, and Millikan.
3. (*a*) Draw a diagram of a modern mass spectrometer and explain how it works.
   (*b*) What are some of its uses?
4. Look up other arrangements of the periodic chart and compare them with the one given in this chapter.
5. (*a*) How were isotopes first discovered? (*b*) When and by whom?

CHAPTER 4

A THEORY FOR THE ARRANGEMENT OF ELECTRONS IN ATOMS

IF A BEAM OF LIGHT passes through a glass prism, two things happen to it: (1) the direction of the beam is changed, or, as we usually say, the light is *refracted*, and (2) the colorless beam is changed to a multicolored band called a *spectrum*. The separation of white light into a colored band is called *dispersion*.

A Continuous Spectrum

A spectrum was first studied by Isaac Newton as early as the 17th Century. Newton allowed a beam of sunlight to pass through a narrow opening into a darkened room, and, as one would expect, a white patch of light appeared on the far wall. He then held a triangular glass prism in the path of the beam. The white patch disappeared at once and in its place, but off to one side, a spectrum appeared. The spectrum of sunlight is a *continuous* band of color, ranging from red at one end—through orange, yellow, green, and blue—to violet at the other. Newton accounted for this phenomenon by stating that sunlight (usually called white light) is made up of many colors, and that each color is bent to a different extent as it passes through a prism. The constituent colors of white light are thus separated to form a spectrum.

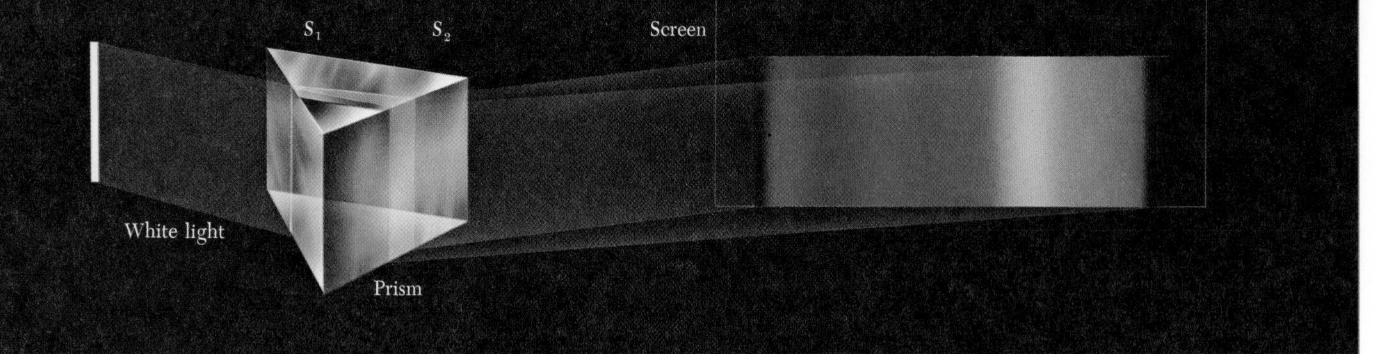

Fig. 4-1 A narrow beam of white light is separated into its constituent colors by a glass prism. The light is refracted and dispersed when it enters the prism at S_1. The colors are again refracted and still further separated when they leave the prism at S_2.

A source of white light more convenient than the sun is a white-hot object such as the incandescent filament of a light bulb. If light from such a filament passes first through a narrow slit and then through a glass prism, as shown in Fig. 4-1, the narrow beam of light can be observed on a screen as a band of spectrum colors. Each color in the white light produces its own image of the slit. That is, a spectrum is really a composite of a vast number of images of the slit arranged side by side. Thus, the colors red, orange,yellow, green, blue, and violet merge into each other, changing gradually and continuously from a deep red at one end to a dark violet at the other.(See Fig. 4-2, *a*.) For this reason a spectrum of white light is called a *continuous* spectrum.

Line Spectra

On the other hand, the spectrum of a luminous gas (a gas heated until it glows) is not continuous, but consists instead of a series of colored lines, often called *bright lines*, separated by *dark bands*. Such spectra are called *line spectra*. Every luminous gas has its own particular line spectrum. Examples of line spectra are shown in Fig. 4-2(*b*)—(*d*) and Fig. 4-3.

Of all gas spectra, hydrogen has the fewest lines. Can this in some way be related to the fact that hydrogen atoms are structurally the simplest kind of atoms?

Figure 4-3 is a diagrammatic illustration of the formation of a hydrogen spectrum. An electric discharge from an induction coil (an electrical device for producing high voltages) is passed through a discharge tube that contains hydrogen gas, which causes the hydrogen to glow with a magenta (or purplish-red) color. However, the line spectrum of hydrogen that is projected is found to consist of at least four unequally spaced lines, one in the red part of the spectrum, one in the blue, and two in the violet.

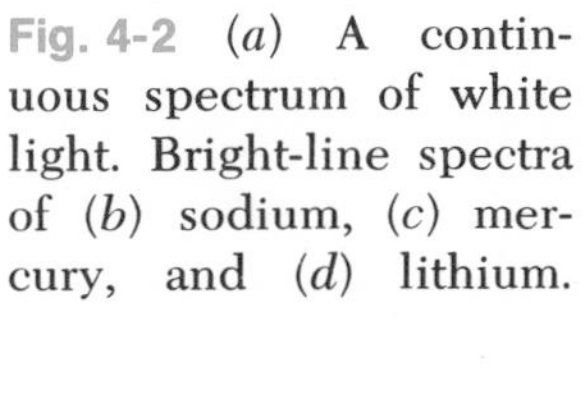

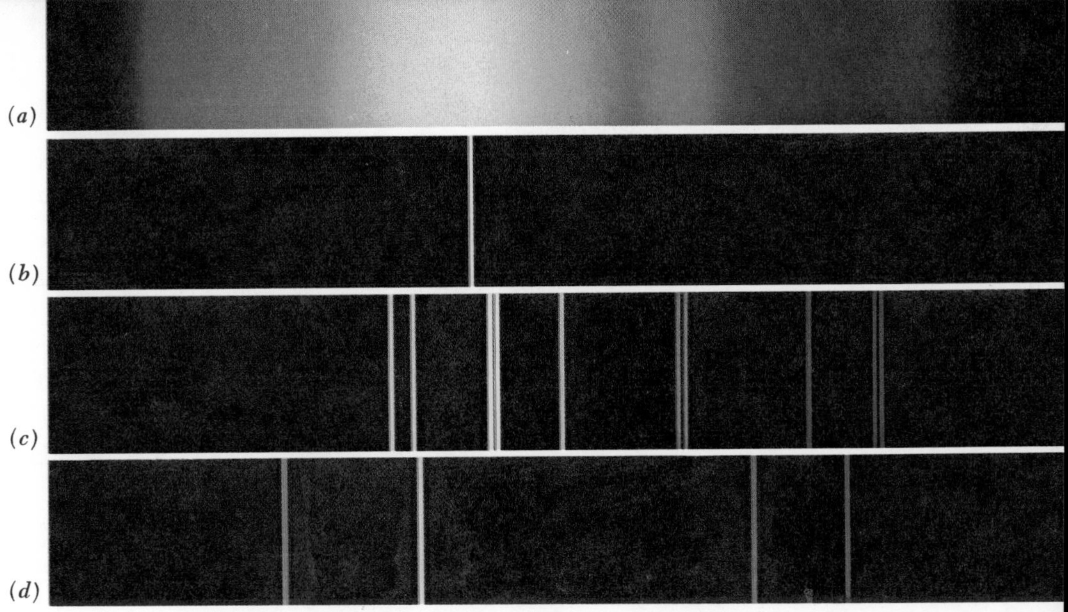

Fig. 4-2 (*a*) A continuous spectrum of white light. Bright-line spectra of (*b*) sodium, (*c*) mercury, and (*d*) lithium.

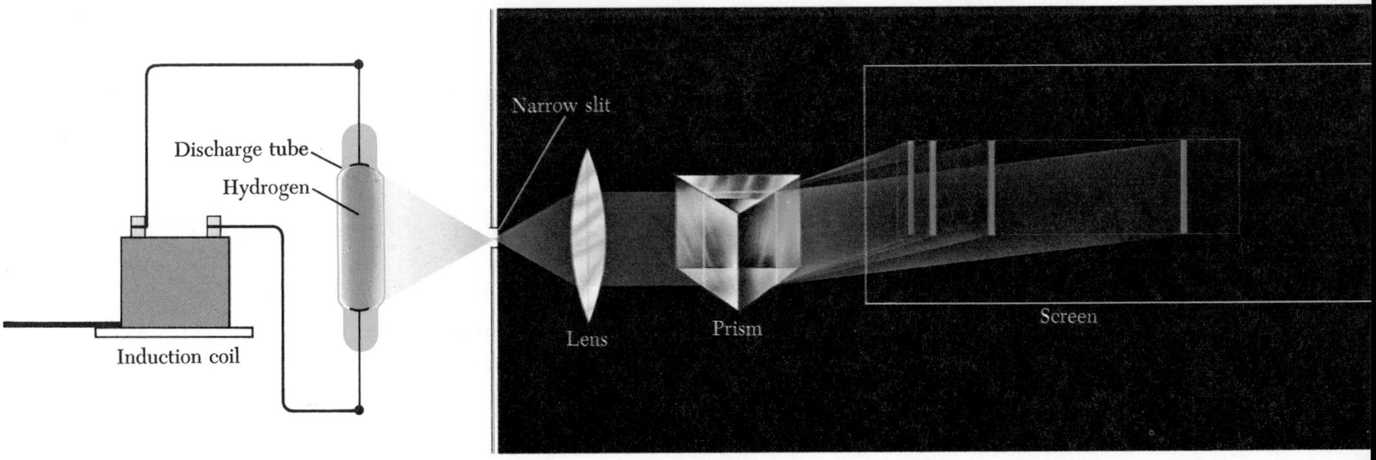

Discharge tube
Hydrogen
Induction coil
Narrow slit
Lens
Prism
Screen

Fig. 4-3 The line spectrum of hydrogen consists of several colored lines.

Fig. 4-4 Diagram of the operating principle of the spectroscope. See page 62.

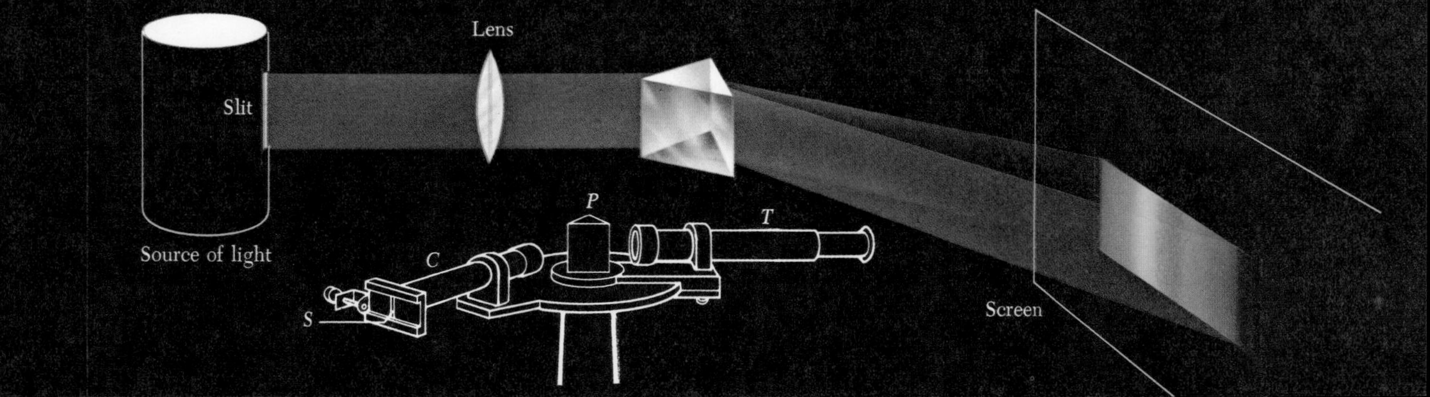

Line spectra are best observed through an instrument called a spectroscope. Figure 4-4 shows the operating principle of the spectroscope. A spectroscope consists essentially of three parts: (1) a collimator (C), (2) a glass prism (P), and (3) a telescope (T) mounted on an arm that rotates. The slit (S) in the collimator admits a narrow beam of light from the luminous source; the prism refracts and disperses the light that passes through the slit; and the telescope focuses the spectrum colors so that they can be observed through the eyepiece (E).

The Wave Theory of Light

What is light? Such common properties of light as reflection and refraction can easily be explained by assuming that light is a wave motion somewhat like the motion of water waves in a shallow pool. If you plunged your finger repeatedly in and out of a shallow tank of water, a succession of circular waves would travel outward from your finger to the sides of the tank where they are reflected. See Fig. 4-5 (a) and (b). Each wave consists of a crest followed by a trough, and this motion would be repeated as long as your finger moved up and down. Notice that the direction of wave motion, which is along the surface, is perpendicular to the motion of your finger, which is up and down. By analogy, we can say that light waves are caused by a rapidly vibrating source, such as oscillating electrical charges, as shown in Fig. 4-6. This explanation of the nature of light is known as the *wave theory*.

The distance between two corresponding points of a water wave, for example, the distance from crest to crest or from trough to trough—is called a *wavelength*. Wavelength is an important characteristic of a wave. Another is *frequency*. Frequency is the number of waves that passes a given point in a given period of time. Suppose, for instance that 20 ripples of water pass a selected point in the tank every second. The frequency in this case is 20 waves/sec.

Light waves are also characterized by wavelength and frequency. The wavelengths of the various colors of the spectrum can be determined by experiment, and they are found to be exceedingly short. For instance, the wavelengths of one shade of red and of one shade of violet light are 6.4×10^{-5} cm and 4.0×10^{-5} cm, respectively. To avoid negative exponents it is customary to

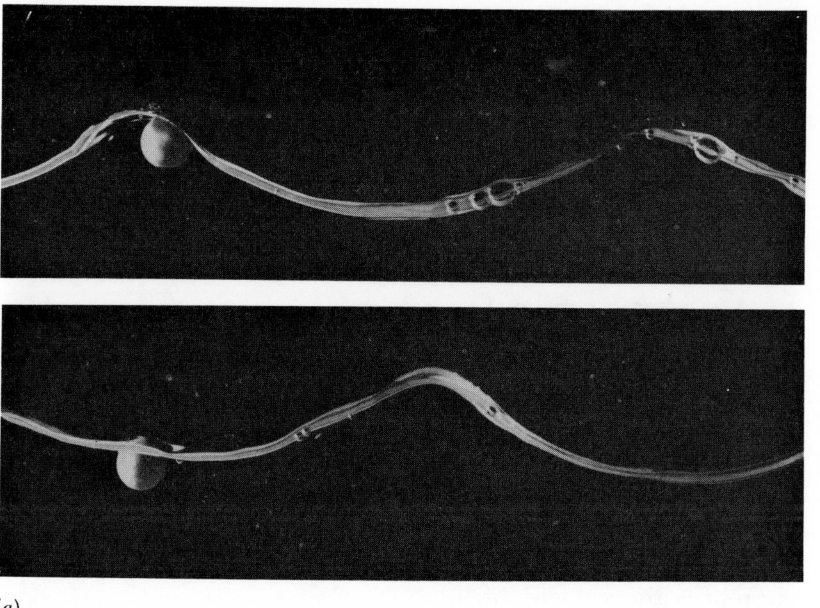

(a)

(b)

Fig. 4-5 (a) A wave is formed on the surface of water disturbed by a finger. (b) Each circular wave consists of a crest and a trough.

express wavelengths in units called angstroms (Å), so that 1 Å equals 10^{-8} cm. Thus, on this scale, the wavelength of red light is about 7500 Å and that of violet light about 4000 Å. What reasons can you suggest to explain why wavelengths of light are expressed in angstroms? Is it a matter of convenience more than anything else?

Equation Relating Frequency and Wavelength

It should be obvious that all the colors making up white light travel through space with the same *velocity*. The shorter the wavelength, the greater is the frequency. Or, expressed another way, wavelength is inversely proportional to frequency. The usual symbol for wavelength is the Greek letter lambda (λ); a convenient symbol for frequency is the Greek letter nu (ν). The formula

Note . . .

Velocity is usually considered to be a *vector* quantity. It has a magnitude (speed) which is expressed as distance per unit of time—and a direction—up, down, north, etc. Here, we are referring to the magnitude of velocity when we use this term.

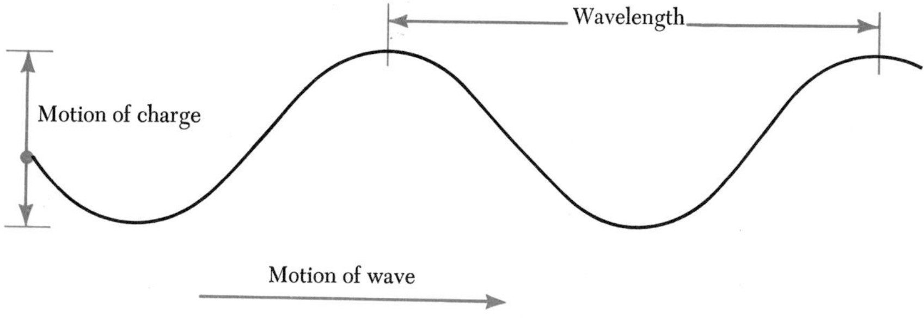

Fig. 4-6 Production of transverse waves by an oscillating electric charge. A transverse wave is a wave that moves in a direction perpendicular to the direction of the motion of the disturbed particles (charges). Could these be light waves?

Note . . .
In recent years frequency has been expressed in terms of the hertz (Hz), a unit named in honor of the German physicist Heinrich Hertz (1857–1894). One hertz equals one cycle (vibration, or movement back and forth) per second.

for frequency therefore, is

$$\lambda \propto \frac{1}{\nu} \tag{4-1}$$

or

$$\lambda \times \nu = k \text{ (a constant)} \tag{4-2}$$

The units of wavelength used here are cm/wave and the units of frequency are vibrations per second (vps). Hence,

$$\lambda \times \nu = \text{cm/wave} \times \text{waves/sec} = \text{cm/sec}$$

Since the units of velocity are cm/sec,

$$\lambda \times \nu = c \tag{4-3}$$

where c is the velocity of light.

The velocity of light is approximately 186,000 mi/sec, or, in metric units, 3×10^8 m/sec or 3×10^{10} cm/sec.

Since the wavelengths of light are very small, the frequencies of vibration are very large. For example, the wavelength of one shade of yellow light is 6×10^{-5} cm, and therefore its frequency is

$$\nu = \frac{c}{\lambda} = \frac{3 \times 10^{10} \text{ cm/sec}}{6 \times 10^{-5} \text{ cm/vibration (wave)}} = 5 \times 10^{14} \text{ Hz}$$

Moreover, each color has a range of wavelengths associated with what we have called a shade of that color. Visible red light, for example, has wavelengths between 6600 and 7600 Å.

The approximate wavelengths and frequencies of the representa-

Table 4-1 Wavelengths and frequencies of spectrum colors

Color	Wavelength (λ)		Frequency (ν) vps (or Hz)
	cm	Å	
Limit of red	7.0×10^{-5}	7000	3.9×10^{14}
Orange	6.2×10^{-5}	6200	4.8×10^{14}
Yellow	5.8×10^{-5}	5800	5.2×10^{14}
Green	5.3×10^{-5}	5300	5.7×10^{14}
Blue	4.6×10^{-5}	4600	6.5×10^{14}
Limit of violet	3.8×10^{-5}	4000	7.9×10^{14}

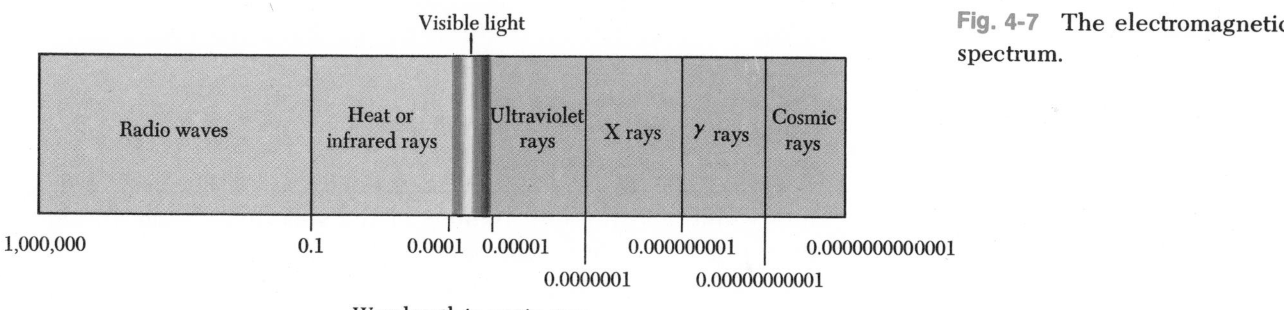

Fig. 4-7 The electromagnetic spectrum.

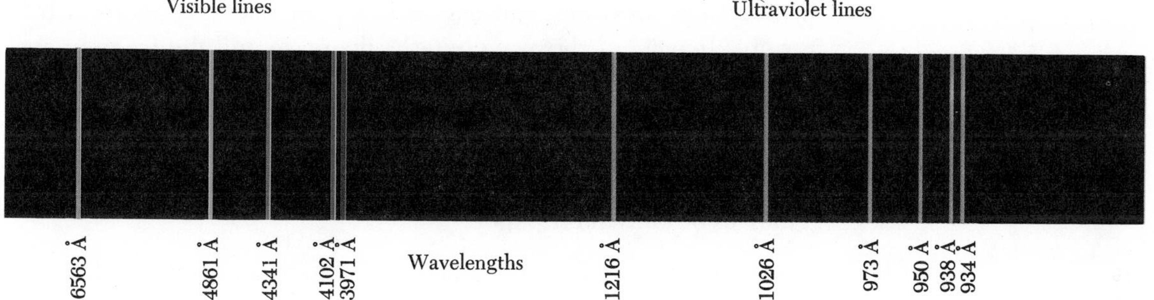

Fig. 4-8 The emission spectrum of hydrogen, showing the visible and ultraviolet regions. What are the colors of the visible lines?

tive shades of colors of the spectrum are given in Table 4-1. The frequency of a color indicates its exact position in the spectrum.

The Electromagnetic Spectrum

A spectrum can be seen by the eye; it can also be recorded on a photographic film. The spectrum recorded on the film, however, is different, and shows that there are waves beyond the red (with longer wavelengths and lower frequencies than the red), as well as beyond the violet (with shorter wavelengths and higher frequencies than the violet). The waves immediately beyond the red are called the *infrared* waves and those immediately beyond the violet are called *ultraviolet*. In other words, a photographic film is more sensitive to a wider range of "colors" than the eye.

The *visible spectrum* (the part detectable by the human eye) is only a very small part of the so-called *electromagnetic spectrum*. The electromagnetic spectrum also includes various bands of "invisible light," referred to as radio waves, infrared, ultraviolet, X rays, gamma (γ) rays, and "cosmic rays." The range in wavelengths of these bands is shown in Fig. 4-7.

Explain . . .
Frequencies can be used to indicate various colors, but wavelengths are used more often. Why?

The Line Spectrum of Hydrogen

As can be shown, the hydrogen spectrum shows lines in the visible, ultraviolet, and infrared regions of the spectrum. Each line in all three regions is an image of the slit of the spectroscope and indicates a particular frequency (and wavelength) emitted by the hydrogen gas. For example, in Fig. 4-8 there is a group of four lines in the visible and another of six lines in the ultraviolet. Observe that the distances between successive lines become smaller from left to right; that is, as the wavelengths decrease and the frequencies increase. This, for reasons to be given later, is an important observation. Actually, there are more than four lines in the visible region and more than six in the ultraviolet. However, at the far end, where the frequencies are highest, the additional lines are too close together to be drawn on paper.

Now let us raise a question: How does hydrogen gas produce its unique spectrum? Why is the spectrum of each element different from that of all the others? Clearly, it is the atoms of the elements that emit special frequencies corresponding to their spectral lines. Moreover, light having frequencies between these lines is not emitted at all. This tells us that a very important property of all atoms is their ability to give off only certain frequencies of light. These frequencies are different for each kind of atom. This must be a clue to the internal structural differences between atoms. For each kind of atom has a different energy-emission pattern. Perhaps we should learn more about energy.

Energy

A body is said to have energy if it has the capacity to do work, that is, if it is able to exert a force through a distance. Energy takes many forms.

Forms of Energy

Interpret . . .
In terms of mechanical energy, potential energy is the product of the weight (F_W) of an object and its height (h). Express this relationship mathematically.

Probably the most familiar form of energy that we see is *mechanical energy*. In Fig. 4-9 a pile driver is shown. The ram is raised to height h. If the ram is allowed to fall, it loses height and gains speed. When it strikes the pile, work is done because the pile is moved through a distance into the earth.

In this discussion of mechanical energy, we may identify two different energy states. Because work was applied to the ram to raise it to height h, the ram had the capacity to do work by virtue of its position. In other words, the ram possessed *potential energy.*

When the ram is released, a second state of energy may be identified. This state of energy is the energy of motion and is called *kinetic energy.* By virtue of its kinetic energy, the ram can do work, as is evident when the pile moves deeper into the earth.

Interpret . . .

If kinetic energy is one-half the product of the mass (m) of an object times its velocity (v) squared, express this relationship in a mathematical formula.

Other Forms of Energy *Electric* energy, *radiant* energy, and *nuclear* energy are all *forms* of energy. An electric current can drive a motor, which is a very common device for doing work. The radiant energy of sunlight comes through cold space, and yet we feel the heating effect of sunlight on our bodies. Nuclear energy is used to drive generators, submarines, and, some day, space vehicles.

Chemical energy is, however, of primary interest in chemistry. We can say that there is chemical energy in a gallon of gasoline because when gasoline burns, the energy produced can be used to do the work necessary to push the piston of an automobile engine. Thus, chemical energy consists of potential and kinetic energy. Do other forms of energy have potential and kinetic energy? Are forms of energy related? The study of chemistry reveals that the different forms of energy can be related one to another. Therefore, to appreciate the subject of chemistry you should be familiar with the various forms energy takes.

Transformation of Energy

If a car is on a slope and the brakes are released, we know by experience that it will coast down the slope even though its engine is not running. Moreover, as the car loses height it gains speed. That is, as the car loses potential energy it gains kinetic energy. This is an example of the *transformation of energy* from one kind to another.

Energy transformations are very common. For example, the car running down the slope can be brought to a standstill by applying the brakes. And, if we touched the brake drums, we would realize they were quite hot. The heat is caused by friction between the brake

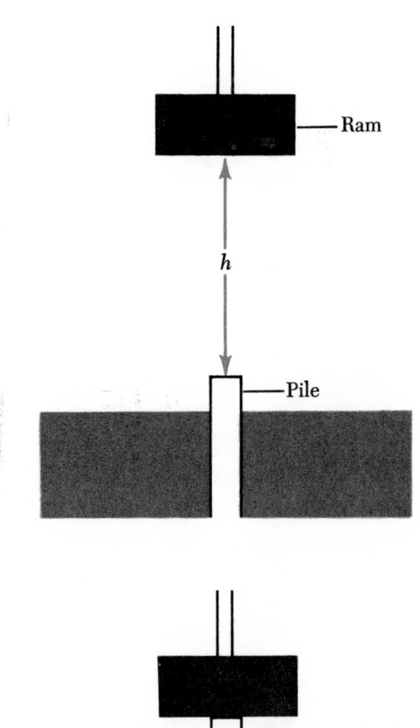

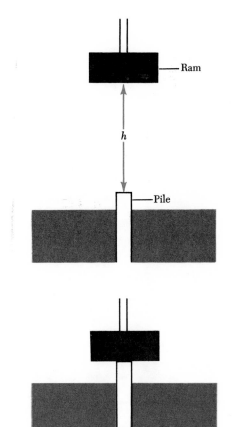

Fig. 4-9 When one uses a pile driver, the potential energy of the ram must be transformed into kinetic energy before it can do work. This happens when the ram drops through the distance h onto the pile.

drum and the wheel. In other words, some of the potential energy originally possessed by the car has been transformed into heat energy. Or, again, we know that gasoline burns and that, in burning, it emits both heat and light. Thus we conclude that potential chemical energy is stored in gasoline and during the process of burning this potential energy is transformed into heat energy and light energy. As we shall read later in the chapter, energy transformations within atoms are very common. For example, if a gas is heated, some of the heat energy overcomes the attractive force between electrons and nuclei so that in consequence electrons of some of the atoms are moved away from their nuclei. Thus, in this process, heat energy is transformed into potential energy. If the elevated electrons then fall back towards the nucleus, another transformation takes place. This time, however, the potential energy is transformed into light energy; the amount of light energy is closely related to the structure of the atom.

The Quantum Theory

At the turn of the century, a German physicist named Max Planck (1859–1947) was puzzled by the results of those who studied the radiations emitted by hot objects. These results could not be explained in terms of the wave theory. But they could be explained by assuming that the energy in matter is emitted in packages or bundles which he called *quanta*. Planck postulated that a quantum of energy is proportional to the frequency (ν) of the radiation. Thus, the higher the frequency, the greater is the energy (E) of the quantum. Or, in symbols, $E \propto \nu$. Hence,

$$E = \nu \times h \qquad (4\text{-}4)$$

where h is a proportionality constant known as Planck's constant. Planck's idea—that energy comes in packets and that the energy contents of a packet are related to the frequency of the radiated energy—is particularly useful because it enables us to express frequencies, which can be determined experimentally, in units of energy. It also suggests that since each kind of atom emits a unique series of frequencies (or wavelengths) of light and no other frequencies, then the internal energy of atoms can change only in steps.

Note . . .
The value of Planck's constant is 6.62×10^{-27} erg-sec.

A Particle Theory of Light

Note . . .
The photon is a quantum of light energy.

In 1906, Einstein used the quantum theory to account for the *photoelectric effect*. The photoelectric effect is the name given to the ejection of electrons from the surface of certain metals when light falls on them. Experimental data connecting the intensity of the light hitting the metal with the number of electrons ejected and their energy could not be explained by a wave model of light. Einstein (1879–1955) explained the data in terms of collisions between the electrons of the metal and bundles (or packets) of light which he called *photons*. In effect, Einstein said that when light is emitted or absorbed by matter, each atom gives off or takes on 1 photon of energy at a time and he showed that the Planck equation ($E = \nu \times h$) applies to photons, where ν is the frequency of the light; h is Planck's constant, and E is the energy of a photon. The equation shows that the energy of a photon is determined by its frequency—the higher the frequency, the greater the energy, and vice versa. Thus, a photon of blue light carries more energy than a photon of red light. Also, a photon of ultraviolet radiation carries more energy than a photon of visible light. On the other hand, a photon of infrared radiation carries less energy than a photon of visible light.

Thus, there are two theories that explain and predict the behavior of light, a wave theory and a particle theory. These theories are so effective that scientists often say that light behaves as both a wave and a particle at the same time. Some light effects can be explained only in terms of waves, other effects can be explained only in terms of particles, while some can be explained either by the wave theory or the particle theory. It was the particle nature of light, however, that led to a new and revolutionary concept concerning the structure of atoms.

The Law of Motion and Rotating Bodies

The Rutherford model of an atom, as you recall, had a positively charged nucleus and rotating electrons. Although Rutherford did not think of electrons as having special orbits, for he assumed that electrons moved in circular orbits determined only by chance, he compared electrons with planets revolving about the sun, and called them *planetary* electrons. However, the concept of electrons rotating around a nucleus contradicted the laws of motion. A body such

Observe . . .
See for yourself. Fasten a rubber ball to a string and whirl it rapidly in a circle. How long does it continue to move in a circle after you stop whirling it?

as a billiard ball can be made to move in a circle at constant speed only if a force is applied to it. If the applied force is withdrawn, the ball loses energy and eventually stops rotating.

By analogy, it was assumed that a steady force had to be applied to an electron to make it revolve around a nucleus, and that if the force were withdrawn, the electron would spiral into the nucleus. But this did not happen.

In 1913, a Danish physicist named Niels Bohr made the bold and controversial suggestion that the laws of physics as applied to large objects did not apply to minute particles such as atoms and electrons. This was a revolutionary idea, but Bohr maintained that it was justified because it was supported by evidence.

Bohr (1885–1962) maintained that electrons can revolve indefinitely in a given orbit without having to absorb energy from an external source. He then assumed that several such orbits could exist in the atom and that the electron would possess a different amount of energy in each of them. If the electron were to move from one orbit to another, a photon of definite frequency would be emitted or absorbed. Using this model, Bohr was able to account for all of the lines in the spectrum of hydrogen.

Bohr's Concept of Hydrogen Atoms

Bohr thought of an electron as revolving freely in a path around the nucleus of a hydrogen atom. He suggested that, if the atoms are heated, the electrons absorb some of the heat energy and jump into another orbit further from the nucleus, thereby increasing their potential energy. Thus, in this process heat energy is transformed into potential energy. Conversely, if the electron falls back to its original orbit, it loses the energy it has gained, emitting the energy as light in the process. If the energy of the electron in the higher energy level or orbit is E_2, and that in the lower energy level or orbit is E_1, the energy radiated during the drop to the lower level is E_2–E_1. In terms of the Planck equation,

$$E_2 - E_1 = h \times \nu$$

or (4-5)

$$\nu = \frac{E_2 - E_1}{h}$$

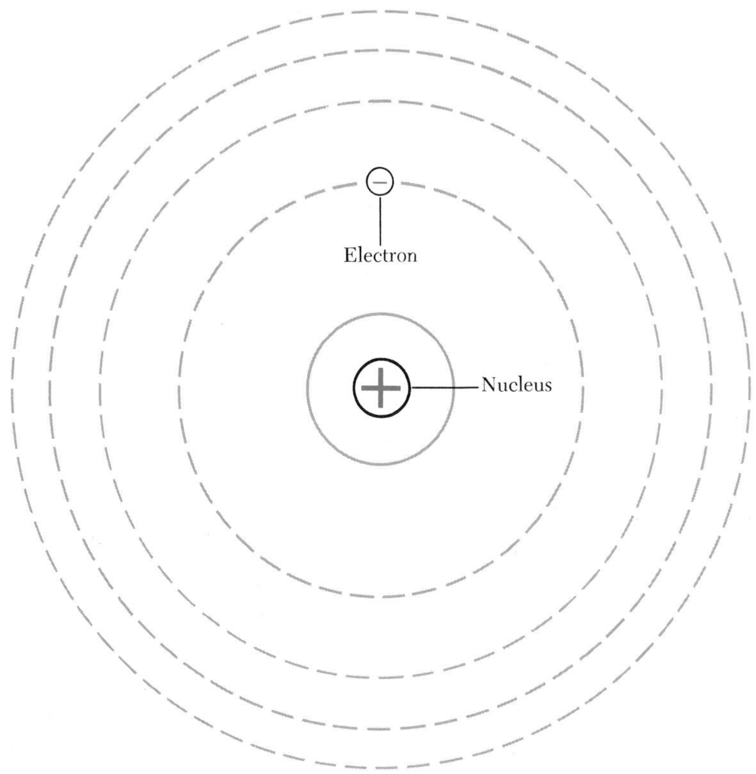

Fig. 4-10 Bohr's model of the hydrogen atom showing several stationary states or energy levels in which the electron might reside.

That is, the energy emitted is in the form of a photon whose frequency is ν.

If light of all wavelengths and frequencies were emitted, then clearly the spectrum would be continuous. But, since only line spectra are obtained, Bohr concluded that electrons travel only in special or permitted orbits. Bohr called the permitted orbits *stationary states*. The orbit closest to the nucleus is the orbit of least energy, and it is called the *ground state*. A Bohr model of a hydrogen atom with some of the permitted orbits is shown in Fig. 4-10. Notice that the distances between orbits diminish the further these orbits are from the ground state.

Another way to think of the Bohr atom is in terms of energy levels (see Fig. 4-11). The electron is normally in the ground state which is level 1. In this ground state the electron is in the condition of least energy and the atom is in the condition of maximum stability. If the atom is heated (as in a discharge tube), the electron overcomes the force of electrostatic attraction of the nucleus. As a result, the

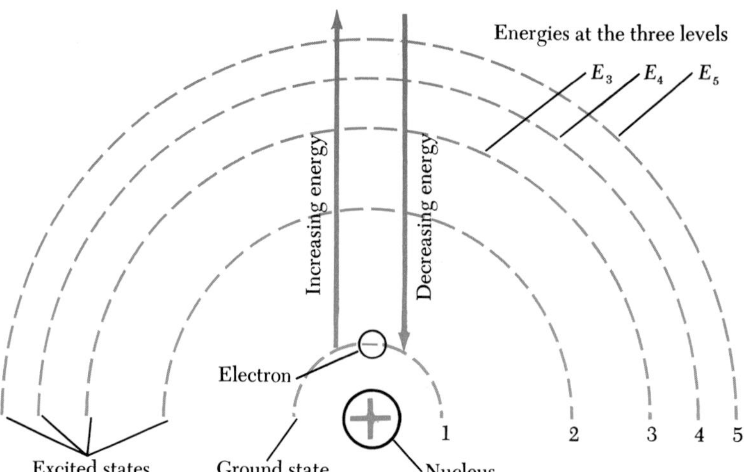

Fig. 4-11 Bohr's model of the hydrogen atom showing that an electron's energy is greater the further the electron is from the nucleus.

electron jumps, from level 1, to levels 2, 3, 4, 5, and so on, depending upon the number of quanta absorbed. That is, the energy of the electron increases from level to level, and the electron with increased energy is said to be in an *excited* state. An electron in an excited state is unstable, so that it "falls" to a lower energy level, and, in doing so, emits a photon of light. If the energy is E_5 at level 5 and E_4 at level 4, the frequency emitted by the photon of light as the electron falls from level 5 to level 4 is given by the equation

$$\nu = \frac{E_5 - E_4}{h} \tag{4-6}$$

Similarly, as the electron falls from level 4 to level 3 the frequency of the light emitted is

$$\nu' = \frac{E_4 - E_3}{h} \tag{4-7}$$

Since the spacing between successive energy levels is not uniform (see Fig. 4-11), the two frequencies ν and ν' are different, and therefore the colors emitted are different.

Energy Emitted by Electrons Expressed in Kilocalories

The energy emitted by a single photon is so small that it is more convenient to consider the energy emitted by a "mole of photons." What is a mole? The term *mole* is considered at some length in Chapter 9, but for our purposes here we can assume that one mole of hydrogen is its atomic mass expressed in grams; that is, 1.0079 g. Moreover, we know that there are 6.02×10^{23} atoms in one mole (1.0079 g) of hydrogen atoms. And, since each hydrogen atom contains one electron, we can say that there are 6.02×10^{23} electrons in 1 mole of hydrogen. (We can also say that this quantity of electrons is a mole of electrons.) What is the mass of a mole of electrons? The mass of one electron is 9.1×10^{-28} g. Thus,

$$9.1 \times 10^{-28}\ \text{g/electron} \times 6.02 \times 10^{23}\ \text{electrons/mole} = 5.4 \times 10^{-4}\ \text{g/mole}$$

If, in forming spectra, each electron emits 1 photon we can say there are 6.02×10^{23} photons in 1 mole. Actually, the amount of energy emitted depends on the amount of heat or electrical energy added, and atoms are constantly being excited and then losing energy.

As already stated, every line in the hydrogen spectrum is the result of electrons falling from one energy level to another and emitting energy in the process. Let us consider the red line in the hydrogen spectrum and compute the energy (in kilocalories) emitted when a mole of these red photons is released by the atoms. The wavelength of this red line is 6560 Å, or 6.56×10^{-5} cm, and therefore its frequency ν is c/λ, or

$$\frac{3.0 \times 10^{10}\ \text{cm/sec}}{6.56 \times 10^{-5}\ \text{cm}} = 4.57 \times 10^{14}\ \text{vps or Hz}$$

$$\text{Energy of photon} = h \times \nu = 6.6 \times 10^{-27}\ \text{erg-sec} \times 4.57 \times 10^{14}\ \text{Hz} = 30.2 \times 10^{-13}\ \text{ergs/photon}$$

$$\begin{aligned}\text{Energy per mole of photons} &= 30.2 \times 10^{-13}\ \text{ergs/photon} \times 6.02 \times 10^{23}\ \text{photons/mole} \\ &= 182 \times 10^{10}\ \text{ergs/mole} \times 2.3 \times 10^{-8}\ \text{cal/erg} \\ &= 420 \times 10^{2}\ \text{cal/mole} \\ &= 42\ \text{kcal/mole}\end{aligned}$$

This figure represents the amount of energy emitted when one mole of electrons "falls" from the third energy level to the second energy level in hydrogen atoms.

Table 4-2
Energy required to raise hydrogen electron from the ground state to higher levels

Energy level change, 1 to —	Energy required, kcal/mole
2	235
3	278
4	293
5	300
6	305
7	307

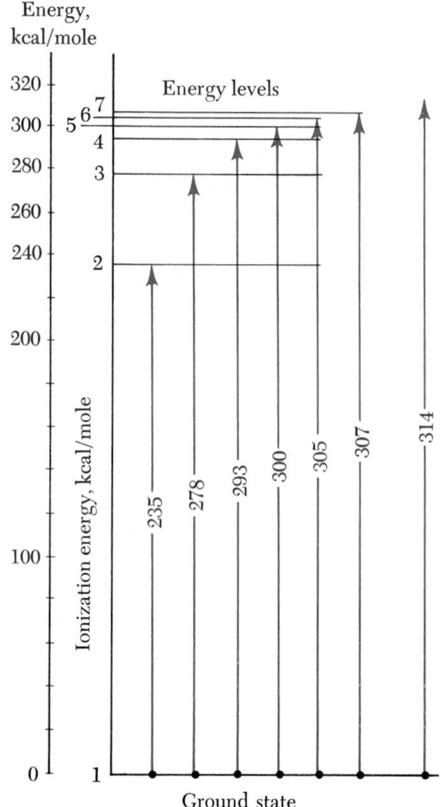

Fig. 4-12 Energy needed to lift electrons in one mole of hydrogen atoms to energy levels.

Input Energy

The amounts of energy needed to raise the electrons in 1 mole of hydrogen atoms from the ground state to the various energy levels was computed by Bohr. They are shown in Table 4-2 and Fig. 4-12.

If 314 kcal of energy are absorbed by a mole of hydrogen atoms, all the electrons can be completely removed from the atoms and hydrogen ions are formed. This reaction is represented by the equation

$$n\text{H (atoms)} \xrightarrow{314\text{ kcal}} n\text{H}^+ + ne^-$$

where $n = 1$ mole.

This value (314 kcal) is called the *ionization energy*. It is apparent that the energies necessary to excite electrons from the ground state to the various levels must be less than the ionization energy.

Visible and Ultraviolet Lines and Energies

In falling toward the ground state, the electron may jump in one step or two steps or in a series of steps. For example, if the electron jumps from level 5 to level 2, the photon emitted is greater in energy than if the jump is from level 5 to level 4, or from level 3 to level 2. The energies emitted when 1 mole of electrons fall to level 2 from levels 7, 6, 5, 4, and 3 can be calculated from Fig. 4-12 and are given in Table 4-3. Each energy output produces a spectral line, and the recorded wavelengths show that all these lines are in the visible spectrum.

Table 4-3 Energy emitted by the hydrogen electron from outer levels to level 2

Electron jump	Energy difference, kcal/mole		Output energy, kcal/mole	Wavelength, Å	Color of line
E_7 to E_2	307 − 235	=	72	3800	violet
E_6 to E_2	305 − 235	=	70	3850	violet
E_5 to E_2	300 − 235	=	65	4100	violet
E_4 to E_2	293 − 235	=	58	4800	blue-green
E_3 to E_2	278 − 235	=	43	6600	red

Now let us consider the energy output as electrons fall from the various levels to the ground state (Fig 4-12 and Table 4-4). It should be clear that the lines in this second group are in the ultraviolet. (Why?) The emission lines in the two groups are shown diagram-

Table 4-4 Energy emitted during jump of hydrogen electron from outer levels to level 1

Electron jump	Energy difference, kcal/mole		Output energy, kcal/mole	Wavelength, Å
E_6 to E_1	305 − 0	=	305	935
E_5 to E_1	300 − 0	=	300	940
E_4 to E_1	293 − 0	=	293	960
E_3 to E_1	278 − 0	=	278	1020
E_2 to E_1	235 − 0	=	235	1210

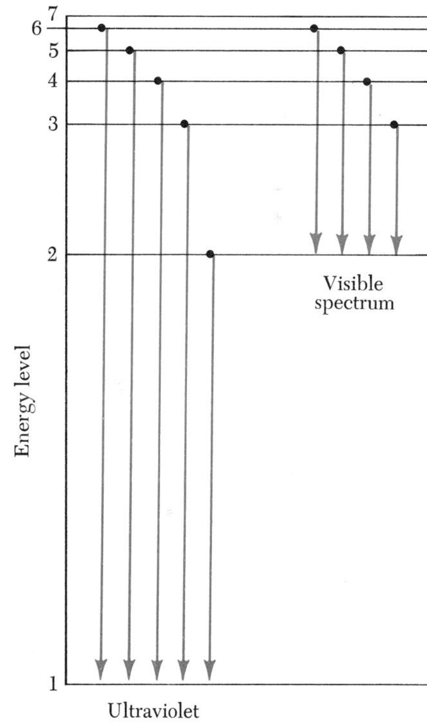

Fig. 4-13 When does an electron produce visible light and ultraviolet radiations?

matically in Fig. 4-14. Lines in the visible region represent the energy emissions when an electron falls to level 2 from any of the higher levels. The lines in the ultraviolet are formed when an electron falls to the ground state from any of the higher levels.

But what of the lines in the infrared region of the spectrum? How are they formed? Radiation in the infrared consists of longer wavelengths and lower frequencies than radiation in the visible region. That is, lines in the infrared represent a smaller emission of energy than do lines in the visible. It can be shown that lines in the infrared region are formed when electrons fall to level 3.

The Limitations of the Bohr Model of the Atom

Using Newton's second law of motion and Coulomb's law of attraction between opposite electric charges, Bohr derived the equation from which he computed the energy of an electron in the various energy levels for the hydrogen atom. With this information, he was able to calculate the light energy emitted when an electron falls from a higher to a lower energy level. In all cases, the calculated values agreed with the experimental values as measured from line spectra. This agreement between theory and experiment was so remarkable that the concept of atomic energy levels has become an important part of physical science.

It is not surprising that the Bohr atomic model for hydrogen was applied to heavier atoms. However, the Bohr model could not account for the spectra of atoms with more than one electron. Thus, Bohr's theory was useful in considering the spectrum of hydrogen and no other. This imposed serious limitations upon the Bohr model and it has therefore been replaced by a newer model.

Recall . . .

Newton's second law:

When a force is applied to an object, the rate of change of momentum is directly proportional to the force producing it, and the change of momentum takes place in the direction of the applied force.

In symbols:

$$F \propto \frac{\Delta mv}{\Delta t}$$

This new model of the atom was developed some 12 years after Bohr proposed his model for a hydrogen atom. It was derived from a new field of study called *quantum mechanics*. The new model accounts not only for the spectral lines of hydrogen but also for the lines of all the heavier elements. The quantum mechanical model deals in *probabilities* rather than the certainties of the older model.

Summary

Light can be described as a wave motion. The wavelength and frequency of light waves can be found by experiment. A white-hot source of light gives a continuous color spectrum. The spectrum of a luminous gaseous element is a series of visible colored bands or lines, in addition to lines in the infrared and ultraviolet regions, which can be photographed, but not seen.

Line spectra can be explained in terms of the quantum theory of light and energy. Energy can be transformed from one kind to another. Potential energy can be transformed into kinetic energy, or heat energy, or even light energy.

Planck's quantum theory asserts that radiant energy is emitted in packages or quanta. This theory was applied to the emission of light from atoms. A particle of light emitted by an atom is called a photon. The energy of a photon is related to the color of the light—the higher the frequency the greater is the amount of energy carried by the photon. The higher the frequency the farther toward the blue or violet portion of the spectrum is the color.

Bohr's atomic model, unlike Rutherford's, is concerned with the particular energy levels of electrons. To justify his model, Bohr made two revolutionary assumptions: (1) an electron can move in its orbit without losing energy, and (2) an electron can exist only in certain permitted orbits. An electron in an atom is normally in the ground state, but if the electron absorbs energy from an external source, its energy content is increased and it is said to be in a higher energy level or in an excited state. If it falls to a lower permitted orbit, it loses energy and emits a photon of light. The magnitude of the energy of the photon determines the frequency (and therefore the color) of the light emitted.

Bohr derived an equation (based on the laws of physics as applied to circular motion) from which he could predict the wavelengths of the lines in the visible spectrum of hydrogen atoms. This independent prediction of the spectral lines gave support to his theory of circular orbits and discrete energy levels. However, Bohr was unable to predict the spectral lines of any element except hydrogen. This failure of the Bohr theory led scientists to adopt a new atom model based on quantum mechanics.

Factual Recall

1. (*a*) What is a continuous spectrum? (*b*) How is it formed?
2. (*a*) What is a line spectrum? (*b*) How is it formed?
3. What are the essential features of the wave theory of light?
4. (*a*) What is the equation relating wavelength and frequency? (*b*) Explain the meaning of the symbols used in this equation.
5. What is meant by: (*a*) ultraviolet, (*b*) infrared, (*c*) electromagnetic spectrum?
6. Discuss the nature of the line spectrum of hydrogen.
7. (*a*) What is (*i*) energy, (*ii*) potential energy, (*iii*) kinetic energy? (*b*) Give an example of the conversion of kinetic energy into potential energy.
8. What are the essential features of the quantum theory?
9. (*a*) Compare the two theories of light. (*b*) Why have scientists proposed the two different theories?
10. In deriving his model of a hydrogen atom, Bohr made a basic assumption that was at variance with the laws of physics. (*a*) What was this assumption and why was it made? (*b*) Why was a new model adopted for atoms in general?
11. What is meant by the terms (*a*) ground state, (*b*) excited state, (*c*) energy level?
12. (*a*) What is meant by ionization energy? (*b*) Why is the energy needed to "lift" one mole of electrons from the ground state to the highest stationary state less than the ionization energy?
13. Under what circumstances are spectral lines of hydrogen formed in (*a*) the infrared region, (*b*) the visible region, (*c*) the ultraviolet region?
14. Draw a diagram, including energy levels, to show how lines in the infrared region are produced.

Apply Your Knowledge!

1. In your opinion, has Bohr's contribution to atomic structure served any useful purpose? Explain.
2. State the wavelength of blue light in angstroms, and compute its frequency, given λ is 4.6×10^{-5} cm and the velocity of light is 3×10^{10} cm/sec.
3. The wavelengths of two of the lines in the ultraviolet region of hydrogen are 1216 Å and 950 Å. Compute the frequencies of these lines. Use Fig. 4-12 to determine the energy levels between which the electrons moved in giving rise to each of these lines.
4. Given that 1 erg of energy is equivalent to 2.39×10^{-8} cal, compute the number of ergs in 1 kcal.
5. The wavelength of the blue line in the hydrogen spectrum is 4860 Å. Compute the energy of this line in kilocalories per mole of photons emitted.
6. Compare the energy of a photon of red light ($\lambda = 6800$ Å) with the energy of a photon of violet light ($\lambda = 4000$ Å).
7. Using Planck's equation, compare the frequencies of light emitted as an electron in the hydrogen atom falls from (*a*) level 3 to level 2, (*b*) level 6 to level 5.
8. The energy emitted when electrons in hydrogen atoms fall from level 3 to the ground state is 278 kcal/mole. Compute (*a*) the wavelength and (*b*) the frequency of the line emitted.

Find Out!

1. Look up the analytical procedure known as "flame testing." How is this related to the topics of this chapter?
2. What is a spectroscope? What are some of its uses?

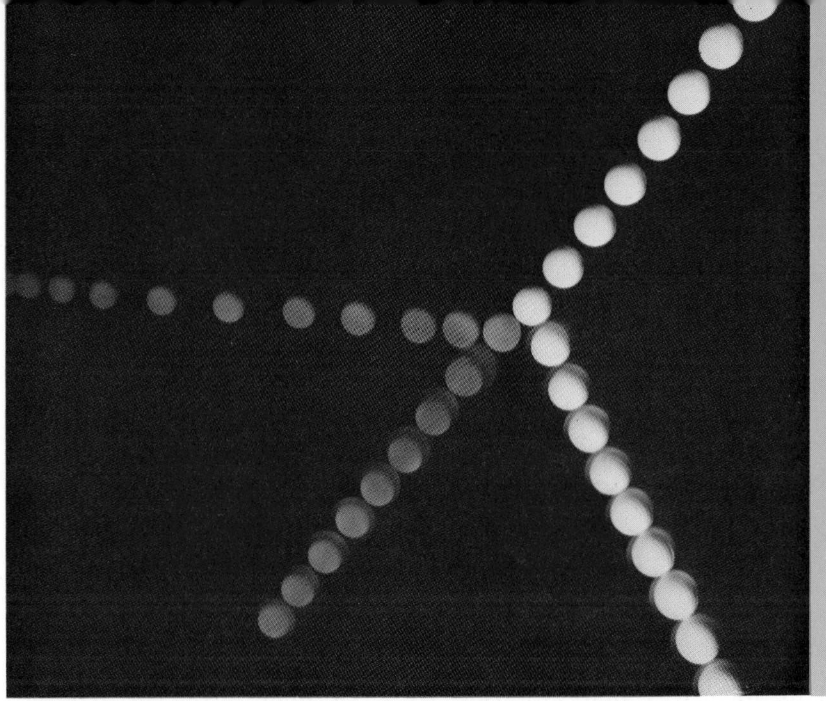

CHAPTER 5

THE QUANTUM MECHANICAL ATOM

CLASSICAL MECHANICS based on Newtonian laws enable the speed and position of moving bodies, like the colliding billard balls in the photograph, to be calculated. Both the position and the speed of large objects, such as moving billiard balls, can be accurately measured. But first the billiard balls must be seen; they must reflect light waves back to the eye of the observer. The impact of the light waves does not perceptibly disturb either the speed or direction of the moving balls. However, this does not appear to be true of the impact of radiations upon such minute particles as moving electrons. The wavelengths of visible light are longer than the diameters of electrons, and experience suggests that light "rides over" electrons, causing no disturbing effects. By contrast, the wavelengths of high-energy radiations such as ultraviolet, X, and γ rays are smaller than the diameters of electrons. In such cases, there is evidence that the jolt of a high-energy photon (for example, an X-ray photon) interacting with the electron changes both the speed and direction of an electron, as shown in Fig. 5-1. But,

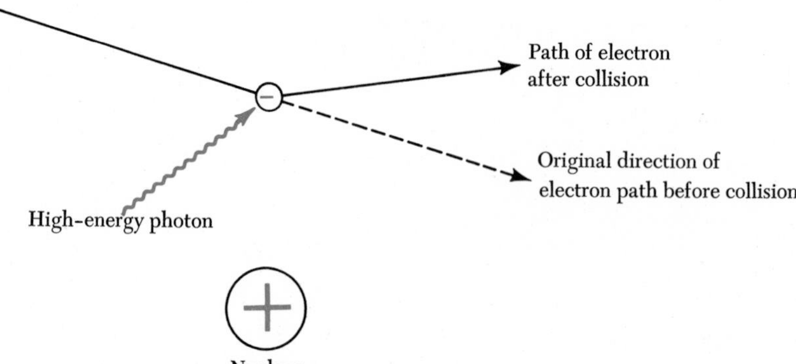

Fig. 5-1 A jolt from a high-energy photon will change the direction of the path of an electron and also its speed.

using light, any attempt to determine the position of the electron prevents the determination of velocity immediately before impact.

This idea was first proposed by a German physicist, Werner Heisenberg (1901–1968). All of this is summarized in Heisenberg's *uncertainty principle*, which states that it is not possible to determine both position and velocity of a minute particle at the same time. If the exact position of an electron near the nucleus is known, its velocity cannot be determined. If a precise velocity is known for an electron, its exact position cannot be found. In other words, if the position of an electron is known, we do not know its speed or direction. Conversely, if we know its speed and direction, its exact position is unknown. From the velocity of the electron we can estimate its energy. Therefore the uncertainty principle tells us that if we know the energy of the electron, we cannot know its exact position in the atom. Because of the importance of the energy-level concept in explaining the behavior of atoms, a knowledge of the energy of the electrons in the atom is of greater value than a knowledge of their positions.

It is for this basic reason that Heisenberg rejected Bohr's concept of definite orbits but retained his idea of energy levels. What, then, is the substitute for Bohr's picture of an electron moving around a nucleus?

Schrödinger's Wave Mechanics

In 1926, the Austrian physicist Erwin Schrödinger (1887–1961) proposed a mathematical approach to quantum theory. This approach, called *wave mechanics*, resulted in a complicated equation known as the wave equation; it gave rise to a new model of an atom, one that has now displaced the older Bohr model. The wave equation deals with the electron's most probable position, or with the region in which it is most likely to be found, rather than with the concept of definite orbits. Using the wave equation, Schrödinger computed the probabilities of finding an electron at certain positions near the nucleus at a given moment of time.

Let us apply this idea to the electron of a hydrogen atom. The position of the electron in space means the distance from the origin (the nucleus) along each of the axes x, y, and z (see Fig. 5-2). These axes are perpendicular to each other and intersect at the origin. Actually, the wave equation involves values on all three axes. However, if for simplicity, the values along the y- and z-axes are imagined to be zero, the probability of finding the electron at various points along the x-axis alone can be computed from the wave equation. The equation then gives a probability distribution along the x-axis like that shown in Fig. 5-3. Notice that the position of maximum probability is near the nucleus (actually 0.53 Å from the nucleus). For distances less than 0.53 Å from the nucleus the probability positions taper off rapidly. For distances greater than 0.53 Å the probability positions taper off more slowly.

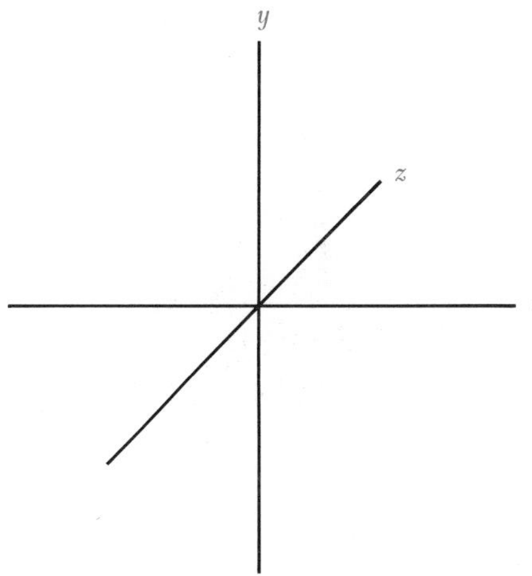

Fig. 5-2 Three axes at right angles to each other are needed to represent the position of a point in space. Why?

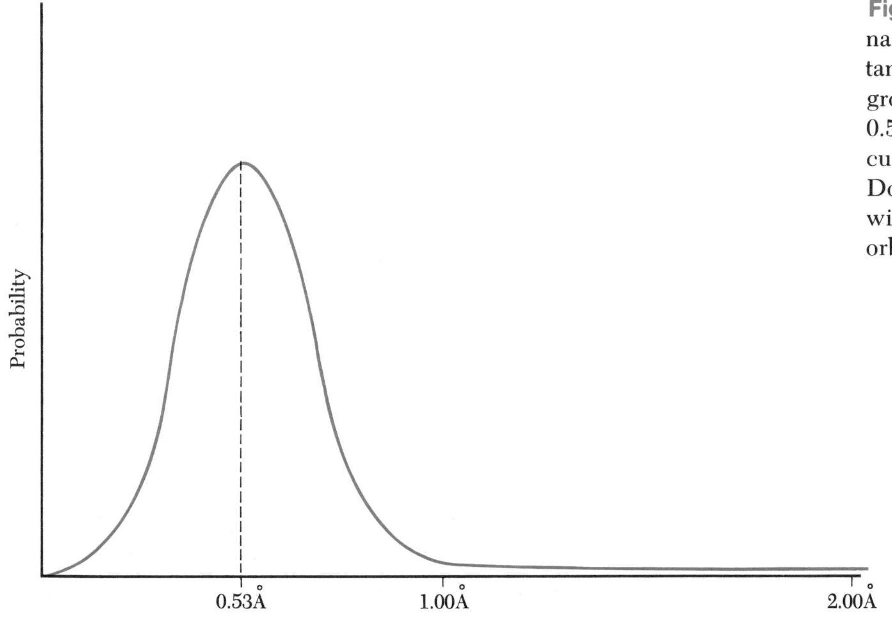

Fig. 5-3 From the laws of classical dynamics Bohr computed that the distance from electron to nucleus in the ground state of a hydrogen atom is 0.53 Å. This diagram is a probability curve based on quantum mechanics. Does the most probable distance agree with Bohr's computed radius of the orbit?

Similarly, a distribution along the y-axis can be found by making $x = 0$ and $z = 0$ in the equation. And, finally, if $x = 0$ and $y = 0$, distributions along the z-axis can be determined. Clearly, there are positions of high probability along each of the axes, and a locus of these high-probability positions gives the region of highest probability, or the region in which the electron appears to spend most of its time. In other words, the wave equation determines the probability of finding the electron at various positions in space in the ground state for a hydrogen atom. It is interesting that the distance from nucleus to the position of maximum probability is precisely the same as the distance from nucleus to electron that Bohr had computed for the ground state of the hydrogen atom. However, it must be emphasized that for Bohr this distance was *fixed and invariable*, whereas for Schrödinger it was the *most probable distance* among thousands of possibilities.

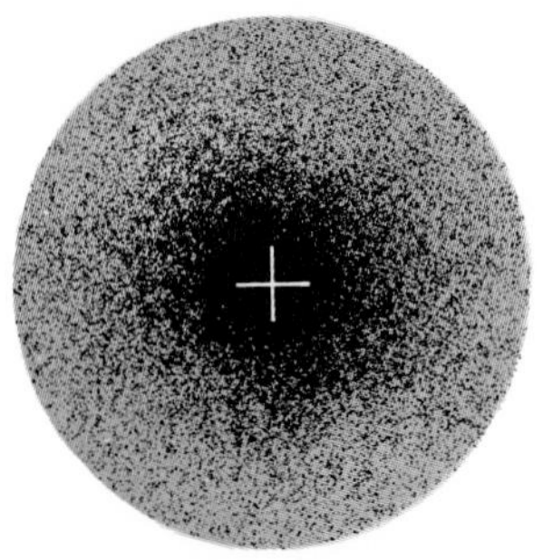

Fig. 5-4 The 1*s* electron forms a spherical charge cloud about the nucleus.

An Electron Cloud

According to this view an electron in an atom has a region in which it is most likely to be found. This region is called an *electron cloud* or *orbital*. An illustration of the electron cloud for the ground state of a hydrogen atom is shown in Fig. 5-4. In the cloud, some possible positions of the electron are represented by dots; the greater the density of dots, the greater is the probability of finding the electron in that particular region. This picture of an electron cloud shows that at any given instant of time the electron will most probably be found near the nucleus. However, there is also a small probability of finding the electron relatively far from the nucleus, and therefore, it is convenient to imagine a boundary for the electron cloud; this boundary is chosen so that the electron has a 95% chance of being within the regions described by the boundary. The diameter of such a spherical hydrogen atom is approximately 10^{-8} cm. A circular cross section of a hydrogen atom is shown in Fig. 5-5. *Could* the electron ever be outside the boundary surface?

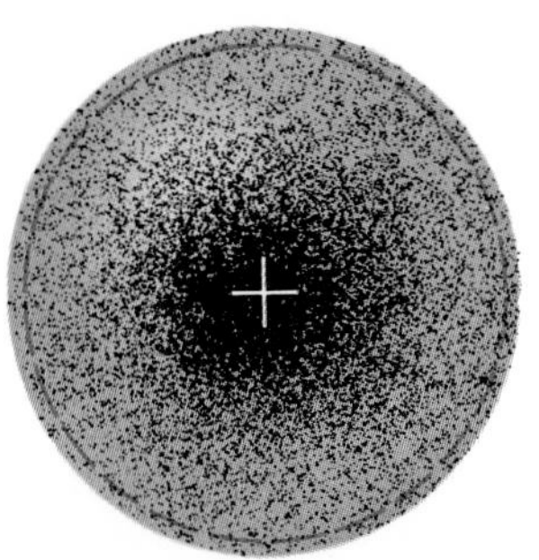

Fig. 5-5 For convenience the charge cloud may be enclosed in a spherical surface. The diameter of such a sphere is taken as 1 Å or 10^{-8} cm. However, there is a slight probability that the electron will be outside the arbitrarily fixed surface.

Quantum Numbers

Some electron clouds or orbitals are spherical, but, as we shall see later, others vary in shape and size as well as in position in space. Spectroscopic studies have led to the conclusion that each orbital is a discrete energy level and that the energy of the electron in a given orbital can be described in terms of a series of numbers—known as *quantum numbers* — similar in many ways to the postal zip code. Quantum numbers make it possible to describe the energies of all the electrons in atoms. Since the chemical and physical properties of atoms are closely related to the electrons within them and the energies of these electrons, a knowledge of quantum numbers is very important.

Principal Quantum Number

The first quantum number, called the *principal quantum number*, refers to the main energy level or shell of which the orbital is a component. The principal quantum number is an integer which can have any of the values 1, 2, 3, 4, 5, etc. These values correspond to the various energy levels in the model of the Bohr atom. Thus, if an electron has a principal quantum number (n) of 1, its orbital will be in the first shell; if 2, the orbital will be a part of the second shell and so on.

Orbital Quantum Number

The second quantum number (l) is related to the shape of an orbital. We shall consider only four different orbital shapes, and these will be discussed later in the chapter. Each shape is designated by one of the letters *s*, *p*, *d*, or *f*. Another way of expressing this idea is to say that each major energy level or shell is made up of sublevels or subshells which contain orbitals designated in terms of their shape as *s*, *p*, *d*, or *f*. Thus, the electron is said to be in a shell whose number is designated by the principal quantum number and in a subshell designated as *s*, *p*, *d*, or *f*.

Magnetic Quantum Number

The third quantum number (m_l) indicates the orbital itself and also its orientation in space in a magnetic field. To explain, let us imagine that the orbital—the region in which that electron spends most of its time—is both an energy level and an electron cloud. As an electron cloud it has a certain shape and possibly a certain preferred direction in space relative to other orbitals. As an energy level it is part of a subshell, designated as *s*, *p*, *d*, or *f* and by the orbital quantum number 0, 1, 2, or 3; and also a part of a shell,

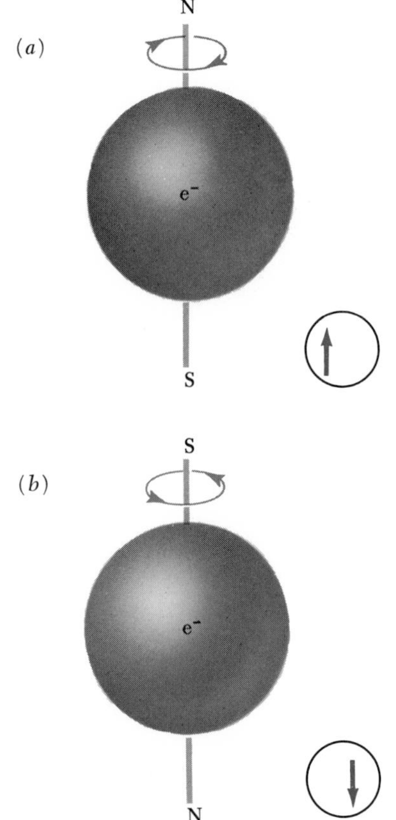

Fig.5-6 A spinning electron has a magnetic effect that gives rise to N and S poles. Explain the magnetic difference between (*a*) and (*b*).

Note . . .
The four quantum numbers are designated as follows:
n is the principal quantum number
l is the orbital quantum number
m_l is the magnetic quantum number
m_s is the spin magnetic quantum number.
The number of orbitals per shell is n^2 and the maximum number of electrons per shell is $2n^2$.

designated by the principal quantum number. If we think of the orbital as analogous to a house, a subshell to a town, and a shell to a state, we see that we could give the house address in terms of three quantum numbers—the state quantum number, the town quantum number, and the house quantum number. In a somewhat similar way we talk about the principal quantum number, the orbital quantum number, and the *magnetic quantum number* for each electron in an atom.

However, the pattern of energy levels for electrons in atoms is not quite as complicated as the state-town-house concept because there are fewer shells, subshells, and orbitals in the atom than there are states, towns, and houses in our country. In fact, spectroscopic studies have shown that there are strict limitations on the numbers of subshells in a shell and on the number of orbitals in a subshell. To be specific, the first shell contains only one subshell—the 1*s* subshell; the second shell contains two subshells—the 2*s* and the 2*p* subshells; the third shell contains three subshells—the 3*s*, 3*p*, and 3*d* subshells, and so on. Moreover, all *s* subshells have only one orbital, all *p* subshells have three orbitals—each with a different orientation in space—all *d* subshells have five orbitals. All *f* subshells have seven orbitals. The *magnetic quantum number* then is a number which designates in which of the various possible orbitals the electron is to be found.

Spin Quantum Number

There is also a fourth quantum number (m_s) which concerns what is called the spin of an electron. To account for certain magnetic effects it has been suggested that an electron, like a top, spins on its axis. For example, an assembly of hydrogen atoms acts as if it were composed of two kinds of magnets. This can be explained by assuming that in half the atoms the electrons have one kind of spin, clockwise perhaps, and in the other half of the atoms the electrons have an opposite counterclockwise spin as shown in Fig. 5-6.

An electron with a clockwise spin develops N and S poles as shown in the diagram. But if the spin is counterclockwise the magnetic poles are opposite to those with a clockwise spin. The *spin quantum numbers* are $+\frac{1}{2}$ or $-\frac{1}{2}$, corresponding to the two spin orientations. Studies show that two electrons with opposite spins can occupy the same orbital at the same time.

Electron Energy Levels in Atoms

A study of line spectra led Bohr to develop the energy-level concept and enabled him to estimate the energy of the electron in each of the various possible energy levels. Subsequent spectroscopic studies showed that the energy-level pattern was more complicated than this, and that shell, subshell, and orbital designations were necessary. These same studies revealed the relative energy spacing between the various energy levels, and these are given in Fig. 5-7. We shall see that all atoms have approximately the same energy-level pattern and therefore we shall use this pattern to predict the arrangement of electrons in all (or nearly all) the known atoms.

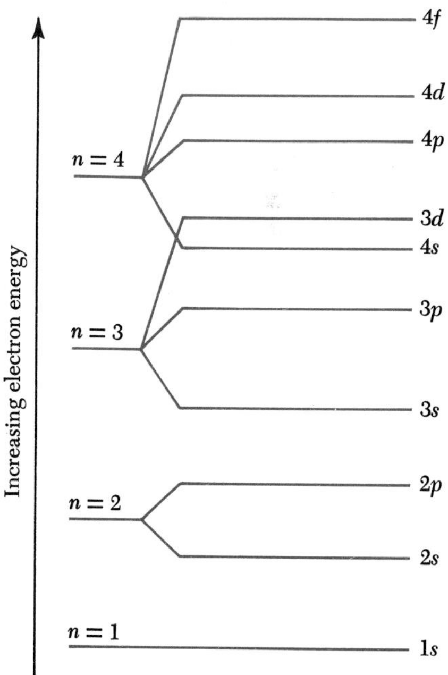

Fig. 5-7 Diagram showing relation between principal quantum numbers and energy levels of electron orbitals.

The Numbers and Shapes of Orbitals

As indicated earlier, there is only one orbital corresponding to the first energy level ($n = 1$), and it is called the 1*s* orbital. The location of the electron is distributed spherically about the nucleus. A diagram of the spherical 1*s* orbital of a hydrogen atom has already been shown in Fig. 5-4.

At the second energy level ($n = 2$) there are four orbitals. What are their shapes? The first is the 2*s* orbital and, like the 1*s* orbital, it is spherical about the nucleus. However, it is further from the nucleus than a 1*s* orbital as is shown in Fig. 5-8. Indeed, all *s* orbitals, whatever the energy level, are spherical electron clouds which increase in radius as the principal quantum number increases. As the quantum number increases, the energy of the orbital increases.

The remaining three orbitals at the second energy level are called 2*p* orbitals. What is their shape? Calculations based on the Schrödinger equation show that they have the shape illustrated in Fig. 5-9. Each of the three orbitals lies along one of the three axes (x, y, and z) which are perpendicular to each other in space. They are often written as p_x, p_y, and p_z orbitals. Hence, an electron in a *p* orbital is said to spend most of its time in the two regions on opposite sides of the nucleus. There are three *p* orbitals at every energy level, provided the quantum number is greater than one.

And what of the *d* and *f* orbitals? For principal quantum number 3, there are 3^2 or nine orbitals. Of these, one is the *s* orbital, three are *p* orbitals, and five are *d* orbitals. Moreover, even for quantum numbers greater than 3, the number of *d* orbitals is always five.

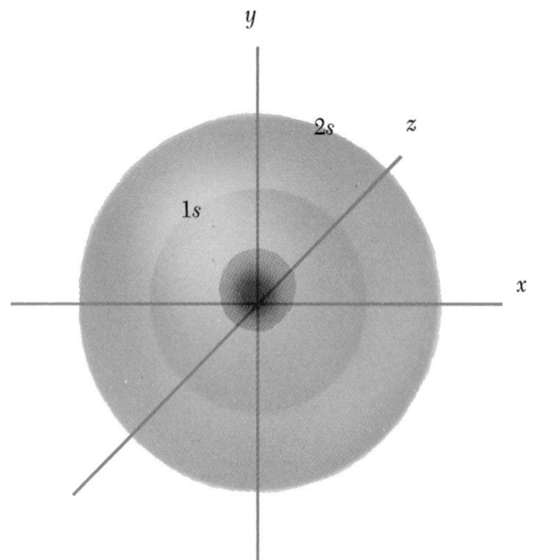

Fig. 5-8 The 2*s* orbital is further from the nucleus than the 1*s* orbital. Both are spherical.

For quantum number 4, there are 4^2 or 16 orbitals; one *s* orbital, three *p* orbitals, five *d* orbitals, and seven *f* orbitals. The *d* and *f* orbitals have much more complicated shapes and orientations in space than the *p* orbitals, and they will not be discussed in this text.

Table 5-1 Orbitals and energy levels

Principal quantum number	Number of orbitals	Energy levels of orbitals	Notation of orbitals
1	1	1 in *s*	1*s*
2	4	1 in *s*	2*s*
		3 in *p*	2*p*
3	9	1 in *s*	3*s*
		3 in *p*	3*p*
		5 in *d*	3*d*
4	16	1 in *s*	4*s*
		3 in *p*	4*p*
		5 in *d*	4*d*
		7 in *f*	4*f*

The Arrangement of Electrons in Atoms

How do these ideas on energy levels enable us to know the arrangement of electrons in atoms? To be more specific, we know that an atom of helium has 2 electrons, an atom of neon has 10 electrons, and an atom of argon 18 electrons. How are the electrons arranged in each of these atoms?

Pauli's Exclusion Principle

A clue was provided by an Austrian scientist, Wolfgang Pauli (1900–1958) in 1925. Pauli saw that if the number of electrons in any given orbital were no more than two, he could use the energy-level pattern to predict the arrangement of electrons in all the atoms, and he formulated a principle, now known as Pauli's *exclusion principle,* which accounted for the lack of overcrowding. The rule is not based upon experimental evidence but rather upon the realization that such a generalization brought order out of near chaos in understanding the electron structure of atoms. The exclusion principle states that *no two electrons in an atom can have the same set of quantum numbers.*

To illustrate the exclusion principle let us consider again the meaning and significance of the four quantum numbers. For an electron to have the same four quantum numbers as another electron means that this electron is in the same shell, the same subshell, the same orbital, and has the same spin. In other words, these two electrons would have identical energies and identical regions of highest probability. By stating that no two electrons in an atom have the same four quantum numbers, Pauli was simply saying that each electron has features of energy or probability that are different from those of all other electrons in an atom. In effect, the Pauli principle tells us that two electrons might have three of the four quantum numbers the same. This could mean that they are in the same shell, subshell, and orbital, but that they must have opposite spins. From this we see that the maximum number of electrons an orbital can accommodate is two. From this information we can tabulate the maximum number of electrons that can occupy the orbitals in the energy-level pattern of Fig. 5-7. This tabulation is in Table 5-2.

Table 5-2 Maximum number of electrons per orbit

Principal quantum number (or shell number), n	Number of orbitals, n^2	Maximum number of electrons per orbital	Maximum number of electrons per shell, $2n^2$
1	1	2	2 (both in 1s orbital)
2	4	2	8 (two in 2s, two in each of three 2p orbitals)
3	9	2	18 (two in 3s, two in each of three 2p orbitals , two in each of five 3d orbitals)

With Pauli's principle in mind and making the reasonable assumption that orbitals of lower energy will be occupied before those of higher energy, we can now assign electrons to the various orbitals of any atom.

Let us now consider a slightly altered version of Fig. 5-7 in which the orbitals are placed at their correct relative energies but each orbital is indicated by a circle rather than a short line. Let us further agree to the convention of representing electrons by arrows, the points of which are related to the possible spin orientations of an electron. Thus, an electron could be represented by ↑ for one spin orientation and by ↓ for the opposite spin orientation. In accordance with the Pauli principle, an orbital can accommodate a

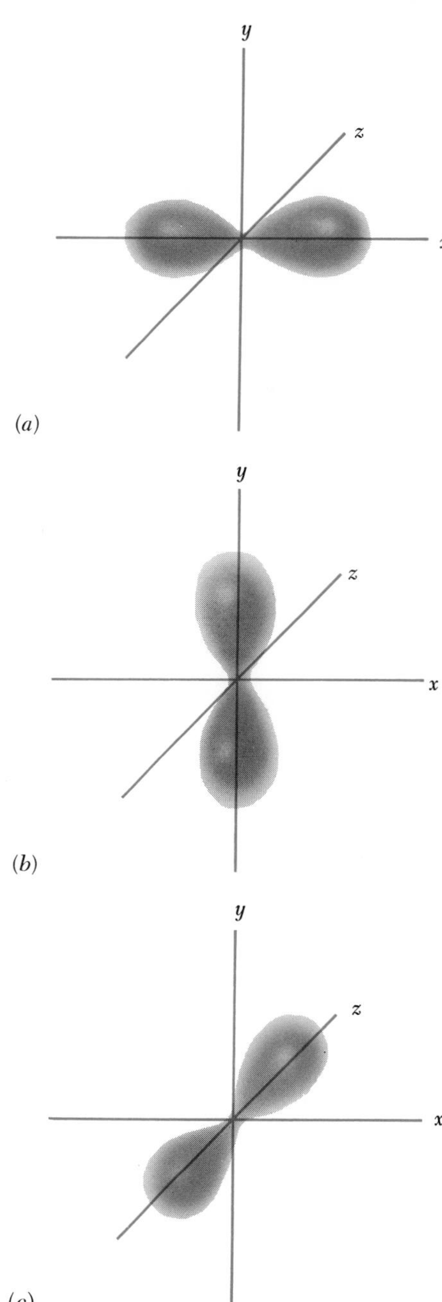

Fig. 5-9 The most probable distribution of a 2p electron is on one of two dumbbell-shaped regions on opposite sides of the nucleus and on each of the axes. (a) The two 2p orbitals on the x axis. (b) The two 2p orbitals on the y axis. (c) The two 2p orbitals on the z axis.

maximum of two electrons, but they must have opposite spins. In this convention and in Fig. 5-10, a filled orbital would be represented by ⑪.

We now have the information needed to enable us to determine the ground-state arrangement of the electrons in atoms. Let us start with the first two elements, hydrogen and helium. These are elements one and two, respectively, which means that hydrogen contains one electron and helium two electrons. Using Fig. 5-10 and the Pauli principle, and filling the energy levels of lowest energy first, you can see that the electrons in these elements will fill orbitals in the manner shown in Fig. 5-11.

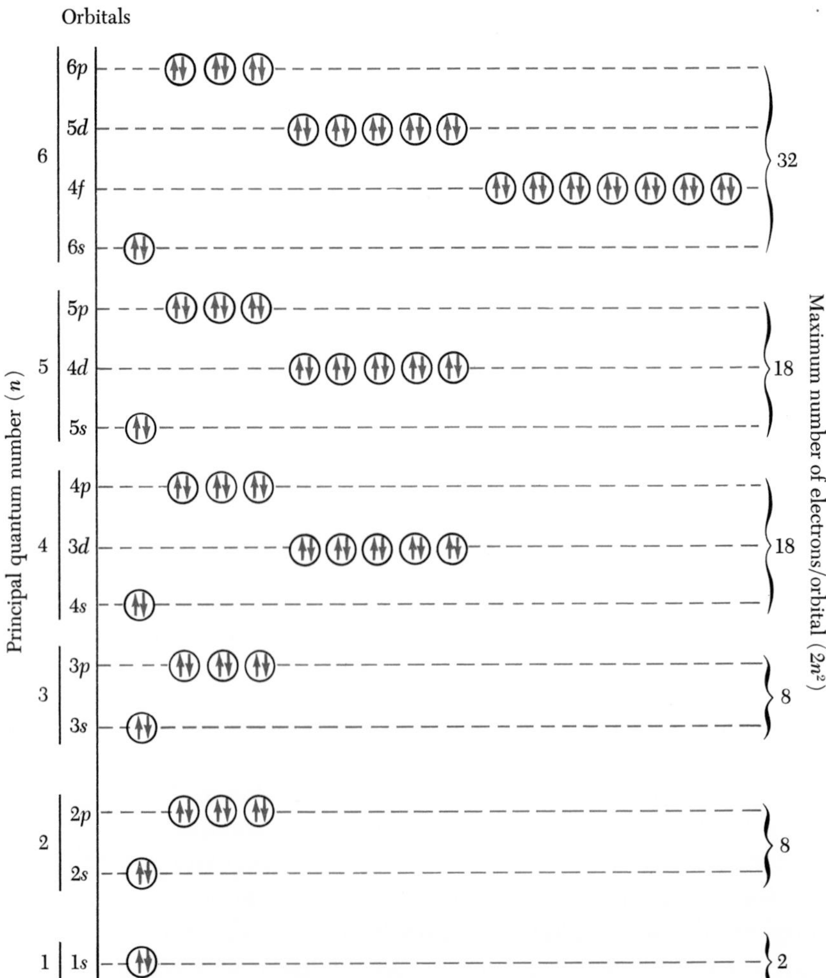

Fig. 5-10 Pictorial representation of the orbitals in energy levels 1, 2, and 3. Since only a single electron occupies the 1*s* orbital, this diagram also represents the ground state of the electron of a hydrogen atom.

Assigning Electrons to Some Atoms

The hydrogen electron will enter the lowest, or 1*s*, energy level and the two electrons in the helium atom also will enter the 1*s* energy level. The assignment of electrons to these energy levels can be written in terms of Fig. 5-11 as H: 1*s* (↑) and He: 1*s* (↑↓) or in what is known as the spectroscopist's notation, H: $1s^1$ and He: $1s^2$. The spectroscopist's notation often is easier to write but it does not convey as much information as is conveyed by Fig. 5-11. Nevertheless, we shall find it helpful to use both notations as we proceed to more complex atoms.

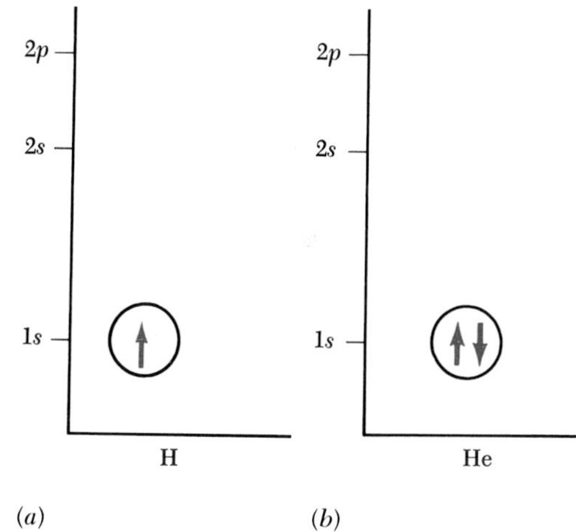

Fig. 5-11 Electronic diagrams of the ground state of (*a*) hydrogen atoms and (*b*) helium atoms.

Now let us consider the ground-state of electrons in elements three through five, i.e., in the elements $_3$Li, $_4$Be, and $_5$B. The three electrons in lithium must be placed so that two are in the lowest energy (1*s*) level and one in the next higher (2*s*) level. In beryllium, the four electrons are placed so that two are in the 1*s* and two in the 2*s* levels. In boron, with five electrons, two are placed in the lowest (1*s*), two in the next higher (2*s*), and one in the next higher (2*p*) levels. In the notation of Fig. 5-11, this becomes:

		2*p* (↑) ○ ○
2*s* (↑)	2*s* (↑↓)	2*s* (↑↓)
1*s* (↑↓)	1*s* (↑↓)	1*s* (↑↓)
$_3$Li	$_4$Be	$_5$B

and in the spectroscopist's notation:

$_3$Li: $1s^2 2s^1$; $_4$Be: $1s^2 2s^2$; $_5$B: $1s^2 2s^2 2p^1$

Can you proceed to assign electron arrangements (or configurations, as they are more often called) to elements beyond boron?

Summary

Using quantum mechanics, Heisenberg derived the *uncertainty principle* which asserts that if the velocity and hence the energy of an electron near the nucleus is known, its position is uncertain. In other words, both the exact position of an electron *and* its velocity cannot be determined at the same time. However, both the energy and the probability of an electron being in a certain region in space can be determined. The highest probability region occupied by an electron is called an *electron cloud* or *orbital*. The size, shape, and position of orbitals are determined by *quantum numbers*. The *prin-*

cipal quantum number (n) is an integer which denotes the main shell or energy level. All shells except the first are made up of sublevels of slightly different energy called subshells and designated by the letters s, p, d, and f. The subshells in turn contain orbitals and the shapes of the orbitals vary; for example, s orbitals are spherical and p orbitals are dumbbell shaped. The number of orbitals per shell is n^2 where n is the principal quantum number. For instance, there are 9 orbitals in the third shell, one in subshell s, three in subshell p and five in subshell d.

Pauli's *exclusion principle* states in effect that the maximum number of electrons in any orbital is two. And, since the total number of orbitals is n^2, the maximum number of electrons per shell is $2n^2$. For example, the maximum number of electrons that can be accommodated in the fourth shell is 2×4^2 or 32. From the relative spacing of the shell and subshell energy levels, the Pauli principle and the assumption that electrons in atoms fill the levels of lowest energy first, it is possible to predict the electron configurations of virtually all the atoms.

Factual Recall

1. (*a*) What is Heisenberg's uncertainty principle?
   (*b*) Point out the conflict between the uncertainty principle and Bohr's concept of the model of an atom.
2. (*a*) What is meant by the term electron cloud?
   (*b*) Draw the electron cloud for the ground state of a hydrogen atom.
3. What is the value of n (the principal quantum number) if the only subshells present are (*a*) s and p (*b*) s, p, and d (*c*) s, p, d, and f?
4. What is the meaning of the symbols (*a*) $2p_x$ (*b*) $3p_y$ (*c*) $4p_z$?
5. Draw a diagram showing the probable distribution of an electron in a p_z orbital.
6. (*a*) State Pauli's exclusion principle. (*b*) What purpose does it serve?

Apply Your Knowledge!

1. Draw a diagram to show the electron configuration of (*a*) a nitrogen atom and (*b*) a neon atom.

2. Use Pauli's principle to compute the maximum number of electrons in the energy level whose principal quantum number is (*a*) 2 (*b*) 4.
3. Try to design a mechanical model to represent an atom of hydrogen. Is it possible? Give your reasons.
4. (*a*) Name the disadvantages in describing the region occupied by an electron as a "cloud". (*b*) What are the advantages?

Find Out!

1. Similar ideas may occur to individuals working independently of one another in the scientific community. Find out if Bohr was the first to suggest the concept of the planetary atom.
2. Look up the source and meaning of the letters *s*, *p*, *d*, and *f* which are used to designate orbitals.

Suggested Readings

Darrow, Karl K., *The Quantum Theory* (SCIENTIFIC AMERICAN #205). San Francisco: Freeman.

Dirac, P.A.M., *The Evolution of the Physicist's Picture of Nature* (SCIENTIFIC AMERICAN Offprint #292). San Francisco: Freeman.

Gamow, G. *The Principle of Uncertainty* (SCIENTIFIC AMERICAN Offprint #212). San Francisco: Freeman.

Hochstrasser, R.M., *Behavior of Electrons in Atoms: Structure, Spectra, & Photochemistry*. New York: W.A. Benjamin. (Paperback)

Nier, A.O.C., *The Mass Spectrometer* (SCIENTIFIC AMERICAN Offprint #256). San Francisco: Freeman.

Schrödinger, E., *What Is Matter?* (SCIENTIFIC AMERICAN Offprint #241). San Francisco: Freeman.

UNIT 

ORBITAL CLASSIFICATION AND BONDING OF ATOMS

ATOMS OF ELEMENTS in Column I in the periodic table contain a single electron in the *s* orbital. Elements in Column II contain 2 electrons in the *s* ortital. In the third element of the second row, there is 1 electron in the *p* orbital. Since there are three *p* orbitals, the second row (and also the third row) must, when filled, be made up of eight elements.

The atoms of elements in Row 4 are in energy level number four. Hence the fourth row consists of 18 elements (two in the single 4*s* orbital, ten in the five 3*d* orbitals, and six in the three 4*p* orbitals). The fourth row is made up of elements of two different principal quantum numbers (3 and 4). Elements with the lower quantum number are *transition elements.*

Elements in the same columns have similar configurations; they are in the same chemical family. All elements in Column I have one electron in the outermost *s* orbital which can be easily detached. Elements that behave this way are metals. The elements in Column VIII are the inactive noble gases. The outermost *s* and *p* orbitals of the noble gases are completely filled with 8 electrons, and therefore show a stable atomic structure. In Column VII all elements have 7 electrons in their outermost shells. In chemical reactions, they attain the stable structure of 8 electrons by gaining an electron. Elements that behave this way are nonmetals.

HISTORICAL CHEMISTRY LABORATORY

From: "Discovery of the Elements," by Mary Elvira Weeks and Henry M. Leicester–J. Chem. Ed. Easton Pa. 1968; pp. 625, 635, 636

Dimitri Mendeleev
(1839–1907)

TABLE II.

THE ATOMIC WEIGHTS OF THE ELEMENTS

Distribution of the Elements in Periods

Groups	Higher Salt-forming Oxides	Typical or 1st small Period	Large Periods 1st	2nd	3rd	4th	5th
I.	R_2O	Li = 7	K 39	Rb 85	Cs 133	—	—
II.	RO	Be = 9	Ca 40	S 87	Ba 137	—	—
III.	R_2O_3	B = 11	Sc 44	Y 89	La 138	Yb 173	—
IV.	RO_2	C = 12	Ti 48	Zr 90	Ce 140	—	Th 232
V.	R_2O_5	N = 14	V 51	Nb 94	—	Ta 182	—
VI.	RO_3	O = 16	Cr 52	Mo 96	—	W 184	Ur 240
VII.	R_2O_7	F = 19	Mn 55	—	—	—	—
VIII.			Fe 56	Ru 103	—	Os 191	—
			Co 58·5	Rh 104	—	Ir 193	—
			Ni 59	Pd 106	—	Pt 196	—
I.	R_2O	H = 1. Na = 23	Cu 63	Ag 108	—	Au 198	—
II.	RO	Mg = 24	Zn 65	Cd 112	—	Hg 200	—
III.	R_2O_3	Al = 27	Ga 70	In 113	—	Tl 204	—
IV.	RO_2	Si = 28	Ge 72	Sn 118	—	Pb 206	—
V.	R_2O_5	P = 31	As 75	Sb 120	—	Bi 208	—
VI.	RO_3	S = 32	Se 79	Te 125	—	—	—
VII.	R_2O_7	Cl = 35·5	Br 80	I 127	—	—	—
		2nd small Period	1st	2nd	3rd	4th	5th
				Large Periods			

From Mendeleev's "Principles of Chemistry," Vol. I

Mendeleev's original Periodic Table of the Elements. The groups are arranged horizontally instead of vertically.

Dimitri Mendeleev evaluated his own discovery (the periodic law) as follows:
"Each law of natural science is of particular value scientifically only when it is possible to draw from it practical consequences, if I may so express it; that is, such logical conclusions as explain what had not previously been explained; which show phenomena not known up to its time; and especially, which permit making predictions that can be confirmed by experiment. Then the value of the law becomes evident and it is possible to test its truth. Then at least it becomes a stimulus for the development of some part of science and so leads on to perfection. Therefore I have given in some detail the consequences of the law of periodicity, namely the following applications: to the system of elements, to the determination of the atomic weights of little-studied elements, to the determination of the properties of still unknown elements, to the correction of the values of atomic weights, to the enrichment of information on the forms of chemical compounds, to the understanding of the so-called molecular compounds, to the study of the physical properties of simple and compound bodies"

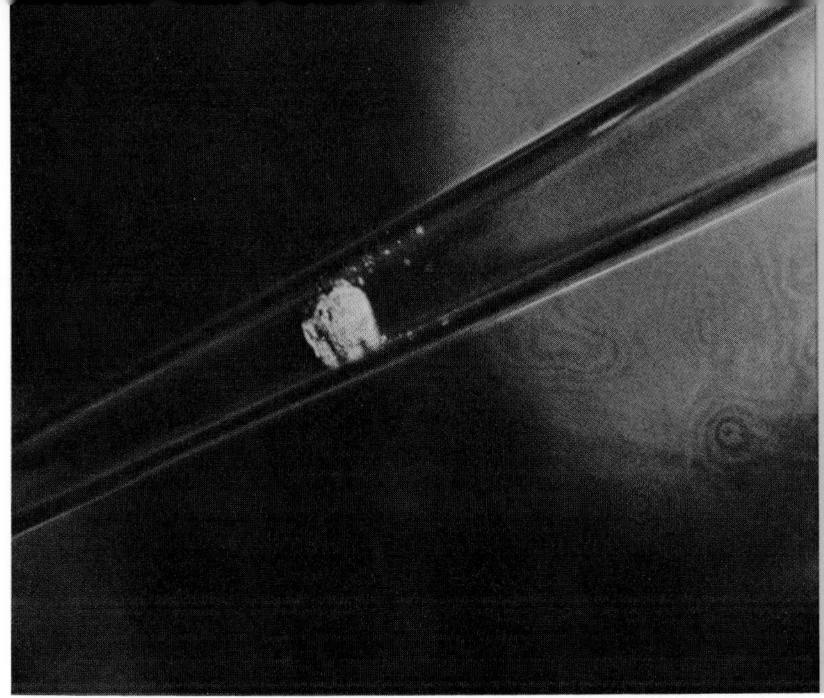

CHAPTER 6

PERIODIC CLASSIFICATION AND ELECTRON CONFIGURATION

IN THE LAST CHAPTER, we considered the electron configurations of the first five elements. We will now consider the configurations of some other elements and relate these configurations to the positions of the elements in the periodic table.

Electron Configurations of Elements in the Second Period

The elements from left to right in the second period (row) of the periodic table are: lithium, beryllium, boron, carbon, nitrogen, oxygen, fluorine, and neon. The electron configurations of lithium, beryllium, and boron are:

$_3\text{Li}$: $1s^2 2s^1$

$_4\text{Be}$: $1s^2 2s^2$

$_5\text{B}$: $1s^2 2s^2 2p^1$

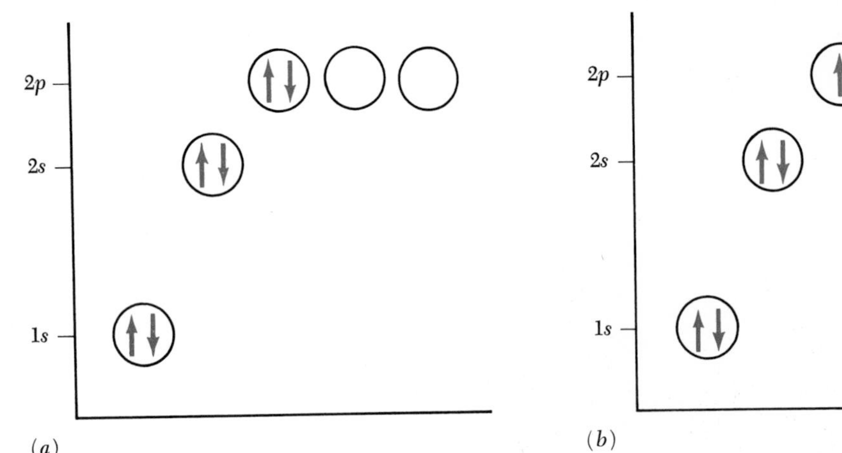

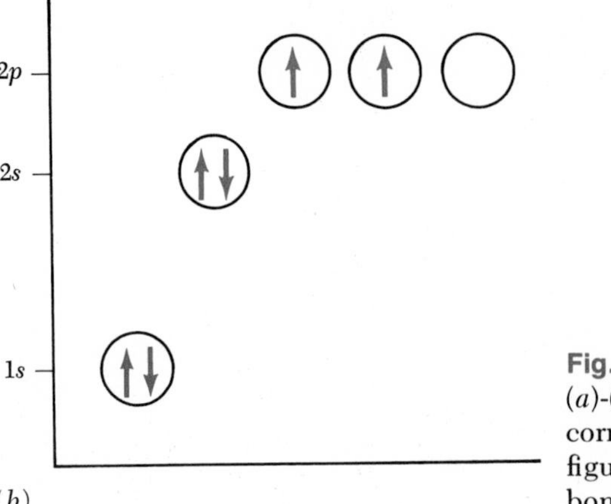

Fig. 6-1 (*a*)-(*b*) Which is the correct electron configuration for the carbon atom?

Boron is the first element to contain an electron in the $2p$ subshell and from Fig. 5-7, we note that this subshell can accommodate more electrons. The five elements immediately following boron (carbon, nitrogen, oxygen, fluorine, and neon) will each have in turn one additional electron in the $2p$ subshell. We may then write the electron configurations of these elements as:

$_6$C: $1s^2 2s^2 2p^2$ $\quad$ $_9$F: $1s^2 2s^2 2p^5$

$_7$N: $1s^2 2s^2 2p^3$ $\quad$ $_{10}$Ne: $1s^2 2s^2 2p^6$

$_8$O: $1s^2 2s^2 2p^4$

However, these notations in some cases obscure an important consideration which can be illustrated with the carbon atom. The key question here is: When the carbon atom adds the second electron to the $2p$ subshell, will this electron enter an empty orbital or an orbital that already contains an electron? This is illustrated in Fig. 6-1.

If we were to attempt to select one of the two configurations, we might reason that since electrons have like charges they repel each other. The electrons will tend to get as far apart as possible. As a result, we might expect that each of the similar orbitals will be only partially filled with one electron. The configuration for a carbon atom is most likely to be that of Fig. 6-1. Interestingly, both spectroscopic and magnetic studies show this to be correct.

By the same argument, the most stable state of a nitrogen atom is that in which all three $2p$ orbitals are only partly filled, as shown in Fig. 6-2.

Fig. 6-2 Electron configuration of the nitrogen atom, showing the three unpaired electrons in the $2p$ subshell.

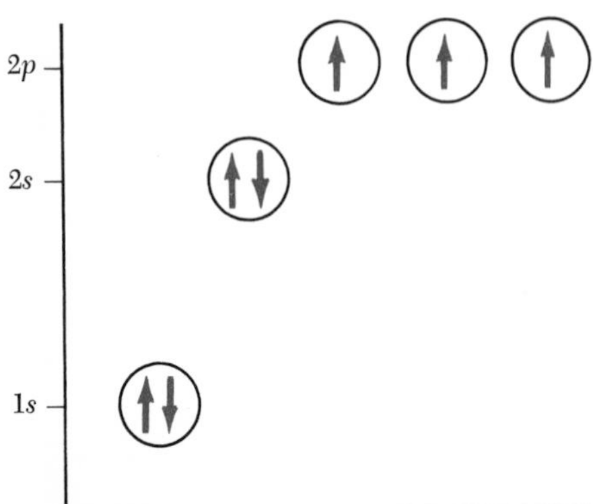

When the next electron, the eighth, is added, it must inevitably enter one of the partially filled orbitals. However, its spin will be opposite to that of the electron already in that orbital. The configuration of an oxygen atom is similar to that shown in Fig. 6-3.

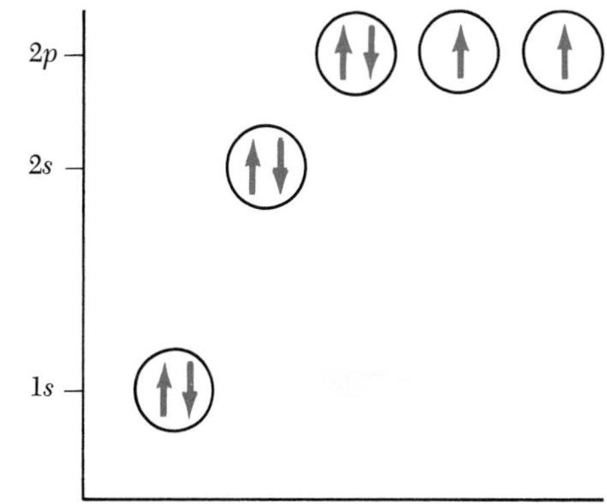

Fig. 6-3 Electron configuration of the oxygen atom.

The atomic number (Z) of the next element (fluorine) is 9, and the ninth electron enters one of the two partially filled $2p$ orbitals.

The configuration of the next element, neon, is shown in Fig. 6-4. What is the orbital notation of this element?

Notice that neon has neither empty nor partially filled orbitals in the second shell. For this reason, neon is unable to take part in chemical reactions; it is a chemically inert element.

Table 6-1 Configuration of elements in period 2

		No. of electrons in orbitals			
		$n=1$	$n=2$		
Element	Z	s	s	p	Electron configuration
Li	3	2	1		$1s^2 2s^1$
Be	4	2	2		$1s^2 2s^2$
B	5	2	2	1	$1s^2 2s^2 2p^1$
C	6	2	2	2	$1s^2 2s^2 2p^2$
N	7	2	2	3	$1s^2 2s^2 2p^3$
O	8	2	2	4	$1s^2 2s^2 2p^4$
F	9	2	2	5	$1s^2 2s^2 2p^5$
Ne	10	2	2	6	$1s^2 2s^2 2p^6$

Configurations of Elements in the Third Period

From left to right, the elements of the third period (row) of the periodic classification are sodium, magnesium, aluminum, silicon, phosphorus, sulfur, chlorine, and argon. The filling of orbitals at the third level follows the same pattern as that at the second level. The electron configuration of phosphorus and argon, chosen as examples, are shown in Figs. 6-5 and 6-6.

Fig. 6-4 Electron configuration of the neon atom.

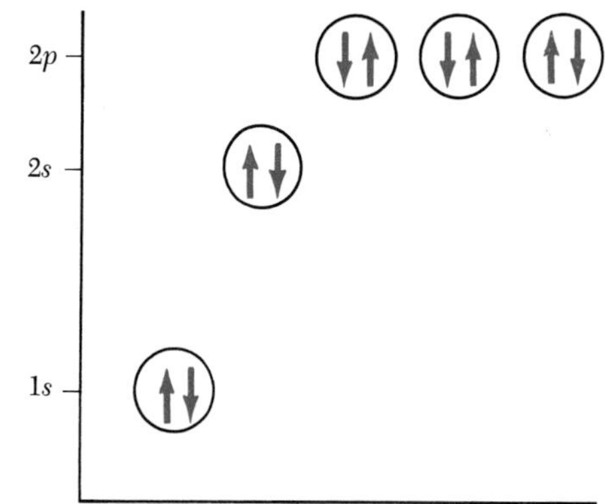

The spectroscopist's notation for phosphorus is $1s^2 2s^2 2p^6 3s^2 3p^3$ and for argon it is $1s^2 2s^2 2p^6 3s^2 3p^6$.

Notice, however, that in the third shell five of the nine orbitals are empty or unoccupied. That is, precisely the same number of orbi-

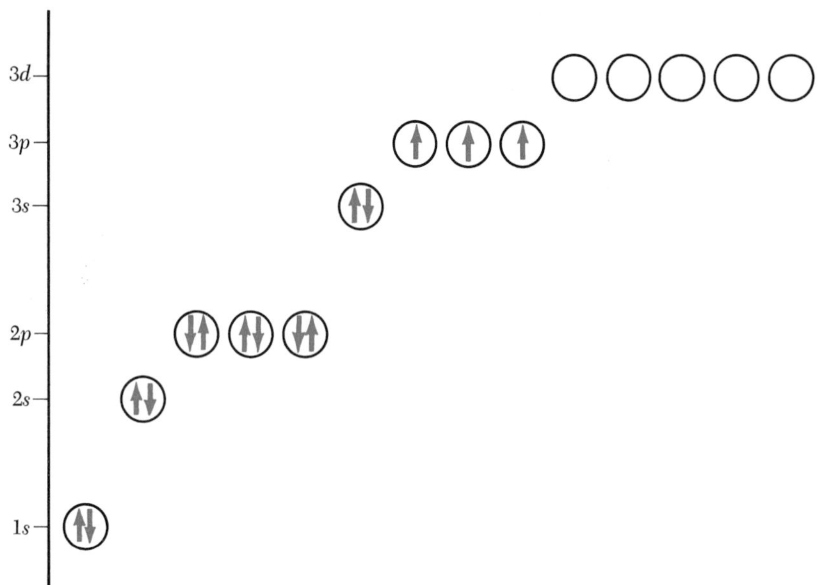

Fig. 6-5 Electron configuration of a phosphorus atom.

tals are occupied in the third shell as in the second shell. Why is this? The answer is related to the unusual stability of a configuration in which there are eight electrons in the outermost shell of the atom.

We have stated earlier that the energy of the electrons at the 4*s* level is a little less than that at the 3*d* level. This was pointed out in Chapter 5 and is shown diagrammatically in Fig. 5-7. Recall that this same inversion of energy levels also occurs in Periods 4, 5, 6, and 7.

Table 6-2 Configuration of elements in period 3

Element	Z	Number of electrons in orbitals					Electron configuration
		$n=1$	$n=2$		$n=3$		
		s	*s*	*p*	*s*	*p*	
Na	11	2	2	6	1		$1s^2 2s^2 2p^6 3s^1$
Mg	12	2	2	6	2		$1s^2 2s^2 2p^6 3s^2$
Al	13	2	2	6	2	1	$1s^2 2s^2 2p^6 3s^2 3p^1$
Si	14	2	2	6	2	2	$1s^2 2s^2 2p^6 3s^2 3p^2$
P	15	2	2	6	2	3	$1s^2 2s^2 2p^6 3s^2 3p^3$
S	16	2	2	6	2	4	$1s^2 2s^2 2p^6 3s^2 3p^4$
Cl	17	2	2	6	2	5	$1s^2 2s^2 2p^6 3s^2 3p^5$
Ar	18	2	2	6	2	6	$1s^2 2s^2 2p^6 3s^2 3p^6$

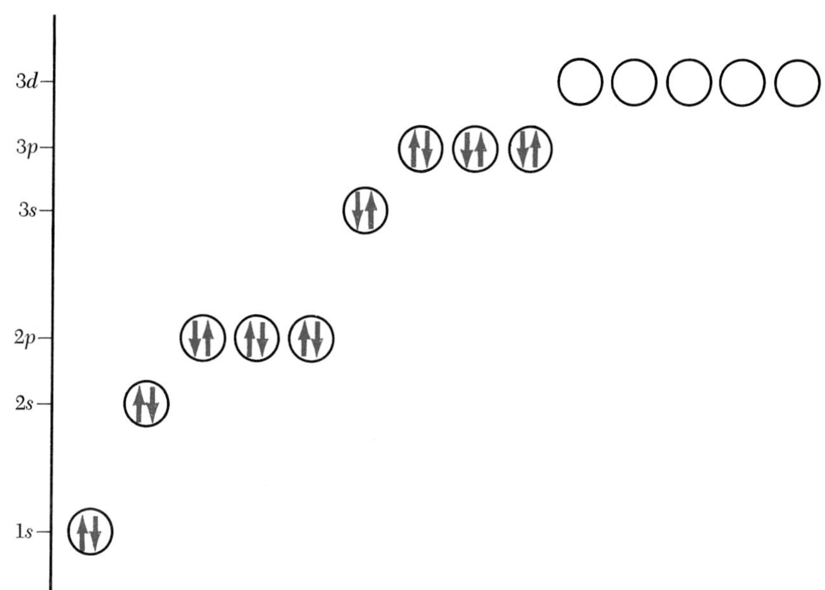

Fig. 6-6 Electron configuration of an argon atom.

Configurations of Elements in the Fourth Period

There are 18 elements in the fourth row, the first being potassium ($Z = 19$) and the last krypton ($Z = 36$). The atoms in this row add electrons to the orbitals of successively higher energy as shown in Fig. 5-7. These orbitals are those in the $4s$, $3d$, and $4p$ subshells. Orbitals of the $3s$ and $3p$ subshells were filled by atoms of third-period elements. However, as shown in Fig. 5-7, the next orbital to be filled is the $4s$ orbital, *not* the $3d$ orbital. This is because the two $4s$ electrons have less energy then the ten $3d$ electrons.

Thus, the configuration for potassium is $1s^2 2s^2 2p^6 3s^2 3p^6 4s^1$

The next added electron also goes into the $4s$ orbital. This electron is contained in the element calcium. What is the electron configuration for the atom of calcium?

With the $4s$ orbital now filled, the next orbitals of lowest energy are those at the $3d$ subshell. These five orbitals contain spaces for 10 electrons, which means that sucessive filling of $3d$ orbitals produces ten different elements. Elements formed by adding electrons to d and f orbitals are called *transition elements.* (Nontransition elements are formed when electrons are added to s and p orbitals.) The first transition element is scandium and its configuration is

$$1s^2 2s^2 2p^6 3s^2 3p^6 3d^1 4s^2$$

Note . . .
We can also state that the transition elements are all metals and, like other metals, they are shiny, lustrous, and good conductors of heat and electricity.

The last element to add an electron to the 3*d* subshell is zinc, and its configuration is

$$1s^2 2s^2 2s^2 2p^6 3s^2 3p^6 3d^{10} 4s^2$$

Thus, the 10 transition elements (Sc, Ti, V, Cr, Mn, Fe, Co, Ni, Cu, and Zn) are a part of the 18 elements that constitute Period 4. These elements are formed after the outer 4*s* orbital has been filled.

With the completion of the last of the transition series of Period 4 (zinc), there still remain three 4*p* orbitals to be filled. The remaining six elements are Ga, Ge, As, Se, Br, and Kr. With this information we can write the electron configurations of the last six elements in Period 4. For example, the configuration for krypton is

$$1s^2 2s^2 2p^6 3s^2 3p^6 3d^{10} 4s^2 4p^6$$

Table 6-3 Configurations of elements in row 4

		Number of electrons in orbitals										
		$n = 1$	$n = 2$		$n = 3$			$n = 4$				
Element	Z	*s*	*s*	*p*	*s*	*p*	*d*	*s*	*p*	*d*	*f*
K	19	2	2	6	2	6		1			
Ca	20	2	2	6	2	6		2			
Sc	21	2	2	6	2	6	1	2			
Ti	22	2	2	6	2	6	2	2			
V	23	2	2	6	2	6	3	2			
Cr	24	2	2	6	2	6	5	1			
Mn	25	2	2	6	2	6	5	2			
Fe	26	2	2	6	2	6	6	2			
Co	27	2	2	6	2	6	7	2			
Ni	28	2	2	6	2	6	8	2			
Cu	29	2	2	6	2	6	10	1			
Zn	30	2	2	6	2	6	10	2			
Ga	31	2	2	6	2	6	10	2	1		
Ge	32	2	2	6	2	6	10	2	2		
As	33	2	2	6	2	6	10	2	3		
Se	34	2	2	6	2	6	10	2	4		
Br	35	2	2	6	2	6	10	2	5		
Kr	36	2	2	6	2	6	10	2	6		

After electrons are added to the $3d$ subshell, the orbitals of this subshell are considered nearer the nucleus than electrons in a $4s$ orbital. *The krypton atom behaves as if it had 8 electrons in its outermost shell rather than the 18 one might expect if the* $4s$, $3d$, and $4p$ subshells were roughly the same distance from the nucleus.

Configurations of Elements in the Fifth Period

Like the fourth row, 18 electrons are added in forming the elements of the fifth row. The $5s$ orbital is filled before the $4d$. Why? The two elements that occupy the $5s$ orbital are, in order, Rb and Sr. Thus, the electron configuration for strontium is

$$1s^2 2s^2 2p^6 3s^2 3p^6 3d^{10} 4s^2 4p^6 5s^2$$

The next ten elements, from Y (Z = 39) to Cd (Z = 48), constitute a second transition series. The electron notation for cadmium is

$$1s^2 2s^2 2p^6 3s^2 3p^6 3d^{10} 4s^2 4p^6 4d^{10} 5s^2$$

and the $4d$ orbitals are filled with 10 electrons. Finally, the next six elements, form indium (Z = 49) to xenon (Z = 54), contain electrons in the $5p$ orbitals. What of the $4f$ orbitals? Fig. 5-7 shows why the elements with $4f$ orbitals are in the sixth row.

Elements in the Sixth Period

The sixth period of elements is the longest; it consists of 32 elements extending from Cs (Z = 55) to Rn (Z = 86). The subshells in this series are $6s$, $4f$, $5d$, and $6p$. Elements in the $4f$ and $5d$ orbitals constitute a third series of transition elements.

The maximum number of electrons in the $6s$ orbital is 2; 14 is the maximum in the $4f$ orbitals, 10 in the $5d$ orbitals, and 6 in the $6p$ orbitals, a total of 32 elements. The first two elements Cs, Z = 55; Ba, (Z = 56) in the series fill the $6s$ orbital. Atoms in the next 15 elements, from La (Z = 57) to Lu (Z = 71), add 1 electron to the $5d$ subshell and 14 electrons to the 4 orbitals. This group of 15 elements constitutes the *lanthanide series* or the *rare earths*. The atoms of the remaining 9 transition elements add electrons to the $5d$ orbitals. They range from Hf (Z = 72) to Hg (Z = 80). The electrons of the last six elements in the sixth period, from Tl (Z = 81) to Rn ($Z = 86$) are in the $6p$ orbitals. The electron configuration for radon, the last element in the sixth row is

$$1s^2 2s^2 2p^6 3s^2 3p^6 3d^{10} 4s^2 4p^6 4d^{10} 4f^{14} 5s^2 5p^6 5d^{10} 6s^2 6p^6$$

The Lanthanide Series

As already stated, the lanthanide series of elements (so called because the first element is lanthanum) is part of a third transition series. The chemical properties of these elements are similar. Many of these elements occur together in nature, and because of their similar chemical properties they are diffcult to separate.

Note . . .
In the lanthanide series, orbitals in the first three shells are fully occupied; they are therefore omitted from Table 6-4.

Table 6-4 Electron configurations of elements of the lanthanide series

Element			Orbitals								
Name	Symbol	Z	4s	4p	4d	4f	5s	5p	5d	5f	6s
Lanthanum	La	57	2	6	10		2	6	1		2
Cerium	Ce	58	2	6	10	2	2	6			2
Praseodymium	Pr	59	2	6	10	3	2	6			2
Neodymium	Nd	60	2	6	10	4	2	6			2
Promethium	Pm	61	2	6	10	5	2	6			2
Samarium	Sm	62	2	6	10	6	2	6			2
Europium	Eu	63	2	6	10	7	2	6			2
Gadolinium	Gd	64	2	6	10	7	2	6	1		2
Terbium	Tb	65	2	6	10	9	2	6			2
Dysprosium	Dy	66	2	6	10	10	2	6			2
Holmium	Ho	67	2	6	10	11	2	6			2
Erbium	Er	68	2	6	10	12	2	6			2
Thulium	Tm	69	2	6	10	13	2	6			2
Ytterbium	Yb	70	2	6	10	14	2	6			2
Lutetium	Lu	71	2	6	10	14	2	6	1		2

Notice that in all members of the lanthanide series the outermost orbital ($6s$) is filled with 2 electrons. These elements are all metals; moreover, their chemical properties are similar, but their physical properties vary somewhat. Can you propose an explanation for this?

Note . . .
One element in this group, promethium ($Z = 61$), has never been found in nature. Its existence was predicted in 1914, but it was isolated in 1947 from a mixture of fission products of uranium from an atomic pile. Again, this is an example of discovery waiting upon technological advance.

Elements in the Seventh Period

The seventh row consists of elements from francium ($Z = 87$) to element 104, only 18 in all. This row does not contain the expected number of 32 elements. Why? The first two elements, francium and radium, have electrons in the 7*s* orbital. After the 7*s* orbital is filled, one electron is added to a 6*d* orbital; then the 5*f* orbitals are filled with 14 electrons. Thus, the elements following radium constitute a fourth transition series.

Note . . .
In the actinide series, orbitals in the first four shells are fully occupied; they are therefore omitted from Table 6-5.

The Actinide Series

This fourth transition series of elements is usually called the actinide series; it is named after the first element in the series. The actinides (which include the elements uranium, neptunium, and thorium) are radioactive. The elements beyond uranium are synthetic—they do not occur in nature. The later elements of the series (americium to lawrencium) are highly unstable and exist for only very short periods of time before they disintegrate.

Table 6-5 Electron configurations of elements in the actinide series

			Orbitals								
Element	Symbol	Z	5*s*	5*p*	5*d*	5*f*	6*s*	6*p*	6*d*	6*f*	7*s*
Actinium	Ac	89	2	6	10		2	6	1		2
Thorium	Th	90	2	6	10		2	6	2		2
Protactinium	Pa	91	2	6	10	2	2	6	1		2
Uranium	U	92	2	6	10	3	2	6	1		2
Neptunium	Np	93	2	6	10	4	2	6	1		2
Plutonium	Pu	94	2	6	10	5	2	6	1		2
Americium	Am	95	2	6	10	7	2	6			2
Curium	Cm	96	2	6	10	7	2	6	1		2
Berkelium	Bk	97	2	6	10	8	2	6	1		2
Californium	Cf	98	2	6	10	9	2	6	1		2
Einsteinium	Es	99	2	6	10	10	2	6	1		2
Fermium	Fm	100	2	6	10	11	2	6	1		2
Mendelevium	Md	101	2	6	10	12	2	6	1		2
Nobelium	No	102	2	6	10	14	2	6			2
Lawrencium	Lr	103	2	6	10	14	2	6	1		2
Kurchatovium*	Ku	104	2	6	10	14	2	6	2		2

*This is a tentative name, not yet completely accepted.

Note . . .
The seventh period of elements is theoretically incomplete. There are only two electrons in the 6*d* orbitals and none at all in the 6*f* and 7*p*. However, chemists believe that more elements will be synthesized in the future, and information on this subject appears in the Appendix.

Summary

The electron configurations of the atoms are related to the periodic arrangement of the elements. Electrons in atoms enter energy

Table 6-6 Periodic table of the elements showing atomic numbers, orbital configurations, and electron configurations

Periods										
1	1 **H** 1									
2	3 **Li** 2 1	4 **Be** 2 2								
3	11 **Na** 2 8 1	12 **Mg** 2 8 2								
4	19 **K** 2 8 8 1	20 **Ca** 2 8 8 2	21 **Sc** 2 8 9 2	22 **Ti** 2 8 10 2	23 **V** 2 8 11 2	24 **Cr** 2 8 13 1	25 **Mn** 2 8 13 2	26 **Fe** 2 8 14 2	27 **Co** 2 8 15 2	28 **Ni** 2 8 16 2
5	37 **Rb** 2 8 18 8 1	38 **Sr** 2 8 18 8 2	39 **Y** 2 8 18 9 2	40 **Zr** 2 8 18 10 2	41 **Nb** 2 8 18 12 1	42 **Mo** 2 8 18 13 1	43 **Tc** 2 8 18 13 2	44 **Ru** 2 8 18 15 1	45 **Rh** 2 8 18 16 1	46 **Pd** 2 8 18 18
6	55 **Cs** 2 8 18 18 8 1	56 **Ba** 2 8 18 18 8 2	57 to 71	72 **Hf** 2 8 18 32 10 2	73 **Ta** 2 8 18 32 11 2	74 **W** 2 8 18 32 12 2	75 **Re** 2 8 18 32 13 2	76 **Os** 2 8 18 32 14 2	77 **Ir** 2 8 18 32 15 2	78 **Pt** 2 8 18 32 17 1
7	87 **Fr** 2 8 18 32 18 8 1	88 **Ra** 2 8 18 32 18 8 2	89 to 103	104 **?** 2 8 18 32 32 10 2	105 **?** 2 8 18 32 32 11 2					

57-71 Lanthanide series (The rare earths)	57 **La** 2 8 18 18 9 2	58 **Ce** 2 8 18 20 8 2	59 **Pr** 2 8 18 21 8 2	60 **Nd** 2 8 18 22 8 2	61 **Pm** 2 8 18 23 8 2
89-103 Actinide series	89 **Ac** 2 8 18 32 18 9 2	90 **Th** 2 8 18 32 18 10 2	91 **Pa** 2 8 18 32 20 9 2	92 **U** 2 8 18 32 21 9 2	93 **Np** 2 8 18 32 22 9 2

								Orbital configurations
							2 He 2	1*s*
		5 B 2 3	6 C 2 4	7 N 2 5	8 O 2 6	9 F 2 7	10 Ne 2 8	1*s* 2*s* 2*p*
		13 Al 2 8 3	14 Si 2 8 4	15 P 2 8 5	16 S 2 8 6	17 Cl 2 8 7	18 Ar 2 8 8	1*s* 2*s* 2*p* 3*s* 3*p*
29 Cu 2 8 18 1	30 Zn 2 8 18 2	31 Ga 2 8 18 3	32 Ge 2 8 18 4	33 As 2 8 18 5	34 Se 2 8 18 6	35 Br 2 8 18 7	36 Kr 2 8 18 8	1*s* 2*s* 2*p* 3*s* 3*p* 3*d* 4*s* 4*p*
47 Ag 2 8 18 18 1	48 Cd 2 8 18 18 2	49 In 2 8 18 18 3	50 Sn 2 8 18 18 4	51 Sb 2 8 18 18 5	52 Te 2 8 18 18 6	53 I 2 8 18 18 7	54 Xe 2 8 18 18 8	1*s* 2*s* 2*p* 3*s* 3*p* 3*d* 4*s* 4*p* 4*d* 5*s* 5*p*
79 Au 2 8 18 32 18 1	80 Hg 2 8 18 32 18 2	81 Tl 2 8 18 32 18 3	82 Pb 2 8 18 32 18 4	83 Bi 2 8 18 32 18 5	84 Po 2 8 18 32 18 6	85 At 2 8 18 32 18 7	86 Rn 2 8 18 32 18 8	1*s* 2*s* 2*p* 3*s* 3*p* 3*d* 4*s* 4*p* 4*d* 4*f* 5*s* 5*p* 5*d* 6*s* 6*p*
								1*s* 2*s* 2*p* 3*s* 3*p* 3*d* 4*s* 4*p* 4*d* 4*f* 5*s* 5*p* 5*d* 5*f* 6*s* 6*p* 6*d* 7*s*

62 Sm 2 8 18 24 8 2	63 Eu 2 8 18 25 8 2	64 Gd 2 8 18 25 8 2	65 Tb 2 8 18 27 8 2	66 Dy 2 8 18 28 8 2	67 Ho 2 8 18 29 8 2	68 Er 2 8 18 30 8 2	69 Tm 2 8 18 31 8 2	70 Yb 2 8 18 32 8 2	71 Lu 2 8 18 32 9 2
94 Pu 2 8 18 32 23 9 2	95 Am 2 8 18 32 25 8 2	96 Cm 2 8 18 32 25 9 2	97 Bk 2 8 18 32 26 9 2	98 Cf 2 8 18 32 27 9 2	99 Es 2 8 18 32 28 9 2	100 Fm 2 8 18 32 29 9 2	101 Md 2 8 18 32 30 9 2	102 No 2 8 18 32 32 8 2	103 Lr 2 8 18 32 32 9 2

levels in such a way that orbitals of lower energy are filled before the orbitals of higher energy. Electrons enter orbitals of the same subshell until every orbital contains 1 electron, then a second electron enters each orbital. Each orbital is filled with 2 electrons. Elements which partly fill the outer orbitals before the inner orbitals are complete are called *transition elements.*

Factual Recall

1. (*a*) What are transition elements? (*b*) Why is scandium ($1s^2 2s^2 2p^6 3s^2 3p^6 3d^1 4s^2$) a transition element? (*c*) Write the notation for the transition element manganese ($Z = 25$).
2. The atoms of sixth-row elements use orbitals $6s$, $4f$, $5d$, and $6p$.
   (*a*) Compute the number of elements in this row.
   (*b*) Compute the number of transition elements in this row.

Apply Your Knowledge!

1. Why is there a debate as to whether zinc is or is not a transition element?
2. Why is gallium more closely related to aluminum than is scandium?
3. What other elements does 104 probably resemble?
4. In which orbital do you think the "last" electron of element 105 will be located? $6f$, $7s$, $7p$? To what other element(s) may it be most closely related?

Find Out!

Look up the "discovery" of the transuranium elements. What methods are likely to be used in producing additional elements beyond 104?

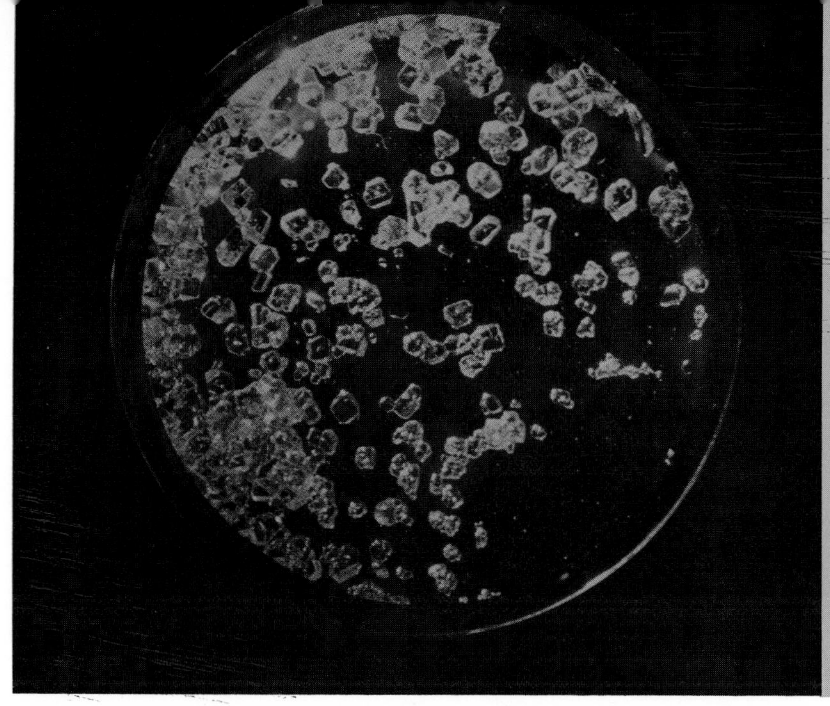

CHAPTER 7

RELATION OF ELECTRON CONFIGURATION TO PROPERTIES

WHAT IS THE RELATION between the electron configurations (or what is sometimes called the *electronic structure* of the atoms) and their properties? The periodic table is both a summary of the periodicity in properties of the elements and a reflection of the structure of atoms, and thus provides important insights into the relationship between the electron configurations of atoms and their properties. Some groups from a modern table are given in Table 7-1.

What similarity exists in the electron configurations of the atoms in any one group? See Table 7-2.

From examination of Table 7-2 we must strongly suspect that there is some relation between the number of electrons an atom holds in its outermost shell and its physical and chemical properties. The outermost shell thus becomes the focus of our attention, and chemists have called this the *valence shell*. The electrons in this shell are referred to as *valence electrons*.

Observe and Classify . . .
Examine the appearance and uses of such elements as carbon, chlorine, copper, iron, oxygen, silicon, silver, sulfur, and tin. *Metals* have luster and are good conductors of heat and electricity. Most metals are malleable (capable of being hammered into sheets) and ductile (capable of being drawn into wire). *Nonmetals* do not have these properties. On the basis of your observations, classify as metals or nonmetals the elements named above. What about carbon and silicon?

Table 7-1 Groups of representative elements

	Group								
Row	IA	IIA		IIIA	IVA	VA	VIA	VIIA	0
1									
2	${}_{3}$Li	${}_{4}$Be		${}_{5}$B	${}_{6}$C	${}_{7}$N	${}_{8}$O	${}_{9}$F	${}_{2}$Hc
3	${}_{11}$Na	${}_{12}$Mg		${}_{13}$Al	${}_{14}$Se	${}_{15}$P	${}_{16}$S	${}_{17}$Cl	${}_{10}$Ne
4	${}_{19}$K	${}_{20}$Ca		${}_{31}$Ga	${}_{32}$Ge	${}_{33}$As	${}_{34}$Se	${}_{35}$Br	${}_{18}$Ar
5	${}_{37}$Rb	${}_{38}$Sr		${}_{49}$In	${}_{50}$Sn	${}_{51}$Sb	${}_{52}$Te	${}_{53}$I	${}_{36}$Kr
6	${}_{55}$Cs	${}_{56}$Ba		${}_{81}$Tl	${}_{82}$Pb	${}_{83}$Bi	${}_{84}$Po	${}_{85}$At	${}_{54}$Xe
7	${}_{87}$Fr	${}_{88}$Ra							${}_{86}$Rn

Transition elements

Table 7-2 Electron configurations of representative groups

Group					
IA		IIA		IIIA	
Element	Configuration	Element	Configuration	Element	Configuration
${}_{3}$Li	$1s^2 2s^1$	${}_{4}$Be	$1s^2 2s^2$	${}_{5}$B	$1s^2 2s^2 2p^1$
${}_{11}$Na	$1s^2 2s^2 2p^6 3s^1$	${}_{12}$Mg	$1s^2 2s^2 2p^6 3s^2$	${}_{13}$Al	$1s^2 2s^2 2p^6 3s^2 3p^1$
${}_{19}$K	$1s^2 2s^2 2p^6 3s^2 3p^6 4s^1$	${}_{20}$Ca	$1s^2 2s^2 2p^6 3s^2 3p^6 4s^2$	${}_{31}$Ga	$1s^2 2s^2 2p^6 3s^2 3p^6 3d^{10} 4s^2 4p^1$
${}_{37}$Rb	$1s^2 2s^2 2p^6 3s^2 3p^6 3d^{10}$ $4s^2 4p^6 5s^1$	${}_{38}$Sr	$1s^2 2s^2 2p^6 3s^2 3p^6 3d^{10}$ $4s^2 4p^6 5s^2$	${}_{49}$In	$1s^2 2s^2 2p^6 3s^2 3p^6 3d^{10} 4s^2 4p^6$ $4d^{10} 5s^2 5p^1$

An examination of the electron configurations of the atoms from the various groups in the periodic table reveals that *the number of valence electrons* in an atom of a representative element is the *same as the group number*. The atoms of all Group I elements have 1 valence electron, all atoms of Group II elements have 2 valence electrons, and all Group VII atoms have 7 valence electrons. In the atoms of Groups III through VII, the valence electrons are in both *s* and *p* subshells. Let us now take a closer look at three groups or *families* of elements.

The Family Of Noble Gases

The elements of the noble gas family were briefly discussed in Chapter 1, where it was stated that these elements are chemically inactive and form very few compounds. Actually, the elements of this family are far less active than those of any other family.

Indeed, no compounds of the noble gas family occur in nature, and it was not until 1962 that the first compound of this family (a compound of xenon and fluorine) was synthesized. (Photo page 107). Since then a few others, chiefly compounds of krypton and radon with fluorine, have been synthesized. However, all these compounds are unstable and readily decompose or react with other substances. All of this suggests that the atoms of the noble gas family have stable valence-shell configurations.

Speculate and Explain . . .
Radon is very radioactive and dangerous to handle. However, work done with very small amounts (about 1×10^{-9} g) has shown that radon reacts with fluorine at 400°C to yield a product that is not gaseous at room temperature. Do you think this product is stable? Explain.

Structure of Noble Gas Atoms

When we wish to concentrate on a certain atom and its valence electrons, we use a shorthand notation. This consists of the symbol of the element surrounded by a number of dots equal to the number of valence electrons in the atom. Some examples are:

Na· Mg: Al: ·Si· ·P: ·S: :Cl: :Ar:

Using this electron-dot notation, let us compare the valence-shell configurations of several noble gas atoms with those of their nearest neighbors in the periodic table. For neon, the nearest neighbors are fluorine and sodium; for argon, they are chlorine and potassium; for krypton, they are bromine and rubidium. Arrange them as in Fig. 7-1.

Compare and Predict . . .
Compare your operational definition of metals and nonmetals, based on physical properties, with the definition based on electron configuration. Using this new definition with the elements you will study in this chapter, predict which elements will be "most" metallic, "least" metallic, "most" nonmetallic, and so on.

The atoms to the left of the noble gases in Fig. 7-1 are those of three of the most reactive *nonmetals*; the atoms to the right of the noble gas atoms are those of three of the most reactive *metals*. Thus, we see in this figure three valence-electron configurations: that found in the most reactive nonmetals, that accompanying the most stable elements, and that of the most reactive metals. What is the relationship of the configurations to the chemical properties?

In the valence shell of the most stable or least reactive atoms, there is a group of 8 electrons called an octet. There are a great many examples of stability associated with atoms containing 8 valence-shells electrons. We shall see, for example, that the fluorine atom which contains 7 valence electrons can, upon reaction, become the stable fluoride ion, :F:⁻ which has an octet in its valence shell, and that the sodium atom, upon reaction, loses its single valence electron to form the less reactive sodium ion; Na^+ also has 8 electrons in what is now its outermost shell.

Fig. 7-1 Electron-dot formulas of members of Groups VII, VIII, and I, respectively.

:F:	:Ne:	Na·
:Cl:	:Ar:	K·
:Br:	:Kr:	Rb·

All the noble gas atoms except helium have an octet of valence

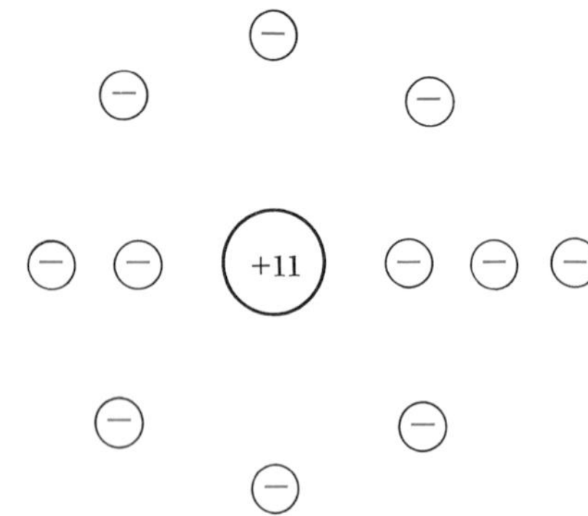

Fig. 7-2 Diagram of a sodium atom.

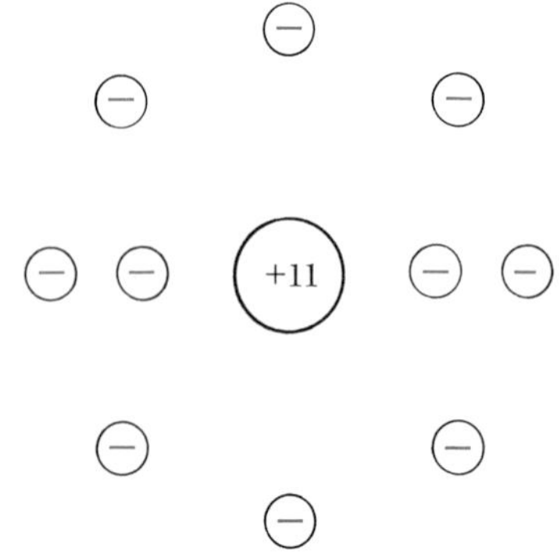

Fig. 7-3 Diagram of a sodium ion.

electrons and are chemically inactive. Helium also is inactive, but it has only 2 valence electrons. Can you offer an explanation for this? Are all elements whose atoms have 2 valence electrons also chemically inactive? On what do you base your answer?

On the basis of what has been said, consider the suggestion that the periodic law should be modified to read: *The properties of the elements are periodic functions of their electron configurations.* What do you think? Can you suggest one feature of the electron configuration of atoms that is characteristic of metals and another feature that is characteristic of nonmetals?

The Alkali Metals

Let us now consider the elements in Group I, a group called the *alkali metals.* This family consists of six elements: lithium (Li), sodium (Na), potassium (K), rubidium (Rb), cesium (Cs), and francium (Fr). We can think of the alkali metals as neighbors of the noble gases as shown in Table 7-3.

Unlike the noble gases, the alkalis are solids. Moreover, they are metals and, like all metals, they are good conductors of heat and electricity. However, unlike most other metals, they are soft and can easily be cut with a knife.

The alkali metals are exceedingly active chemically. They even react violently with water. How can this chemical activity be explained? The atomic number (Z) of sodium is 11; a sodium atom has 11 electrons: 2 in the first shell, 8 in the second, and 1 in the third (Fig. 7-2). Since the single valence electron is farthest from the nucleus, the electrical force of attraction between this electron and the nucleus is less than that between the nucleus and the other electrons. Indeed, this electron is only weakly held in the atom and therefore it is easily detached. When this happens, a chemical change is said to take place and the metal atom becomes an *ion* (Fig. 7-3).

If a sodium atom loses its valence electron, it then has 8 electrons in its outer shell. It then has the same electronic arrangement as a neon atom. As we would expect, a sodium ion is electronically stable and chemically reactive. The nuclear charge (total positive charge) on a sodium ion is +11, whereas its total electronic charge is −10. The formation of the ion from the atom can be shown as

$$\underset{\text{sodium atom}}{\text{Na}} - 1e^- \longrightarrow \underset{\text{sodium ion}}{\text{Na}^+} \qquad (7\text{-}1)$$

Since all alkali metals have atoms with single valence electrons, all these metals may lose this electron and form ions of the type M^+. Is this a general characteristic of metals?

A Definition of Metals

Hitherto we have thought of metals as elements that have luster and that are good conductors of heat and electricity. Now metals can also be defined in other terms. *A metal is an element whose nuclei exert a relatively small force of attraction upon their outermost electrons.* As a result, metals commonly react chemically by losing one or more electrons, thereby forming positive ions.

Table 7-3 Lists of elements in group I and VIII

Group			
VIII		I	
Element	Z	Element	Z
He	2	Li	3
Ne	10	Na	11
Ar	18	K	19
Kr	36	Rb	37
Xe	54	Cs	55
Rn	86	Fr	87

The Halogen Family

The halogen family occupies Group VII of the periodic table just to the left of the noble gas family. This family consists of the elements fluorine (F), chlorine (Cl), bromine (Br), iodine (I), and astatine (At). A comparison of the two families with their atomic numbers (Z) is shown in Table 7-4.

Table 7-4 Halogen and noble gas families

Group			
VII		VIII	
Element	Z	Element	Z
		He	2
F	9	Ne	10
Cl	17	Ar	18
Br	35	Kr	36
I	53	Xe	54
At	85	Rn	86

Although the atoms of each of the halogens have only one electron less than the corresponding atoms of the noble gases, the two families differ markedly in both physical and chemical properties. Fluorine is a yellowish gas, violently active and dangerous to handle. Chlorine is a greenish gas, very active chemically and poisonous. Bromine is a dark-red, corrosive liquid with an unpleasant odor; it is less active chemically than either fluorine or chlorine. Iodine is a black, shiny solid that is only moderately active chemically. As an example of their chemical activity, all the halogens readily combine with the element hydrogen. Why the marked difference in properties? Let us examine the electronic configurations of the halogens (Table 7-5):

Table 7-5 Characteristics of the halogen family

Element	Z	Electron configuration
F	9	$1s^2\ 2s^2\ 2p^5$
Cl	17	$1s^2\ 2s^2\ 2p^6\ 3s^2\ 3p^5$
Br	35	$1s^2\ 2s^2\ 2p^6\ 3s^2\ 3p^6\ 3d^{10}\ 4s^2\ 4p^5$
I	53	$1s^2\ 2s^2\ 2p^6\ 3s^2\ 3p^6\ 3d^{10}\ 4s^2\ 4p^6\ 4d^{10}\ 5s^2\ 5p^5$

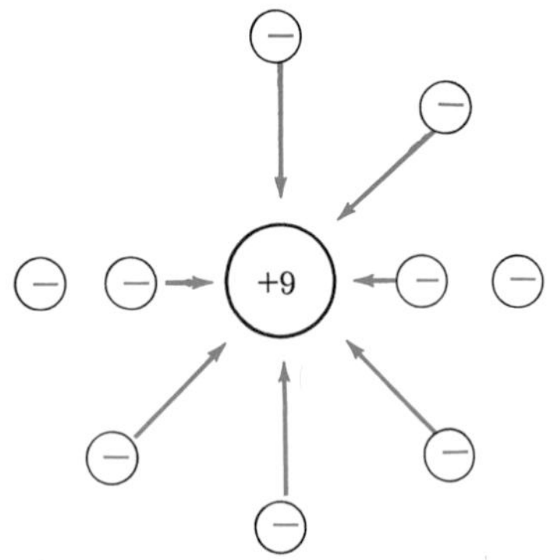

Fig. 7-4 Diagram of a fluorine atom.

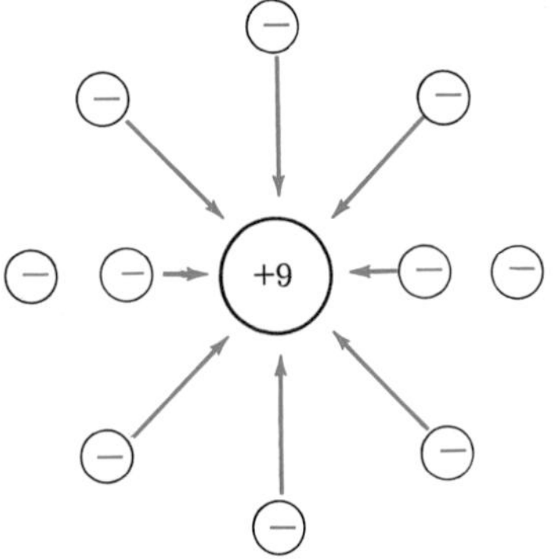

Fig. 7-5 Diagram of a fluoride ion.

In all cases these atoms have seven valence electrons with the highest level *p* orbitals containing 5 electrons. They need only one more electron to attain the stable structure of the noble gases. One would therefore predict that the nuclear charge of a fluorine atom (Fig. 7-4) is able to attract an extra electron into its outer shell. When this happens, the fluorine atom becomes a negatively charged *fluoride ion* (F^-). Thus, in symbols, the reaction can be written as

$$\underset{\text{fluorine atom}}{F} + 1e^- \longrightarrow \underset{\text{fluoride ion}}{F^-} \qquad (7\text{-}2)$$

Similarly, all the halogens tend to fill their outer shells, or, specifically, their outermost *p* orbitals, and in doing so they form the corresponding negatively charged halide ions.

A Definition of Nonmetals

This characteristic reaction of the halogens is the opposite of the characteristic reaction of the alkali metals and it serves to characterize the nonmetals. How then can we define nonmetals? Judging from the halogen reactions, we can say that *nonmetals* are *elements whose nuclei have a relatively high attraction for their outermost electrons*. The halogens are also poor conductors of heat and electricity. Both families are discussed further in Chapters 21 and 22.

The Position of Hydrogen in the Periodic Table

A hydrogen atom has a single electron in its 1*s* orbital. If a hydrogen atom loses this electron, it forms a hydrogen ion.

$$\underset{\text{hydrogen atom}}{H} - 1e^- \longrightarrow \underset{\text{hydrogen ion}}{H^+} \qquad (7\text{-}3)$$

In this respect, hydrogen behaves like the alkali metals—but with this difference. If the outermost electron is removed from the atom of an alkali metal, the remaining ion has the stable arrangement of 8 electrons (2 in the case of lithium) in its outer shell. But if the outermost electron is removed from a hydrogen atom, the remaining ion has *no electrons at all.* This remaining nucleus is very small and its charge is concentrated in a tiny volume, so the H^+ ion is very unstable.

A hydrogen atom that gains an electron would behave like a halogen.

$$\underset{\text{hydrogen atom}}{H} + 1e^- \longrightarrow \underset{\text{hydride ion}}{H^-} \quad (7\text{-}4)$$

Thus, hydrogen may undergo either the loss or the gain of an electron and, in this respect, it is unique. Theoretically, therefore, hydrogen could be placed in Group I with the alkali metals or in Group VII with the halogens. In practice, however, hydrogen shows a much greater tendency to lose an electron than to gain one, and is usually placed with the alkali metals.

Note . . .

The hydrogen ion exists as such only in the gaseous state, and when there are virtually no other atoms in the container. However, H^+ produced in the presence of water results in an aquated species, the hydronium ion, H_3O^+, which is a component of all aqueous acids.

Structure and Properties of Elements in a Period (or Row)

As we pass from element to element in a given row (say from left to right), there is a regular change in the electron configurations of the atoms, and it is reasonable to suppose that this should result in a gradual change in the properties of the elements. Let us, for example, consider the eight elements (Na, Mg, Al, Si, P, S, Cl, and Ar) in the third row of the periodic table. These elements constitute a natural sequence, because successive additions of electrons, one at a time, gradually fill the 3*s* and 3*p* orbitals.

Sodium

The first atom, sodium, has one electron in its 3*s* orbital. It readily loses this electron in chemical reactions to form the ion Na^+. Therefore, sodium is an active metal; and, because it loses an electron, it is said to have a valence (or combining power) of +1.

Magnesium

The second atom, magnesium, has two electrons in its 3*s* orbital. However, the nuclear charge for magnesium is +12, whereas for sodium it is +11. Therefore, the two 3*s* electrons of magnesium are held by the nuclear charge more strongly than is the corresponding 3*s* electron of sodium. That is, magnesium loses its valence electrons less readily than does sodium, and in consequence magnesium is a less active metal than sodium. Magnesium, like sodium, forms a positively charged ion:

$$\underset{\text{magnesium atom}}{Mg} - 2e^- \longrightarrow \underset{\text{magnesium ion}}{Mg^{+2}}$$

Notice, however, that the charge on its ion is +2; this means that magnesium has a valence of +2.

Aluminum

The next element, aluminum, has three outer electrons, two in the 3*s* orbital and one in the 3*p*. The nuclear charge for aluminum is +13, so an aluminum atom loses its valence electrons less readily than does a magnesium atom. If it loses the three electrons, it forms an aluminum ion with a charge of +3.

$$\underset{\text{aluminum atom}}{Al} - 3e^- \longrightarrow \underset{\text{aluminum ion}}{Al^{+3}} \qquad (7\text{-}5)$$

What is the valence of aluminum? Why?

Silicon

The fourth element in the series is silicon. It has four valence electrons in the 3*s* and 3*p* orbitals and a nuclear charge of +14. This nuclear charge exerts such a strong attractive force on the outer electrons that they are difficult to dislodge. Indeed, it is just as easy for a silicon atom to gain electrons as to lose them. Thus, silicon is an intermediate between metal and nonmetal.

Phosphorus

The next atom, phosphorus, has five valence electrons (two in the 3*s* orbital and three in the 3*p* orbitals) and a nuclear charge of +15. Phosphorus tends to gain electrons rather than lose them; it fills its 3*p* orbitals by adding three electrons. Therefore, phosphorus is a nonmetal.

Sulfur

The next atom, sulfur, is also a nonmetal. Why? Why is it a more active nonmetal than phosphorus? What is its valence? Why?

Chlorine

The seventh atom, chlorine, is one of the halogens. As stated earlier, a chlorine atom has seven electrons in its outer *s* and *p* orbitals. Since its nuclear charge is +17, the attractive force tending to fill its *p* orbitals is greater than that in the sulfur atom.

Argon

What of the element argon? Is it a metal or a nonmetal? Since argon takes no part in chemical reactions, this question cannot be answered in terms of loss or gain of electrons. On the basis of its physical properties, it can be regarded as a nonmetal.

Transition: From Metals to Nonmetals

It should now be apparent that, as we pass from left to right in any given period, the nonmetallic properties of the elements become more marked and, on the other hand, in passing from right to left the metallic properties become more marked. Or, in general, elements on the left of the table are metals, those on the right are nonmetals, and those in between show a progressive change in properties from metals to nonmetals.

Structure and Properties of Elements in a Column or (Group)

Group I

First, we will examine a column of metals, Group I. The higher the atomic number the greater is the distance between the outermost electrons and the nucleus, and the more active is the metal. Can you explain why? As the atomic number (Z) increases, the distance from nucleus to outermost electrons also increases and, as a result, the attractive force between nucleus and outer electrons diminishes. For example, in Group I a cesium atom loses the electron in its outermost *s* orbital much more easily than does a lithium atom. *The metallic properties of the elements in a given group become more pronounced as their atomic numbers increase.*

Group VII

In nonmetal Group VII, the most reactive halogen is fluorine and the least reactive is iodine. From this fact we may conclude that *the lower the atomic numbers of elements in a given group of nonmetals, the more marked are the nonmetallic properties of the elements.*

Elements Form Compounds

When chemically active elements combine they form *compounds*. And the *compound* often is more stable than its constituent elements. This implies that there must be a *chemical bond* between the "parts" of a compound. What is the nature of a chemical bond? And does the chemical nature of a compound depend upon the particular kind of bond? How is the formation of a compound related to the electron and orbital configurations of its component atoms? We shall seek answers to these questions in Chapter 8.

Summary

The "modern" periodic table shows that the properties of the elements are a periodic function of their electron configurations. For example,—except for helium—all members of the noble gas family have 8 electrons in their highest energy level, and their outer *s* and *p* orbitals are filled to capacity. Since the noble gases are chemically inactive, the outermost 8-electron structure must be a stable electron system.

Factual Recall

1. The electronic notations of oxygen and sulfur are $1s^2 2s^2 2p^4$ and $1s^2 2s^2 2p^6 3s^2 3p^4$, respectively. (*a*) Write the electron configuration for the element selenium ($Z = 34$). (*b*) Why are these elements (oxygen, sulfur, and selenium) in the same group?
2. The periodic law can be stated: *The properties of the elements are periodic functions of their electronic configurations.* Illustrate this statement by reference to the first three alkali metals.

Apply Your Knowledge!

1. Suppose that you have discovered element 108. Where would it fit in the periodic table? Why?
2. Why are all the transition elements metals?

Find Out!

1. Examine tables of electron configurations of elements in the *Handbook of Chemistry and Physics.* List places where irregularities occur.
2. Write a report on the formation of compounds of krypton and xenon. Include information on the orbitals involved.

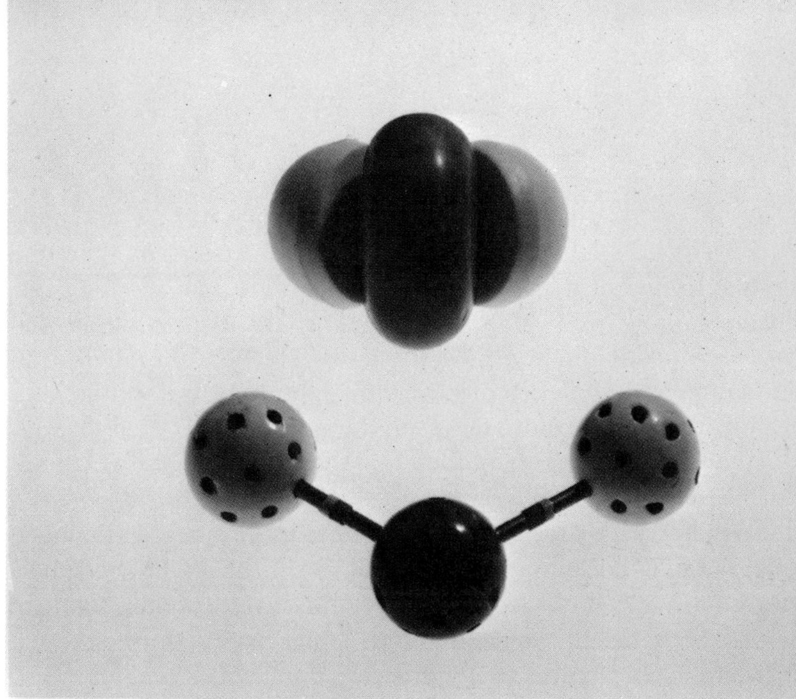

CHAPTER 8

CHEMICAL BONDS

AN ESSENTIAL CONDITION for a reaction between two atoms is that their electron configurations change in such a way that rearrangement of the electrons results in a *chemical bond* between them. Essentially all bonds result from the simultaneous attraction of electrons to two or more nuclei. There are at least three kinds of chemical bonds and we will consider each in turn.

Ionic Bonds

The alkali metals are active metals and the halogens are active nonmetals. Therefore, it should not be surprising that the alkali metals and the halogens readily react with each other. For example, sodium metal combines with chlorine gas to form a white crystalline compound, sodium chloride, often called common salt. Expressed in symbols the reaction is

$$Na + Cl \longrightarrow NaCl \qquad (8\text{-}1)$$

Why does this reaction take place?

Infer . . .
Is electron-dot notation a model?

We found in Chapter 7 that the sodium atom can lose its single valence electron and thereby acquire an electron configuration identical to that of the inactive neon atom. We also saw how the chlorine atom, with 7 valence electrons, could acquire a more stable electron configuration by gaining one electron, thereby bringing its number of valence electrons to eight. In fact, if sodium and chlorine atoms come close together, the weakly held outer electron of the sodium atom may be pulled into the third shell or level of the chlorine atom. When this happens, the chlorine atom becomes a chloride ion with 8 electrons in its third level or outer shell and, at the same time, the sodium atom empties its third shell to become a sodium ion, with 8 electrons in its second level or outer shell. In this way, both the chlorine and sodium atoms have acquired the stable electronic structures of neighboring noble gas elements.

The reaction in Eq. (8-1) can now be summarized as

$$\dot{\text{Na}} + :\dot{\underset{\cdot\cdot}{\text{Cl}}}: \longrightarrow \text{Na}^+ + :\overset{\cdot\cdot}{\underset{\cdot\cdot}{\text{Cl}}}:^- \qquad (8\text{-}2)$$

and the number of protons and electrons in the reactants and products are shown in Table 8-1.

Table 8-1 Number of charged particles in related atoms and ions

	Reactants		Products	
Charged particles	Sodium atom (Na)	Chlorine atom (Cl)	Sodium ion (Na^+)	Chloride ion (Cl^-)
Protons	11	17	11	17
Electrons	11	17	10	18

Since sodium and chloride ions are oppositely charged, there is an electrostatic force of attraction between them. *The attractive force between oppositely charged ions constitutes a so-called ionic bond, and compounds that are formed by the transfer of electrons are known as ionic (or electrovalent) compounds.*

Explain . . .
Greater "strength" results from condensation into a solid, since each positive (+) is surrounded by negatives (−) and vice versa. Why?

The elements lithium and fluorine also combine to form the ionic compound lithium fluoride. Here the lithium atom may lose its single valence electron to the fluorine atom which has seven valence electrons. The stability of these atoms would be increased if the lithium atom lost an electron and the fluorine atom gained one. Why? These oppositely charged lithium and fluoride ions are held together by strong ionic bonds to form the stable compound lithium fluoride. And now comparing the compounds sodium chloride and lithium fluoride, which in your opinion has the stronger ionic bonds? That is, which is the more stable compound?

Actually, ionic bonds are strong enough to bind the ions into a solid lattice called a crystal. A crystal of sodium chloride, for example, consists of equal numbers of sodium and chloride ions packed together as shown in Fig. 8-1. Notice that every sodium ion is surrounded by six chloride ions and every chloride ion is surrounded by six sodium ions.

It should now be apparent that the formation of ionic bonds is favored in compounds formed by metals with nonmetals. For example, atoms of elements of Group I and Group VII easily lose or gain one electron to form ionic compounds. Similarly, ionic bonds are common in compounds formed from elements of Group II with elements from Group VII. For example, magnesium chloride is an ionic compound and a crystalline solid. The same reasoning applies to pairs of elements in Group I and Group VI, and also to members of Groups II and VI.

This discussion might lead us to assume that hydrogen and oxygen atoms are held together by ionic bonds and that water (H_2O) is an ionic compound. This, however, is not true. What then is the nature of the bond between hydrogen and oxygen? Before answering this important question it will be helpful to consider ionic bonding in terms of *electron-dot notation.*

Electron-dot Notation for Ionic Reactions

Using ordinary symbols, the reaction between sodium and chlorine is represented by

$$\mathrm{Na} + \mathrm{Cl} \longrightarrow \mathrm{Na}^+ + \mathrm{Cl}^- \tag{8-3}$$

Using electron-dot symbols (as discussed in Chapter 7) this becomes

$$\dot{\mathrm{Na}} + :\underset{\cdot\cdot}{\dot{\mathrm{Cl}}}: \longrightarrow \mathrm{Na}^+ + :\underset{\cdot\cdot}{\ddot{\mathrm{Cl}}}:^-$$

These notations show that the valence electron of a sodium atom is transferred to a chlorine atom, thereby filling its outer energy level with eight electrons. Notice that an electron-dot formula shows at a glance the valence of an element. *The number of electrons gained or lost in completing or emptying the outer shell is the valence*

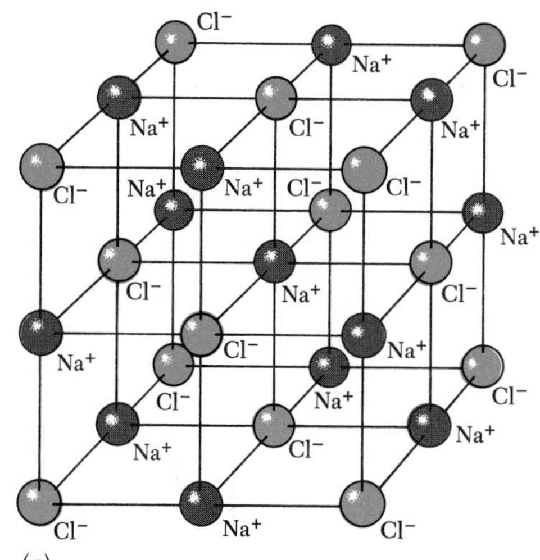

(*a*)

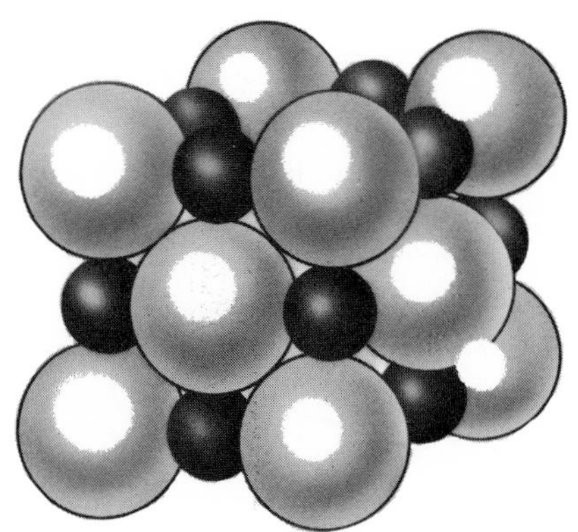

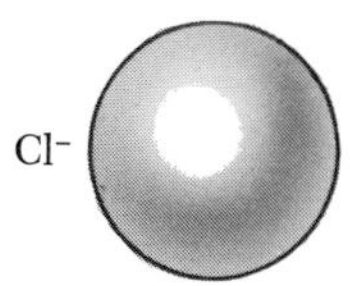

(*b*)

Fig. 8-1 (*a*) Sodium chloride is a lattice of sodium and chloride ions held together by electrostatic forces of attraction. (*b*) Detail of sodium chloride lattice.

Fig. 8-2 Electron-dot formula of Al_2S_3.

Al :S:
:S:
Al :S:

number. If electrons are gained, the valence is negative; if electrons are lost, the valence is positive. Thus, the electron-dot symbol for potassium is K· and its valence is +1; the symbol for magnesium is Mg· and its valence is +2; for aluminum (·Al) the valence is +3; for fluorine (·F:) it is −1; and for sulfur (·S·), it is −2. Hence, the ordinary formula for magnesium fluoride is MgF_2 and its electron-dot formula is

:F: Mg :F:

Similarly, the ordinary formula for aluminum sulfide is Al_2S_3 and the electron-dot formula is shown in Fig. 8-2.

Covalent Bonds

As stated earlier, various atoms can combine to form a stable unit which, unlike an ion, carries no net charge. A collection of atoms that forms such a unit is called a *molecule* and the simplest of all molecules is that of hydrogen. It can be shown that each molecule of hydrogen consists of two atoms; that is, a hydrogen molecule is *diatomic* and its formula is H_2. What is the nature of the bond that binds two atoms of hydrogen together into a single unit? Both atoms are identical, each consisting of one proton and one electron. We would not expect two identical atoms to transfer an electron from one atom to the other. Why? Obviously, hydrogen molecules are not held together by ionic bonds. What then is the nature of the bond?

Fig. 8-3 Electrostatic forces of attraction and repulsion between two nearby hydrogen atoms.

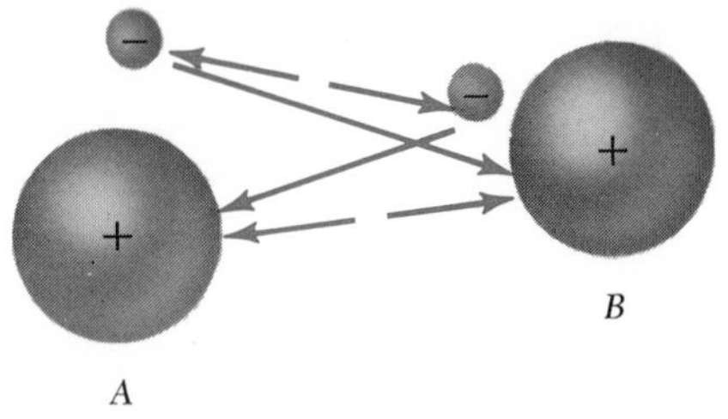

Covalent Bonding in a Hydrogen Molecule

If two hydrogen atoms, *A* and *B*, approach each other, they are affected by at least four electrostatic forces. The nucleus of atom *A* (which is a proton) attracts the electron of atom *B*, and the nucleus of atom *B* attracts the electron of atom *A*. At the same time, the two protons repel each other and the two electrons also repel each other. In other words, there are two forces of attraction and two of repulsion. This is illustrated in Fig. 8-3. However, since we know that two atoms of hydrogen combine to form a molecule, the attractive forces must be the stronger so that there is a net force of attraction between the atoms.

Speculate . . .
In the light of this discussion, would you expect the molecule H_3 to be stable or unstable? For what reason?

A diagrammatic representation of the formation of a hydrogen molecule is shown in Fig. 8-4. In (*a*) each hydrogen atom comes under the electrical influence of the other. Then, as shown in (*b*) their 1*s* orbitals overlap until the forces of attraction and repulsion are at a minimum. The two electrons, each experiencing the influence of the two nuclei, may be said to occupy a *molecular orbital* rather than separate atomic orbitals. When this happens, the two atoms are bonded together into a stable configuration, and the molecular orbital of this spatial arrangement is thought to be somewhat as shown in (*c*). In the molecular orbital, the two electrons are *shared* equally by each of the atoms so that the electron pair occupies the whole of the space of the ellipsoid-shaped cloud. However, as one would expect, the probability of finding the electron pair is greatest between the two nuclei. The sharing of pairs of electrons by different nuclei is called *covalence* and the chemical bond that results from such a sharing is called a *covalent bond.* In general, the strongest covalent bonds are formed between atoms of nonmetals.

Fig. 8-4 Formation of hydrogen molecule from two hydrogen atoms.

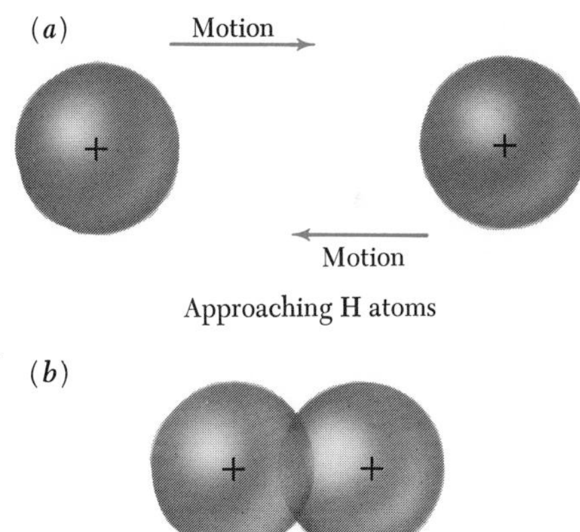

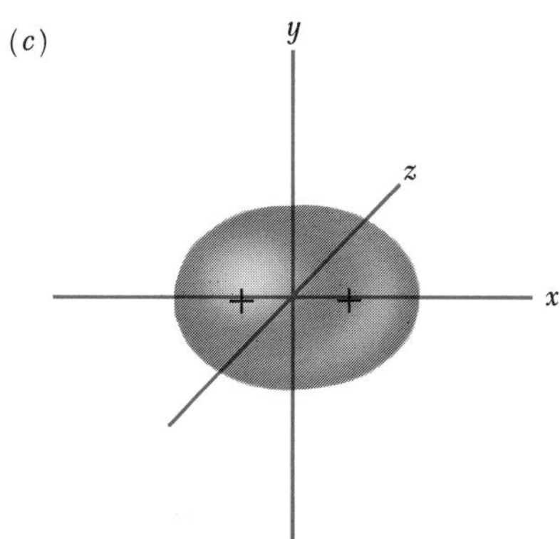

The overlapping spherical orbitals are distorted to form a combined egg-shaped orbital of a hydrogen molecule.

The electron-dot notation showing the combination of two hydrogen atoms to form a molecule is

$$\text{H}\cdot \quad + \quad \cdot\text{H} \longrightarrow \text{H}:\text{H} \tag{8-4}$$

The double dot represents a shared pair of electrons. That is, each hydrogen atom shares the valence electron of the other and, as a result, the first shells (the *s* orbitals) of both atoms become filled. And this, as you know, is a stable structure, the structure of helium.

Nonpolar Covalent Bonds In a hydrogen molecule the two atoms share the electron pair equally (the number of protons equals the number of electrons), and therefore a molecule of hydrogen is electrically neutral. Since the electrons are equally attracted to either nucleus, there is no residual electric charge and therefore the bond in a hydrogen molecule is said to be *nonpolar* and the bonds in nonpolar molecules are called *nonpolar covalent bonds.*

Hydrogen is by no means the only diatomic molecule. Experiments prove that, except for the noble gases, the molecules of most gaseous elements are diatomic; the formula for a molecule of fluorine is F_2, for chlorine Cl_2, for oxygen O_2, for nitrogen N_2, and so on. Moreover, the pairs of atoms of all diatomic molecules are held together by nonpolar bonds. Let us consider the bonding in a molecule of fluorine.

The electronic configuration of a fluorine atom is $1s^2 2s^2 2p^5$. Two of the three $2p$ orbitals are filled, with two electrons each, and the third $2p$ orbital contains only one electron. Therefore, the electron in the third $2p$ orbital is available for covalent bonding. The $2p$ orbitals of a fluorine atom are shown in Fig. 8-5.

If two fluorine atoms approach each other, a bond is formed when the half-filled p orbital of one atom overlaps the half-filled orbital of the other, thereby forming a covalent bond. The covalent bond of a fluorine molecule is shown in Fig. 8-6. Notice that the front lobes of the overlapping orbitals are larger than the other orbitals and the back lobes are smaller. This is because the probability of finding the electron pair *between* the two nuclei has been increased by the bond; in addition, the chance of finding the electron pair *beyond* the nuclei has been decreased.

Speculate . . .
Would you expect a covalent bond to form between two lithium atoms or two sodium atoms? Explain your answer.

The reaction between two fluorine atoms expressed in electron-dot notation is

$$:\ddot{\underset{..}{F}}\cdot + \cdot\ddot{\underset{..}{F}}: \longrightarrow :\ddot{\underset{..}{F}}:\ddot{\underset{..}{F}}: \tag{8-5}$$

This representation shows that, by sharing a pair of electrons, the outer shells of both atoms become filled with eight electrons—a stable structure.

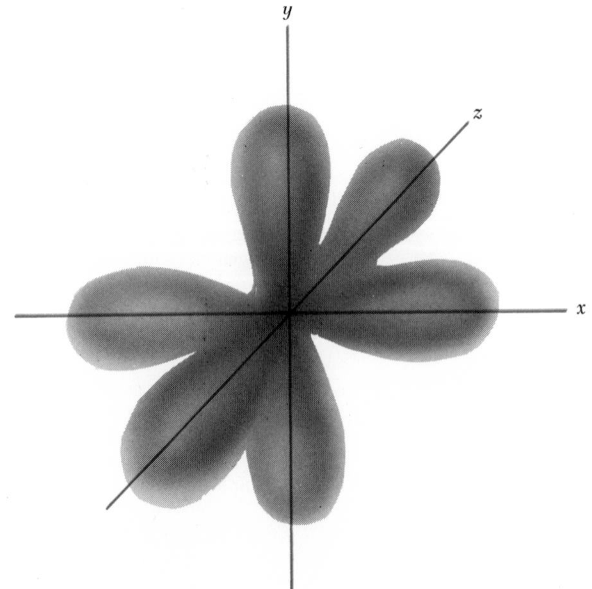

Fig. 8-5 The $2p$ orbitals of the fluorine atom. Two of the three are filled; the third is half-filled. How is it used in forming covalent bonds with other fluorine atoms?

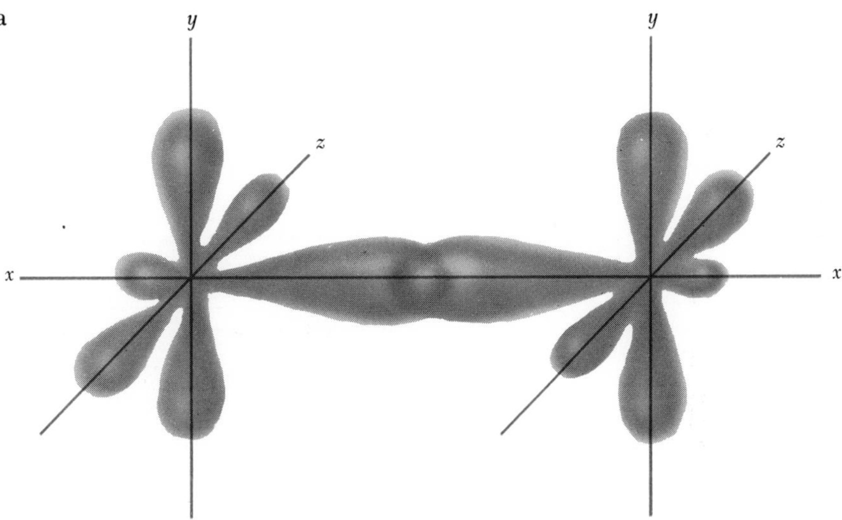

Fig. 8-6 A nonpolar covalent bond in a molecule of fluorine.

Similarly, the reaction between two chlorine atoms is

$$:\underset{\cdot\cdot}{\overset{\cdot\cdot}{\mathrm{Cl}}}\cdot + \cdot\underset{\cdot\cdot}{\overset{\cdot\cdot}{\mathrm{Cl}}}: \longrightarrow :\underset{\cdot\cdot}{\overset{\cdot\cdot}{\mathrm{Cl}}}:\underset{\cdot\cdot}{\overset{\cdot\cdot}{\mathrm{Cl}}}: \qquad (8\text{-}6)$$

The chlorine molecule is therefore nonpolar because a pair of electrons is shared equally by the two chlorine atoms.

Polar Covalent Bonds Let us now consider the reaction between hydrogen and fluorine to form the gaseous compound hydrogen fluoride. In the compound, the bond is caused by the overlapping of the $1s$ orbital of a hydrogen atom and the available $2p$ orbital of a fluorine atom. This is an example of another kind of covalent bond, and a model showing the overlapping orbitals in a molecule of hydrogen fluoride is shown in Fig. 8-7.

Since the two atoms in the molecule are not identical, and since each has a different ability to attract electrons, where is the shared pair of electrons located? Remember that (1) the greater the nuclear charge, the greater is the attractive force between nucleus and electrons in the outer shell, and (2) the greater the distance from nucleus to electrons the less is the attractive force between them. The position of the shared pair is determined by the stronger of the two opposing effects. The nuclear charge of a fluorine atom is +9; for a hydrogen atom, it is +1. Measurements show that apparently the greater nuclear charge of the fluorine atom more than offsets the effect of the greater distance of its outer electrons; and

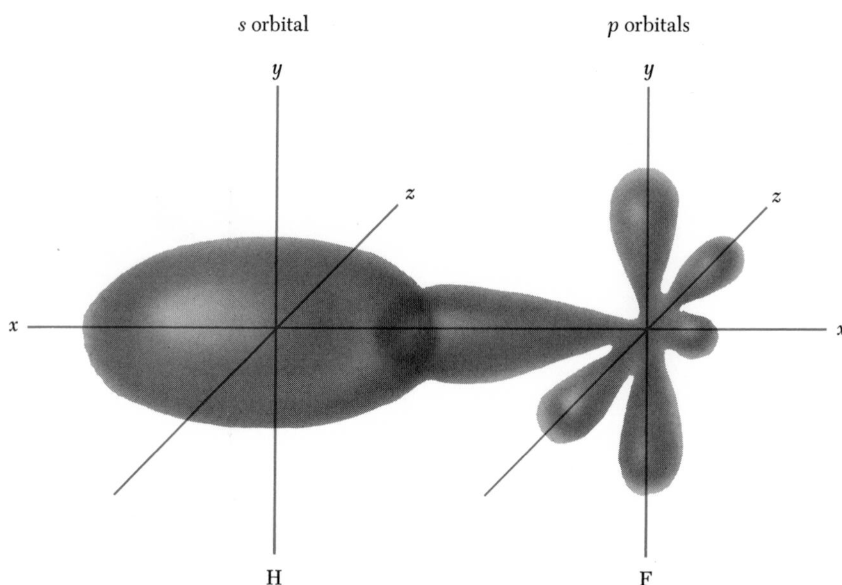

Fig. 8-7 A polar covalent bond in a molecule of hydrogen fluoride (HF).

thus the fluorine atom has a stronger attraction for electrons than has the hydrogen atom. As a result the shared pair of electrons is closer to the fluorine nucleus than to the hydrogen nucleus. Expressed in quantum terms, the shared pair of electrons is nearer the fluorine nucleus for the greater part of the time. The electron-dot notation expresses this idea by placing the shared pair closer to F than to H, as in H $:\ddot{\underset{..}{F}}:$. Thus, the reaction can be shown as

$$H\cdot + \cdot\ddot{\underset{..}{F}}: \longrightarrow H\ :\ddot{\underset{..}{F}}: \tag{8-7}$$

This unequal sharing means that although the molecule is itself electrically neutral, the hydrogen part of the molecule is slightly positive (its nucleus is more exposed) and the fluorine part is slightly negative. In other words, a molecule of hydrogen fluoride appears to have a positive end and a negative end. Such a molecule is called a *polar molecule* or a *dipole* and the bond is called a *polar covalent bond.* A polar bond is an intermediate between an ionic bond and a nonpolar covalent bond.

It is often convenient to represent a covalent bond (a pair of electrons) by a dash. Thus the dash in the formula H—F means that the atoms H and F share one pair of electrons. Hydrogen chloride is also a polar covalent compound, its electron-dot formula being H $:\ddot{\underset{..}{Cl}}:$ and its dash formula H—Cl.

Water, A Polar Molecule

Probably the most important polar compound is water. As you know, the usual formula for water is H_2O and there must be two oxygen—hydrogen bonds per molecule (Fig. 8-8). In electron-dot notation, the oxygen atom has six valence electrons: two in the 2*s*, two in one of the 2*p*, and one in each of the other 2*p* orbitals. This can be written $:\dot{\underset{..}{O}}\cdot$. The hydrogen atoms have single 1*s* electrons represented as H· and H· If we visualize that each of the *s* orbitals of the hydrogen atom overlaps one of the half-filled *p* orbitals in the oxygen atoms, we can picture the formation of two covalent bonds. The electron-dot picture then would be

$$\begin{array}{l} \text{H} \\ :\overset{..}{\underset{..}{\text{O}}}:\ \text{H} \end{array}$$

Fig. 8-8 If the two O—H bonds in a water molecule were in line, would the molecule be polar or nonpolar?

An orbital picture of the water molecule is given in Fig. 8-9. If these bonds were in the same straight line, as in H—O—H, the electrical pulls of the two hydrogen-atom bonds would be in opposite directions, so that the electrical effects of the two bonds would neutralize each other and the molecule could not possibly be polar. What then is the structure of a water molecule?

Deduce . . .
You know the valence of hydrogen is +1. Could the structure then be H—H—O?

In water, each H—O bond is a polar covalent bond, because the electron is attracted more to the O than to the H. Since these two bonds are *not* on opposite ends of the O, and the molecule as a whole is balanced we find that the water molecule as a whole is polar. How can this be explained? We expect that each of the shared pairs of electrons is attracted more strongly by the oxygen nucleus than by the hydrogen nucleus. Why? If this is true the electron pair has a greater probability of being closer to the oxygen nucleus than to the hydrogen nucleus. As a result, the oxygen part of the molecule acts as a negative pole and the combined effect of the two hydrogen atoms acts as a positive pole. Thus the molecule is said to be a dipole as is shown in Fig. 8-10. Therefore the bonds between the oxygen atom and the hydrogen atoms are clearly of the polar covalent kind.

Fig. 8-9 Orbital model of a water molecule showing the overlapping of two half-filled *p* orbitals in oxygen with the half-filled *s* orbital of hydrogen.

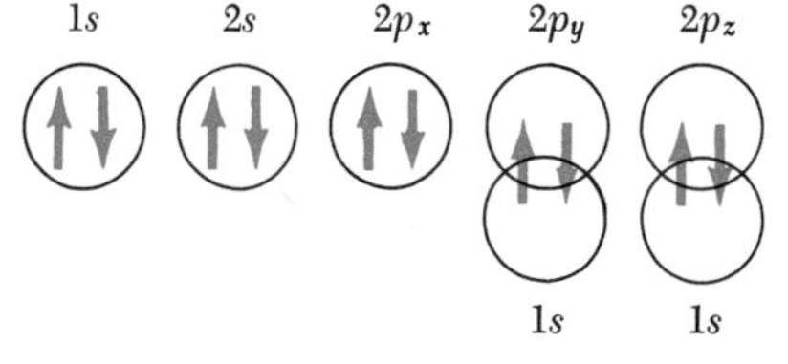

In the oxygen atom in Fig. 8-9 the *p* orbital on the *x*-axis is filled with two electrons, but there is only one electron in each of the *p* orbitals on the *y*-and *z*-axes. Hence the $2p_y$ electron can share an orbital with the 1*s* electron of a hydrogen atom and the $2p_z$ electron can share its orbital with the electron of the other hydrogen atom.

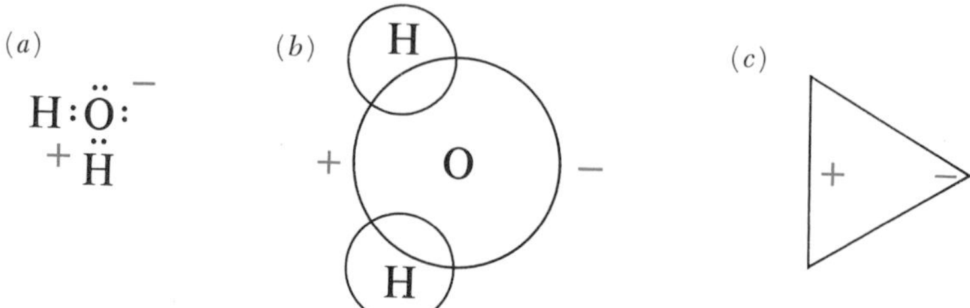

Fig. 8-10 Three representations of the water dipole.

As a result, two covalent bonds are formed. A model of a water molecule is shown in Fig. 8-11. In this diagram, the *s* orbitals of two hydrogen atoms overlap the partially filled orbitals of an oxygen atom, thereby forming two covalent bonds. Since *p* orbitals are perpendicular to one another, the axes of the bonded orbitals in this diagram form an angle of 90°. This is called the *bond angle*.

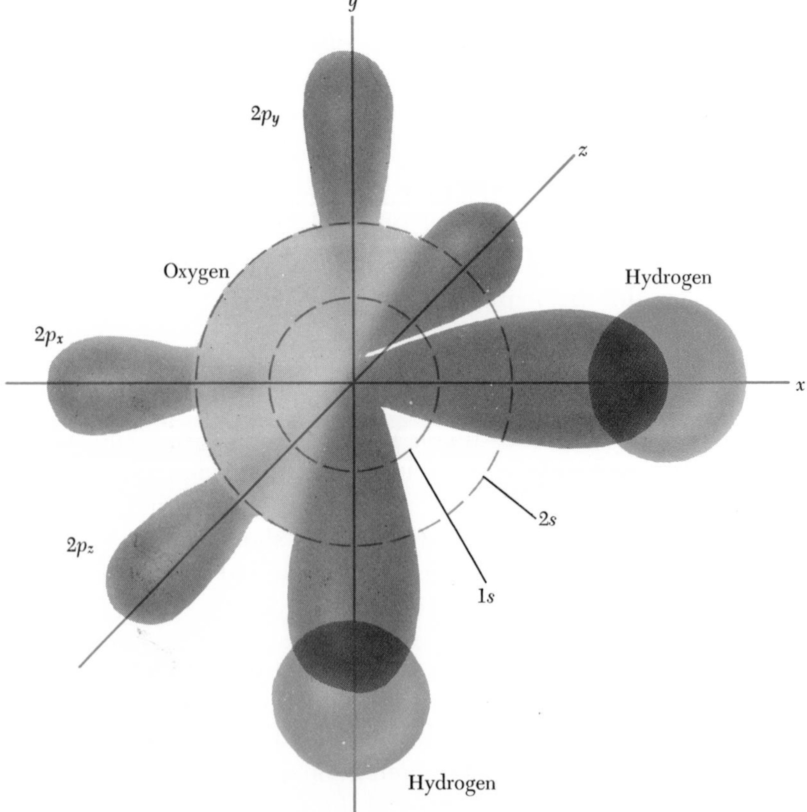

Fig. 8-11 Spatial model of the water molecule, showing the space orientation of oxygen orbitals which give rise to the angular shape of the molecule.

However, the bond angle can be determined experimentally from spectroscopic studies and it is found to be 105°, rather than 90° as shown in the model (Fig. 8-11). Why do these values differ? One contributing factor might be the force of repulsion between the somewhat exposed nuclei of the two hydrogen atoms, which spreads these atoms farther apart. This force would increase the bond angles beyond 90°.

Some Unique Properties of Water

Because water molecules are polar in nature they cling together in clusters such as those in Fig. 8-12. This behavior of molecules is called *association*, and association accounts for the fact that water is a peculiar liquid—it has some unique physical and chemical properties.

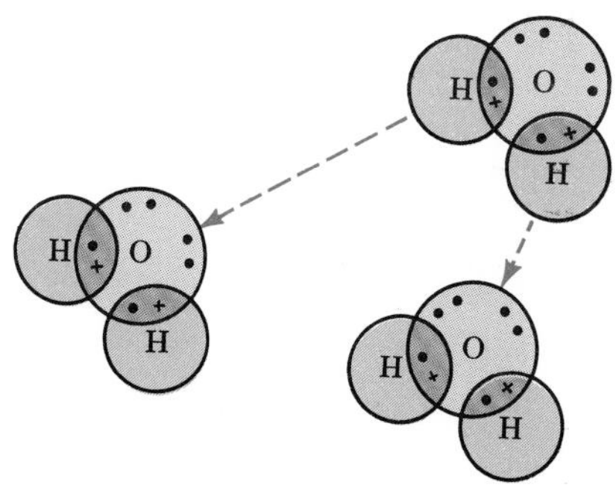

Fig. 8-12 Water tends to form aggregates of molecules.

One of its peculiar properties is that water is a liquid at ordinary temperatures. As you know, its freezing point is 0 °C and its boiling point is 100 °C. If we compare these temperatures with the freezing and boiling temperatures of the corresponding compounds in the same family, we realize that they are unexpectedly high.

Oxygen, sulfur, selenium, and tellurium are in the same chemical family. We would therefore expect that compounds of these elements with some other element such as hydrogen would have properties that change in a regular and predictable manner as we pass from hydrogen oxide (H_2O) to hydrogen sulfide (H_2S), hydrogen selenide (H_2Se), and hydrogen telluride (H_2Te). Let us compare a few of their properties. Hydrogen oxide (water) is a tasteless, odorless, and potable liquid. But hydrogen sulfide is a poisonous gas with a foul smell, as are hydrogen selenide and hydrogen telluride. Moreover, the freezing and boiling temperatures of these compounds, (Table 8-2), show that water does not follow the general trend. The trends of these freezing and boiling

Table 8-2 Properties of water and its analogs

Compound	Formula mass	Freezing temperature, °C	Boiling temperature, °C
H_2O	18	0	100
H_2S	34	−83	−60
H_2Se	81	−66	−41
H_2Te	130	−48	− 2

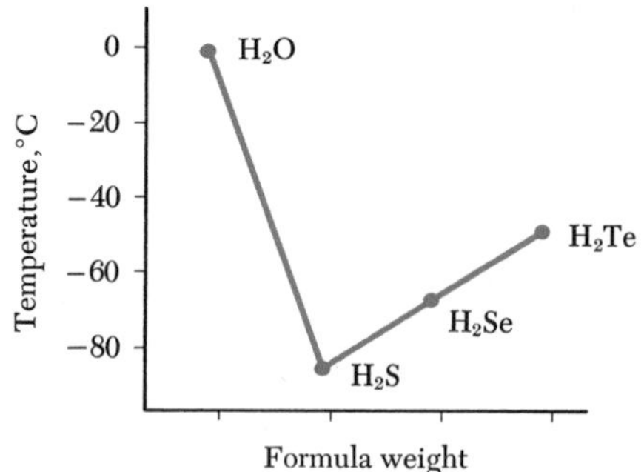

Fig. 8-13 Melting points of water and its analogs. Does a regular variation of melting point with formula weight appear here?

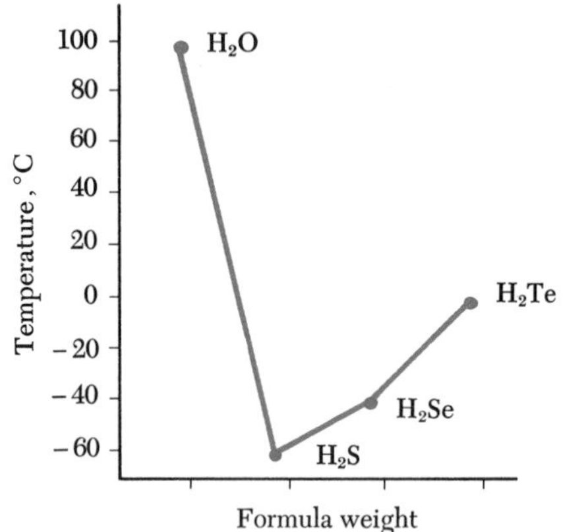

Fig. 8-14 Boiling points of water and its analogs. Is there a regular variation of boiling point with formula weight?

temperatures are clearly seen by plotting them on a graph (see Figs. 8-13 and 8-14). Judging from the general trend shown by the other compounds, we would expect water to be a gas at ordinary temperatures.

The molecules of H_2S, H_2Se, and H_2Te also are bent, but the S, Se, and Te atoms do not attract electrons as strongly as does the O atom in water. Therefore, the bonds in H_2S, H_2Se, and H_2Te are much less polar and these molecules do not associate to form clusters as readily as do water molecules. Water molecules also form "hydrogen bonds" with each other. These bonds facilitate the clustering of the molecules.

When water boils, it changes to steam (or water vapor), and it can be proved experimentally that the vapor molecules are single molecules of H_2O. That is, molecules of water vapor are not associated. Therefore, before liquid water can be vaporized, the electrical bonds between the associated molecules must be broken. This can be done by heating the water sufficiently, as shown in Eq. (8-8),

$$(H_2O)_n\ (l) \xrightarrow{\text{heat}} nH_2O(g) \tag{8-8}$$

where n is the number of water molecules, (l) refers to the liquid state, and (g) to the vapor state of water. It should now be apparent why water has an abnormally high boiling point. It is fortunate that water molecules are polar. Otherwise life as we know it could not exist.

Still another remarkable property of water is its ability to dissolve substances; water is by far the most important of all solvents. Its dissolving power is also due to the fact that water molecules are polar. As you will learn in Chapter 14, a solid dissolves because the electrical attraction of the water dipoles is able to overcome the weaker forces of attraction that hold together the particles of a solid substance. As a result, the solid disintegrates and dissolves. The fact that a vast number of chemical reactions take place in water solution is an example of the unusual dissolving power of water. Moreover, all biological reactions take place in water solutions or water suspensions.

The Shapes of Molecules

The fact that the water molecule is bent rather than linear suggests that other molecules containing three or more atoms may also have preferred space orientations of their atoms. This has been verified by a vast quantity of experimental data and as a consequence chemists have found the concept of *molecular shape* a powerful tool in understanding molecular behavior.

One of the simplest rules of thumb for predicting the shape of molecules is: *The electron pairs in the valence shell of the "central" atom of the molecule tend to arrange themselves so as to get as far from one another as possible, and the atoms bonded to some or all of these electron pairs assume positions in space accordingly.* To illustrate this rule, let us consider the molecule of boron trichloride, BCl_3. The electron-dot formula for this molecule is shown in Fig. 8-15. We see here that the central atom in the molecule is boron and that it contains 3 pairs of electrons in the valence shell. Now according to the rule for predicting molecular shape, these 3 pairs of electrons are expected to repel one another so as to get as far apart as possible. A little thought will show that this condition prevails when the 3 pairs lie in the same plane as the boron atom and each is at a 120° angle from its neighbors. We must imagine then that the boron atom and its 3 electron pairs assume such positions and that the three chlorine atoms remain attached to the boron atom through these electron pairs. With this model in mind, we would predict that the BCl_3 molecule would consist of a boron atom surrounded by three chlorine atoms all of which lie in the same plane and each of which is at an angle of 120° from its neighbors as in Fig. 8-16. This is the known shape of the BCl_3 molecule.

Fig. 8-15 Electron-dot formula of BCl_3.

```
 ..      ..
:Cl: B :Cl:
 ..  ..  ..
    :Cl:
     ..
```

Fig. 8-16 Plane structure of BCl_3.

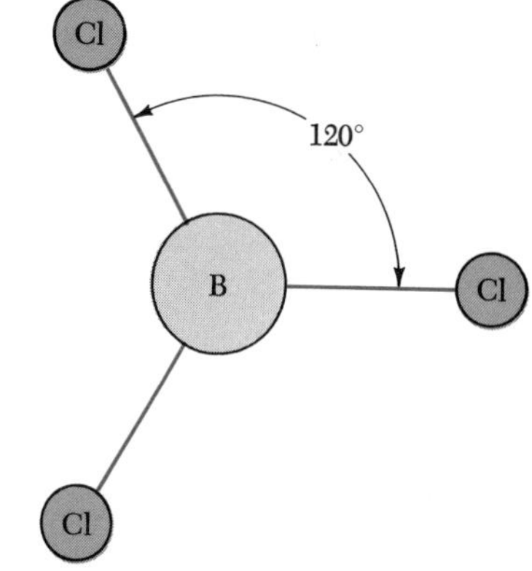

Let us now try to predict the shapes of several other simple molecules. For convenience we choose $BeCl_2$, CH_4, NH_3, H_2O, and SF_6. All of these are covalent substances and we can write electron-dot formulas for each of these molecules by pairing the valence-shell electrons of the central atom with one electron from the valence shells of each of the other atoms in the molecule. (See Fig. 8-17.)

Fig. 8-17 Electron-dot formulas of various compounds.

```
 ..      ..        H           H
:Cl:Be:Cl:      H:C:H       H:N:
 ..      ..        H           H
    (a)          (b)         (c)

                 F
  ..         F . .. . F
 :O:H         : S :
  H          F . .. . F
                 F
  (d)           (e)
```

For beryllium chloride (Fig. 8-17*a*), there are 2 pairs of valence electrons around beryllium. If these assume positions as far apart as possible, they will be found on opposite sides of the central atom and the structure will be linear Cl—Be—Cl—as has been confirmed by experiment. For methane, CH_4, (Fig. 8-16 *b*) there are 4 pairs of electrons around carbon in the molecule. What orientation of these 4 pairs will place them as far apart as possible? This

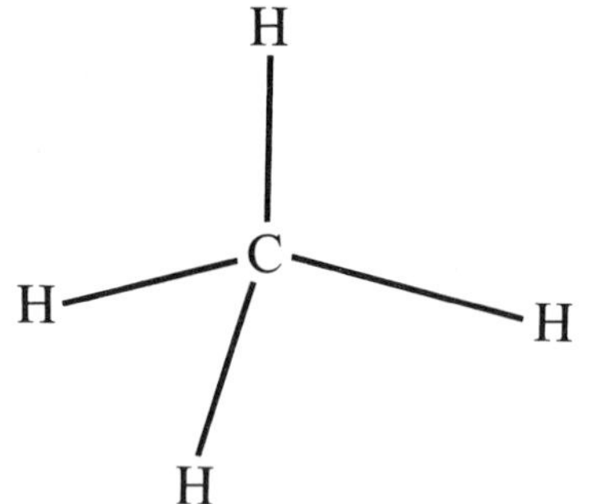

Fig. 8-18 Tetrahedral skeleton of methane.

Fig. 8-19 Tetrahedral structure of methane.

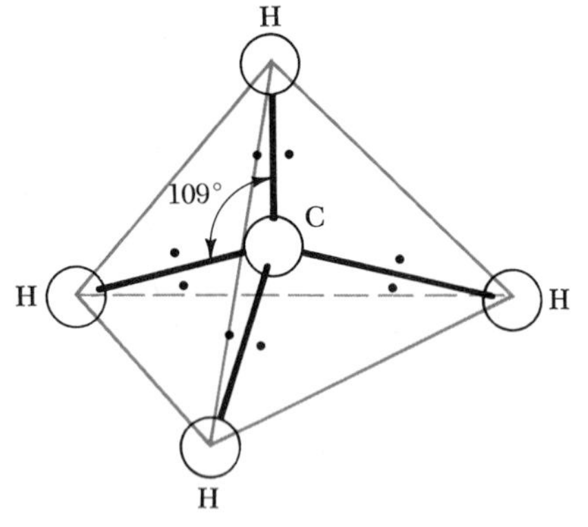

is the so-called *tetrahedral* arrangement illustrated by Fig. 8-18. In Fig. 8-19, the covalent bonds appear to be directed from the carbon atom to the four corners of a regular tetrahedron.

In ammonia, NH_3 (Fig. 8-17*c*), there are also 4 pairs of electrons around the central atom, and again we predict that they would be oriented toward the four corners of a tetrahedron. However, only 3 pairs are bonded to hydrogen atoms; the fourth is not bonded and is known as a lone pair. What then is the predicted shape of the ammonia molecule? Would it not be the same as methane but with one hydrogen removed? This has been called a *pyramidal* shape with the nitrogen atom at the apex and is shown in Fig. 8-20.

In water (Fig. 8-17*d*), the oxygen atom has 4 pairs of electrons in its valence shell and again we imagine a tetrahedral arrangement of electron pairs (Fig. 8-21). In this case there are two bonded and two lone pairs. As we know, the shape of the water molecule is angular. Is this consistent with electron-pair repulsion ideas? The angle between bonds in the tetrahedral structure is 109°. How does this compare with the known bond angle in water?

Finally, we can predict the shape of the SF_6 molecule (Fig. 8-17*e*). Here the sulfur atom has 6 pairs of electrons in its valence shell. Symmetrically arranged, they would assume positions in which each pair points toward the corner of a regular octahedron, that is, with 4 pairs arranged symmetrically in a plane around the "equator" of the sulfur atom, 1 pair directed above, and 1 pair below this

Fig. 8-20 Two representations of a molecule of ammonia. (*a*) Pyramidal skeleton. (*b*) Pyramidal structure.

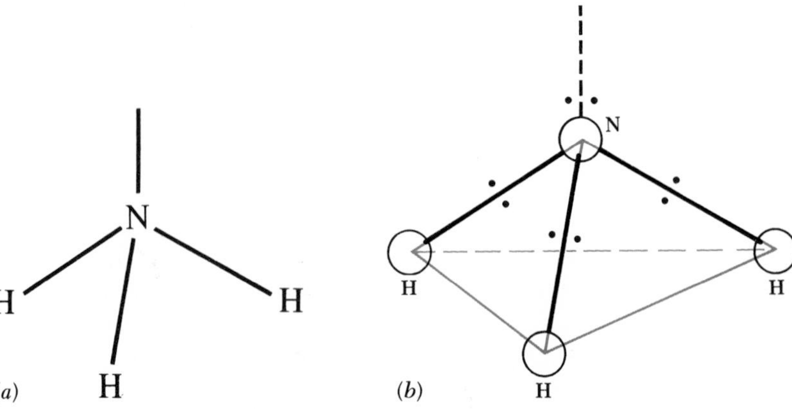

plane. This arrangement is pictured in Fig. 8-22. Measurements show that sulfur hexafluoride has this octahedral structure.

This method of predicting molecular shape can be used to predict correctly the shape of a great number of molecules.

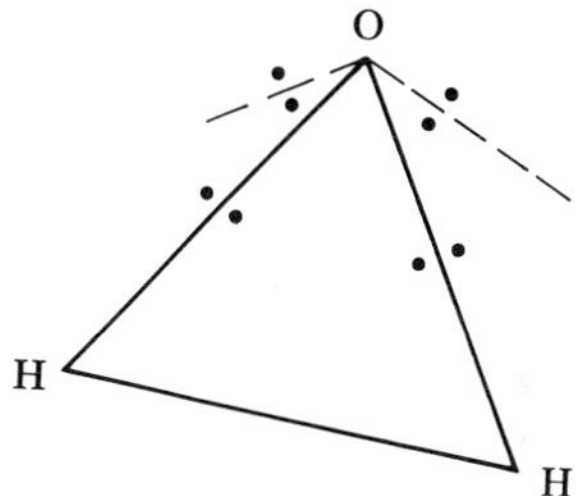

Fig. 8-21 The structure of water suggests a tetrahedron.

Metallic Bonds

We have now considered ionic bonds and covalent bonds. Does either of these types of bonding apply to metals? With the exception of mercury, all metals are solids at ordinary temperatures. This means metal bonds are strong, strong enough to hold the atoms together in a metal crystal. What is the nature of a metallic bond?

Fig. 8-22 Octahedral structure of sulfur hexafluoride.

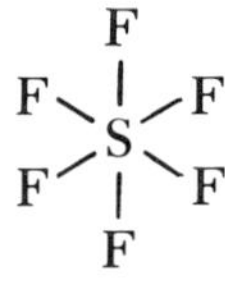

All metals have loosely held valence electrons which can easily be detached from the rest of the atom, usually called the *kernel*. For example, the electron configuration for a sodium atom is $1s^2 2s^2 2p^2 2p^6 3s^1$. That is, a sodium atom has only one valence electron, the electron in its $3s$ orbital. Therefore, a sodium atom has four available valence orbitals (one partially filled $3s$ and three empty $3p$ orbitals) which could be occupied by other electrons.

Let us consider the forces exerted upon a single atom of sodium in a crystal of sodium metal. It can be shown that each atom of sodium is surrounded by eight similar atoms, some of which are shown in Fig. 8-23. Evidently then, an atom (for example, atom A) cannot share its electron with all its neighboring atoms, and this in turn means that covalent bonding between metal atoms is unlikely. However, the loosely held valence electron can move easily in and out of the empty valence orbitals of nearby atoms. The positively charged kernels repel each other, but exert an attractive force upon the moving valence electrons. This attractive force, which is called a *metallic bond*, binds the whole into a rigid lattice. To be more specific, we can say that a metallic bond is the force of attraction between the kernel of a metal atom and all the electrons that come under the influence of this atom. Notice again that in a metallic bond the metal atoms are held together in a rigid lattice or crystal because valence electrons are free to move throughout the whole crystal.

Fig. 8-23 In a metallic bond, valence electrons wander between atoms and are attracted by the positive kernels of these atoms.

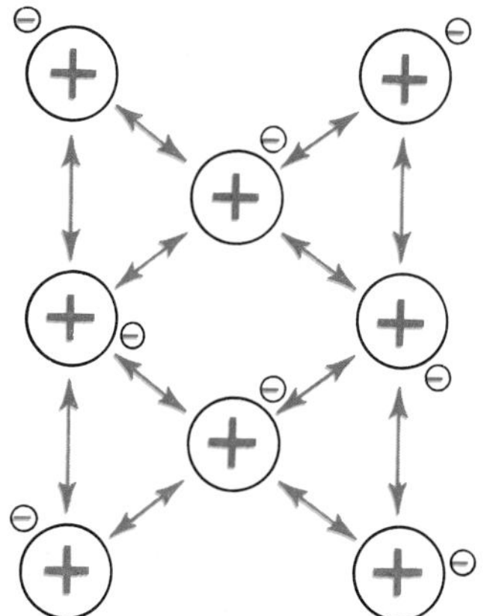

One of the characteristics of all metals is that they are good conductors of electricity. How can conductivity be accounted for?

Define . . .
Define the kernel of an atom.

Suppose a metal wire is connected to the terminals of a dry cell as shown in the schematic diagram in Fig. 8-24. Electrons from the negative terminal of the cell enter the metal crystal, displacing some of the valence electrons of the metal atoms. The displaced electrons are pushed along between the kernels of the atoms displacing other electrons, until eventually electrons emerge at the other end of the wire, where they enter the positive terminal of the cell. Thus, although valence electrons are being constantly displaced, their total number remains unchanged. Why?

Summary

The atoms in molecules are held together because the total forces of attraction are dominant over the forces of repulsion.

An *ionic bond* is formed when an atom of a nonmetal accepts an electron (or electrons) from an atom of a metal. The strong electrostatic attraction between the oppositely charged ions constitutes the bond.

A *covalent bond* is formed by the sharing of electrons in pairs when nonmetals react with each other. If the electron pair is shared equally by the two atoms, the covalent bond is *nonpolar*. If the electron pair is shared unequally by the atoms, it is closer to one nucleus than to the other. An unequally shared pair constitutes a *polar covalent bond*.

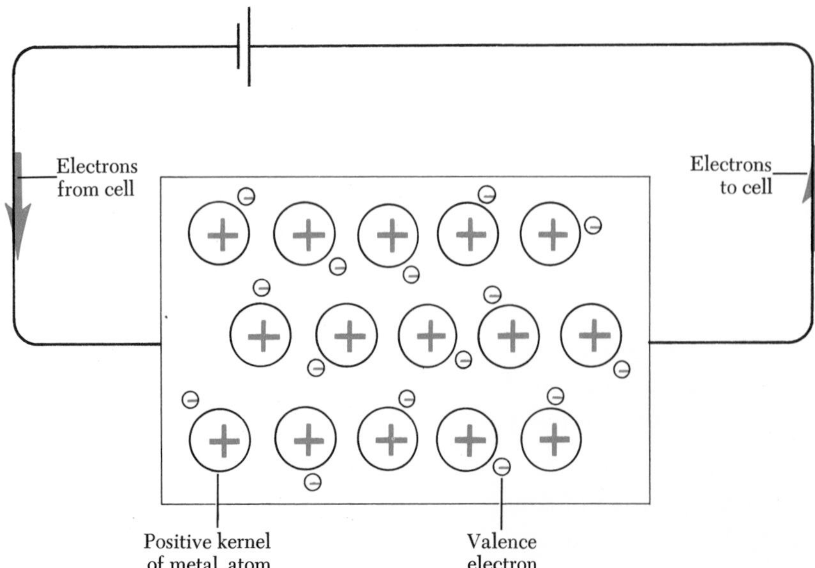

Fig. 8-24 Metals are electrical conductors because electrons from an outside source displace valence electrons of metal atoms which are then free to migrate.

Polar molecules appear to have positive and negative ends. The polar nature of water molecules accounts for many of the unusual properties of liquid water.

The shapes of simple molecules can be predicted accurately by remembering that the electron pairs in the valence shell of the central atoms arrange themselves as far from one another as possible. All atoms of BCl_3 (boron trichloride) are in the same plane, whereas atoms of CH_4 (methane) form a tetrahedron with the four hydrogen atoms at the corners and the carbon atom at the geometric center.

A *metallic bond* is formed by the attraction between loosely held valence electrons from the positive kernels of metal atoms. The valence electrons wander freely throughout the metal crystal, being attracted by many different kernels. The intensity of this force of attraction determines the strength of the metallic bond and the freedom of movement of valence electrons determines the electrical conductivity of a metal.

Factual Recall

1. (*a*) What is an ionic bond? (*b*) Illustrate your answer by reference to the formation of magnesium chloride from its elements.
2. (*a*) Write the equations for the reaction between (*i*) lithium and fluorine and (*ii*) calcium and fluorine. (*b*) Write the electron configuration of all atoms and ions in these reactions.
3. (*a*) What is a covalent bond? (*b*) Illustrate your answer by reference to the bonding in a molecule of fluorine.
4. Compare a nonpolar covalent bond with a polar covalent bond.
5. A water molecule is said to be polar. Explain why.
6. What is meant by the term bond angle?
7. State experimental evidence which supports the fact that a water molecule is not linear, as is implied in the formula H—O—H.
8. (*a*) What is meant by the term *association*? (*b*) Explain how polar forces account for the abnormally high boiling point of water.

9. (*a*) What is a metallic bond? (*b*) Explain the difference between a metallic bond and an ionic bond. (*c*) Why are metals good conductors of electricity?

Apply Your Knowledge!

1. (*a*) Compare the ionic bonds in sodium chloride and lithium fluoride. (*b*) Which compound has the stronger bonds? Why?
2. Predict the shape of the following molecules: H_2S, NF_3, PH_3, CCl_4, $SiCl_4$, IF_5, IF_7, XeF_6.
3. Metallic sodium is soft and melts easily; magnesium is harder than sodium and has a higher melting point. Give a possible explanation of these facts.
4. Considering the relative diameters of the ions involved, how would CsCl compare with NaCl? What similarities and what differences would you predict?
5. Why are the transition elements metallic?
6. Predict the type (or types) of bonding we would expect to find in S_8, $CaCO_3$, SiF_4, CsBr, NH_4Cl, and solid Mg.

Find Out!

1. Look up crystal lattice structures for such compounds as $MgCl_2$ and Al_2O_3.
2. Construct 3-dimensional models of the molecular "shapes" of compounds of the second-row elements discussed on page 29.
3. (*a*) Predict the shapes of the following ions: PCl_6^-, NH_4^+, SiF_6^{-2}(*b*) Account for the charge on each ion in (*a*).
4. Draw or build a model showing how two $AlCl_3$ molecules could bond to form Al_2Cl_6.
5. Look up the structure of SiO_2 (silica) and compare its bonding to that in CO_2.

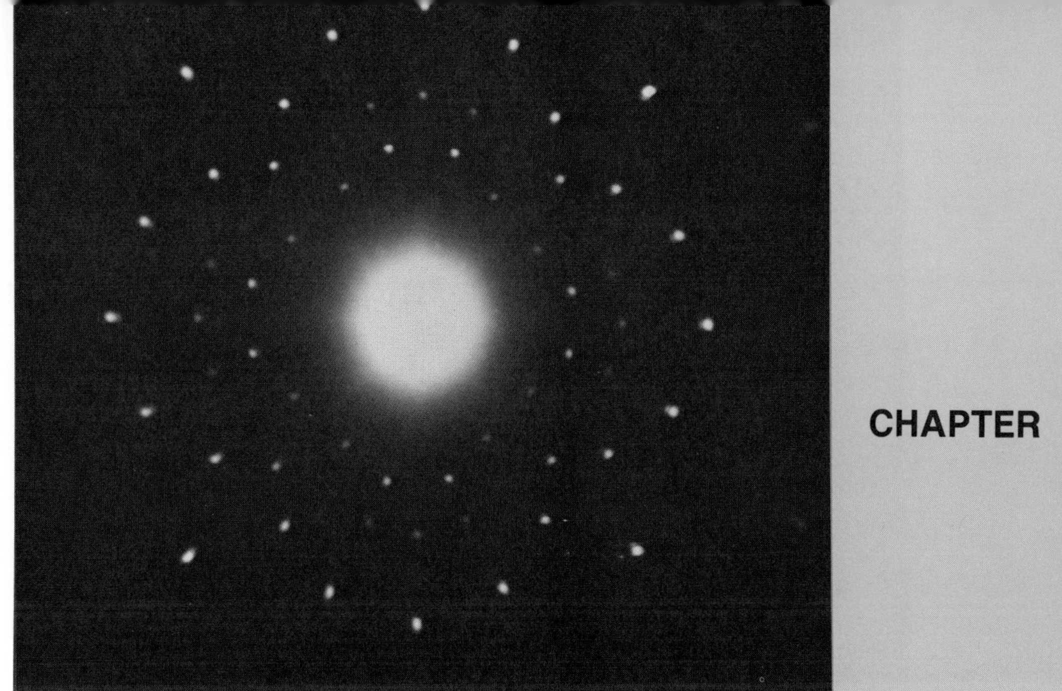

CHAPTER 9

ATOMS AND IONS

IN ADDITION TO THE PERIODICITY of atoms and their structure, size is a quality which helps to prove an atom's reality.

Sizes of Atoms and Ions

Covalent Radii of Atoms

Half of the distance between the nuclei of two atoms of an element in a covalent molecule is defined as the *covalent radius* of the atom. The measured distance between the nuclei of a hydrogen molecule (H_2) is 0.74 Å, and therefore the effective covalent radius of a hydrogen atom is 0.37 Å. Atomic distances are expressed in angstroms rather than centimeters. Similarly, the measured internuclear distance for a molecule of fluorine (F_2) is 1.44 Å, and therefore the covalent radius of a fluorine atom is 0.72 Å. Radii of other atoms have been determined. See Fig. 9-1.

There is a progressive decrease in the atomic radii of the elements from left to right along a row. In any period the radii of atoms get smaller as the atomic numbers of the elements increase. In addition, as we examine one period after the other, there is a marked

Research . . .
Look up at least one method by which atomic radii are measured.

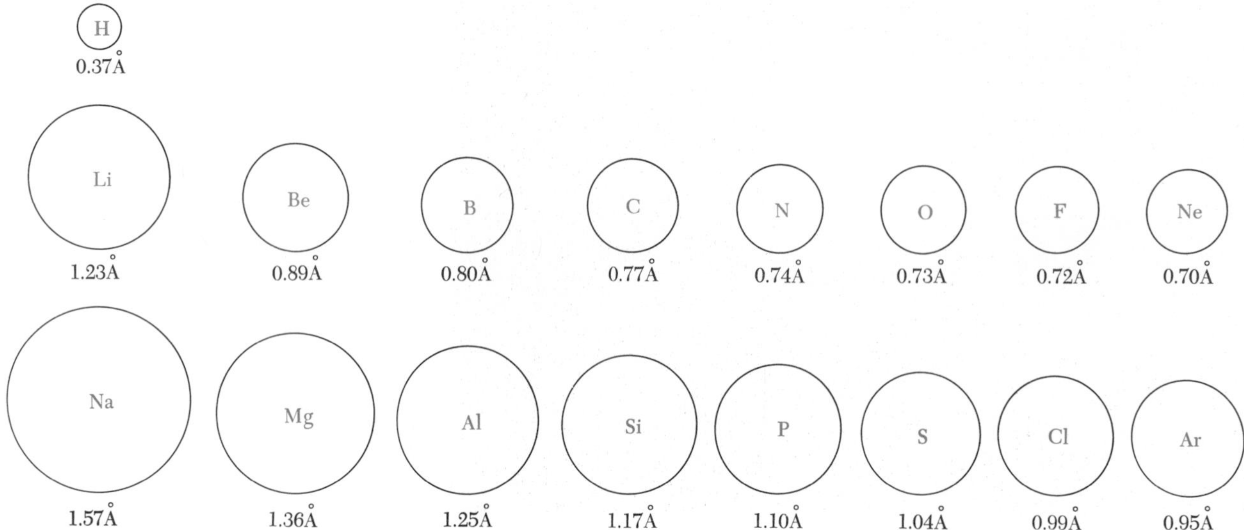

Fig. 9-1 Covalent radii of atoms of elements in the first three rows of the periodic table, the radius of helium (not shown) is 0.5A.

increase in atomic radii. Finally, we observe that within a group (or family) the atomic radii increase from the top to the bottom of the periodic table. For example, the radius of Na is greater than the radius of Li. How can we explain these observations?

All these facts fit into a pattern when we consider the orbital configurations of the atoms. First, why do the radii of atoms in any row of the periodic table *decrease* in order from left to right? The nuclear charge of each element in the row is greater by one unit than the charge in the preceding element; at the same time, each element gains an electron in the outer shell, that is to the *s* or *p* orbitals. The increase in nuclear charge pulls the electrons closer to the nucleus, thereby decreasing the effective radius of the atom.

Let us now consider the marked *increase* in atomic radius from one period to the next. Why, for example, is a sodium atom larger than a fluorine atom? In a fluorine atom, all the electrons are in the 1*s*, 2*s*, and 2*p* orbitals, but in the sodium atom the 1*s*, 2*s*, and 2*p* orbitals are filled with 10 electrons and the eleventh electron is in the 3*s* orbital, which is farther from the nucleus than the 2*p* orbitals.

Radii of Ions

The distances between the nuclei of adjacent ions can be measured by X-ray examination of crystal structures and from these distances the radii of ions are computed. Atoms and ions differ markedly in size, as is shown in Table 9-1, which gives the radii (in angstroms) of a few selected atoms and ions.

Table 9-1 Comparison of atomic and ionic radii of selected elements

Row	Element	Atom		Ion	
		Symbol	Radius, Å	Symbol	Radius, Å
1	Lithium	Li	1.23	Li^{+}	0.60
	Beryllium	Be	0.89	Be^{+2}	0.31
	Oxygen	O	0.73	O^{-2}	1.40
	Fluorine	F	0.72	F^{-}	1.36
2	Sodium	Na	1.57	Na^{+}	0.95
	Magnesium	Mg	1.36	Mg^{+2}	0.65
	Sulfur	S	1.04	S^{-2}	1.84
	Chlorine	Cl	0.99	Cl^{-1}	1.81

Let us compare the values for sodium and chlorine. The effective radius for an atom of sodium is 1.57 Å, whereas its ionic radius is 0.95 Å. That is, a sodium atom is larger than a sodium ion. Why the difference? A sodium ion has its $2p$ orbitals filled, but its $3s$ orbital is vacant. On the other hand, in a sodium atom the $2p$ orbitals are filled and, in addition, there is an electron in the $3s$ orbital.

In the case of chlorine, the ion is larger than the atom. Why? Both the chlorine atom and the chloride ion have the same number of orbitals. However, the atom has 5 electrons in its $3p$ orbitals whereas the ion has 6 electrons. That is, the atom gains an extra electron in forming an ion. This extra electron repels the five already present in the $3p$ orbitals, and this repulsive force has a greater effect than the attraction of the added electrons by the nucleus. The result is that the ionic radius is greater than the atomic radius.

Ionization Energy

Energy is needed to remove a valence electron from an atom, and in the process an ion is formed. This process can be summarized as

$$\text{atom} + \text{energy} \longrightarrow \text{ion} + \text{electron} \qquad (9\text{-}1)$$

And, as stated in Chapter 4, the energy needed to dislodge the most loosely held electron in an atom is called the *ionization energy* of that particular atom (or element). The ionization energy of an element can be found by bombarding that element in a gaseous state with a stream of electrons. For instance, if a voltage or potential difference is applied to the terminals of a discharge tube containing hydrogen gas, electrons are forced out of the negative electrode and they in turn bombard the atoms of hydrogen. If the voltage is increased, the energy of the bombarding electrons is also increased until, eventually, valence electrons are dislodged from some of the atoms and positive ions are formed. The positive ions then flow to the negative terminal. The voltage at which this occurs is called the *ionization potential* for any particular element. For hydrogen, a current flows when the applied voltage is 13.6 V; this, then, is the ionization potential of hydrogen. However, it is customary to measure the *energy* needed to dislodge an electron rather than the *applied voltage*. The simplest way to express this kind of energy is in terms of electron-volts. *An electron-volt is the energy acquired by an electron as it falls through a potential difference of one volt.* Therefore, the ionization energy (of each atom) of hydrogen is 13.6 electron-volts (or, for short, 13.6 eV).

Review . . .
Do you remember a previous definition of the mole?

Recall that in ordinary chemical reactions energy changes are usually expressed in kilocalories per mole. A mole is 6.02×10^{23} atoms, ions, or molecules of the substance in question. Thus, for example 1 mole of carbon atoms contains 6.02×10^{23} atoms of carbon, and 1 mole of oxygen molecules contains 6.02×10^{23} molecules of oxygen; 94.0 kcal of heat are released when 1 mole of carbon dioxide is formed from 1 mole of carbon atoms and 1 mole of oxygen molecules.

Conversion of Electron-volts to Kilocalories per Mole

To express electron-volts in calories we use the conversion factor:

$$1\ \text{eV} = 3.82 \times 10^{-20}\ \text{cal}$$

$$\begin{aligned}\text{Thus,}\quad 1\ \text{eV/atom} &= 3.82 \times 10^{-20}\ \text{cal/atom} \qquad (9\text{-}2)\\ &= 3.82 \times 10^{-20} \times 6.02 \times 10^{23}\ \text{cal/mole of atoms}\\ &= \frac{3.82 \times 10^{-20} \times 6.02 \times 10^{23}\ \text{kcal/mole of atoms}}{10^{3}\ \text{cal/kcal}}\\ &= 23.0\ \text{kcal/mole of atoms}\end{aligned}$$

Using this factor, the ionization energy of hydrogen is

$$13.6 \times 23.0\ \text{kcal/mole} = 313\ \text{kcal/mole}$$

That is, the amount of energy needed to remove an electron from every atom in 1 mole of hydrogen atoms is 313 kcal.

Periodicity in Ionization Energies

In Fig. 9-2 the ionization energies of the elements in Table 9-2 are plotted against their atomic numbers (Z). Notice that, except for a few slight irregularities, in each row of the periodic table the ionization energies increase from left to right. That is, as the atomic number increases so does the value of the ionization energy, being smallest for the alkali metals and largest for the noble gas elements. How can this be explained?

Starting with lithium, the number of protons in the nucleus increases by one from one element to the next. The added electrons are all in the 2*s* or 2*p* orbitals and the attractive force on these electrons in the same shell increases. Therefore the ionization energy increases until the stable octet arrangement is reached in neon.

Notice also that there is a marked drop in ionization energy as we go from one *period* to the next, for example from neon to sodium, from argon to potassium. Why does this occur? If we consider

Table 9-2 Ionization energies of elements 1 through 20

Element		Ionization energy	
Symbol	Z	eV/atom	kcal/mole
H	1	13.6	313
He	2	24.6	567
Li	3	5.4	124
Be	4	9.3	215
B	5	8.3	191
C	6	11.3	260
N	7	14.5	335
O	8	13.6	313
F	9	17.4	402
Ne	10	21.6	497
Na	11	5.1	118
Mg	12	7.6	175
Al	13	6.0	138
Si	14	8.2	188
P	15	11.0	242
S	16	10.4	239
Cl	17	13.0	300
Ar	18	15.8	363
K	19	4.3	100
Ca	20	6.1	141

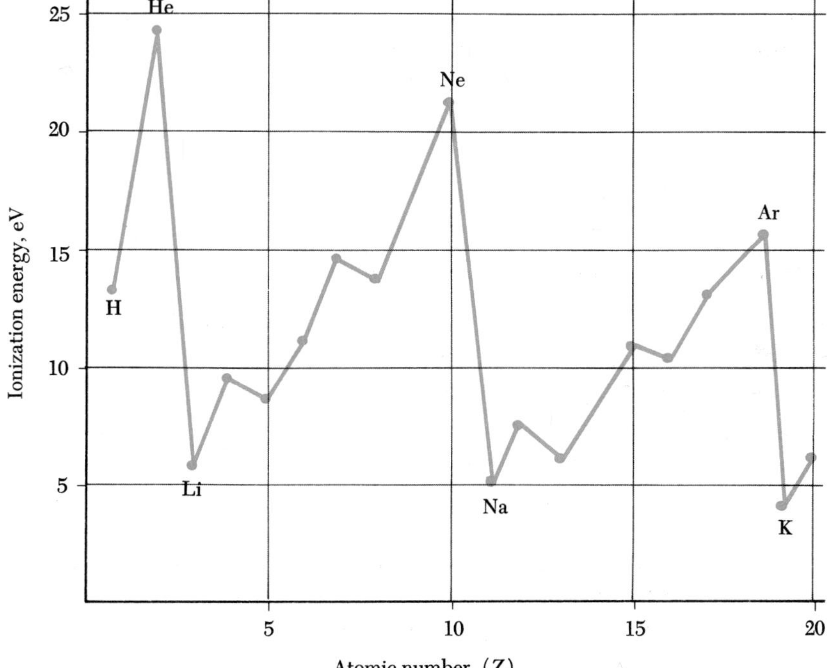

Fig. 9-2 In this graph, how do the atomic numbers change with increasing ionization energy?

elements in the same *group* or family, we note that the ionization energies as shown in Fig. 9-2 decrease as the atomic numbers increase. How can this observation be explained? Let us consider the three alkali metals: lithium, sodium, and potassium.

Table 9-3 Properties of three alkali metals

Element	Z	Electron configuration	Ionization energy, kcal/mole
Li	3	$1s^2 2s^1$	124
Na	11	$1s^2 2s^2 2p^6 3s^1$	118
K	19	$1s^2 2s^2 2p^6 3s^2 3p^6 4s^1$	100

Although the nuclear charge of a sodium atom (+11) is greater than that of a lithium atom (+3), the radius of the valence 3*s* orbital in sodium is greater than the radius of the 2*s* (valence) orbital in lithium. Thus, there are two opposing factors, charge and distance, affecting ionization energy. But the effect of an increase in charge is less than the effect of an increase in distance. The effect of distance is reinforced by the fact that the shells of electrons between the valence shell and the nucleus screen or shield the valence electrons from the nuclear charge. Therefore, the net result is that the 3*s* electron in sodium is held less strongly than the 2*s* electron in lithium. For this reason, less energy is needed to dislodge the valence electron in a sodium atom than to ionize a lithium atom.

Other Ionization Energies

So far we have stated the quantity of energy needed to remove *one* electron from a neutral atom to form an ion. However, an ion also has electrons. Can electrons be detached from an ion?

Ionization Energy of Helium If the potential applied at the electrodes of a discharge tube containing helium is gradually increased, there is a large surge of current when the voltmeter reads 25 V. At this voltage an electron has been removed from each atom, and the surge occurs when the electrons flow to the positive electrode. After the surge the current flow falls. But if the applied potential is further increased to 54 V, there is another surge of current. This second surge occurs when the second electron is being detached from the nucleus. Thus, helium has two ionization energies:
25 eV atom (or 567 kcal/mole) and 54 eV/atom (or 1250 kcal/mole).

Why is the second ionization energy approximately twice as great as the first? In a helium atom the two electrons are in the 1*s* orbital, and in the diagram in Fig. 9-3 these electrons are labeled *A* and *B*. Electron *B* is repelled by electron *A* but attracted by the two protons in the nucleus. If electron *A* is detached when a potential of 25 V is applied, what will be the attractive force between the nucleus and electron *B*? The only force now acting on *B* is the attraction of the two protons. There is no repulsive force on the electron and it has been pulled closer to the nucleus. Therefore, considerably more energy is needed to detach electron *B* when *A* is absent as to detach *A* when both are present.

(*a*)

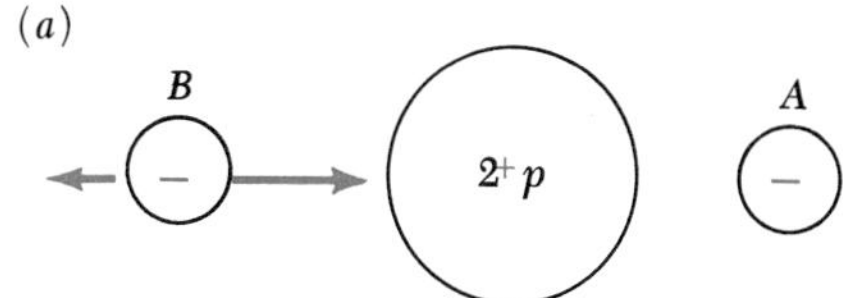

(*b*)

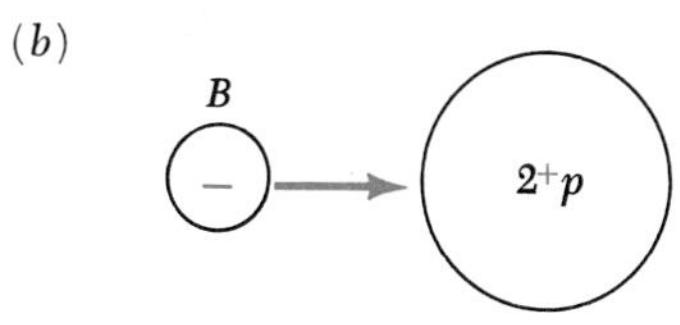

Fig. 9-3 Electron *B* in (*b*) is attracted to the nucleus with twice as much force as electron *B* in (*a*).

Ionization Energy of Lithium In the case of lithium, the ionization energies are 5.4 eV/atom (or 124 kcal/mole) for the first electron, 76 eV/atom (or 1740 kcal/mole) for the second electron, and 122 eV/atom (or 2820 kcal/mole) for the third. Why is this true? The first ionization energy is much smaller than the second, about one-fourteenth as much. This is true because the first electron to be dislodged is in the 2*s* orbital, whereas the second and third electrons are in the 1*s* orbital. Why is the third ionization energy larger than the second?

Ionization Energy of Magnesium The first four ionization energies and the changes in electron configuration of magnesium are shown in Table 9-4. Why is the ionization energy of electron 2 greater than that of 1, but much less than that of 3? Why is the ionization energy of electron 4 greater than that of electron 3?

Table 9-4 Ionization of magnesium

Electron no.	Electron configuration			Ionization energy	
	Before ionization		After ionization	kcal/mole	eV/atom
1	$1s^2 2s^2 2p^6 3s^2$	$\longrightarrow$	$1s^2 2s^2 2p^6 3s^1$	176	7.6
2	$1s^2 2s^2 2p^6 3s^1$	$\longrightarrow$	$1s^2 2s^2 2p^6$	347	15.0
3	$1s^2 2s^2 2p^6$	$\longrightarrow$	$1s^2 2s^2 2p^5$	1850	79.7
4	$1s^2 2s^2 2p^5$	$\longrightarrow$	$1s^2 2s^2 2p^4$	2520	109

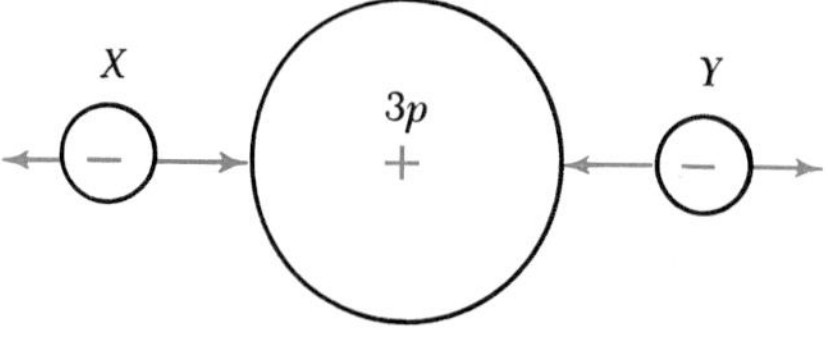

(*a*)

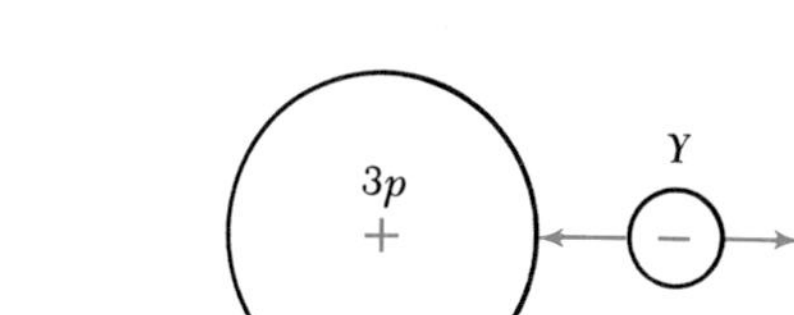

(*b*)

Fig. 9-4 In a lithium atom the second ionization energy, (the removal of electron *X* in *a*), is about two-thirds of the third ionization energy (the removal of electron *Y* in *b*).

Electron Affinity

The ionization energy of the *metal* lithium is 124 kcal/mole and the value for the *nonmetal* fluorine (which is in the same period) is 402 kcal/mole. Clearly, lithium loses an electron much more readily than does fluorine, but this does not necessarily mean that lithium is a more chemically active element than fluorine. Why not? Nonmetals, unlike metals, usually react by gaining electrons, and they release energy in doing so. Such a reaction can be expressed:

$$\text{nonmetallic atom} + \text{electron} \longrightarrow \text{ion} + \text{energy} \qquad (9\text{-}3)$$

The amount of energy released when an atom gains an electron is called *electron affinity*.

Electron affinity is not simply the opposite of ionization energy. In the case of fluorine, for example, the ionization energy is the energy required to remove one of nine electrons from the control of a nucleus containing nine protons. The product here is a *positive ion*. By contrast, the electron affinity is the energy released when a tenth electron is added and the product is a *negative ion*. Of all elements, fluorine has the strongest tendency to gain an electron and it is therefore the most active nonmetal.

It is difficult to determine electron affinities experimentally. A somewhat related property, however, can be studied. This property is defined as the *ability of one atom to attract electrons from another*, and it is called *electronegativity*.

Electronegativity

Linus Pauling (1901-), an American chemist, devised an arbitrary scale with a maximum value of 4.0 to indicate the electronegativities of the elements. A partial list of the Pauling electronegativity values is given by families in Table 9-5. Observe that the electronegativity values are periodic. Notice also that no values are given for the family of noble gases. Why? The difference in the electronegativity values between two elements determines the nature of the chemical bond between them. Let us see how.

Table 9-5 Pauling electronegativity values

H	2.1												
Li	1.0	Be	1.5	B	2.0	C	2.5	N	3.0	O	3.5	F	4.0
Na	0.9	Mg	1.2	Al	1.5	Si	1.8	P	2.1	S	2.5	Cl	3.0
K	0.8	Ca	1.0	Ga	1.6	Ge	1.8	As	2.0	Se	2.4	Br	2.8
Rb	0.8	Sr	1.0	In	1.7	Sn	1.8	Sb	1.9	Te	2.1	I	2.5
Cs	0.7	Ba	0.9	Tl	1.8	Pb	1.8	Bi	1.9				

Electronegativity and Chemical Bonds

Suppose atom X combines with atom Y to form a compound XY. The bond between X and Y can be one of three kinds.

Ionic Bonds First, if the electronegativity of Y is much greater than that of X, an electron is completely transferred from X to Y and the ionic compound X^+Y^- is formed. A specific example is the case of NaCl. The electronegativities for Cl and Na are 3.0 and 0.9, respectively. The difference between these quantities is 2.1, which is an unusually large number in terms of the values in Table 9-5. Hence, the bond is ionic and, as you know, the compound can be shown as $\mathrm{Na}^+ \; :\underset{\cdot\cdot}{\ddot{\mathrm{Cl}}}:^-$

Nonpolar Covalent Bonds Second, if the electronegativities of X and Y are equal, two electrons are shared midway between the two atoms as in $X:Y$. This kind of bond between X and Y is, you recall, a nonpolar covalent bond. For example, Table 9-5 shows that the electronegativity of both hydrogen and phosphorus is 2.1. Therefore, the bonding in the compound phosphorus trihydride (phosphine) is covalent and is shown in Fig. 9-5.

Fig. 9-5 Electron-dot formula of phosphine.

$$\begin{array}{c} \mathrm{H} \\ \mathrm{H} : \underset{\cdot\cdot}{\ddot{\mathrm{P}}} : \mathrm{H} \end{array}$$

Similarly, electronegativity values show that the bond between two hydrogen atoms or two fluorine atoms is nonpolar, as in Fig. 9-6.

Fig. 9-6 Electron-dot formulas showing covalent bonding in (*a*) hydrogen and (*b*) fluorine.

$$\underset{(a)}{\mathrm{H} : \mathrm{H}} \qquad \text{and} \qquad \underset{(b)}{:\underset{\cdot\cdot}{\ddot{\mathrm{F}}} : \underset{\cdot\cdot}{\ddot{\mathrm{F}}}:}$$

Polar Covalent Bonds And, finally, if the electronegativity of Y is greater than that of X, but not great enough to cause electron transfer, an electron from X is pulled toward Y so that the shared pair is no longer midway, but is nearer Y than X, as in $X\;:Y$. Such a bond is intermediate, partly ionic and partly covalent, and is called polar covalent. A specific example is the bond between hydrogen and chlorine. The electronegativity values are 2.1 and 3.0, respectively, a difference of 0.9, and the sharing can be shown as $\mathrm{H}\;\;:\underset{\cdot\cdot}{\ddot{\mathrm{Cl}}}:$

Summary

Sizes of atoms and ions can be determined by several experimental methods.

An atom may be larger or smaller than its ion, depending upon whether it adds or loses electrons in forming the ion. For a sodium atom, the 3*s* orbital contains one electron; for a sodium ion, the 3*s* orbital is empty. Therefore the atom is larger than the ion. For chlorine, the atom is smaller than the ion. This has been attributed to an increase in the repulsion among the valence-shell electrons upon addition of another electron. This repulsion is too large to be compensated for by the additional attractive force between the added electron and the nucleus. Therefore, the valence shell of the ion is expanded and the ion is larger than the atom.

Factual Recall

1. Comparing the size of atoms in the same row of the periodic table, the atomic volume of silicon is less than that of sodium but greater than that of chlorine. Explain why.
2. What is meant by the terms (*a*) ionization potential, (*b*) ionization energy, (*c*) electron-volt?
3. The ionization energy of potassium ($Z = 19$) is less than that of lithium ($Z = 3$). Explain why.
4. In each row of the periodic table, the noble gas element has the highest ionization energy. Explain why.
5. (*a*) What is meant by (*i*) the second ionization energy, and (*ii*) the third ionization energy of an element? (*b*) The second and third ionization energies of magnesium are 350 kcal/mole and 1850 kcal/mole, respectively. Why is the value of the third so much larger than the value of the second?
6. What is the essential difference in concept between electronegativity and ionization energy?
7. (*a*) Write the electron configurations for (*i*) sodium (*ii*) magnesium. (*b*) Which element has the greater first ionization energy? Why? (*c*) Which element has the greater second ionization energy? Why?

Apply Your Knowledge!

1. Which is the larger, a calcium atom or a calcium ion? Explain your answer.
2. Which is the larger, a sulfur atom or a sulfide ion? Explain your answer.
3. Compare the strengths of the bonds in (*a*) H_2O and H_2S, (*b*) H_2S and HCl.
4. Sodium combines directly with both chlorine and fluorine. Does sodium transfer electrons more readily to chlorine or to

fluorine? Base your answer upon the electronegativities of these elements.

5. Predict the first four ionizations energies for Ca, using Mg as a model.

6. (*a*) What is characteristic of the ionization energy of (*i*) an element that forms positive ions? (*ii*) an element that form negative ions? (*b*) How do these compare as to electronegativity?

Find Out!

1. Look up the second and third ionization energies for elements 3-20; plot these, and compare the plot with a plot of the first ionization energies of these same elements.

2. Pauling's scale of electronegativites is described as an "arbitrary" scale. (*a*) What does this mean? (*b*) Have other such scales been set up?

3. Look up the life of Linus Pauling.

4. (*a*) Predict the first four ionization energies for Al. (*b*) Check your values against those in a reliable reference. (*c*) How do you account for a larger relative difference between the first and second energies than that between the second and third.

Suggested Readings

Bragg, L., *X-Ray Crystallography* (SCIENTIFIC AMERICAN Offprint #325). San Francisco: Freeman.

Fullman, R.L., *The Growth of Crystals* (SCIENTIFIC AMERICAN Offprint #260). San Francisco: Freeman.

UNIT 

THE BEHAVIOR OF GASES

GASES BEHAVE QUITE DIFFERENTLY from liquids and solids, and a theory has been devised to account for their properties. The theory states that at ordinary temperatures gas molecules are in a state of rapid motion. If moving gas molecules strike a surface, they exert a pressure upon that surface.

Another statement of the theory is that the average speed of the molecules increases as the temperature rises. Similarly, as the temperature falls the molecular speeds decrease. And, if the temperature were to drop far enough molecular motions would stop altogether. The temperature at which all molecular motions cease is called absolute zero, and it is apparent that at absolute zero gas molecules would not be able to exert any pressure whatever.

The volume of a gas is the sum of the volume of the molecules and the volume of the space through which the molecules move. However, the volume of the molecules is so small, that it is of no significance. We conclude that equal volumes of all gases must contain the same number of molecules provided the gases are at the same temperature and pressure. This statement is known as Avogadro's hypothesis.

HISTORICAL CHEMISTRY LABORATORY

This is an excerpt from Avogadro's essay in which he proposed an important hypothesis.

Amadeo Avogadro (1776–1856)

There is a consideration which appears at first sight to be opposed to the admission of our hypothesis with respect to compound substances. It seems that a molecule composed of two or more elementary molecules should have its mass equal to the sum of the masses of those molecules and that in particular, if in a compound one molecule of one substance unites with two or more molecules of another substance, the number of compound molecules should remain the same as the number of molecules of the first substance. Accordingly, on our hypothesis when a gas combines with two or more times its volume of another gas, the resulting compound, if gaseous, must have a volume equal to that of the first of these gases. Now, in general, this is not actually the case. For instance, the volume of water in the gaseous state is, as M. Gay-Lussac has shown, twice as great as the volume of oxygen which enters into it, or what comes to the same thing, equal to that of the hydrogen instead of being equal to oxygen. But a means of explaining facts of this type in conformity with our hypothesis presents itself naturally enough; we suppose, namely, that the constituent molecules of any simple gas whenever (i.e., the molecules which are at such a distance from each other that they cannot exercise their mutual action) are not formed of a solitary elementary molecule, but are made up of a certain number of these molecules united by attraction to form a single one; and further, that when molecules of another substance unite with the former to form a compound molecule, the integral molecule which should result splits up into two or more parts (or integral molecules) composed of half, quarter, etc., the number of elementary molecules going to form the constituent molecules of the first substance, combined with half, quarter, etc. the number of constituent molecules of the second substance that ought to enter into combination with one constituent molecule of the first substance (or what comes to the same thing, combined with a number equal to this last of half-molecules, quarter-molecules, etc., of the second substance); so that the number of integral molecules of the compound becomes double, quadruple, etc., what it would have been if there had been no splitting-up and exactly what is necessary to satisfy the volume of the resulting gas.

CHAPTER 10

AVOGADRO'S HYPOTHESIS

THE WORD *molecule* came into scientific language much later than the word atom. Molecule was used in the early part of the 19th Century to explain the way gases combine chemically, or rather to account for the volumes of gases in gas reactions.

Gay-Lussac's Law of Volumes

A French chemist named Joseph Louis Gay-Lussac (1778-1850) investigated a large number a gas reactions and, in all cases, he measured the volumes of the reacting gases and also the volumes of the gaseous products. From his experimental data, and using the term *volume* to mean parts by volume, he found for example that

$$\text{1 volume of hydrogen} + \text{1 volume of chlorine} \longrightarrow \text{2 volumes of hydrogen chloride} \qquad (10\text{-}1)$$

$$\text{2 volumes of hydrogen} + \text{1 volume of oxygen} \longrightarrow \text{2 volumes of water vapor} \qquad (10\text{-}2)$$

$$\text{1 volume of nitrogen} + \text{3 volumes of hydrogen} \longrightarrow \text{2 volumes of ammonia} \qquad (10\text{-}3)$$

The numbers representing gas volumes in these reactions are

$$(a)\ 1 + 1 \longrightarrow 2 \quad (b)\ 2 + 1 \longrightarrow 2 \quad (c)\ 1 + 3 \longrightarrow 2$$

These numbers show a simple and striking relationship. First they are whole numbers and not fractional numbers as one might have expected. Indeed, Gay-Lussac found this whole-number volume relationship in all the gas reactions he investigated, and it was apparent that he had discovered a scientific law. This law, now known as Gay-Lussac's Law of Volumes, is usually stated: *The ratios of volumes of combining gases are always small whole numbers provided the volumes are measured at the same temperature and pressure.* The next important observation is that the gas volumes in these reactions are not necessarily additive

$$1+1=2,\quad 2+1=2, \text{ not } 3 \quad 1+3=2, \text{ not } 4$$

Explanations of Gay-Lussac's Law

The first attempt to explain Gay-Lussac's Law was made by Dalton. Indeed, Gay-Lussac discovered the law of volumes in the same year (1808) that Dalton published his atomic theory. It therefore was not surprising that Dalton should try to account for the simple relationship between the combining volumes of gases. To do this he assumed that equal volumes of gases at the same temperature and pressure contain the same number of atoms, but he ran into difficulty when he applied this assumption to the reaction between hydrogen and chlorine. Let us see why. At that time, the word *molecule* was not a term in scientific language and the word *atom* was applied to compounds as well as elements; the smallest possible particle of a compound was called a *compound atom.*

Gay-Lussac had stated that

1 volume of chlorine + 1 volume of hydrogen $\longrightarrow$ 2 volumes of hydrogen chloride

Accepting Dalton's assumption, it followed that

n atoms of chlorine + n atoms of hydrogen $\longrightarrow$ $2n$ compound atoms of hydrogen chloride

Think . . .
Why is Dalton's assumption that equal volumes of gases at the same temperature and pressure contain the same number of particles reasonable? How could this assumption be argued?

Clearly, this reaction can take place only if every atom of hydrogen and every atom of chlorine can be split into two parts However, according to Dalton's atomic theory atoms were not divisible into smaller particles. Therefore Dalton's assumption that equal volumes of gases at the same temperature and pressure contain the same number of *atoms* was untenable. A solution to this difficulty was offered in 1811 by an Italian scientist named Amadeo Avogadro (1776–1856).

Avogadro's Hypothesis

Avogadro suggested that particles of gaseous elements are made up of *groups of atoms*, usually 2 atoms per group. This new idea turned out to be one of great significance. For example, he said that if each of the normal particles of hydrogen and chlorine contained two atoms rather than one, the experimental facts concerning the gas volumes could be accounted for. Let us see how. But first let it be said that Avogadro coined the word *molecule* for these little groups of atoms. (The word *molecule* is derived from Latin and means *a small heap or cluster.*) Therefore, the word *molecule* can be substituted for the word *atom* in Dalton's statement. This revised version was called Avogadro's hypothesis, and it states: *Equal volumes of all gases contain the same number of molecules provided they are measured at the same temperature and pressure.*

Let us now apply Avogadro's hypothesis to the hydrogen–chlorine reaction:

1 volume of hydrogen + 1 volume of chlorine $\longrightarrow$
2 volumes of hydrogen chloride

According to Avogadro,

n molecules of hydrogen + n molecules of chlorine $\longrightarrow$
$2n$ molecules of hydrogen chloride

Or dividing out the factor n,

1 molecule of hydrogen + 1 molecule of chlorine $\longrightarrow$
2 molecules of hydrogen chloride (10-4)

Each molecule of hydrogen (and also each molecule of chlorine) contributes to the formation of two molecules of hydrogen chloride. Therefore each molecule of hydrogen and chlorine must be made up of at least 2 atoms; that is, the molecules are *diatomic* and their formulas are H_2 and Cl_2, respectively. The noble gases are an exception because they are monatomic. Therefore, the symbol for neon is the same as for an atom of neon.

Fig. 10-1 Gay-Lussac's law of volumes diagrammatically represented by one volume of hydrogen combining with one volume of chlorine to product two volumes of hydrogen chloride.

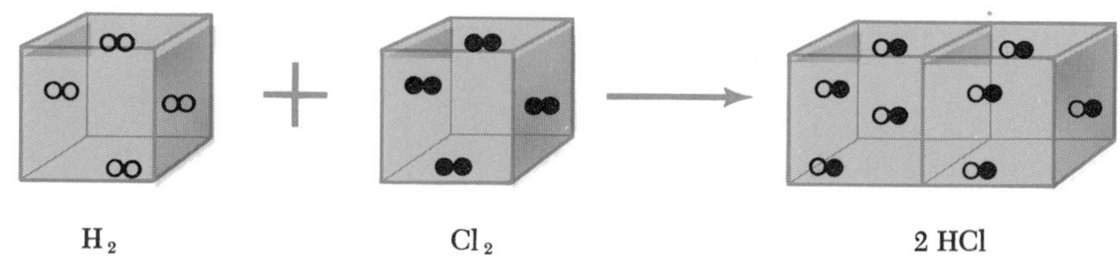

Using Avogadro's hypothesis, we can represent Gay-Lussac's law of volumes diagrammatically (see Fig. 10-1). The diagram for the hydrogen–chlorine reaction shows that each molecule of hydrogen and chlorine consists of two atoms and that a molecule of hydrogen chloride consists of one atom of hydrogen and one atom of chlorine. It also shows that equal volumes of hydrogen, chlorine, and hydrogen chloride contain the same number of molecules.

Remember that Gay-Lussac also proved experimentally that two volumes of hydrogen (80 ml, for example) combine with one volume of oxygen (40 ml) to form two volumes of water vapor (80 ml). In this case, there is a reduction in volume from three volumes (or 120 ml) to 2 volumes (or 80 ml) as shown in Fig. 10-2. In this diagram, the two volumes of hydrogen contain eight molecules, the volume of oxygen contains four molecules, and the two volumes of water vapor contain eight molecules. Thus, the reduction in total volume is possible because two atoms (or one molecule) of hydrogen combine with one atom (or one-half of a molecule) of oxygen to form one molecule of water vapor.

Finally, the reaction between nitrogen and hydrogen is represented diagrammatically in Fig. 10-3. How can you explain the change in volume, from four volumes of reactants to two volumes of product?

Gas Densities and Molecular Masses

The first convincing experimental evidence in favor of Avogadro's hypothesis was the determination of the molecular masses of gaseous elements and compounds. This was possible because a

Fig. 10-2 Application of Avogadro's reasoning to the reaction of hydrogen combining with oxygen to produce water.

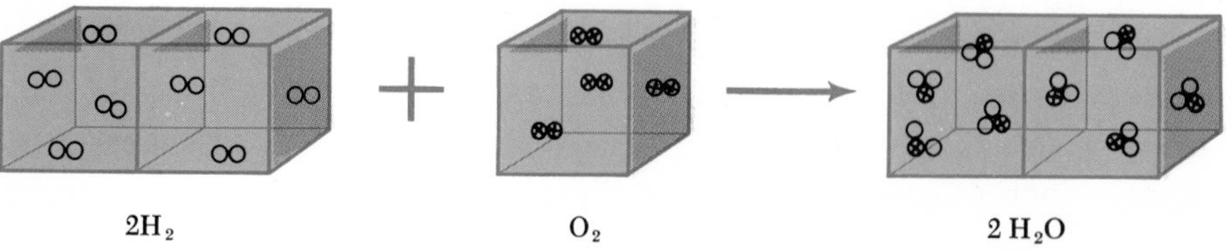

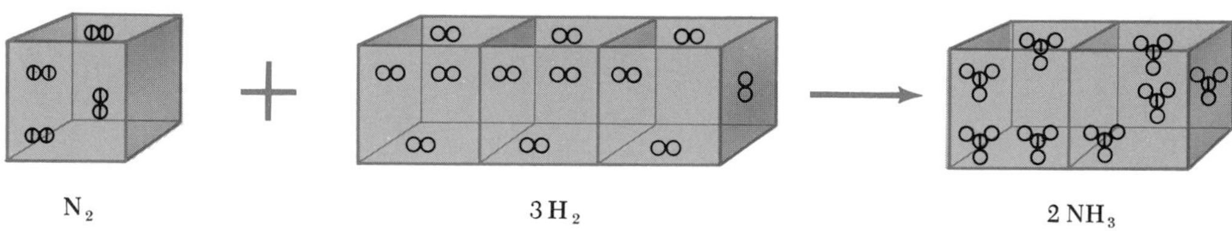

Fig. 10-3 How is it possible for one volume of nitrogen and three volumes of hydrogen to give two volumes of ammonia?

French chemist named Jean-Baptiste Dumas (1800–1884) had, in the middle of the 19th Century, concentrated upon the problem of finding the densities of various gases. Density is defined as mass per unit volume or, in symbols, $D = M/V$. As noted in Chapter 1, densities of gases are expressed in grams per liter (g/1). Thus Dumas' problem was to find the mass of a known volume of gas and then to make the computation. This sounds simple enough, but in practice the experimental technique is quite difficult.

Dumas used a flask with a stopcock in the neck so that the flask could be evacuated by an air pump. (See Fig. 10-4.) First the volume of the flask (up to the stopcock) was measured by filling the flask with water and then weighing the water. (One gram of water occupies one milliliter at 20°C.) Dumas next poured out the water, then evacuated the flask of air and weighed it (M_1). He then filled the flask with a gas (oxygen, for example) at atmospheric pressure and again weighed it (M_2). The mass of the gas in the flask is clearly the difference between these two masses ($M_2 - M_1$). Actually, the mass of the gas is exceedingly small compared with the mass of the flask and only by skillful techniques could the mass of gas be found with the desired degree of accuracy. Moreover, gas density depends upon both temperature and pressure, and Dumas determined the gas densities at a pressure of one atmosphere and a temperature of 25°C. Under these conditions he found the density of hydrogen to be 0.083 g/l, nitrogen to be 1.15 g/l, oxygen 1.31 g/l and carbon dioxide 1.81 g/l.

Fig. 10-4 Flask similar to the one used by Jean Baptiste Dumas to determine the molecular masses of gases.

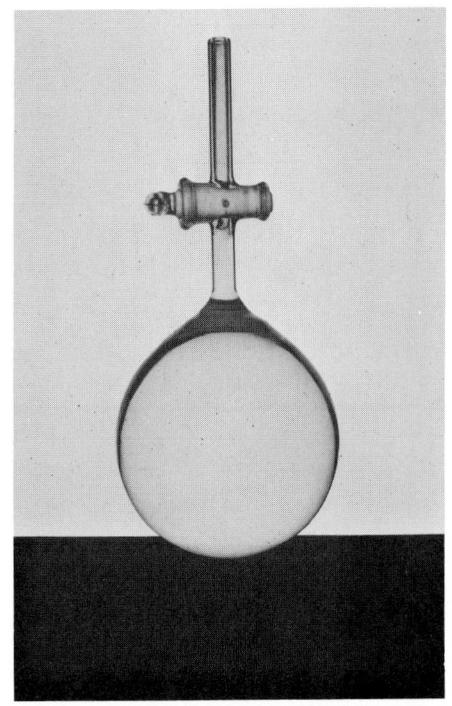

Then, by applying Avogadro's hypothesis to gas densities, the molecular masses of the gases could be computed. Since by Avogadro's hypothesis equal volumes of gases contain the same number of molecules, there must be the same number of molecules (n) in 1 liter of all gases. Thus, we can compute the molecular mass of nitrogen by comparing the masses of n molecules of nitrogen and n molecules of oxygen and by assuming that oxygen molecules are diatomic.

$$\frac{\text{mass of } n \text{ molecules of nitrogen}}{\text{mass of } n \text{ molecules of oxygen}} = \frac{1.15 \text{ g}}{1.31 \text{ g}} = 0.878$$

Therefore,

$$\frac{\text{mass of one molecule of nitrogen}}{\text{mass of one molecule of oxygen}} = 0.878$$

You recall that in the late 19th Century the atomic mass scale was based on the value of oxygen as 16.000 atomic mass units (amu). On this scale, the mass of a diatomic molecule of oxygen (the molecular mass of oxygen) would be 32.000 amu. Therefore, the molecular mass of nitrogen must be 32.000 amu × 0.878 or 28.0 amu. The molecular masses of other gases were found in the same way. For example, the density of carbon monoxide was found to be 1.15 g/l at 25 °C. By the same reasoning,

$$\frac{\text{mass of } n \text{ molecules of carbon monoxide}}{\text{mass of } n \text{ molecules of oxygen}} = \frac{1.15 \text{ g}}{1.31 \text{ g}} = 0.878$$

Therefore the molecular mass of carbon monoxide is 32.000 amu × 0.878 = 28.0 amu.

Example 10-1

The density of the gas methane (marsh gas) is 0.653 g/l at 760 mm of mercury and 25°C. Find the molecular mass of methane.

Solution

$$\frac{\text{mass of } n \text{ molecules of methane}}{\text{mass of } n \text{ molecules of oxygen}} = \frac{0.653 \text{ g}}{1.31 \text{ g}} = 0.500$$

Therefore the molecular mass of methane is

32.00 amu × 0.500 = 16.000 amu

It should now be apparent that the molecular mass of a gaseous element or compound is the mass of one molecule of the element (or compound) compared to the mass of an atom of oxygen, arbitrarily chosen as 16.000 atomic mass units. Although this standard is no longer used—as was stated earlier in this book—we will use it for computational convenience in the discussions and examples that follow. Using C = 12 amu as a standard, as chemists have done since 1961, the molecular mass of oxygen is actually 31.9988.

Fig. 10-5 This graduated cylinder contains almost 1 gram-molecular mass of water or approximately 18 g. How many water molecules does the cylinder contain?

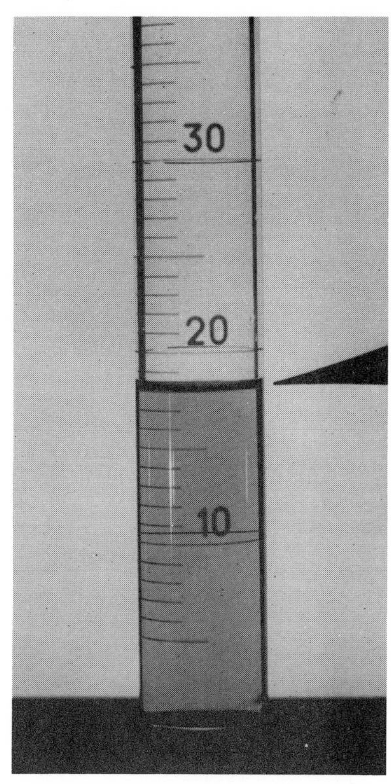

Avogadro's Number

The actual mass of one molecule of oxygen is 5.4×10^{-25} g. This is an exceedingly cumbersome number to use in computations and is a quantity much smaller than could be used in the laboratory. A unit of more practical value would be the relative molecular mass expressed in grams or, as it is usually called, a gram-molecular mass. By agreement among chemists, the gram-molecular mass of oxygen is 32 g (actually 31.9988 g), that of nitrogen is 28 g (actually 28.0144 g), and that of chlorine, 71 g (actually 70.906 g). Clearly, there must be the same number of molecules in a gram-molecular mass of any substance. This number is called Avogadro's number in honor of the scientist who first introduced the concept of molecules. Avogadro's number is a very important constant; it is approximately 6×10^{23}; or to be more exact, it is 6.02×10^{23}. This is a vast number, far beyond the imagination. However, some idea of its magnitude can be conveyed by an analogy.

> Suppose a counting machine could be set to count continuously at the rate of one per second. At the end of 1 hour the machine would have counted to 3600, at the end of a 24-hour day the count would be 86,400, and at the end of 1 week it would be 604,800. But, to reach Avogadro's number, the machine would have to count continuously for 19,000,000,000,000,000 (or 1.9×10^{16}) years!

Avogadro's number has been determined experimentally in a number of ways. Knowing Avogadro's number, the mass of a single molecule or even the mass of a single atom can be computed. Thus, to find the mass of a molecule of water, we start with the gram-molecular mass of water, which is 18.02 g. Therefore the mass of a water molecule is

$$\frac{18.02 \text{ g/gram-molecular mass}}{6.02 \times 10^{23} \text{ molecules/gram-molecular mass}} = 2.99 \times 10^{-23} \text{ g/molecule}$$

Fig. 10-6 This cube represents 1 gram-molecular volume or 22.4 l. It measures 28.2 cm on each edge. At STP, how many grams of hydrogen would occupy this volume?

How can the mass of a single atom, for example an oxygen atom, be computed? First we must apply Avogadro's number to a gram-atomic mass of it. Since 32 g of oxygen contain 6.02×10^{23} molecules and since each oxygen molecule consists of two atoms, 32 g of oxygen must contain $2 \times 6.02 \times 10^{23}$ atoms. Therefore, a gram-atomic mass of oxygen (or 16.0 g of it) contains Avogadro's number of atoms, and the mass of one atom of oxygen is

$$\frac{16.0 \text{ g/gram atomic mass}}{6.02 \times 10^{23} \text{ atoms/gram atomic mass}} = 2.66 \times 10^{-23} \text{ g/atom}$$

The Mole

As already stated, a convenient quantity for comparing the mass of different substances which have the same number of molecules is the gram-molecular mass. This quantity was originally called a mole. When originally defined in this way the number of molecules in 1 mole had not been determined. However, the term *mole*, as now defined, includes Avogadro's number. Specifically, 1 mole of a substance contains 6.02×10^{23} particles, either molecules or atoms, of the substance. Thus, 1 mole of oxygen molecules consists of 6.02×10^{23} molecules, and the total mass is 32 g. Similarly, one mole of oxygen atoms consists of 6.02×10^{23} atoms, and the total mass is 16 g. In other words, the term *mole* applies to an *Avogadro number of atoms or molecules.* For example, 23.0 g of sodium constitutes 1 mole of sodium atoms, and 32.0 g of sulfur constitutes 1 mole of sulfur atoms. Expressed the other way around, 35.5 g of chlorine is equivalent to 1 mole of chlorine atoms. As a final example, what is the new significance of the formula HCl as applied to the gaseous compound hydrogen chloride? The formula HCl means 1 mole of HCl molecules, and 1 mole of HCl molecules contains 1 mole of hydrogen atoms and also 1 mole of chlorine atoms.

Molar Volumes

About the middle of the 19th Century the research of an Italian chemist named Stanislao Cannizzaro (1826–1910) gave still further support to Avogadro's hypothesis. By assuming the validity of the hypothesis, Cannizzaro first proved that 1 mole of any gas occupies a volume of 22.4 liters at 1 atmosphere pressure and 0 °C. With this information, he determined both molecular and atomic masses from his experimental data. In deriving a gas volume of 22.4 liters, Cannizzaro argued somewhat in the following manner.

Fig. 10-7 The substance in the dish is approximately 32 g of sulfur. How many moles of sulfur does this represent?

> If, as Avogadro states, 1 mole of every gas contains the same number of molecules, then the volume of 1 mole of some selected gas must be precisely the same as the volume of 1 mole of any other gas. This theoretical conclusion can easily be checked by experiment. However, we must bear in mind that gas volumes are affected by pressure and temperature, and therefore any comparison of gas volumes must be made under the same conditions of temperature and pressure. The standard of comparison is 0°C and 760 mm mercury pressure, usually referred to as *STP* (*standard temperature and pressure*). For example, at STP the density of oxygen is 1.43 g/l and the density of hydrogen is 0.090 g/l.
>
> What is the volume occupied by 1 mole of oxygen?
>
> $$\text{density} = \frac{\text{mass}}{\text{volume}} \quad \text{or} \quad D = \frac{M}{V} \quad \text{and} \quad V = \frac{M}{D}$$
>
> Hence the volume of oxygen is
>
> $$\frac{\text{molar mass of oxygen}}{\text{density of oxygen}} = \frac{32.0\ \text{g/mole}}{1.43\ \text{g/l}}$$
>
> $$= 22.4\ \text{l/mole}$$
>
> Similarly, the volume occupied by 1 mole of hydrogen is
>
> $$\frac{\text{molar mass of hydrogen}}{\text{density of hydrogen}} = \frac{2.02\ \text{g/mole}}{0.090\ \text{g/l}}$$
>
> $$= 22.4\ \text{l/mole}$$
>
> Similar computations for other gases show that the volume of 1 mole of any gas at STP is 22.4 l. This volume is an important gas constant; it is called the *molar volume*. (See Fig. 10-6)

To Find the Molecular Mass of a Gas from its Molar Volume

The formula $D = M/V$ can also be rearranged to read $M = D \times V$, and in this form it has practical importance. In words, the formula means that the molecular mass of a gas equals the density of the gas times its molar volume. For example, the density of carbon dioxide can be computed from data obtained experimentally in the laboratory. The molecular mass can then be found from the density and the molar volume (22.4 l) at STP, as in the following example.

Example 10-2

Experimental Data:

Mass of carbon dioxide	= 0.545 g
Volume of carbon dioxide	= 297 ml
Temperature of carbon dioxide	= 22 °C or 295 °K
Pressure of carbon dioxide	= 766 mm (mercury)

Solution

Since our calculation of the molar mass depends on knowing the molar volume at STP, the first step is to find the volume of the gas at STP. This is done by using the combined gas laws as described in the next chapter. Such a computation shows the volume at STP is 277 ml or 0.277 l.

Hence the density of carbon dioxide is

$$\frac{\text{mass}}{\text{vol. at STP}} = \frac{0.545\text{g}}{0.277\text{ l}} = 1.97 \text{ g/l}$$

Using the relation $M = D \times V$, the molar mass of carbon dioxide is 1.97 g/l × 22.4 l/mole = 44.1 g/mole.

Therefore the molecular mass of carbon dioxide as determined in this way is 44.1 amu.

Fig. 10-8 The volume of gas in the plastic bag can be determined by the amount of water displaced from the flask. How could the volume of water displaced be measured? The difference in mass between the full bag and the empty bag is the mass of the gas itself. Once volume and mass are determined, the density of the gas can be calculated for any given temperature and pressure.

Cannizzaro's Method of Finding Atomic Masses

To find the atomic mass of an element, Cannizzaro first determined the molecular masses of a number of compounds which contained the particular element. He also analyzed these compounds and found their percentage compositions. Obviously his method was limited to those elements that formed gaseous compounds under easily attainable laboratory conditions. Carbon, hydrogen, and chlorine are three such elements. We will examine the experimental data of a number of compounds of these elements as shown in Table 10-1, and then determine their atomic masses.

The values in columns 1 and 2 of Table 10-1 are obtained from experimental data, and the masses in column 3 are derived from the values in columns 1 and 2. Let us examine the values for carbon in grams per mole in column 3. Cannizzaro assumed that the atomic mass of the element is the smallest mass to be found in 1 mole of a number of its compounds. Or, expressed another way, the atomic mass of an element is the largest common divisor in masses per mole of its compounds. On the basis of this information, therefore, the atomic mass of carbon is 12.0 amu. Similarly, the atomic masses of hydrogen and chlorine are 1.01 and 35.5 respectively.

Determination of the Formulas of Compounds

The data such as given in Table 10-1 enabled Cannizzaro to determine the formulas of compounds. Let us see how. The mass of an element in 1 mole of a compound is found by multiplying the molecular mass of the compound by the percentage of the element in it. Thus, the mass of chlorine in 1 mole of carbon tetrachloride is 154.1 g × 92.2% or 142 g. The number of atoms of an element in a molecule of a compound equals the mass (in grams) of the element

Table 10-1 Computation of molecular formulas

Substance	1 Mol. mass (mass of 22.4 l at STP)	2 Percentage composition			3 Mass of element, g/mole			4 Atoms/molecule			5 Formula
		H	C	Cl	H	C	Cl	H	C	Cl	
Methane	16.0	25.2	74.8		4.03	12.0		4	1		CH_4
Ethane	30.1	20.2	79.8		6.05	24.0		6	2		C_2H_6
Benzene	78.1	7.7	92.3		6.05	72.0		6	6		C_6H_6
Chloroform	119.5	0.84	10.1	89.1	1.01	12.0	106.5	1	1	3	$CHCl_3$
Carbon tetrachloride	154.1		7.8	92.2		12.0	142		1	4	CCl_4
Hydrogen chloride	36.5	2.8		97.2	1.01		35.5	1		1	HCl
Chlorine	71.0			100			71			2	Cl_2

in 1 mole of that compound divided by the gram-atomic mass of a molecule of that element. Therefore, the number of atoms of chlorine in one molecule of carbon tetrachloride is equal to 142 g/35.5 g = 4. In a like manner the number of each kind of atom per mole of the compounds listed in Table 10-1 has been computed and recorded in column 4. With this information it is a simple matter to write the formulas of the compounds, as shown in column 5. Thus the formula for ethane is C_2H_6 and for carbon tetrachloride it is CCl_4.

Cannizzaro published his work about 1860 and, with his monumental contribution to chemical knowledge, the evidence for Avogadro's hypothesis was indisputable. Avogadro's hypothesis became universally accepted by chemists as Avogadro's law.

Equations for Gas Reactions

As stated earlier, the gases hydrogen and chlorine combine to form the gas hydrogen chloride. The formula for a molecule of hydrogen is H_2, that of chlorine Cl_2, and that of hydrogen chloride HCl. The reaction can be represented as

$$H_2 + Cl_2 \longrightarrow HCl$$

However, in this expression there are four atoms on the left of the arrow and only two on the right. Since atoms are never destroyed in a chemical reaction, the number of atoms in the product (or products) must be precisely the same as the total number in the reactants. Thus, to write an accurate expression, the coefficient 2 should be placed before the formula HCl. The expression then becomes

$$H_2 + Cl_2 \longrightarrow 2HCl \qquad (10\text{-}5)$$

Observe that the number of atoms in the reactants equals the number of atoms in the products or, as we usually say, atoms are conserved. An expression in which atoms are conserved is called an equation and the equation is said to be balanced. Notice also that in an equation reactants and products are usually connected by an arrow, and the coefficient 1 representing one molecule is omitted just as it is in an algebraic expression. Thus, although

$$1H_2 + 1Cl_2 \longrightarrow 2HCl$$

would be an accurate statement, it is common practice to omit the coefficient 1.

In writing Eq. (10-5) we referred to molecules. Moles, however, are larger quantities and can be weighed. Chemists prefer to think in terms of moles rather than of molecules. Sometimes it is convenient to think of relative gram masses and sometimes, if the compounds are gases, or relative volumes. Now rewrite Eq. (10-5) and place below the formulas the various kinds of information given.

H_2	$+$	Cl_2	$\longrightarrow$	$2\ HCl$	(10-5)
If we take 2 atoms of H_2	and	2 atoms of Cl_2,	we can get	2 molecules of HCl.	(*a*)
Or					
if we take 1 molecule of H_2	and	1 molecule of Cl_2,	we can get	2 molecules of HCl.	(*b*)
Or					
if we take 1 mole of H_2	and	1 mole of Cl_2,	we can get	2 moles of HCl.	(*c*)
Or					
if we take x moles of H_2	and	x moles of Cl_2,	we can get	$2x$ moles of HCl.	(*d*)
Or					
if we take 2 g of H_2	and	71 g of Cl_2,	we can get	73 g of HCl.	(*e*)
Or					
if we take 1 volume of H_2	and	1 volume of Cl_2,	we can get	2 volumes of HCl, at the same temperature and pressure.	(*f*)
Or					
if we take 22.4 l of H_2	and	22.4 l of Cl_2,	we can get	44.8 l of HCl at STP.	(g)

Summary

Gay-Lussac made the experimental observation that the ratios of the volumes of gases involved in chemical reactions are small whole numbers. Then, to explain Gay-Lussac's observation, Avogadro proposed the hypothesis that equal volumes of all gases contain the same number of molecules under the same conditions of temperature and pressure.

Further studies of gases led to the idea that the molar volume of a gas is 22.4 liters at STP and that a molar volume of a gas contains 6.02×10^{23} molecules. This number (6.02×10^{23}) is called

Avogadro's number. From these concepts the formulas, molecular masses, and atomic masses of gaseous elements and compounds were determined. Finally the idea of representing a reaction between gases in terms of a chemical equation emerged.

Factual Recall

1. State Gay-Lussac's law of volumes.
2. (*a*) State Avogadro's hypothesis. (*b*) Prove that an oxygen molecule is diatomic given the experimental fact that two volumes of hydrogen plus one volume of oxygen yield two volumes of water vapor.
3. (*a*) What is the value of Avogadro's number ? (*b*) What does this number mean?
4. What is meant by the term *molar volume*?
5. (*a*) Write the equation for the reaction of hydrogen and nitrogen to give ammonia. (*b*) Under each symbol in the equation write the number of atoms, moles, grams, and volumes that the symbol can represent. (*c*) Is there a conservation of (*i*) atoms, (*ii*) moles, (*iii*) volumes?

Apply Your Knowledge!

1. Compute the molecular mass of chlorine if the densities at STP of oxygen and chlorine are 1.43 g/l and 3.17 g/l, respectively.
2. Compute the molecular mass of nitrogen, assuming that 250 ml of nitrogen weigh 0.313 g at STP.
3. The experimental values of the molecular masses of ethane, ethyl alcohol, methane, and carbon dioxide are 30, 46, 16, and 44 respectively. The experimental values of the percentage of carbon by mass are 80%, 52%, 75%, and 27% respectively. Compute the atomic mass of carbon.

Find Out!

If one mole (18 ml) of water with specially "labeled" molecules were placed in the oceans and allowed to mix completely, how many specially labeled molecules would be in each cup (about 250 ml) of water taken later from the oceans? N.B. The quantity of water in the oceans is 3.2×10^8 mile^3 and 4.2×10^{12} l = 1 mile^3.

CHAPTER 11

THE GAS LAWS

SCIENTISTS IN THE 17TH CENTURY discovered that gases, when confined, behave according to simple laws. What are these laws? Before answering this question, we must first answer another: What is meant by gas pressure and how is it measured?

Gas Pressure

Gas pressure is defined as *the force exerted by a gas per unit area of surface*—per square centimeter, for example. In practice it is difficult to measure gas pressure directly, but there are several devices or instruments that will measure it indirectly. One of these is a mercury barometer.

The first mercury barometer was devised by an Italian scientist named Evangelista Torricelli (1608–1647) in the early part of the 17th Century. Even today, Torricelli's barometer is used to measure atmospheric pressure. A Torricelli barometer is made from a long glass tube filled with mercury. The open end of the tube is sealed temporarily by a finger, as shown in Fig. 11-1 (*a*), and the tube is then inverted and immersed in a dish of mercury. The finger is then removed. Some mercury flows out of the tube, creating a vacuum above the column of mercury which remains steady at a height of about 76 cm (or 760 mm). This situation is shown in Fig.

Infer . . .
Why does the mercury barometer give only an indirect measurement of air pressure?

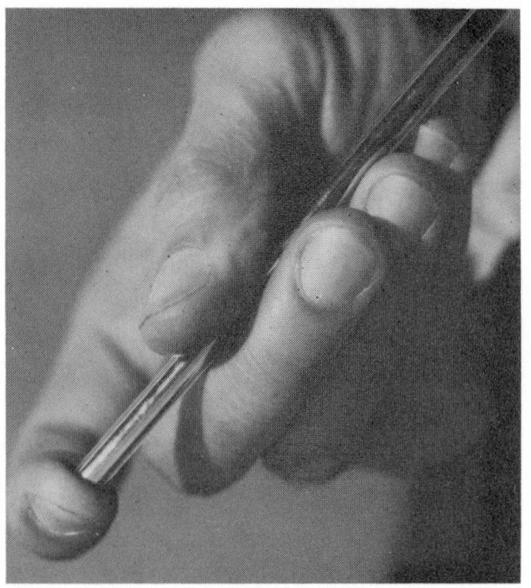

(*a*)

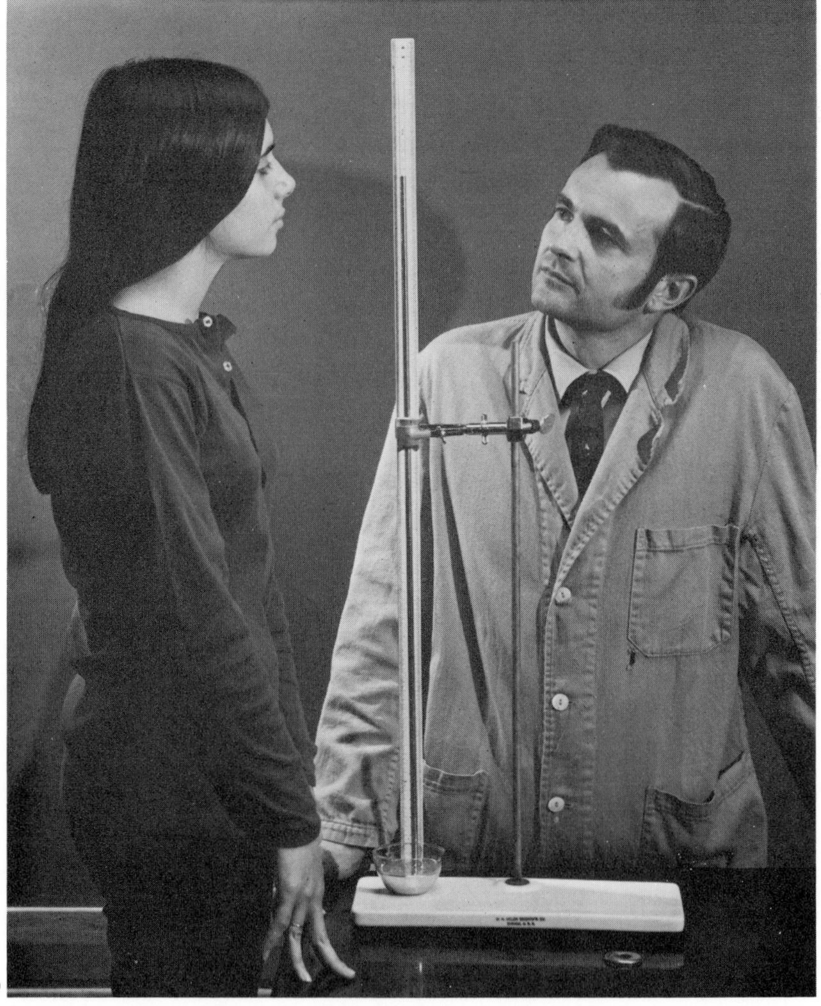

(*b*)

Fig. 11-1(*a*) Since mercury is extremely dense, the filled tube must be inverted carefully to avoid breaking it. (*b*) Notice the girl is reading the height of the mercury column at eye level. Why is an eye-level reading necessary?

11-1 (*b*). What supports the mercury column at this particular height?

Note . . .
Mercury is a poison. Avoid prolonged contact with your skin, and do not inhale its vapors.

Because of its weight, the mercury in the tube exerts a downward pressure, P_d. On the other hand, the pressure of the atmosphere (P) on the surface of the mercury in the dish is transmitted through the mercury and exerts an upward pressure, P_u, on the mercury in the tube. If P_d is greater than P_u, mercury falls out of the tube until the opposing pressures balance each other; that is, until $P_d = P_u$. Thus, the height of the mercury column (the barometric reading) is an *indirect* way of measuring the pressure of the atmosphere. Atmospheric pressure varies slightly from day to day, but for purposes of comparison, a mercury column 760 mm in height is taken as stand-

Define . . .
What is a standard atmosphere?

ard. *If the mercury column is 760 mm in height, the gas pressure is exactly one atmosphere (1 atm) or 760 torr* (in honor of Torricelli). Similarly, a height of 900 mm indicates a gas pressure of

$$\frac{900 \text{ mm}}{760 \text{ mm/atm}} \quad \text{or} \quad 1.18 \text{ atm}$$

This is called a pressure of 900 torr. A pressure of 550 torr is equivalent to 0.723 atm.

Define . . .
If 760 mm of mercury are equal to 760 torr, what is a torr?

If a gas is in a container, its pressure can be measured by a device called a manometer, — shown in Fig. 11-2 — which operates like a barometer. The container is first completely evacuated of air and the mercury levels in the two arms of the manometer are then equal. If a sample of gas is now admitted into the container, mercury is forced down the left arm and up the right, and the difference in height (h) between the two mercury levels is a measure of the pressure of the gas in the container.

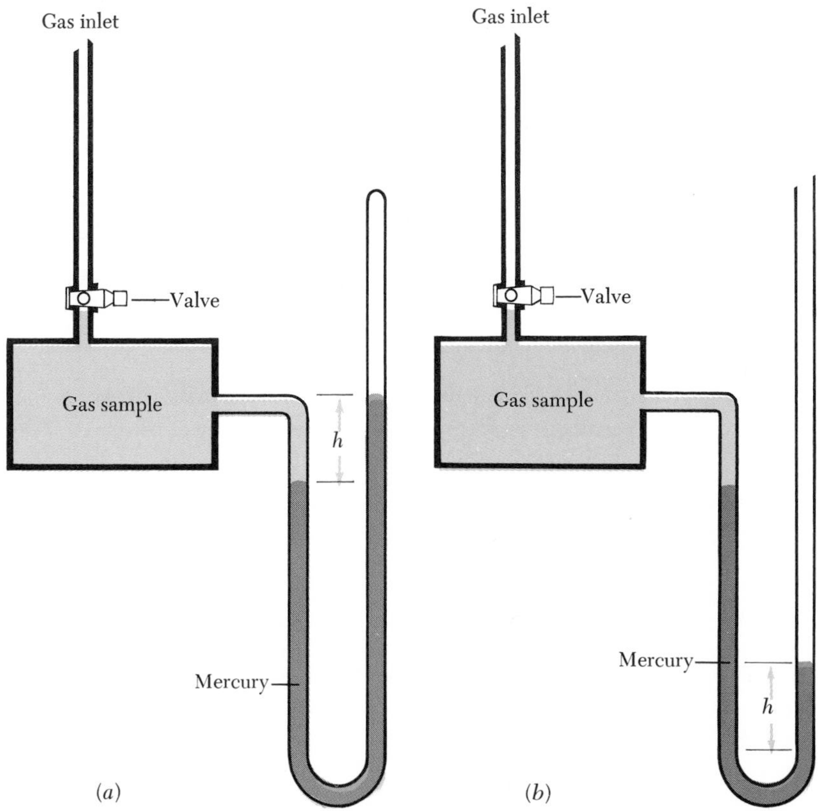

Fig. 11-2 (*a*) This is a closed-end manometer. The pressure of the gas is equal to the difference in height (mm of Hg) between the two columns. (*b*) This is an open-end manometer. The pressure of the gas is equal to atmospheric pressure (mm of Hg) minus the height (mm of Hg) of the long arm. Notice that both manometers show the same amount of pressure. Which kind of manometer would measure pressure greater than 1 atm?

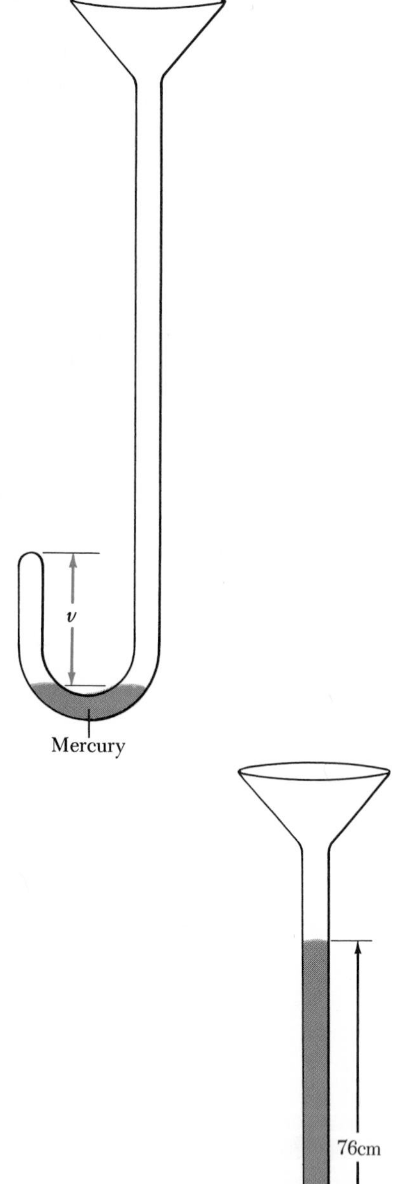

The Relationship between the Volume and the Pressure of a Gas

Boyle's Law

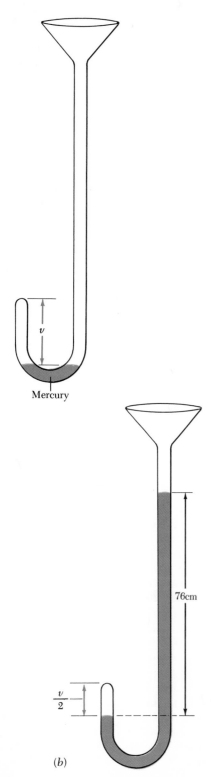

In 1660 a British scientist named Robert Boyle (1627–1691) investigated the changes that occur in the volume of a sample of air when the pressure exerted by the air is changed. For this purpose he used the simple device shown in Fig. 11-3. It is a J-shaped tube, the long arm of which is open and the short arm closed. If a small quantity of mercury is poured into the open arm, a definite quantity of gas is trapped in the closed arm, and if the mercury surfaces in the arms are at the same level, as shown in Fig. 11-3 (*a*), the pressure of the confined gas must be equal to the pressure of the atmosphere.

The volume of the gas column equals its length (or height) times the area of the cross section. Since the cross-sectional area is constant, the volume is proportional to the length; therefore the length (or height) of the gas column can be used as a measure of its volume. The symbol *V* in the diagram indicates this volume.

Boyle measured the height of the gas column when the levels of mercury in the two arms were the same. He then poured more mercury into the open tube and the levels of both mercury columns rose, but not at the same rate. The mercury column rose much faster in the open arm than in the closed arm. Can you explain why? In the situation shown in Fig. 11-3 (*b*) the volume of trapped gas has been halved, that is, its volume has been changed from V to $V/2$ and the distance (h) between the two mercury levels was found to be 30 inches. What did this indicate?

A length of 30 inches is equivalent to 760 mm, and therefore a 30-inch column of mercury exerts a pressure of 1 atmosphere or 760 torr. Hence the pressure exerted on the layer of mercury at *B* in the long arm is 2 atmospheres (1 atmosphere of pressure caused by the mercury column and 1 atmosphere pressure caused by air pressure

Fig. 11-3 Boyle's law apparatus. (*a*) The pressure of the confined volume (*V*) of gas is equal to atmospheric pressure (760 torr) Why? (*b*) If the difference between the two mercury columns is 76 cm, the volume is halved and the pressure is doubled. How much is this new pressure in mm of Hg? To answer this question, you must convert centimeters to millimeters. How much is this new pressure in torr?

on the mercury surface in the open tube). What then is the pressure of the confined gas on surface A, which is at the same level as B? The evidence proves that if the volume of a confined gas is diminished by one-half, the pressure of the gas is *increased* twofold (in this case from 1 atmosphere to 2 atmospheres).

Predict . . .
Could a relationship between volume and pressure have been established in Boyle's experiment had the temperature of the gas not been kept constant?

Boyle poured more mercury into the open tube until the volume of gas was reduced to one third of its original volume, and he found that the pressure of the trapped gas was increased to three times the original value. He then decreased the volume to one fourth of the original volume and found that the gas pressure was increased to four times its original value. Continuing in this way he eventually obtained enough data to indicate a pattern which pointed to a natural law. The law, now known as Boyle's Law, is usually stated: *The volume of a given mass of gas, kept at constant temperature, varies inversely as its pressure.*

Boyle's law can also be expressed in graphical form. For example, consider the set of data in Table 11-1, which is used to plot the graph in Fig. 11-4.

In the graph (Fig. 11-4), heights or relative volumes are plotted against the corresponding pressures. The curve is a hyperbola, and you may recall from your geometry that the equation for a hyperbola, is $xy = c$ (a constant). What exactly does this mean?

The Equation of Boyle's Law

Mathematically, Boyle's law can be expressed as

$$V \propto 1/P \qquad \text{or} \qquad P \times V = c$$

where c is a constant. Observe, in the third column in Table 11-1, that the product of all the pairs of values for P and V is a constant: 8.0. If P_1 and V_1 represent the original pressure and volume of a sample of gas, and P_2 and V_2 the final pressure and volume of the same sample, we can say P_1V_1 is a constant quantity, and P_2V_2 is the same constant. We may conclude, therefore, that

$$P_1V_1 = P_2V_2 \tag{11-1}$$

which is known as the Boyle's law equation.

The equation 11-1 can be used to solve volume–pressure gas problems such as Example 11-1.

Table 11-1
The product of P and V is constant

Height of gas column, cm V	×	Pressure of gas, atm P	=	Constant PV
8.0	×	1.00	=	8.0
6.0	×	1.33	=	8.0
4.0	×	2.00	=	8.0
3.0	×	2.67	=	8.0
2.0	×	4.00	=	8.0
1.0	×	8.00	=	8.0

Fig. 11-4 A graph showing how the volume of gas varies with the pressure when the temperature is constant.

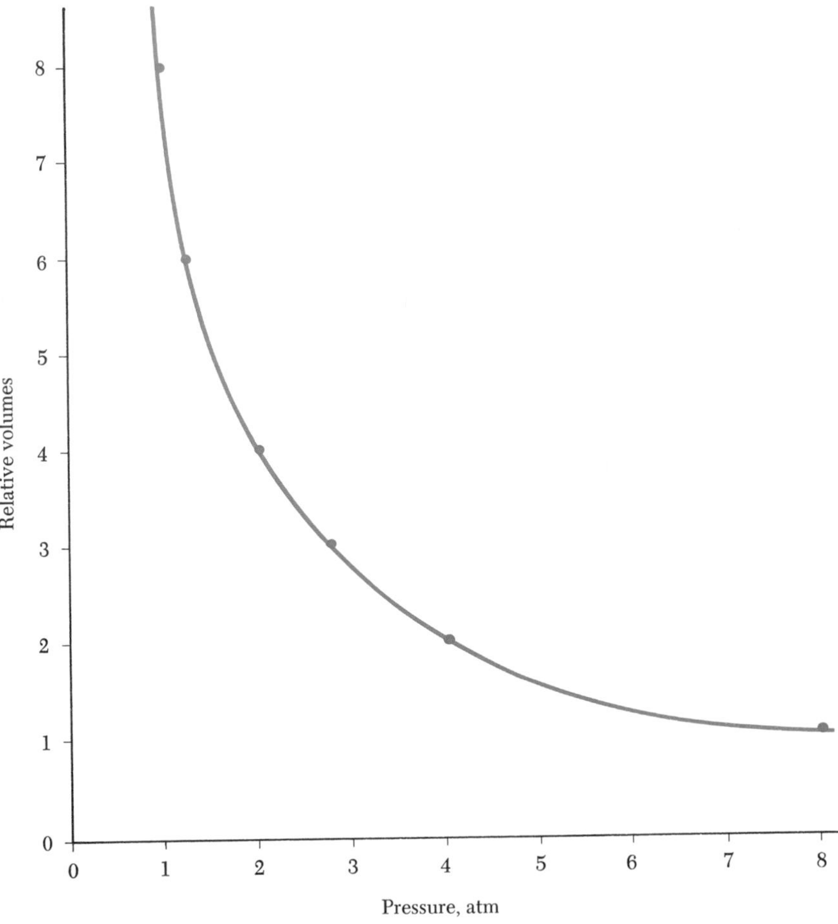

Fig. 11-5 A modification of Boyle's law apparatus. The pressure on the confined gas in the tube is changed as the height of reservoir of mercury is raised or lowered. Would raising the reservoir increase pressure?

Example 11-1

If the volume of a gas is 500 ml at normal pressure (760 torr), what will be its volume if the pressure is reduced to 730 torr?

Solution

$P_1 = 760$ torr, $V_1 = 500$ ml, and $P_2 = 730$ torr.

$$V_2 = \frac{P_1 V_1}{P_2}$$

$$= \frac{760 \text{ torr} \times 500 \text{ ml}}{730 \text{ torr}}$$

$$= 521 \text{ ml}$$

The problem can also be solved by common sense so that we do not have to depend upon a memorized formula. We can say that since the pressure is decreased from 760 torr to 730 torr the original volume (500 ml) is increased by a factor of 760/730; and

$$V_2 = 500 \text{ ml} \times 760/730 = 521 \text{ ml}$$

Definition . . .
To extrapolate means to extend the graph into a region where no data have been obtained.

Explain . . .
V plotted against *P* cannot be extrapolated through the origin. Can you explain why this statement is true? To answer this question, think what values *V* and *P* must have in order to be at the origin.

To Plot the Volume of a Confined Gas against the Reciprocal of its Pressure

Since the volume of a confined gas varies inversely as the pressure, it follows that *the volume varies directly as the reciprocal of the pressure.* This conclusion can be checked by using the data in Table 11-1 and drawing a graph of *V* plotted against $1/P$ (Fig. 11-6).

Notice that the graph is a straight line which, if extrapolated, approaches the origin. Mathematically, such a line means that the values on the vertical axis (the ordinate) are directly proportional to

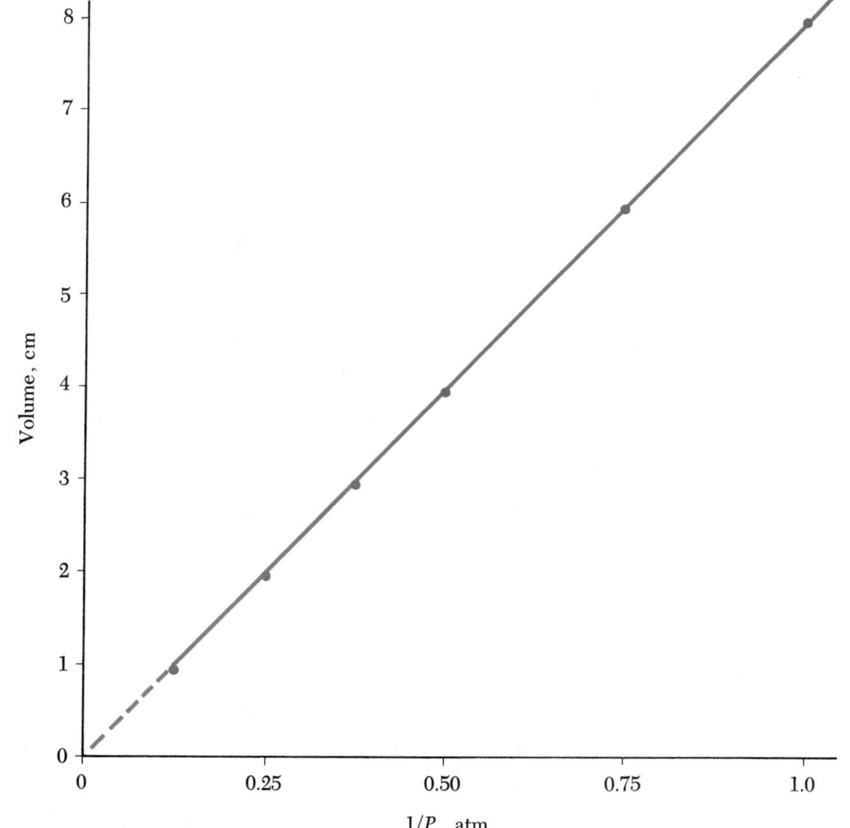

Fig. 11-6 A graph showing how the volume of a gas varies with the reciprocal of pressure when the temperature is constant.

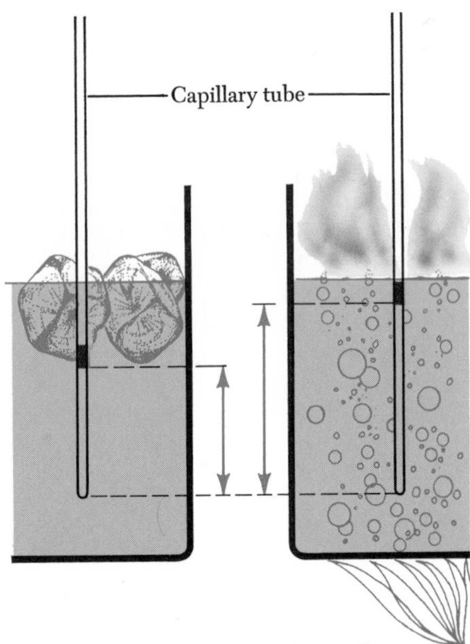

Fig. 11-7 What will happen to the height of the mercury pellet as the temperature of the gas in the capillary tube increases?

Table 11-2 Variation of relative volume of air column with temperature.

Temperature, °C	Length of air column, cm
0	24.2
40	27.8
70	30.4
100	33.1

the values on the horizontal axis (the abscissa), which confirms the above conclusion.

The Relationship between the Volume and Temperature of a Gas

Charles' Law

A French scientist named Jacques Charles (1746–1823) discovered that *all gases have the same coefficient of expansion.* A simple way to find the volume coefficient of expansion (α_v) of a gas (in this case air) is to use a capillary tube in which a small column of air is trapped between the closed end of the tube and a globule of mercury. If the capillary tube is immersed in a mixture of ice and water as shown in Fig. 11-7, the length of the air column can be measured at 0 °C. If the ice–water mixture is then slowly heated, the length of the air column can be determined at various temperatures. Table 11-2 is a typical set of readings obtained in such an experiment.

For a temperature rise of 40 C° the length of the air column increases by

$$27.8 \text{ cm} - 24.2 \text{ cm} = 3.6 \text{ cm}$$

By definition, the coefficient of volume expansion of a gas is the increase in volume per Celsius degree rise in temperature. Since the cross section is constant and volume is proportional to length, it follows that the coefficient of volume expansion is

$$\frac{3.6 \text{ cm}}{24.2 \text{ cm} \times 40 \text{ C}^\circ} = 0.00372/\text{C}^\circ$$

The volume coefficient of expansion can also be computed by using two other values for rise in temperature and increase in length. For example, if for a rise in temperature of 100 C°, the increase in length is 8.9 cm, the coefficient of volume expansion is

$$\frac{8.9 \text{ cm}}{24.2 \text{ cm} \times 100 \text{ C}^\circ} = 0.00368/\text{C}^\circ$$

The apparatus used by Charles was more elaborate than the capillary tube with its globule of mercury and, as a result, his experimental data were more accurate than those shown in Table 11-2. Actually, Charles found that the coefficient of expansion of a gas is 0.00366/C° or, expressed as a fraction, 1/273. Stated in words: *A gas expands by 1/273 of its volume at 0 °C for each Celsius degree that the temperature rises if the pressure remains constant.* This statement is known as *Charles' law.*

The Absolute or Kelvin Scale of Temperature

Let us now examine the volume–temperature relationship by means of a graph, using the data shown in Table 11-3. If these data are plotted on a graph, as is shown in Fig. 11-8, it is apparent that the four points lie on a straight line.

If the line were extrapolated downwards, it would cut the temperature axis at $-273\,°C$. This suggests that if the gas remained as a gas throughout this temperature range, its volume would become zero at $-273\,°C$.

Charles' law can also be stated: *At constant pressure a gas contracts by 1/273 of its volume at 0°C for each Celsius degree that the temperature falls.* Thus, if the temperature continued to fall, the volume of the gas theoretically would become zero at $-273\,°C$. In practice however, all gases liquefy before this temperature is reached. Moreover, a temperature of—273 °C has never quite been reached, although modern techniques have enabled scientists to come within a fraction of a degree of it. Nonetheless. this is clearly an important temperature and it is called the *absolute zero* of temperature.

Table 11-3 Variation of gaseous volume with temperature at constant pressure.

Temperature, °C	Volume of gas, ml
50	173
100	200
150	226
250	254

Speculate . . .
What might *absolute zero* mean? For example, temperature is a measure of kinetic energy. Might all molecular motion of any kind (such as the rotation of electrons) stop at absolute zero? Can matter have an absolute zero state of energy?

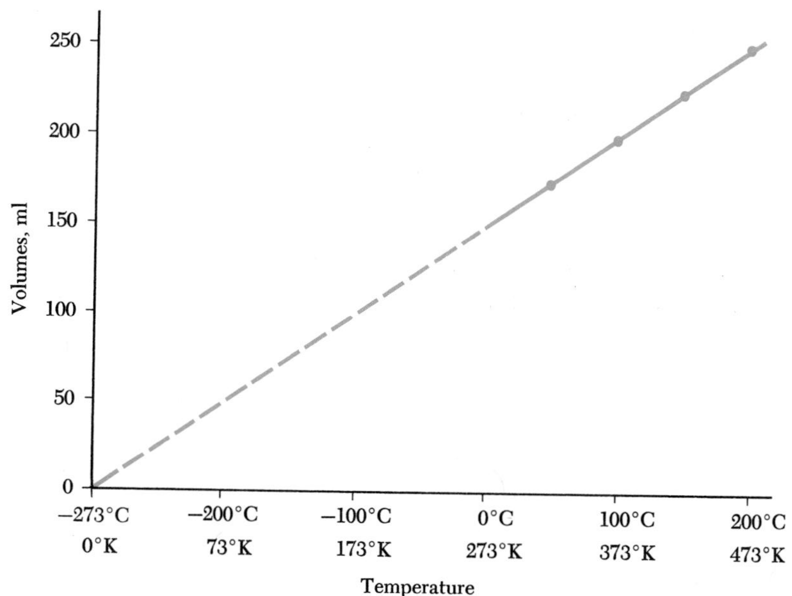

Fig. 11-8 How does the volume of a gas vary with changes in temperature if pressure is constant?

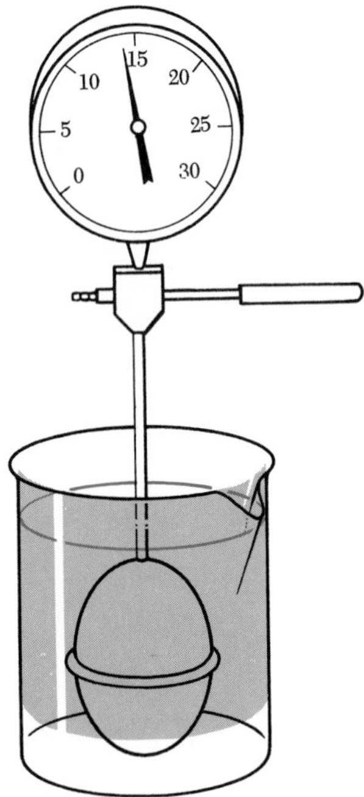

Fig. 11-9 Gay-Lussac apparatus used to determine an experimental value for absolute zero. Varying the temperature of the metal bulb having a fixed volume and containing a fixed amount of air causes corresponding changes in pressure in lb/in². If the pressure changes are plotted against temperature changes, a zero pressure value can be extrapolated. An experimental value for absolute zero is, then, obtained.

To permit convenient use of this concept, a new temperature scale was devised: $-273\,°C$ is the zero point and the degrees are the same size as those on the Celsius scale. This scale is called the *absolute* or *Kelvin* scale in honor of the British scientist Lord Kelvin (1824–1907), who first suggested that $-273\,°C$ was the lowest possible temperature. The letter K or A is used to signify temperatures on this scale. From the relationship $-273°C = 0°K$, it should be apparent that to convert a Celsius temperature to an absolute temperature, the number 273 must be added to the Celsius reading. Thus,

$$100\,°C = 373\,°K \qquad \text{and} \qquad -30\,°C = 243\,°K$$

Conversely, to convert absolute temperature to Celsius, 273 must be subtracted from the absolute reading. For example, $200\,°K = -73\,°C$. A comparison of some absolute and Celsius temperatures is shown in Fig. 11-10.

Notice that temperatures are marked in absolute as well as Celsius degrees in the graph (Fig. 11-8). If we think of 0°K as the origin, then the graph is a straight line which passes through the origin, and therefore *the volume of a gas (at constant pressure) is proportional to its absolute temperature.* This statement is the usual way of expressing Charles' law.

The Equation of Charles' Law

Charles' law can be expressed *mathematically* as $V \propto T$, where V is the volume of a gas and T the absolute temperature. Therefore,

$$V = T \times k \qquad \textit{or} \qquad V/T = k$$

where k is a constant.

If a gas of volume V_1 at absolute temperature T_1 is heated at constant pressure to absolute temperature T_2,, it expands to a new volume V_2. Thus, V_1/T_1 is a constant and V_2/T_2 is the same constant. Therefore,

$$\frac{V_1}{T_1} = \frac{V_2}{T_2} \qquad \text{or} \qquad \frac{V_1}{V_2} = \frac{T_1}{T_2}$$

Either of these Charles' law equations can be used to solve problems that involve temperature and volume changes. One such problem follows.

Note . . .
The famous physicist Lord Kelvin was not born to this title. His work was done under the name of William Thomson.

Example 11-2

What would be the new volume of hydrogen at 150 °C if its volume is 1.63 l at −10°C? Assume that the pressure remains constant.

Solution

First, the Celsius temperatures must be changed to Kelvin temperatures.

$T_1 = -10\ °C = 263\ °K$

$T_2 = 150\ °C = 423\ °K.$

$V_1 = 1.63\ l$

$$V_2 = \frac{T_2}{T_1} \times V_1$$

$$= \frac{423\ °K}{263\ °K} \times 1.63\ l$$

$$= 2.62\ l$$

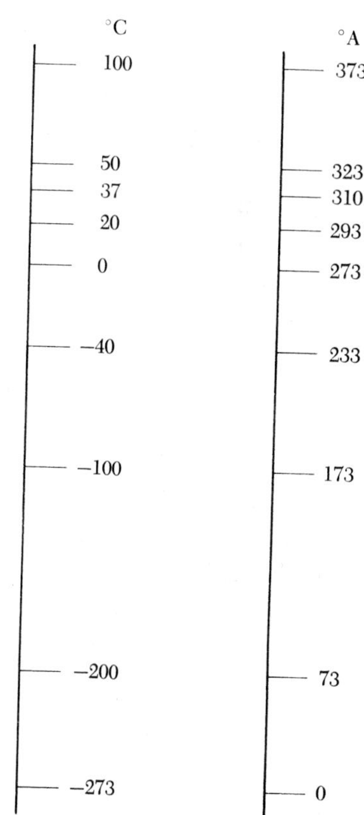

Fig. 11-10 A comparison between Celsius and absolute temperature scales.

The situation we have considered concerns the changes in volume and temperature of a gas at constant pressure. Suppose, however, the gas is kept in a container at constant volume. What will happen if the temperature is raised? Clearly, if the temperature is raised and the volume kept constant, the pressure of the gas will be increased. Indeed, it can be shown that *at constant volume the pressure of a gas increases by 1/273 of its pressure at 0°C* for each Celsius degree rise in temperature. This statement is another version of Charles' law which is usually expressed: *The pressure of a sample of a gas at constant volume varies as its absolute temperature.*

In mathematical terms, this statement of the law can be written as

$$P \propto T$$

Hence, P/T is a constant, and therefore

$$\frac{P_1}{T_1} = \frac{P_2}{T_2} \quad \text{or} \quad \frac{P_1}{P_2} = \frac{T_1}{T_2}$$

Fig. 11-11 The relationship between temperature and volume can be indicated using this apparatus. Changes in volume (indicated by the syringe) plotted against change in temperature can roughly determine at what temperature the air in the flask would theoretically be zero. Can a gas ever occupy no volume at all?

This is called the pressure–temperature equation, and it is used to solve problems like in Example 11-3.

Example 11-3

Suppose the original pressure and temperature of a gas in a container are 750 torr and 22 °C. To what temperature must the gas be heated so that it will exert a pressure of 1400 torr?

Solution 1

$$T_1 = 22\,°\text{C} + 273 = 295\,°\text{K}$$

$$T_2 = \frac{P_2}{P_1} \times T_1$$

$$= \frac{1400\text{ torr} \times 295\,°\text{K}}{750\text{ torr}} = 550\,°\text{K} \quad \text{or} \quad 277\,°\text{C}$$

Solution 2

The problem can be solved from first principles without using a formula. Since the gas pressure is increased from 750 torr to 1400 torr, the absolute temperature must be raised by a factor of 1400/750. Therefore, the final absolute temperature is

$$T_2 = 1400/750 \times 295\,°\text{K}$$

$$= 550\,°\text{K}$$

The Combined Gas Law

Sometimes changes in volume, pressure, and temperature all occur at the same time. You may recall that one of the rules of proportionality states that if a certain quantity (x) is proportional to two other quantities (y and z) then x is also proportional to the product of y and z ($x \propto y \times z$). In the gas laws, V is proportional to T and $1/P$. That is,

$$V \propto \frac{T}{P} \quad \text{and hence } V = \frac{T}{P} \times k$$

where k is a constant. Or,

$$\frac{PV}{T} = k$$

If the specific values are P_1, V_1, and T_1,

$$\frac{P_1V_1}{T_1} = k$$

and if the values are P_2, V_2, and T_2,

$$\frac{P_2V_2}{T_2} = k$$

Therefore,

$$\frac{P_1V_1}{T_1} = \frac{P_2V_2}{T_2} \qquad (11\text{-}2)$$

which is known as the *combined gas law equation.*

Units in Computations

It should be emphasized that both numbers and units are involved in the solution of gas law problems. This also applies to all kinds of chemical problems. Let us see why. There are two essential factors in any particular quantity, (1) the number itself and (2) the units of the properties with which we are dealing. A particular mass, for example, might be 10 g, or 10 kg, or 10 lb. And the same algebraic processes that apply to numbers apply also to units. That is, units can be multiplied and divided, or even added and subtracted. A computation involving numbers is usually complicated enough to require a slide rule. But a computation of units is very simple and usually involves only a dividing out of similar units. Thus, if a mass is being determined, the unit left after dividing out should be grams, or kilograms, or pounds. But if the calculation shows mass expressed in centimeters (a wrong unit), then clearly there has been an error in setting up the problem. In other words, by using units an error of this kind is revealed. That is why it is important to use units in all computations. The role of units is illustrated in the solution to Example 11-4.

Example 11-4

What is the mass of 250 ml of mercury expressed in (*a*) grams (*b*) kilograms (*c*) pounds, given the density of mercury as 13.6 g/ml?

Solution

(*a*) $\text{density} = \dfrac{\text{mass}}{\text{volume}} \quad \text{or} \quad M = D \times V$

$$\therefore M = \frac{13.6\ \text{g}}{\cancel{\text{ml}}} \times 250\ \cancel{\text{ml}}$$

$$= 3400\ \text{g}$$

Notice that similar units (ml) divide out and that the the computed unit of mass is in grams.

(*b*) The conversion factor is 1 kg/1000 g.

$$M = 3400\ \cancel{\text{g}} \times \frac{1\ \text{kg}}{1000\ \cancel{\text{g}}}$$

$$= 3.40\ \text{kg}$$

Again similar units (g) divide out.

(*c*) The conversion factor here is 2.20 lb/kg.

$$M = 3.40\ \cancel{\text{kg}} \times \frac{2.20\ \text{lb}}{\cancel{\text{kg}}}$$

$$= 7.48\ \text{lb}$$

The overall solution is

$$M = \frac{13.6\ \cancel{\text{g}}}{\cancel{\text{ml}}} \times 250\ \cancel{\text{ml}} \times \frac{1\ \cancel{\text{kg}}}{1000\ \cancel{\text{g}}} \times \frac{2.20\ \text{lb}}{\cancel{\text{kg}}}$$

$$= 7.48\ \text{lb}$$

The Gas Constant

Recall . . .
STP stands for *standard temperature and pressure.* What does this mean?

Let us now apply both the gas laws and Avogadro's hypothesis to a given number of moles of gas, say n moles. According to Avogadro, one mole of any gas at STP occupies 22.4 l. The total gas volume is proportional to the number of moles, or $V \propto n$. However, Charles' Law states that $V \propto T$ and Boyle's Law states that $V \propto 1/P$. Therefore

$$V = R \times n \times T \times \frac{1}{P}$$

where R is the proportionality constant, called the *gas constant*. The equation

$$PV = nRT \qquad (11\text{-}3)$$

is known as the perfect gas law since it applies only to gases at low pressures and high temperatures.

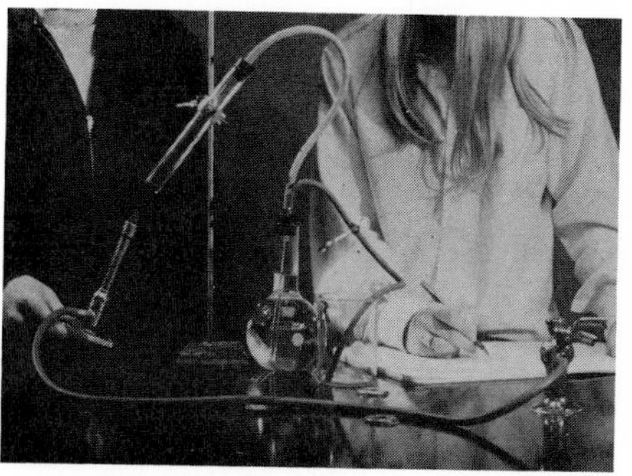

Fig. 11-12 The general gas constant can be calculated using this apparatus in which oxygen is being produced by the decomposition of a known amount of potassium chlorate. The number of moles (n) of oxygen produced, oxygen's pressure (atmospheric pressure), its volume (ml of water displaced), and its temperature (room temperature) can be calculated in order to compute R.

What are the units of R? Rearranging the expression it becomes $R = PV/nT$. If P is measured in atmospheres, V in liters, n in moles, and T in degrees absolute, the units of R are liter-atmospheres/mole-degree.

What is the numerical value of the gas constant R? From Avogadro we know that one mole of any gas occupies 22.4 l at STP. Substituting the values of STP in Eq. 11-3, we find that

$$R = \frac{1 \text{ atm} \times 22.4 \text{ l}}{1 \text{ mole} \times 273\ °\text{K}}$$

$$= 0.0821 \text{ liter-atmosphere/mole-degree}$$

This value of R applies to all gases; it is an important gas constant which has many applications. For example, it can be used to determine the molecular masses of gases *directly* rather than from their molar volumes as was discussed in Chapter 10.

Example 11-5

Find the molecular mass of carbon dioxide from the given data, using the gas law.

The data: $V = 0.297$ l;

$T = 22 + 273 = 295\ °\text{K}$; $P = 766$ torr or

766/760 atmosphere = 1.01 atm;

the mass of the sample is 0.545 g.

Solution

$$n = \frac{PV}{RT}$$

$$= \frac{1.01 \text{ atm} \times 0.297 \text{ l}}{0.0821 \text{ l-atm/mole-°K} \times 295\text{°K}}$$

$$= 0.0124 \text{ mole}$$

From this we know that the 0.545 g of carbon dioxide contains 0.0124 mole. Hence,

$$1 \text{ mole} = \frac{0.545 \text{ g}}{0.0124 \text{ mole}}$$

$$= 44.0 \text{ g/mole}$$

Therefore the molecular mass of carbon dioxide is 44.0 amu.

Summary

Gas pressure is the force exerted by a gas per unit area of surface. Atmospheric pressure is measured by a barometer; gas pressure is measured by a manometer. However, in both these devices pressure is usually expressed in millimeters of mercury or torr.

Boyle investigated the volume-pressure relationship of gases. Boyle's law states that at constant temperature the pressure and volume of a definite mass of gas are inversely related; if one increases, the other decreases by a corresponding amount. Mathematically, Boyle's law can be expressed as $PV =$ a constant.

Charles investigated the volume–temperature relationship of a gas. Charles' law states that at constant pressure all gases expand (or contract) by the same fraction of their volume at 0 °C when heated (or cooled) through the same range of temperature. Mathematically, Charles' law can be expressed as $V/T =$ a constant

A graph of a volume of gas versus temperature upon extrapolation crosses the temperature axis at −273 °C. This temperature (−273 °C) is called the absolute zero of temperature (0 °K).

The three gas law equations are

(1) Boyle's (at constant temperature) $P_1V_1 = P_2V_2$

(2) Charles' (at constant pressure) $\frac{V_1}{V_2} = \frac{T_1}{T_2}$

(3) Charles' (at constant volume) $\frac{P_1}{P_2} = \frac{T_1}{T_2}$

These equations can be combined to give the combined gas law equation

$$\frac{P_1V_1}{T_1} = \frac{P_2V_2}{T_2}$$

Applying Avogadro's law to the combined gas equation we may derive the perfect gas law

$$PV = nRT$$

where R, the gas constant, is 0.0821 l-atm/mole-°K.

Factual Recall

1. What holds up the mercury in a Torricelli barometer?
2. How does a manometer differ from a barometer?
3. Explain how the pressure of a gas can be determined by a manometer?
4. Draw a Boyle's law curve and explain what it means.
5. Describe an experiment which verifies Charles' law.
6. (*a*) Draw a graph to illustrate Charles' law. (*b*) What does it mean? (*c*) Is extrapolation of this graph necessary? (*d*) Is extrapolation of this graph justifiable?
7. What is meant by the statement "All gases have the same coefficent of expansion"?
8. Why is the Kelvin scale useful?
9. Derive the combined gas law equation from the equations that express Boyle's law and Charles' law.

Apply Your Knowledge!

1. The boiling points of the following liquids are: helium, −269°C; hydrogen, −253 °C; oxygen, −183 °C; carbon monox-

ide, −192°C; neon, −246°C; chlorine, −35°C. Express each of these temperatures on the Kelvin scale.

2. The freezing points of the following liquids are: hydrogen, 14°K; nitrogen, 63°K; chlorine, 166°K; ammonia, 240°K. Express each of these temperatures on the Celsius scale.
3. The volume of gas is 2.24 l at 380 torr and 273°C. Find the volume at STP.
4. Find the volume of a gas at 1520 torr and 25 °C if its volume is 2.00 l at 760 torr and 25 °C.
5. A volume of 500 ml of hydrogen is collected at 25°C and 760 torr pressure. The temperature drops to 10°C and the volume is kept constant by adjusting the pressure. What is the final pressure of the hydrogen?
6. A volume of gas is 900 ml at a temperature of 27°C. If the temperature of the gas increases 50 C° at a constant pressure, what would be the new volume of the gas?
7. The volume of a gas is 150 l when the pressure is 760 torr and the temperature is 20°C, and becomes 200 l when the pressure is raised to 1000 torr. Calculate the final temperature.
8. The pressure of a gas in a sealed flask at 20°C is increased from 700 torr to 1000 torr by raising the temperature. Find the final temperature of the gas.
9. A helium sample, 100 ml in volume at STP, is subjected to a temperature of 136.5°C and a pressure of 570 torr. Find its new volume.
10. A gas is heated from 136.5°K to 136.5°C, the pressure remaining constant. Calculate the final volume if the initial volume is 100 ml.
11. A sample of carbon dioxide at STP was heated to 273°C and, at the same time, the pressure was doubled. Find the new volume of the gas if the initial volume was 3.65 l.

Find Out!

Look up a discussion of "perfect" or "ideal" gases in a physics or college chemistry text.

CHAPTER 12

The Kinetic Molecular Theory

THE FOLLOWING LIST is a summary of the postulates of the *Kinetic Molecular Theory*:

(1) Gases are composed of molecules which are relatively far apart.

(2) Gas molecules are always in motion. Their speeds depend upon temperature; the higher the temperature of the gas the greater are the speeds of the molecules.

(3) Gas molecules collide with each other and with the walls of their containers, and when they collide both their direction and speed are changed. Hence gas molecules travel in all directions and at different speeds; that is, their motion is said to be random.

(4) The collisions of gas molecules are frictionless so that no energy is lost as heat. Such collisions are said to be perfectly *elastic*. Therefore, although the speeds of molecules are changed (increased or decreased) by collisions, the total kinetic energy of the colliding molecules is the same after the impact as it was before.

Infer and Evaluate . . .

The idea that the behavior of gases could be explained in terms of the motion of molecules occurred to several people over a span of some 100 years; such as D. Bernoulli in 1738, J. P. Joule in 1851, and A. Kronig in 1856. The theory was developed in detail following 1858 by R. J. E. Clausius, J. C. Maxwell, L. Boltzmann and others. What implications about a theory's development might you draw from the history of this one idea?

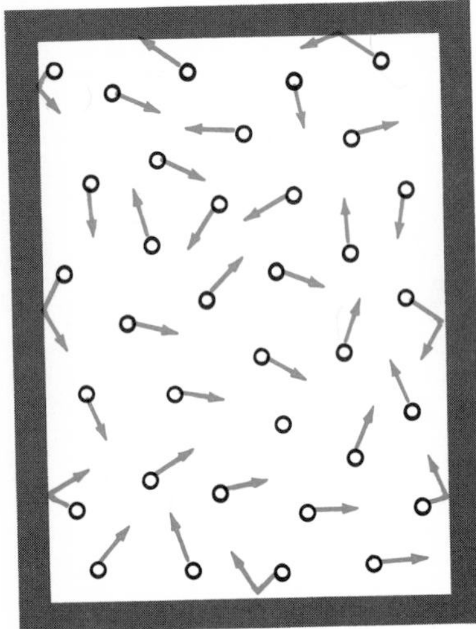

Fig. 12-1 Gas pressure is due to the bombardment of a surface by moving molecules.

How does the kinetic molecular theory account for Boyle's law, Charles' law, and Avogadro's law?

Boyle's Law and the Kinetic Theory

If a gas is enclosed in a container, the moving molecules strike the walls of the container and rebound as shown in Fig. 12-1. At the moment of impact each molecule exerts only a tiny force upon the wall. But, since there are billions of collisions per square centimeter of surface every second, the actual pressure (force per unit area) is considerable.

Let us now imagine a situation in which a certain volume (V) of gas is enclosed in a cylinder with a gas-tight movable piston as shown in Fig. 12-2 (*a*). The gas pressure P is determined by the number of molecular impacts on the underside of the piston. Suppose the piston is now pushed down so that the volume of the gas is halved; that is, the volume now becomes $V/2$ as shown in Fig. 12-2 (*b*). How does this affect the gas pressure? The numbers of molecules in (*b*) and (*a*) are the same, but in (*b*) they occupy only half the space occupied in (*a*). Hence the rate of molecular bombardment is doubled and therefore the gas pressure is doubled; that is, it is now $2P$.

Let us now return to the situation as shown in Fig. 12-2 (*a*), but this time the piston is raised until the gas volume is twice the original volume, or $2V$ as shown in Fig. 12-2 (*c*). What is the pressure in this case? In (*c*) there are only half the number of molecules per unit volume as in (*a*). Hence in (*c*) only half as many molecules strike each unit area of surface as in (*a*), and therefore the gas pressure in case (*c*) is $P/2$. These results are listed in Table 12-1 and verify Boyle's law.

Table 12-1 Relation of gas pressure to volume

Gas volume	Gas pressure
V	P
$V/2$	$2P$
$2V$	$P/2$

Charles' Law and the Kinetic Theory

As stated earlier, gas molecules do not move at the same speed even at the same temperature; some move faster than others. Therefore, at a given temperature there is a considerable variation in the kinetic energy of individual molecules, as is shown in Fig. 12-3. However, since there is a vast number of molecules in even a small volume, we are concerned with *average* kinetic energy. One

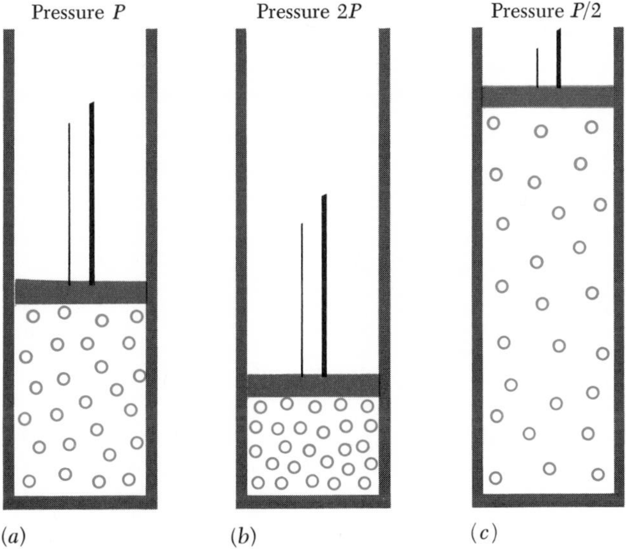

Fig. 12-2 The volume of a gas varies inversely with pressure.

of the fundamental assumptions of the kinetic theory is that all gas molecules, even different kinds of molecules, have the same average kinetic energy at the same temperature. This means for example that for two different gases, $\frac{1}{2} m_1 v_1^2 = \frac{1}{2} m_2 v_2^2$ where m_1 and m_2 are the masses of different molecules and v_1 and v_2 are their velocities. It is therefore apparent that if the different molecules have the same kinetic energy, the lighter molecules must travel faster than the heavier ones. As a result, the lighter molecules strike the walls of the container more frequently than the heavier and slower molecules, but that the total bombarding effect of the two kinds of molecules is the same.

If the temperature of a particular gas is raised, the average speed of its molecules is increased and therefore its average kinetic energy is also increased. In other words, *the absolute temperature of a gas is a measure of the average kinetic energy of the individual gas molecules*. Why is the absolute temperature used rather than the Celsius temperature? If the temperature of a gas were to fall continuously, the average speed of the molecules would also decrease continuously, until eventually the molecules would have an absolute minimum of energy. The temperature at which this would happen is absolute zero. Hence, in terms of the kinetic theory, the absolute zero of temperature is that temperature at which molecules would have lost all of the heat they possibly could lose. The absolute zero is therefore the lowest temperature attainable; it is

Fig. 12-3 At a given temperature there is a wide variation in the kinetic energies of gas molecules.

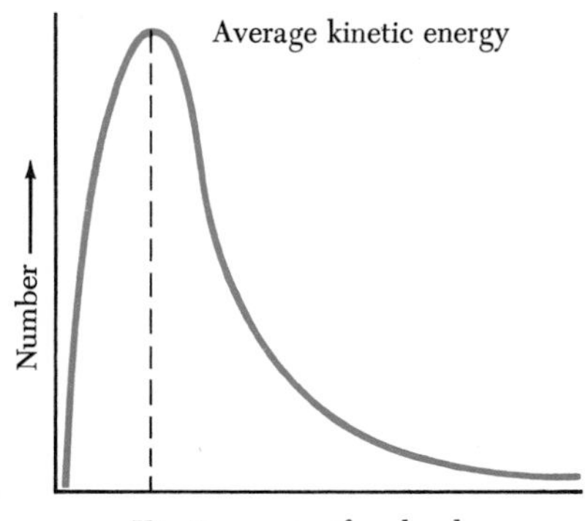

Note . . .
It is a popular misconception that all molecular motion would cease at absolute zero. In fact, at this temperature molecules are locked in the lowest allowed energy level of vibration.

the natural zero of temperature; it is the temperature at which, in principle at least, both the pressure and volume of a gas would be zero. Thus it is that *the volume of a gas (at constant pressure) or the pressure (at constant volume) is proportional to the temperature on the absolute scale.* This is a statement of Charles' law.

Avogadro's Law and the Kinetic Theory

Consider the situation where two vessels of the same volume contain different gases, A and B, at the same temperature and pressure. The pressure of each gas depends upon two factors: (1) the average kinetic energy per molecule, and (2) the number of molecules in each vessel. However, since the temperatures of the gases are the same, the kinetic energy for gas A is the same as for gas B. And, since the gas pressures in the two vessels are alike, the number of gas molecules in vessel A must be precisely the same as the number in vessel B. Hence, *two equal volumes of different gases at the same temperature and pressure contain the same number of molecules.* This is a statement of Avogadro's law.

Gas Diffusion

Calculate . . .
How many miles per hour is 4.5×10^4 cm/sec?

Because of their motion, gas molecules readily occupy any space that is available to them. This spreading into space is a characteristic property of all gas molecules; it is called *diffusion.* How fast do gas molecules move? That is, what is their rate of diffusion? It can be shown that, at ordinary temperatures, molecules of air (oxygen and nitrogen) have average speeds of almost 4.5×10^4 cm/sec. Although this is a very high *speed,* we must remember that the *directions* of the molecules are constantly changing. There are billions of molecules of oxygen and nitrogen in every milliliter of air. Moreover, these molecules undergo countless collisions so that they follow a zig-zag path as shown in Fig. 12-4. As a result, their forward progress is slowed down.

Fig. 12-4 A gas molecule follows a zig-zag path because it collides with other molecules.

Let us apply the kinetic theory to the problem of diffusion. First, let us compare the rates of diffusion of hydrogen and oxygen. If v_H and m_H represent the average velocity and mass of a hydrogen molecule and v_0 and m_0 the corresponding symbols for an oxygen molecule, we know that, at a given temperature,

$$\tfrac{1}{2} m_H v_H^2 = \tfrac{1}{2} m_O v_O^2$$

Hence,

$$\frac{v_H^2}{v_O^2} = \frac{m_O}{m_H} \quad \text{or} \quad \frac{v_H}{v_O} = \sqrt{\frac{m_O}{m_H}}$$

But the molecular masses of oxygen and hydrogen are (approximately) 32 and 2 respectively. Therefore,

$$\frac{v_H}{v_O} = \sqrt{\frac{32}{2}} = \frac{4}{1}$$

That is, according to the kinetic theory, hydrogen molecules move four times as fast as oxygen molecules at the same temperature. This deduction from the theory has been confirmed repeatedly by experiments.

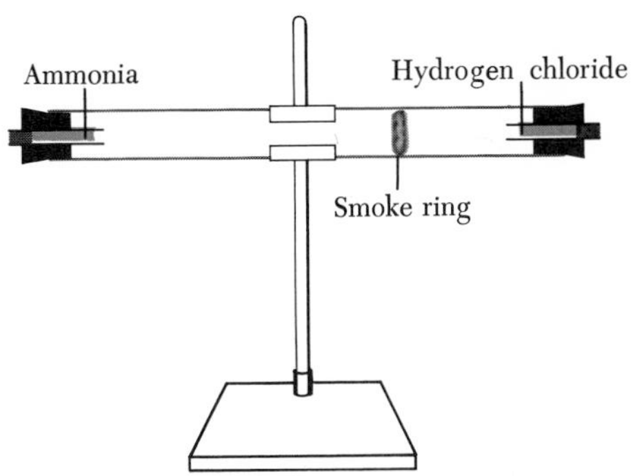

Fig. 12-5 Molecules of ammonia move more than half the length of the tube before they meet and react with molecules of hydrogen chloride. Why?

Graham's Law of Diffusion

Actually, the relationship between the velocities of gases and their molecular masses was investigated in 1830 by an English scientist named Thomas Graham (1805–1869), about 30 years before the kinetic theory was propounded. Graham discovered a fundamental law of diffusion which states: *The rates of diffusion of gases are inversely proportional to the square roots of their molecular masses.*

Applying Graham's law to the rates of diffusion (v) of NH_3 and HCl, we can say

$$v_{NH_3} \propto \frac{1}{\sqrt{\text{mol. mass of } NH_3}} \quad \text{and} \quad v_{HCl} \propto \frac{1}{\sqrt{\text{mol. mass of HCl}}}$$

$$\frac{v_{NH_3}}{v_{HCl}} \propto \sqrt{\frac{\text{mol. mass HCl}}{\text{mol. mass } NH_3}} \propto \sqrt{\frac{36.5}{17}} \propto \sqrt{2.14} \propto \frac{1.46}{1}$$

Hence the rate of diffusion of ammonia is 1.46 times as fast as the diffusion rate of hydrogen chloride.

The Law of Partial Pressures

In a mixture of gases the pressure exerted by each gas is called the *partial pressure* of that particular gas. Dalton discovered that each gas in a mixture of gases exerts the same pressure that it would if it

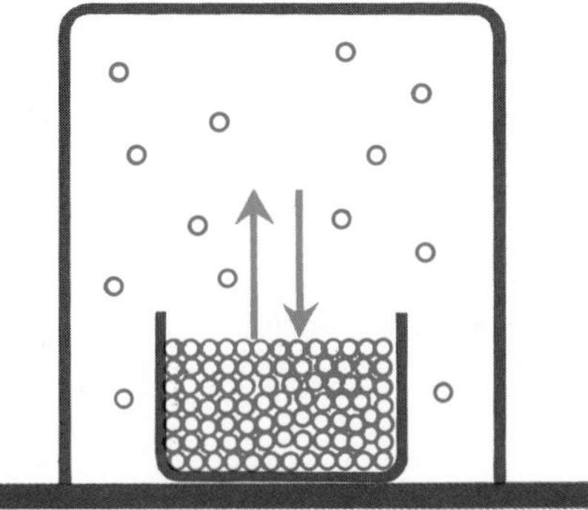

Fig. 12-6 At equilibrium the rate of evaporation equals the rate of condensation.

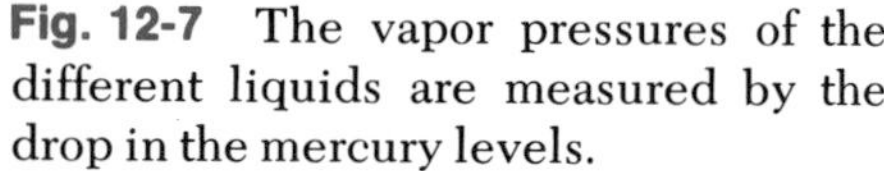

Fig. 12-7 The vapor pressures of the different liquids are measured by the drop in the mercury levels.

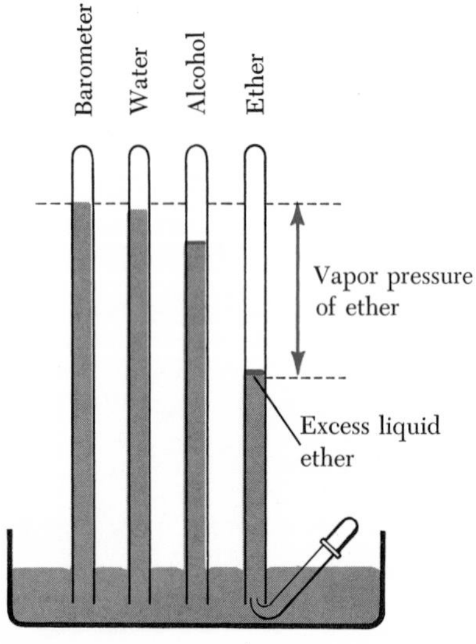

were alone in its container, and *that the total pressure of the gas mixture is the sum of the partial pressures exerted by each of the constitutents.* This is known as the *law of partial pressures.* Thus air is a mixture of roughly, nitrogen 78%, oxygen 21%, and argon 1%. If the total pressure is 760 torr, the partial pressure of nitrogen is 593 torr (760 torr × 0.78). Similarly, the partial pressure of oxygen is 160 torr (760 torr × 0.21), and the partial pressure of argon is 8 torr (760 × 0.01).

The kinetic theory also offers a simple explanation of the law of partial pressures. According to the kinetic theory there are relatively large distances between gas molecules and therefore we would expect each gas molecule to behave independently of all others, and to contribute its own particular share of the total pressure.

Vapor Pressure of Water

Imagine that a battery jar is placed over a beaker of water as shown in Fig. 12-6. Molecules of water will evaporate to fill the space enclosed by the jar. During evaporation, molecules of water escape into the closed space above the water surface, thereby becoming molecules of water vapor, which is a gas. If these molecules strike the surface of the water, one of two things will happen: (1) some will rebound, thereby creating a pressure on the surface, and (2) others will break the surface, and re-enter the water. When vapor molecules re-enter water we say that molecules in the gaseous phase become molecules in the liquid phase, a process called *condensation.* Eventually, the rate of condensation catches up with the rate of evaporation, and a condition of *equilibrium* is said to exist between water and water vapor. The space above the water is then *saturated* with water vapor at that particular temperature, and the pressure exerted by the water vapor at saturation is called its *vapor pressure.* Therefore, we can say: *The vapor pressure of a liquid is the pressure the vapor exerts when the liquid and vapor phases are in equilibrium.* It is important to observe that, at equilibrium, the rate of evaporation is the same as the rate of condensation, so that these opposing processes produce no net measurable effect. Moreover, you probably know that during evaporation heat is absorbed (causing a drop in temperature) and during condensation heat is released (causing a drop in temperature). At equilibrium these effects neutralize each other; there is no net temperature change.

Let us now consider a specific example. If the temperature of the water in the beaker is 20°C, the pressure exerted by the vapor steadily increases until it is equivalent to 18 mm of mercury, when it remains constant. That is, the vapor pressure of water at 20°C is 18 torr. The pressure of the vapor is a specific property of the water so that it is the same whether it is measured in air or in a vacuum. Vapor pressure can readily be demonstrated and even measured by using a mercury barometer, as shown in Fig. 12-7.

If the opening of a medicine dropper, which contains water, is held just below the end of the barometer tube, a slight squeeze of the bulb causes a few drops of water to rise up the mercury column. When the water reaches the space above the mercury, some water collects as a layer of liquid on top of the mercury column, and some of it vaporizes, thereby saturating the space with water vapor. At the same time the mercury column in the tube falls about 2 centimeters. Here, then, is a condition of equilibrium between water and water vapor inside the barometer tube, and the depression of the mercury column is a measure of the vapor pressure at this temperature.

Pressure of a Gas Collected over Water

If a graduated tube is filled with water and then inverted with the open end under water in a beaker, the water still completely fills the tube. If a gas, hydrogen for example, is now bubbled into the tube, water is displaced and the hydrogen collected as shown in Fig. 12-8. Let us consider the case where the water levels inside and outside the tube are alike, the temperature of the gas is 20°C, and the barometric reading is 750 torr. Since the hydrogen was bubbled through water, the space in the tube is saturated with water vapor. And, further, since the inside and outside water levels are equal, the sum of the partial pressures of hydrogen (P_H) and water vapor (P_W) must be equal to the pressure of the atmosphere (P_A). Or, in symbols,

$$P_A = P_H + P_W$$

Therefore,

$$P_H = P_A - P_W = 750 \text{ torr} - 18 \text{ torr} = 732 \text{ torr}$$

Fig. 12-8 The pressures of hydrogen and water vapor equal the pressure of the atmosphere.

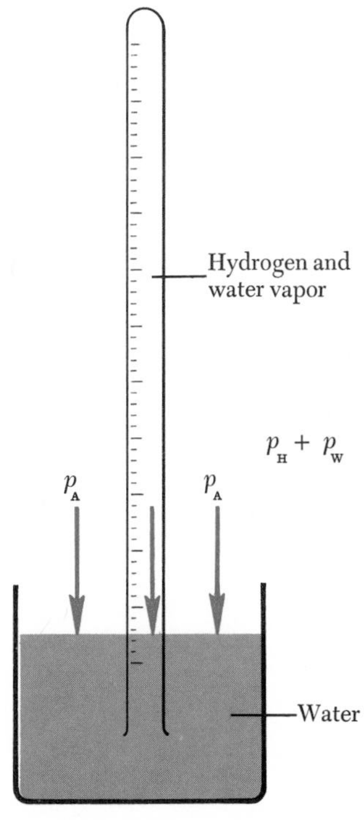

Deviations from the Gas Laws

Since all gases condense to form liquids or solids and since this in itself constitutes a deviation of the gas from the behavior predicted by the gas laws, it is reasonable to expect that all gases, even before they condense, will deviate from the gas laws. There are several ways in which gases deviate somewhat from the properties one would expect from the gas laws and the kinetic theory. In other words, the behavior of *real* gases is not perfect or, as we usually say, *ideal*. Why is it that the actual properties of gases are not quite the same as the predicted properties? Do some of the postulates of the kinetic theory need to be modified? Actually gas molecules attract each other and they also occupy space. But the kinetic theory makes no mention of these factors.

It is true that PV is *almost* a constant at pressures of 1 atm or less, but if the gas is subjected to high pressures, say pressures of 5 to 10 atm, PV is certainly not a constant. How can this be explained? Remember that PV=constant is explained by the kinetic theory which assumes (1) that gas molecules exert no attractive forces upon each other and (2) that, being perfectly elastic, they rebound after collision without any loss of energy. How valid are these assumptions?

The fact that all gases condense to liquids when sufficiently cooled strongly suggests that, as the molecules are slowed down, they stick to each other. Therefore there must be a force of attraction between them. As a result, when molecules rebound from each other energy must be expended to overcome the attractive forces. In other words, gases are not perfectly elastic. At low pressures gas molecules are relatively far apart so that the intermolecular attractive forces are very small indeed—too small to be significant. At high pressures, however, gas molecules are close together and the attractive forces are great enough to become effective. Thus at high pressures, the net effect of these attractive forces is that molecules strike the walls of the container with a force slightly less than they exert at ordinary pressure. Hence, the pressure is slightly less than expected and therefore the product PV is slightly less than that expected.

Let us consider a specific example. If the volume of a sample of oxygen is 2.000 liters at 20°C and 1 atm pressure, the value of PV= 2.000 l-atm. If the pressure is now increased to 2 atm, we would expect the volume of the gas to be 1.000 liter when we apply the formula PV = constant. But experiment shows that the volume is 0.991 l, so that the actual value of $PV = 1.982$ l-atm, which is slightly less than that for an ideal gas.

Another source of deviation of gases from ideal behavior is related to the actual compressible space in a gas sample. The kinetic theory assumes that the entire volume of a gas is empty and hence compressible space. This implies that the volume occupied by the molecules themselves is so small that it can be disregarded. At high pressures, however, the free or compressible space is greatly reduced so that the volume of the molecules themselves becomes significant and cannot be disregarded.

If, for instance, we assume that the molecules of a gas at high pressure occupy as much as one-tenth the volume of the container, then clearly the compressible space is only nine-tenths of the recorded gas volume. If this gas is compressed still further, the volume will not shrink proportionately and the experimental value of PV will be slightly greater than the ideal value.

Notice that the first assumption, namely that molecules of gases attract one another, results in a slightly diminished value for PV, whereas the second assumption—that gas molecules occupy a significant portion of the recorded volume—results in a slightly increased PV value. In other words, the two effects of (1) intermolecular attractions and (2) the volume occupied by the molecules tend to offset each other and as a result, the gas laws are reasonably accurate at ordinary temperatures and pressures. Nonetheless, there are slight discrepancies in the experimentally determined values for both PV and molar volume.

The precise molar volume of an ideal gas at STP is 22.414 l so that the approximate value to three significant figures is 22.4 l. However, the experimentally determined molar volumes for hydrogen, oxygen, methane, and hydrogen chloride are respectively 22.432 l, 22.392 l, 22.377 l, and 22.247 l. Notice that variations occur only in the third significant figures, but these variations reflect the differences between actual (or real) gas volumes and ideal volumes.

Summary

The kinetic molecular theory was developed in the years following 1858 into a detailed theory. It is a set of assumptions, about gas molecules, postulated to account for Avogadro's hypothesis and the gas laws. From these assumptions the pressure–volume–temperature relationship of a gas (Boyle's and Charles' laws) can be explained.

The behavior of a real gas deviates from that of any ideal gas. This is reflected in such results as (1) the failure of the *PV* product of Boyle's law to remain constant over a wide pressure range and (2) molar volumes at STP not quite equal to 22.1 l.

Factual Recall

1. State the main postulates of the kinetic theory of gases.
2. Derive Boyle's law from the kinetic theory.
3. Derive Charles' law from the kinetic theory.
4. Derive Avogadro's law from the kinetic theory.
5. (*a*) State the law of partial pressures. (*b*) Discuss the significance of the law in computing the pressure of a gas collected over water.

Apply Your Knowledge!

1. A gas mixture consists of 60% carbon dioxide and 40% carbon monoxide by volume. Compute the number of moles of each gas in 22.4 l of the gas mixture at STP.
2. At 20°C, 200 ml of hydrogen are collected over water, and the total gas pressure is 720 torr. What is (*a*) the pressure of the water vapor? (*b*) the partial pressure of the hydrogen? (*c*) the pressure of the dry hydrogen?

Find Out!

Look up the vapor pressure of mercury at 20°C. How many mercury molecules would be in a space above the mercury in a barometer if the volume of the space is 5 ml?

CHAPTER 13

FORMULAS, EQUATIONS, AND CHEMICAL CALCULATIONS

THE FORMULA OF A COMPOUND is a way of expressing the composition of the compound in chemical symbols. To find the formula, a compound must first be analyzed. Then, from the mass of the constituent elements, the number of moles of atoms of each element can be computed.

Empirical Formulas

The formula obtained by the chemical analysis of a compound represents the ratio of atoms of each element in the compound. It tells nothing about molecules. In earlier chapters we referred to sodium chloride as NaCl. This formula was obtained by analysis of a sample of sodium chloride. However, there are no molecules in a crystal of sodium chloride, and so the formula NaCl is an empirical formula, not a molecular formula. The formula for tin oxide (another ionic compound) is empirical rather than molecular. Let us compute the empirical formula of tin oxide.

Example 13-1

In one experiment 2.50 g of tin were burned in air and 3.18 g of tin oxide were formed. Calculate the empirical formula for tin oxide.

Solution

$$\text{Mass of tin (Sn)} = 2.50 \text{ g}$$

$$\text{Mass of oxygen} = 3.18 \text{ g} - 2.50 \text{ g} = 0.68 \text{ g}$$

$$\text{Moles of tin atoms} = \frac{\text{mass Sn}}{\text{gram atomic mass of Sn}} = \frac{2.50 \text{ g}}{117 \text{ g/mole}} = 0.00213 \text{ mole}$$

$$\text{Moles of oxygen atoms} = \frac{\text{mass O}}{\text{gram atomic mass of O atoms}} = \frac{0.68 \text{ g}}{16 \text{ g/mole}} = 0.00425 \text{ mole}$$

$$\frac{\text{Moles of Sn atoms}}{\text{Moles of O atoms}} = \frac{0.00213}{0.00425} = \frac{1}{2}$$

Therefore in tin oxide there is 1 mole of tin atoms for every 2 moles of oxygen atoms, and the empirical formula is SnO_2.

In Example 13-2, the formula is found from the percentage composition although, as in Example 13-1, it could be computed directly from the actual masses.

Example 13-2

In one experiment 1.44 g of copper (Cu) were heated with sulfur (S), and 1.80 g of copper sulfide were formed. Find the percentage composition and the empirical formula of the compound.

Solution 1: *Percentage composition of copper sulfide*

Mass of S = 1.80 g of copper sulfide − 1.44 g of copper
= 0.36 g

$$\% \text{ Cu} = \frac{\text{mass copper}}{\text{mass copper sulfide}} \times 100\%$$

$$= \frac{1.44 \text{ g}}{1.80 \text{ g}} \times 100\%$$

$$= 80.0\%$$

$$\% \text{ S} = \frac{\text{mass sulfur}}{\text{mass copper sulfide}} \times 100\%$$

$$= \frac{0.36 \text{ g}}{1.80 \text{ g}} \times 100\%$$

$$= 20.0\%$$

Solution 2: *Empirical formula for copper sulfide*

Atomic masses of Cu and S are 63.5 amu and 32.1 amu, respectively.

$$\text{Moles of Cu atoms} = \frac{80.0 \text{ g}}{63.5 \text{ g/mole}}$$

$$= 1.26 \text{ mole}$$

$$\text{Moles of S atoms} = \frac{20.0 \text{ g}}{32.1 \text{ g/mole}}$$

$$= 0.625 \text{ mole}$$

$$\frac{\text{Moles of Cu}}{\text{Moles of S}} = \frac{1.26\text{mole}}{0.625 \text{ mole}} = \frac{2}{1}$$

The empirical formula for copper sulfide is therefore Cu_2S.

Molecular Formulas

A molecular formula tells the number and kind of atoms in a molecule of the substance. Thus, before we can assign a molecular formula to a substance we must first be sure that the molecular mass of substance is composed of molecules. After that the molecular mass of the substance must be determined.

You may recall that in Chapter 8 water was discussed in detail as a substance composed of molecules. By analysis, the percentage composition of water by mass is found to be 11.1% hydrogen and 88.9% oxygen. What is the empirical formula for water?

$$\text{Moles of H} = \frac{11.1\text{ g}}{1.01\text{ g/mole}} = 11.0\text{ moles}$$

$$\text{Moles of O} = \frac{88.9\text{ g}}{16.0\text{ g/mole}} = 5.6\text{ moles}$$

$$\frac{\text{Moles H}}{\text{Moles O}} = \frac{11.0}{5.6} = \frac{2}{1}$$

Hence the empirical or simplest formula is H_2O.

In the molecular formula, the atoms of hydrogen and oxygen must therefore be in the ratio of 2:1. Therefore the formula *could* be H_2O, H_4O_2, H_6O_3, or in general $(H_2O)_n$, and only the molecular mass as found by experiment can determine which of these alternatives is correct. As explained in Chapter 10 the gram-molecular mass of a gaseous compound is the mass in grams of 22.4 l of the gas at STP. For water, this value is found to be 18.0 g so that its molecular mass is 18.0 amu. Therefore $(H_2O)_n = 18$. Substituting atomic masses for symbols, the equation can be written

$$(2 + 16)_n = 18 \qquad \text{or} \quad n = 1$$

Hence the molecular formula for water is H_2O. For this compound, the molecular formula is the same as the empirical formula.

Empirical and Molecular Formulas of Acetylene and Benzene

Acetylene is a gas at ordinary temperatures, and benzene is a low-boiling liquid. Both are compounds of carbon and hydrogen, and chemical analysis shows that both have the same percentage composition by mass, namely carbon 92.3% and hydrogen 7.73%, and therefore the same empirical formula.

$$\text{Moles of C} = \frac{92.3\text{ g}}{12.0\text{ g/mole}} = 7.69\text{ moles}$$

$$\text{Moles of H} = \frac{7.73\text{ g}}{1.01\text{ g/mole}} = 7.65\text{ moles}$$

It should be apparent that the empirical formula for both compounds is CH.

The molecular masses of both compounds must be determined experimentally to find their molecular formula. For acetylene the mass of 22.4 l at STP is 26 g, and for benzene vapor the mass of 22.4 l at STP is 78 g. That is, the molecular mass of acetylene is 26 amu and the molecular mass of benzene is 78 amu.

Acetylene

$$(CH)_n = 26 \text{ or } (12 + 1)_n = 26 \text{ and } n = 2$$

Therefore, the molecular formula is C_2H_2.

Benzene

$$(CH)_n = 78 \text{ or } (12 + 1)_n = 78 \text{ and } n = 6$$

Therefore, the molecular formula is C_6H_6.

Hence the molecular formula of acetylene is twice its empirical formula, whereas the molecular formula for benzene is six times its empirical formula.

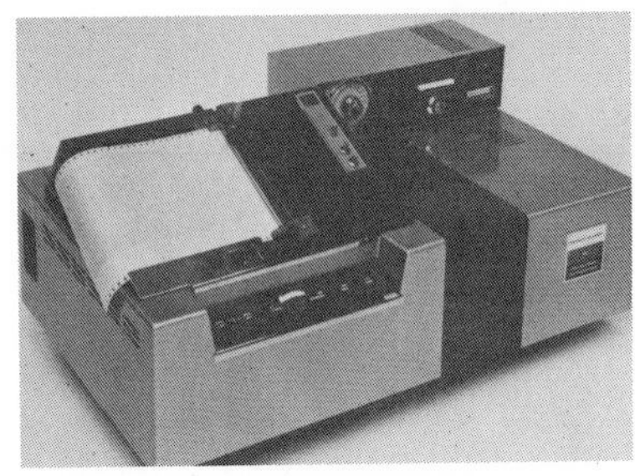

Fig. 13-1 To write the formula for an unidentified compound, the elements contained in it must be known. This particular model of an atomic absorption spectrophotometer can identify sixty-three metallic elements and was used to analyze rocks taken from the moon.

Formula Masses

We have already stated that the term *molecular mass* cannot be applied to ionic compounds. However, the term *formula mass* can be applied. *The formula mass of an ionic compound is the sum of the atomic masses of all atoms in its empirical formula.* Thus, the formula mass of sodium chloride, NaCl, is 58.5 amu (23 + 35.5), and that of aluminum oxide, Al_2O_3, is 102 amu ($2 \times 27 + 3 \times 16$).

Of course, the term formula mass also applies to substances that have molecular masses. In such cases formula masses are the same as molecular masses. Thus, for water (H_2O) the formula mass is 18, for carbon dioxide (CO_2) it is 44, and for oxygen (O_2) it is 32.

Valence and Formulas

In Chapter 8 we discussed ionic and covalent bonds, and we used the term *valence* to express the combining capacity of atoms. In ionic bonding, the valence of an atom is the number of electrons the atom loses or gains. In polar covalent bonding, valence is the number of electron pairs shared by a particular atom. If the atom loses electrons either entirely (as in an ionic bond), or partially (as in a

Table 13-1 A useful short list of valences

Element	Valence	Element	Valence
Hydrogen	+1	Zinc	+2
Sodium	+1	Aluminum	+3
Potassium	+1	Tin	+4
Silver	+1	Fluorine	−1
Magnesium	+2	Chlorine	−1
Calcium	+2	Oxygen	−2
Lead	+2	Sulfur	−3

polar covalent bond), the valence is positive. Conversely, the valence is negative if the atom either gains electrons entirely or attracts them more strongly than the other atom. With this in mind, what general statement can be made concerning valences of atoms?

Elements in Group I of the periodic classification (the alkali metals) have a valence of +1; elements in Group II (the alkaline earths) have a valence of +2; elements in Group III have a valence of +3. Elements in Group VII(the halogens)have a valence of −1, at least this is true of halogens in binary compounds. Elements in Group VI show a valence of −2 when they combine with metals. A useful list of valences is found in Table 13-1.

Writing Formulas

In writing the formula of a compound we must bear in mind two simple rules which are applicable in most cases:

(1) The first element is the one with the more positive valence and the last is the one with the more negative valence.

(2) Valence numbers must balance each other so that the net charge in the molecule (or in the compound) is zero.

To show how these rules apply, we will write the formula for calcium chloride.

Speculate . . .
A binary compound is made up of two elements. What do you think a ternary compound is?

Calcium chloride Calcium has a more positive valence than chlorine and so is written first. The valence of Ca is +2; that of Cl is −1. Therefore two chlorine atoms are needed to balance electrically one calcium atom, and the formula is $CaCl_2$. Notice that the number 2 (the number of atoms of chlorine) is written as a subscript to the right of the symbol. Names of all binary compounds end in *-ide*; for example, oxide, sulfide, chloride, fluoride, and nitride.

Multivalent Elements

Some of the transition metals form two or even more different compounds with a nonmetal. Why is this? You recall that the first row of transition elements (Sc to Zn) have two outer 4*s* electrons (except for Cu which has one) plus 3*d* electrons which vary in number from 1 to 10. Thus, an atom of iron may lose its two 4*s* electrons to form the ion Fe^{+2}, and in addition it may lose one of its six 3*d* electrons to form the ion Fe^{+3}. Furthermore, a copper atom may lose its 4*s* electron to become Cu^+ and it may also lose one of its 3*d* electrons to become Cu^{+2}. In general, it can be said that the number of electrons involved in bonding can vary for many of the transition elements, depending upon the conditions imposed upon the reaction. The result is that many of the transition elements exhibit more than one valence. You will study the multivalence of transition elements later, but at this time it is enough to consider only the two common valences of the elements shown in Table 13-2.

Table 13-2 Common valences of some multivalent elements

Element	Valences
Copper	+1 and +2
Mercury	+1 and +2
Chromium	+2 and +3
Iron	+2 and +3
Tin	+2 and +4

If copper is heated in air, two entirely different oxides are possible (one a red solid and the other black), depending upon the temperature and the amount of oxygen available. What are the formulas for these oxides? According to the rules, the formula of the oxide with monovalent copper is Cu_2O, and the formula of the oxide of divalent copper is CuO. What are the names of these oxides?

Research . . .
What is the origin of the words "ferrous" and "stannous"?

Actually there are two systems of nomenclature still in use. As you learned in Chapter 2, the modern and internationally accepted system uses a Roman numeral to indicate the valence. In this system Cu_2O is called copper (I) oxide, and CuO is called copper (II) oxide. In the older system, the metal has a particular ending to indicate its valence; the ending *-ous* indicates the lower valence and the ending *-ic* indicates the higher valences. Thus the older name for Cu_2O is cuprous oxide, and for CuO it is cupric oxide. Similarly, $FeCl_2$ is called iron (II) chloride or ferrous chloride and $FeCl_3$ is called iron (III) chloride or ferric chloride. Still another example is SnS, called tin (II) sulfide or stamious sulfide. And, finally, it should now be apparent that the correct name for SnO_2, the compound made by heating tin in air, is tin (IV) oxide rather than tin oxide. Also, the modern name for Cu_2S is copper (I) sulfide rather than cuprous sulfide.

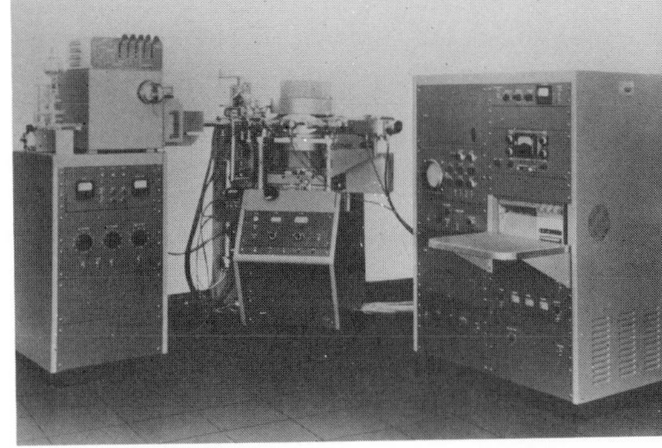

Fig. 13-2 A mass spectrometer. This machine can calculate the molecular mass of an unidentified compound.

To Calculate the Percentage Composition of a Compound from its Formula

You already know that the formula of a compound may be determined from its percentage composition and the atomic mass of its constituent elements. The reverse is also true; that is, the percentage composition of a compound can be computed from its formula.

Remember that the quantitative meaning of a symbol of an element in a formula is a mole of atoms of that particular element. The percentage composition of a compound, therefore, can be computed from its formula.

Example 13-3

Calculate the percentage composition by mass of glucose from its formula, $C_6H_{12}O_6$.

Solution

Molecular mass of $C_6H_{12}O_6 = 72 + 12 + 96 = 180$ amu

$$\%\text{ carbon} = \frac{\text{mass of 6 moles of C atoms}}{\text{mass of one mole of glucose}} \times 100$$

$$= \frac{72\text{ g}}{180\text{ g}} \times 100 = 40.0\%$$

$$\%\text{ hydrogen} = \frac{\text{mass of 12 moles of H atoms}}{\text{mass of one mole of glucose}} \times 100$$

$$= \frac{12\text{ g}}{180\text{ g}} \times 100 = 6.7\%$$

$$\%\text{ oxygen} = \frac{\text{mass of 6 moles of O atoms}}{\text{mass of one mole of glucose}} \times 100$$

$$= \frac{96\text{ g}}{180\text{ g}} \times 100 = 53.3\%$$

Equations

In Chapter 10 you learned that a chemical equation is a summary of a reaction. For instance, hydrogen burns in chlorine to form hydrogen chloride. The formulas for these substances are H_2, Cl_2, and HCl respectively, and so we can write

$$H_2 + Cl_2 \longrightarrow HCl \qquad (13\text{-}1)$$

However, since atoms are neither created nor destroyed, there must be the same number of atoms in the product as in the reactants. Equation (13-1) is clearly unbalanced, but it can be balanced by writing a coefficient of 2 in front of the HCl formula:

$$H_2 + Cl_2 \longrightarrow 2HCl \qquad (13\text{-}2)$$

Recall . . .
What scientific law states that the number of reactant atoms must equal the number of product atoms?

In this reaction all the substances are gases and this fact can be included in the equation by placing the letter g in parentheses after each of the substances,

$$H_2(g) + Cl_2(g) \longrightarrow 2HCl(g) \quad (13\text{-}3)$$

A more complicated equation is the one showing the reaction between metallic aluminum and zinc oxide. The facts are that hot aluminum reacts with zinc oxide to form zinc and aluminum oxide. We begin by writing the known formulas,

$$Al + ZnO \longrightarrow Zn + Al_2O_3 \quad (13\text{-}4)$$

In Eq. (13-4) zinc atoms are conserved but not aluminum and oxygen atoms. To conserve aluminum atoms the symbol Al requires a coefficient of 2, and to conserve oxygen atoms the formula ZnO needs a coefficient of 3. As amended, the statement now reads:

$$2Al + 3ZnO \longrightarrow Zn + Al_2O_3 \quad (13\text{-}5)$$

The only atoms not now conserved are zinc atoms and this can be done by adding a coefficient of 3 to the symbol Zn. Thus the balanced equation is

$$2Al + 3ZnO \longrightarrow 3Zn + Al_2O_3 \quad (13\text{-}6)$$

Since all substances are solids, another way to write Eq. (13-6) is

$$2Al(s)+3ZnO(s) \longrightarrow 3Zn(s)+Al_2O_3(s) \quad (13\text{-}7)$$

where the (s) stands for solid.

Still more complicated is the equation for the reaction between hot iron (II) sulfide and oxygen to form iron (III) oxide and sulfur dioxide. The equation can be balanced in three steps.

The formulas of reactants and products give the unbalanced statement, Eq. (13-8):

$$FeS + O_2 \longrightarrow Fe_2O_3 + SO_2 \quad (13\text{-}8)$$

Step 1 To conserve oxygen atoms in O_2 and Fe_2O_3, the coefficients must be 3 and 2, respectively. Hence

$$FeS + 3O_2 \longrightarrow 2Fe_2O_3 + SO_2 \quad (13\text{-}9)$$

Step 2 To conserve iron and sulfur atoms, the coefficient of FeS must be 4 and the coefficient of SO_2 must be 4. Therefore,

$$4FeS + 3O_2 \longrightarrow 2Fe_2O_3 + 4SO_2 \quad (13\text{-}10)$$

Step 3 Iron and sulfur atoms are now conserved, but not oxygen atoms. In the product $2Fe_2O_3$ there are 6 atoms of oxygen and in $4SO_2$ there are 8, a total of 14. Therefore, the coefficient of the reactant O_2 must be changed from 3 to 7. This gives the balanced equation:

$$4FeS + 7O_2 \longrightarrow 2Fe_2O_3 + 4SO_2 \tag{13-11}$$

Iron (II) sulfide and iron (III) oxide are solids; oxygen and sulfur dioxide are gases. Equation (13-11) can then be amended to read:

$$4FeS(s) + 7O_2(g) \longrightarrow 2Fe_2O_3(s) + 4SO_2(g) \tag{13-12}$$

Calculations of Mass and Volume Using Equations

A formula can be interpreted in terms of molecules or moles. Similarly, all the items in a balanced equation can be expressed in terms of molecules or moles.

In Eq. (13-11), we can write

$$4 \text{ moles} + 7 \text{ moles} \longrightarrow 2 \text{ moles} + 4 \text{ moles}$$

and we can use these molar relationships as conversion factors, as in the following problem.

Example 13-4

How many moles of iron (III) oxide are formed if 4.30 moles of oxygen react with iron (II) sulfide?

Solution

The conversion factor needed to convert moles of O_2 to moles of Fe_2O_3 is

$$\frac{2 \text{ moles } Fe_2O_3}{7 \text{ moles } O_2}$$

Therefore,

$$\text{Moles } Fe_2O_3 = 4.30 \text{ moles } O_2 \times \frac{2 \text{ moles } Fe_2O_3}{7 \text{ moles } O_2}$$

$$= 1.23 \text{ moles } Fe_2O_3$$

The quantitative relationships between the masses of reactants and products in a reaction (or between the volumes of gaseous substances) is called *stoichiometry*. There are at least three kinds of stoichiometric problems: (1) mass-mass, (2) mass-volume, and (3) volume–volume.

Analyze . . .
To solve stoichiometric problems, why is a balanced equation required?

Mass-Mass Problems

A quantity in a chemical reaction is usually expressed in grams, or in liters if the substance is a gas. By means of an equation we can compute the quantity of any other substance involved in the reaction. In the mass–mass type of problem we are given the mass of one of the substances in the reaction and can compute the mass of another. Example 13-5 is a mass–mass problem.

Example 13-5

Compute the mass of iron (III) oxide formed if 43.5 g of iron (II) sulfide react completely with oxygen.

Solution

Every calculation of this kind involves at least three steps:

(1) The units of the given mass (such as grams) are changed to moles.

(2) The number of moles of the required substance is computed from the conversion factor of the equation.

(3) The number of moles of the substance asked for is changed to the corresponding units of mass.

First, a balanced equation must be written for the reaction:

$$4FeS + 7O_2 \longrightarrow 2Fe_2O_3 + 4SO_2 \qquad (13\text{-}11)$$

Step 1

The conversion factor for converting grams to moles is

$$88 \text{ g FeS/mole} \quad \text{or} \quad \frac{1 \text{ mole FeS}}{88 \text{ g FeS}}$$

Deduce . . .
If stoichiometric problems are directly related to the ratio of reactants to products, what simple mathematical concept is used to solve these problems?

"If four apples cost 35 cents, how much would eight apples cost?"
"As in stoichiometric problems, 70 cents."

Therefore,

$$\text{moles FeS} = 43.5 \text{ g FeS} \times \frac{1 \text{ mole FeS}}{88 \text{ g FeS}}$$

$$= 0.495 \text{ mole FeS}$$

Step 2
From the equation the conversion factor for computing moles of Fe_2O_3 is

$$\frac{2 \text{ moles } Fe_2O_3}{4 \text{ moles FeS}}$$

Therefore,

$$\text{moles } Fe_2O_3 = 0.495 \text{ mole FeS} \times \frac{2 \text{ moles } Fe_2O_3}{4 \text{ moles FeS}}$$

$$= 0.247 \text{ mole } Fe_2O_3$$

Step 3
The conversion factor for converting moles to grams is

$$160 \text{ g } Fe_2O_3/\text{mole} \quad \text{or} \quad \frac{160 \text{ g } Fe_2O_3}{1 \text{ mole } Fe_2O_3}$$

Therefore,

$$\text{grams } Fe_2O_3 = 0.247 \text{ mole } Fe_2O_3 \times \frac{160 \text{ g } Fe_2O_3}{1 \text{ mole } Fe_2O_3}$$

$$= 39.6 \text{ g } Fe_2O_3$$

These three steps can be combined into a single overall expression:

$$\underset{(1)}{43.5 \, \cancel{\text{g FeS}}} \times \underset{(2)}{\frac{1 \, \cancel{\text{mole FeS}}}{88 \, \cancel{\text{g FeS}}}} \times \underset{(3)}{\frac{2 \, \cancel{\text{moles } Fe_2O_3}}{4 \, \cancel{\text{moles FeS}}}} \times \underset{(4)}{\frac{160 \text{ g } Fe_2O_3}{\cancel{1 \text{ mole } Fe_2O_3}}}$$

$$= 39.6 \text{ g } Fe_2O_3$$

Multiplying term (1) by term (2) gives moles of FeS. Then multiplying by term (3) gives moles of Fe_2O_3; finally, multiplying by term (4) gives grams of Fe_2O_3.

If a large number of terms is involved, similar terms (that is, similar formulas and similar units) should be divided out as in arithmetic. The remaining unit and formula will then show at a glance if the problem has been correctly set up. Notice that in this problem six items in the numerator divide out six items in the denominator; the remaining item is g Fe_2O_3, which is what we expect.

Mass-Volume Problems

If a gas is evolved in a reaction, the volume of the gas at STP can be determined from the equation, provided the mass of one of the reactants is known. Or, conversely, if the volume of the gas is known, the mass of any of the reacting substances can be computed. This kind of problem is called the mass–volume type and is illustrated by Example 13-6

Example 13-6

How many liters of oxygen (measured at STP) are needed to react with 15.0 g of iron (II) sulfide?

The balanced equation is

$$4FeS + 7O_2 \longrightarrow 2Fe_2O_3 + 4SO_2 \qquad (13\text{-}11)$$

Solution

The conversion factors are

(1) $FeS = \frac{88\ g}{mole}$

(2) $\frac{moles\ O_2}{moles\ FeS} = \frac{7}{4}$

(3) $O_2 = \frac{22.4\ l}{mole}$

Volume of O_2 equals

$$15.0\ g\ FeS \times \frac{1\ mole\ FeS}{88\ g\ FeS} \times \frac{7\ moles\ O_2}{4\ moles\ FeS} \times \frac{22.4\ l\ O_2}{1\ mole\ O_2}$$

$$= 6.68\ l\ O_2$$

If the oxygen is collected under temperature and pressure conditions other than STP, then two additional conversion factors are required to solve the problem.

Volume - Volume Problems

Volume–volume problems concern gases, and this kind of problem has already been referred to in Chapter 10. You recall that, at the same temperature and pressure, one mole of all gases occupies the same volume. Therefore, the volumes of any two gases in a chemical reaction are proportional to the number of moles of these gases. This number in turn is indicated by the coefficients of the formulas in the equation. Example 13-7 is a volume–volume problem.

Example 13-7

Compute the volume of sulfur dioxide formed at STP if 30.0 l of oxygen react with iron (II) sulfide.

The balanced equation is

$$4FeS + 7O_2 \longrightarrow 2Fe_2O_3 + 4SO_2 \qquad (13\text{-}11)$$

Solution

The conversion factor from the equation is

$$\frac{\text{moles } SO_2}{\text{moles } O_2} = \frac{\text{vol } SO_2}{\text{vol } O_2}$$

$$= \frac{4 \times 22.4\ \text{l}}{7 \times 22.4\ \text{l}} = \frac{4}{7}$$

Therefore,

volume of SO_2 =

$$30.0\ \text{l} \times \frac{4}{7} = 17.2\ \text{l}\ SO_2$$

Notice that temperature and pressure conditions are not involved unless there is a *change* in pressure or temperature, and the computation is valid for any temperature and pressure, as in Example 13-8.

Example 13-8

Compute the volume of oxygen needed to react with iron (II) sulfide and produce 25.0 l of sulfur dioxide, assuming the gas volumes are measured at 25°C and 720 torr pressure.

Solution

$$V_{O_2} = V_{SO_2} \times \frac{\text{moles } O_2}{\text{moles } SO_2}$$

$$= 25.0 \text{ l} \times \frac{7 \text{ moles}}{4 \text{ moles}}$$

$$= 43.8 \text{ l } O_2$$

Where V_{O_2} is the volume of O_2 and V_{SO_2} is the volume of SO_2.

In some reactions all reactants and products are gases, as in the burning of methane.

$$CH_4(g) + 2O_2(g) = CO_2(g) + 2H_2O(g) \qquad (13\text{-}12)$$

That is, at the temperature of the flame, water exists as vapor.

Summary

In writing formulas, the element with the more positive valence is written first. The element with the more negative valence is written last. *The sum of the valences of the atoms in the formula of a compound is zero.*

Balancing equations is principally governed by the Law of Conservation of Matter. The number of atoms of the elements making up the reactants must equal the number of atoms of the elements making up the products. Stoichiometric relationships are determined by ratios of the reactants and products in a *balanced* equation.

Factual Recall

1. What does an empirical formula indicate?

2. What does a molecular formula indicate?
3. What chemical property of a compound determines whether or not a molecular formula can be used to represent the compound?
4. How do *formula mass* and *molecular mass* differ from each other?
5. What factor must be known about the elements in a compound to derive the empirical formula from the percentage composition of the compound?

Apply Your Knowledge!

Writing Formulas

1. Write formulas for (*a*) potassium oxide, (*b*) magnesium chloride, (*c*) sodium sulfide, (*d*) calcium nitride, (*e*) lead bromide, (*f*) aluminum nitride, (*g*) manganese (II) fluoride.
2. Write formulas for (*a*) copper (I) sulfide, (*b*) iron (III) oxide, (*c*) tin (IV) nitride, (*d*) mercury (II) oxide, (*e*) iron (II) chloride, (*f*) copper (II) iodide, (*g*) mercury (I) bromide.

Molecular or Formula Mass

3. Calculate the molecular or formula mass of (*a*) Ne, (*b*) F_2, (*c*) O_3, (*d*) HCl, (*e*) $FeCl_2$.
4. Calculate the molecular or formula mass of (*a*) magnesium nitride, (*b*) aluminum sulfide, (*c*) phosphorus trioxide, (*d*) sodium peroxide, (*e*) boron fluoride.

Writing Balanced Equations

5. Using symbols, write balanced equations for
   (*a*) hydrogen + oxygen $\longrightarrow$ water
   (*b*) tin + oxygen $\longrightarrow$ tin (II) oxide
   (*c*) copper + sulfur $\longrightarrow$ copper (I) sulfide
   (*d*) copper (I) chloride + chlorine $\longrightarrow$ copper (II) chloride
   (*e*) iron (II) oxide + oxygen $\longrightarrow$ iron (III) oxide
   (*f*) aluminum bromide + chlorine $\longrightarrow$
   aluminum chloride + bromine

Empirical Formulas

6. Find the empirical formula of an oxide of sulfur which contains 40.0% sulfur and 60.0% oxygen.
7. An oxide of iron contains 77.7% iron. What is the empirical formula of the oxide?
8. If 3.90 g of an oxide of mercury are decomposed by heat, 0.15 g of oxygen is liberated. Find the empirical formula of the oxide and give its name.

Percentage Composition

9. Calculate the percentage of hydrogen in (*a*) H_2O_2 (*b*) HF (*c*) $NaHCO_3$ (*d*) NH_4OH (*e*) $(NH_4)_2SO_4$ (*f*) $CaCl_2 \cdot 6H_2O$.

Gases

10. Find the mass of 1 l of carbon dioxide at 50 °C and 700 torr pressure.
11. Find the number of moles of carbon dioxide in 10.01 of the gas at 273 °C and 380 torr pressure.

Stoichiometry

12. Compute the mass of (*a*) hydrogen (*b*) oxygen required to give 100 g of water.
13. Hydrogen peroxide (H_2O_2) is easily decomposed to give oxygen and water. How many moles of oxygen are liberated when 102 g of the peroxide is decomposed?

Find Out!

Look up some commercial process and write equations for as many steps as possible (example: manufacture of sulfuric acid).

Suggested Readings

Adler, B.J., and T.E. Wainwright, *Molecular Motions* (SCIENTIFIC AMERICAN Offprint #265). San Francisco: Freeman.

Sienko, M.J., *Chemistry Problems*. New York: W.A. Benjamin.

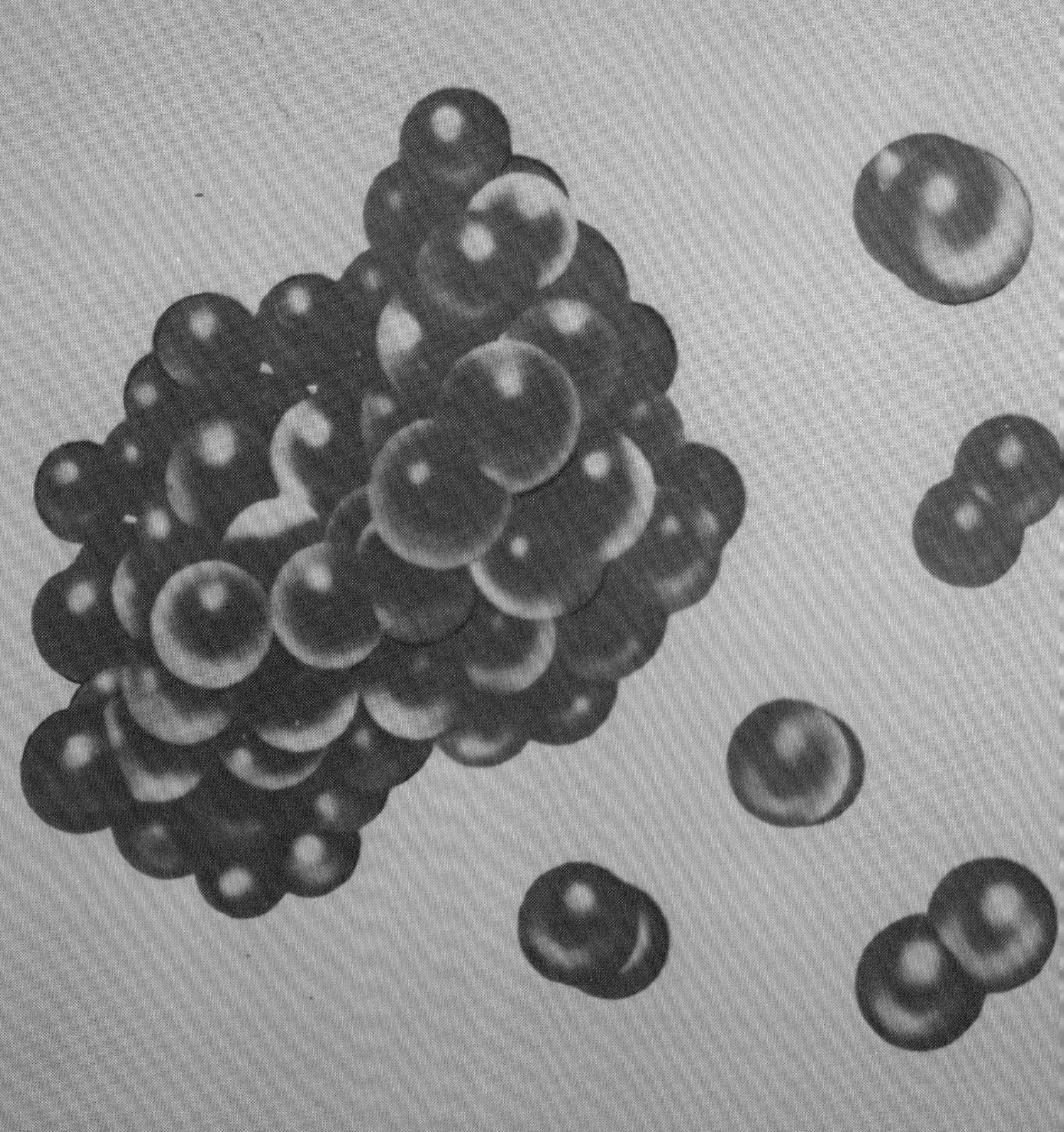

UNIT IV

SOLUTIONS AND IONIZATION

A SOLID IS A SOLID because the electrical attractions between its particles are strong enough to hold them together. If a solid is dropped into water, the attractive force of the water molecules may be strong enough to separate the particles. When this happens, the solid is said to have *dissolved* in the water to form a *solution.*

In the case of salts as solids, the particles are ions. The molecular dipoles of H_2O tend to break the bonds between the ions. The ions are free to move in solution and the salt is said to be ionized.

Polar covalent compounds such as HCl are also ionized by water. Molecules of water attach themselves to HCl molecules and these hydrated (aquated) units split into hydronium ions H_3O^+ (commonly abbreviated to H^+ and called hydrogen ions) and chloride ions $Cl(aq)^-$ (abbreviated as Cl^-). A solution with a relatively large number of hydrogen ions is called an *acid.* A *base*, on the other hand, contains hydroxide ions (OH^-) even in the solid state. If a solution of an acid is mixed with a solution of a base, the hydrogen ions react with the hydroxide ions to form water

$$H^+ + OH^- \longrightarrow H_2O$$

And if the two solutions are in the right proportions, neither an excess of hydrogen ions nor an excess of hydroxide ions remain in solution after the reaction. In such a case both acid and base are said to be neutralized and the process is called *neutralization.*

HISTORICAL CHEMISTRY LABORATORY

This is a translation of excerpts from a paper published in 1882 by Francois-Marie Raoult. The original work appeared in the French scientific periodical ***Comptes rendus hebdomadaires des séances d'Académie de Science Française.***

François-Marie Raoult (1830–1901)

GENERAL LAW OF THE FREEZING OF SOLUTIONS

If A is the lowering of the freezing point due to the presence of 1 gram of a substance dissolved in 100 grams of solvent; M the molecular weight of the dissolved substance, supposedly anhydrous, calculated according to the atomic formula H = 1, O = 16. . .; T its molecular lowering of the freezing point (that is, the lowering of the freezing point caused by one molecule dissolved in 100 grams of liquid), then, if the solutions are dilute,

$$MA = T$$

My previous studies have shown that, in the same liquid, the molecular lowering, T, is a nearly constant number for very numerous groups of compounds of the same type. Since then I have made new experiments using as solvents the following compounds whose freezing points can always be determined with extreme precision.

	Freezing Point, Degrees
Water	*0.00*
Benzene	*4.96*
Nitrobenzene	*5.28*
Ethylene dibromide	*7.92*
Formic acid	*8.52*
Acetic acid	*16.75*

Lack of space prevents me from giving details here... .

Conclusions. These experiments...agree in establishing the following:

All bodies, on dissolving in a definite liquid compound which can solidify, lower the freezing point.

In all liquids, the molecular lowering of the freezing point due to the different compounds approaches two values, invariable for each liquid, of which one is double the other. The larger is more often found and constitutes the normal molecular lowering. The lesser corresponds to the case where the molecules of the dissolved body are joined two to two.

The normal molecular lowering of the freezing point varies with the nature of the solvent: it is 37 for water and 117 for ethylene dibromide.

To make water agree with the general rule, it is enough to admit that the physical molecules which compose it are formed from three chemical molecules joined together, at least near the freezing point. Then, indeed, this solvent gives a number which does not differ from the mean of the five others. The following law can then be formulated:

One molecule of any compound dissolved in 100 molecules of any liquid of a different nature lowers the freezing point of this liquid by a nearly constant quality, close to 0.62 degrees.

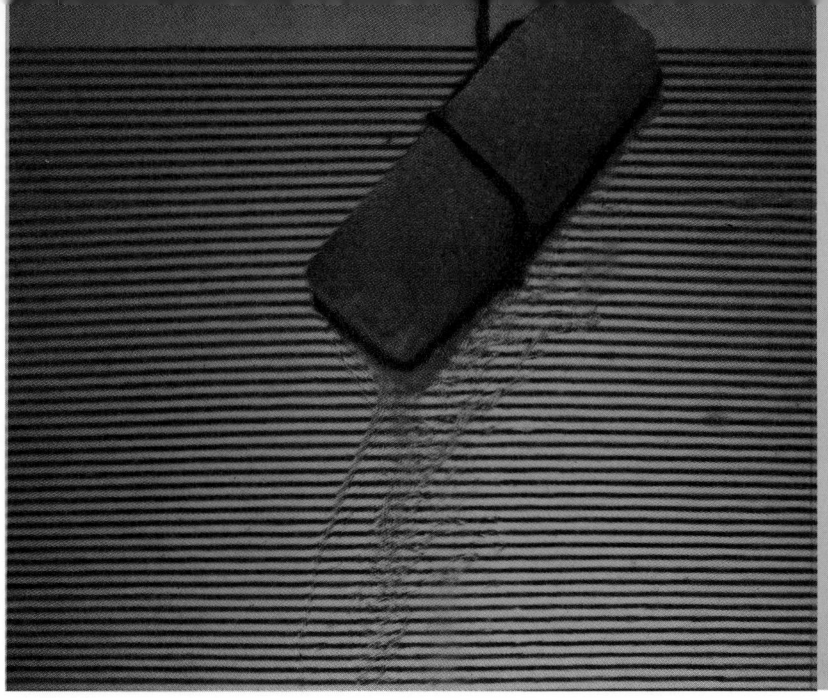

CHAPTER 14

SOLUTIONS

What is a Solution?

MANY CHEMICAL REACTIONS TAKE PLACE in water *solution*. What is a solution? A solution is made by dissolving a solid, or a liquid, or even a gas in water (or in any other liquid). Thus, there are *two* essential *ingredients* in any solution: (1) a dissolved substance called a *solute* and (2) a dissolving liquid called a *solvent*.

Definition . . .
If one ingredient of a solution is present in larger amount than the other(s), it may be called the *solvent*; the other ingredient(s) will be called *solute*.

In general terms, we can say that a *solution is a homogeneous mixture of solute and solvent*. If sugar is dissolved in water, sugar is the solute and water the solvent; if alcohol is dissolved in water, alcohol is the solute and water the solvent; if iodine is dissolved in alcohol, iodine is the solute and alcohol is the solvent.

Water is the most common solvent, and for our purposes we shall be mostly concerned with water (or *aqueous*) solutions of solids. How does a solid dissolve in water? In the process of solution a crystalline solid, such as salt or sugar, ceases to exist as such and becomes part of the liquid. How is this possible? Clearly, before a

Inquiry . . .
There are also solid/solid solutions. An alloy such as brass is a good example of such a solution. How many others can you name?

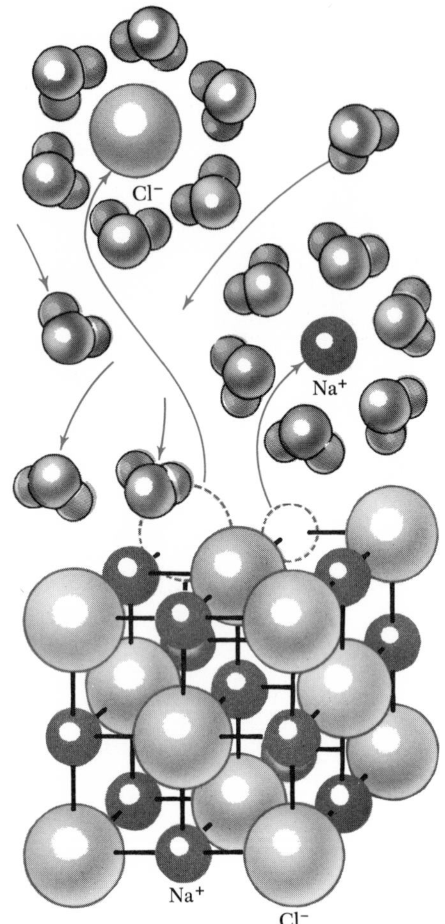

Fig.14-1 A model for the solution of an ionic solid.

solid can dissolve in water the interionic forces, as in common salt, or the intermolecular forces, as in sugar, must be overcome.

Most ionic solids are soluble in water. But some—like aluminum oxide and silver chloride—are almost insoluble. Why?

How Ionic Solids Dissolve

Let us consider the dissolving action of water on sodium chloride. As stated in Chapter 8, water molecules are dipoles, and it is the dipole nature of the molecules that accounts for the dissolving property of water. You recall that a crystal of sodium chloride consists of sodium ions and chloride ions held in place by strong ionic bonds. If a crystal of salt is dropped into water, the water molecules orient themselves around the ions. The number of water molecules which act upon the ion depends upon both the charge on the ion and its size. The positive ends of the water molecules are attracted by chloride ions and the negative ends by sodium ions, illustrated by Fig. 14-1. Water molecules line up in this way and insulate the opposite charges from one another, thereby reducing markedly the attraction between oppositely charged ions. The hydrated ions move away from the crystal and into the solution. When this happens, the salt is said to *dissolve* or go into solution. A number of water molecules remain attached to the dissolved ions, forming a kind of shell around them as shown in Fig. 14-2. This effect is called *hydration* (*aquation*), and dissolved ions are always *hydrated* (*aquated*) *ions*. In the case of ionic solids which are only slightly soluble, the attraction of the ions in the crystal may be so great that insulation by water molecules is not effective.

How Molecular Compounds Dissolve

Many substances (solids, liquids, and gases) are made up of molecules rather than ions. How and why do molecular compounds dissolve in water? The most important factor that determines the solubility of a molecular substance is the nature and strength of its attractive forces. In general, two types of intermolecular attractive forces are recognized. These are van der Waals forces and polar forces; van der Waals forces are present in *all* intermolecular interactions. Polar forces are present only between polar substances, that is, between those molecules in which there is an *unsymmetrical* charge distribution, such as in water molecules and other dipoles. The strengths of both the van der Waals and the polar forces vary widely, depending upon the composition and shape of the molecules. The tetrahedral methane (CH_4) molecule is nonpolar. It is *symmetrical* in shape, with the carbon atom at the center of the tetrahedron and a hydrogen atom at each of the four corners, as shown in Fig. 14-3. Such a symmetrical molecule has no resultant electrical charge from the C—H bonds. Therefore, methane molecules are nonpolar; being nonpolar, methane molecules do not attract water molecules. This statement, in effect, means that methane does not dissolve in water to any marked degree. Both methane and water molecules exhibit van der Waals forces, but in this case the polar forces between water molecules are dominant, keeping the water molecules segregated from the methane.

Molecules of sugar, $C_{12}H_{22}O_{11}$, on the other hand, are *unsymmetrical* in shape so that the polar bonds are not completely counterbalanced electrically. As a whole, a sugar molecule is a dipole and can be represented diagrammatically as

Polar molecules attract each other and the aligned molecules can be shown as

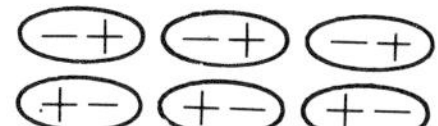

Such an alignment of molecules may result in the formation of a liquid (such as alcohol) or a solid (such as sugar). However, the intermolecular bonds in a crystal of sugar are much weaker than interionic bonds in a crystal of sodium chloride. One way to compare the strength of the bonds is to compare the melting temperature of the crystals: in general, the higher the melting point, the stronger are the bonds. The melting point of sugar is about 180 °C, whereas for salt it is about 800 °C.

The polar molecules of any solid lattice attract polar molecules of water, as shown in Fig. 14-4. And when the force of attraction between solid polar molecules and water is greater than the attraction between the molecules themselves, solid molecules are insulated from their neighbors in the solid and go into solution. That is what happens to a crystal of sugar in the presence of water.

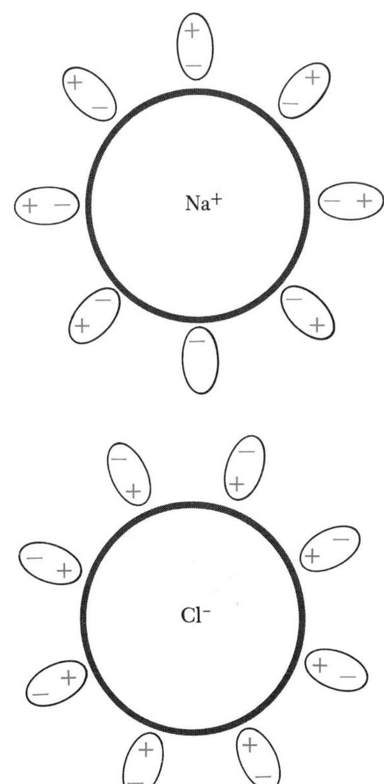

Fig. 14-2 Diagrammatic representation of hydration.

Fig. 14-3 A molecule of methane has four angles, all equal to 109 °.

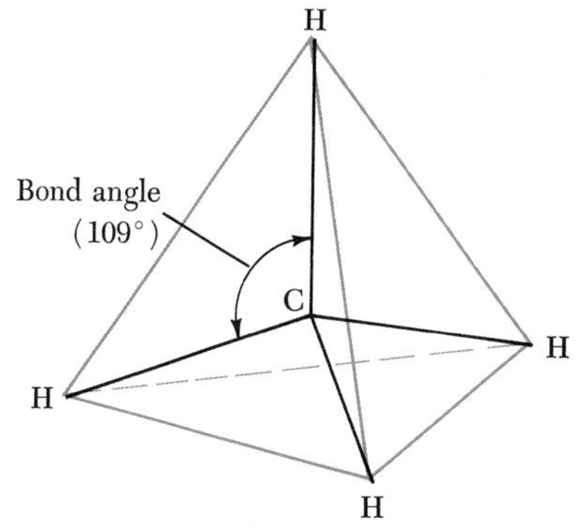

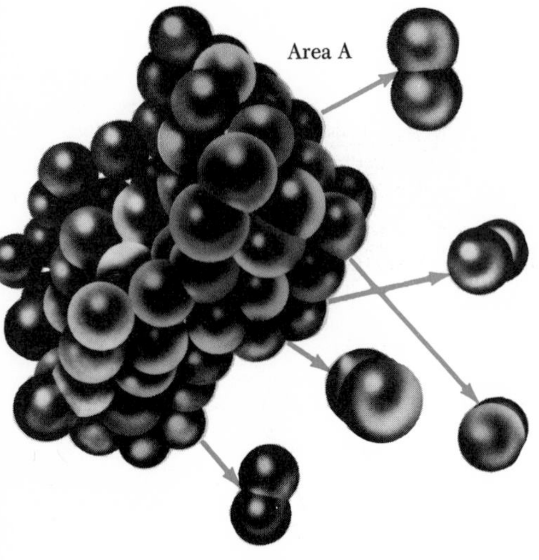

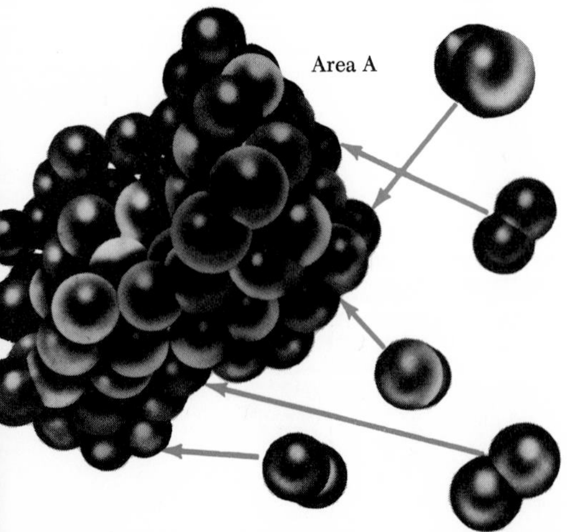

Fig. 14-4 The dynamic equilibrium of solubility.

Saturated Solutions

Let us consider what happens if a little powdered potassium nitrate is placed in a test tube and shaken with water. Solid potassium nitrate (KNO_3) consists of a lattice of oppositely charged ions: potassium ions (K^+) and nitrate ions (NO_3^-). Because water is a dipole, it is attracted by both ions, and the lattice begins to break down; that is, some of the potassium nitrate dissolves, resulting in free hydrated ions. As soon as some ions are in solution, a reverse effect is set up; that is, some of the solute particles leave the solution and redeposit (precipitate) on the crystals. Thus, there are two opposing processes taking place at the same time, a solution process and a deposition process. However, if only a small amount of salt and a large amount of water are used, more ions of potassium nitrate go into solution than come out of solution, and the net effect is that the solid dissolves completely.

Now suppose that more potassium nitrate is added to the solution. What happens? Obviously more ions from solution are deposited on the crystals. And if still more potassium nitrate is added, the rate of crystallization increases still further. Eventually, the rate at which solute particles (or ions) leave the solution to rejoin the solid equals the rate at which particles (or ions) leave the solid and go into solution. When this happens, the solution is said to be *saturated*. Thus, in a saturated solution the solute dissolves at the same rate as it crystallizes or, as we usually say, *a condition of equilibrium exists* between the solid and the particles in solution (see Fig. 14-5). These opposing processes can be represented by reversible arrows, and a saturated solution can be expressed as

$$\text{solid particles (undissolved)} \underset{\text{crystallization}}{\overset{\text{solution}}{\rightleftharpoons}} \text{dissolved particles}$$

So far, we have assumed that the saturated solution has been kept at a constant temperature. If, however, the saturated solution is heated, the potassium nitrate will eventually dissolve completely. Why? At the higher temperature, the number of collisions between water molecules and solid particles of KNO_3 increases, and so more of the solid goes into solution. As more ions go into solution, the rate of return to the crystalline form also increases. At the higher temperature, a new solubility equilibrium is established. In this equilibrium the concentration of the ions in solution is greater. We now have a saturated solution at the higher temperature.

Le Châtelier's Principle

Henri Le Châtelier (1850–1936) was a French scientist. In 1888 he stated a principle (or law) that applies to any system in equilibrium and it predicts what happens to the system if the conditions at equilibrium are disturbed. It has wide application, and the solubility process is only one of many systems to which the principle can be applied. The principle states: *If a stress is imposed upon any system in equilibrium, an opposing process is automatically set up which tends to counteract the effects of the applied stress, and to establish a new point of equilibrium.*

What is meant by the term *stress*? A stress means some sort of change in the conditions that prevail at that time. First let us apply Le Châtelier's principle to the water–vapor equilibrium system already discussed in Chapter 12. If the system of water and saturated vapor is heated, then clearly the temperature of the system is raised. What does Le Châtelier's principle predict concerning the vapor pressure under the new conditions? The applied heat constitutes a stress and the principle predicts that a change will take place to counteract this stress; that is, if the water–vapor system is heated the pressure exerted by the vapor will also increase until a new water-vapor equilibrium is established. As you know, this prediction is in agreement with experimental facts.

Fig. 14-5 *Let's go into solution!*

Solubility

Solubility is defined as *the mass of a substance required to form a saturated solution in 100 grams of water at a given temperature.* This mass can be expressed in grams or moles of solute. Thus, the solubility of potassium nitrate at 20 °C is 31.6 g or 0.313 mole of KNO_3 per 100 g of water. As you have learned, the higher the temperature the greater is the solubility of KNO_3. At 30°C, for example, it is found to be 45.8 g or 0.454 mole.

Solubilities can be found experimentally at any reasonable temperature, and in Table 14-1 the solubility values for KNO_3 are given at intervals of 10° within the range of 0°C to 100°C. A solubility graph obtained by plotting these data is shown in Fig. 14-6. In this graph, temperatures are plotted along the abscissa and solubilities (in grams) along the ordinate. The graph is an upward curve which increases in steepness as the temperature rises.

Table 14-1 Variation of solubility of temperature

	Solubility	
Temperature, °C	g/100g H_2O	Moles/100g H_2O
0	13.3	0.132
10	20.9	0.207
20	31.6	0.313
30	45.8	0.454
40	63.9	0.633
50	85.5	0.845
60	110	1.09
70	138	1.37
80	169	1.67
90	202	2.00
100	246	2.44

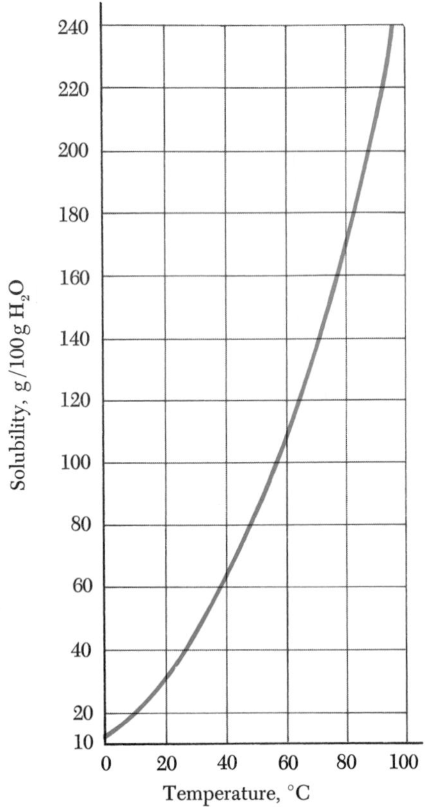

Fig. 14-6 Curve showing changes with temperature of the aqueous solubility of KNO_3.

The solubilities of different substances vary widely and the solubility curves for six selected salts are shown in Fig. 14-7. Notice that the solubility curve for sodium chloride is almost a horizontal line; that is, the solubility of sodium chloride increases only slightly as the temperature rises. Notice also that the solubility of potassium chloride is lower than that of sodium chloride at low temperatures but greater at high temperatures. In contrast, the solubility of silver nitrate is high even at low temperatures.

Temperature Changes during Solution

If a thermometer is placed in the test tube as potassium nitrate is being dissolved, it registers a marked drop in temperature. A process that absorbs heat is called *endothermic* and the term applies to the dissolving of many salts. In a few cases, however, there is a rise in temperature; that is, heat is evolved during solution. Such a change is called *exothermic*. What factors determine whether the solution process is exothermic or endothermic?

To bring ions into solution, heat energy is required to overcome the attractive forces in the solute. This is an endothermic change because energy is absorbed. However, energy is released as ions are attracted to water molecules in the hydration process. This is an exothermic change. If the *net* change is endothermic (as it often is), there is a drop in temperature as solution takes place.

Heat of Solution

The change in heat content per mole of solute dissolved under carefully specified conditions is called the *heat of solution*. Table 14-2 contains a few examples of heats of solution. Notice the two signs. The negative sign indicates an exothermic change. Why is a negative sign associated with an exothermic change? If the change is exothermic, some heat is evolved and in consequence there is a rise in temperature. Therefore the total energy content in the solution must be *less* than that of the original energy content of the separate components—solute and water—before solution takes place. Conversely, if the change is endothermic, the reverse is true and the heat of solution is said to be positive.

Table 14-2 Heats of solution of various substances.

Substance	Heat of solution, kcal/mole
KNO_3	+ 8.5
KCl	+ 4.1
NaCl	+ 0.9
$MgCl_2$	−37.0
NaOH	−10.1

The Temperature–Solubility Relationship

Let us further examine the solubility of potassium nitrate. Experimental facts indicate that potassium nitrate dissolves with an absorption of heat (or a drop in temperature). Moreover, the higher the temperature of the system, the greater is the solubility of potassium nitrate. How does Le Châtelier's principle account for these facts? If the solution is heated, its temperature rises, and the heat input constitutes a stress. To counteract this stress, a change must take place which will absorb heat. This change is the solution of more potassium nitrate. That is why more and more potassium nitrate goes into solution as long as an external source of heat continues to raise the temperature of the solid–solution system.

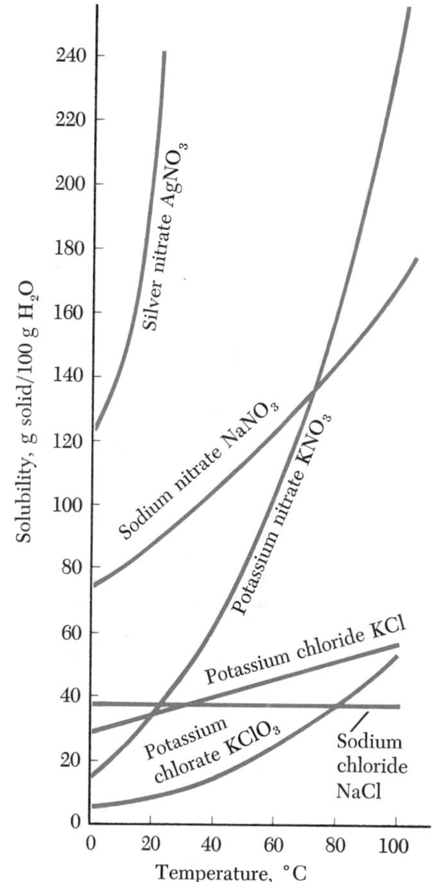

Fig. 14-7 Solubility curves for six compounds.

The Solubility of Gases

You have probably noticed that tiny bubbles of gas escape from water when it is heated. These are bubbles of air (oxygen and nitrogen), so it is apparent that air is less soluble in hot water than in cold. Indeed, the solubility of most gases decreases as the temperature of the aqueous gas solution is raised. This is the opposite of the temperature–solubility effect for many aqueous solutions of solids. How can this be explained?

When a gas dissolves in water there are no ionic bonds of a crystal lattice to be broken; therefore, the solution process is invariably exothermic. According to Le Châtelier's principle, adding heat to this system would displace the position of equilibrium to the left and make the gas less soluble.

Concentration of Solutions

Molarity

A chemist often wants to know how concentrated a solution is; that is, he wants to know the relative amounts of solute and solvent. The words *dilute* and *concentrated* are used to express concentration in a qualitive way. The term *dilute* means that the solution contains a relatively small amount of solute, and the term *concentrated* means that the solution contains a relatively large amount of solute.

A much more precise way of expressing concentration is in terms of *molarity. Molarity is defined as the number of moles of solute per liter of solution.* For instance, if a sucrose solution contains 1 mole of $C_{12}H_{22}O_{11}$ (that is, 342 g) per liter of solution, the concentration

Calculate . . .
Sucrose is the chemists' name for table sugar (cane sugar). Its formula is $C_{12}H_{22}O_{11}$. Calculate its molecular mass.

Fig. 14-8 The steps in making a volumetric solution. The final step, not shown, is mixing the solution by inverting it 40-50 times.

of the solution is said to be 1 molar. The abbreviation 1*M* represents 1 molar, 2*M* represents 2 molar, 0.5*M* is 1/2 molar, and so on.

It is important to note that in molar concentrations it is the volume of the *solution* that is significant, not the volume of solvent. It is, therefore, a simple matter to prepare molar solutions. All that is needed is a volumetric flask like that shown in Fig. 14-8. Note that the flask has a circular mark etched around the neck to indicate the exact volume (for example, 1 l, 500 ml, 100 ml, etc.)

One liter of 1 *M* solution of urea [$CO(NH_2)_2$, molecular mass 60] could be prepared by weighing out exactly 60 g of urea and dissolving the urea in water in a 1-l volumetric flask. Water is then added until the level of the solution in the neck of the flask coincides with the mark on the flask. Similarly, a 4*M* solution of urea would be prepared by dissolving 240 g of urea in water and then making the solution up to 1 l by adding water. Or again, a 0.2*M* solution of sodium chloride could be prepared by dissolving 5.85 g of NaCl (1 mole of NaCl equals 58.5 g) in water and making the volume of the solution up to 500 ml.

Molarity can be expressed in terms of moles of solute (n) and volume of solution (v). If v l of a solution contain n moles of solute, then clearly the molarity (M) of the solution equals n/v. This relationship

$$M = n/v \qquad (14\text{-}1)$$

can be used to solve problems such as the examples that follow.

Example 14-1

Find the mass(M) of urea [$CO(NH_2)_2$] in 62 ml of a 4*M* solution.

Solution

$n = M \times v$

$= 4.0 \text{ mole/l} \times 0.062 \text{ l} = 0.248 \text{ mole}$

$\text{mass} = 0.248 \text{ mole} \times 60.0 \text{ g/mole}$

$= 14.9 \text{ g}$

Example 14-1 points to one of the advantages of expressing concentrations in terms of molarity: the *mass* of the solute can be determined from the volume of the solution. Clearly, it is much easier to pour out a given volume of solution than to weigh a solute on a balance.

Equation 14-1 can also be used to solve problems such as Example 14-2. When you have read Example 14-2 carefully, find the molarity of the solution formed when 5.85 g of NaCl are dissolved in enough water to make 250 ml of solution.

Measure . . .

Make up a 0.1*M* solution of NaCl. Note that the water level in the neck of the flask forms a curve or meniscus. The flask is "filled to the mark" when the lowest point of the meniscus coincides with the mark. Adjusting the volume can be tricky. Practice until you acquire skill.

Example 14-2

Calculate the volume of 0.200*M* NaCl needed to give 4.68 g of solute.

Solution

$$n = \frac{4.68 \text{ g}}{58.5 \text{ g/mole}} = 0.0800 \text{ mole}$$

$$v = n/M$$

$$= \frac{0.0800 \text{ mole}}{0.200 \text{ mole/l}} = 0.400 \text{ l}$$

If water is added to a solution of known concentration, both the molarity and the volume of the solution are changed but the total number of moles of solute remains the same. Therefore,

$$n = M_1 v_1 = M_2 v_2 \qquad (14\text{-}2)$$

where M_1 and M_2 represent the molarities, and v_1 and v_2 the volumes, before and after dilution. Equation 14-2 can be used to solve problems such as Example 14-3.

Example 14-3

To what volume must 10 ml of 3*M* H_2SO_4 be diluted to change the concentration to 0.20*M*?

Solution

$$v_2 = \frac{M_1 v_1}{M_2}$$

$$= \frac{3M \times 10 \text{ ml}}{0.20M} = 150 \text{ ml}$$

It should now be apparent that equal volumes of equimolar solutions of different substances contain the same *number of moles* of each of the solutes. This is an important observation which can be readily confirmed mathematically by working Example 14-4.

Example 14-4

Compute the number of moles of (*a*) cane sugar (sucrose), $C_{12}H_{22}O_{11}$ and (*b*) urea, $CO(NH_2)_2$, in 500 ml of each of their 5*M* solutions.

Solution

$$n_{\text{sugar}} = M_1 v_1$$

$$= 5 \text{ moles/l} \times 0.500 \text{ l}$$

$$= 2.5 \text{ moles}$$

$$n_{\text{urea}} = M_2 v_2$$

$$= 5 \text{ moles/l} \times 0.500 \text{ l}$$

$$= 2.5 \text{ moles}$$

Molality

In *molar* solutions we know the *mass of solute* but *not* the *mass of solvent*. In different solutions of identical molarity, the mass of solvent (water, for example) varies according to the volume occupied by the solute. For example, it can be shown that 1 l of 5*M* HCl contains 900 g of H_2O, whereas 1 l of 5*M* H_2SO_4 contains only 796 g of H_2O. Sometimes we wish to know the mass of water as well as the mass of solute. At such times we use *molality*, rather than *molarity*. *The molality of a solution, or the molal concentration, is the number of moles of solute per kilogram of solvent* (usually water).

The usual abbreviation for molality is *m*. Thus, 1 molal (1 *m*) NaCl contains 1 mole (58.5 g) of NaCl for each kilogram of water. Similarly, 0.5 *m* K_2CO_3 contains 0.5 mole K_2CO_3 (69 g) for each kilogram of water.

Example 14-5 is a typical problem involving molality.

Example 14-5

Compute the mass of urea needed to prepare a 0.25 *m* solution in 200 g of water.

Solution

A 0.25 *m* solution of urea contains 60/4 g $CO(NH_2)_2$/kg H_2O or 60/(4 × 5) g $CO(NH_2)_2$/200 g H_2O. Thus the mass of urea is 3.0 g.

Comparison of Molarity and Molality

Molarity (*M*) expresses moles of solute per liter of solution, whereas molality (*m*) expresses moles of solute per kilogram of solvent. Molarity is concerned with the volume occupied by the solute but molality is not. If a solution is exceedingly dilute, the volume occupied by the solute is negligible and the molarity of a given solution is then approximately the same as the molality. However, as the solution becomes more and more concentrated the difference between molarity and molality increases.

Another important observation is that equimolal solutions containing the same mass of water (solvent) contain the same number of moles of solute. For example, 0.5 *m* solutions of urea (mol. mass = 60) and sucrose (mol. mass = 342) are prepared respectively by dissolving 30 g of urea in 1 kg H_2O and 171 g of sucrose in 1 kg H_2O. In each solution, the number of molecules of solute in solution is one-half of Avogadro's number, or 3.01×10^{23} molecules.

An important application of molality concerns the freezing and boiling points of the solution. Actually, it is the concentration of dissolved particles (either molecules or ions) that determines the temperature at which the liquid solvent of a solution freezes or boils.

Explain . . .
When 1000 g of water are added to 1 mole of solute, is the resulting solution 1 *M* or 1 *m*? Why?
When a solvent is added to 1 mole of solute to make 1000 ml of solution, is the resulting solution 1 *M* or 1 *m*? Why?

Freezing and Boiling Points of Solutions

It has long been known that an aqueous solution of a solid freezes at a temperature below the freezing point of pure water. The freezing

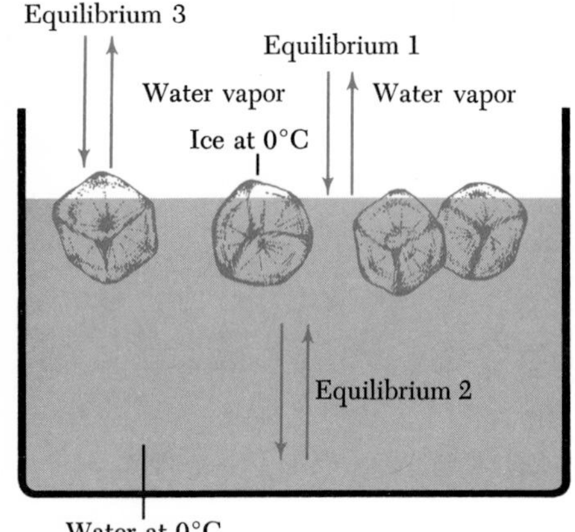

Fig. 14-9 At 0°C, there are three different pairs of equilibria between water, water vapor, and ice.

point of sea water, for example, is lower than that of river water. Dissolved liquids also depress the freezing point. Thus, an antifreeze [such as methyl alcohol (CH_3OH) or ethylene glycol, $(CH_2OH)_2$] prevents water in an automobile radiator from freezing in winter. How does a solute depress or lower the freezing point of water?

If we add enough ice to water in a beaker, the temperature of the ice, water, and water vapor are in equilibrium, as shown in Fig. 14-9. That is, at this temperature there are three different sets of equilibria:

(1)	ice	$\rightleftharpoons$	water
(2)	water	$\rightleftharpoons$	water vapor
(3)	ice	$\rightleftharpoons$	water vapor

Moreover, at 0°C the vapor pressure of ice must be the same as the vapor pressure of water, otherwise the substance with the greater vapor pressure would gradually disappear. This situation is shown in Fig. 14-10 where both the "water curve" and the "ice curve" indicate the vapor pressure of water and ice at various temperatures. The temperature of point P where these two curves meet is 0°C, the freezing point of water or the melting point of ice.

How is vapor pressure affected by dissolving a solid such as sugar or urea in water? Since they are solids at room temperature, sugar and urea have a very low vapor pressure at this temperature. Therefore, when they are dissolved in water, urea molecules or sugar molecules serve to replace water molecules with a less volatile species. This results in a reduction in the number of water molecules per unit volume available to excape as vapor, so the vapor pressure of the solution is less than the vapor pressure of pure water at the same temperature. This situation is also shown in the graph, where the vapor–solution curve is below the vapor–water curve. The point P_1 where the solution curve meets the ice curve is the freezing point of the solution ($-t$°C). If the solution were more concentrated, the freezing point would be lower.

It should be observed that P_1 is the *initial* freezing point of the dilute solution. As more ice is formed, the remaining solution becomes more concentrated and its freezing point is progressively lowered. Thus, the freezing point would decrease continuously until, ultimately, the solution becomes saturated; at this point the freezing point would remain steady.

It should now be apparent that *the depression of the freezing point depends upon the concentration of particles (molecules or ions) of solute in solution*; that is, the greater the proportion of molecules of solute to molecules of water the greater is the depression of the freezing point. However, 1 mole of sugar and 1 mole of urea contain the same number of molecules. Therefore, if 1 mole of each of these substances is dissolved in the same mass of water (1 kg, for example) we would expect the depression of the freezing point to be the same for each solution. This conclusion can readily be verified by experiment.

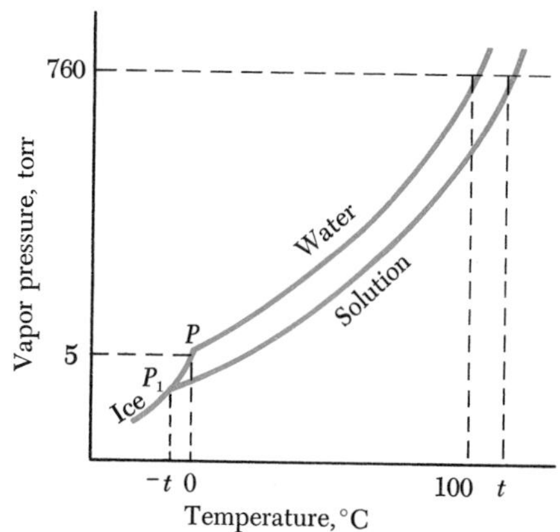

Fig. 14-10 At 0°C the vapor pressure of ice is the same as the vapor pressure of water. At the same temperature the vapor pressure of a solution is less than the vapor pressure of water.

Raoult's Law

In 1882, a French scientist named F. M. Raoult (1830–1901) discovered a relationship between the depression and the concentration of solutions. This relationship applies to very dilute solutions and only approximately to more concentrated solutions. First, he showed experimentally that the depression of the freezing point depended upon the ratio of the number of moles of solute to the mass of water in the solution. If, for example, a solution contains x moles of solute in y kilograms of water, the depression of the freezing point is proportional to

$$\frac{x \text{ moles solute}}{y \text{ kg water}}$$

This fraction expresses the number of moles of solute per kilogram of water, which is the molality of the solution. One way, then, of stating Raoult's law is: *The depression of the freezing point of a solution is proportional to its molality.* If the symbol Δt represents the depression of the freezing point and m the molality, the law can be written as

$$\Delta t \propto m \qquad \text{or} \qquad \Delta t = m \times k$$

where k is a constant. This constant can be determined by making a 1 m solution (by dissolving 1 mole of a solute in 1 kg H_2O) and finding the initial freezing point of the solution. For this solution,

$$k = \frac{\Delta t}{m} = \frac{\Delta t}{1 \text{ mole solute/kg } H_2O} \tag{14-3}$$

If urea is selected as the solute, experiment shows that a solution containing 1 mole (60 g) of urea dissolved in 1 kg of water begins to freeze at $-1.86C°$. Hence, the molal freezing-point depression (Δt) is $1.86C°$. Substituting this value in Eq. (14-3),

$$k = 1.86\text{C}°/\text{ mole of solute/kilogram of water}$$

Or, expressed another way, $k = 1.86C°$ per Avogadro number (6.02×10^{23}) of molecules of solute per kilogram of water.

Molecular Masses of Dissolved Substances

You have already learned how to find the molecular masses of gases. Many substances are not gases under ordinary conditions, but if a substance (solid or liquid) dissolves in water and does not ionize, its molecular mass probably can be determined by the depression of the freezing point of a solution of known molal concentration. In Example 14-6, the molecular mass of glucose is computed from experimental data.

Example 14-6

Given the following data, find the molecular mass of glucose.

mass of glucose = 2.50 g

mass of H_2O used to dissolve the glucose = 20.0 g or 0.0200 kg

initial freezing point of solution = −1.29 °C

molecular mass of glucose = ?

Solution

$$m = \frac{\Delta t}{k} = \frac{1.29\text{C}°}{1.86\text{C}°/\text{mole/kg H}_2\text{O}}$$

$$= \frac{1.29\text{C}° \times \text{mole}}{1.86\text{C}° \times 1\text{ kg H}_2\text{O}}$$

$$= 0.695\text{ mole/kg H}_2\text{O}$$

$$\text{mass of glucose in 1 kg H}_2\text{O} = \frac{2.50\text{ g} \times 1\text{ kg}}{0.0200\text{ kg}} = 125\text{ g}$$

Hence

$$0.695 \text{ mole glucose} = 125 \text{ g}$$

$$1 \text{ mole glucose} = \frac{125 \text{ g}}{0.695 \text{ mole}} = 180 \text{ g/mole}$$

Therefore the molecular mass of glucose is 180 amu.

Example 14-7 illustrates Raoult's law.

Example 14-7

Find the molality of a solution of urea that freezes at $-0.50\,°C$.

Solution

$$m = \frac{\Delta t}{k}$$

$$= \frac{0.50C° \times 1 \text{ mole}}{1.86C° \times 1 \text{ kg } H_2O}$$

$$= 0.27 \text{ mole/kg } H_2O$$

The molality of the urea solution is 0.27 *m*.

Boiling Points of Solutions

Since a dissolved nonvolatile solute lowers the vapor pressure of the solvent, an aqueous solution must be heated to a temperature above 100 °C before its vapor pressure equals the pressure of the atmosphere. In other words, a dissolved solute *raises the boiling point of the solvent.* Note the vapor pressures of water as shown in Fig. 14-11. Notice that when the vapor pressure is 760 torr, the boiling point of pure water is 100°C, but the boiling point of the aqueous solution is higher than 100°C.

The same relation exists for elevation of the boiling point as for depression of the freezing point, and another part of Raoult's law is: *The elevation of the boiling point of a solution is proportional to*

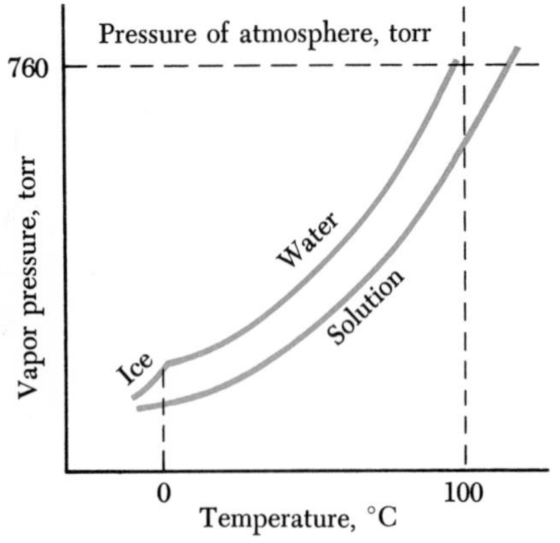

Fig. 14-11 The vapor pressure of a solution is less than the vapor pressure of water at corresponding temperatures.

its molality. Hence,

$$\Delta t \propto m \qquad \text{or} \qquad \Delta t = k \times m$$

where k is a constant, Δt is the elevation of the boiling point, and m is the molality.

The value of the molal boiling point constant, however, is quite different from the freezing-point constant. Experiment shows that a solution containing 1 mole of solute in 1 kg of water boils at 100.51 °C. Hence, the boiling-point constant is 0.51° per mole per kilogram of water. The elevation of the boiling point can also be used to determine the molecular mass of a solute as in Example 14-8.

Example 14-8

Find the molecular mass of urea if a solution of 2.50 g of urea in 20.0 g of H_2O boils at 101.06 °C.

Solution

$$m = \Delta t / k$$

$$= \frac{1.06^\circ \times \text{mole}}{0.51^\circ \times 1 \text{ kg } H_2O}$$

$$= 2.08 \text{ moles/kg } H_2O$$

$$\text{mass of urea in 1 kg water} = \frac{2.50 \text{ g}}{0.0200 \text{ kg}} \times 1 \text{ kg}$$

$$= 125 \text{ g}$$

$$2.08 \text{ moles urea} = 125 \text{ g}$$

$$1 \text{ mole urea} = \frac{125 \text{ g}}{2.08 \text{ moles}} = 60.0 \text{ g/mole}$$

Therefore the molecular mass of urea is 60 amu.

Freezing Points of Solutions of Soluble Ionic Compounds

Experiment shows that the freezing point of a 1 m solution of NaCl is about −3.72 °C. That is, the depression of the freezing point is almost twice as large as the value computed from the Raoult equation:

$$\Delta t = m \times 1.86°$$

Why the abnormally large depression? Does Raoult's law not apply to solutions of ionic compounds? As you recall, a crystal of NaCl consists of a lattice of Na^+ ions and Cl^- ions, and the addition of water breaks the lattice bonds and separates the ions. In other words, 1 mole of sodium chloride contains 2 moles of ions. That is, a solution containing 1 mole of NaCl contains twice Avogadro's number of ions (6.02×10^{23} Na^+ ions and 6.02×10^{23} Cl^- ions, or 12.04×10^{23} in all).

You recall that the lowering of the vapor pressure (and therefore the depression of the freezing point) depends upon the concentration of particles in solution, whatever their size. And, since there are twice as many *ions* in 1 mole of sodium chloride as there are *molecules* in 1 mole of urea, we would expect the freezing-point depression for sodium chloride to be twice the depression calculated from the Raoult equation.

Summary

An ionic solid dissolves in water, provided the attractive force between the water dipoles and the ions is strong enough to overcome the mutual attraction of oppositely-charged ions. If a substance is made up of molecules rather than ions, it will usually dissolve in water if the molecules are polar; if the molecules are nonpolar, the substance is usually not very soluble in water.

In a saturated solution, there is an equilibrium between the rate at which the solid dissolves and the rate at which dissolved particles crystallize (precipitate).

Le Châtelier's principle applies to all systems in equilibrium, and to both physical and chemical changes. It states: *If a system in equilibrium is subjected to a stress, the system responds so as to relieve (or oppose) the stress and to establish a new equilibrium.*

A one-molar (1 *M*) solution contains 1 mole of solute per liter of *solution.* A one molal (1 *m*) solution contains 1 mole of solute per kilogram of solvent, usually water (or, per liter of water at 4°C).

Raoult's law concerns molal solutions. It states: *The depression of the freezing point of the liquid solvent of a solution (or the elevation of the boiling point of the solvent) is proportional to the molality of the solution.*

Factual Recall

1. What is (*a*) a solution, (*b*) a saturated solution, (*c*) an unsaturated solution?
2. Explain how water dissolves an ionic compound.
3. Explain how water dissolves a nonionic compound.
4. Explain why carbon tetrachloride (CCl_4) is almost insoluble in water.
5. The heat of solution of potassium nitrate is −8.5 kcal/mole. Explain (*a*) the term *heat of solution*, and (*b*) the significance of the negative sign.
6. (*a*) State Le Châtelier's principle.

   (*b*) Explain by Le Châtelier's principle why some of the dissolved KNO_3 is precipitated if the saturated solution is cooled.
7. Compare and contrast molar and molal solutions.

Apply Your Knowledge!

If 44.9 g of a saturated solution of KNO_3 at 40 °C are evaporated to dryness and 17.5 g of solid remain, compute the solubility of KNO_3 at 40 °C.

Find Out!

By analysis, the composition of a substance by mass is 38.7% carbon, 9.7% hydrogen, and 51.6% oxygen. A solution of 0.150g of the substance in 10.0 g of water freezes at −0.43 °C.

(*a*) What is the experimental value for the molecular mass of the substance?

(*b*) Find the simplest formula of the substance.

(*c*) Find the molecular formula of the substance.

(*d*) What is the correct molecular mass value?

CHAPTER 15

IONIZATION

THE THEORY OF IONIZATION can be used to explain and to correlate a great many of the properties of matter. Some of the most important of these are the properties of solutions of electrolytes. To understand more about this interesting area of chemistry we must go back to the work of Michael Faraday (1791–1867), an English scientist who first used the term *ion*.

Electrolytes and Nonelectrolytes

In the early part of the 19th Century, Faraday discovered two natural laws which opened up the new field of electrolysis. Using an apparatus similar to that shown in Fig. 15-1, he dipped the electrodes into solutions of hydrogen chloride (hydrochloric acid), sodium hydroxide, and sodium chloride. In each case the evolution of gas proved that each solution conducted an electric current. This phenomenon will be further discussed in Chapter 18. The apparatus used today resembles Fig. 15-2. When the electrodes are dipped into solutions of HCl, NaOH, and NaCl, the light bulb glows very brightly, proving that each solution conducts an

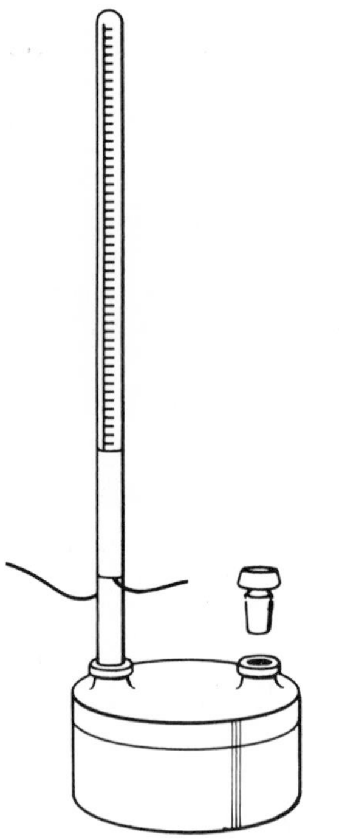

Fig. 15-1 Faraday's apparatus for measuring electrical conductivity.

electric current. However, when the electrodes are dipped into solutions of sugar, urea, and alcohol, the light bulb does not glow. What does this indicate?

On the basis of these experiments, Faraday classified compounds into two categories, *electrolytes* and *nonelectrolytes*, depending upon the conductivity or nonconductivity of their solutions. He defined *electrolytes as substances whose water solutions conduct electricity*. Of the three electrolytes mentioned above, hydrochloric acid is an acid, sodium hydroxide a base, and sodium chloride a salt. If the electrodes are dipped into solutions of other acids, bases, and salts, the bulb lights up every time. We therefore conclude that *acids, bases, and salts are electrolytes*.

Why do solutions of electrolytes conduct a current? Faraday said that solutions of electrolytes must contain electrically charged particles that travel to the electrodes. He called these charged particles *ions*, a word derived from a Greek word meaning "going."

Faraday's experiments on electrolysis were performed about 1820. Some 60 years later, in 1887, a Swedish chemist named Svante Arrhenius (1859–1927) proposed a theory of ionization to account for the electrical properties of solutions of electrolytes. Arrhenius' theory not only explained the conductivity of solutions, it also accounted for their chemical and physical properties. As we compare Arrhenius' theory with the modern theory of ionization we must bear in mind that in 1887 nothing was known about electrons, protons, or the structure of atoms.

Arrhenius' Theory of Ionization

The main points of Arrhenius' theory can be summarized as follows:

1. Electrolytes produce positive and negative ions when dissolved in water.
2. Since a solution is electrically neutral, the number of *negative charges* on the negative ions must equal the number of *positive charges* on the positive ions.
3. An acid gives hydrogen ions (H^+) in water solution, and a base gives hydroxide ions (OH^-).

Predict . . .
Remember that ions in aqueous solution, especially hydrogen ions, exist in hydrated form. Does this fact change these concepts in any way?

Notice that Arrhenius did not state *how* water caused ionization. He did not know; in his day nothing was known about dipoles. Arrhenius did state that the number of negative *charges* equals the number of positive *charges*. He did not refer to an equality between positive and negative *ions*. Why not?

Consider, for example, the ionization of a molecule of sulfuric acid:

$$H_2SO_4 \longrightarrow 2H^+ + SO_4^{-2}$$

Clearly the total number of positive charges on the hydrogen ions equals the number of negative charges on the sulfate ions. However, the number of *hydrogen ions* does *not* equal the number of *sulfate ions*. Finally, Arrhenius defined acids and bases in terms of their characteristic ions. These turned out to be most useful concepts but the Arrhenius concepts had to be expanded to include modern ideas on acids and bases.

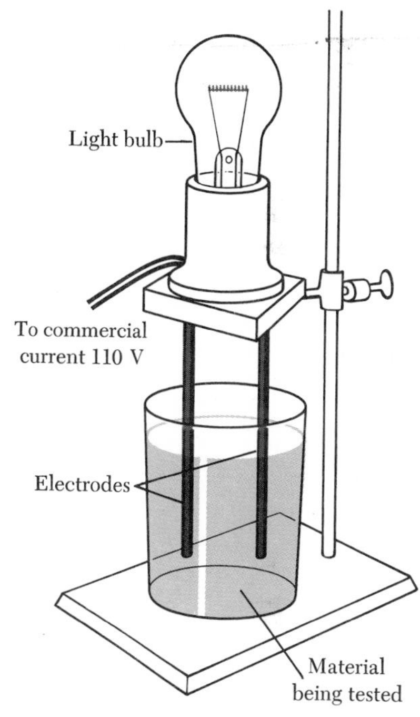

Fig. 15-2 Modern conductivity tester.

Chemical Evidence in Support of the Arrhenius Theory

If solutions of sodium chloride and silver nitrate are mixed, a white precipitate forms. The formation of a precipitate shows that a chemical reaction has taken place. What is the nature of the reaction? According to Arrhenius, sodium chloride and silver nitrate dissociate into ions when dissolved in water:

$$NaCl \xrightarrow{H_2O} Na^+ + Cl^- \quad (15\text{-}1)$$

$$AgNO_3 \xrightarrow{H_2O} Ag^+ + NO_3^- \quad (15\text{-}2)$$

Thus, there are four ions present when the solutions are mixed. Will the ions react? There are four possibilities for such reactions:

$$Na^+ + Cl^- \longrightarrow NaCl \quad (15\text{-}3)$$

$$Ag^+ + NO_3^- \longrightarrow AgNO_3 \quad (15\text{-}4)$$

$$Na^+ + NO_3^- \longrightarrow NaNO_3 \quad (15\text{-}5)$$

$$Ag^+ + Cl^- \longrightarrow AgCl \quad (15\text{-}6)$$

The compounds NaCl, $AgNO_3$, and $NaNO_3$ are soluble in water and therefore there is no evidence that reactions (15-3), (15-4), and (15-5) take place. Silver chloride, however, is only very slightly soluble, so there is a marked tendency for free silver ions and chloride ions to combine to form the white solid AgCl. In other words, reaction (15-6) is favored and the ionic equation for this reaction is

$$Na^+ + Cl^- + Ag^+ + NO_3^- \longrightarrow Na^+ + NO_3^- + AgCl\downarrow \quad (15\text{-}7)$$

A downward arrow is sometimes used to indicate a precipitate, an insoluble substance.

Speculate . . .
Do the downward arrows (Eqs. 15-7 and 15-8) have *exactly* the same meaning as the (s) in Eq. 15-9?

Notice that the ions Na^+ and NO_3^- are present in both the reactants and the products. Therefore they take no part in the reaction; they are merely *spectator ions* and can be omitted from the equation. The amended equation then becomes

$$Ag^+ + Cl^- \longrightarrow AgCl\downarrow \quad (15\text{-}8)$$

and it includes only those ions that take part in the reaction.

Another way to write the equation is

$$Ag^+(aq) + Cl^-(aq) \longrightarrow AgCl(s) \quad (15\text{-}9)$$

where (aq) means that the ions are in aqueous solution, and the symbol (s) represents a slightly soluble solid.

Experiment . . .
Place four test tubes (labeled *A,B,C,* and *D*) in a rack. Into *A* pour 10 ml of dilute HCl; into *B*, 10 ml of 0.1 *M* KCl; into *C*, 10 ,; pf 0.1 *M* $CaCl_2$; and into *D*, 10 ml of tap water. To each tube add 10 drops of 0.1 *M* $AgNO_3$. Observe and explain what happens.

Concerning this reaction, Arrhenius maintained that the precipitation of silver chloride is quite independent of the source of chloride ions. That is, he predicted that if a solution of HCl, or KCl, or $CaCl_2$ is added to a solution of $AgNO_3$, the same white precipitate will be formed. Does this also apply to lead chromate? See Fig. 15-3.

Physical Evidence in Support of the Arrhenius Theory

Arrhenius believed (1) that electrolytes, when pure, were made up of molecules and (2) that in a solution of an electrolyte, a condition of equilibrium existed between molecules and ions, so that, as water was added, more molecules changed to ions. There seemed to be ample experimental evidence to support this view. For instance, he argued that the equilibrium in a concentrated solution of sodium chloride is

$$\underset{\text{molecules}}{n\,NaCl} \rightleftharpoons \underset{\text{ions}}{n\,Na^+ + n\,Cl^-} \quad (15\text{-}10)$$

Explain . . .
Relate this theory to Le Châtelier's principle.

If water is added to this concentrated solution, its electrical conductivity is found to increase; this fact seemed to confirm the molecule-ion equilibrium idea. Or, as Arrhenius stated, the greater the dilution of the solution the greater is the degree of ionization until, eventually, the electrolyte is completely ionized. This statement also seemed to be supported by data on the depression of the freezing point.

Table 15-1 Change of freezing point depression with molality of sodium chloride solution

Molality, m	Freezing point, °C	Freezing point depression per mole NaCl, C°	Apparent ionization, %
1	−3.42	3.42	84
0.1	−0.347	3.47	88
0.01	−0.0361	3.61	93
0.001	−0.00366	3.66	97
0.0001	−0.000372	3.72	100

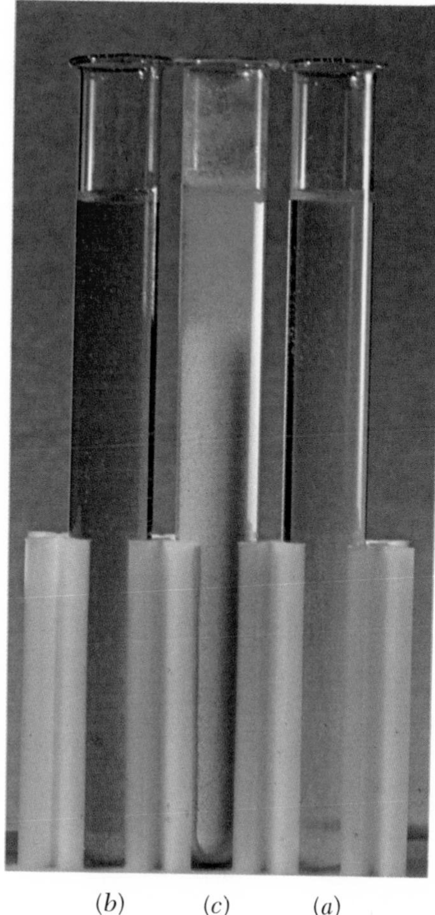

(*b*) (*c*) (*a*)

Fig. 15-3 Making chrome yellow. Lead nitrate (*a*), when mixed with potassium chromate (*b*), forms lead chromate (*c*), which is the pigment chrome yellow.

How can these figures be interpreted? Arrhenius said that a depression of 3.72° (or 2 × 1.86°) shows that every molecule of the electrolyte has yielded two ions or, in other words, the solute is completely ionized. On the other hand, a freezing point of −3.42°C shows that the solute is only partially ionized and the amount of *abnormality* (or the number of degrees below −1.86°C) indicates the degree of ionization. Since the abnormality is 1.56° (3.42° − 1.86°) he argued that 1.56/1.86 or 84% of the NaCl in a 1 M solution is ionized, and the rest (16%) is molecular.

This explanation seemed reasonable, and it was generally accepted that ordinary solutions of electrolytes were indeed mixtures of molecules and ions. However, when X-ray analysis showed that salts in crystal form are completely ionized, the molecular-ionic concept had to be reconsidered. But why do electrolytes appear to be incompletely ionized in solution? Why is there an *apparent degree of ionization* if the salts are indeed completely ionized. There was no satisfactory answer to this question until 1923 (almost 40 years after Arrhenius stated his theory), when two European scientists, P.J.W. Debye (Dutch) and W.F.K. Hückel (German), propounded a theory that accounted for the properties of ionic solutions in terms of attraction between oppositely charged ions.

The Debye-Hückel Theory

Debye (1884–1966) and Hückel (1895–19__) assumed that strong electrolytes like NaCl are completely ionized at all times. However, in solution there is a mutual attraction between ions of opposite charges and, as a result, every positive ion is surrounded by a slight excess of negative charge and every negative ion is surrounded by a

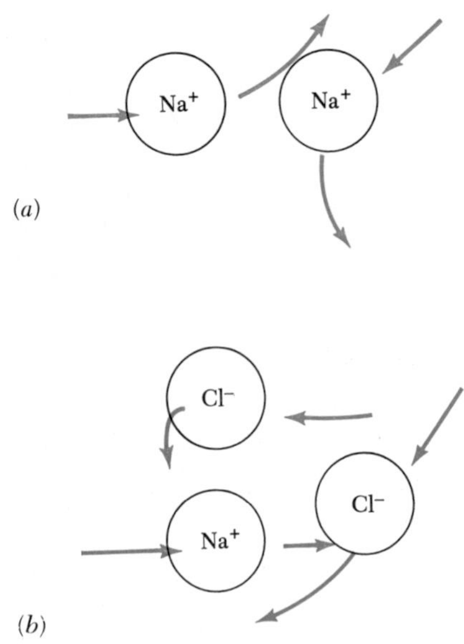

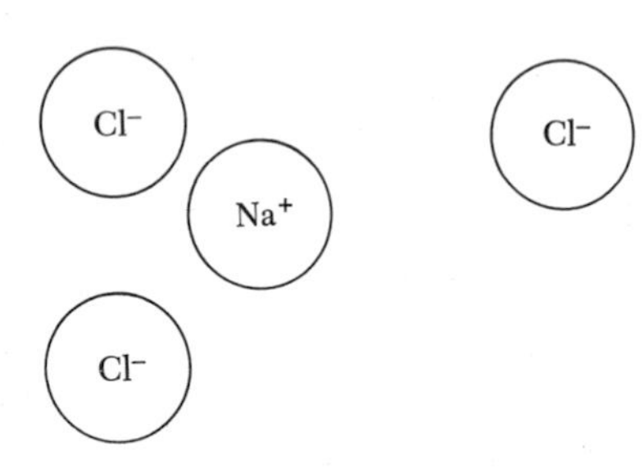

(c)

Fig. 15-4 Behavior of ions in solution. (*a*) Sodium ions are repelled as they approach each other. (*b*) Chloride ions are attracted to moving sodium ions. (*c*) What happens as a net result?

slight excess of positive charge. (See Fig. 15-4.) Moreover, a certain percentage of the oppositely charged ions would be so close together that they would behave like single particles. This, in turn, would decrease the number of "particles" in solution, thereby increasing the vapor pressure and reducing the expected freezing point depression. At infinite dilution, however, the ions are so widely separated that interionic attraction is at a minimum and, as a result, the depression of the freezing point reaches a maximum value. Thus, the Debye-Hückel theory accounts for the *apparent* incomplete ionization of salts, but supports the concept of complete ionization. Finally, although Arrhenius' molecule–ion equilibrium concept for electrolytes has long been disproved, his statement that electrolytes give rise to free ions in water solution is still accepted today.

The Ionization of Covalent Molecules

Some covalent compounds also form ions when dissolved in water. Hydrogen chloride is an example of such a compound. Experiment shows that neither liquid hydrogen chloride nor hydrogen chloride dissolved in benzene conducts a current, and we therefore conclude that no ions are present in this compound. However, if water is added to hydrogen chloride (thereby forming hydrochloric acid), the solution conducts a current very well. Hydrochloric acid therefore contains ions, and it is apparent that these ions must have been formed by a reaction between molecules of hydrogen chloride and molecules of water. How is this possible?

As you learned in Chapter 9, chlorine is more electronegative than hydrogen. (The electronegativity of chlorine is 3.0 and that of hydrogen is 2.1.) Thus, in a molecule of hydrogen chloride the shared pair of electrons is closer to the chlorine atom than to the hydrogen atom, thereby forming a polar covalent bond. As a result, one end of the molecule (the hydrogen end) is positive and the other (the chlorine end) is negative. That is, the molecule is polar, as is shown in the following electron-dot formula:

$$H^{+}\ :\overset{\cdot\cdot}{\underset{\cdot\cdot}{Cl}}:^{-}$$

Since a water molecule is also polar, the negative end of a water molecule will be attracted to the positive end of a hydrogen chloride molecule, and vice versa, to form a doubly hydrated molecule. Such an arrangement is represented in Eq. (15-11):

$$\mathrm{H}:\underset{\mathrm{H}}{\overset{\cdot\cdot}{\underset{\cdot\cdot}{\mathrm{O}}}}: + \mathrm{H}\ :\overset{\cdot\cdot}{\underset{\cdot\cdot}{\mathrm{Cl}}}: + \mathrm{H}:\underset{\mathrm{H}}{\overset{\cdot\cdot}{\underset{\cdot\cdot}{\mathrm{O}}}}: \longrightarrow \mathrm{H}:\underset{\mathrm{H}}{\overset{\cdot\cdot}{\underset{\cdot\cdot}{\mathrm{O}}}}:\mathrm{H}\ :\overset{\cdot\cdot}{\underset{\cdot\cdot}{\mathrm{Cl}}}:\ \mathrm{H}:\underset{\mathrm{H}}{\overset{\cdot\cdot}{\underset{\cdot\cdot}{\mathrm{O}}}}: \tag{15-11}$$

If the attraction between the oxygen end of the water molecule and the proton of a hydrogen chloride molecule is greater than the attraction of the hydrogen and chlorine atoms for each other, the hydrated hydrogen chloride molecule will break apart with the proton attached to the water molecule. There is evidence that something like this actually happens and the reaction is shown in Eq. (15-12):

$$\mathrm{H}:\underset{\mathrm{H}}{\overset{\cdot\cdot}{\underset{\cdot\cdot}{\mathrm{O}}}}:\mathrm{H}\ :\underset{\mathrm{H}}{\overset{\cdot\cdot}{\underset{\cdot\cdot}{\mathrm{Cl}}}}:\ \mathrm{H}:\underset{\mathrm{H}}{\overset{\cdot\cdot}{\underset{\cdot\cdot}{\mathrm{O}}}}: \longrightarrow$$

$$[\mathrm{H}:\underset{\mathrm{H}}{\overset{\cdot\cdot}{\underset{\cdot\cdot}{\mathrm{O}}}}:\mathrm{H}]^{+} + [\ :\overset{\cdot\cdot}{\underset{\cdot\cdot}{\mathrm{Cl}}}:\ \mathrm{H}:\underset{\mathrm{H}}{\overset{\cdot\cdot}{\underset{\cdot\cdot}{\mathrm{O}}}}:\ ]^{-} \tag{15-12}$$

In this equation, simple hydrated ions are formed; Eq. (15-12) can also be written:

$$HCl + 2H_2O \longrightarrow H_3O^+ \text{ (or } H^+ \cdot H_2O) + Cl^- \cdot H_2O \tag{15-13}$$

In practice, however, the number of water molecules attached to the ions is probably greater than one, so that the reaction is more accurately expressed in Eq. (15-14):

$$HCl + nH_2O \longrightarrow [H \cdot xH_2O]^+ + [Cl \cdot yH_2O]^- \tag{15-14}$$

where the letters n, x, and y are integers whose actual values are unknown. However, simplified forms of Eq. (15-14) are acceptable. Usually it is written as Eq. (15-15) to show only a hydrated hydrogen ion (called a hydronium ion).

$$HCl + H_2O \longrightarrow H_3O^+ + Cl^- \tag{15-15}$$

But sometimes it is convenient to write the reaction in its simplest form, without showing any hydrated ions at all:

$$HCl \longrightarrow H^+ + Cl^- \tag{15-16}$$

In an equation such as Eq. (15-16), the hydration of ions is, of course, always assumed.

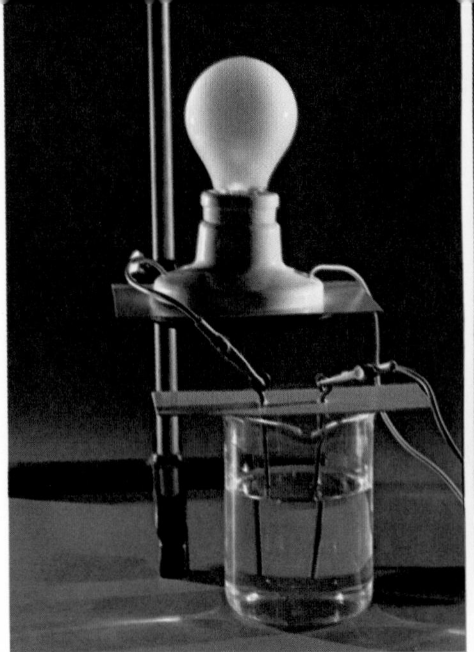 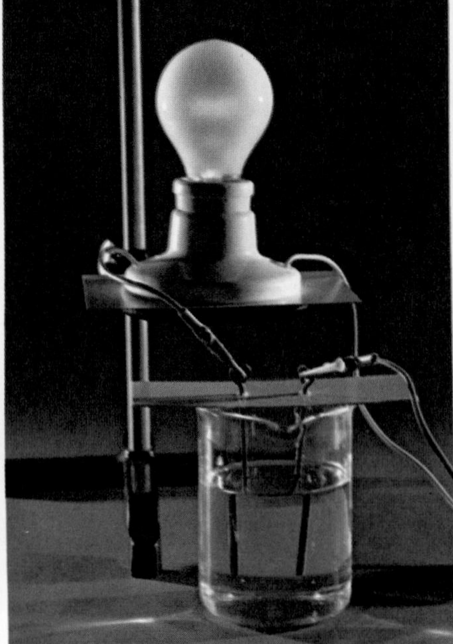 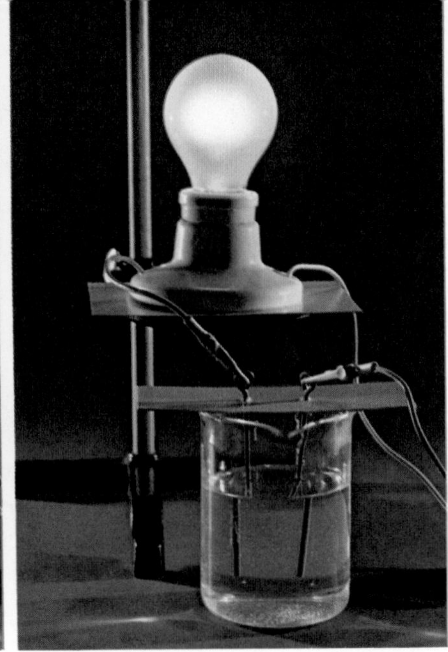

Fig. 15-5 Conductivity tester in operation. Which set up contains the strongest electrolyte? The weakest?

Strong and Weak Electrolytes

So far we have considered some ionic compounds and one compound (HC1) that is not ionic. As you know, ionic compounds consist of ions even as solids, and in water solution they are also completely ionized. Hydrogen chloride is also thought of as completely ionized in dilute solutions. Substances that are completely ionized in dilute solution are called *strong* electrolytes. Some compounds, however, ionize to only a slight degree when dissolved in water and these are called *weak* electrolytes. For example, carboxylic acids are weak electrolytes. One such acid is acetic acid, CH_3COOH.

Definition . . .
Carboxylic acids comprise a large number of carbon-containing acids that also have in common a —COOH group, known as a carboxyl group.

If the electrodes of the conductivity apparatus (Fig. 15-5) are dipped into pure acetic acid (which is a liquid at ordinary temperatures), the bulb does not light up. If water is added to the acetic acid the bulb glows dimly; the bulb never gets much brighter no matter how much water is added. How can this be explained? It is assumed that molecules of acetic acid ionize only to a slight degree, forming hydronium ions and acetate ions.

$$CH_3COOH + H_2O \xrightleftharpoons[\longleftarrow]{\rightharpoonup} H_3O^+ + CH_3COO^- \qquad (15\text{-}17)$$

The short arrow pointing to the right is meant to indicate that ionization takes place to only a slight extent.

Notice that in this case there *is* an equilibrium between molecules and ions. This you recall was one of the postulates of the original Arrhenius theory. In other words, this postulate of Arrhenius is true insofar as it is applied to *weak electrolytes.*

How can the "weakness" of acetic acid be accounted for? The electron-dot formula for acetic acid is shown in Fig. 15-6.

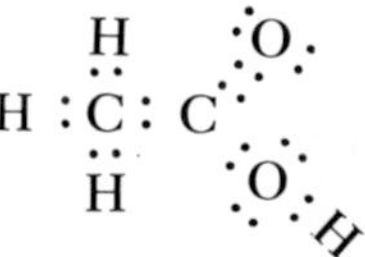

Fig. 15-6 Electron-dot formula for acetic acid.

The covalent bond between hydrogen and oxygen in acetic acid must be much stronger than the bond between hydrogen and chlorine in hydrogen chloride. That is, the O H bond in acetic acid shows a large covalent tendency but only a slight ionic tendency.

The base ammonia also is a weak electrolyte. The reaction of ammonia with water is represented by

$$NH_3(g) + H_2O \rightleftharpoons NH_4^+ + OH^- \qquad (15\text{-}18)$$

Here the NH_3 molecule takes a proton from water, leaving OH^- ions. The equilibrium in this reaction is similar to that of acetic acid and water in that the concentrations of NH_4^+ and OH^- are not large. Liquid ammonia, like pure acetic acid, does not conduct electricity.

Some Characteristic Properties of Acids

Long before Arrhenius' time acids and bases were recognized as important groups of chemical compounds which have their own characteristic properties. The three properties commonly associated with acids are

(1) They have a sour taste.
(2) They turn blue litmus red.
(3) They react with certain metals, releasing hydrogen gas.

When Arrhenius defined an acid in terms of hydrogen ions, all the properties listed were ascribed to hydrogen ions.

Sour Taste

The juices of such citrus fruits as lemons and limes have a sharp or acid taste which, according to Arrhenius, is caused by the hydrogen ions in the weak acids they contain. Therefore, these fruit juices have relatively low hydrogen-ion concentration and thus are pleasant to taste. However, even dilute solutions of laboratory acids such as sulfuric acid and nitric acid contain hydrogen ions in such high

Fig. 15-7 Litmus indicator paper at work. Which test tube contains the acid?

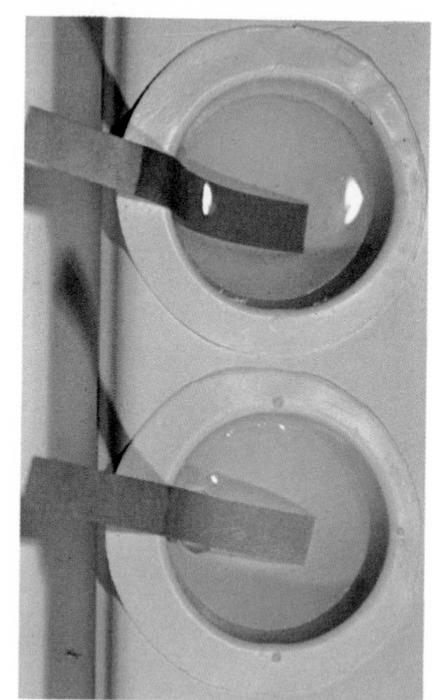

concentration that their taste is most unpleasant; furthermore their effect on tissues is harmful. They should *never* be tasted.

The Color of Litmus

Litmus is a vegetable dye which has two different structures, one blue and the other red (See Fig. 15-7). The particular structure which is present at any given time depends upon the concentration of hydrogen ions present. Hydrogen ions react chemically with the blue structure and change it to the red structure. Thus, when an acid is present the red structure will be formed and the dye will appear red. Conversely, bases react with the red structure to produce the blue structure. The reaction is completely reversible.

Reactions of Acids with Certain Metals

When metals such as magnesium and zinc react with dilute sulfuric acid or dilute hydrochloric acid, hydrogen is released from the acid. Before anything was known about ionization the equations for these reactions were written:

$$Mg + H_2SO_4 \longrightarrow MgSO_4 + H_2\uparrow \qquad (15\text{-}19)$$
$$Zn + H_2SO_4 \longrightarrow ZnSO_4 + H_2\uparrow \qquad (15\text{-}20)$$
$$Mg + 2HCl \longrightarrow MgCl_2 + H_2\uparrow \qquad (15\text{-}21)$$
$$Zn + 2HCl \longrightarrow ZnCl_2 + H_2\uparrow \qquad (15\text{-}22)$$

where the upward-pointing arrow indicates a gas is released.

The ionic equation for the reaction between magnesium and dilute sulfuric acid can be written:

$$Mg + 2H^+ + SO_4^{-2} \longrightarrow Mg^{+2} + SO_4^{-2} + H_2(g) \qquad (15\text{-}23)$$

Or, omitting the spectator ion (SO_4^{-2}),

$$Mg + 2H^+ \longrightarrow Mg^{+2} + H_2(g) \qquad (15\text{-}24)$$

Equation (15-24) can also be written:

$$Mg(s) + 2H^+(aq) \longrightarrow Mg^{+2}(aq) + H_2(g) \qquad (15\text{-}25)$$

Or, expressing hydrogen ion as hydronium ion,

$$Mg(s) + 2H_3O^+ \longrightarrow Mg^{+2} + H_2(g) + 2H_2O \qquad (15\text{-}26)$$

The simplest equation (Eq. 15-24) shows that the chemical change is essentially a reaction between magnesium metal and hydrogen ions. Why does the reaction take place? You recall that a chemical reaction will take place between two substances provided that both can increase their stability by doing so. We know that a magnesium atom has two loosely held electrons—two $3s$ electrons. The metal atoms tend to lose these electrons because, in doing so, they form ions with the stable configuration of the noble gas neon. On the other hand, hydrogen ions are protons. If two protons each gain an electron, they form two hydrogen atoms and if these atoms share each other's valence electron to form a hydrogen molecule, the s orbitals of both atoms are filled. And this, you recall, is the stable structure of helium, another of the noble gases. This suggests that if the metal magnesium is in contact with hydrogen ions, the two valence electrons of a magnesium atom are transferred to two hydrogen ions, thereby increasing the stability of both reactants:

$$Mg - 2e^- \longrightarrow Mg^{+2} \qquad (15\text{-}27)$$

and

$$2H^+ + 2e^- \longrightarrow 2H \longrightarrow H_2(g) \qquad (15\text{-}28)$$

Some Characteristic Properties of Bases

It has long been known that bases, like acids, have a number of characteristic properties. For example, properties attributed to solutions of bases are:

(1) They have a brackish ("soapy") taste.
(2) They turn red litmus blue.
(3) They neutralize acids.

Arrhenius defined bases as substances which contain hydroxide ions (OH^-) in water solution and he ascribed the three listed characteristic properties of bases to these ions. The two most common bases are sodium hydroxide (NaOH) and potassium hydroxide (KOH).

Taste

Solutions of NaOH and KOH should never be tasted—they are harmful to tissue and cause burn-like wounds. However, it is safe to taste a soap solution which is basic. And, as you probably know by experience, it has a characteristic brackish taste. It also turns red litmus blue.

Note . . .
In older chemical literature, the—OH group is usually called *hydroxyl*. Keep this in mind when you do literature research.

According to Arrhenius, the reaction between sodium hydroxide and water is

$$NaOH \xrightarrow{\text{water}} Na^+ + OH^- \qquad (15\text{-}29)$$

We now know from X-ray analysis that many bases, like salts, form ionic lattices in the solid state, and that the addition of water breaks the lattice bonds, thereby releasing the ions. Thus, a more accurate representation of the ionization of a base is

$$\underset{\text{solid}}{n\,[Na^+\,OH^-]} \xrightarrow{H_2O} \underset{\text{solution}}{n\,Na^+ + n\,OH^-} \qquad (15\text{-}30)$$

Neutralization

The *neutralization* of an acid by a base *means that a base neutralizes or counteracts the characteristic properties of the acid.* Stated in words, a neutralization reaction is

$$\text{acid} + \text{base} \longrightarrow \text{salt} + \text{water} \qquad (15\text{-}31)$$

A specific example is

$$HCl + NaOH \longrightarrow NaCl + H_2O \qquad (15\text{-}32)$$

The ionic equation for this neutralization (Eq. 15-32) is

$$H^+ + Cl^- + Na^+ + OH^- \longrightarrow Na^+ + Cl^- + H_2O \qquad (15\text{-}33)$$

Or, omitting spectator ions,

$$H^+ + OH^- \longrightarrow H_2O \qquad (15\text{-}34)$$

That is, *neutralization is a reaction between the hydrogen ion of an acid and the hydroxide ion of a base.* It is therefore the same chemical reaction whatever the acid or base. Neutralization will be discussed at greater length in the next chapter.

Salts The salt formed in the neutralization reactions (15-32) and (15-33) is sodium chloride, NaCl. *A salt is an ionic compound of the positive ion of a base and the negative ion of an acid.*

Ternary Acids and Their Salts

Sulfuric acid contains three elements: H, O, and S. Acids that contain three elements are called *ternary* acids. All ternary acids contain hydrogen and almost all contain oxygen: therefore the third element distinguishes the kind of acid and its name is used in the prefix when naming the acid. For example, the third element in H_2SO_4 is sulfur and so the acid is called *sulfuric* acid. Similarly, H_2CO_3 is called *carbonic* acid. Notice also that the name ending for a ternary acid is sometimes *-ic*. And the name ending for a salt formed from an *-ic* acid is *-ate*, as in Table 15-2.

Table 15-2 Naming the salts of three ternary acids

Acid	Typical salt		Name ending of salt
	Formula	Name	
Sulfur*ic*	Na_2SO_4	sodium sulf*ate*	*ate*
Carbon*ic*	Na_2CO_3	sodium carbon*ate*	*ate*
Phosphor*ic*	Na_3PO_4	sodium phosph*ate*	*ate*

Sometimes two different acids are formed from the same three elements. In such cases, there is a difference in the number of oxygen atoms per molecule. The names of acids with fewer oxygen atoms per molecule end in *-ous*. For example, H_2SO_3 is sulfur*ous* acid and H_3PO_3 is phosphor*ous* acid. The name of a salt formed from an *-ous* acid ends in *-ite* as in Table 15-3.

Table 15-3 Naming salts of ternary acids with fewer oxygen atoms

Acid	Typical salt		Name ending of salt
	Formula	Name	
Sulfur*ous*	Na_2SO_3	sodium sulf*ite*	*ite*
Phosphor*ous*	Na_3PO_3	sodium phosph*ite*	*ite*

Complex Ions

As stated earlier, sodium sulfate is a salt and, even as a crystalline solid, it exists as ions, Na^+ ion and SO_4^{-2} ion. The sulfate ion (SO_4^{-2}) is called a *complex ion*. Complex ions often are quite stable: if this is the case, they remain intact in reaction in solution. That is, they normally behave like an ion consisting of only a single atom. Complex ions are very common and they usually carry a negative charge. Examples are sulfate ion (SO_4^{-2}), carbonate ion (CO_3^{-2}), nitrate ion (NO_3^-), chlorate ion (ClO_3^-), and phosphate ion (PO_4^{-3}). The only common complex ion with a positive charge is the ammonium ion, NH_4^+.

Research . . .
The polyatomic units which we now call *complex ions* were formerly called *radicals.* Find out why this term was used. Why is the modern term more correct?

The charge on the complex ion is sometimes called its valence. What determines the "valence"of a complex ion? The "valence" is the net charge that remains after the atoms of the ion have bonded with each other. Let us consider a chlorate ion which consists of three atoms of oxygen and one atom of chlorine. This ion has a -1 charge and hence its "valence" is -1. However, it is reasonable to ask how this -1 charge can be explained. Perhaps the easiest way to explain this is to write the electron-dot formula for chlorate ion, recognizing that both the oxygen and chlorine atoms will be stabilized when they have eight valence electrons and that the structure of this ion is known to be that of a chlorine atom surrounded by three oxygen atoms. The electron-dot formula can be written

$$-\!\!{}^{\times}\overset{\times\times}{\underset{\times\times}{O}}\,\overset{\circ}{\underset{\times}{}}\,\overset{\circ\circ}{Cl}\,\overset{\circ}{\underset{\circ}{}}\,\overset{\times\times}{\underset{\times\times}{O}}\,\overset{\times}{\underset{\times}{}}$$
$$\overset{\circ\circ}{\underset{\times\times}{{}^{\times}_{\times}O^{\times}_{\times}}}$$

where the dots represent electrons from chlorine and the x's electrons from oxygen. With this structure, it should be clear that there are not enough valence electrons on the four atoms to give a structure with eight valence electrons for all atoms. If, however, one more electron is added, all the atoms will have eight valence electrons and the structure will be stable. Hence the chlorate ion, in becoming stable, must acquire one more electron than its atoms can supply. When it acquires this additional electron it also acquires its -1 charge. To complete the picture, the electron-dot formula for chloric acid ($HClO_3$) is

$$\overset{\times\times}{{}^{\times}_{\times}O^{\times}_{\times}}$$
$$H\underset{\times}{-}\overset{\times\times}{\underset{\times\times}{O}}\,{}^{\times}_{\circ}\,\overset{\circ\circ}{\underset{\circ\circ}{Cl}}\,{}^{\circ}_{\circ}\,\overset{\times\times}{\underset{\times\times}{O}}{}^{\times}_{\times}$$

Here, the additional electron, represented by the dash, is supplied by the hydrogen atom. Another chlorine-oxygen acid is perchloric acid ($HClO_4$).

Table 15-4 contains a list of some of the common complex ions—their names, formulas, and valences.

Compounds with Complex Ions

Formulas In writing formulas, we must bear in mind the rule stated in Chapter 13, namely that valence numbers must balance so

Table 15-4 Common complex ions

Name of complex ion	Formula of complex ion	Valence of complex ion
Ammonium	NH_4^+	+1
Chlorate	ClO_3^-	−1
Hydroxide	OH^-	−1
Nitrate	NO_3^-	−1
Carbonate	CO_3^{-2}	−2
Sulfate	SO_4^{-2}	−2
Sulfite	SO_3^{-2}	−2
Phosphate	PO_4^{-3}	−3
Phosphite	PO_3^{-3}	−3

that the net charge on the compound is zero. For example, the formulas for ammonium sulfate, calcium nitrate, and magnesium phosphate are $(NH_4)_2SO_4$, $Ca(NO_3)_2$, and $Mg_3(PO_4)_2$, respectively.

Equations Again, as you learned in Chapter 13, in writing equations, matter (atoms) must be conserved—there must be the same total number of atoms in the products as in the reactants. Thus, the equation for the reaction

$$\text{sodium carbonate} + \text{iron III nitrate} \xrightarrow{\text{gives}} \text{sodium nitrate} + \text{iron (III) carbonate} \quad (15\text{-}35)$$

is

$$3Na_2CO_3 + 2Fe(NO_3)_3 \longrightarrow 6NaNO_3 + Fe_2(CO_3)_3 \quad (15\text{-}36)$$

and for the reaction

$$\text{potassium chlorate} \xrightarrow{\text{gives}} \text{potassium chloride} + \text{oxygen} \quad (15\text{-}37)$$

the equation is

$$2KClO_3 \longrightarrow 2KCl + 3O_2 \quad (15\text{-}38)$$

Problems Problems involving complex ions are solved by the methods discussed in Chapter 13. We are not concerned with ionization, so non-ionic equations are adequate. In Example 15-1, only mass and volume are involved.

Example 15-1

Compute the volume of oxygen collected at 25°C and 700 torr pressure if 12.25 g of potassium chlorate are decomposed by heat.

Solution

$$2KClO_3 \longrightarrow 2KCl + 3O_2\uparrow$$

$$\text{Volume of oxygen} = 12.25\ \cancel{g}\ \cancel{KClO_3} \times \frac{1\ \cancel{mole}\ \cancel{KClO_3}}{122.5\ \cancel{g}\ \cancel{KClO_3}} \times \frac{3\ \cancel{moles}\ \cancel{O_2}}{2\ \cancel{moles}\ \cancel{KClO_3}} \times \frac{22.4\ l\ O_2}{1\ \cancel{mole}\ \cancel{O_2}} \times \frac{298\ \cancel{°K}}{273\ \cancel{°K}} \times \frac{760\ \cancel{torr}}{700\ \cancel{torr}}$$

$$= 3.99\ l$$

Slightly Soluble Bases

Sodium hydroxide and potassium hydroxide are very soluble in water. However, as a class, bases are only sparingly soluble. This is because the electrostatic force of attraction between ions in the lattices of most bases is so strong that the attractive force of water dipoles is unable to pull them apart. A case in point is iron (III) hydroxide.

If a solution of iron (III) chloride is added to a solution of sodium hydroxide, a red-brown precipitate is formed. The ionic equation for this reaction is

$$Fe^{+3} + 3Cl^- + 3Na^+ + 3OH^- \longrightarrow 3Cl^- + 3Na^+ + Fe(OH)_3\downarrow \qquad (15\text{-}39)$$

Or, omitting spectator ions,

$$Fe^{+3}\,(aq) + 3OH^-(aq) \longrightarrow Fe(OH)_3(s) \qquad (15\text{-}40)$$

It is apparent that iron (III) hydroxide is only slightly soluble. Indeed, it is often spoken of as an insoluble substance. However, there is no such thing as a *completely insoluble* substance, and even iron III hydroxide yields a few free ions in water solution. The separation of its ions in solution can be shown as

$$Fe^{+3}(OH^-)_3 \rightleftharpoons Fe^{+3} + 3OH^- \qquad (15\text{-}41)$$

However, the concentration of hydroxide ion is so low that it does not change red litmus to blue. The same is true of copper (II) hydroxide

$$Cu^{+2}(OH^-)_2 \rightleftharpoons Cu^{+2} + 2OH^- \qquad (15\text{-}42)$$

and also of the hydroxides of other heavy metals.

Calcium hydroxide is intermediate in solubility—much less soluble than NaOH but much more soluble than $Fe(OH)_3$. Its solubility and ionization are shown in Eq. (15-43).

$$\underset{\text{solid}}{Ca^{+2}(OH^-)_2} \rightleftharpoons \underset{\text{solution}}{Ca^{+2} + 2OH^-} \qquad (15\text{-}43)$$

Obviously, any solution of calcium hydroxide (which is called limewater) is of necessity always a dilute solution. Nonetheless the concentration of hydroxide ion is sufficient to turn red litmus blue; moreover, it is the only solution of a common base that is safe to taste.

Summary

Measurements on the conductivity of solutions appeared to indicate that electrolytes are not completely ionized except in very dilute solution. Arrhenius "explained" this effect in terms of an equilibrium between molecules and ions. But the modern theory of Debye and Hückel assumes, correctly, that salts and many bases are completely ionized, whatever the degree of dilution, and states that the *apparent* incomplete ionization is due to attraction between oppositely charged ions which interfere with the free migration of these ions.

Factual Recall

1. State the main postulates of the Arrhenius theory of ionization.
2. Write balanced equations for:
   (*a*) aluminum sulfate + calcium hydroxide ⟶ aluminum hydroxide + calcium sulfate
   (*b*) silver nitrate + sodium chloride ⟶ silver chloride + sodium nitrate
   (*c*) magnesium chloride + phosphoric acid ⟶ magnesium phosphate + hydrochloric acid

3. Write ionic equations for:
   (*a*) iron (II) chloride + sodium hydroxide ⟶ iron (II) hydroxide + sodium chloride
   (*b*) barium chloride + sulfuric acid ⟶ barium sulfate + hydrochloric acid
   (*c*) zinc sulfate + hydrogen sulfide ⟶ zinc sulfide + sulfuric acid
4. Write simplest ionic equations for the following reactions:
   (*a*) aluminum with dilute sulfuric acid
   (*b*) zinc with hydrochloric acid
   (*c*) calcium hydroxide solution with nitric acid

Apply Your Knowledge!

1. Molten potassium nitrate conducts a current. Does this experimental fact support or refute the Arrhenius theory of ionization? Explain.
2. An excess of dilute H_2SO_4 is added to 5.40 g of aluminum. Compute the (*a*) mass of acid consumed, (*b*) moles of salt formed, (*c*) volume of gas liberated at STP.
3. If 22.4 l of oxygen at STP are to be produced by the decomposition of potassium chlorate, (*a*) what mass of chlorate must be used, and (*b*) how many moles of solid product are formed?
4. A solution containing 11.10 g of $CaCl_2$ is added to a solution containing 6.90 g of K_2CO_3. Calculate the moles of $CaCO_3$ that precipitate.
5. Five grams of Al metal are added to 0.50 mole of HCl. Compute the (*a*) mass of salt produced, (*b*) volume of gas liberated at STP, (*c*) volume of gas liberated at 25 °C and 700 torr pressure.
6. Calculate the volume of gas produced at 20 °C and 760 torr pressure if 0.250 mole of Al reacts completely with dilute H_2SO_4.
7. If 0.0100 mole $KClO_3$ is decomposed by heat, compute (*a*) the volume of gas product at STP, (*b*) the moles of solid product.

Find Out!

In a physiology text, look up the importance of ions in nerve conductivity.

CHAPTER 16

ACIDS AND BASES

WATER IS A DIPOLE; its molecules behave as though they have positive and negative ends. As a result, single molecules are able to cluster into groups, a process called *association*. For instance, two molecules of water could associate as in Eq. (16-1):

$$\mathrm{H{:}\ddot{\underset{..}{O}}{:}^{-}}_{\;\overset{+}{}\mathrm{H}} + \mathrm{H{:}\ddot{\underset{..}{O}}{:}^{-}}_{\;\overset{+}{}\mathrm{H}} \longrightarrow \mathrm{H{:}\ddot{\underset{..}{O}}{:}H{:}\ddot{\underset{..}{O}}{:}^{-}} \tag{16-1}$$

In the same way, three molecules of water could associate to form a larger molecule,

$$\mathrm{H{:}\underset{\overset{+}{}H}{\ddot{\underset{..}{O}}}{:}H{:}\underset{H}{\ddot{\underset{..}{O}}}{:}H{:}\underset{H}{\ddot{\underset{..}{O}}}{:}^{-}}$$

$$\mathrm{H{:}\underset{H}{\ddot{\underset{..}{O}}}{:}\overset{X}{\mid}H\overset{Y}{\mid}{:}\underset{H}{\ddot{\underset{..}{O}}}{:}}$$

Fig. 16-1

In Fig. 16-1, the large molecule $(H_2O)_2$ might be imagined to break along either broken line, X or Y. If the split occurred along X, the molecule would revert to two ordinary molecules of water. But if the split occurred along Y, it is apparent that both hydronium ions and hydroxide ions would be formed. Omitting the intermediate step, the reaction between two water molecules can be represented as

$$H_2O + H_2O \rightleftharpoons H_3O^+ + OH^- \tag{16-2}$$

Recall . . .
What is the special contribution of acids to aqueous solutions?

Thus we can think of this reaction as the transfer of a proton from one molecule of water to another. An even simpler way of representing the reaction is as an equilibrium between molecules of liquid water and hydrogen ions $H^+(aq)$ plus hydroxide ions $OH^-(aq)$:

$$H_2O(l) \rightleftharpoons H^+(aq) + OH^-(aq) \qquad (16\text{-}3)$$

Equation (16-3) is useful in making certain calculations, although protons do not exist as such in pure water.

Water as a Weak Electrolyte

Conventionally, ion concentrations are represented by square brackets. Thus $[H^+]$ means the number of moles of hydrogen ion per liter of pure water. Similarly, $[OH^-]$ means the number of moles of hydroxide ion per liter of water. In the water ionization expression [Eq. (16-3)] the product $[H^+] \times [OH^-]$ is called the *ion product* for water. This product is a constant (K_W) and its value is found to be 10^{-14} at 25°C; that is,

$$K_W = [H^+][OH^-] = 10^{-14} \qquad (16\text{-}4)$$

Note . . .
Units for K_w are moles per liter × moles per liter, or $(\text{moles})^2$ per $(\text{liter})^2$.

Units are usually omitted from the value for K_W. But, in pure water for every hydrogen ion there is one hydroxide ion, as is indicated in Eq. (16-3). Therefore,

$$[H^+] = [OH^-]$$

Substituting x for $[H^+]$ and $[OH^-]$, we may say that

$$x \cdot x = 10^{-14}$$
$$x^2 = 10^{-14}$$
$$x = \sqrt{10^{-14}} = 10^{-7} \qquad (16\text{-}5)$$

Therefore,

$$[H^+] = [OH^-] = 10^{-7} \text{ mole/l} \qquad (16\text{-}6)$$

That is, the concentration of either hydrogen ions or hydroxide ions in pure water is 10^{-7} mole per liter. Therefore,

$$[H^+] = 10^{-7}\,M \qquad [OH^-] = 10^{-7}\,M$$

Since the concentration of hydrogen ions is 10^{-7} mole/l, it follows that there is only 1 mole of hydrogen ions (1.0079 g) in 10^7 (or 10 million) liters of pure water. Of, if the mass of 1 liter of water is 10^3 g, there is 1 mole of hydrogen ions in 10^{10} g of water, which equals 55.5×10^7 moles $[10^{10}$ g/(18 g/mole)$]$ of water. Similarly, there is 1 mole (17 g) of hydroxide ions in 10^7 l of water. Clearly, therefore, water is an exceedingly weak electrolyte.

The extent of ionization of water is so slight that, at first sight, it looks as though its effect in chemical reactions would be negligible. Yet, strangely enough, this slight amount of dissociation of water is one of its most important properties and many reactions depend upon it. Let us see why.

The Effect of Adding Hydrogen Ion to Water

As already stated, the numerical value of the ionization constant for water is 10^{-14}. Experiments show that, at normal room temperature,

$$[H^+] \times [OH^-] = 10^{-14}$$

not only in water *but also in all aqueous solutions, even in solutions of acids and bases.*

If a strong acid such as HCl is added to water, then clearly the concentration of hydrogen ion exceeds 10^{-7} mole/l. Therefore, at that instant, the product $[H^+] \times [OH^-]$ is greater than 10^{-14} and, in consequence, the equilibrium

$$H_2O \rightleftharpoons H^+ + OH^- \qquad (16\text{-}7)$$

is disturbed. The addition of H^+ constitutes a stress and, according to Le Châtelier's principle, the reaction to the left is favored, and hydrogen ions will combine with an equal number of hydroxide ions until the value of the ionization constant (10^{-14}) is restored. Thus it is that a solution of any acid contains hydroxide ions as well as hydrogen ions, but the concentration of hydrogen ions is greater than (and that of hydroxide ion is less than) 10^{-7} mole/l. Let us consider a specific example.

Example 16-1

Suppose 0.01 mole of hydrogen chloride is dissolved in water and that more water is added until the volume of the solution is exactly 1 l. What is the concentration of hydroxide ion in this acid solution?

Solution

Since hydrochloric acid ionizes completely, if the concentration of hydrogen ion is increased, there must be a corresponding decrease in the concentration of hydroxide ion.

$[H^+] = 10^{-2}$ mole/l $= 10^{-2}\,M$

But, $[H^+] \times [OH^-]$ must remain at 10^{-14} mole²/l².

Hence,

$$[OH^-] = \frac{10^{-14}\text{ mole}^2/\text{l}^2}{10^{-2}\text{ mole/l}} = 10^{-12}\text{ mole/l}$$

The addition of 0.01 mole of HCl to 1 l of water in Ex. 16-1 reduces the concentration of hydroxide ion from 10^{-7} to 10^{-12}, that is by a factor of 10^5 (100,000), as shown in Fig. 16-2.

Definitions of Acids and Bases

Acids and bases can be defined in terms of the concentration of hydrogen ions or hydroxide ions. If the concentration of hydrogen ions is greater than that of hydroxide ions, the solution is acidic. If the concentration of hydroxide ions is greater than that of hydrogen ions, the solution is basic. Or, *an acidic solution has a hydrogen-ion concentration greater than* 10^{-7} *mole per liter and a basic solution has a hydrogen-ion concentration less than* 10^{-7} *mole per liter.*

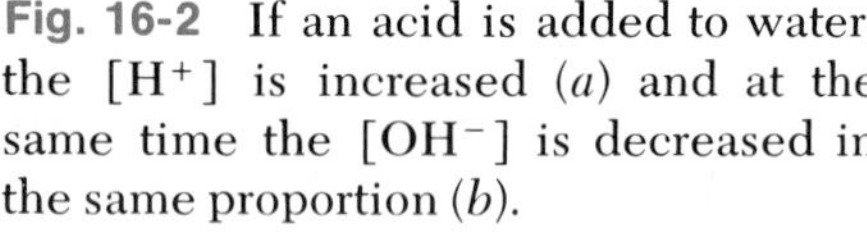

Fig. 16-2 If an acid is added to water, the $[H^+]$ is increased (*a*) and at the same time the $[OH^-]$ is decreased in the same proportion (*b*).

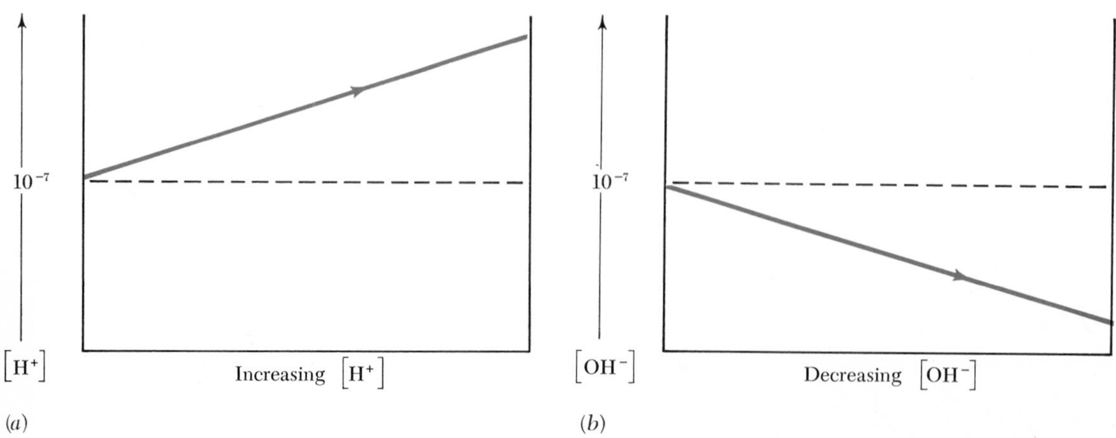

The pH Scale for Measuring Acidity

Many of the chemical reactions taking place in living organisms are especially sensitive to the hydrogen-ion concentration of the medium. The blood of a normal person is slightly basic. Actually, the hydrogen-ion concentration of the blood should be $10^{-7.4}$, and a marked deviation from this value is indicative of disorder. However, $10^{-7.4}$ is an awkward reference number for the acidity of normal blood. It would clearly be much more convenient if a scale could be devised on which the acidity is expressed not as an exponential or as a negative number but as a positive number—such as 7.4 in this case. Such a scale was devised in 1909 by a Danish chemist, S.P.L. Sörensen (1868–1939). He did this by using the index (or logarithmic function) of the hydrogen-ion concentration and changing the sign. He called it a pH scale—the letter p stands for *potenz* (the Danish word for power) and H stands for hydrogen ion. Thus, the Sörensen pH device is

Definition . . .
The $\log_{10}$ of a number is the power to which (base) 10 must be raised to equal that number.

$$[H^+] = 10^{-pH} \quad \text{or} \quad -pH = \log_{10} [H^+] \qquad (16\text{-}8)$$

From this it follows that

$$pH = -\log [H^+] = \log \frac{1}{[H^+]} \qquad (16\text{-}9)$$

Predict . . .
What are $[H^+]$ and $[OH^-]$ in solutions in which pH = 14?

Therefore,by definition: *The pH of a solution is minus one times the logarithm of the concentration of the hydrogen ion.*

Consider a specific example.

Example 16-2

Suppose the molar concentration of hydrogen ions is $0.0000001 = 10^{-7}$. What is the pH?

Solution

$\log 10^{-7} = -7$
Multiplying this by -1 gives the pH, which is 7. That is, the pH for a neutral solution, or pure water, equals 7.

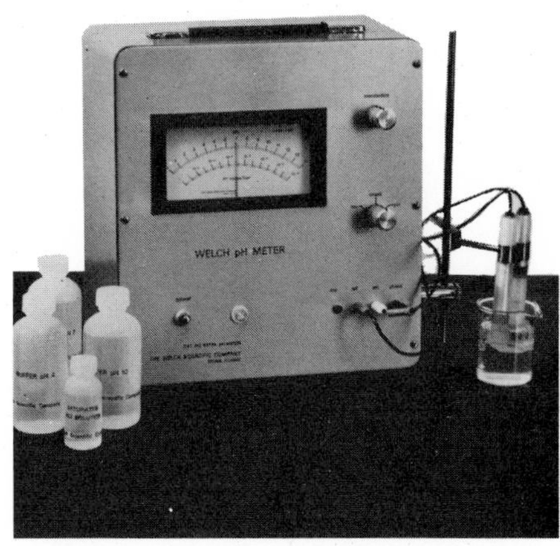

Fig. 16-3 The pH meter provides a rapid means of accurately determining pH.

If the pH is less than 7, the solution is acidic and if the pH is greater than 7, the solution is basic. A pH scale with a range from 0 to 14

Table 16-1 pH Values of common substances

Substance	pH
1.0 M HCl	0
0.1 M HCl	1.1
Gastric or stomach juice	1.0–3.0
Lemon juice	2.2–2.4
Vinegar	2.4–3.4
Grapefruit juice	3.0–3.3
Orange juice	3.0–4.0
Grape juice	3.5–4.5
Sour milk	4.4
Banana juice	4.5–4.7
Urine	4.8–8.4
Fresh milk	6.3–6.6
Water (distilled)	7.0
Blood (human plasma)	7.3–7.5
Seawater	7.36–8.21
Milk of magnesia	10.5
0.1 M NH_3	11.1
Limewater (saturated)	12.4
0.1 M NaOH	13.0
1.0 M NaOH	14.0

has been devised to indicate at a glance the degree of acidity or alkalinity of various substances.

We must remember that the pH scale is a logarithmic scale, so that a decrease of one in the scale number represents a tenfold increase in the degree of acidity. Thus, a solution with a pH of 3 is 10 times as acid as a solution with a pH of 4, 100 times as acid as a solution of pH 5, and 1000 times as acid as a solution of pH 6.

pH Calculations

Table 16-1 indicates that the pH of many common substances is known. Apparently this knowledge is of importance. How then is the pH determined? There are two kinds of pH calculations. In one type, the hydrogen-ion concentration is given and the pH computed. In the other type the pH is given and the hydrogen-ion concentration is computed. Both types are illustrated in Examples 16-3 and 16-4, which can also be solved by inspection.

Example 16-3

What is the pH of 0.001 M HCl solution?

Solution

Because HCl is completely ionized, $[H^+] = 10^{-3}$ mole/l in this example.

Therefore,

$$pH = -\log [H^+]$$

$$= -\log 10^{-3} = 3$$

Or

$$pH = \log \frac{1}{[H^+]}$$

$$= \log \frac{1}{10^{-3}}$$

$$= \log 10^3 = 3$$

Definition . . .
The antilog of 0.5 is the number whose log is 0.5. It can be determined either by using log tables or from the D and L scales of a slide rule.

Example 16-4

Find the hydrogen-ion concentration of an acid solution with a pH of 6.5.

Solution

$$\log [H^+] = -pH = -6.5 = 0.5 - 7$$

Therefore

$$[H^+] = \text{antilog } 0.5 \times \text{antilog } -7$$
$$= 3.2 \times 10^{-7} \text{ mole/l}$$

Fig. 16-4 Litmus paper can be used to test the pH of foods. Is the lemon acidic or basic?

A quick way to find the pH of a solution is to use a so-called acid–base indicator. An acid–base indicator is a complex organic compound—usually a weak acid—which changes color when the pH of its solution is changed. Thus, a given indicator changes color at a certain concentration of hydrogen ions. The commonest indicator is litmus. The color of litmus is red when the solution is strongly acid, pink when weakly acid, pale blue when weakly basic, and deep blue when strongly basic. However, these color changes are not sharp and often they take place over a rather wide range of pH values, from about pH 4.5 to about pH 8.5. Other indicators show a sharper change in color over a relatively small pH range, and are therefore more sensitive than litmus. A series of indicators can be selected that cover a wide range of pH values. For example, the indicators listed in Table 16-2 cover a pH range from roughly 2 to 12

Table 16-2 Ranges and color changes of common indicators

Indicator	pH Range of color change	Color at lower pH	Color at higher pH
Thymol blue	1.2–2.8	red	yellow
Methyl orange	3.1–4.4	red	yellow
Methyl red	4.2–6.6	red	yellow
Litmus	4.5–8.5	red	blue
Phenolphthalein	8.0–9.8	colorless	red
Alizarin yellow	10.0–12.0	yellow	red

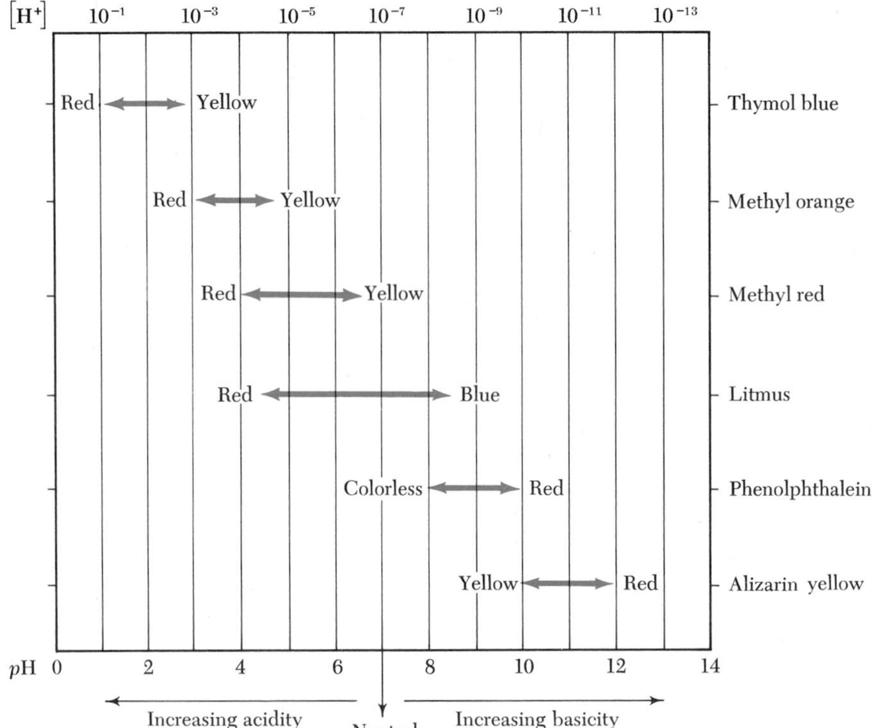

Fig. 16-5 Different indicators change color at different hydrogen-ion concentrations.

The range of these indicators is plotted in Fig. 16-5. Thus, to find the *p*H of a solution, a few drops of each indicator is added in turn to separate samples of the solution, and when a color change occurs the approximate *p*H is indicated in the table.

Investigate . . .
What kind of instrument could be used to determine *p*H? If your school has such equipment, learn how to use it.

Another way to find *p*H is to use a specially prepared paper such as Gramercy Universal Indicator or Hydrion ® Paper and a color chart. Such a paper is prepared by dipping it into a solution of a mixture of indicator dyes, and then letting it dry. This prepared paper gives a characteristic color for each *p*H when dipped into a solution whose *p*H is to be determined. By matching the color of the indicator paper with one of the colors in the color chart supplied with the universal indicator, the *p*H of the solution can be read on the chart. See Fig. 16-7.

Acid–Base Neutralization

The ionic equation for the neutralization of the strong acid HCl by the strong base NaOH is

$$H^+(aq) + Cl^-(aq) + Na^+(aq) + OH^-(aq) \longrightarrow Na^+(aq) + Cl^-(aq) + H_2O \qquad (16\text{-}10)$$

Notice that there is no reaction between sodium ions and chloride ions. Why not? Clearly, because these ions are stable chemically. See Fig. 16-6.

Fig. 16-6 How do these models explain the structure of hydrogen chloride.

They have the noble gas structure; sodium ion has the same electron configuration as a neon atom, and a chloride ion has the same configuration as an atom of argon. It could be argued, however, that hydrogen ions and hydroxide ions also have stable structures, which is true. Then why do they react?

The answer is related to the equilibrium between $H^+(aq)$ and $OH^-(aq)$ which we have been discussing. Suppose the concentrations of acid and base are 0.1 *M*. That is,

$$[HCl] = 0.1\,M \quad \text{and} \quad [NaOH] = 0.1\,M$$

Then,

$$[H^+] = 0.1\,M = 10^{-1} \text{ mole/l}$$

and

$$[OH^-] = 0.1\,M = 10^{-1} \text{ mole/l}$$

Hence,

$$[H^+] \times [OH^-] = 10^{-2}$$

which is higher than the ionization constant by a factor of 10^{12}. Therefore $H^+(aq)$ and $OH^-(aq)$ will combine to form water until the product $[H^+] \times [OH^-]$ is reduced to 10^{-14}. This same argument applies to reactions between all strong acids and bases.

Titration

The concentration of a solution of an acid or base can be determined by a process called *titration*. A titration is essentially a neutralization reaction in which the exact volumes of acid and base solutions are measured with burets (see Fig. 16-8). To do this the acid solution is poured into one buret and the base solution is poured into another, as shown in Fig. 16-9. Then a known volume (say, 20 ml) of acid is run into an Erlenmeyer flask, and 1 or 2 drops of indicator, such as phenolphthalein, added. The base solution is then run slowly into the flask until the indicator changes color, from colorless to red. The color change occurs at the point of neutralization, which is called the *end point*.

Fig. 16-7 Color changes in various acid–base indicators at different pH values. In (*a*) and (*b*) the top row is before change, the bottom row, after. (*a*) Left to right: thymol blue (pH 1.2–2.8); methyl orange (pH 3.1–4.4); bromcresol green (pH 3.8–5.4); chlorophenol red (pH 4.8–6.4); bromthymol blue (pH 6.0–7.6). (*b*) Left to right: neutral red (pH 6.8-8.0); thymol blue (pH 8.0–9.6); phenolphthalein (pH 8.0–9.6); thymolphthalein (pH 9.3–10.5); alizarin yellow G (pH 10.1–12.0). Colors found for various pH levels with (*c*) Gramercy universal indicator and (*d*) Hydrion ® paper.

(*a*)

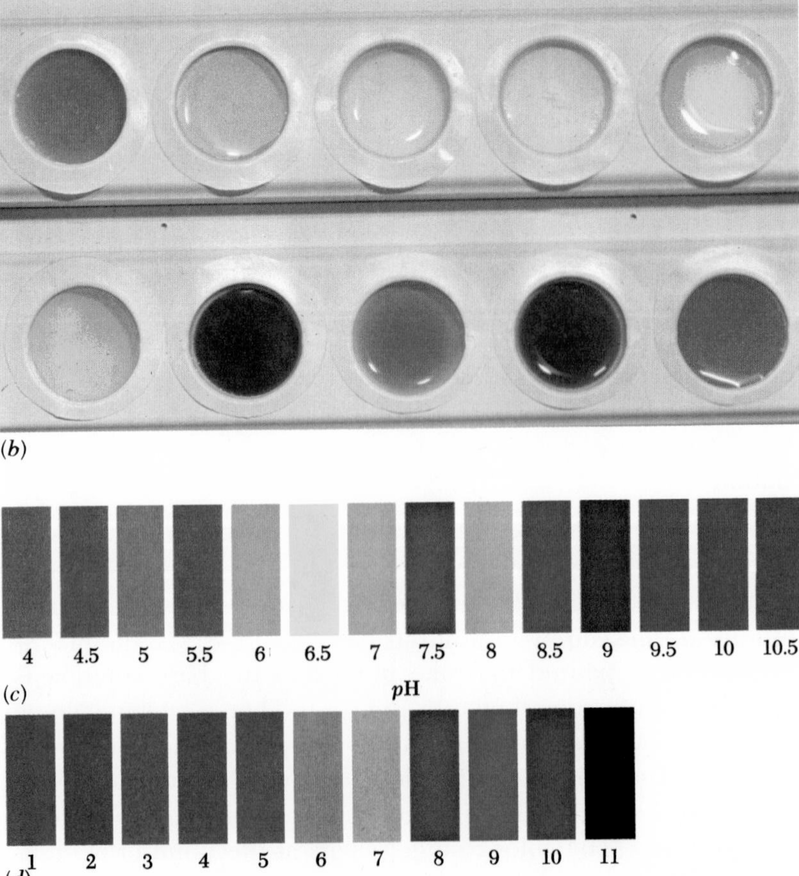

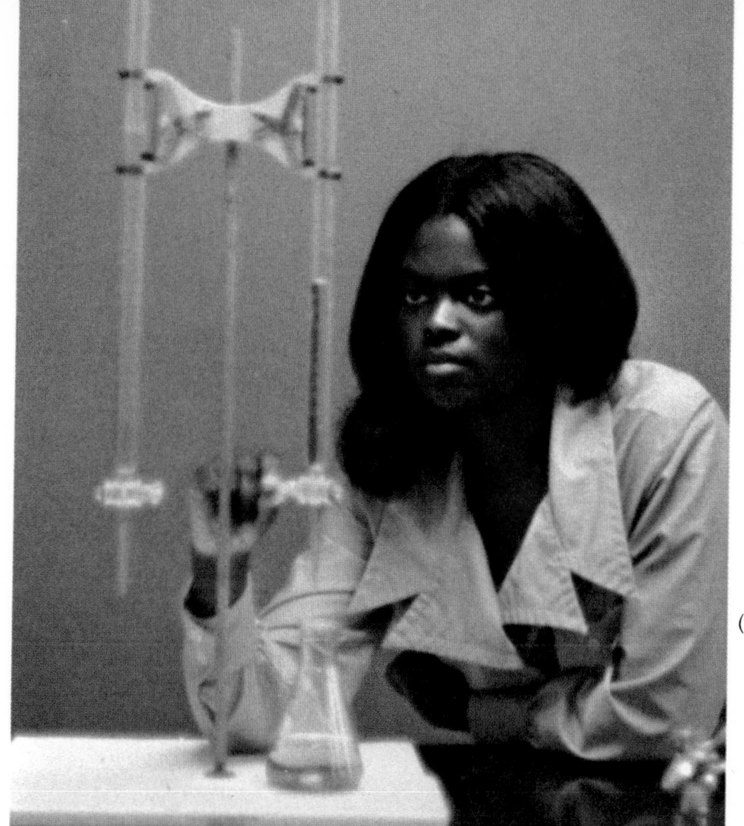

(a)

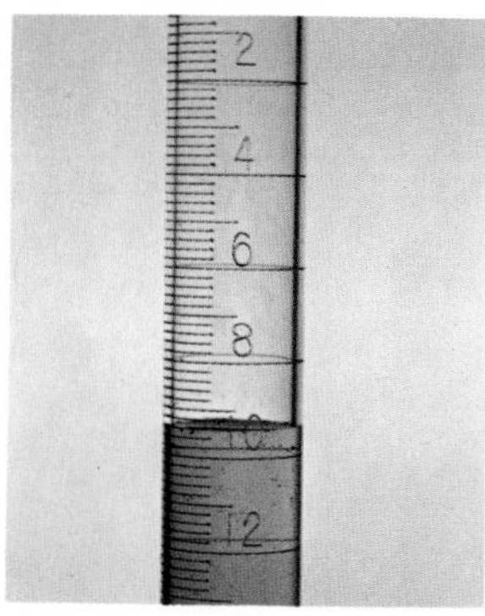

(b)

Fig. 16-8 (a) Performing a titration with burets. (b) Detail of buret showing meniscus.

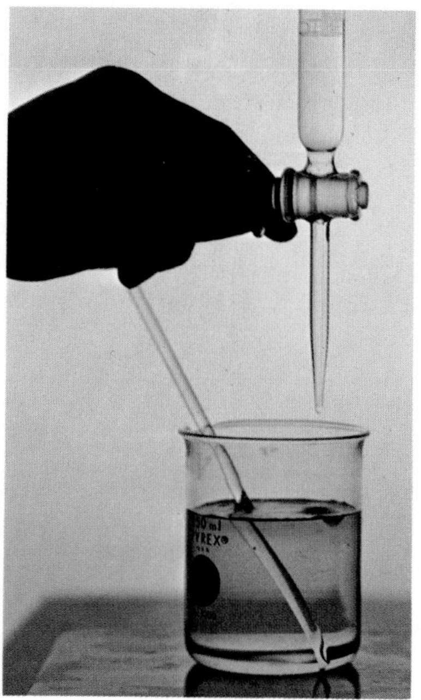

Fig. 16-9 Nearing the end point of a titration. One drop from the buret will permanently change the color of the indicator.

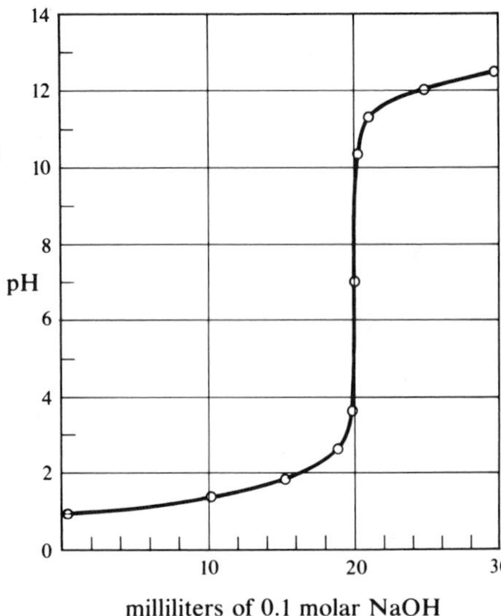

Fig. 16-10 Graph showing changes in *p*H as 0.1 *M* NaOH is added to 20 ml of 0.1 *M* HCl.

To determine the concentration of the acid solution the concentration of the base solution must be known and, conversely, the concentration of the acid solution must be known before the concentration of the base can be determined. The solutions of known concentration are called *standard* solutions, and clearly they must be prepared beforehand.

The End Point

As stated earlier, when neutralization occurs in titrations of strong acids with strong bases, the concentrations of $H^+(aq)$ and $OH^-(aq)$ are the same, namely 10^{-7} mole/l. Thus it looks as though we should select an indicator which changes color when the *p*H is 7. Actually, however, this may not be necessary. Let us see why.

The graph, Fig. 16-10 shows the change in the *p*H of 20 ml of a 0.1 *M* HCl solution as various volumes of a standard 0.1 *M* NaOH solution are added to it. At first the change in *p*H is quite gradual and then, near the point of equivalence, the change is very rapid. The graph shows that near the equivalence point just 2 or 3 drops of the base changes the *p*H of the solution from 2 to 10. Or expressed in other terms, $[H^+]$ is reduced from 10^{-2} *M* to 10^{-10} *M* (that is, by a factor of 10^8) by adding only 2 or 3 drops of the base that although phenolphthalein changes color over a *p*H range of 8.0 to 9.8 (that is, in a basic solution) yet it can be used in this case to indicate the point at which neutralization occurs.

To Compute Molarity of an Acid Solution

Suppose acid and base are HCl and NaOH, respectively. Suppose further that the standard NaOH solution is 0.100 *M* and that in the titration 17 ml of NaOH are needed to neutralize 20 ml of HCl. Then:

$$\text{number of moles of NaOH} = 0.100 \text{ mole/l} \times 0.017 \text{ l}$$
$$= 0.0017 \text{ mole}$$

Since 1 mole of NaOH [or of $OH^-(aq)$] will exactly neutralize 1 mole of HCl [or of $H^+(aq)$] then, the number of moles of HCl is 0.0017 mole, and

$$[\text{HCl}] = \frac{0.0017 \text{ mole}}{0.020 \text{ l}}$$
$$= 0.085\ M$$

Strong and Weak Acids

Acids that are completely (or almost completely) ionized are called *strong acids*; those that are only slightly ionized are called *weak acids*. The terms *strong* and *weak* are somewhat confusing. They do not, as might be expected, refer to the stability of the acid, but rather to the degree of ionization. For example, acetic acid is weak but stable,

$$CH_3COOH \rightleftarrows H^+ + CH_3COO^- \tag{16-11}$$

On the other hand, carbonic acid is weak and unstable,

$$H_2O + CO_2 \rightleftharpoons H_2CO_3 \rightleftarrows H^+ + HCO_3^- \tag{16-12}$$

Thus, in carbonic acid there are at least two sets of equilibria. One deals with the ionization of the molecule and the other deals with the decomposition of the molecule into H_2O and CO_2. We shall see that a third equilibrium also exists:

$$HCO_3^- \rightleftarrows H^+(aq) + CO_3^{-2} \tag{16-13}$$

The relative strengths of weak acids can be expressed in terms of their ionization constants (K_A). Thus, if the weak acid HX gives rise to the ions H^+ and X^-, the equation for the reversible reaction is

$$HX \rightleftarrows H^+ + X^-$$

and the ionization constant is

$$K_A = \frac{[H^+] \times [X^-]}{[HX]} \tag{16-14}$$

For a solution of acetic acid,

$$K_A = \frac{[H^+] \times [CH_3COO^-]}{[CH_3COOH]} \tag{16-15}$$

and, if the various concentrations are determined experimentally, computation shows that the value for K_A at 25 °C is 1.8×10^{-5}.

The ionization constants for a few weak acids are given in Table 16-3. Notice that the relative strength of acetic acid (CH_3COOH) is between that of hydrofluoric (HF) and carbonic (H_2CO_3) acids; that is, it is weaker than HF but stronger than H_2CO_3. Notice also that hydrochloric acid, nitric acid, and sulfuric acid are omitted from the table. Why is this ? Both HCl and HNO_3 are found to be completely dissociated in water solution. Hence the values of [HCl] and $[HNO_3]$ can be set equal to zero. Therefore the value of the ionization constant for HCl as computed from

$$K_A = \frac{[H^+][Cl^-]}{[HCl]} \tag{16-16}$$

is infinitely large. Similarly, the ionization constant for HNO_3 is also infinitely large.

Table 16-3 Values of K_A for selected weak acids

Acid	Reaction	Value of K_A at 25 °C
Hydrofluoric	$HF(aq) \rightleftarrows H^+ + F^-$	6.7×10^{-4}
Acetic	$CH_3COOH(aq) \rightleftarrows H^+ + CH_3COO^-$	1.8×10^{-5}
Carbonic	$H_2CO_3(aq) \rightleftarrows H^+ + HCO_3^-$	4.4×10^{-7}
Bicarbonate ion	$HCO_3^-(aq) \rightleftarrows H^+ + CO_3^{-2}$	4.7×10^{-11}
Hydrosulfuric	$H_2S(aq) \rightleftarrows 2H^+ + S^{-2}$	1.0×10^{-21}

The Value of K_A for Water

You have learned that water is a weak electrolyte,

$$H_2O \rightleftarrows H^+ + OH^- \tag{16-17}$$

However, since hydrogen ions are released, it is also a weak acid and the ionization constant can be computed in the usual way.

$$K_A = \frac{[H^+] \times [OH^-]}{[H_2O]} \tag{16-18}$$

In pure water, $[H_2O] = \dfrac{1000 \text{ g}}{18.0 \text{ g/mole}} = 55.5$ moles

and both $H^+(aq)$ and $OH^-(aq)$ are 10^{-7} *M*.

Therefore, $K_A = \dfrac{10^{-7} \times 10^{-7}}{55.5} = 1.8 \times 10^{-16}$

It should be apparent that water is a weak base as well as a weak acid. This acid-base concept is discussed later in the chapter.

Polybasic Acids

Some acids have more than one replaceable hydrogen ion. Such acids are called *polybasic acids* (or polyprotic acids) and a common example is sulfuric acid. Sulfuric acid ionizes in two steps:

$$H_2SO_4 \rightleftarrows H^+(aq) + HSO_4^- \text{ (bisulfate ion)} \quad (16\text{-}19A)$$
$$HSO_4^- \rightleftarrows H^+(aq) + SO_4^{-2} \text{ (sulfate ion)} \quad (16\text{-}19B)$$

Each step has its own particular ionization constant. In the first step, sulfuric acid is almost completely ionized. It is a strong acid, and at room temperature

$$K_A = \frac{[H^+][HSO_4^-]}{[H_2SO_4]} = 10^4$$

This is a very high value. However, in the second step, HSO_4^- is only slightly ionized and its K_A value at room temperature is low:

$$\frac{[H^+][SO_4^{-2}]}{[HSO_4^-]} = 1.2 \times 10^{-2}$$

In other words, H_2SO_4 is strong but HSO_4^- is relatively weak.

Another polybasic acid is phosphoric acid (H_3PO_4) which ionizes in 3 steps as shown in Table 16-4. These K_A values show that phosphoric acid is a fairly weak acid and that $H_2PO_4^-$ and HPO_4^{-2} are very weak acids. Observe that the ionization constant decreases sharply at each of the subsequent steps: K_A for step 2 is less than K_A for step I, and K_A for step 3 is less than K_A for step 2. This is typical of all polybasic acids.

Table 16-4 Ionization of H_3PO_4

Step	Reaction	K_A
1	$H_3PO_4 \rightleftarrows H^+(aq) + H_2PO_4^-$	7.5×10^{-3}
2	$H_2PO_4^- \rightleftarrows H^+(aq) + HPO_4^{-2}$	6.2×10^{-8}
3	$HPO_4^{-2} \rightleftarrows H^+(aq) + PO_4^{-3}$	1.0×10^{-12}

Finally, let us refer to the two ionization constants for carbonic acid given in Table 16-3. The first ionization step is

$$HCO_3^- \rightleftarrows H^+(aq) + HCO_3^- \text{ (bicarbonate ion)} \quad (16\text{-}20)$$

$$K_A = \frac{[H^+] \times [HCO_3^-]}{[H_2CO_3]} = 4.4 \times 10^{-7} \quad (16\text{-}21)$$

and the second ionization step is

$$HCO_3 \rightleftarrows H^+(aq) + CO_3^{-2} \text{ (carbonate ion)} \quad (16\text{-}22)$$

$$K_A = \frac{[H^+] \times [CO_3^{-2}]}{[HCO_3^-]} = 4.7 \times 10^{-11} \quad (16\text{-}23)$$

A comparison of these data for the three acids shows that carbonic acid is much weaker than phosphoric acid, but that phosphoric acid is much weaker than sufuric acid.

Typical Problems Involving Ionization Constants

The methods used in solving the following two problems are typical and may be used for most problems of this type.

Example 16-5

What is the hydrogen-ion concentration in 1 *M* acetic acid?

Solution

The equilibrium reaction is:

$$CH_3COOH \rightleftarrows H^+(aq) + CH_3COO^-$$

We know that $[H^+] = [CH_3COO^-]$

and we can set this equal to x. In this case

$$[CH_3COOH] = 1 - x$$

because x also represents the number of moles of the acid per liter that has ionized. However, acetic acid is a weak electrolyte and practically all the acid is in the molecular form. This means that x is very small and $1-x$ is very nearly 1. We are therefore justified in assuming that the concentration of molecular acetic acid in a 1 *M* solution is one. Thus,

$$\frac{[H^+][CH_3COO^-]}{[CH_3COOH]} = \frac{x \times x}{1} = 1.8 \times 10^{-5}$$

Therefore,

$$x^2 = 1.8 \times 10^{-5} \quad \text{and} \quad x = \sqrt{18 \times 10^{-6}} = 4.2 \times 10^{-3}$$

In other words,

$$[H^+] = 4.2 \times 10^{-3} \text{ or } 0.0042\,M$$

Example 16-6

Compute the percentage ionization in 1 M acetic acid.

Solution

$$\% \text{ ionization} = \frac{[H^+]}{[CH_3COOH]} \times 100$$

$$= \frac{0.0042\,M}{1.0\,M} \times 100 = 0.42\%$$

Hydrolysis of Salts

Since a solid salt is made up of positive and negative ions, it looks, at first sight, as though solutions of all salts would be neutral, but this will not be true if one or both kinds of ions react with the water to produce H^+(aq) or OH^-(aq). We find that this occurs and as a result solutions of some salts are neutral, whereas others are basic and still others are acidic. Why the difference?

Salts can be classified according to the kind of acid and base from which they are derived. They may be the product of a reaction between (1) a weak acid and a strong base, (2) a strong acid and a strong base, or (3) a strong acid and a weak base. The *p*H values of each of these solutions are quite different. Let us see why.

Salts of Weak Acids and Strong Bases

Typical examples of salts of a weak acid and a strong base are sodium acetate and sodium carbonate. What happens when sodium acetate is dissolved in water? First, the ionic lattice breaks down so that the sodium ions (Na^+) and acetate ions (CH_3COO^-) can be imagined to be free to move,

$$CH_3COO^- + Na^+ \xrightarrow{\text{water}} CH_3COO^-(aq) + Na^+(aq) \qquad (16\text{-}24)$$

Now we know that in acetic acid (HAc) solutions there are many more acetic acid molecules than acetate ions. This suggests that acetate ions are not very stable in water but that they can be stabilized by forming acetic acid molecules. Therefore the reaction in Eq. (16-25) is expected to occur. This does indeed appear to be the case, and sodium acetate solutions are basic because of the $OH^-(aq)$ produced:

$$CH_3COO^- + H_2O \rightleftharpoons CH_3COOH + OH^- \tag{16-25}$$

Hence, $[OH^-]$ becomes greater than 10^{-7} (or the pH is greater than 7) and therefore the solution is basic.

Thus the principal chemical reaction that occurs when sodium acetate dissolves in water is that in Eq. (16-25). This kind of reaction (the reaction of a salt with water to form either a basic solution or an acidic solution) is called *hydrolysis.*

Salts of Strong Acids and Strong Bases

Sodium chloride is formed by a reaction between the strong acid HCl and the strong base NaOH. Does NaCl undergo hydrolysis in water solution? The four ions in solution can be shown as

$$\begin{aligned} & Na^+ + Cl^- \\ H_2O \rightleftharpoons\ & OH^- + H^+ \end{aligned} \tag{16-26}$$

Both sodium and chloride ions are stable in water; neither react with it to give $H^+(aq)$ or $OH^-(aq)$. Why not? Therefore, the water equilibrium is not disturbed and hydrolysis does not occur. Expressed another way, a solution of sodium chloride is neutral and its pH is 7.

On the basis of the foregoing discussion, explain why solutions of NH_4Cl and $CuCl_2$ are acidic.

The Brönsted-Lowry Theory of Acids and Bases

In the ionization process water reacts chemically with acids and bases, just as it does with salts in the process of hydrolysis. This important role played by water led to a new acid–base concept, first proposed in 1923 by two scientists working independently: J. N. Brönsted (1870–1947), a Dane, and T. M. Lowry (1874–1936), an Englishman.

According to the Brönsted-Lowry theory, *an acid is a donor of protons (or hydrogen ions) and a base is an acceptor of protons.* This concept greatly extended the Arrhenius definition of acids and bases. It includes all acids and bases as defined by Arrhenius and it also includes a number of molecules and ions that could not be classed as acids and bases under his definition.

The Brönsted-Lowry Concept of an Acid

As stated earlier, there is much experimental evidence which indicates that hydrogen ions do not exist as free protons, but rather as hydrated protons. The simplest hydrated hydrogen ion is the hydronium ion H_3O^+. Applying this idea to the reaction when hydrogen chloride gas dissolves in water, we can write,

$$\mathrm{HCl\ (g) + H_2O \longrightarrow H_3O^+ + Cl^-} \qquad (16\text{-}27)$$

That is, a molecule of hydrogen chloride donates a proton and a molecule of water accepts the proton. Thus, according to the Brönsted-Lowry definitions, HCl is an acid and water is a base. Or,

$$\underset{\text{acid}}{\mathrm{HCl}} + \underset{\text{base}}{\mathrm{H_2O}} \longrightarrow \mathrm{H_3O^+ + Cl^-} \qquad (16\text{-}28)$$

Notice again the extension of the Arrhenius concept. According to Arrhenius, water is not a base—only hydroxides belong to this category.

The Brönsted-Lowry Concept of a Base

The gas ammonia reacts with water to form ammonium ions and hydroxide ions. In this reaction, a molecule of ammonia accepts a proton from a water molecule. Therefore, according to the Brönsted-Lowry theory, water is an acid and ammonia is a base even though it does not yield hydroxide ions. In symbols, the reaction is

$$\underset{\text{base}}{\mathrm{NH_3(g)}} + \underset{\text{acid}}{\mathrm{H_2O}} \longrightarrow \mathrm{NH_4^+ + OH^-} \qquad (16\text{-}29)$$

Expressed as electron-dot formulas, the equation is

$$\underset{\text{base}}{\mathrm{H:\overset{\displaystyle H}{\underset{\displaystyle H}{\ddot{\underset{..}{N}}}}:}} + \underset{\text{acid}}{\mathrm{H:\overset{\displaystyle H}{\underset{..}{\ddot{O}}}:}} \longrightarrow \left[\mathrm{H:\overset{\displaystyle H}{\underset{\displaystyle H}{\ddot{\underset{..}{N}}}}:H}\right]^+ + \left[\mathrm{:\overset{\displaystyle H}{\underset{..}{\ddot{O}}}:}\right]^- \qquad (16\text{-}30)$$

Notice that, in order to accept a proton, the molecule of a base must have an unshared pair of electrons; and when the proton is accepted, a coordinate covalent bond is formed.

Acid–Base Pairs

The reaction between acetic acid and water is reversible,

$$CH_3COOH + H_2O \rightleftharpoons CH_3COO^- + H_3O^+ \qquad (16\text{-}31)$$

In the forward reaction a molecule of acetic acid donates a proton to a molecule of water. Therefore it is an acid–base reaction. In the reverse reaction, a hydronium ion donates a proton to an acetate ion. Therefore, the reverse reaction is also acid–base, H_3O^+ acting as an acid and CH_3COO^- as a base. Thus the equation becomes

$$\underset{\text{acid}}{CH_3COOH} + \underset{\text{base}}{H_2O} \rightleftharpoons \underset{\text{base}}{CH_3COO^-} + \underset{\text{acid}}{H_3O^+} \qquad (16\text{-}32)$$

In this reaction, there are two pairs of reacting substances which differ only by a single proton: (1) CH_3COOH and CH_3COO^-, and (2) H_2O and H_3O^+. Such substances are called *acid–base pairs* or *conjugate pairs*. Thus acetate ion is the conjugate base of acetic acid, and hydronium ion is the conjugate acid of the base water.

The reaction between ammonia and water is also reversible,

$$\underset{\text{base}}{NH_3} + \underset{\text{acid}}{H_2O} \rightleftharpoons \underset{\text{acid}}{NH_4^+} + \underset{\text{base}}{OH^-} \qquad (16\text{-}33)$$

and the conjugate acid–base pairs are (1) NH_3 and NH_4^+ and (2) H_2O and OH^-.

In general, the conjugate pairs can be expressed as (1) acid_1–base_1 and (2) acid_2–base_2. So the general expression for an acid–base reaction is

$$\text{acid}_1 + \text{base}_2 \rightleftharpoons \text{base}_1 + \text{acid}_2 \qquad (16\text{-}34)$$

Since strong acids are, by definition, acids with a strong tendency to release protons, their conjugate bases must be weak. The reaction of sulfuric acid with water illustrates this point.

$$\textit{Step 1}\ \underset{\text{strong acid}}{H_2SO_4} + H_2O \rightleftharpoons H_3O^+ + \underset{\text{weak conjugate base}}{HSO_4^-} \qquad (16\text{-}35A)$$

$$\textit{Step 2}\ \underset{\text{moderately strong acid}}{HSO_4^-} + H_2O \rightleftharpoons H_3O^+ + \underset{\text{moderately weak conjugate base}}{SO_4^{-2}} \qquad (16\text{-}35B)$$

Let us revert to the reaction between two molecules of water discussed in the early part of this chapter:

$$H_2O + H_2O \rightleftharpoons H_3O^+ + OH^- \qquad (16\text{-}36)$$

Using electron-dot formulas this reaction is

$$\begin{array}{c} H:\ddot{\underset{..}{O}}: \\ H \end{array} + \begin{array}{c} H:\ddot{\underset{..}{O}}: \\ H \end{array} \rightleftharpoons \begin{array}{c} H:\ddot{\underset{..}{O}}:H \\ H \end{array} \quad \begin{array}{c} :\ddot{\underset{..}{O}}: \\ H \end{array}$$

$$\rightleftharpoons \left[\begin{array}{c} H:\ddot{\underset{..}{O}}:H \\ H \end{array}\right]^+ + \left[\begin{array}{c} :\ddot{\underset{..}{O}}: \\ H \end{array}\right]^- \qquad (16\text{-}37)$$

If the split occurs along the broken line, then one molecule of water accepts a proton and the other donates one. In other words, according to the Brönsted-Lowry theory this also is an acid–base reaction,

$$\underset{\text{base}_2}{H_2O} + \underset{\text{acid}_1}{H_2O} \rightleftharpoons \underset{\text{acid}_2}{H_3O^+} + \underset{\text{base}_1}{OH^-} \qquad (16\text{-}38)$$

Finally, let us consider again the dissolving of sodium acetate in water, and the resulting reaction,

$$CH_3COO^- + H_2O \rightleftharpoons CH_3COOH + OH^- \qquad (16\text{-}39)$$

which gives rise to the basic solution. In this reaction, acetate ion acts as a base, water as an acid, with CH_3COOH being the conjugate acid of acetate ion and hydroxide ion the conjugate base of water. In the light of this would you say sodium acetate is a base, a salt, or both? Justify your answer.

Summary

Water is a weak electrolyte and its ionization constant is very small. $K_W = [H^+] \times [OH^-] = 1.0 \times 10^{-14}$.

The *acidity* of a solution can be expressed on a *p*H scale. For a neutral solution, the $pH = 7$, for an acid solution the $pH < 7$, and for a basic solution $pH > 7$.

Hydrolysis is the reaction of the ions of certain salts with water.

According to the Brönsted-Lowry definition, an acid is a *proton donor* and a base is a *proton acceptor.* The two pairs of reacting substances are called conjugate acid–base pairs.

Factual Recall

1. If a little sodium hydroxide is added to water, the concentration of hydrogen ion in the solution is less than 10^{-7} mole/l. Explain why by referring to Le Châtelier's principle.
2. Define a base in terms of (*a*) hydrogen ion concentration, (*b*) *p*H.
3. (*a*) Define *p*H. (*b*) The *p*H of a neutral solution is 7. Why? (*c*) State a *p*H value that an acid solution could have and state a value that it could not have. Give a reason for your answer.
4. (*a*) What is an indicator? (*b*) Name three common indicators. (*c*) State the color changes of the indicators named in (*b*) in acid–base solutions. (*d*) Discuss the relative merits of each of these indicators.
5. Why is the ionization constant limited to weak acids?
6. Write the expression for the ionization constant for water, and compute its value.
7. What is meant by the primary, secondary, and tertiary ionization constants for phosphoric acid?
8. (*a*) What is hydrolysis? (*b*) Is a solution of sodium sulfide acidic, basic, or neutral? Why?
9. (*a*) Name one kind of salt that does not hydrolyze. (*b*) Give three examples of this kind of salt.

Apply Your Knowledge!

N.B. In Problems 1-6, assume that strong acids and strong bases are completely dissociated.

1. Calculate the concentration in moles per liter of hydrogen ion for each of the following: (*a*) 1.825 g of HCl in 100 ml of solution, ((*b*) 0.00063 g of HNO_3 in 500 ml of solution, (*c*) 8.1 g of HBr in 500 ml of solution, (*d*) 1.28 g of HI in 100 ml of solution.
2. Compute the *p*H of each of the solutions in Problem 1.
3. Calculate the concentration in moles per liter of hydroxide ion for each of the following: (*a*) 4.0 g of NaOH in 250 ml of solution, (*b*) 1.85 g of $Ca(OH)_2$ in 100 ml of solution, (*c*) 11.2 g of KOH in 5.0 l of solution.

4. Compute the *p*H of each of the solutions in Problem 4.
5. Calculate the hydrogen-ion concentration for a solution whose p*H* is (*a*) 0, (*b*) 4.0, (*c*) 10.0, (*d*) 2.3, (*e*) 4.4, (*f*) 12.5, (*g*) 1.5, (*h*) −0.5.
6. The *p*H of a salt solution is 10.0. (*a*) What is the hydroxide-ion concentration in the solution? (*b*) What would be the color of (*i*) phenolphthalein, (*ii*) methyl orange, (*iii*) thymol blue in the solution?

Find Out!

1. Prepare an indicator by boiling red cabbage leaves in a minimum of water until the solution has a deep color. (The pigment in the leaves may be extracted with other solvents also.) Test this indicator by preparing solutions with *p*H values of 1 to 14 and checking the color of a few drops of indicator in a sample of each of the prepared solutions.
2. Use this indicator on commercially prepared solutions or test paper (such as Hydrion paper) to check the *p*H of common substances as on page 252.
3. Titrate a weak acid and strong base and a strong base and weak acid and prepare curves as on page 258.
4. Look up the Lewis acid–base definition in a college text and compare this to the Arrhenius and Brönsted-Lowry concepts.

Suggested Readings

Behrman, A.S., *Water Is Everybody's Business: The Chemistry of Water Purification.* Garden City, N.Y.: Doubleday-Anchor. (Paperback)

Buswell, A., and W. Rodebush, *Water* (SCIENTIFIC AMERICAN Offprint #262). San Francisco: Freeman.

Derjaguin, B.V., *The Force between Molecules* (SCIENTIFIC AMERICAN Offprint #266) San Francisco: Freeman.

Wahl, A.C., "Chemistry by Computer," *Scientific American*, April 1970.

UNIT 

ELECTROCHEMISTRY

IN THE REACTION $A + B \longrightarrow C + D + \text{energy}$, the potential energy in the products is less than the potential energy in the reactants. The energy may be released as heat energy. For instance, if metallic zinc is dropped into a solution of copper (II) sulfate, the reaction is

$$Zn + Cu^{+2} \longrightarrow Zn^{+2} + Cu + \text{heat energy} \qquad \text{(V-1)}$$

In other words, there is a loss of chemical potential energy if electrons are transferred from zinc atoms to copper ions, and this energy is released as heat.

If zinc and zinc ions are placed in one beaker, and copper and copper ions in another, the reaction will still take place, if zinc and copper are connected by a wire and the gap between the solutions in the beakers is bridged by a conducting solution. In this reaction the difference in potential energy between reactants and products is transformed into electrical energy, and the apparatus used for such a purpose is called a *voltaic cell*. Reactions in voltaic cells occur automatically (no external aid is needed) and they are called spontaneous reactions.

We would expect that if enough energy is supplied from an outside source, the direction of the reaction could be reversed. If a battery of dry cells in series is connected to the zinc and copper terminals of a Daniell cell, the reaction can be driven backwards:

$$Cu + Zn^{+2} + \text{electrical energy} \longrightarrow Cu^{+2} + Zn \qquad \text{(V-2)}$$

A cell of this kind is called an *electrolytic cell*. Reactions in electrolytic cells are non-spontaneous.

HISTORICAL CHEMISTRY LABORATORY

This extract is from the works of Michael Faraday. The article first appeared in the defunct British journal, ***Philosophical Transactions*** (1837), in which he proposed some important concepts of electrochemistry.

Michael Faraday
(1791–1867)

The theory which I believe to be a true expression of the facts of electrochemical decomposition, and which I have therefore detailed in a former series of these researches, is so much at variance with those previously advanced, that I find the greatest difficulty in stating results, as I think correctly, whilst limited to the use of terms which are current with a certain accepted meaning. Of this kind is the term pole, with its prefixes of positive and negative, and the attached ideas of attraction and repulsion. The general phraseology is that the positive pole attracts oxygen, acids, &c., or more cautiously, that it determines their evolution upon the surface; and that the negative pole acts in an actual manner upon hydrogen, combustibles, metals, and bases. According to my view, the determining force is not at the poles, but within the decomposing body; and the oxygen and acids are rendered at the negative extremity of the body, whilst hydrogen, metals, &c., are evolved at the positive extremity.

To avoid, therefore, confusion and circumlocution, and for the sake of greater precision of expression than I can otherwise obtain, I have deliberately considered the subject with two friends, and with their assistance and concurrence in framing them, I purpose henceforward using certain other terms, which I will now define. The poles, as they are usually called, are only the doors or ways by which the electric current passes into and out of the decomposing body; and they of course, when in contact with that body, are the limits of its extent in the direction of the current. The term has been generally applied to the metal surfaces in contact with the decomposing substance; but whether philosophers generally would also apply it to the surfaces of air and water, against which I have effected electrochemical decomposition, is subject to doubt. In place of the term pole, I propose using that of electrode, and I mean thereby that substance, or rather surface, whether of air, water, metal, or any other body, which bounds the extent of the decomposing matter in the direction of the electric current.

CHAPTER 17

OXIDATION-REDUCTION

WHEN THE ROLE OF ELECTRON TRANSFER in the formation of ionic bonds was understood, this new concept was applied to the processes of oxidation and reduction. Thus, in the reaction

$$2Na^{\cdot} + \ddot{\underset{\cdot\cdot}{O}}\!: \longrightarrow 2Na^{+} + :\ddot{\underset{\cdot\cdot}{O}}\!: \qquad (17\text{-}1)$$

the valence electrons of the sodium atoms are pulled away by the oxygen atom. Here sodium is oxidized and oxygen is the oxidizing agent. With this in mind, we can say that an *oxidizing agent is a substance that attracts electrons*. If sodium were to react with fluorine or chlorine, a similar transfer of electrons would occur. Therefore we could call both fluorine and chlorine oxidizing agents.

The term *reduction* was first used in metallurgy centuries ago to describe the process in which a large pile of metallic ore was changed to metal. Thus, in the blast furnace process, iron ore is heated with coke and metallic iron is formed. The reaction can be represented as

$$2Fe_2O_3 + 3C \longrightarrow 4Fe + 3CO_2 \qquad (17\text{-}2)$$

Fig. 17-1 Magnesium ribbon burning in oxygen is an example of rapid oxidation. Write a balanced equation to show how electrons are lost and gained in this reaction. Is oxygen reduced? Powdered antimony reacting with chlorine is also an example of rapid oxidation. Write a balanced equation for this reaction to show electron transfer. Is antimony oxidized?

In the reaction iron ore is said to be *reduced* and coke is said to be the *reducing agent*. What is meant by a reducing agent in terms of electrons?

In Fe_2O_3, iron exists as iron (III) ions symbolized by Fe^{+3}. In the course of this reaction these iron ions are converted to iron atoms symbolized by Fe. Evidently the Fe^{+3} ions have each accepted three electrons in the process and the reducing agent—carbon in this case—must have supplied these electrons. Thus we can define a *reducing agent as a substance that provides or loses electrons.*

Oxidation-Reduction in Ionic Reactions

The common laboratory method of preparing hydrogen is to place some pieces of zinc metal in a dilute solution of either sulfuric acid or hydrochloric acid. Why does zinc react with an acid? You recall that the electron configuration of a zinc atom is $1s^2 2s^2 2p^6 3s^2 3p^6 3d^{10} 4s^2$. The two electrons in the $4s$ orbital are only loosely held and so are readily captured by hydrogen ions. This transfer of electrons can be represented in two steps:

$$Zn - 2e^{-1} \longrightarrow Zn^{+2} \tag{17-3}$$

$$2H^+(aq) + 2e^{-1} \longrightarrow 2H \longrightarrow H_2 \tag{17-4}$$

and the net ionic reaction can be written as

$$Zn + 2H^+(aq) \longrightarrow Zn^{+2} + H_2 \tag{17-5}$$

Notice that this is also an oxidation-reduction reaction or, as it is sometimes called, a *redox* reaction. Since electrons are transferred from zinc metal to the hydrogen ion, the oxidizing agent is the hydrogen ion and the reducing agent is the metallic zinc. In passing, it should be observed that the hydrogen ion (H^+) often acts as an oxidizing agent, whereas hydrogen (H_2) often acts as a reducing agent.

A Comparison of the Chemical Activity of Zinc and Copper

If several pieces of zinc are placed in a test tube containing a solution of copper (II) sulfate, several things happen:

(1) The blue color of the solution becomes fainter and may even disappear altogether.

(2) The zinc becomes coated with a dark red deposit.
(3) The test tube becomes warm and therefore the reaction is exothermic.

How can these observations be explained?

The blue color is due to copper (II) ions and the dark red deposit is copper metal. Hence the equation for the reaction is

$$Zn + Cu^{+2} \longrightarrow Zn^{+2} + Cu + \text{heat} \qquad (17\text{-}6)$$

This net reaction is nothing more than the sum of two half-reactions in which two electrons are transferred from each zinc atom to each copper (II) ion.

$$Zn \longrightarrow Zn^{+2} + 2e^{-1} \qquad (17\text{-}7)$$
$$Cu^{+2} + 2e^{-1} \longrightarrow Cu \qquad (17\text{-}8)$$

This is clearly a redox reaction in which the copper (II) ion is the oxidizing agent and metallic zinc the reducing agent. *The tendency of a metal to give up electrons can be used as a measure of its chemical activity.* The greater the tendency of a certain metal to give up electrons the greater is the activity of the metal, and, conversely, the greater the tendency of metal ions to form atoms the less is the activity of the metal. In other words, zinc atoms are reactive compared with copper atoms, which under these conditions are inactive.

Fig. 17-2 This mask is made of gold and is over 1000 years old. Is gold a chemically active metal?

Comparing the activity of the metals zinc and copper with hydrogen, the order is

Zinc
Hydrogen
Copper

This list can be expanded to include other metals. Table 17-1 is such a list, called an *activity list.* In summary metals above hydrogen in the activity list release electrons more readily than hydrogen atoms and they are called active metals. On the other hand, metals below hydrogen release electrons less readily than hydrogen atoms. The least reactive of these are known as the *noble metals.* They include gold and platinum.

Table 17-1 Order of activity of metals

No.	Element	Symbol
1	Potassium	K
2	Calcium	Ca
3	Sodium	Na
4	Magnesium	Mg
5	Aluminum	Al
6	Zinc	Zn
7	Iron	Fe
8	Lead	Pb
9	Hydrogen	H
10	Copper	Cu
11	Mercury	Hg
12	Silver	Ag
13	Platinum	Pt
14	Gold	Au

The Release of Heat Energy in the Zn–Cu^{+2} Reaction

The release of heat energy in the Zn-Cu^{+2} reaction means that there is more chemical energy in the reactants than in the products.

Suppose we now place the zinc metal and copper (II) ions in separate beakers and connect them by a wire (Fig. 17-1*a*). Electrons clearly cannot move from zinc atoms to copper (II) ions directly. But will electrons flow from zinc to copper (II) ions along the wire? This is clearly an important question since it raises the possibility of using chemical reactions as a source of electric energy in a so-called *electrochemical* or *galvanic* cell.

A Galvanic Cell

A galvanic cell consists of two half-cells, each made up of a metal and a solution of suitable ions. For our purpose, a strip of zinc is placed in a beaker containing zinc ions (a solution of zinc sulfate, for example) and a strip of copper is placed in another beaker containing copper (II) ions (a solution of copper (II) sulfate). The zinc and copper strips are connected by a wire which, in turn, is connected to an ammeter as shown in Fig. 17-3(*a*). However, there still remains a gap between the beakers so that no current can flow. To bridge the gap, the two half-cells are connected by a so-called *salt bridge* which is an inverted U-tube filled with a strong electrolyte such as zinc sulfate solution or potassium chloride solution. Such a salt bridge is shown in Fig. 17-3(*b*).

In practice, as soon as the salt bridge is lowered into place to bridge the gap, an electric current flows through the circuit and the needle of the ammeter is deflected. Moreover, the direction in which the needle is deflected proves that electrons flow from zinc to copper in the external circuit, that is, along the wire.

The Chemical Reaction in a Galvanic Cell

Zinc metal releases electrons, thereby forming zinc ions. The released electrons flow along the wire and combine with copper (II) ions in the other beaker. The two half-reactions are

$$\mathrm{Zn} \longrightarrow \mathrm{Zn}^{+2} + 2\mathrm{e}^{-1} \tag{17-7}$$

$$\mathrm{Cu}^{+2} + 2\mathrm{e}^{-1} \longrightarrow \mathrm{Cu} \tag{17-8}$$

By addition, the *net* reaction is

$$\mathrm{Zn} + \mathrm{Cu}^{+2} \longrightarrow \mathrm{Zn}^{+2} + \mathrm{Cu} \tag{17-9}$$

The number of electrons is the same on both sides of the equation. Therefore there is no net gain or loss of electrons, and for this reason electrons are usually omitted from the net equation.

Speculate . . .
Examine the net reaction of the galvanic cell. Is it conceivable that an electric current might be applied to the products of the reaction and there by reverse it?

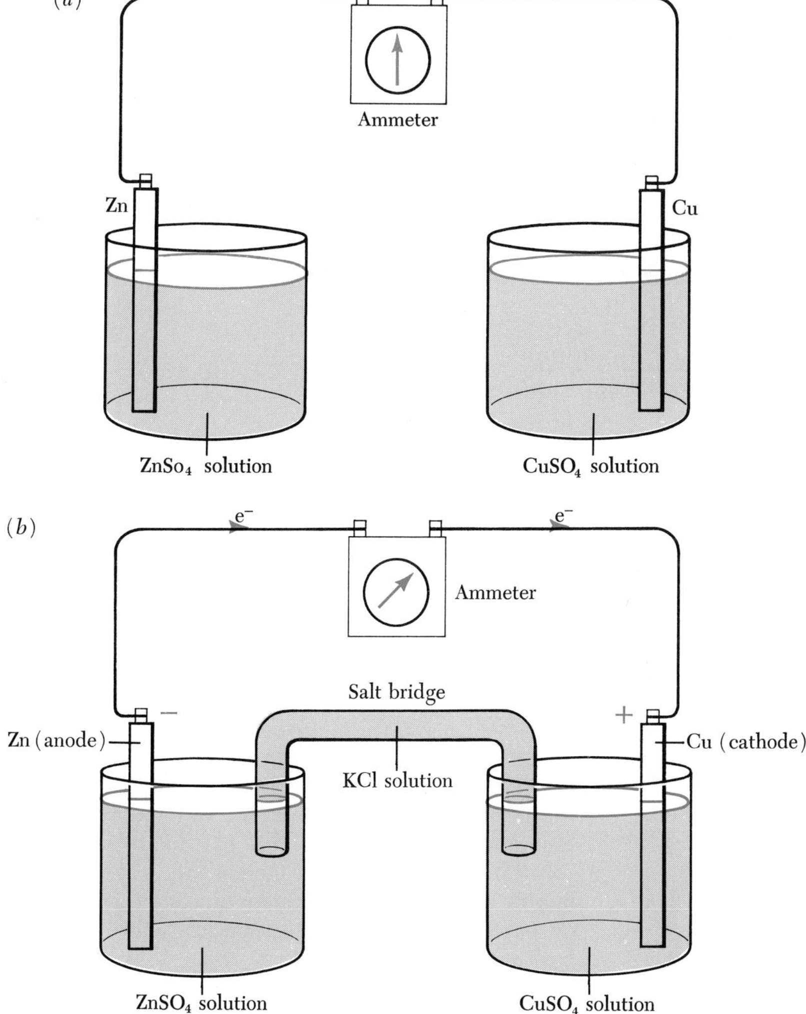

Fig. 17-3 *(a)* A galvanic cell is made up of two half-cells. The electrical circuit is not complete. Why? *(b)* A current flows when the half-cells are connected by a salt bridge. Compare this diagram with diagram *(a)*.

Both zinc metal and copper ions are gradually used up. Hence the blue color the the copper ions fades away and metallic copper is deposited on of copper strip. Also the half-reactions occur at the metal strips where electrons either leave or enter the cell. The metal terminals in a cell are called *electrodes.*

Since electrons are released by the metal zinc, the half-reaction at the zinc electrode is oxidation and the electrode at which oxidation takes place is called *the anode.* On the other hand, the half–reaction at the copper electrode is reduction and the electrode at which reduction occurs is called *the cathode.* Positively charged copper (II) ions flow towards the cathode.

Note . . .
The two half-reactions of a cell must of necessity take place at the same time. It is therefore impossible to find the *absolute* electrode potential of a single metal directly.

Electrical Measurements—Coulombs, Amperes, and Volts

In Fig. 17-3 (*b*), the ammeter inserted in the external circuit shows that a current flows through the wire. What does an ammeter really measure? In Chapter 3 it was stated that the unit of quantity of electricity is called a *coulomb*. It was also stated that the charge on an electron is 1.60×10^{-19} C. Therefore the number of electrons in one coulomb is

$$\frac{1 \text{ coulomb}}{1.60 \times 10^{-19} \text{ coulomb/electron}} = 6.3 \times 10^{18} \text{ electrons}$$

The rate of flow of electrons (or the electric current) is the amount of charge that passes a point (on a conductor) in one second. The

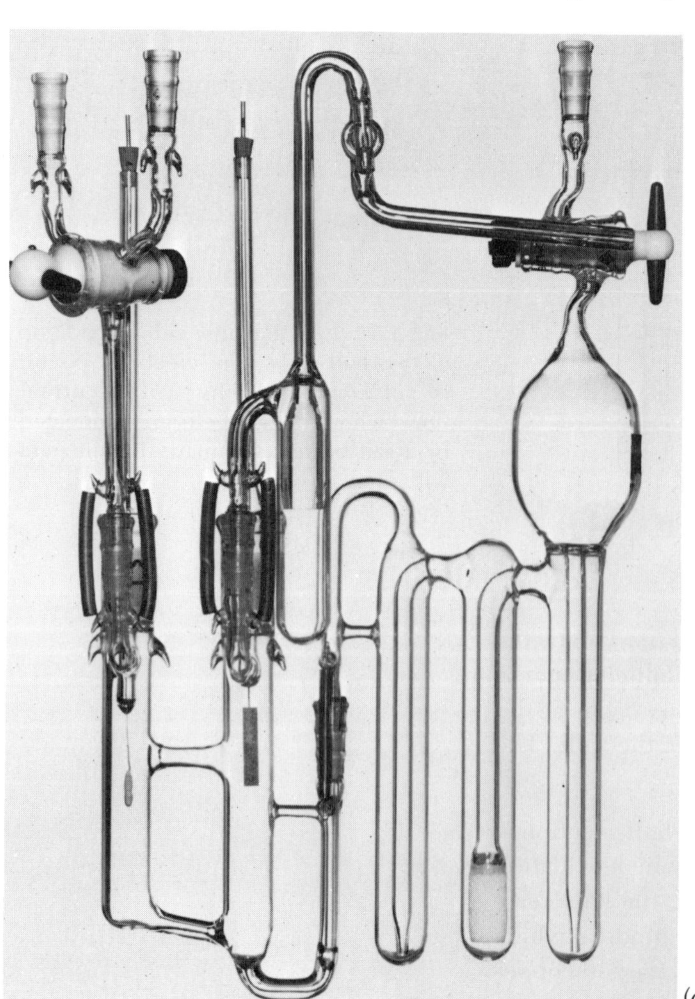

(*a*)

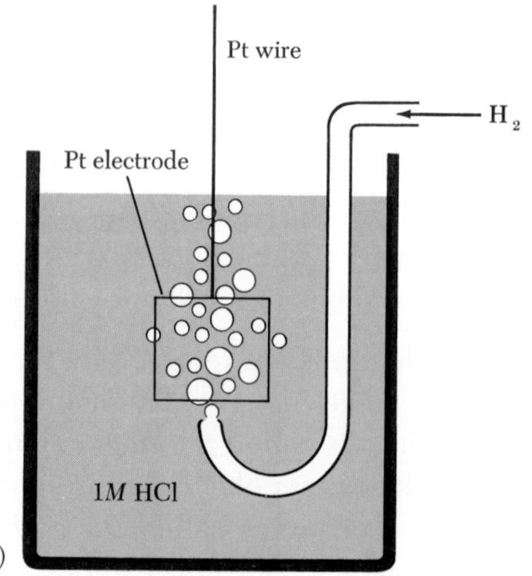

(*b*)

Fig. 17-4 (*a*) The glass apparatus which appears in the photograph is used by the National Bureau of Standards to determine the *p*H value of buffer solutions, some of which have a medical use. It is known as a standard hydrogen electrode and works on essentially the same principle as the standard hydrogen electrode shown in (*b*).

unit of current is called the *ampere* and is defined as *the quantity of electricity, measured in coulombs, which passes a given point of a conductor in one second.* One ampere (A) equals one coulomb per second. An ammeter measures current in amperes.

Voltage, on the other hand, concerns *electric pressure or potential.* It corresponds to water pressure in a standpipe and it determines the rate at which electrons flow in a conductor. That is, voltage is a measure of electrical potential. The higher the voltage of a cell, the greater is its capacity to do the work needed to force electrons along the conductor—usually a wire. It should now be apparent that, in any electrochemical cell, electrons flow from the electrode of higher potential to the electrode of lower potential. The electric potential difference between the two electrodes of a cell can be measured by a voltmeter and is expressed in volts (V).

The Standard Hydrogen Electrode

Every galvanic cell is made up of two half-cells, each containing a different metal immersed in a solution of its particular ion. The tendency of a metal to yield electrons (as in Eq. 17-7 or 17-8) is called its *electrode potential.* How can the electrode potential of a metal be measured?

A relative value can be found by comparing the electrode potential of a metal with a suitable standard of reference, just as atomic masses are based on the standard value of 12.000 for the most common isotope of carbon. The standard of reference is a hydrogen half-cell which consists of hydrogen gas in a solution of hydrogen ions. A hydrogen half-cell, or a standard hydrogen electrode, is shown in Fig. 17-4 (*b*).

Note . . .
The symbol C is used as the standard abbreviation for coulomb both in international usage and in publications of the American Chemical Society.

The hydrogen half-cell consists of a piece of platinum metal immersed in a 1 *M* solution of HCl. Platinum is an inactive (or noble) metal and does not react with dilute acid. However, platinum is an excellent adsorber of hydrogen gas and therefore becomes covered with a layer of hydrogen. Thus, in effect, the platinum plate becomes a hydrogen electrode.

The half-reaction in this hydrogen gas–hydrogen ion cell is

$$H_2(g) \rightleftharpoons 2H^+(aq) + 2e^{-1} \qquad (17\text{-}10)$$

and an electrode potential of 0.00 *V* is assigned to this reaction.

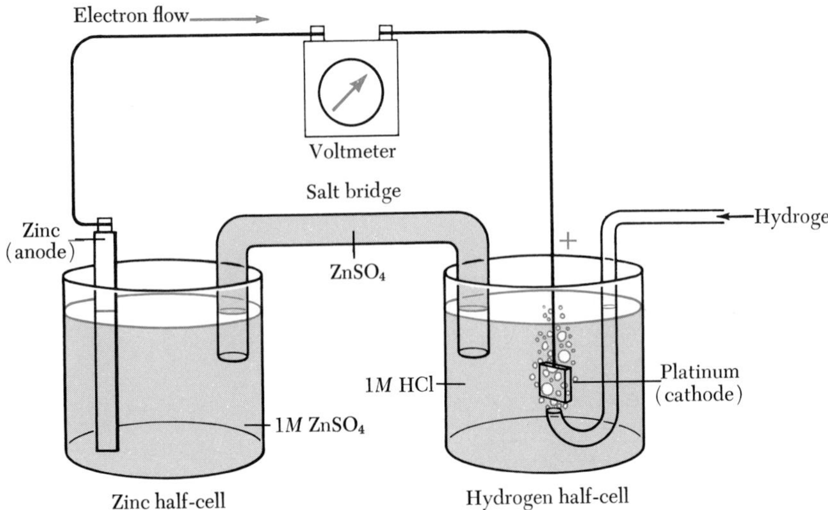

Fig. 17-5 The electrode potential of zinc is measured by connecting a zinc half-cell to a hydrogen half-cell.

To Measure Electrode Potentials

Electrode potentials of various metals can be measured by connecting the metal half-cell to a hydrogen half-cell by means of a salt bridge. The apparatus for measuring the electrode potential of zinc is shown in Fig. 17-5. The zinc half-cell consists of a zinc rod immersed in 1 *M* solution of $ZnSO_4$. The voltage is registered on a voltmeter placed in the external circuit. The reading of the voltmeter is 0.76 V. What does this indicate?

The reactions in the two half-cells are

$$Zn(s) \longrightarrow Zn^{+2}(1\,M) + 2e^{-1} \quad (17\text{-}11)$$

$$2H^{+}(aq)\ (1\,M) + 2e^{-1} \longrightarrow H_2(g) \quad (17\text{-}12)$$

and therefore the zinc electrode is the negative terminal (or anode) and the hydrogen electrode is the positive terminal (or cathode). The net reaction is

$$Zn(s) + 2H^{+}(aq)\ (1\,M) \longrightarrow Zn^{+2}(1\,M) + H_2(g) \quad (17\text{-}13)$$

That is, the zinc electrode dissolves and hydrogen gas is released at the hydrogen electrode. Notice also that this is precisely the same equation as the reaction between zinc and dilute hydrochloric acid in a test tube *except that the ion concentrations are precisely specified.* The voltage of the cell depends on these concentrations. Therefore, the voltage of this cell is 0.76 V when the ion concentration is 1 *M*.

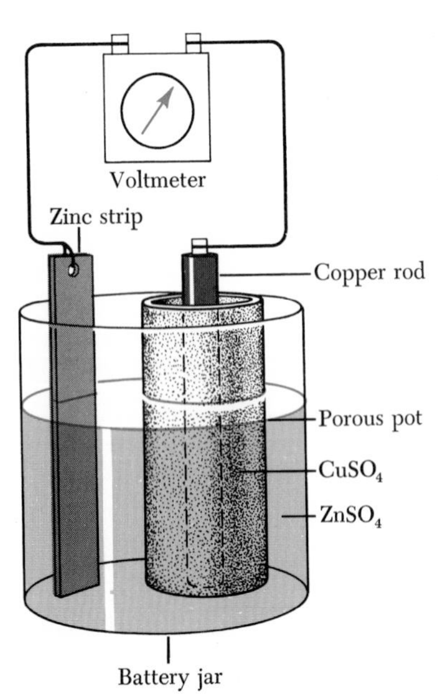

Fig. 17-6 A Daniell cell.

The symbol E^0 is used to indicate standard electrode potential with 1 M ion concentration. A E^0 value of 0.00 V is assigned to the half-reaction

$$H_2(g) \rightleftharpoons 2H^+(aq)(1\,M) + 2e^{-1} \qquad (17\text{-}14)$$

and, therefore, it follows that $E^0 = 0.76$ V for the reaction

$$Zn(s) \longrightarrow Zn^{+2}(1\,M) + 2e^{-1} \qquad (17\text{-}15)$$

This last reaction, you will recall, is an oxidation reaction (Zn is oxidized to Zn^{+2}) and for this reason it is sometimes convenient to speak of *oxidation potentials* rather than electrode potentials.

Finally, since E^0 for zinc is greater than E^0 for hydrogen, it follows that the $Zn–Zn^{+2}$ half-reaction releases electrons more readily than the $H_2–2H^+(aq)$ reaction. For this reason a positive sign is written for the standard oxidation potential (E^0) for zinc and this becomes +0.76 V.

A Zinc–Copper Cell

Suppose we now make an electrochemical cell by combining the two half—cells, $Zn–Zn^{+2}$ (1 M) and $Cu–Cu^{+2}$ (1 M) as shown in Fig. 17-6. What is the voltage of such a cell?

At a 1 M concentration, the potential of the zinc electrode relative to hydrogen is 0.76 V; also, in a Cu-H cell the potential of the hydrogen electrode is 0.34 V greater than that of the copper elec-

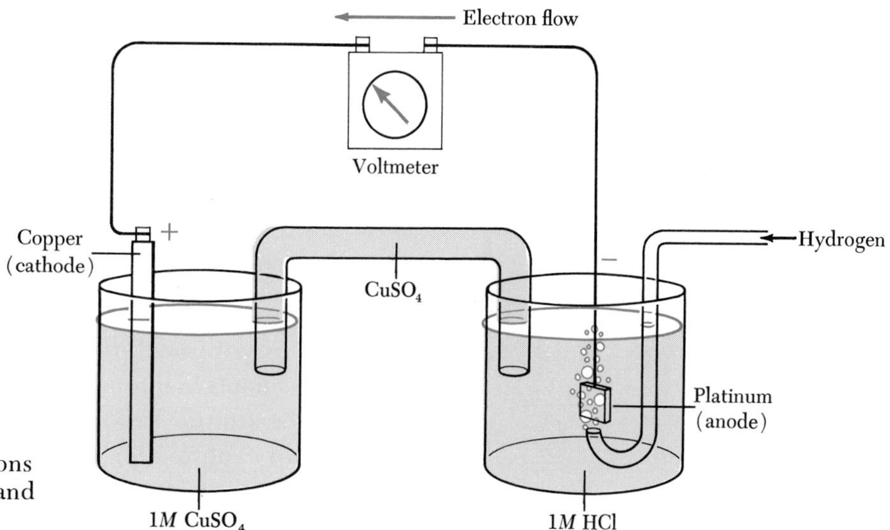

Fig. 17-7 A Cu-H cell. Electrons flow toward the copper electrode and the voltmeter reads 0.34 V.

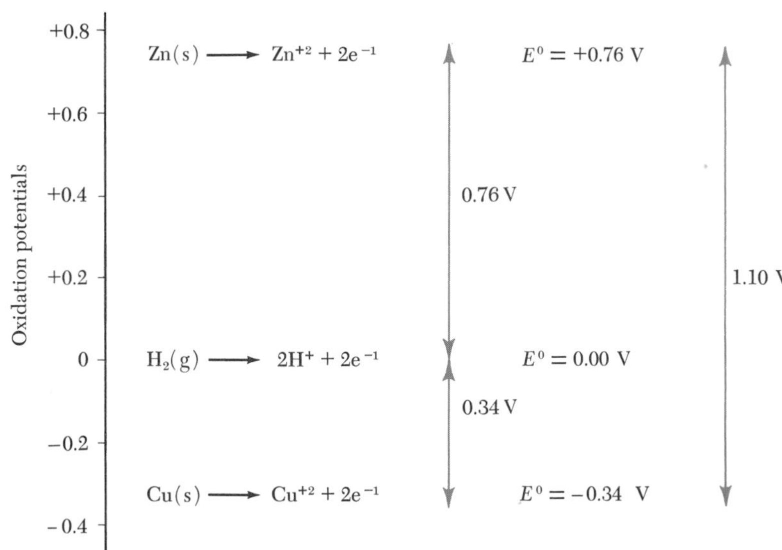

Fig. 17-8 The voltage of a cell is the algebraic sum of the oxidation potentials of the half-cells.

trode. Therefore if a zinc–copper cell containing the ions at a concentration of 1 *M* is prepared, we expect the voltage to be 1.10 V. This is found to be correct. In general, the voltage of a cell (or potential difference as it is usually called) is the algebraic sum of the oxidation potentials of the half-cells. See Fig. 17-8.

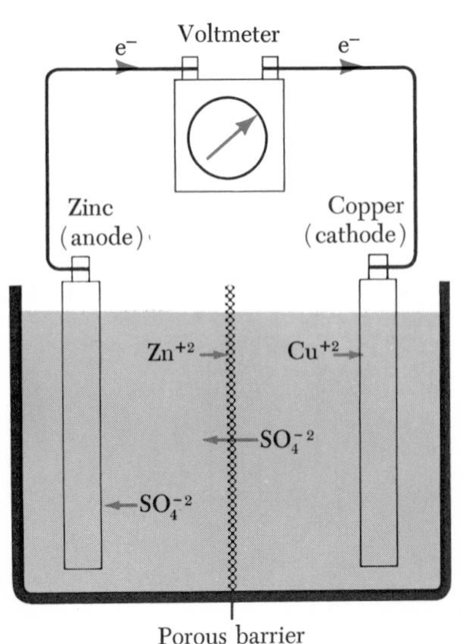

Fig. 17-9 The porous barrier in the zinc-copper cell prevents Cu^{+2} ions from reaching the zinc electrode.

The Flow of Ions in a Daniell Cell As stated earlier, the zinc strip is the anode in a Daniell cell. For every two electrons released from the zinc electrode a zinc ion is formed so that, as electrons flow through the wire, zinc ions accumulate around the electrode.

Since electrons flow from zinc to copper in the wire, the copper electrode is the cathode of the cell. Thus, copper (II) ions flow towards the copper electrode where they are discharged to give copper metal. On the other hand, negatively charged sulfate ions flow towards the zinc electrode. This ion flow in opposite directions is shown in Fig. 17-9.

Ions must pass through the porous pot barrier, otherwise electrons could not flow through the wire. Why not? The great advantage of the porous pot is that it prevents rapid movement of copper (II) ions towards the zinc electrode. If Cu^{+2} ions reached the zinc electrode, they would capture electrons directly from the zinc, and the reaction would take place at that point. Therefore, the electron flow in the wire would be reduced and possibly prevented altogether.

Standard Oxidation Potentials

The standard oxidation potentials of a large number of half-cell reactions have been determined by experiment, and some of them are included in Table 17-2,

The metal on the left-hand side of each equation constitutes the reduced state of the element and the ion on the right-hand side constitutes the oxidized state. Half-cell potentials can be used to predict the potential of a cell made up of any two of the half-cells in the table. For example, what would be the voltage of an iron–silver electrochemical cell? From Table 17-2,

$$Fe \longrightarrow Fe^{+2} + 2e^{-1} \qquad E^0 = +0.44\ V$$
$$Ag \longrightarrow Ag^{+} + e^{-1} \qquad E^0 = -0.80\ V$$

If we reverse the second equation and double the coeffecient, we get

$$2Ag^{+} + 2e^{-1} \longrightarrow 2Ag \qquad E^0 = +0.80\ V \tag{17-16}$$

Let us compute the net value.

$$\begin{aligned} Fe &\longrightarrow Fe^{+2} + 2e^{-1} & E^0 &= +0.44\ V \\ 2e^{-1} + 2Ag^{+} &\longrightarrow 2Ag & E^0 &= +0.80\ V \\ Fe + 2Ag^{+} &\longrightarrow Fe^{+2} + 2Ag & E^0 &= +1.24\ V \end{aligned}$$

A positive value for the net E^0 indicates that the reaction is spontaneous.

Table 17-2 Oxidation potentials for some selected half-reactions.

Half-reaction	E^0, V
$Mg \longrightarrow Mg^{+2} + 2e^{-1}$	+2.34
$Al \longrightarrow Al^{+3} + 3e^{-1}$	+1.66
$Zn \longrightarrow Zn^{+2} + 2e^{-1}$	+0.76
$Fe \longrightarrow Fe^{+2} + 2e^{-1}$	+0.44
$Ni \longrightarrow Ni^{+2} + 2e^{-1}$	+0.25
$H_2 \longrightarrow 2H^{+} + 2e^{-1}$	0.00
$Cu \longrightarrow Cu^{+2} + 2e^{-1}$	−0.34
$Hg \longrightarrow Hg^{+} + e^{-1}$	−0.79
$Ag \longrightarrow Ag^{+} + e^{-1}$	−0.80

Oxidation Numbers

Oxidation numbers are assigned for convenience to atoms and ions that take part in redox reactions. Since atoms are electrically neutral their oxidation numbers are chosen as 0. Hence, in the reaction (Eq. 17-17),

$$2Cu + Cl_2 \longrightarrow 2CuCl \tag{17-17}$$

the oxidation number for Cu is 0 and for Cl_2 it is also 0. If an atom loses an electron, the sign of the oxidation number of the resulting ion is positive, and the value of the number equals the number of electrons lost. Conversely, if an atom gains an electron, the sign of the oxidation number is negative. The oxidation numbers of some atoms and ions are listed in Table 17-3.

Table 17-3 Oxidation numbers of selected atoms and ions.

Atom or ion	Oxidation number
Cu	0
Cu^{+}	+1
Cu^{+2}	+2
Cl (or Cl_2)	0
Cl^{-1}	−1

Oxidation numbers are also used to define the terms oxidation, reduction, reducing agent, and oxidizing agent. Let us see how. In the following two half-reactions it is apparent that (1) copper is the reducing agent (and is oxidized) and (2) chlorine is the oxidizing agent (and is reduced).

$$\underset{\text{reducing agent}}{Cu} - 2e^{-1} \xrightarrow{\text{oxidation}} Cu^{+2} \tag{17-18}$$

$$\underset{\text{oxidizing agent}}{Cl_2} + 2e^{-1} \xrightarrow{\text{reduction}} 2Cl^{-1} \tag{17-19}$$

Thus, in general terms we can say that *oxidation involves an increase in the oxidation number of the reactant* and *reduction involves a decrease in the oxidation number of the reactant.* Also, *a reducing agent is a substance (atoms or ion) that increases its oxidation number in a reaction, whereas an oxidizing agent is a substance that decreases its oxidation number.*

Oxidation Numbers of Atoms in Covalent Molecules

Both copper (I) chloride and copper (II) chloride are ionic compounds. Indeed, the term oxidation number was first applied to elements in compounds in which an electron transfer had taken place. However, in the large majority of compounds, electrons are shared, not transferred; that is, in the majority of compounds, bonds are covalent, not ionic. How are the oxidation numbers of elements assigned in covalent molecules?

The electronegativity scale is used to assign the oxidation number of an atom as positive or negative. And, with this proviso, elements in covalent compounds are treated in the same way as elements in ionic compounds. First, let us consider a covalent bond in which the shared pair is midway between the two nuclei—as in a molecule of hydrogen. In such a case, neither of the atoms appears to have either a negative or positive charge and therefore the oxidation number is 0. Similarly, the oxidation number of a chlorine atom in a molecule of chlorine is 0. Thus, by this argument we arrive at the same result as when we state that the oxidation number of an element (either atom or molecule) is 0.

The Oxidation Numbers of H, Cl, and O in Covalent Compounds

What of the oxidation numbers of unlike atoms in a covalent molecule? What, for example, are the oxidation numbers of hydrogen and chlorine in a molecule of hydrogen chloride? The electronegativity of chlorine is 3.0 and of hydrogen it is 2.1. *The more electronegative element has the negative oxidation number and the less electronegative element has the positive oxidation number.* That is, the oxidation numbers of chlorine and hydrogen are −1 and +1, respectively. This makes sense because, as you learned earlier, the shared pair of electrons is nearer the chlorine nucleus than the hydrogen nucleus. Thus the chlorine atom appears to have gained an electron, so that its oxidation number is −1. On the other hand, the hydrogen atom appears to have lost an electron and its oxidation number is +1.

What are the oxidation numbers of hydrogen and oxygen in a molecule of water? The electronegativity of oxygen is 3.5 and therefore the oxidation number of oxygen has a negative sign. In a water molecule, two hydrogen atoms share two pairs of electrons with one oxygen atom. Moreover, the two pairs of electrons are pulled towards the oxygen nucleus. That is, the oxygen atom appears to have gained two electrons (one from each hydrogen atom). Therefore the oxidation number of oxygen is −2, and of hydrogen it is +1. Indeed, the oxidation number of oxygen is −2 in almost all of its compounds and, by the same token, the oxidation number of hydrogen in its compounds is almost always +1.

The Oxidation Number of Carbon in Covalent Compounds

Based on the electronegativity rule, the oxidation number of carbon may be positive or negative. For example, let us compute the oxidation number of C in (1) carbon monoxide (CO), (2) carbon dioxide (CO_2), and (3) methane (CH_4). The three electronegativities are: H, 2.1; C, 2.5; and O, 3.5. Hence the oxidation number of carbon in CO is +2, in CO_2 it is +4, and in CH_4 it is −4.

Rules for Assigning Oxidation Numbers to Elements in Compounds

Carbon is by no means the only element that can have several oxidation numbers or, as we usually say, exist in several oxidation states. Indeed, we have already discussed the different oxidation states of the metals iron, copper, tin, and mercury. Moreover, the metals manganese and chromium can exist in a relatively large number of oxidation states. The oxidation numbers of all elements can readily be computed from a set of seven rules which can be summarized as follows:

1. The oxidation number of all elements in the free state is 0.
2. The oxidation number of hydrogen is $+1$ in all its compounds, except in metals hydrides when it is -1.
3. The oxidation number of oxygen is -2 in all its compounds, except in peroxides when it is -1.
4. The oxidation numbers of all metals are positive. For the alkali metals the number is $+1$, for the alkaline earths it is $+2$, and for aluminum $+3$.
5. The oxidation number of the halogens is -1 in binary compounds.
6. In compounds of elements not covered by the foregoing rules, the oxidation number of the element with the higher electronegativity has a negative sign.
7. The algebraic sum of the oxidation numbers of all atoms in any formula is equal to the charge on the formula.

The following two examples illustrate the use of these rules.

Example 17-1

What is the oxidation number of manganese in potassium permanganate ($KMnO_4$)?

Solution

Rule 4 Oxidation number of K $= +1$.

Rule 3 Oxidation number of $O_4 = 4 \times -2 = -8$.

Rule 7 Sum of oxidation numbers of $Mn + K + O_4 = O$.

$+1 + Mn + (-8) = 0$

Therefore, the oxidation number of Mn $= +7$.

The total oxidation numbers can now be written above the atoms in the formula

$$\overset{+1}{K}\ \overset{+7}{Mn}\ \overset{-8}{O_4}$$

Example 17-2

What is the oxidation number of chromium in dichromate ion, $Cr_2O_7^{-2}$?

Solution

Rule 3 Total oxidation number for $O_7 = -2 \times 7 = -14$.

Total oxidation number for $Cr_2 = -2 - (-14) = +12$

Therefore, the oxidation number of each chromium atom is $+6$.

The total oxidation numbers are

$$\overset{+12}{Cr_2}\overset{-14}{O_7}{}^{-2}$$

Balancing Equations of Redox Reactions by Oxidation Numbers

The equations of some redox reactions are complicated and difficult to write by using the technique of conserving atoms as was done in an earlier chapter. Equation writing is simplified if we consider the principle of the conservation of oxidation numbers as well as conservation of atoms. As in previous examples, the correct formulas of reactants and products must be written first. In addition, two further rules are necessary:

(1) Discover which element is oxidized and which is reduced by comparing oxidation numbers of all atoms in the reactants and products.

(2) Make the increase in oxidation number of the element being oxidized equal to the decrease of oxidation number of the element being reduced by writing suitable coefficients for reactants and products.

Let us apply these rules to the following example.

Example 17-3

A solution of potassium permanganate reacts with iron (II) sulfate and dilute sulfuric acid to form potassium sulfate, ferric sulfate, manganous sulfate, and water.

Write the equation for the reaction.

Solution

The unbalanced reaction is

$$\overset{+7}{KMnO_4} + \overset{+2}{FeSO_4} + H_2SO_4 \longrightarrow K_2SO_4 + \overset{+2}{MnSO_4} + \overset{2(+3)}{Fe_2(SO_4)_3} + H_2O$$

Oxidation numbers of atoms on the left are:

K = +1; Mn = +7; 0 = −2; Fe = +2; S = +6; H = +1.

Oxidation numbers of atoms on the right are:

K = +1; Mn = +2; 0 = −2; Fe = +3; S = +6; H = +1.

From this it is evident that the oxidation number of Mn is decreased from +7 to +2, that is by 5, and that the oxidation number of Fe is increased from +2 to +3, that is by 1. Since the amount of oxidation must equal the amount of reduction in any reaction, we can see that we need five iron (II) ions for each manganese atom. Therefore we shall assign coefficients of 1 to $KMnO_4$ and 5 to $FeSO_4$. Thus the expression becomes

$$1KMnO_4 + 5FeSO_4 + H_2SO_4 \longrightarrow K_2SO_4 + 1MnSO_4 + 2.5Fe_2(SO_4)_3 + H_2O$$

The rest of the equation is now balanced by inspection.

$$1KMnO_4 + 5FeSO_4 + 4H_2SO_4 \longrightarrow 0.5K_2SO_4 + 1MnSO_4 + 2.5Fe_2(SO_4)_3 + 4H_2O$$

or, to avoid fractional coefficients,

$$2KMnO_4 + 10FeSO_4 + 8H_2SO_4 \longrightarrow K_2SO_4 + 2MnSO_4 + 5Fe_2(SO_4)_3 + 8H_2O$$

Fig. 17-10 The oxidation-reduction reaction of potassium permanganate, iron (II) sulfate, and sulfuric acid. Pictured from left to right are a test tube of potassium permanganate, and a test tube of iron (II) sulfate. The third tube is a mixture of these solutions. The fourth tube contains both solutions and dilute sulfuric acid.

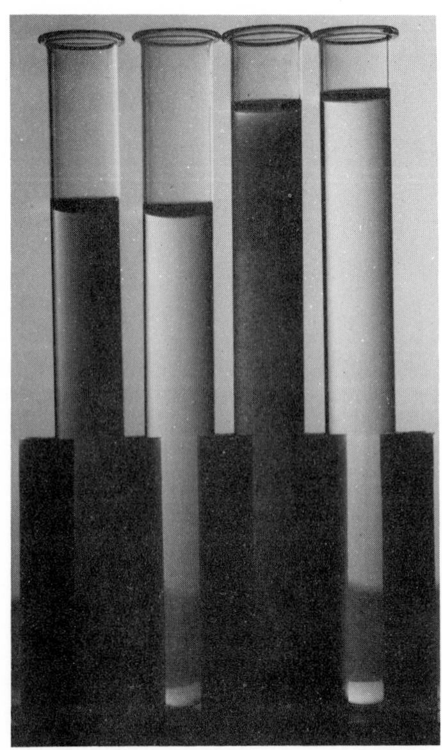

Balancing Redox Equations by the Ion–Electron Method

Another way to balance an equation is to consider the electron exchange in the two half-reactions wherein the same number of electrons must be transferred from one half-reaction to the other.

Example 17-4

Let us use the ion-electron method to balance the equation for the reaction of potassium permanganate with iron (II) sulfate in the presence of sulfuric acid to give potassium sulfate, manganous sulfate, iron (III) sulfate, and water.

Solution

The unbalanced ionic expression is

$$K^+ + MnO_4^- + Fe^{+2} + SO_4^{-2} + H^+ + SO_4^{-2} \longrightarrow K^+ + SO_4^{-2} + Mn^{+2} + SO_4^{-2} + Fe^{+3} + SO_4^{-2} + H_2O$$

The two half-reactions are

$$MnO_4^- + 8H^+(aq) + 5e^{-1} \longrightarrow Mn^{+2} + 4H_2O$$
$$5Fe^{+2} \longrightarrow 5Fe^{+3} + 5e^{-1}$$

Adding the two half reactions, the sum of the electrons is zero, and the balanced ionic equation is

$$MnO_4^- + 5Fe^{+2} + 8H^+(aq) \longrightarrow Mn^{+2} + 5Fe^{+3} + 4H_2O$$

Notice that this equation is balanced both chemically and electrically. That is, there are the same number of atoms or ions of Fe, Mn, H, and O on both sides of the equation. Moreover, the net electrical charge on each side of the equation is also balanced.

"Someone thinks the man of the future won't have much muscle."
"Balancing redox equations may save us!"

Summary

An oxidation-reduction (redox) reaction is one in which one of the reactants (the oxidizing agent) gains electrons from the other (the reducing agent). If redox reactants are mixed in a test tube, electrons can be imagined to pass from one reactant to the other. But if the reactants are parts of an electrochemical cell, electrons pass along the wire from one reactant to the other; that is, the electron transfer is *indirect.* The *anode* or the cell is the electrode at which oxidation occurs; the *cathode* is the electrode where reduction occurs.

Every electrochemical cell consists of two parts (two half–cells).

Oxidation occurs in one half–cell, reduction in the other. Clearly, a single half–cell connot operate by itself. The oxidation potential of a substance is measured in volts. Experimentally, it can be determined by combining a hydrogen half–cell (to which a value of zero potential is arbitrarily assigned) with another half–cell whose electrode system contains the substance under consideration. If the substance releases electrons more readily then hydrogen, its oxidation potential is positive. Conversely, if it releases electrons less readily than hydrogen, its oxidation potential is negative. The voltage of a galvanic cell can be computed from the values of the two half–cell reactions but it depends on the concentrations of the ions in the cell.

An *oxidation number* is assigned to atoms in various ions and molecules. While this has no physical significance, as "bookkeeping," the concept is very useful because it enables us to keep track of the amount of oxidation or reduction in chemical reactions.

Redox reactions can be balanced by assigning oxidation numbers to all atoms in the unbalanced equation and then adjusting the coefficients so that the increase in oxidation number for atoms of one reactant equals the decrease in oxidation number for atoms of the other reactant.

Factual Recall

1. (*a*) Define (*i*) oxidation, (*ii*) reduction. (*b*) Write ionic equations for the reaction of (*i*) zinc with copper (II) sulfate solution, (*ii*) nitric acid with potassium hydroxide. (*c*) Are the foregoing reactions of the oxidation-reduction type? Give a reason for your answer.

2. Explain why reaction (*a*) takes place and why reaction (*b*) does not take place.

   (*a*) $Mg + 2H^+(aq) \longrightarrow Mg^{+2} + H_2$
   (*b*) $Mg^{+2} + H_2 \longrightarrow Mg + 2H^+(aq)$

3. (*a*) Explain the meaning of the term *oxidation potential.* (*b*) What is a hydrogen electrode? (*c*) Explain why a hydrogen electrode is a necessary standard of comparison in measuring oxidation potentials.

4. The half-reaction associated with the oxidation potential for iron is

$$Fe \longrightarrow Fe^{+2} + 2e^- \qquad E^0 = +0.44V$$

Draw a diagram of the apparatus you would use to measure this oxidation potential and explain how the apparatus works.

5. Define the terms (*a*) anode, (*b*) cathode, (*c*) anion, (*d*) cation.

6. (*a*) What is meant by the term *oxidation number*? (*b*) Define oxidation in terms of oxidation number. (*c*) Give an example of the definition in (*b*).

7. Write the oxidation numbers of (*a*) nitrogen in nitric acid, (*b*) nitrogen in nitrous acid (HNO_2), (*c*) sulfur in sodium sulfide, (*d*) sulfur in sodium sulfite, (*e*) hydrogen in sodium hydride, (*f*) carbon in ethane (C_2H_6).

8. Hydrogen sulfide reacts with $KMnO_4$ in the presence of dilute H_2SO_4 to yield S, $MnSO_4$, and H_2O. Write the equation for this reaction.

9. If NaBr is added to a solution of $K_2Cr_2O_7$ (potassium dichromate) which has been acidified with H_2SO_4, $Cr_2(SO_4)_3$ [chromium (III) sulfate], Br_2, and H_2O are formed. (*a*) Balance the equation for this reaction by the ion-electron method. (*b*) Check the charges in reactants and products and show that both are equal to +6.

Apply Your Knowledge!

1. A voltaic cell consists of a magnesium half–cell (magnesium strip immersed in 1 *M* $MgSO_4$) connected by a salt bridge with a copper half-cell (a copper strip immersed in 1 *M* $CuSO_4$). What is the E^0 of the cell?

2. A voltaic cell consists of an iron-cell (an iron strip immersed in 1 *M* $FeSO_4$) connected by a salt bridge with a copper half-cell (a copper strip immersed in 1 *M* $CuSO_4$). (*a*) What is the E^0 of the cell? (*b*) At which terminal are cations reduced?

3. The reaction between zinc and a strong acid liberates 1.12 liters of hydrogen at STP. (*a*) How many moles of oxiding agent are consumed? (*b*) What mass of reducing agent is consumed? (*c*) How many moles of the oxidation product are

formed? (*d*) What volume of 6.00 *M* hydrogen-ion solution is required?

4. A gas mixture, prepared from 22.4 liters of hydrogen at STP and one mole of oxygen, is ignited by a spark. Calculate (*a*) the moles of water formed, (*b*) the mass in grams of oxidizing agent consumed, (*c*) the mass in grams of substance reduced.

5. The skeleton equation for a redox reaction is

$$MnO_4^- + H^+(aq) + I^- \longrightarrow Mn^{+2} + I_2 + H_2O$$

If 2.54 g of iodine are formed in this reaction, compute (*a*) the volume of 0.500 *M* MnO_4^- solution used, (*b*) the moles of Mn^{+2} produced, (*c*) the mass in grams of H^+ consumed, (*d*) the moles of I^- used.

6. The skeleton equation for a redox reaction is

$$Al + H^+(aq) + NO_3^- \longrightarrow Al^{+3} + H_2O + N_2$$

If 10.01 ml of 1.59 *M* NO_3^- solution are consumed in this reaction, compute (*a*) the moles of aluminum metal used up, (*b*) the volume of nitrogen gas liberated at 20 °C and 700 torr pressure, (*c*) the mass in grams of aluminum ion formed.

Find Out!

1. There are about 100 common oxidizing agents and about 100 common reducing agents in aqueous solution. Find out how many possible oxidation-reduction reactions there might be. Do you need to research this question?

2. Since there is a large number of possible oxidation-reduction reactions, find out how they are systematized.

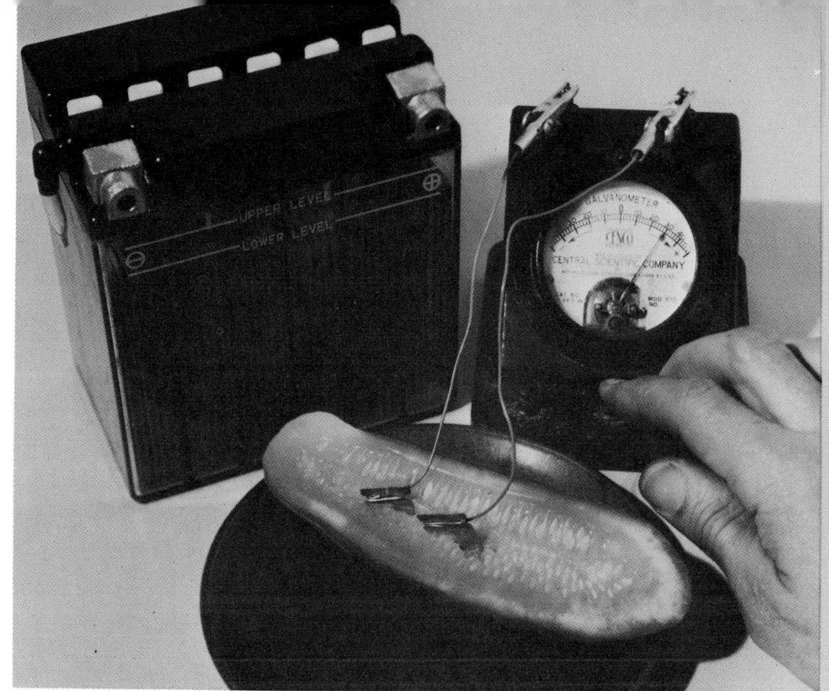

CHAPTER 18

CHEMICAL EFFECTS OF AN ELECTRIC CURRENT

IN THE ELECTROLYTIC CELL in Fig. 18-1 the negative terminal of the dry cell is connected to the strip of copper and the positive terminal of the dry cell is attached to the silver. The dry cell is, in fact, an electrochemical cell and, as you learned in the last chapter, the negative terminal of a dry cell is the terminal from which electrons leave the cell. Therefore the copper terminal receives electrons and electrons flow out of the silver terminal. Thus the half-reactions are

$$2Ag - 2e^- \longrightarrow 2Ag^+ \quad (18\text{-}1)$$

and

$$Cu^{+2} + 2e^- \longrightarrow Cu \quad (18\text{-}2)$$

That is, silver metal is oxidized to Ag^+ ion, and Cu^{+2} ion is reduced to metallic copper. Therefore the silver terminal is the anode and the copper terminal is the cathode. This is the reverse of the situation. Fig. 18-2, which shows an electrochemical cell.

Recall . . .
In an electrochemical (or voltaic) cell, reactions occur spontaneously. In an electrolytic cell, reactions are not spontaneous; they are instead induced by electrical energy supplied from an outside source; such as a dry cell.

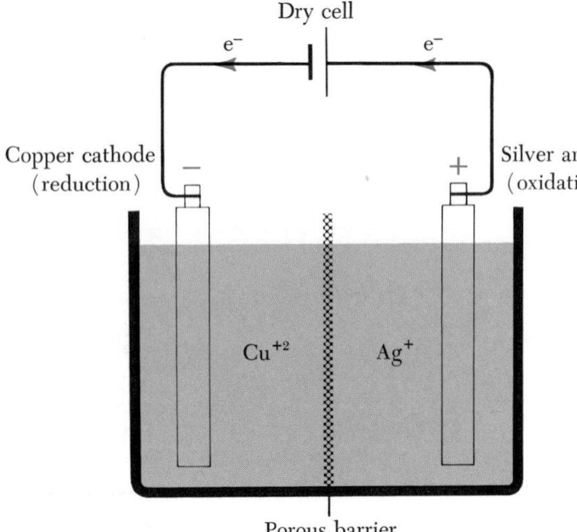

Fig. 18-1 A copper-silver electrolytic cell. In which direction are the electrons flowing? What supplies the electrical energy that makes non-spontaneous reactions,

$$Cu^{+2} + 2Ag \longrightarrow Cu + 2Ag^{+}$$ take place?

Notice that the copper electrode is marked negative, and the silver terminal is marked positive in both the electrochemical and the electrolytic cell. This may be confusing unless we understand the reason for these (+) and (−) signs. In the electrochemical cell, the copper terminal is marked (−) because electrons escape from it, leaving behind positive ions. In the electrolytic cell, the copper terminal is marked (−) because it is attached to the negative terminal of the battery. However, let it be said that the signs (+) or (−) on the terminals are of little or no significance. The *important* thing to know is the *direction of the electron flow*. If electrons flow out of a terminal, oxidation takes place at that terminal and the *oxidation* terminal is called the *anode*. And so we always associate the term

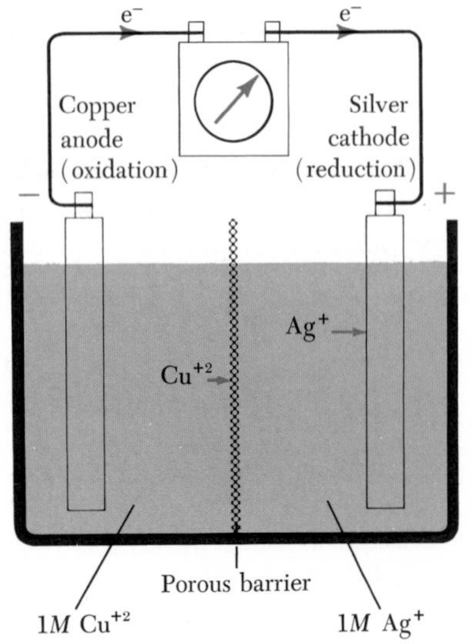

Fig. 18-2 A copper-silver electrochemical cell.

anode with *oxidation*, whatever the kind of cell. Similarly, reduction takes place at the terminal where electrons flow in. The *reduction terminal* is called the *cathode* and so we always associate the term *cathode* with *reduction*.

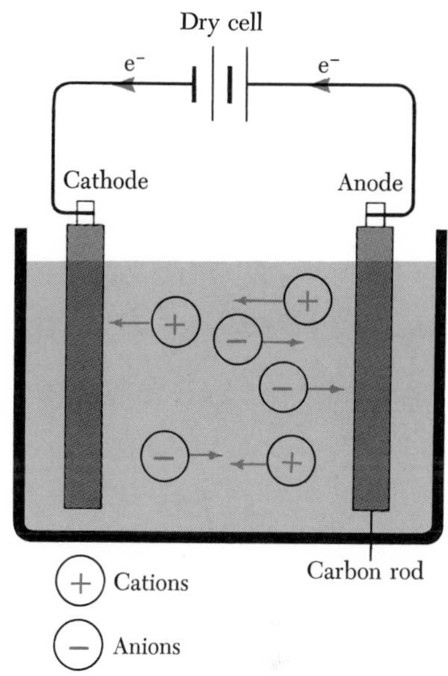

Fig. 18-3 An electrolytic cell. Both electrodes are carbon rods. Why?

An Electrolytic Cell

An electrolytic cell consists essentially of three parts: (1) a source of electrons such as a battery of dry cells, (2) a solution of an electrolyte, and (3) two electrodes, which should be chemically inactive. That is, the electrodes should not react with the substances released at the electrodes nor with the ions in solution. Carbon rods often are satisfactory for this purpose as are small pieces of platinum foil. A simple electrolytic cell is shown in Fig. 18-3.

The battery of the electrolytic cell consists of two dry cells connected in series, as shown in Fig. 18-4. A common dry cell has a zinc case (the anode) and a central carbon rod (the cathode) surrounded by a moist paste composed mainly of ammonium chloride which is an electrolyte. The zinc electrode is the electron source, $Zn \longrightarrow Zn^{+2} + 2e^-$, and for this reason it is the negative electrode. As electrons are released at the zinc anode, an equal number must be pulled into the carbon rod. Therefore, the carbon rod is the positively charged electrode.

The usual diagrammatic representation of a battery of two dry cells is

—|‖|—

The short vertical line represents the negative terminal and the longer line represents the positive terminal Thus we can think of a battery of cells as a kind of electron pump which continuously forces electrons out of the zinc terminal, along the wire, and into the carbon terminal.

Returning now to the electrolytic cell Fig. 18-3, it is apparent that electrons are pushed by the electron pump or battery on to the carbon rod on the left which therefore becomes negatively charged; it is the cathode. At the same time, an equal number of electrons are pulled away from the carbon rod on the right. Therefore this carbon rod becomes positively charged; it is the anode.

Fig. 18-4 In which direction do electrons flow in this pair of dry cells?

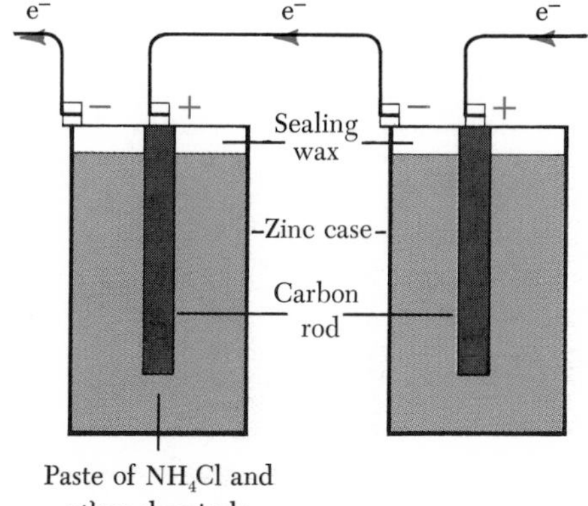

Associate . . .

The sense of naming negative ions *anions* is made clear if you associate the fact that negative ions are those most likely to be oxidized with the fact that oxidation occurs at the anode. A similar association applies to the term *cation*.

What is the source of these anode electrons? Since carbon is an inert substance, it cannot be the electron source. The only other possibility is the electrolyte in which the carbon rod is immersed. The electrolyte consists of positive and negative ions. The negative ions are attracted to the anode where they transfer their excess electrons to this positively charged electrode. These ions are known as *anions*. The released electrons then flow into the positive terminal of the battery. Positive ions, called *cations*, take on electrons drawn from the battery at the cathode and often form a free element. Thus an oxidation–reduction reaction takes place in the cell. Oxidation or a loss of electrons occurs at the anode and reduction or a gain of electrons occurs at the cathode. In the electrolysis of a solution of copper (II) chloride, for example, copper (II) ions are reduced to copper metal at the cathode and chloride ions are oxidized to chlorine gas at the anode. The overall chemical reaction of the cell could be represented as

$$Cu^{+2} + 2Cl^- \xrightarrow{\text{electricity}} Cu + Cl_2 \qquad (18\text{-}3)$$

The Electrolysis of Hydrochloric Acid

A simple arrangement for the electrolysis of hydrochloric acid is shown in Fig. 18-5 (*a*).

The beaker contains two carbon rods and a 1 *M* solution of HCl; that is, 1 *M* in $H^+(aq)$. The external circuit includes two dry cells connected in series, an ammeter, a rheostat, and a switch. The voltage of each dry cell is about 1.5 V so that if the rheostat is in the position of minimum resistance, a potential of about 3.0 V can be applied to the carbon electrodes. A voltmeter attached separately to the electrodes will indicate the actual voltage that is applied to the electrodes.

Note . . .

A *rheostat* is a device that provides an electrical circuit with variable resistance. A popular application of such a device dims or brightens an electric light.

The rheostat is first arranged to offer its maximum reistance and the switch is closed. In this situation no current flows through the circuit and the ammeter reading is zero. If the resistance is now gradually reduced, the voltage applied to the cell is gradually increased. When the voltmeter reads about 1.4 V the ammeter needle is deflected, showing that a current is flowing through the circuit. At the same time, bubbles of gas are released at each of the electrodes. If the applied voltage is still further increased by further decreasing the resistance, the ammeter then registers a larger current and gas bubbles are evolved more rapidly. What are these gases?

As is shown in Fig. 18-5 (*b*) the cathode reaction is

$$2H^+(aq) + 2e^- \longrightarrow H_2 \tag{18-4}$$

and the anode reaction is

$$2Cl^- \longrightarrow Cl_2 + 2e^- \tag{18-5}$$

The net reaction is

$$2H^+(aq) + 2Cl^- \longrightarrow H_2(g) + Cl_2(g) \tag{18-6}$$

The gases are hydrogen and chlorine. However, chlorine gas is fairly soluble in water so that fewer chlorine than hydrogen bubbles will be seen.

Notice again that this is an oxidation–reduction reaction. The oxidation potentials of these half-reactions are

$$\begin{array}{lrcll} & 2H^+(aq) + 2e^- & \longrightarrow & H_2 & E^0 = 0.00\text{ V} \\ & 2Cl^- & \longrightarrow & Cl_2 + 2e^- & E^0 = -1.36\text{ V} \\ \hline \text{Net reaction is} & 2H^+(aq) + 2Cl^- & \longrightarrow & H_2 + Cl_2 & E^0 = -1.36\text{ V} \end{array}$$

The negative sign for the potential of the cell indicates that the reaction is not spontaneous. The reverse reaction, namely

$$H_2 + Cl_2 \longrightarrow 2HCl \longrightarrow 2H^+(aq) + 2Cl^-$$

is of course spontaneous. The actual value for E^0 for the cell (−1.36 V) indicates that an applied voltage of at least 1.36 V is necessary to overcome the natural tendency of the reaction. We can now understand why no current flowed through the circuit until the reading of the voltmeter was about 1.4 V.

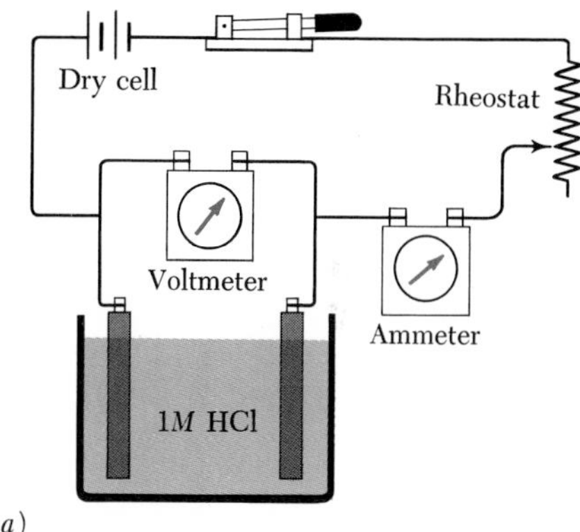

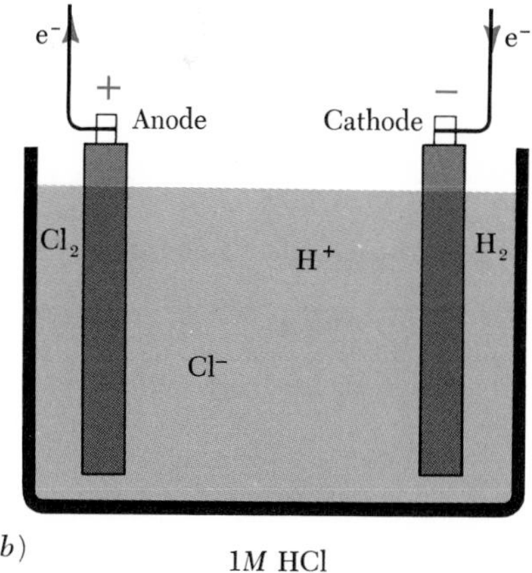

Fig. 18-5 (*a*) The battery supplies the energy to cause the electrolysis of hydrochloric acid, a reaction that does not occur spontaneously. (*b*) In the electrolysis of hydrochloric acid, hydrogen ions are discharged at the cathode and chloride ions are discharged at the anode.

The Electrolysis of Dilute Sulfuric Acid

The electrolysis of dilute sulfuric acid can be studied by the apparatus shown schematically in Fig. 18-6. Small pieces of platinum foil are soldered to the ends of two copper wires. The wires are bent into a beaker of water. Two test tubes, filled with water, are supported over the platinum terminals and the wires are connected to a circuit which includes an ammeter, a switch, and a battery of five or six dry cells connected in series. When the switch is closed, the ammeter needle is not deflected indicating that no current

Note . . .
The capital letter V is internationally used among scientists as an abbreviation for *volts*.

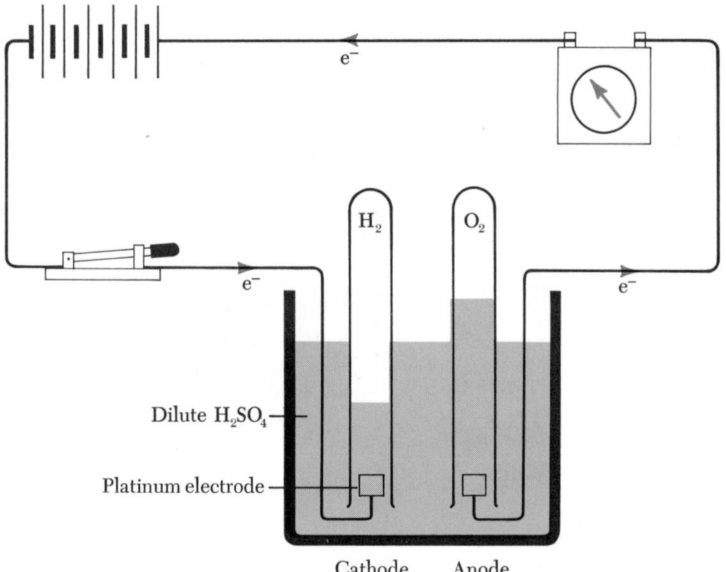

Fig. 18-6 The electrolysis of dilute sulfuric acid is essentially the decomposition of water.

flows along the wire. If the test tubes are now withdrawn, filled with dilute sulfuric acid and replaced, the ammeter shows that a current flows through the circuit. At the same time, bubbles of gas are released at both electrodes. Moreover, the volume of gas collected at the cathode is twice that collected at the anode. What are these gases?

Chemical tests prove that the gas released at the cathode is hydrogen and that the gas released at the anode is oxygen. Hence the ratio by volume of the reaction products is

$$2 \text{ volumes } H_2 : 1 \text{ volume } 0_2$$

Applying Avogadro's hypothesis, the simplest ratio by molecules is

$$2 \text{ molecules } H_2 : 1 \text{ molecule } 0_2$$

Therefore, the equation for the reaction is

$$2H_2O \longrightarrow 2H_2 + O_2$$

In other words, the electrolysis of dilute sulfuric acid is essentially the decomposition of water. How is this possible? What is the function of sulfuric acid in this reaction?

The electrolyte, sulfuric acid, supplies the ions $H^+(aq)$, HSO_4^-, and SO_4^{-2}. In addition, there are molecules of water (H_2O) and also traces of OH^- ion from the water. Which of the ions or molecules will react at the electrodes?

The only possible cathode reactions are the reduction of hydrogen ions or water molecules. Actually, it is much easier to reduce hydrogen ions than water molecules so that the half-reaction at the cathode is

$$4H^+(aq) + 4e^- \longrightarrow 2H_2 \qquad (18\text{-}8)$$

At the anode where oxidation (loss of electrons) occurs, there are several possibilities, namely the oxidation of HSO_4^-, SO_4^{-2}, or OH^- ions, or of H_2O molecules. Actually, H_2O molecules are more easily oxidized than are the other ions. Hence, the half-reaction at the anode is

$$2H_2O - 4e^- \longrightarrow O_2 + 4H^+(aq) \qquad (18\text{-}9)$$

That is, oxygen gas and hydrogen ions are produced at the anode. The oxidation potentials of these half-reactions are

Cathode reaction:	$4H^+(aq) + 4e^- \longrightarrow 2H_2$	$E^0 = 0.00\text{ V}$
Anode reaction:	$2H_2O \longrightarrow O_2 + 4H^+ + 4e^-$	$E^0 = -1.23\text{ V}$
Net reaction:	$2H_2O \longrightarrow 2H_2 + O_2$	$E^0 = -1.23\text{ V}$

Notice that water molecules are decomposed at the anode, releasing hydrogen ions and electrons. At the cathode, the same number of hydrogen ions and electrons, released from the decomposition of water, are used up. Why then is sulfuric acid necessary? What part does the acid play in this reaction? Perhaps its most significant role is as a conductor of electricity in the solution. Just as electrons are the electrical conductors in a wire, so are positive and negative ions the electrical conductors in a solution. Without the acid and its ions the resistance of the solution would be too great to permit much current to flow.

Fig. 18-7 The electrolysis of an aqueous solution of potassium iodide. This reaction is somewhat like the electrolysis of an aqueous solution of sodium chloride. When iodine is formed, it combines with the iodide ion of the electrolyte solution to form the complex ion I_3^-. Is iodine formed at the anode or cathode?

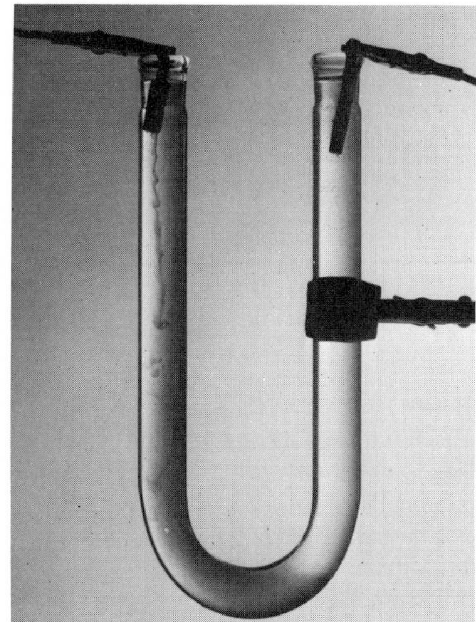

The Electrolysis of Sodium Chloride Solution

What happens when a potential is applied to a solution of sodium chloride? The solution contains (1) Na^+ and Cl^- ions in abundance, (2) traces of $H^+(aq)$ and OH^- ions, and (3) water molecules.

What reaction takes place at the cathode? Several reactions are possible, namely

$$Na^+ + e^- \longrightarrow Na \qquad (18\text{-}10)$$

$$2H^+(aq) + 2e^- \longrightarrow H_2 \qquad (18\text{-}11)$$

$$2H_2O + 2e^- \longrightarrow H_2 + 2OH^- \qquad (18\text{-}12)$$

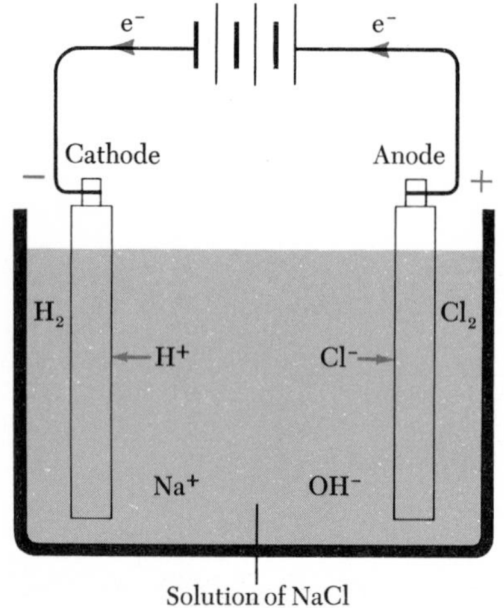

Fig. 18-8 The electrolysis of an aqueous solution of sodium chloride.

The actual reaction that occurs depends upon the electrode potential and the abundance of the ions. Since the reaction at the cathode is a reduction reaction, we are interested in the reduction potentials of the ions rather than their oxidation potentials. These are

$$\begin{array}{llll} Na^+ & + e^- \longrightarrow Na & & E^0 = -2.71\ V \\ 2H^+(aq) & + 2e^- \longrightarrow H_2 & & E^0 = \ \ 0.00\ V \\ 2H_2O & + 2e^- \longrightarrow H_2 + 2OH^- & & E^0 = -0.83\ V \end{array}$$

Clearly a much smaller potential is needed to reduce water molecules than sodium ions. By the same argument, hydrogen ions are more easily reduced than water molecules. However, we must remember that the concentration of $H^+(aq)$ ion is exceedingly low, so that the principal cathode reaction is

$$2H_2O + 2e^- \longrightarrow H_2 + 2OH^- \qquad (18\text{-}12)$$

What of the anode reaction? Three oxidation reactions are possible. These reactions with their oxidation potentials are

$$\begin{array}{llll} 2Cl^- - 2e^- \longrightarrow Cl_2 & & E^0 = -1.36\ V & (18\text{-}13) \\ 4OH^- - 4e^- \longrightarrow 2H_2O + O_2 & & E^0 = -1.21\ V & (18\text{-}14) \\ 2H_2O - 4e^- \longrightarrow 4H^+(aq) + O_2 & & E^0 = -1.23\ V & (18\text{-}15) \end{array}$$

Hydroxide ion is present only in trace amounts and,as a practical matter, the oxidation of chloride ions is easier than the oxidation of water molecules. The principal anode reaction is Eq. (18-17). However, in dilute solutions oxygen also is found in the products.

The net reaction is therefore the sum of these two half-reactions.

$$\begin{array}{lll} \text{Anode reaction:} & 2Cl^- - 2e^- \longrightarrow Cl_2 & (18\text{-}13) \\ \text{Cathode reaction:} & 2H_2O + 2e^- \longrightarrow H_2 + 2OH^- & (18\text{-}12) \\ \hline \text{Net reaction:} & 2Cl^- + 2H_2O \longrightarrow Cl_2 + H_2 + 2OH^- & (18\text{-}16) \end{array}$$

That is, as shown in Fig. 18-8, chlorine is liberated at the anode and an equal volume of hydrogen is liberated at the cathode.

Infer . . .
From what you know about the terms of electrochemistry, is the metal to be plated the anode or the cathode? Is the negative terminal of the battery the anode or the cathode?

Electroplating

Electroplating is an important industrial application of electrolysis. Copper, silver, (see Fig. 18-9) and chromium plating are common examples of this process in which a thin coating of metal is deposited upon the object to be plated. In all cases of electroplating, there are three essential conditions:

(1) The article to be plated is attached to the negative terminal of the battery.
(2) The anode must be of the same metal as the one to be plated.
(3) The electrolyte must contain ions of the metal to be plated.

For example, in copper plating the anode must be of pure copper, the electrolyte solution should be copper (II) sulfate, and, for purposes of class demonstration, the cathode could be a carbon rod. This electroplating arrangement is shown in Fig. 18-10. How does the cell operate?

As is shown in Fig. 18-10, the solution contains Cu^{+2} and SO_4^{-2} from the electroyte, traces of $H^+(aq)$ and OH^- ions from water, and H_2O molecules in abundance.

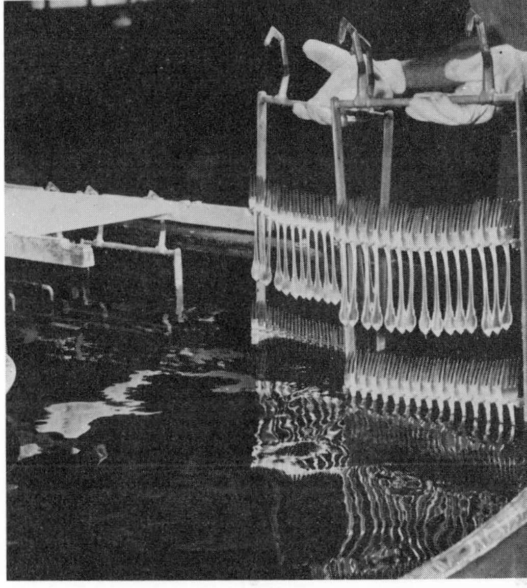

Fig. 18-9 Silver plating must be carefully done. To silver plate these forks, should they be placed at the anode or the cathode?

The Cathode Reaction

Copper (II) ions are more easily reduced than H^+ ions or H_2O molecules, and therefore the only reaction at the cathode is the reduction of Cu^{+2} ions

$$Cu^{+2} + 2e^- \longrightarrow Cu \qquad (18\text{-}2)$$

That is, at the cathode Cu^{+2} ions pick up electrons from the battery and copper atoms are deposited or, as we usually say, copper is plated.

The Anode Reaction

Four reactions are possible at the anode: the loss of electrons by SO_4^{-2} ions, by OH^- ions, by H_2O molecules, or by Cu atoms. Actually, copper atoms are the most easily oxidized so that the anode reaction is

$$Cu - 2e^- \longrightarrow Cu^{+2} \qquad (18\text{-}17)$$

Thus a Cu^{+2} ion is formed at the anode for each Cu^{+2} ion reduced at the cathode. To summarize:

Anode reaction:

$$Cu \longrightarrow Cu^{+2} + 2e^- \qquad (18\text{-}17)$$

Fig. 18-10 Electroplating copper consists essentially of the transfer of copper from a copper anode to the cathode which is plated.

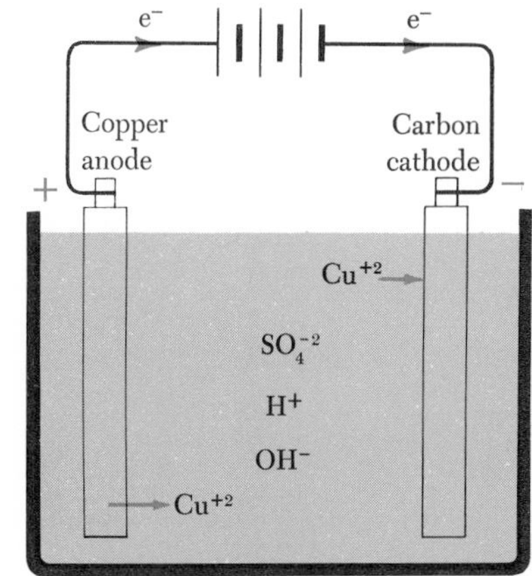

Cathode reaction:

$$Cu^{+2} + 2e^- \longrightarrow Cu \qquad (18\text{-}2)$$

And therefore the net reaction is

$$Cu\ (anode) + Cu^{+2} \longrightarrow Cu\ (cathode) + Cu^{+2} \qquad (18\text{-}18)$$

That is, the concentration of Cu^{+2} ion remains constant and the only change that takes place is the transfer of copper metal from the anode to the cathode.

Electrolytic Refining of Copper

Industrially, metallic copper is manufactured from copper ore. First, copper (II) oxide is made from the ore. Copper (II) oxide is then reduced to copper metal by heating a mixture of the oxide and coke in a furnace

$$CuO + C \longrightarrow Cu + CO(g) \qquad (18\text{-}19)$$

The furnace copper is called "blister" copper. However, blister copper is not pure; it contains various metals in small amounts, about 2% in all. The chief impurities are iron, zinc, silver, and gold. These must be removed, because copper is used mainly as a conductor of electricity, and even small amounts of metallic impurities greatly reduce its conductivity. How can these impurities be removed? This is done by making an electrolytic cell which contains a solution of copper (II) sulfate, an anode of blister copper,

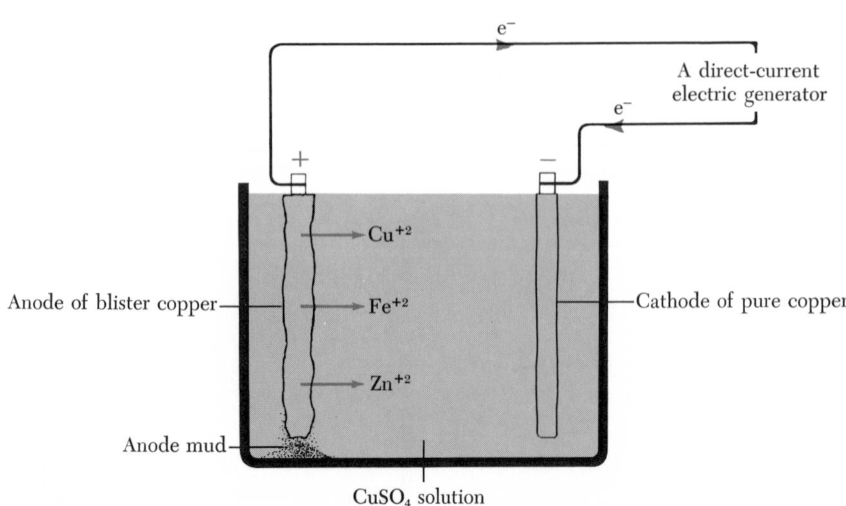

Fig. 18-11 Refining copper. By maintaining the right voltage, only pure copper is deposited on the copper cathode.

and a cathode of pure copper. Such an arrangement is shown in Fig. 18-11.

Oxidation potentials of various metals are given in Table 18-1. The table shows that if the potential supplied by the battery is controlled at about 0.4 V, atoms of zinc, iron, and copper at the anode will lose their outermost electrons and go into solution as ions. However, at this voltage neither silver nor gold atoms are oxidized. Instead, they fall to the bottom of the cell as an anode "mud," and from this mud the precious metals can be recovered.

Table 18-1
The oxidation potentials of the various metals

Metal	Products	E^0
Zn	$\longrightarrow Zn^{+2} + 2e^-$	+0.76 V
Fe	$\longrightarrow Fe^{+2} + 2e^-$	+0.44 V
Cu	$\longrightarrow Cu^{+2} + 2e^-$	−0.34 V
Ag	$\longrightarrow Ag^+ + e^-$	−0.80 V
Au	$\longrightarrow Au^+ + e^-$	−1.68 V

Notice also that an applied potential of 0.4 V is high enough to discharge Cu^{+2} ions but not high enough to discharge Zn^{+2} and Fe^{+2} ions. Why not? Therefore the only reaction at the cathode is the deposition of Cu (Eq. 18-17).

On an industrial scale, blister copper from the furnace is cast into thick rectangular slabs. A number of these slabs are connected in parallel, placed in a tank containing copper (II) sulfate solution, and attached to the positive terminal of an electric generator. The cathode consists of a number of thin sheets of pure copper which are also connected in parallel. The cathode sheets are suspended alternately between the thick anode slabs and attached to the negative terminal of the generator. The arrangement is shown in Fig. 18-12. When the current is turned on and the applied voltage maintained at 0.40 V, only pure copper is transferred from the anode slabs to the cathode sheets.

Fig. 18-12 Lifting copper cathodes out of the electrolyte tank. The metal sheets are at least 99.9 % copper, pure enough for electrical transmission.

Faraday's Laws of Electrolysis

As stated in Chapter 15 the first scientist to treat electrolytic phenomena quantitatively was Michael Faraday. Indeed, he discovered two laws of electrolysis which are still of great importance in theory and technology.

In one series of experiments Faraday investigated both the mass of an element deposited on the cathode of an electrolytic cell and the quantity of electricity needed to deposit this mass. An apparatus used to deposit silver is shown in Fig. 18-13. It consists of two electrodes: an anode of silver and a cathode of an inert metal, such as platinum, in a solution of silver nitrate. The external circuit includes a battery of dry cells, an ammeter, a rheostat, and a switch.

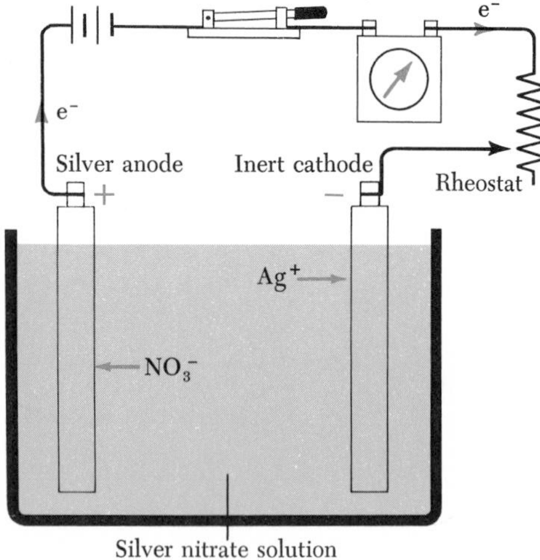

Fig. 18-13 The electrolytic deposition of silver.

Fig. 18-14 Faraday passed a current through a number of cells arranged in series.

If a current of electricity (I amperes) is allowed to flow through the circuit for a given time (t seconds), the quantity of electricity can be computed from the equation $Q = I \times t$ where Q is the quantity of electricity, expressed in coulombs. To find the mass deposited, the cathode is weighed before and after the flow of current. The increase in the mass of the cathode is, of course, the mass of silver deposited. If the experiment is repeated and the time interval doubled, it is found that the mass deposited on the cathode is also doubled. After numerous variations of both time and current, Faraday discovered that *the mass of an element deposited on (or liberated at) an electrode is proportional to the quantity of electricity that passes through the circuit.* This statement is now known as *Faraday's first law of electrolysis.* The law can be written as $m \propto Q$, where m is the mass deposited in grams and Q is the quantity of electricity in coulombs.

The Faraday

Experiment proves that 1.0000 g of silver is deposited by 894.5 C of electricity, which is 894.5 C/g. Or, expressed another way, 1 coulomb will deposit

$$\frac{1.000\ \text{C}}{894.5\ \text{C/g}} = 0.001118\ \text{g of silver}$$

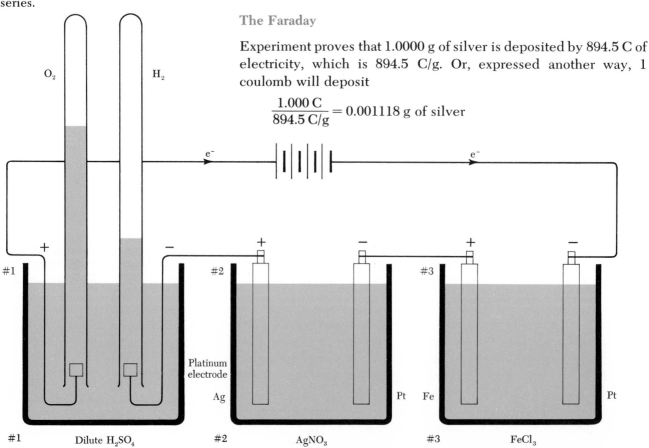

The atomic mass of silver = 107.87 amu and 1 mole of silver is 107.87 g. We can now compute the number of coulombs needed to deposit 1 mole of silver.

$$\begin{aligned}\text{Number of coulombs} &= 894.5\ \text{C/g} \times 107.9\ \text{g/mole}\\ &= 96{,}500\ \text{C/mole}\\ &= 9.65 \times 10^4\ \text{C/mole}\end{aligned}$$

Similarly, this quantity can also be experimentally determined for other elements. For example, expressed in C/mole, the quantity is found to be 9.65×10^4 for sodium, 19.3×10^4 for magnesium, and 19.3×10^4 for copper. Indeed, for all substances released at an electrode during an electrolysis, the quantity of electricity needed is either 9.65×10^4 C/mole or an integral multiple of this value. Clearly 9.65×10^4 C is a significant unit of electric quantity; it consists of 1 mole of electrons. This quantity of electricity is called the *faraday* (**F**) in recognition of Faraday's pioneer work in electrolysis.

To summarize,

$$1F = 9.65 \times 10^4\ \text{C} = 1\ \text{mole of electrons}$$

Definition . . .
The coulomb is defined as one ampere-second or the quantity of electricity equal to the combined charge on 6.24×10^{18} electrons. In the scientific community, the internationally accepted abbreviation for this unit is C.

Define . . .
In the scientific community, the letter *F* represents *Faraday's constant* Define both the faraday and Faraday's constant.

Faraday's Second Law

In another set of experiments, Faraday passed a current through a number of electrolytic cells arranged in series, and measured the quantities of products collected at or deposited on the electrodes. Let us consider the circuit shown in Fig. 18-14, in which cell 1 contains dilute sulfuric acid and platinum electrodes; cell 2 contains a solution of silver nitrate, a silver anode, and an inert cathode such as platinum; and cell 3 contains a solution of iron (III) chloride, an anode of pure iron, and a cathode of platinum. Clearly, the same quantity of electricity passes through each cell when the current flows. In cell 1, oxygen is collected at the anode and hydrogen at the cathode; in cell 2, silver is deposited on the cathode, and in cell 3 iron is deposited on the cathode, and the quantities of the gases collected or metals deposited can be determined. Faraday repeated this experiment with a variety of cells and he discovered that *the masses of various elements liberated at the electrodes of electrolytic cells by the same quantity of electricity are proportional to the equivalent masses of the elements.* This statement is known as Faraday's second law of electrolysis. What did *Faraday* mean by the term *equivalent mass*?

Equivalent Masses

The *equivalent masses* (or combining masses) of elements is a decsriptive term for the various masses of elements that combine with each other. For this purpose 1.00 g of hydrogen is selected as a standard and the equivalent masses of all other elements are expressed in terms of this standard. That is, *the equivalent mass of an element is that mass of it which combines with or replaces 1.00 g of hydrogen.*

The equivalent mass of an element can be found by considering the composition of a suitable compound. For example, in the compound water (H_2O) 2.00 g of hydrogen have combined with 16.0 g of oxygen. Therefore the equivalent mass of oxygen is 8.00 g. Similarly, by considering the composition of the compound HCl, it is apparent that the equivalent mass of chlorine is 35.5 g. We can therefore extend the definition and say: *The equivalent mass of an element is that mass of it which combines with 1.00 g of hydrogen or 8.00 g of oxygen or 35.5 g of chlorine.* Thus, considering the compound silver chloride (AgCl), the equivalent mass of silver is 108 g, and in $FeCl_3$ the equivalent mass of iron is 56/3 or 18.6 g.

From these examples it is apparent that the equivalent mass of an element may be the same as its gram-atomic mass; it may be one half or one third of its gram-atomic mass or, in the case of the element tin, one fourth of it.

Why is the mass of an element deposited on an electrode proportional to its equivalent mass rather than its atomic mass? The number of atoms of an element that are deposited depends upon the number of charges on its ion. Let us, for example, compare the discharge of $H^+(aq)$ ions and Cu^{+2} ions. One H^+ ion is reduced by one electron

$$H^+(aq) + e^- \longrightarrow H \qquad (18\text{-}4)$$

Therefore, Avogadro's number of electrons (6.02×10^{23} electrons,) will reduce 6.02×10^{23} H^+ ions, which is 1.0079 g of hydrogen ion. The product (1.0079 g of hydrogen) is both an equivalent mass and a gram-atomic mass of hydrogen.

On the other hand, two electrons are needed to reduce one Cu^{+2} ion.

$$Cu^{+2} + 2e^- \longrightarrow Cu \qquad (18\text{-}2)$$

Therefore 6.02×10^{23} electrons will discharge only 3.01×10^{23} Cu^{+2} ions, thereby producing 64/2 or 32 g of copper which is an equivalent mass of copper but only one half of its gram-atomic mass.

Similarly, in the reaction

$$Fe^{+3} + 3e^- \longrightarrow Fe \qquad (18\text{-}20)$$

it is apparent that 6.02×10^{23} electrons will deposit only 2.01×10^{23} atoms of iron which weigh 56/3 or 18.6 g.

With this in mind we can now restate Faraday's second law in more specific terms: *An equivalent mass of any cation is deposited on the cathode of an electrolytic cell by one faraday or 96,500 coulombs of electricity.*

Problems Involving Faraday's Laws

Following are typical problems based on Faraday's laws.

Example 18-1

How many coulombs are needed to deposit 5.00 g of silver in an electrolytic cell? (Equivalent mass of Ag is 108 g.)

Solution

$$\text{Number of faradays} = \frac{5.00\text{ g}}{108\text{ g/}\mathbf{F}} = 0.0463\ \mathbf{F}$$

$$\text{Number of coulombs} = 0.0463\ \mathbf{F} \times 9.65 \times 10^4 \frac{\text{C}}{\mathbf{F}}$$

$$= 4.47 \times 10^3\ \text{C}$$

Example 18-2

A current of 2.00 A is maintained for 3.00 hr in the electrolysis of sodium chloride solution. Compute the mass of chlorine released at the anode. (Equivalent mass of Cl is 35.5 g.)

Recall . . .
Define the ampere, which is here represented by the internationally accepted abbreviation A.

Solution

$$Q = I \times t$$

$$= 2.00\ \text{A} \times 3\ \text{hr} \times 60\ \text{min/hr} \times 60\ \text{sec/min} \times \frac{1\ \text{C}}{\text{A-sec}}$$

$$= 2.16 \times 10^4\ \text{C}$$

$$\text{Mass of chlorine} = 2.16 \times 10\ \text{C} \times \frac{1\ \text{F}}{9.65 \times 10^4\ \text{C}} \times \frac{35.5\ \text{g}}{\text{F}}$$

$$= 7.95\ \text{g}$$

The Lead Storage Cell

In Chapter 17 we discussed voltaic cells that *yield* electricity. We have also discussed electrolytic cells which require electricity.

We shall now discuss the so-called lead storage cell which is capable of operating as either a voltaic cell or an electrolytic cell. As you probably know, it is used as a voltaic cell in automobiles to start the motor and to operate the headlights and other electrical equipment. The voltage of the lead cell is about 2 V, and the common automobile battery consists of six lead cells connected in series, so that the total voltage is about 12 V. What is a lead cell?

Fig. 18-15 A cross-section of a storage cell. Notice that a number of negative plates made of lead are connected by a negative strap and that a number of positive plates of lead dioxide are connected by a positive strap.

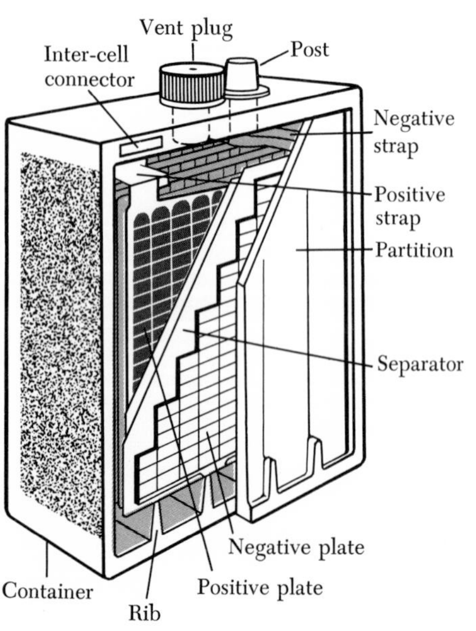

One electrode of a lead cell is made of metallic lead(Pb) and the Other of lead (IV) oxide (PbO_2), a dark-brown solid. The electrodes are immersed in dilute H_2SO_4. A number of lead plates are arranged close together and parallel to each other and connected. This group of lead plates constitutes the negative terminal (or anode) during discharge. The positive terminal (or cathode) is also made up of a number of parallel lead plates. However, these plates are coated with a paste of lead (IV) oxide so that the positive electrode is, in effect. lead (IV) oxide, not lead. The anode plates of lead are fitted between the plates of lead (IV) oxide, and the two sets of plates are separated by thin sheets of porous insulating material such as plastic or glass fibers. A cutaway view of a storage cell is shown in Fig. 18-15. How does a lead cell operate?

A Lead Cell as a Voltaic Cell: The Discharging Process

Lead is oxidized more readily than lead (IV) oxide. That is, the lead electrode releases electrons, and the reaction is

$$Pb \longrightarrow Pb^{+2} + 2e^- \tag{18-21}$$

Therefore the lead electrode is the anode, as shown in Fig. 18-16. The Pb^{+2} ions released at the anode immediately combine with SO_4^{-2} ions in the solution to form a white insoluble salt, lead sulfate:

$$Pb^{+2} + SO_4^{-2} \longrightarrow PbSO_4(s) \tag{18-22}$$

The net reaction at the anode is

$$Pb + SO_4^{-2} \longrightarrow PbSO_4 + 2e^- \tag{18-23}$$

Electrons released at the anode flow along the connecting wire to the cathode and reduce the lead (IV) oxide. Moreover, for every SO_4^{-2} ion used up at the anode, two H^+ ions must be used up at the cathode. Therefore, the reacting substances at the cathode are PbO_2, H^+, and H_2SO_4 (as ions), and the equation for the net reaction at the cathode is

$$PbO_2 + 4H^+(aq) + SO_4^{-2} + 2e^- \longrightarrow PbSO_4(s) + 2H_2O \tag{18-24}$$

Notice that, in this reduction reaction at the cathode, the oxidation number of lead is reduced from +4 in PbO_2 to +2 in $PbSO_4$. Notice also that the product ($PbSO_4$) is deposited on the surface of the lead (IV) oxide cathode.

Infer. . . .
Lead (IV) oxide is also known as lead dioxide. Can you think of another appropriate name for this compound?

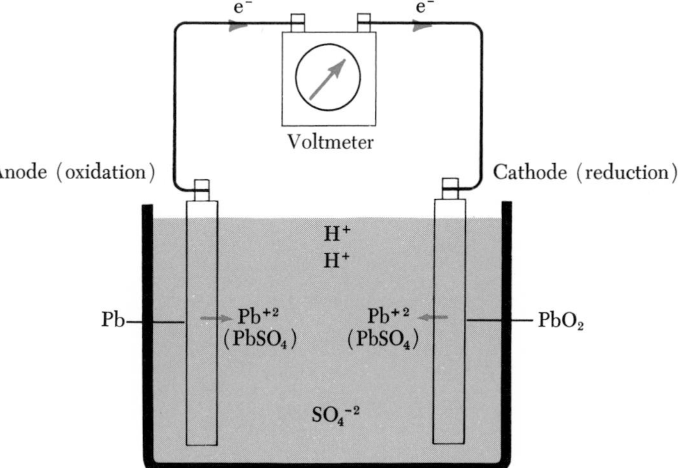

Fig. 18-16 The discharging process of a lead cell.

The oxidation potentials of these half-reactions are shown below.

Anode reaction:

$$Pb + SO_4^{-2} \longrightarrow PbSO_4 + 2e^- \qquad E^0 = +0.36\ V$$

Cathode reaction:

$$PbO_2 + 4H^+ + SO_4^{-2} + 2e^- \longrightarrow PbSO_4 + 2H_2O \qquad E^0 = +1.68\ V$$

Net reaction:

$$Pb + PbO_2 + 4H^+ + 2SO_4^{-2} \longrightarrow 2PbSO_4 + 2H_2O \qquad E^0 = 2.04\ V$$

Thus, the potential difference of the cell is approximately 2 V and this value would be registered by the voltmeter shown in Fig. 18-16.

Lead sulfate which is of very low solubility is a product of both half-reactions. If both electrodes were to become completely covered with lead sulfate, the cell would be unable to produce current. Moreover, in the discharge process sulfuric acid is used up and water is formed. Thus during the discharge the acid becomes more dilute and its density decreases. A garage mechanic makes use of this fact by measuring the density of the acid to check the condition of an automobile battery. Actually, the density of sulfuric acid solution should be about 1.2 g/ml; if the density drops as low as 1.05 g/ml, the battery needs to be recharged.

A Lead Cell as an Electrolytic Cell: The Charging Process

If a lead cell is to supply current continuously, the deposit of lead sulfate on the electrodes must be removed. This is done by supplying current from an external source: The charging current must be opposite in direction to the discharging current. Why?

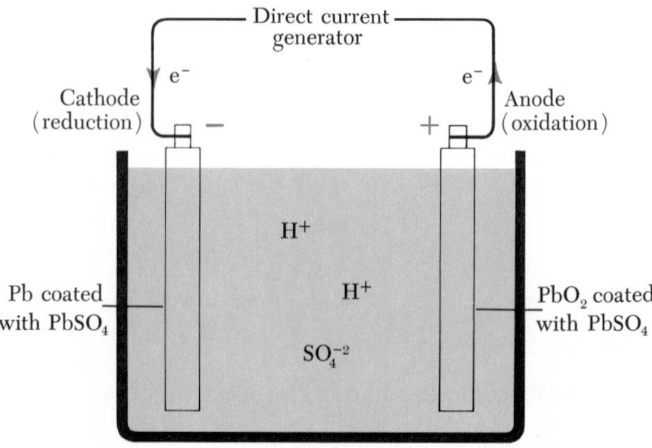

Fig. 18-17 The charging process of a lead cell.

Actually, the cell is automatically recharged by the current from the generator run by the automobile motor. The charging process is shown in Fig. 18-17.

The negative terminal of the generator is attached to the lead plate and the positive terminal to the lead (IV) oxide plate. Thus the lead plate, which was the anode during discharge, becomes the cathode during the charging process. Conversely, the lead (IV) oxide plate, which was the cathode during discharge, becomes the anode. Therefore the two half-reactions during charging are

Cathode reaction: $$PbSO_4 + 2e^- \longrightarrow Pb + SO_4^{-2} \quad (18\text{-}28)$$

Anode reaction: $$PbSO_4 + 2H_2O - 2e^- \longrightarrow PbO_2 + SO_4^{-2} + 4H^+ \quad (18\text{-}29)$$

Net reaction:
$$2PbSO_4 + 2H_2O \longrightarrow Pb + PbO_2 + 4H^+ + 2SO_4^{-2} \quad (18\text{-}30)$$

The net equation for the reaction shows that during the charging process the two electrodes are restored to their original condition by the removal of lead sulfate, and the concentration of the acid is increased.

Although the battery is automatically recharged as the motor runs, the cells, nevertheless, slowly deteriorate and more drastic treatment may be needed to restore them. When this happens, the battery is removed from the automobile and recharged for a period of several hours by current from an outside source. But even this is only a temporary expedient. Some lead sulfate continuously falls away from the plates which, in turn, means that both lead and lead (IV) oxide plates are slowly consumed and the battery must finally be replaced.

Fig. 18-18 This car is powered with lead batteries and a 6-kW hydrogen-air fuel battery. Its top speed is 55 miles per hour and it does not pollute the atmosphere.

Summary

Electrolysis is a redox reaction that takes place only if electrical energy is put into the system. Such redox reactions are not spontaneous. During electrolysis, negative ions are attracted to the anode and often oxidized, and positive ions are attracted to the cathode and often reduced. Thus, uncharged atoms or molecules are released at the electrodes.

Faraday's laws concern the masses of substances released at the electrodes during the electrolytic process. The first law states that the mass of an element liberated at an electrode is proportional to the quantity of electricity that passes through the circuit. The second law states that one faraday of electricity (96,500 coulombs) will discharge an electrochemical equivalent mass of any element at the electrode.

Factual Recall

1. An electrolytic cell contains 1 *M* hydrochloric acid. No reaction occurs if a voltage of 1.0 V is applied to the electrodes. But if the applied voltage is increased to 1.5 V a reaction occurs at each electrode. Give reasons for these experimental observations.
2. For the reaction, $Cu \longrightarrow Cu^{+2} + 2e^-$, the oxidation potential is −0.34 V. (*a*) What does this statement mean? (*b*) What is the reduction potential of this same reaction? Why?
3. Describe the experiment that led Faraday to state his first law of electrolysis.
4. (*a*) What is a faraday? (*b*) What is its significance?
5. In one experiment the mass of hydrogen released at the cathode of a dilute sulfuric acid cell was 0.0200 g and the mass of lead deposited on the cathode of a lead–lead nitrate cell was 2.07 g. From this evidence prove that the charge on a lead ion is twice as large as the charge on a hydrogen ion.

Apply Your Knowledge!

1. The electrolysis of a dilute H_2SO_4 solution for 8.00 hr gives 33.61 of anode gas product at 273 °C and 380 torr pressure. What is the current?
2. The cathode gains mass at the rate of 23.9 g/hr during the electrolysis of copper (II) sulfate solution, using a current of 20.0 A. Compute the equivalent mass of copper (II).
3. When a current of 4.00 A is used in the electrolysis of a salt of an inactive metal, the cathode gains 19.7 g in mass in 2.00 hr. (*a*) What is the equivalent mass of the metal? (*b*) If the valence of the metal is 3, what is its atomic mass? (*c*) What is the metal?
4. A current of 1.50 A is maintained for 50 min in the electrolysis of copper (II) sulfate solution, using a copper anode. Calculate

(*a*) the gain in mass of the cathode, and (*b*) the change in mass of the anode.

5. One liter of 5.00 *M* NaCl solution is electrolyzed for 60 min by a current of 2.68 A. (*a*) How many electrons are involved in the cathode reaction? (*b*) How many moles of anode product are formed? (*c*) What is the volume in liters of cathode product? (*d*) What is the *p*H of the solution at the end of the electrolysis?
6. The electrolysis of a molten salt by a current of 1.34 A for 2 hr deposits 1.74 g of metal product on the cathode. Calculate the (*a*) equivalent mass of the metal, (*b*) atomic mass of the metal if its valence is 3.
7. A dry cell forces a current of 0.100 A through an external circuit for 10.0 min. (*a*) Compute the number of electrons delivered to the circuit. (*b*) Compute the number of coulombs of electricity delivered by the cell. (*c*) Compute the mass in grams of zinc ion formed at the anode of the cell.

Find Out!

What is a cadmium cell? Describe how it works and compare it with the standard lead battery.

Suggested Readings

Shamos, M.H. (Ed.), *Great Experiments in Physics.* New York: Halt, 1960. pp. 146–157.

UNIT VI

CHEMICAL DYNAMICS

THE MOTIONS OF GAS PARTICLES (molecules or atoms) can be compared with the motions of billiard balls on a billiard table. The balls move in all directions at different speeds and they frequently collide with each other. Two different kinds of gas molecules can be represented by balls of different colors, say white and red. If a red ball (*R*) travels faster than a white one (*W*), R will ultimately overtake *W* provided both are traveling in the same direction and in line. When collision occurs, ball *R* transfers some of its kinetic energy to ball *W* and, in consequence, the speed of *R* is decreased and the speed of *W* is increased.

This collision theory accounts for a number of properties of gas molecules, some of which have been discussed in the chapter on kinetic theory. However, the billiard ball model cannot explain why gas molecules react with each other chemically. We must remember that the electrons of an atom also possess energy and that a collision between atoms (or molecules) will disturb some of the electrons, particularly those in the outer shells. If the outer electrons of an atom of *W* gain energy on impact, they will be lifted to a higher level, further from the nucleus. These electrons are then less tightly held by the nucleus and they are said to be *activated*. Precisely the same thing can happen to the outer electrons of an atom of *R* when it collides with another atom. If the activated atoms of *R* and *W* now approach each other sufficiently closely there will be a transfer or sharing of the loosely held electrons; that is, under these conditions there will be a chemical reaction between atoms *W* and *R*.

HISTORICAL CHEMISTRY LABORATORY

The following selection gives the basic formulation of the law of mass action as it was stated in a paper published in 1879 by C.M. Guldberg and P. Waage.

C. M. Guldberg (1836–1902) P. Waage (1833–1900)

In the year 1867, we presented a study under the title of "Etudes sur les affinités chimiques" in which we were concerned chiefly with chemical mass action. We expressed the view that the result of a chemical process depends not only on the substances which enter into the new compound but also on all other substances which are present in the process. The latter we called foreign substances, in so far as they exert a noticeable influence, even though they do not themselves undergo any chemical change during the process. The solvent is considered one of these foreign substances.

The chemical forces which come into effect between the substances are dependent on temperature, pressure, the aggregate condition, and the mass ratios.

We differentiate two chief groups of chemical forces: the true affinity forces which bring about the formation of new chemical compounds, and the secondary forces whose action can be referred back to the foreign substances.

The chemical processes which are most suitable for the study of the chemical forces in them are, in our view, those in which an equilibrium state exists between the forces, or, in other words, processes in which the chemical reaction goes equally in two opposite directions. As examples, we will mention.

1. A metal is oxidized by water vapor, and the metal oxide under the same conditions is reduced by hydrogen.

2. Dissociation of a body AB, in which both parts A and B and the original substances AB are present at the same time.

3. Two dissolved substances give rise to a double decomposition: thus alcohol and acetic acid go partly into ester and water, and reversibly, ester and water go partly into alcohol and acetic acid.

4. A soluble and an insoluble salt partly exchange their acids . . .

These last classes of chemical compounds were those which we chiefly made the subject of our experimental studies.

From our own experimental studies combined with already known material, we deduced the law for chemical mass action which we stated as follows:

If two substances A and B change into two new substances A′ and B′ the chemical strength with which A and B are held together is measured by the mass of new substances A′ and B′ formed in unit time.

The mass with which a definite substance enters the unit volume of the body in which the chemical process proceeds we have called the active mass of the substance.

CHAPTER 19

RATES AND HEATS OF CHEMICAL REACTIONS

THE SPEEDS OF CHEMICAL REACTIONS vary a great deal depending upon the particular reactants involved. For example, a piece of dry white phosphorus soon bursts into flame in air. In contrast, a dry piece of iron rusts very slowly, while a piece of sulfur is not affected at all. The rates of reaction of substances with water also vary a great deal. Sodium reacts violently with water, releasing hydrogen, while the reaction between magnesium and water is exceedingly slow. Further, calcium oxide and water react at a rapid rate, but aluminum oxide and water do not react at all.

Temperature and Rate of Reaction

The rate of reaction between two substances is always increased by raising the temperature. A rough rule of thumb is that a rise of 10 C° doubles the reaction rate. For example, if a reaction proceeds to, say 90% completion in 12 sec at 20 °C, then at 30 °C the reaction will proceed to the same extent in about 6 sec, and at 40 °C the elapsed time will be approximately 3 sec. How can this be explained?

In order to react, molecules (or ions) must first collide with each other. The kinetic theory tells us that the higher the temperature the higher is the average speed of the particles. Obviously, the higher the speed the greater is the number of collisions between the particles. However, when particles collide they may or may not react. Usually they do not, they merely rebound. Actually, the exchange of energy in each collision is a much more important factor than the number of collisions.

Activation Energy

As you know, temperature is a measure of the *average* speed of particles, but even at the same temperature individual particles move at different speeds, and a small number of them move at exceedingly high speeds. You recall that kinetic energy is proportional to the square of the velocity (K.E. $= \frac{1}{2} mv^2$) and therefore the particles with the highest speeds have the greatest kinetic energies. Some of the chemical bonds of a particle may weaken or break on impact. When this happens a reaction can occur, and the particle is said to have acquired the *activation energy* needed for the particular reaction in question. Thus we conclude that before two particles are able to react chemically, they must have acquired a certain minimum of energy. This essential minimum is called the *energy of activation.* Figure 19-1 shows how the kinetic energies of molecules are distributed at a given temperature (T_1). A small number of

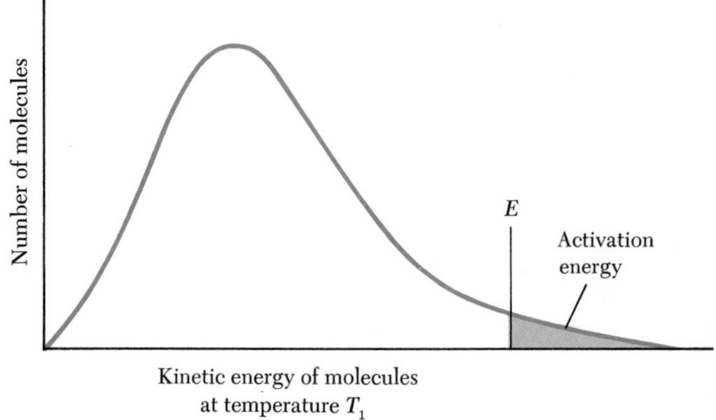

Fig. 19-1 Curve showing distribution of kinetic energy of molecules at a given temperature T_1. Only the molecules in the colored part of the graph have achieved activation energy.

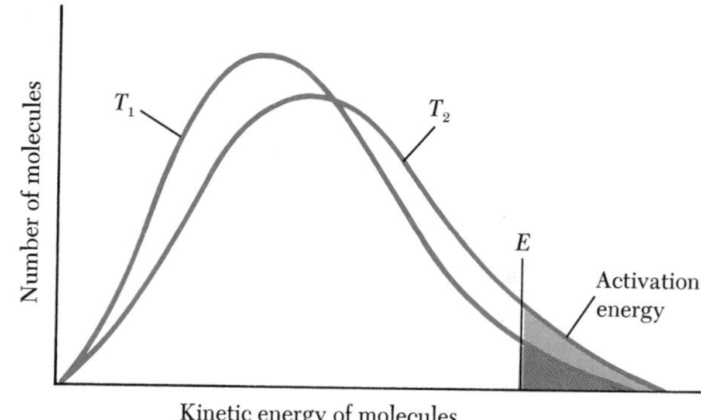

Fig. 19-2 Curves showing change in activation energy with change in temperature from T_1 to T_2.

the molecules (shown in the colored area) have energies equal to or greater than the activation energy.

The whole area under the curve represents a certain number of molecules, and the shape of the curve indicates distribution of kinetic energies among the molecules. The line marked E corresponds to the activation energy.

Therefore, molecules to the right of line E have enough energy to react when collision occurs, but molecules to the left of the line will not react. Thus, it is apparent that only a very small fraction of the colliding molecules have enough energy to react.

What happens to the kinetic energies of the molecules if the temperature is raised from T_1 to T_2? Clearly the average speed of the molecules increases and therefore a larger fraction of the molecules acquires activation energy. This situation is shown in Fig. 19-2 where the distribution curve at temperature T_2 is superimposed upon the T_1 curve of Fig. 19-1. Since the total number of molecules remains the same, the area under each of the curves is also the same. However, the T_2 curve is flatter than the T_1 curve and the shaded area for T_2 is greater than that for T_1. It should therefore be apparent that the higher the temperature the greater is the number of molecules that crosses the barrier and acquires the energy of activation.

Heat of Reaction

A mixture of hydrogen and oxygen is inactive at ordinary temperatures. However, if the temperature is raised to about 800°C, the gases combine with explosive violence and a great deal of heat is released. The equation for this reaction is

$$2H_2(g) + O_2(g) \xrightarrow{\text{heat}} 2H_2O(g) + \text{heat} \qquad (19\text{-}1)$$

Obviously there is more energy in the reactants (hydrogen and oxygen) than in the product (water vapor). Suppose that the heat content is H_1 in the reactants and H_2 in the product. The *difference* in heat content between reactants and product is released as heat (H) and is usually represented by the symbol ΔH, Δ being the Greek letter *delta*. Hence

$$\Delta H = H_2(\text{products}) - H_1\ (\text{reactants})$$

Actual measurements show that 56.7 kcal of heat are released for each mole of water vapor formed:

$$H_2(g) + \tfrac{1}{2}O_2(g) \longrightarrow H_2O(g) + 56.7\ \text{kcal} \qquad (19\text{-}2)$$

Moreover, since the potential energy of the product is less than the potential energy of the reactants, ΔH must have a negative value. In other words, $\Delta H = -56.7$ kcal/mole.

Fig. 19-3 An exothermic reaction. The temperature rises when concentrated H_2SO_4 is added to H_2O, causing Thermomelt ® Crayon mark (100 °F, 38 °C) on frosted glass slab to melt and disappear below level of liquid, while other marking (200 °F, 93 °C) is not affected.

Suppose, however, that all substances are measured at room temperature, say 25 °C. That is, the hydrogen-oxygen mixture at 25 °C is exploded and the product (water vapor) is then allowed to cool to 25 °C. The vapor first condenses to water at 100 °C and the liquid then cools to 25 °C. In this case, the equation for the reaction is

$$H_2(g) + \tfrac{1}{2}O_2(g) \longrightarrow H_2O(l) \qquad (19\text{-}3)$$

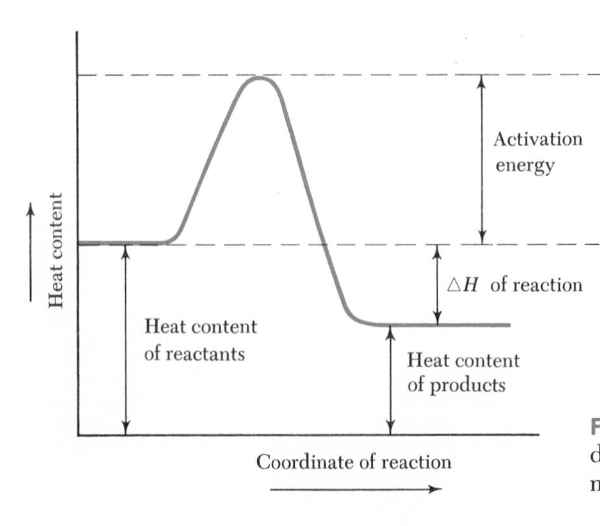

Fig. 19-4 An energy diagram of an exothermic reaction.

In condensing from steam to water at 25 °C, heat of vaporization (10.5 kcal/mole) is evolved:

$$H_2O(g) \longrightarrow H_2O(1) + 10.5\,\text{kcal} \qquad (19\text{-}4)$$

Hence ΔH in this condensing process is -10.5 kcal/mole, and the total amount of heat released in the reaction in Eq. (19-3) is $-(56.7+10.5)$ kcal/mole, that is $\Delta H = -68.2$ kcal/mole.

Heat of Reaction and Activation Energy

In the reaction in Eq. (19-1), heat energy is needed to break the covalent bonds of the hydrogen and oxygen molecules, but heat is released when the bonds of water molecules are formed. As already stated, the net process is exothermic. (See Fig. 19-3.) We also know that before molecules can react they must acquire activation energy, otherwise they would merely bounce away intact when they collide. The relationship between activation energy and heat of reaction is shown in Fig. 19-4. In this reaction the heat content of the products is less than that of the reactants. Therefore Fig. 19-4 is a diagram of an *exothermic reaction.*

In an endothermic reaction heat is absorbed, and therefore the heat content of the products must be greater than the heat content of the reactants. This is shown in Figs. 19-5 and 19-6.

Since $\Delta H = H_2$ (products) $- H_1$ (reactants), and since H_2 (products) is greater then H_1 (reactants), the sign of ΔH is positive in an en-

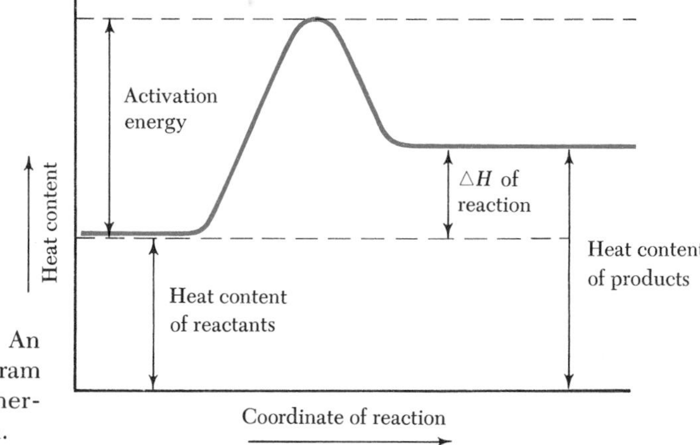

Fig. 19-5 An energy diagram of an endothermic reaction.

Fig. 19-6 When "photographers' hypo" is added to water, moisture condenses on the outside of the beaker. Why does this prove that an endothermic reaction has occurred?

dothermic reaction. For example, in the following reaction,

$$H_2 \longrightarrow 2H \tag{19-5}$$

energy is needed to split hydrogen molecules into atoms. For reaction (19-5), $\Delta H = +52.1$ kcal/mole of H atoms, and in reaction (19-6),

$$Cl_2 \longrightarrow 2Cl \quad \text{or} \quad \tfrac{1}{2}\,Cl_2 \longrightarrow Cl \tag{19-6}$$

$\Delta H = +28.9$ kcal/mole of Cl atoms.

Concentration and Reaction Rate

Suppose that a solution containing 1 mole/l of substance *A* and 1 mole/l of substance *B* is prepared, and that the speed or rate of the reaction between *A* and *B* is determined. How would this rate of reaction compare with the reaction rate for a solution in which the concentrations of *A* and *B* are each 2 moles/l? The chance of collision between particles in the second solution is clearly greater than the collision probability of the first solution. Thus it is reasonable to conclude that if the concentration of a reactant is increased, the rate of reaction is also increased.

Let us also consider reacting gases. Hydrogen, for example, reacts with iodine vapor to form the gas hydrogen iodide:

$$H_2(g) + I_2(g) \longrightarrow 2HI(g) \tag{19-7}$$

What happens if we change the concentration of the reactants? Suppose we double the concentration of hydrogen but maintain the initial concentration of iodine. Since the number of collisions between hydrogen and iodine molecules is doubled, we might expect the reaction rate also to be double, and experiment proves that this occurs. Hence we conclude that reaction rate is proportional to the concentration of hydrogen:

$$R \propto [H_2] \tag{19-8}$$

where R stands for rate of reaction.

If, however, we double the concentration of iodine gas and maintain the original concentration of hydrogen, the number of intermolecular collisions is again doubled. From this we conclude that

$$R \propto [I_2] \tag{19-9}$$

and therefore,

$$R \propto [H_2] \times [I_2] \tag{19-10}$$

The Law of Mass Action

Let us now consider the effect of changing the concentrations of both gases at the same time. If the concentration of hydrogen is doubled and the iodine concentration trebled, the number of molecular collisions is increased six times as shown in Fig. 19-7 Therefore the rate of reaction is increased six times, which is what we expect from the products of the concentrations. Although not all reactions show such a simple dependence of reaction rate on concentration of reactants, it is generally true that increasing the concentration of reactants increases the reaction rate. This relationship between reaction rate and the concentration of reactants is known as the *Law of Mass Action*.

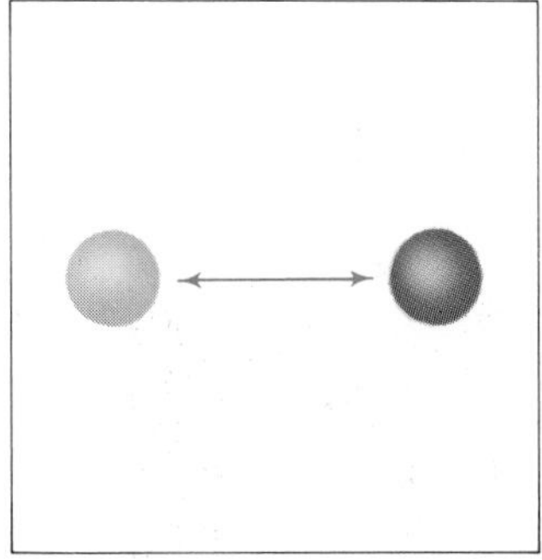

1 Collision

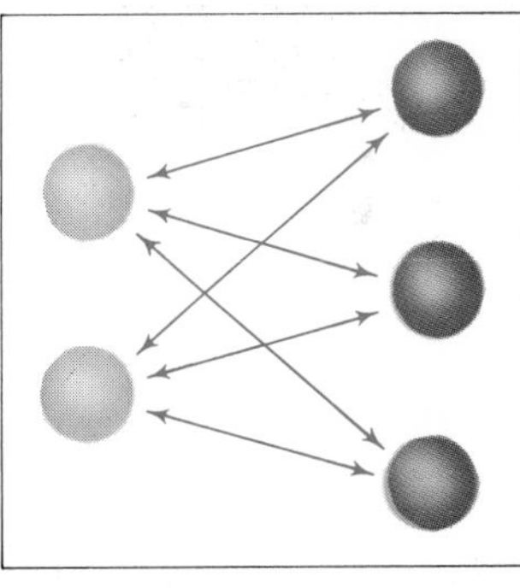

6 Collisions

Fig. 19-7 If the concentration of one of the gases is doubled and the other tripled, how much is the rate of reaction increased?

Concentration and Gas Pressure

If A and B are gases, concentration can be expressed in moles of gas reactant per liter of volume (that is, the space occupied by the gas mixture). Moreover, the concentration of a gas depends upon the pressure of the gas; in fact the concentration of the gas is directly proportional to its pressure. For example, if 0.01 mole of reaction mixture has a volume of 1 l, the pressure of the reaction mixture (at 0 °C) is 0.224 atm. And, if the pressure is increased to 2.24 atm (at the same temperature, 0 °C), the volume of the reaction mixture is reduced to 0.1 l so that a tenfold increase in pressure has increased the concentration ten times.

Remember that the pressure of a reaction mixture is equal to the sum of the pressures of its components (the reactants). Therefore the rates of reactions among gases are found to depend upon the partial pressures of the individual gases in the reaction mixture.

Let us now apply the law of mass action to the reaction in Eq. (19-7).

From Eq. (19-10) we find that

$$R = [H_2] \times [I_2] \times k \qquad (19\text{-}11)$$

where k is the *rate constant*. The value of k can be determined as follows. If $[H_2] = 1$ mole H_2/l and $[I_2] = 1$ mole/l,

$$R = 1 \times 1 \times k \qquad \text{or} \qquad R = k$$

under these conditions.

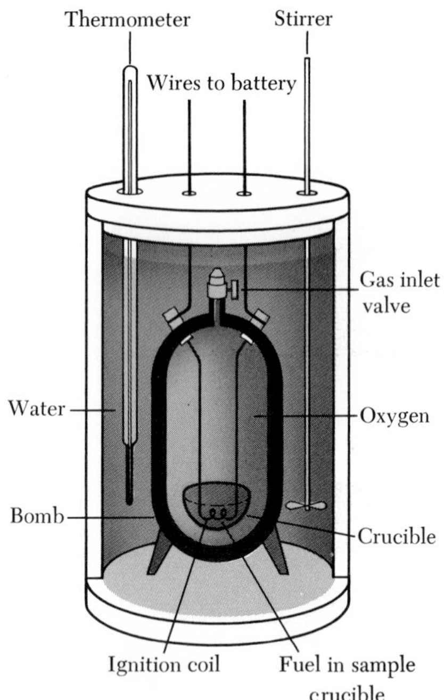

Fig. 19-8 Diagram of a calorimeter used to find heats of reaction. The fuel sample and oxygen under pressure are enclosed in the bomb which is then immersed in water. The reaction is started by a current which flows through an ignition coil situated in a crucible within the bomb.

Example 19-1 is a typical mass-action law problem.

Example 19-1

Compute the rate of reaction in Eq. (19-7) if $[H_2]$ is 2 moles/l and $[I_2]$ is 4 moles/l.

Solution

$$R = [H_2] \times [I_2] \times k$$
$$= 2 \times 4 \times k$$
$$= 8k$$

That is, the rate of reaction is eight times as fast as it is when the concentration of each reactant is 1 mole/l. Of course, if the value of the rate constant, k, is known, then the exact reaction rate can be calculated.

Heat of Combustion

The term *heat of reaction* applies to reactions in general. We discussed the reaction

$$H_2(g) + \tfrac{1}{2}O_2(g) \longrightarrow H_2O(l) + 68.2\text{ kcal} \qquad (19\text{-}12)$$
$$\Delta H = -68.2\text{ kcal}$$

where $\Delta H = H_2$ (heat content of products) $-$ H_1 (heat content of reactants).

A special case of heat of reaction is *heat of combustion*, a term that refers to the combustion of 1 mole of a fuel. The hydrogen–oxygen reaction is obviously a combustion reaction. However, *heat of reaction* is defined as the *heat released in the formation of one mole of product* whereas we define *heat of combustion* as *the heat released during the combustion of one mole of fuel.*

Heats of combustion can be determined experimentally by mixing a known mass of fuel with oxygen in a calorimeter, the calorimeter being immersed in a known mass of water as shown in Fig. 19-8. The heat evolved in the reaction warms the water and the amount of heat produced can be computed from the mass of water and the rise in temperature. It is then a simple matter to compute the heat evolved per mole of fuel burned.

Let us consider the heats of combustion of two fuels: carbon and carbon monoxide. Pure carbon burns in oxygen and releases 94.0 kcal/mole,

$$C(s) + O_2(g) \longrightarrow CO_2(g) + 94.0 \text{ kcal} \qquad (19\text{-}13)$$

From Eq. (19-13) we see that $\Delta H = -94.0$ kcal/mole of carbon. This exothermic reaction is represented graphically in Fig. 19-9.

The equation for the combustion of carbon monoxide is

$$2CO(g) + O_2(g) \longrightarrow 2CO_2(g) + 135.3 \text{ kcal} \qquad (19\text{-}14)$$

And, rewriting the equation for one mole of fuel,

$$CO(g) + \tfrac{1}{2}O_2(g) \longrightarrow CO_2(g) + 67.6 \text{ kcal} \qquad (19\text{-}14A)$$

Therefore, $\Delta H = -67.6$ kcal/mole of CO.

In a limited amount of oxygen, carbon burns to form carbon monoxide:

$$2C(s) + O_2(g) \longrightarrow 2CO(g) \qquad (19\text{-}15)$$

However, in practice, it is impossible to heat carbon in oxygen so that it yields *only* carbon monoxide. For this reason, the *experimental* value of the heat of combustion of carbon in forming carbon monoxide is unreliable, but it can be computed from the two known reliable values found in Eqs. (19-13) and (19-14A). In making the computation, we must know how much heat is needed to decompose 1 mole of CO_2 into CO and O_2. This value is given by reversing Eq. (19-14A). If 67.6 kcal of heat are released when 1 mole of CO_2 is formed from CO and O_2, then, by the law of conservation of energy, 67.6 kcal of heat will decompose 1 mole of CO_2 into CO and O_2. Hence,

$$C + O_2 \longrightarrow CO_2 + 94.0 \text{ kcal} \qquad (19\text{-}13)$$

$$CO_2 \longrightarrow CO + \tfrac{1}{2}O_2 - 67.6 \text{ kcal} \qquad (19\text{-}14B)$$

The heat of combustion of carbon monoxide is then obtained by adding Eqs. (19-13) and (19-14B).

$$C + O_2 + CO_2 \longrightarrow CO_2 + CO + \tfrac{1}{2}O_2 + 26.4 \text{ kcal} \qquad (19\text{-}16)$$

Or

$$C + \tfrac{1}{2}O_2 \longrightarrow CO + 26.4 \text{ kcal} \qquad (19\text{-}15A)$$

Therefore, $\Delta H = -26.4$ kcal/mole of CO formed.

Fig. 19-9 Heat is released in the burning of carbon, an exothermic reaction.

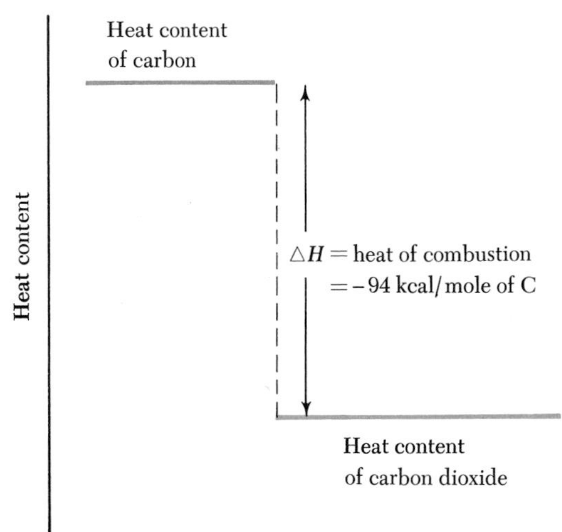

Speculate . . .
What has replaced water gas as a fuel? Why?

An Endothermic Reaction

Water gas was at one time a common fuel gas. It is made by passing steam over hot coke.

$$C(s) + H_2O(g) \longrightarrow CO(g) + H_2(g) \qquad (19\text{-}17)$$

That is, water gas is a mixture of carbon monoxide and hydrogen. We can compute the *heat of reaction* in the water-gas preparation from previously determined values:

Since

$$H_2(g) + \tfrac{1}{2} O_2(g) \longrightarrow H_2O(g) + 56.7 \text{ kcal} \qquad (19\text{-}2)$$

therefore

$$H_2O(g) \longrightarrow H_2(g) + \tfrac{1}{2} O - 56.7 \text{ kcal} \qquad (19\text{-}2A)$$

Since

$$CO(g) + \tfrac{1}{2} O_2(g) \longrightarrow CO_2(g) + 67.6 \text{ kcal} \qquad (19\text{-}14A)$$

therefore

$$CO_2(g) \longrightarrow CO(g) + \tfrac{1}{2} O_2(g) - 67.6 \text{ kcal} \qquad (19\text{-}14B)$$

Heats of reaction used in the computation are

$$C(s) + O_2(g) \longrightarrow CO_2(g) + 94.0 \text{ kcal} \qquad (19\text{-}13)$$

$$H_2O(g) \longrightarrow H_2 + \tfrac{1}{2} O_2 - 56.7 \text{ kcal} \qquad (19\text{-}2)$$

$$CO_2(g) \longrightarrow CO(g) + \tfrac{1}{2} O_2(g) - 67.6 \text{ kcal} \qquad (19\text{-}14B)$$

By addition

$$C(s) + H_2O(g) \longrightarrow H_2(g) + CO(g) - 31.4 \text{ kcal} \qquad (19\text{-}18)$$

Therefore, $\Delta H = 31.4$ kcal/mole.

Infer . . .
Look up the definition of steam in your dictionary. Why do scientists usually say "water vapor" when nonscientists might say "steam"?

Thus, the water-gas reaction is endothermic; that is, as "steam" combines with hot coke there is an absorption of heat energy and an inevitable drop in temperature. This endothermic reaction is represented graphically in Fig. 19-10.

Effect of Catalysts on Rate of Reaction

Some reactions can be speeded up by the use of substances called *catalysts*. For instance, in preparing oxygen, either from potassium chlorate or a solution of hydrogen peroxide, the reactions proceed much faster if manganese dioxide is used as a catalyst,

$$2KClO_3(s) \xrightarrow{MnO_2(s)} 2KCl(s) + 3O_2(g) \tag{19-19}$$

$$2H_2O_2(aq) \xrightarrow{MnO_2(s)} 2H_2O(l) + O_2(g) \tag{19-20}$$

In industry, one of the steps in the manufacture of sulfuric acid is the oxidation of sulfur dioxide gas by oxygen to form sulfur trioxide gas,

$$2SO_2(g) + O_2(g) \longrightarrow 2SO_3(g) \tag{19-21}$$

The reaction in Eq. (19-21) proceeds very slowly at room temperature. But if metallic platinum or vanadium pentoxide (which is a white solid) is introduced into the reaction vessel holding the gas mixture, the reaction proceeds rapidly,

$$2SO_2(g) + O_2(g) \xrightarrow{\text{Pt or } V_2O_5} 2SO_3(g) \tag{19-21A}$$

Both the platinum and vanadium pentoxide are intact at the end of the reaction—they are not chemically changed in any way. What is the mechanism by which they change the rate of the reaction? It is thought that the gases SO_2 and O_2 are adsorbed on the surface of the platinum and as a result the gases are brought into closer contact so that intermolecular collisions take place more frequently.

Sometimes, however, a catalyst is a gas; in this case the mechanism is certainly not a surface effect. Thus, sulfur trioxide will combine rapidly with water vapor to form sulfuric acid in the presence of the gas nitrogen dioxide (NO_2):

$$H_2O(g) + SO_3(g) \xrightarrow{NO_2(g)} H_2SO_4(l) \tag{19-22}$$

Here it is thought that the catalyst reacts with the reactants in a series of steps to form an *activated complex* from which the catalyst can be easily regenerated. In other words, in some way a catalyst provides a different route for the reaction—an easier route that requires less activation energy than the uncatalyzed reaction. The effect of using a catalyst is shown in Fig. 19-11. Notice that the catalyst reduces the activation energy and therefore lowers the barrier between reactants and products. It should be emphasized that a catalyst does not start a reaction nor does it affect the products of a reaction. In other words, the heat contents of reactants and products and also the heat of reaction (ΔH) are precisely the same, whether a

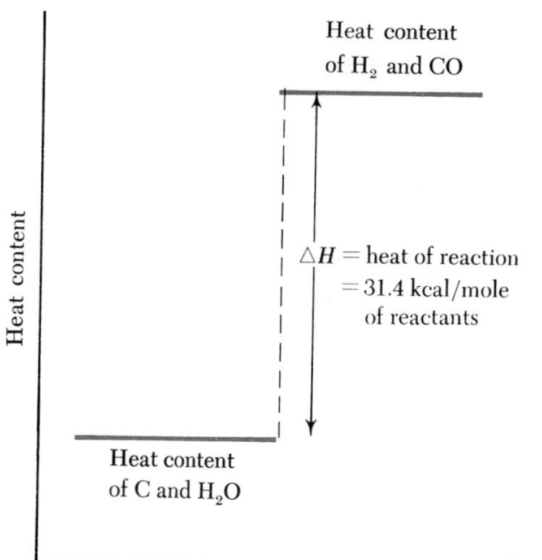

Fig. 19-10 Heat is absorbed in the formation of water gas, an endothermic reaction.

Explain . . .
When chemists write equations, they frequently indicate conditions under which a reaction occurs by means of symbols over or under the arrow. Justify this practice.

Infer . . .
Explain the difference between adsorption and absorption. Why do you think platinum gauze or powdered platinum, rather than lumps of platinum, is used as a catalyst?

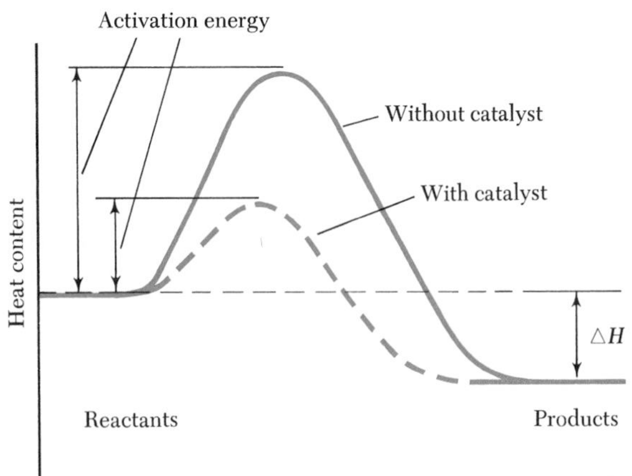

Fig. 19-11 The energy curve of a catalyzed reaction compared with the curve of a noncatalyzed reaction. The catalyst reduces the energy of activation. Does it affect the heat of reaction?

catalyst is present or not. Catalysts are widely used in industrial chemical processes.

State of Division of Reacting Substances

A piece of coal burns slowly in air. If the coal is smashed into small pieces it burns more rapidly, and if it is crushed to a powder and ignited when suspended in air, it burns with explosive violence. Indeed, many of the explosions in coal mines are due to the ignition of coal dust. The finer the state of division the greater is the surface area of the coal exposed to the oxygen of the air and therefore the greater is the number of molecular collisions between carbon and oxygen molecules.

Recall . . .
What is a phase? What are the phases of matter?

A reaction between a solid and a gas is called a *heterogeneous reaction* because the reactants are in different phases. For reactions of this kind, the rate of reaction is proportional to the *area of contact* between the reactants. But in a homogeneous mixture, such as a mixture of gases, the molecules are already mixed in the most intimate way possible. And that is why many gases react with considerable violence.

Summary

Rates of chemical reactions vary a great deal. Some are exceedingly slow and others are so fast that they are explosive. The reaction rates depend mainly upon three factors: (1) the nature of the reacting substances, (2) the concentration of the reactants, and (3) the temperature.

The law of mass action concerns rate of reaction as applied to the concentrations of the reactants. Before colliding molecules are able to react they must have a certain minimum energy called *activation energy*. Thus, a rise in temperature *always* increases the reaction rate between the reactants. If a catalyst is used, the reaction follows a different route. The activation energy is less along the new path than along the uncatalyzed path, and the catalyst speeds up the rate of reaction.

In a chemical reaction heat energy may be released or absorbed, depending upon the difference in chemical potential energy between reactants and products. In an exothermic reaction the potential energy of the reactants is greater then the potential energy of the products; in an endothermic reaction the reverse is the case.

Factual Recall

1. (*a*) What is meant by the term *activation energy*?
   (*b*) Draw a kinetic energy distribution curve for n gas molecules at temperature T_1, and explain what the curve means.
2. (*a*) Draw a kinetic energy distribution curve for n gas molecules at temperature T_2.
   (*b*) Explain how and why the curve in Question 2 differs from the curve in Question 1.
3. (*a*) What is meant by the symbol ΔH?
   (*b*) Explain why ΔH has a negative value in an exothermic reaction.
4. The higher the temperature the greater is the chance of reaction between colliding gas molecules. Explain why.
5. (*a*) State the law of mass action.
   (*b*) Derive an equation for the equilibrium constant for the hypothetical reaction

   $A + B \rightleftarrows C + D$
6. (*a*) What is a catalyst?
   (*b*) Describe the function of a catalyst in a reaction between gases.
7. Explain why wood dust burns more rapidly in air than does a log of wood.

Apply Your Knowledge!

1. (*a*) Compute the heat of reaction for

$$\tfrac{1}{2}\ N_2(g) + O_2(g) \longrightarrow NO_2(g)$$

given

$$N_2(g) + O_2(g) \longrightarrow 2NO(g) \qquad \Delta H_1 = +21.6\ \text{kcal/mole}$$

and

$$2NO(g) + O_2(g) \longrightarrow 2NO_2(g) \qquad \Delta H_2 = -13.5\ \text{kcal/mole}$$

(*b*) Is the reaction exothermic or endothermic?
(*c*) Why?

2. $C\ (\text{diamond}) + O_2(g) \longrightarrow CO_2(g) + 94.5\ \text{kcal}$

and

$$C\ (\text{graphite}) + O_2(g) \longrightarrow CO_2(g) + 94.05\ \text{kcal}$$

(*a*) What is the ΔH for making diamonds from graphite?

(*b*) Why do you suppose that this is a difficult process?

Find Out!

1. Look up the work of Henry Eyring on activated complexes.
2. What is meant by calling an enzyme an "organic catalyst"?

CHAPTER 20

CHEMICAL EQUILIBRIUM

IF A CURRENT OF STEAM is forced over a layer of hot iron as shown in Fig. 20-1 (*a*), hydrogen is formed and can be collected by displacing water. Indeed, this is one method of preparing hydrogen in the laboratory. The equation for the reaction is

$$3Fe + 4H_2O(g) \xrightarrow{\text{heat}} Fe_3O_4 + 4H_2(g) \qquad (20\text{-}1)$$

If, on the other hand, a stream of hydrogen is forced over a layer of hot iron oxide, the hydrogen reduces the oxide to metallic iron (as shown in Fig. 20-1(*b*)- The equation for this reaction is

$$Fe_3O_4 + 4H_2(g) \xrightarrow{\text{heat}} 3Fe + 4H_2O(g) \qquad (20\text{-}2)$$

Reaction (20-2) is the reverse of reaction (20-1). Stated in other terms, the reaction can go either way. Such a reaction is said to be *reversible* and the equation is usually written with reversible arrows:

$$3Fe + 4H_2O(g) \overset{\text{heat}}{\rightleftharpoons} Fe_3O_4 + 4H_2(g) \qquad (20\text{-}3)$$

Recall . . .

Steam (visible) is a mixture of hot water vapor (invisible) carried in minute drops of water (visible) and dust particles (visible) in the air.

If the product hydrogen escapes as soon as it is formed, the reaction proceeds completely to the right. If, on the other hand, water (as steam) is removed as soon as it is formed, the reaction proceeds

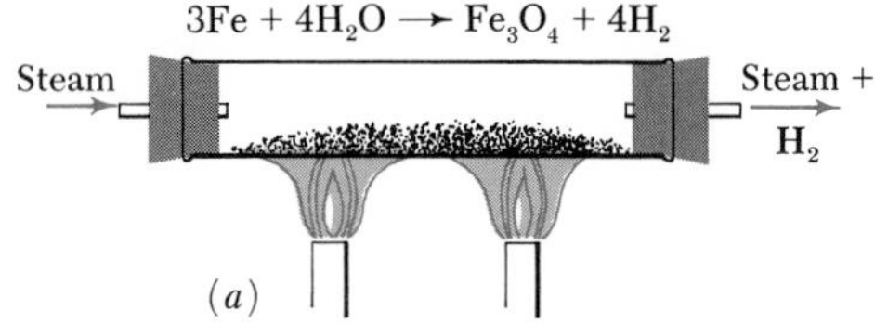

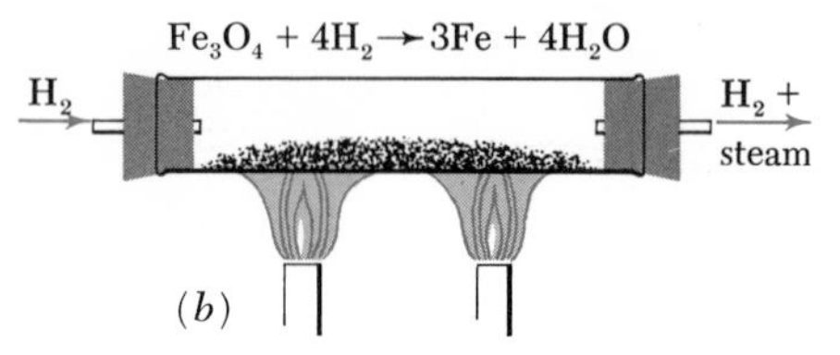

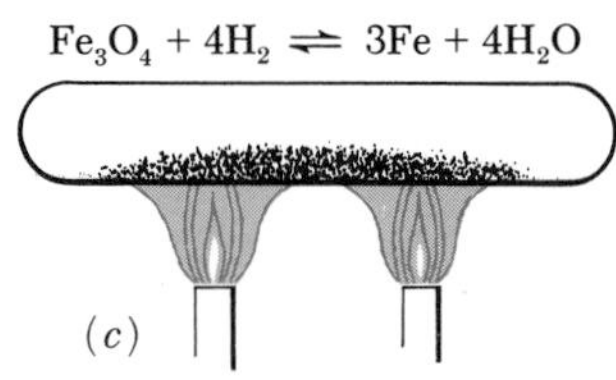

Fig. 20-1 (*a*) The conversion of iron to iron oxide by steam. (*b*) The conversion of iron oxide to iron by hydrogen. (*c*) The equilibrium between iron, iron oxide, steam, and hydrogen in a sealed tube.

completely to the left. What happens if the container is sealed so that neither hydrogen nor steam can escape? (Fig. 20-1 *c*). Or, better still, what happens if a mixture of iron oxide and hydrogen is heated in a sealed container? Clearly iron oxide and hydrogen react to form iron and water as shown in Eq. (20-2). But as soon as iron and water are formed they too begin to react, forming iron oxide and hydrogen as shown in Eq. (20-1). However, the two reactions do not take place at the same rate. At first, the concentration of hydrogen is much greater than the concentration of steam, so that the rate of reaction in Eq. (20-2) is much faster than the rate in Eq. (20-1). However, as more steam and iron are formed, the rate of of the reaction in Eq. (20-1) increases while the rate of reaction in Eq. (20-2) decreases, until, eventually, the two rates are equal. When this happens, the rate of the reaction to the right in Eq. (20-3) equals the rate to the left and the reaction is said to be in a state of *equilibrium*. It should be observed that at equilibrium the reaction *appears* to have come to a standstill, although actually the forward and backward reactions are proceeding at the same rate. For this reason it is better to speak of *dynamic equilibrium*, rather than just equilibriu, because the word *dynamic* implies motion.

The Equilibrium Constant

Let us now consider a hypothetical reversible reaction,

$$A + B \rightleftharpoons C + D \qquad (20\text{-}4)$$

in which reactants A and B combine to form the products $C$and D and, at the same time, the products C and D react to form A and B. This situation is shown in Fig. 20-2. At the moment of mixing, the reaction rate of A and B is a maximum, whereas the reaction rate of C and D is zero. Why? However, as A and B are used up, the rate of the forward reaction decreases and the rate of the reverse reaction increases until, eventually, the two reaction rates are equal, and equilibrium is then established. Why?

What are the concentrations at equilibrium? Are the concentrations of reactants and products alike? Before answering these questions let us apply the law of mass action to this situation. The rate to the right (R_1) is proportional to the product of the concentrations of A

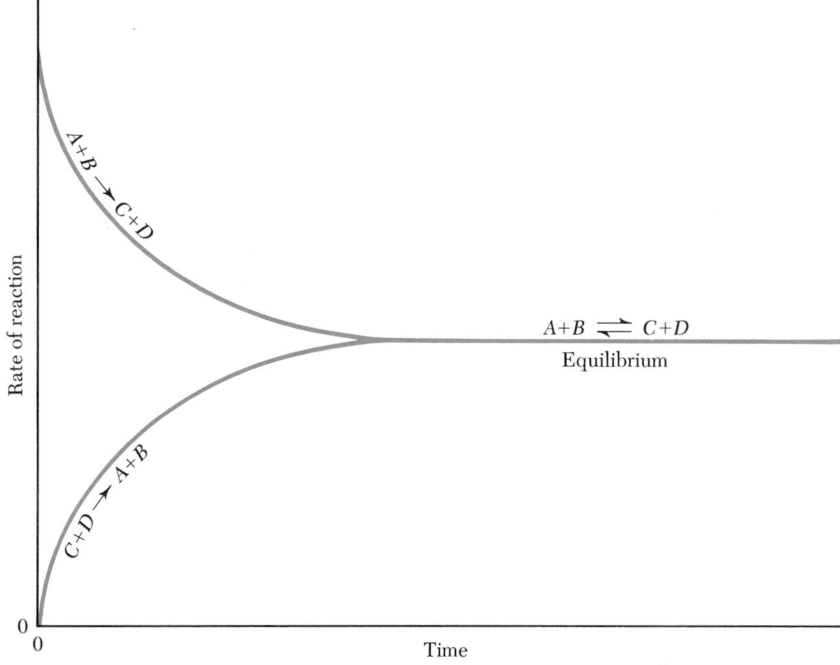

Fig. 20-2 A graph of rate of reaction versus time for the reversible reaction $A + B \rightleftharpoons C + D$. At first the rate of the forward reaction is greater than the rate of the reverse reaction. What happens to the two rates at equilibrium?

and B. That is,

$$R_1 = k_1 \times [A] \times [B]$$

where k_1 is the rate constant for the reaction to the right. The law of mass action also applies to the reverse reaction. Therefore,

$$R_2 = k_2 \times [C] \times [D]$$

where R_2 is the rate for the reaction to the left and k_2 is the rate constant for this reaction.

At equilibrium, $R_1 = R_2$ and therefore

$$k_1\ [A]\ [B] = k_2\ [C]\ [D]$$

and, by rearranging the terms,

$$\frac{k_1}{k_2} = \frac{[C]\,[D]}{[A]\,[B]}$$

Since k_1 and k_2 are constants, the quotient k_1/k_2 is also a constant for this reaction. This constant is known as the *equilibrium constant* and its symbol is K. Thus,

$$\frac{[C]\,[D]}{[A]\,[B]} = K$$

In general terms, the equilibrium constant is the product of the molar concentrations of the products divided by the product of the molar concentrations of the reactants. All chemical reactions in closed containers can be imagined to proceed to equilibrium and all chemical equilibria can be represented by equilibrium constants. These constants tell us something about the distribution of material, i.e., the relative amounts of products and reactants in a reaction mixture at equilibrium.

The Case of Varying Coefficients

In the reaction in Eq. (20-4), one molecule of A plus one molecule of B form one molecule of C plus one molecule of D. What is the equilibrium constant in a reaction with different numbers of reacting molecules such as Eq. (20-5)?

$$2A + 3B \rightleftharpoons C + 2D \qquad (20\text{-}5)$$

Equation (20-5) can be rewritten

$$A + A + B + B + B \rightleftharpoons C + D + D \qquad (20\text{-}5A)$$

and according to the mass action law, R_1, the speed to the right is

$$R_1 \propto [A]\,[A]\,[B]\,[B]\,[B]$$

Hence,

$$R_1 = k_1\,[A]^2 \times [B]^3$$

Similarly, for the speed to the left,

$$R_2 = k_2\,[C] \times [D]^2$$

Therefore the equilibrium constant expression is

$$K = \frac{[C]\,[D]^2}{[A]^2\,[B]^3}$$

Or, for the general case,

$$mA + nB \rightleftharpoons rC + sD \qquad (20\text{-}6)$$

and

$$K = \frac{[\mathrm{C}]^r\,[\mathrm{D}]^s}{[\mathrm{A}]^m\,[\mathrm{B}]^n}$$

where m, n, r, and s represent the numbers of molecules of A, B, C, and D, respectively.

The Value of the Equilibrium Constant

The value of the equilibrium constant for a reaction is determined experimentally from the molar concentrations of reactants and products in the equilibrium mixture. It is a constant for each reaction at a given temperature. Once it is known, for example, we can tell at a glance, at least roughly, how far a reaction will proceed before equilibrium is reached. Let us see how.

If the value of K is large, the numerator of the fraction must be larger than the denominator. That is, the product of the molar concentrations of the products is greater than the product of the molar concentrations of the reactants. This in turn means that, at equilibrium, the reaction will have proceeded well to the right of "midpoint," the point at which the product of the concentrations of the reactants equals the product of the concentrations of the products. If, on the other hand, K has a small value, the concentration product of the reactants must be greater than the concentration product of the products. And this can only mean that the reaction did not proceed very far to the right before equilibrium was reached; in other words, it did not reach the so-called midpoint.

A Specific Example of an Equilibrium Constant

Let us consider the reaction,

$$H_2 + I_2 \rightleftharpoons 2HI \qquad (20\text{-}7)$$

In this example of equilibrium in gases, the temperature should be above 400°C to insure that the iodine is completely vaporized.

For this reaction,

$$K = \frac{[HI]^2}{[H_2][I_2]}$$

In one experiment, at 425°C, the concentrations of the various species at *equilibrium* were found to be:

$$[H_2] = 3.56 \times 10^{-3} \text{ mole/l}$$
$$[I_2] = 1.25 \times 10^{-3} \text{ mole/l}$$
$$[HI] = 15.6 \times 10^{-3} \text{ mole/l}$$

From these, a value for the equilibrium constant can be calculated.

$$K = \frac{(15.6 \times 10^{-3})^2\,(\text{mole/l})^2}{3.56 \times 10^{-3} \times 1.25 \times 10^{-3}\ \text{mole/l} \times \text{mole/l}}$$

$$= \frac{15.6^2}{3.56 \times 1.25} = 54.7$$

Note that K has a value larger than one, indicating that at equilibrium the concentration of product HI is greater than that of the reactants H_2 and I_2.

In another experiment, at a different temperature (490°C), the equilibrium concentrations are:

$$[H_2] = 8.62 \times 10^{-3}\ \text{mole/l}$$
$$[I_2] = 2.63 \times 10^{-3}\ \text{mole/l}$$
$$[HI] = 10.2 \times 10^{-3}\ \text{mole/l}$$

and

$$K = \frac{(10.2 \times 10^{-3})^2}{8.62 \times 10^{-3} \times 2.63 \times 10^{-3}} = 4.60$$

Hence, as we would expect, the value of the equilibrium constant depends upon the temperature. However, at a given temperature, whatever the molar concentrations of reactants and products, the value of the equilibrium constant does not change. For example, three sets of experimental values for the molar concentrations of H_2, I_2, and HI at 425 °C as well as the three corresponding values of K, are given in Table 20-1.

Table 20-1 Data for the reaction in Eq.(20-7)

Experiment	Molar concentrations			$K = \frac{[HI]^2}{[H_2][I_2]}$
	$[H_2]$	$[I_2]$	$[HI]$	
1	1.14×10^{-3}	1.14×10^{-3}	8.41×10^{-3}	54.6
2	1.83×10^{-3}	3.13×10^{-3}	17.7×10^{-3}	54.7
3	2.91×10^{-3}	1.71×10^{-3}	16.5×10^{-3}	54.7

It should be apparent that if two of the three factors in this equilibrium reaction are known, the third can be computed. For instance, if we know the value of the equilibrium constant (54.7 at 425°C) and the molar concentrations of the reactants, we can compute the molar concentration of the product as in Example 20-1, which follows.

Example 20-1

One liter of an equilibrium mixture of H_2, I_2, and HI at 425°C contains 3.00×10^{-3} mole of H_2 and 1.00×10^{-3} mole of I_2. What is the molar concentration of HI in the mixture?

Solution

$$[HI]^2 = K \times [H_2] \times [I_2]$$

$$= 54.7 \times 3.00 \times 10^{-3} \times 1.00 \times 10^{-3}$$

$$= 1.64 \times 10^{-4}$$

$$[HI] = \sqrt{1.64 \times 10^{-4}}$$

$$= 1.28 \times 10^{-2} \text{ mole/l}$$

N.B.: A square root is obtained from the A and D scales of a slide rule. The number (1.64 in this case) on scale A gives the square root value on scale D.

Factors that Affect Equilibrium

Can the point of equilibrium of a reversible reaction be changed? At least two factors other than temperature change may affect the equilibrium of a reaction: (1) a change in the molar concentration of one (or more) of the reacting substances, and (2) a change in pressure, provided that at least one of the reacting substances is a gas. A change in temperature changes the value of K (the equilibrium constant), but a change in concentration or pressure does not change the K value. Let us consider each of these effects in turn.

The Effect of Changing Concentration

Nitrogen combines with hydrogen to form ammonia gas, according to the equation,

$$N_2 + 3H_2 \rightleftharpoons 2NH_3 \qquad (20\text{-}9)$$

Actually, this is the way ammonia is manufactured on an industrial scale, so it is important to set up conditions that will produce the greatest possible yield of ammonia from the raw materials.

Suppose that a mixture of nitrogen and hydrogen in a container has reacted to form ammonia and that equilibrium has been reached. What will happen if more nitrogen is forced into the container? An increase in the concentration of nitrogen causes an increase in the rate of reaction between molecules of nitrogen and hydrogen. As a result, more hydrogen is used up and more ammonia is produced. But the formation of more ammonia speeds up the reaction to the left until, eventually, the rate to the left equals the rate to the right. Clearly, this new rate is not the same as the original rate. By the same argument, if ammonia is added to the equilibrium mixture, the rate at which ammonia decomposes is increased and therefore the concentrations of nitrogen and hydrogen are increased, so again a new point of equilibrium is established. In summary, a change in the concentration of one ingredient results in a change in the concentrations of all other ingredients, which in turn affects the rates of both forward and backward reactions and establishes a new point of equilibrium. However, *the value of the equilibrium constant is not affected by a change in concentration.* Why not?

Recall and evaluate . . .
Is this consistent with Le Châtelier's principle?

The Effect of a Change in Pressure

Liquids and solids are not markedly affected by changes in pressure, but gases are. A change in pressure changes the concentration of a gas. Does a change in concentration shift the point of equilibrium and thereby affect the percentage yield of the product? Let us again consider the reaction,

$$\underset{\text{1 mole}}{N_2} + \underset{\text{3 moles}}{3H_2} \rightleftharpoons \underset{\text{2 moles}}{2NH_3} \qquad (20\text{-}9A)$$

Equation (20-9A) shows that 1 mole of nitrogen plus 3 moles of hydrogen produce 2 moles of ammonia, or that 4 molecules on the left produce 2 molecules on the right. What happens if the pressure on the equilibrium mixture is increased? The concentration of all the gases (N_2, H_2, and NH_3) will be increased. However, the effect of the increase on the concentration of N_2 and H_2 will be greater than that on NH_3. This is the result of their larger coefficients, which appear as exponents in the equilibrium constant. As a result, the increase in the reaction rate to the right will be greater than the increase to the left, and eventually a new equilibrium will be reached with the shift in the point of equilibrium to the right. That is, the yield of ammonia will be increased if the

Recall . . .
How does Boyle's law apply here?

pressure is increased. But again it must be emphasized that a change in pressure (or concentration) does not affect the equilibrium constant K.

Let us now consider the reaction that occurs between the gases oxygen and nitrogen. In the presence of a suitable catalyst these gases react to form the gas nitric oxide (NO), which in turn decomposes to nitrogen and oxygen. That is, it is a reversible reaction,

$$\underset{\text{1 mole}}{N_2} + \underset{\text{1 mole}}{O_2} \rightleftharpoons \underset{\text{2 moles}}{2NO} \qquad (20\text{-}10)$$

What will be the effect of increasing the pressure in this reaction? Again the concentration of all three gases are increased and so the rates of both the forward and backward reactions are also increased. Will the percentage yield of nitric oxide be increased in this case? Since 1 mole of O_2 plus 1 mole of N_2 produce 2 moles of nitric oxide (which means that the exponents add up to the same sum in the numerator and denominator of the equilibrium constant), an increase in pressure will increase the speeds of the forward and backward reactions equally. That is, a change in pressure favors neither reactants nor product, and the percentage yield of NO is not changed.

Speculate . . .
What would be the effect of increasing the pressure upon gases that react to form products with an increase in the number of molecules?

The Effect of Changing Temperature

When nitrogen and hydrogen combine to form ammonia, heat is evolved; it is an exothermic reaction:

$$N_2 + 3H_2 \rightleftharpoons 2NH_3 + \text{heat} \qquad (20\text{-}9B)$$

What happens if the temperature of the equilibrium mixture is raised? The application of heat (or raising the temperature of the equilibrium mixture) will favor the reaction that absorbs heat; that is, the decomposition of ammonia. Thus, if the temperature of the mixture is raised, the concentration of NH_3 is decreased and the concentrations of N_2 and H_2 are increased. Or, considering the fraction

$$\frac{[NH_3]^2}{[N_2][H_2]^3}$$

it is apparent that a rise in temperature decreases the numerator and increases the denominator. Therefore, the value of the equilibrium constant changes with temperature. That is why the particular temperature of reaction must be stated whenever the value of K is listed in tables.

Finally, let us again consider the effect of temperature change upon the nitrogen, oxygen, nitric oxide reaction,

$$N_2 + O_2 \rightleftharpoons 2NO \qquad (20\text{-}10A)$$

This is an endothermic reaction and so the equation can be written as

$$N_2 + O_2 \rightleftharpoons 2NO - \text{heat} \qquad (20\text{-}10B)$$

Since nitric oxide is formed with an absorption of heat, raising the temperature of the reaction mixture will favor the formation of more nitric oxide. Will the equilibrium constant for this reaction be increased or decreased by raising the temperature?

Applications of Le Châtelier's Principle

Le Châtelier's principle is also applicable if stresses are applied to systems in chemical equilibrium. Let us apply Le Châtelier's principle to reaction (20-9).

$$N_2 + 3H_2 \rightleftharpoons 2NH_3 \qquad (20\text{-}9)$$

A Pressure Change

In considering the effect of a change in pressure, we must know the relative number of molecules in the reactants and products:

$$\underset{4n\ \text{molecules}}{N_2 + 3H_2} \rightleftharpoons \underset{2n\ \text{molecules}}{2NH_3} \qquad (20\text{-}9C)$$

Since $4n$ molecules of N_2 and H_2 form $2n$ molecules of NH_3, it is apparent that if these gases are in a closed container, the greater the amount of NH_3 produced the smaller will be the total pressure exerted by the gas mixture. You recall that Le Châtelier's principle states: *If a stress is applied to a system in equilibrium the point of equilibrium will shift in the direction that relieves the stress.* If the pressure upon this gas system is increased, will the yield of ammonia be increased or decreased? The increase in pressure constitutes a stress and therefore, according to Le Châtelier, a reaction will take place to relieve the stress; that is, to diminish the pressure. Hence the equilibrium will shift to the right and the yield of ammonia will be increased. By the same argument, if the pressure is decreased, the yield of ammonia will also be decreased.

A Temperature Change

Bear in mind that the formation of NH_3 is an exothermic reaction and the decomposition of ammonia is an endothermic reaction. Suppose the temperature of the reaction mixture is lowered. Is the yield of ammonia increased or decreased? The lowering of the temperature constitutes a stress and therefore the equilibrium shifts to relieve this stress; that is, to raise the temperature by evolving heat. Therefore the reaction to the right is favored and the yield of ammonia is increased. By the same argument, the yield of ammonia is decreased if the temperature of the gas mixture is raised.

Combining the effects of pressure and temperature, we predict that a good yield of ammonia would be obtained if the pressure is high and the temperature is low. This prediction is confirmed by the experimental data in Table 20-2.

At first sight it looks as though a temperature of 200°C and a pressure of 200 atm would be the best conditions for the preparation of ammonia on an industrial scale. Actually, however, in the Haber process (Figs. 20-3 and 20-4) mixture of N_2 and H_2 is heated in

Fig. 20-3 A simplified diagram of the Haber process. Nitrogen and hydrogen combine in the catalyst chamber. The ammonia is cooled, liquefied, and drawn off from time to time. The residual gas mixture of nitrogen and hydrogen is recirculated through the catalyst chamber. Why?

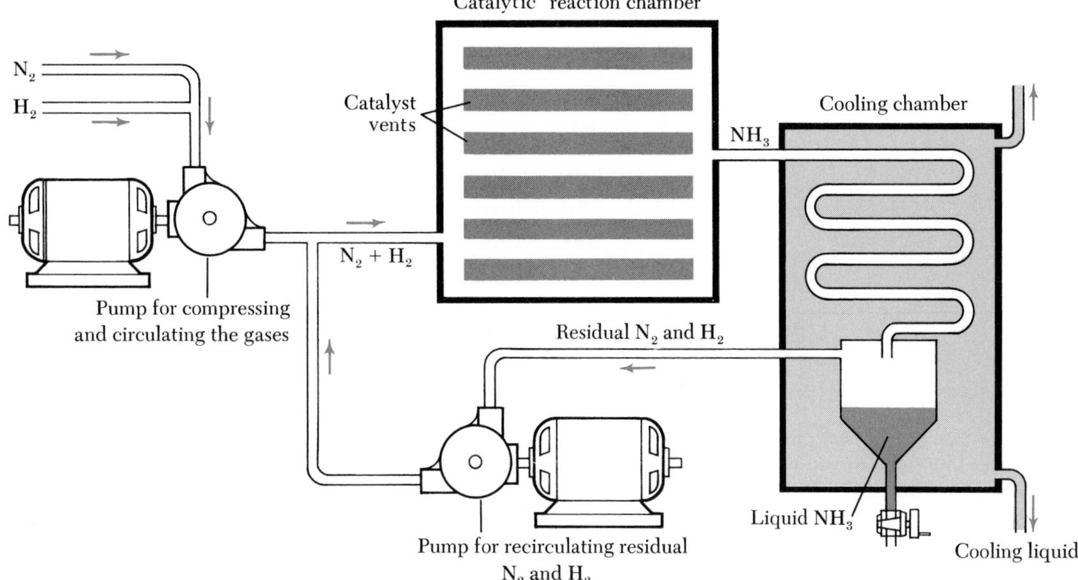

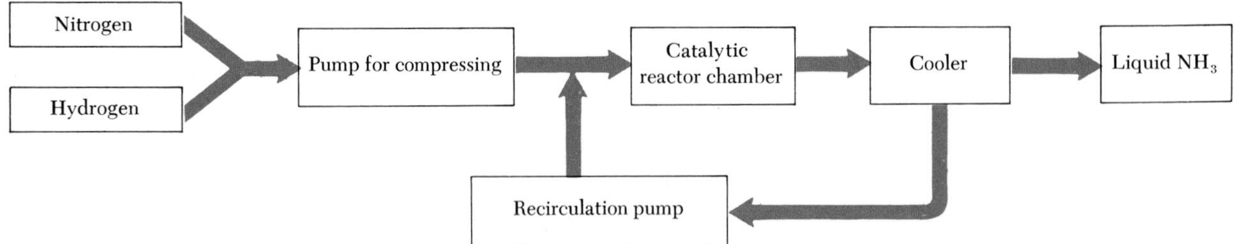

Fig. 20-4 Flow diagram of the Haber process.

the presence of a catalyst at a temperature of about 500°C and under a pressure of about 700 atm. Under these conditions the yield of NH_3 is only about 25%. Can you give a reason for the three conditions: (1) a catalyst, (2) a temperature of 500°C rather than 200°C, and (3) a pressure of 700 atm rather than 200 atm?

Research . . .
Look up the Haber method and at least two others for production of NH_3. Why was the old name for ammonia "spirits of hartshorn"?

Table 20-2 Ammonia yields at varying temperatures and pressures

	Yield of ammonia, %	
Temperature, °C	Pressure: 1 atm	Pressure: 200 atm
200	15.3	86.0
500	0.13	17.6
1000	0.004	0.9

Ionic Equilibria

Ionic compounds in aqueous solution may be strong or weak electrolytes. Hydrochloric acid, you recall, is a strong electrolyte and in dilute solution it is found that the molar concentration of hydrogen ion is practically the same as the molar concentration of the hydrogen chloride in the gas from which the solution was prepared. Thus we assume that hydrogen chloride is completely ionized in dilute solution; the solution contains practically no molecules of hydrogen chloride. What is the equilibrium constant for this compound? Or rather what is its *ionization constant*, since this is the term used for ionic compounds? As previously stated, the concentration of molecular HCl, [HCl], in the dilute acid solution is nearly zero. Therefore the equilibrium constant for

$$\frac{[H^+][Cl^-]}{[HCl]}$$

is infinitely large; that is, it approaches infinity. Thus for strong electrolytes the term ionization constant really has no meaning.

Note . . .
For convenience, acetic acid is frequently written HAc rather than CH_3COOH, and the acetate ion is likewise indicated by Ac^- rather than CH_3COO^-. Such "shorthand" notation is often used by chemists.

What about the constants for weak electrolytes? Let us consider a dilute solution of a weak acid—acetic acid, for example,

$$CH_3COOH \rightleftharpoons H^+(aq) + CH_3COO^- \qquad (20\text{-}11)$$

In this case, the concentration of hydrogen ion, which can be easily measured, is only a very small fraction of the concentration of the undissociated acid, which can also be measured. We therefore conclude that a dilute solution of acetic acid contains a high percentage of undissociated molecules. Table 20-3 presents experimental values for equilibrium concentrations (in moles per liter) of acetic acid molecules and hydrogen ions at 25 °C. The values of undiluted [HAc] and $[H^+]$ were measured and [HAc] in the dilute solution was computed by difference. Since all solutions of electrolytes are electrically neutral, we now have sufficient information to calculate a value for the ionization constant K_i of acetic acid at 25°C. Thus:

$$[H^+] = [CH_3COO^-]$$

$$K_i = \frac{[H^+][CH_3COO^-]}{[CH_3COOH]}$$

$$= \frac{0.317 \times 10^{-3} \times 0.317 \times 10^{-3}}{5.59 \times 10^{-3}}$$

$$= 1.80 \times 10^{-5} \text{ or } 0.000018$$

Table 20-3

Equilibrium concentration of acetic acid molecules and hydrogen ions in dilute solution

Substance	Equilibrium concentration, *M*
[HAc], initial	5.91×10^{-3}
$[H^+]$, measured in dilute solution	0.317×10^{-3}
[HAc], in dilute solution	5.59×10^{-3}

Ionization Constants of Bases

Strong bases such as NaOH and KOH are completely ionized both as solids and in solution. Therefore, ionization constants for strong bases have little or no meaning. However, if ammonia gas is dissolved in water it acts as a weak base (and the water acts as a weak acid). The reaction is

$$NH_3 + H_2O \rightleftharpoons NH_4^+ + OH^- \qquad (20\text{-}12)$$

Concentration measurements show that ammonium ions and hydroxide ions are in equilibrium with ammonia molecules. Hence,

$$K = \frac{[NH_4^+][OH^-]}{[NH_3]}$$

In one experiment, the following equilibrium concentrations (in moles/liter) were determined at 25°C:

$$\text{Initial } [NH_3] \text{ (measured)} = 0.0100 = 1.00 \times 10^{-2}$$

$$[OH^-] \text{ at equilibrium (measured)} = 0.00041 = 4.1 \times 10^{-4}$$

Hence

$$[NH_4^+] \text{ at equilibrium} = 0.00041 = 4.1 \times 10^{-4}$$

and

$$\begin{aligned}[NH_3] \text{ at equilibrium (by difference)} &= 0.0100 - 0.0004 \\ &= 0.00096 \\ &= 9.6 \times 10^{-3}\end{aligned}$$

We then can calculate K_i as follows:

$$\begin{aligned}K_i &= \frac{[NH_4^+][OH^-]}{[NH_3]} \\ &= \frac{4.1 \times 10^{-4} \times 4.1 \times 10^{-4}}{9.6 \times 10^{-3}} \\ &= 1.75 \times 10^{-5}\end{aligned}$$

It should be observed that the ionization constants of $CH_3COOH(aq)$ and $NH_3(aq)$ are very small. Indeed, small constants are typical of all weak acids and bases. But this is what we expect since ionization takes place to only a slight extent.

The Ionization Constant for Water

In Chapter 16 you learned that water ionizes to a very slight degree and that molecules and ions are in equilibrium.

$$H_2O \rightleftharpoons H^+(aq) + OH^-$$

Clearly, water has an ionization constant which can be computed from

$$K = \frac{[H^+][OH^-]}{[H_2O]}$$

where H_2O represents the concentration of nonionized water. One liter of water weighs approximately 1000 g and therefore its molar concentration is

$$\frac{1000\ \text{g}}{18\ \text{g/mole}} = 55.5\ M$$

Since the molar concentrations of $H^+(aq)$ and OH^- are extremely small, there is no appreciable difference between the molar concentration of pure water (which is slightly ionized) and nonionized water. Hence, $[H_2O] = 55.5\,M$ which is a constant. Therefore.

$$K = \frac{[H^+][OH^-]}{55.5}$$

Or,

$$[H^+] \times [OH^-] = K \times 55.5$$

But $K \times 55.5$ is the product of two constants and is therefore also a constant. This constant is accepted as the ionization constant for water, and is designated K_W rather than K. And, as was stated in Chapter 16

$$K_W = [H^+] \times [OH^-] = 10^{-14}$$

Solubility Product

If a solution of silver nitrate is added to a solution of sodium chloride, a white precipitate of silver chloride is instantly formed. The reaction can be written:

$$Ag^+(aq) + NO_3^-(aq) + Na^+(aq) + Cl^-(aq) \longrightarrow AgCl(s) + Na^+(aq) + NO_3^-(aq) \quad (20\text{-}15)$$

Or, omitting spectator ions,

$$Ag^+(aq) + Cl^-(aq) \longrightarrow AgCl(s) \quad (20\text{-}15A)$$

Silver chloride is said to be insoluble. However, there is no such thing as a completely insoluble substance—all "insoluble" compounds are slightly soluble. For instance, a slight amount of solid silver chloride dissolves, and in a saturated solution the rate of solution equals the rate of recrystallization:

$$AgCl(s) \rightleftharpoons Ag^+ + Cl^- \quad (20\text{-}15B)$$

Here is another example of ionic equilibrium, and the equilibrium constant can be expressed as

$$K_1 = \frac{[Ag^+][Cl^-]}{[AgCl]}$$

However, in this case the denominator is a solid and its concentration is therefore unchangeable. Hence, [AgCl] is a constant, K_2.

Therefore,

$$K_1 = \frac{[Ag^+][Cl^-]}{K_2} \text{ or } [Ag^+][Cl^-] = K_1 \times K_2 = K_{sp}$$

This new constant, called the *solubility product*, is designated $\boldsymbol{K_{sp}}$ Thus, the term solubility product applies only to slightly soluble ionic compounds and *it is a product of the molar concentrations of the ions in a saturated solution, each concentration raised to the power of its coefficient in the balanced equation.* Units are usually omitted from the $\boldsymbol{K_{sp}}$ values.

Example 20-2

The solubility of silver chloride is found to be 0.00187 g/l at 25°C.
Calculate the value of K_{sp} for silver chloride.

Solution

In moles per liter the solubility is

$$\frac{1.87 \times 10^{-3} \text{ g/l}}{143.5 \text{ g/mole}} = 1.3 \times 10^{-5} \text{ mole/l}$$

From this we can calculate a value for the K_{sp} of silver chloride:

$$[Ag^+] = [Cl^-] = 1.3 \times 10^{-5}$$

Therefore,

$$\begin{aligned} K_{sp} &= [Ag^+][Cl^-] \\ &= 1.3 \times 10^{-5} \times 1.3 \times 10^{-5} \\ &= 1.7 \times 10^{-10} \end{aligned}$$

Thus, at equilibrium the product of the concentrations of Ag^+ and Cl^- must be equal to 1.7×10^{-10}. If the value of $[Ag^+] \times [Cl^-]$ is greater than 1.7×10^{-10}, some of the ions Ag^+ and Cl^- will be precipitated as AgCl and precipitation will continue until $[Ag^+] \times [Cl^-]$ equals 1.7×10^{-10}. Conversely, if the product of the ion concentrations is less than the K_{sp} value, some solid AgCl will dissolve until the product of the ion concentrations equals 1.7×10^{-10}, when ionic equilibrium will be restored.

Solubility Products of Various Compounds

As one would expect, solubility product values are small numbers. These values can be found in a book of tables such as the *Handbook of Chemistry and Physics*. The solubility products of a few common compounds are given in Table 20-4.

If the solubility product of a compound is known, the molar concentrations of the ions in a saturated solution or the solubility of the salt can be computed, as in Example 20-3.

Table 20-4
Solubility products of common compounds

Compound	K_{sp} at 25 °C
AgCl	1.7×10^{-10}
AgBr	7.7×10^{-13}
$BaCO_3$	4.9×10^{-9}
$CaCO_3$	4.8×10^{-9}
$PbCO_3$	1.6×10^{-13}
$BaSO_4$	1.5×10^{-9}
$PbSO_4$	1.9×10^{-8}
$Mg(OH)_2$	1.5×10^{-11}
$Fe(OH)_2$	1.6×10^{-14}
$Fe(OH)_3$	1.1×10^{-36}
ZnS	4.5×10^{-24}
PbS	3.4×10^{-28}
CuS	8.5×10^{-43}

Example 20-3

What are the solubility of AgBr and the concentration of Ag^+ ion in a saturated solution of AgBr at 25 °C?

For AgBr, $K_{sp} = 7.7 \times 10^{-13}$.

Solution

In a saturated solution

$$[Ag^+][Br^-] = 7.7 \times 10^{-13}$$

But,

$$[Ag^+] = [Br^-] = \text{solubility } (S) \text{ of AgBr in moles/liter}$$

Therefore,

$$K_{sp} = [Ag^+][Br^-] = S^2 = 7.7 \times 10^{-13}$$

and

$$[S] = \sqrt{7.7 \times 10^{-13}} = \sqrt{77 \times 10^{-14}} = 8.7 \times 10^{-7} \text{ mole/l}$$

Thus, $[S]$ is $8.7 \times 10^{-7}\ M$. Since $[S] = [Ag^+]$, the concentration of silver ions in the saturated solution also is $8.7 \times 10^{-7}\ M$.

"Leave us alone! The equilibrium has shifted!"

The Common Ion Effect

As stated earlier, the equilibrium of a reversible reaction can be shifted by changing the temperature or concentration. It can also be shifted by adding a common ion. Adding a common ion means the addition of an ion that is already present in the solution. Thus, acetate ion is the common ion in solutions of acetic acid and sodium acetate. What happens if a solution of sodium acetate is added to dilute acetic acid?

The equation representing the ionization of acetic acid is

$$CH_3\,COOH \rightleftharpoons H^+(aq) + CH_3COO^-(aq) \qquad (20\text{-}11)$$

and the ionization constant is

$$K_i = \frac{[H^+][CH_3COO^-]}{[CH_3COOH]}$$
$$= 1.8 \times 10^{-5}$$

Sodium acetate is completely ionized so that the addition of even a small quantity of this solution greatly increases the concentration of acetate ion. The addition of acetate ion constitutes a stress in the reaction (Eq. 20-11), and to relieve the stress (according to Le Châtelier) some of the excess acetate ions will combine with hydrogen ions to form molecules of acetic acid. That is, the concentration of hydrogen ion is decreased and the point of equilibrium is shifted to the left. This effect is known as the *common ion effect*.

The common ion effect can also be deduced from the mass-action law. If sodium acetate is added to acetic acid, $[Ac^-]$ is greatly increased and therefore the ratio $[H^+]\,[Ac^-]/[HAc]$ is temporary increased beyond 1.8×10^{-5}. But since the ionization constant cannot be changed, the effect of increasing $[Ac^-]$ is to decrease $[H^+]$ in the numerator and to increase $[HAc]$ in the denominator. This is borne out by pH measurements. The pH of 0.1 M acetic acid is approximately 3, but the pH of a mixture of 0.1 M acetic acid and 0.1 M sodium acetate is approximately 5, an increase by a factor of 100.

The common ion effect applies to all kinds of ionic equilibria and affects the solubility of solutes. What, for example, is the effect of adding a solution of sodium chloride to a saturated solution of silver chloride? Here the common ion is chloride ion. If Cl^- is added, in

$$AgCl(s) \rightleftharpoons Ag^+ + Cl^- \qquad (20\text{-}15B)$$

the concentration of Cl^- is increased; and therefore, by Le Châtelier's principle the equilibrium is shifted to the left. That is, silver chloride is less soluble in a solution of sodium chloride than in pure water. The effect of adding solid AgCl to a 0.1 M solution of NaCl can also be computed. For silver chloride,

$$K_{sp} = [Ag^+]\,[Cl^-] = 10^{-10}$$

and since $[Ag^+] = [Cl^-]$ in a saturated solution of AgCl in pure water, $[Ag^+] = 10^{-5}\,M$ in pure water. In 0.1 M NaCl the $[Cl^-]$ is 0.1 M. But,

$$[Ag^+] \times 0.1 = 10^{-10}$$

and

$$[Ag^+] = 10^{-9}\,M$$

Therefore the concentration of Ag^+ is reduced from $10^{-5}\,M$ in water solution to $10^{-9}\,M$ in a solution of 0.1 M sodium chloride. That is, the concentration of silver ion is reduced by a factor of 10,000.

Summary

In a closed system, a chemical reaction is always reversible. Starting with only reactants, the forward reaction proceeds relatively rapidly but the reverse reaction gradually speeds up until its rate eventually equals the steadily decreasing rate of the forward reaction. The reaction is then said to be in a state of equilibrium. If the system is open, rather than closed, the reverse reaction may or may not be able to occur. For example, if a gaseous product escapes from the system, the reverse action cannot take place.

For the general reaction,

$$aA + bB \rightleftharpoons cC + dD$$

the law of chemical equilibrium can be expressed as

$$\frac{[C]^c \times [D]^d}{[A]^a \times [B]^b} = K \text{ (a constant)}$$

For a given reaction at a given temperature the numerical value of the constant does not change. Therefore, if one of the concentrations is changed, the changes that occur in the other three concentrations can be computed.

Le Châtelier's principle also enables us to predict the effect of changes in pressure or temperature upon the position of equilibrium with respect to the midpoint.

Factual Recall

1. Express the equilibrium constant for the reaction,

   $$A + 3B \rightleftharpoons 2C + 2D$$

   Show all the steps in your argument.

2. Explain why, in the reaction,

   $$N_2 + 3H_2 \rightleftharpoons 2NH_3$$

   the equilibrium constant is *not* changed if the applied pressure is increased.

3. Show why the equilibrium constant in the reaction

   $$N_2 + 3H_2 \rightleftharpoons 2NH_3$$

   is *not* changed if the concentration of a reactant is changed.

4. Explain the effect of raising the temperature on the equilibrium constant for the reaction

   $$\text{heat energy} + N_2 + O_2 \rightleftharpoons 2NO$$

5. In the reversible reaction,

   $$A + B \rightleftharpoons C + D$$

   the yield of C and D is poor. If A is expensive and B is cheap, how would you proceed to convert A more completely into C and D?

6. In the reversible reaction,

   $$A + B \rightleftharpoons C + D - \text{heat energy}$$

   would raising the temperature improve the yields of C and D? Explain.

7. The ionization constant for the reaction,

   $$NH_3 + H_2O \rightleftharpoons NH_4^+ + OH^-$$

   is 1.8×10^{-5}. What does this mean?

Apply Your Knowledge!

1. Compute the ionization constant for a weak acid (HA) if a 0.100 *M* solution of it in water is 4% ionized.
2. Compute the ionization constant for a weak base (MOH) if a 2.0*M* solution of it in water is 1% ionized.
3. Compute the percent ionization of a 1 *M* solution of a weak acid (HA) if the ionization constant of the acid is 10^{-7}.
4. Find the percent ionization of 0.050 *M* NH_4OH, given the ionization constant of 1.8×10^{-5} for the weak base.

Find Out!

1. Look up the process for commercial production of sulfuric acid and describe if any of the conditions discussed in connection with the Haber process apply.
2. If the constant for ionization of an acid is small, the amount which ionizes may be ignored in determining the concentration of H^+ ion in a solution, but if it is large it should be considered. Convince yourself that this is true by working these two problems in which the initial concentration of the acid is 0.1 and the equilibrium concentration is $0.1 - [H^+]$.
   (*a*) K_A for $C_6H_5COOH = 6.6 \times 10^{-5}$ $(C_6H_5COOH \rightleftharpoons C_6H_5COO^- + H^+)$
   (*b*) K_A for $HSO_4^- = 1.3 \times 10^{-2}$ $(HSO_4^- \rightleftharpoons H^+ + SO_4^{2-})$

Suggested Readings

Campbell, J.A. *Why Do Chemical Reactions Occur.* Englewood Cliffs, N.J.: Prentice-Hall. (Paperback)

King, E.L., *How Chemical Reactions Occur.* New York: W.A. Benjamin, 1964. (Paperback)

Mahan, B.H., *Elementary Chemical Thermodynamics.* New York: W.A. Benjamin. (Paperback)

Wilson, M., *Energy.* New York: Time. Inc., 1963. (Paperback)

UNIT VII

VERTICAL COLUMNS OF ELEMENTS (CHEMICAL FAMILIES) AND HORIZONTAL ROWS OF ELEMENTS

ATOMS ARE LARGELY COMPOSED of three fundamental particles—protons, neutrons, and electrons. As the number of protons in each nucleus increases, one at a time, the number of neutrons in the nucleus increases proportionately; otherwise the nucleus would not remain intact. As the number of protons in the nucleus increases, the number of electrons in the outer orbitals must also increase in order to keep the atom electrically neutral.

As the number of electrons increases, a similar pattern of outer *s* and *p* orbitals recurs again and again. Atoms with the same electron patterns are arranged in vertical columns, and a vertical column of elements constitutes a chemical family.

Chemical properties of elements are determined by the electron configurations of their atoms. Therefore, we would expect elements in the same family to have similar properties. However, the properties, while similar, are by no means identical. This is because the distances between nucleus and valence electrons vary from atom to atom and, in consequence, the forces that hold the electrons in their orbitals also vary.

HISTORICAL CHEMISTRY LABORATORY

The following extracts are taken from the writings of Sir Humphry Davy who isolated both sodium and potassium in metallic form.

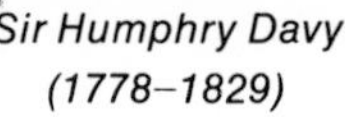

Sir Humphry Davy
(1778–1829)

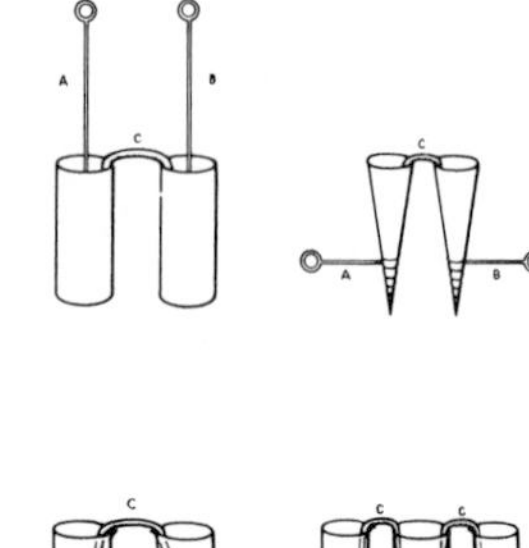

Davy apparatus

A small piece of potash, which had been exposed for a few seconds to the atmosphere so as to give conducting power to the surface, was placed upon an insulated disc of platina, connected with the negative side of the battery of the power of 250 of 6 and 4, in a state of intense activity; and a platina wire, communicating with the positive side, was brought in contact with the upper surface of the alkali. The whole apparatus was in the open atmosphere.

Under these circumstances a vivid action was soon observed to take place. The potash began to fuse at both its points of electrization. There was a violent effervescence at the upper surface; at the lower, or negative, surface, there was no liberation of elastic fluid; but small globules having a high metallic lustre, and being precisely similar in visible characters to quicksilver, appeared, some of which burnt with explosion and bright flame, as soon as they were formed, and others remained, and were merely tarnished, and finally covered by a white film which formed on their surfaces.

These globules, numerous experiments soon shewed to be the substance I was in search of, and a peculiar inflammable principle the basis of potash. I found that the platina was in no way connected with the result, except as the medium for exhibiting the electrical powers of decomposition; and a substance of the same kind was produced when pieces of copper, silver, gold, plumbago, or even charcoal were employed for compleating the circuit. (Oct. 6, 1807)

With the battery of 100 of 6 inches in full activity I obtained good results from pieces of potash weighing from 40 to 70 grains, and of a thickness which made the distance of the electrified metallic surfaces nearly a quarter of an inch; but with a similar power it was impossible to produce the effects of decomposition on pieces of soda of more than 15 or 20 grains in weight, and that only when the distance between the wires was about one-eighth or one-tenth of an inch. The substance produced from potash remained fluid at the temperature of the atmosphere at the time of its production; that from soda, which was fluid in the degree of heat of the alkali during its formation, became solid on cooling, and appeared having the lustre of silver.

*From Davy, H., "The Decomposition of the Fixed Alkalies and Alkaline Earths," Alembic Club Reprint No.6, Chicago: Univ. Chicago Press, 1902. **

*Weeks, M.E., and H. Leicester *Discovery of the Elements*, Easton, Pa.: J. Chem. Ed., 1968. (pp. 444-445)

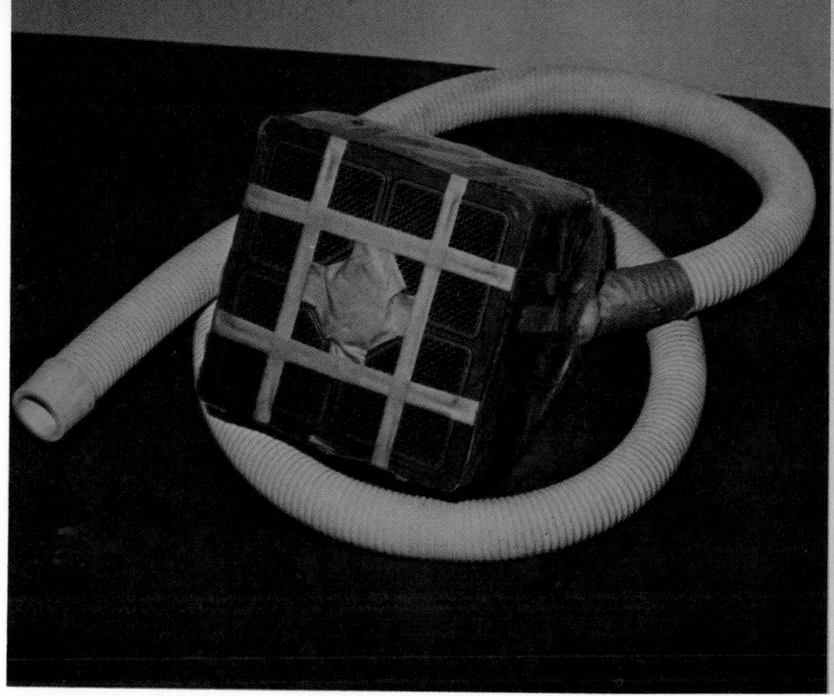

CHAPTER 21

THE ALKALI METALS

THE PERIODIC CLASSIFICATION of the elements was discussed in Chapters 6 and 7. We shall now discuss two families in some detail, the alkali metals in this chapter and the halogens in Chapter 22.

The Alkali Metals

The family of alkali metals consists of the six elements lithium, sodium, potassium, rubidium, cesium, and francium. All these elements are exceedingly active chemically so, as one would expect, they do not occur free in nature. Sodium and potassium are abundant, occurring as Na^+ and K^+ ions (Fig. 21-1). Lithium is also fairly common in nature, occurring as Li^+ ions. Rubidium and cesium, however, are rare elements. They were not discovered until 1860 when two German scientists, R.W. Bunsen (1811-1899) and G. R. Kirchhoff (1824-1887), using their newly invented spectroscope, spotted some unfamiliar spectra which, in turn, led to the discovery of these elements. Francium is radioactive and has been

Infer . . .
How did francium receive its name?

Hypothesize . . .
What is the significance of the measurement of atomic radii? Would the radius of a hydrogen atom in diatomic hydrogen be of a different length than that of a hydrogen atom in HF gas? Under what conditions is the length of atomic radii measured? Consider also under what conditions *ionic* radii are measured. Would you expect the radius of a certain ion to be different in length in different compounds?

produced only in minute quantities. Because it is highly unstable, its active life is little more than 60 minutes and little is known about its chemical properties. Therefore, francium will not be discussed extensively here.

Some Common Properties of the Alkali Metals

A characteristic property of the alkali metals is that they are soft and can easily be cut with a knife. They have relatively low melting points, much lower than the melting points of metals in other families. They are also good conductors of electricity and heat. Chemically they are very active, especially with chlorine, oxygen, and water. When freshly cut, their surfaces are bright and silvery. However, they tarnish rapidly, and, to slow down oxidation, they are generally stored under kerosene.

Table 21-1 Properties of the alkali metals

Element	Z	Melting point, °C	Oxidation number	Radius of atom, Å	Radius of ion, Å	Ionization energy, kcal/mole
Lithium	3	179	+1	1.33	0.68	124
Sodium	11	98	+1	1.54	0.97	119
Potassium	19	63	+1	1.96	1.33	100
Rubidium	37	39	+1	2.06	1.47	96
Cesium	55	29	+1	2.18	1.67	90

Notice that, with the exception of the oxidation number, there is a gradual change in the properties: the melting points gradually decrease from 179 °C for Li to 29 °C for Cs; the radii of both atoms and ions gradually increase, while the value of the ionization energies of the elements gradually decreases. How can these changes be explained? Clearly they are determined by the structure of the atoms; that is, by the composition of their nuclei and their electron configurations.

Properties and Atomic Structure

Investigate . . .
What percentage of your blood is NaCl?

As you learned in Chapter 7, each of the alkali metals has a single valence electron in its outermost *s* orbital. The energy needed to dislodge the valence electron (that is, to ionize the atom) depends upon at least three factors: (1) the charge on the nucleus, (2) the distance of the outer electron from the nucleus, and (3) the shield-

(*a*)

(*b*)

Fig. 21-1 (*a*) The Bonneville salt flats in Utah are at the location of an extinct prehistoric lake. The surface of the salt is so hard that the area is used for an auto race track. (*b*) A gallery in the Avery Island (Louisiana) salt mine. The ceiling here is 140 feet above the floor and the truck in the background is dwarfed in these surroundings.

ing effect. For example, the nuclear charge on a sodium atom is +11, whereas on a lithium atom the nuclear charge is +3. Thus, considering only the nuclear charge, electrons would be attracted more strongly by sodium atoms than by lithium atoms. However, the distance from nucleus to valence electron is greater for sodium than for lithium, and the greater the distance the weaker is the attraction for electrons. Moreover, a sodium atom has eight more electrons between the nucleus and the valence electron than has a lithium atom. These intervening electrons repel the valence electron and so make it easier for it to become detached. This effect is called a shielding effect. Why the word *shielding*? The intervening electrons tend to shield the outermost electron from the attractive force of the nucleus. As compared with a lithium atom, the shielding and distance effects for a sodium atom more than offset the effect of its greater nuclear charge. Thus a sodium atom loses its valence electron more readily than does a lithium atom and is, in consequence, more active chemically. In short, lithium is the least chemically active of the alkali metals and francium is the most active. Indeed francium, in the lower left corner of the periodic table, is the most active of all metals.

Ionization Energies of the Alkali Metals

Since the valence electrons of the alkali metals are only loosely held, it should not be surprising that their ionization energies are relatively low, much lower than the values of corresponding elements in other families. This is shown in Table 21-2.

Table 21-2 Ionization energies of lithium and sodium compared with those of neighboring elements.

Element	Z	Electron configuration	Ionization energy, kcal/mole
He	2	$1s^2$	567
Li	3	$1s^2 2s^1$	124
Be	4	$1s^2 2s^2$	215
Ne	10	$1s^2 2s^2 2p^6$	497
Na	11	$1s^2 2s^2 2p^6 3s^1$	119
Mg	12	$1s^2 2s^2 2p^6 3s^2$	176

Notice also that the ionization energy values of the alkali metals steadily decrease in value as we go down the group. But this is to be expected. Why? The low values of the ionization energies account for the physical and chemical properties of the alkali metals. All these metals form a lattice of positively charged kernels and the loosely held valence electrons move freely between the kernels.

What happens if the temperature of a lattice is raised? The kernels vibrate more rapidly, the weak attractive forces of the valence electrons are no longer able to hold them in place, and the lattice melts; that is, the alkali metals have low melting points. How do you explain the fact that the melting point steadily decreases from lithium to cesium?

Some Chemical Properties of the Alkali Metals

Since the valence electrons are only loosely held, it is not surprising that the alkali metals are exceedingly active chemically. They are all powerful reducing agents, as is shown by their reaction with chlorine. Chlorine gas readily combines with hot sodium to form solid sodium chloride with the release of heat energy:

$$2Na(s) + Cl_2(g) \longrightarrow 2NaCl(s) + 197\ \text{kcal} \qquad (21\text{-}1)$$

In this reaction every sodium atom releases its valence electron and every chlorine atom gains an electron. The oppositely charged ions then form the crystalline compound sodium chloride. As you recall, bonding caused by electron transfer is called ionic bonding.

This reaction is typical of all the alkali metals; that is, each of the alkali metals reacts with chlorine to form a crystalline product held together by ionic bonds:

$$2Li + Cl_2 \longrightarrow 2LiCl + 195\ \text{kcal} \qquad (21\text{-}2)$$

$$2K + Cl_2 \longrightarrow 2KCl + 209\ \text{kcal} \qquad (21\text{-}3)$$

$$2Rb + Cl_2 \longrightarrow 2RbCl + 210\ \text{kcal} \qquad (21\text{-}4)$$

$$2Cs + Cl_2 \longrightarrow 2CsCl + 213\ \text{kcal} \qquad (21\text{-}5)$$

The Reaction of Alkali Metals with Water

All the alkali metals react vigorously with water to form hydrogen and a metallic hydroxide. In all these reactions a great deal of heat energy is released, the amount of heat increasing as we go from metal to metal down the list. Indeed, the released heat generated may ignite the escaping hydrogen with explosive violence. Thus, if the test is made, only a small amount of metal should be used, and great care should be exercised in performing the experiment.

Chemically, the reactions of alkali metals with water are similar to those with chlorine. That is, an alkali metal reduces hydrogen in water (with an oxidation number of +1) to free hydrogen. All hydroxides of the alkali metals are soluble in water and the solutions are strongly basic, or alkaline. Indeed, it is this typical reaction with water that gives rise to the generic term *alkali metals*. The equation for the reaction between sodium and water is

$$2Na(s) + 2H_2O \longrightarrow 2Na^+(aq) + 2OH^-(aq) + H_2(g) + \text{heat} \qquad (21\text{-}6)$$

You should now be able to write the equations for the reactions of the other four alkali metals with water.

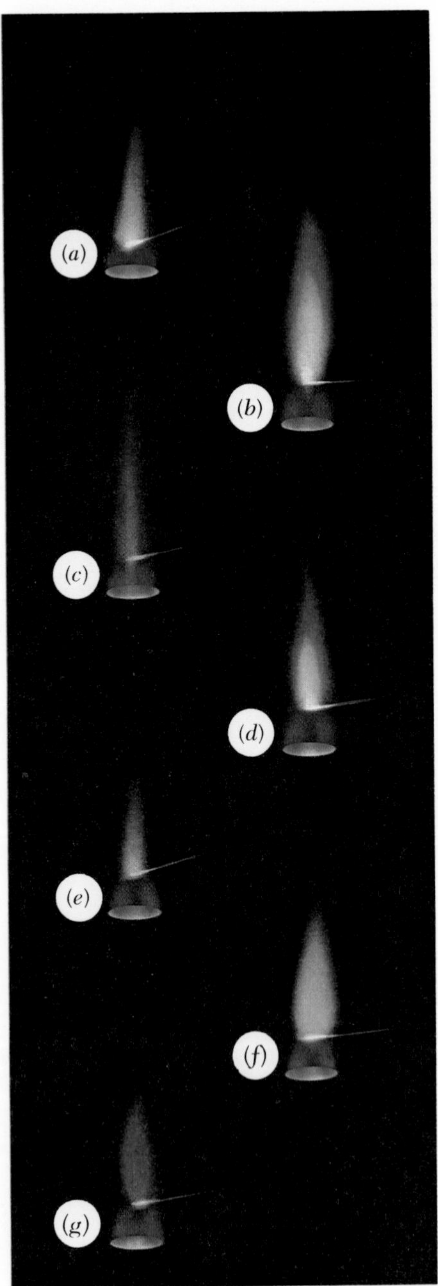

Fig. 21-2 Characteristic colored flames of (*a*) barium, (*b*) calcium, (*c*) copper, (*d*) lithium, (*e*) potassium, (*f*) sodium, and (*g*) strontium.

Spectrum Colors of Vapors of Alkali Metals

Atoms of the alkali metals are easily excited; even the flame of a Bunsen burner can detach the valence electron of the various atoms. As the electrons fall back to lower energy levels, they impart characteristic colors to the flame: lithium, red; sodium, yellow; potassium, violet. These colors can be seen by the eye if a piece of platinum wire is dipped in a salt solution (such as NaCl, KCl, or LiCl) and then held in a Bunsen flame. Indeed this procedure constitutes a so-called *flame test* by which alkali metals can be recognized. See Fig. 21-2.

If the colored vapors are observed through a spectroscope, the line spectra of these metals can be seen. As shown in Fig. 4-2 (page 61), when the red flame of lithium is analyzed in this way it is found to consist of at least four lines, one in the red, one in the yellow, one in the blue, and one in the violet. On the other hand, the yellow flame of sodium is found to consist of one color only—its spectrum consists of two lines very close together in the yellow part of the spectrum. See Fig. 21-4.

Fig. 21-3 The Downs cell.

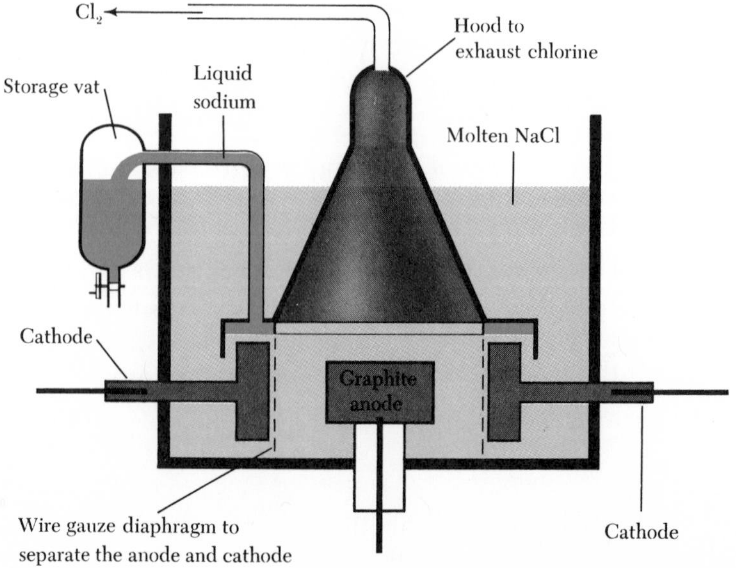

Fig. 21-4 Spectra of some members of Group I: (*a*) potassium, (*b*) rubidium, and (*c*) cesium. Do you see a feature common to each one?

The Occurrence of the Alkali Metals

Since the alkali metals react readily with oxygen and water vapor, they are never found free in nature. However, their salts are stable and many are found in nature, the salts of sodium and potassium being particularly abundant. As you probably know, sodium chloride is found in huge subterranean deposits and it also constitutes about 3% of the weight of sea water. Potassium salts are not abundant in sea water, but the ashes of plants contain a high percentage of potassium carbonate and little or no salts of sodium.

The Preparation of the Alkali Metals

Because the alkali metals are exceedingly reactive, the only economical way to prepare them is by the electrolysis of the fused salt. Sodium, for example, is manufactured on a large scale in a so-called *Downs cell* by the electrolysis of molten sodium chloride.

The Downs cell consists of an iron chamber which contains an iron cathode and a graphite anode. The anode projects through the bottom of the cell and the circular cathode encloses the anode as shown in Fig. 21-3. The melting point of sodium chloride is high, actually 800 °C, and it would be an expensive process to operate at this high temperature. However, if a little sodium carbonate is added, the melting point of the sodium chloride is lowered to about 600 °C, and this is the temperature at which the operation is carried out.

Observe and speculate . . .
Place four test tubes in a rack. Label them NaCl, KCl, LiCl, and HCl. Into each of the first three tubes, pour 10 ml of the appropriate salt solution. Into the fourth tube pour 10 ml of 6 *M* HCl. Obtain a platinum or nichrome wire loop and clean it by heating it strongly in your Bunsen burner flame and then dipping it into the HCl. Repeat the cleaning until you see no flare of yellow flame. Then dip the clean wire into the LiCl solution and heat it in the flame. Observe the color, clean the wire, and then see what happens with each of the other two solutions. Clean the wire with fresh portions of 6 *M* HCl after each flame test. Obtain a square of cobalt (blue) glass. Repeat the experiment, but this time watch the colored flames through the glass. What happens? Why?

The cathode reaction is

$$Na^+ + e^- \longrightarrow Na \qquad (21\text{-}7)$$

The molten sodium rises through a pipe and enters a container where it is protected from air and from which it is drawn off.

The chlorine released at the anode is a valuable by-product and is led off through an outlet and collected.

Uses of Alkali Metals

Since the alkali metals react with air and water, there are relatively few uses for them. Indeed, sodium is the only alkali metal of any commercial importance. Sodium is used in atomic reactors—this is probably its most important use. Liquid sodium is an excellent conductor of heat and (either alone or as an alloy with potassium) is used as a coolant within the atomic furnace, as described in Chapter 29. It is also used to transfer heat from the reactor to water boilers. Sodium has a low melting point so that liquid sodium can be pumped through pipes from the atomic furnace where it picks up heat to water boilers where it releases heat. The heat from the sodium changes water into steam which in turn operates an electric generator. This process is discussed further in Chapter 29. Sodium is also used as a reducing agent in the production of other metals and some organic compounds.

Fig. 21-5 This experimental ion-drive engine is being tested on a block. On February 17, 1970 a satellite powered by such an engine started orbiting earth in a six-month endurance test. Such engines may be used to send unmanned probes to Jupiter and further.

Cesium is used in photocells, in TV color tubes, and in ion drive engines for space vehicles (Fig. 21-5). Ribidium is used like cesium, and is also used for special electric equipment and in coloring glass.

Sodium Compounds

Common salt can be obtained from sea water by evaporation or mined from underground deposits. As you already know, it is one of the most plentiful and useful minerals on earth. It is used in the manufacture of such substances as sodium, chlorine, hydrogen, sodium hydroxide, hydrochloric acid, and sodium carbonate. Sodium carbonate (common name, sal soda) is a basic chemical in a number of industrial processes; it is a necessary ingredient in the manufacture of glass, paper, and laundry soap; it is also used as a

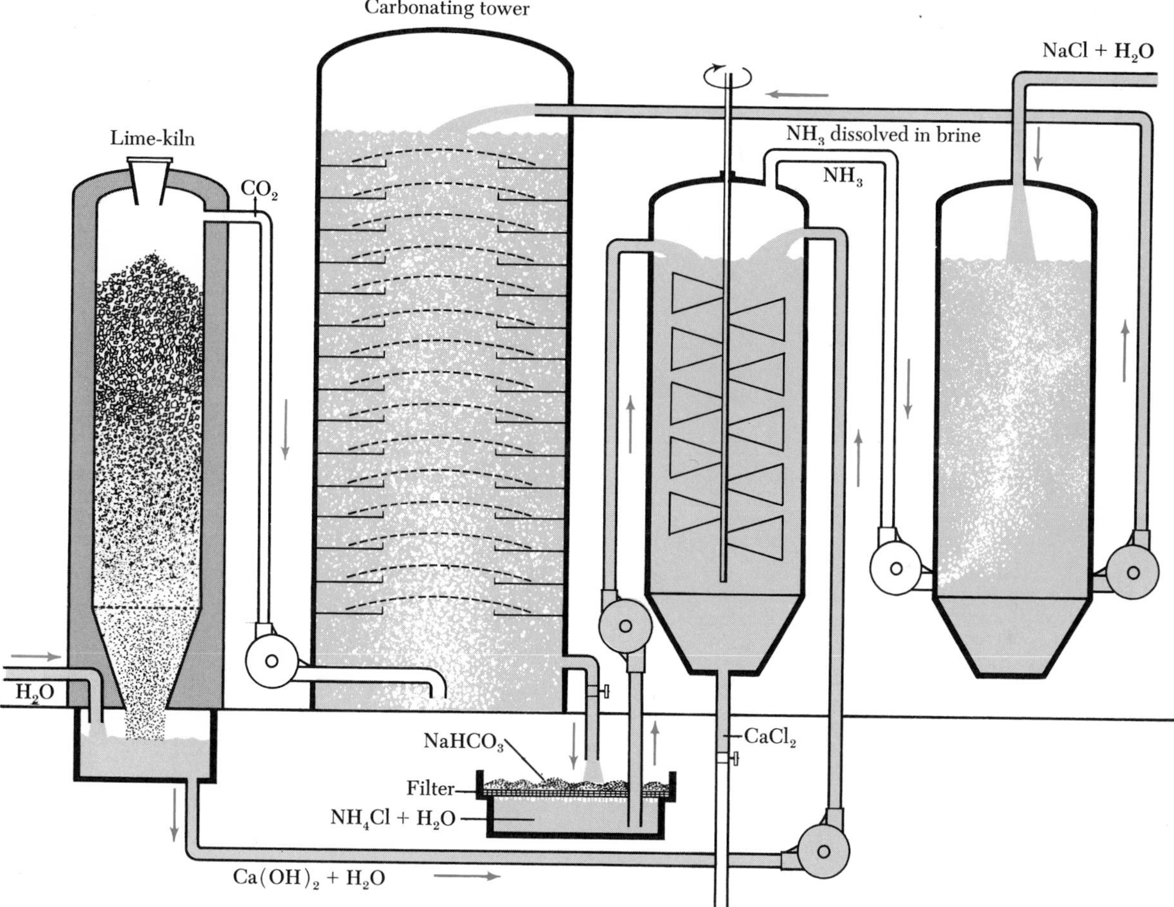

Fig. 21-6 Diagram of a chemical plant for making sodium carbonate by the Solvay process.

water softener. We shall briefly describe the manufacture of sodium carbonate by the *Solvay process*. Fig. 21-6.

The Solvay Process

The Solvay process is an unusually efficient industrial chemical operation in which three raw materials (limestone, common salt, and ammonia) are used in a series of reactions so designed that a product of one reaction becomes a starting substance in another. As a result, waste is avoided and the process becomes a profitable commercial enterprise. Of the three starting materials, limestone and common salt occur in abundance in nature. Therefore they are cheap. Ammonia, however, does not occur in nature. It is manufactured from nitrogen and hydrogen in the Haber process. So ammonia is a relatively expensive starting substance and it must be con-

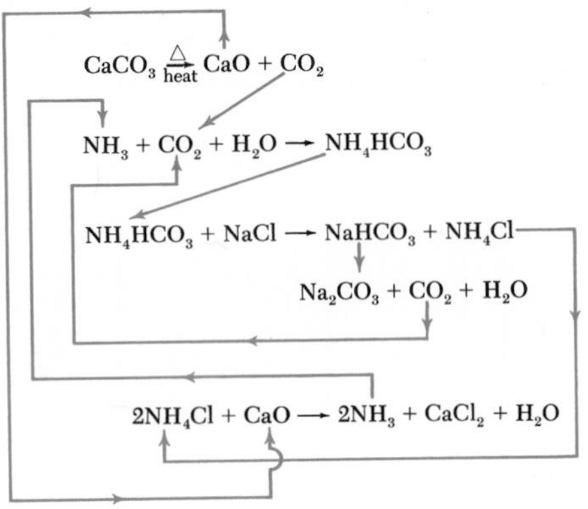

Fig. 21-7 Flowsheet of the Solvay process.

served if the Solvay process is to compete with other industrial methods of manufacturing sodium carbonate.

The following steps constitute the overall Solvay process:

1. Limestone is strongly heated in a lime kiln to yield carbon dioxide and calcium oxide (lime). The reaction is

$$CaCO_3 \longrightarrow CaO(s) + CO_2(g) \tag{21-8}$$

2. In the second operation, gaseous NH_3 and CO_2 are bubbled through a cold saturated solution of NaCl. First the ammonia, carbon dioxide, and water combine to form ammonium ions and bicarbonate ions.

$$NH_3(g) + H_2O + CO_2(g) \rightleftharpoons NH_4^+(aq) + HCO_3^-(aq) \tag{21-9}$$

The HCO_3^- ion then reacts with Na^+ ion to give a precipitate of the only slightly soluble $NaHCO_3$. This is represented by Eq. (21-10):

$$NH_4^+(aq) + HCO_3^-(aq) + Na^+(aq) + Cl^-(aq) \longrightarrow NaHCO_3(s) + NH_4^+(aq) + Cl^-(aq) \tag{21-10}$$

3. The sodium bicarbonate is filtered off and dried. It is then decomposed by heat; sodium carbonate is one of the products of decomposition:

$$2NaHCO_3(s) \longrightarrow Na_2CO_3(s) + H_2O(g) + CO_2(g) \tag{21-11}$$

The CO_2 released in this reaction is used in operation 2 as an additional source of CO_2.

4. The fourth operation is designed to recover the ammonia from the ammonium chloride solution, one of the products in operation 2. To do this, CaO (formed in operation 1) is added to the ammonium chloride solution and the mixture is heated to release the gaseous NH_3:

$$CaO(s) + 2NH_4^+(aq) + 2Cl^-(aq) \longrightarrow CaCl_2(aq) + H_2O(g) + 2NH_3(g) \tag{21-12}$$

The ammonia released in this reaction is used again in operation 2. Thus ammonia, the expensive ingredient, can be used again and again in the cycle of operations. The many ramifications of the various substances are shown in the flowsheet (Fig. 21-7). Notice that five of the products (CaO, CO_2, NH_4HCO_3, $NaHCO_3$, and

NH_3) in one reaction are used again as reactants in another reaction. But one substance, calcium chloride, is not used again—it is the only by-product in the whole series of operations.

Summary

The family of alkali metals constitutes the six elements in Group I of the periodic classification. They are lithium (Li), sodium (Na), potassium (K), rubidium (Rb), cesium (Cs), and francium (Fr). All the alkali metals have a single electron in their outermost *s* orbitals. If this outer electron is dislodged, the atom attains the stable structure of the nearest noble gas. The electron configuration of Li is $1s^2 2s^1$; that of Cs is $1s^2 2s^2 2p^6 3s^2 3p^6 3d^{10} 4s^2 4p^6 4d^{10} 5s^2 5p^6 6s^1$. The valence electron ($6s^1$) for Cs is much less strongly held than the valence electron ($2s^1$) for Li. Therefore cesium is more chemically active than lithium.

By losing an electron, an alkali metal forms an ion with a charge of +1. Ions of alkali metals have the electron orbital structure of the noble gas next door. As a result, ions of alkali metals are exceedingly stable.

Factual Recall

1. Compare the orbital configurations of sodium and potassium.
2. (*a*) What is meant by the term *shielding effect?*
   (*b*) Which have the greater shielding effect, sodium atoms or potassium atoms? Why?
3. Which element has the greater ionization energy, sodium or potassium? Why?
4. Which is the more chemically active element, sodium or potassium? Why?
5. (*a*) Write the equation for the reaction between lithium and water.
   (*b*) Is this reaction exothermic or endothermic? Why?
6. (*a*) What is the flame test for sodium?
   (*b*) Explain why sodium readily responds to a flame test whereas aluminum does not.
7. Describe how metallic sodium is prepared on an industrial scale.

8. Potassium carbonate cannot be prepared from potassium chloride by applying the procedure of the Solvay process. Why not?

Apply Your Knowledge!

1. How long would it take to produce 1000 kg of sodium metal by the electrolysis of molten sodium chloride, using a current of 5000 A?
2. How much heat energy is liberated when 0.250 mole of chlorine gas reacts with (*a*) lithium, (*b*) sodium, (*c*) potassium?

Find Out!

1. From the properties given for other members of this family predict properties for francium.
2. Follow the historical developments resulting in the discoveries of the alkali metals.

CHAPTER 22

THE HALOGENS

AS YOU LEARNED IN CHAPTER 6, the family of elements that occupies Group VII of the periodic table is called the *halogens*. The family consists of the five elements fluorine (F), chlorine (Cl), bromine (Br), iodine (I), and astatine (At). All the elements are chemically active so that none are found free in nature. The first four occur in various compounds of varying degrees of abundance. However, the fifth, astatine, is exceedingly rare and so will not be studied as a member of the halogen family.

Note . . .
Astatine is an unstable element having many isotopes, none of them stable. This element has been found in minute traces in uranium ores by some investigators, and was first synthesized in 1940 at the University of California. Unlike the rest of the halogen family, it is the only element not showing stability. Its name is derived from the Greek word *astatos* meaning unstable.

You recall that at ordinary temperatures all elements in the noble gas family are gases, whereas all the alkali metals are solids. The halogens, on the other hand, ordinarily exist in a variety of phases. Fluorine and chlorine are gases, bromine is a liquid, and iodine is a solid. Fluorine and chlorine can be changed to liquids and solids if the temperature is lowered sufficiently. How can this variety of physical forms be explained? The boiling and melting points of the halogens are given in Table 22-1.

Fig. 22-1 Steel wool burning in chlorine. What is produced?

Table 22-1 Boiling and melting points of the halogens

Element	Z	Boiling point, °C	Melting point, °C
Fluorine	9	−188	−220
Chlorine	17	− 35	−101
Bromine	35	59	− 7
Iodine	53	184	114

Notice that, as the atomic numbers increase, there is a rise in both the boiling and melting temperatures. How can these facts be accounted for? Before answering these questions, we must consider the nature of the bonding in the gas molecules of the halogens, and in particular the bonding in fluorine molecules.

Bonding in Fluorine Molecules

As stated in Chapter 8 the electronic configuration of a fluorine atom is $1s^2 2s^2 2p^5$. Hence two of the three p orbitals contain 2 electrons each, and the third p orbital contains one single electron which is therefore available for bonding.

As is shown in Fig. 22-2 a bond is formed when a pair of these $2p$ electrons (one from each of two atoms) is attracted by the two nuclei equally. When this happens, the position of greatest probability for the moving electron pair will be midway between the two nuclei. The electron-dot notation for this kind of bonding is

$$:\ddot{\underset{\cdot\cdot}{F}}\cdot + {}^{\times}\overset{\times\times}{\underset{\times\times}{F}}\overset{\times}{\times} \longrightarrow :\ddot{\underset{\cdot\cdot}{F}}\overset{\cdot}{\times}\overset{\times\times}{\underset{\times\times}{F}}\overset{\times}{\times} \qquad (22\text{-}1)$$

In these formulas, only valence electrons are shown for each atom. This same argument applies to the other halogens. Therefore, in the gaseous state all the halogens form covalent diatomic molecules: F—F, Cl—Cl, Br—Br, I—I.

Fig. 22-2 Electron configuration for two bonded fluorine atoms.

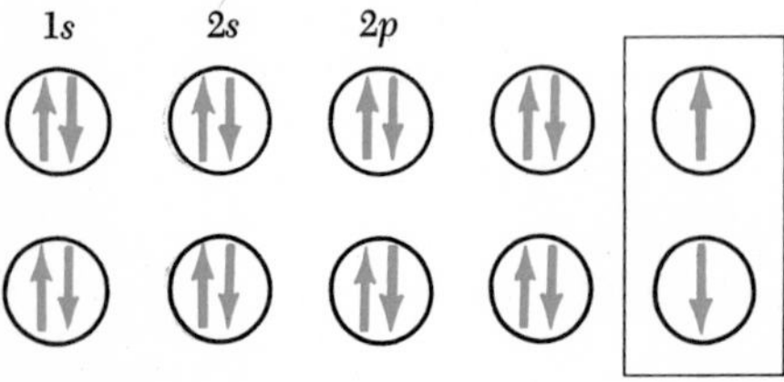

If fluorine gas cooled to −188 °C, it becomes a liquid (the condensation temperature of a gas is the same as the boiling temperature of its liquid), and if the liquid is cooled to −220 C, it becomes a solid (the freezing temperature of a liquid is the same as the melting temperature of the solid). Therefore, to hold molecules together to form liquids or solids, there must be an attractive force *between* the molecules, as distinct from the forces *within* the molecules. What is the nature of this force? How is it possible for nonpolar molecules to attract each other? The attractive forces between non-polar molecules are called *van der Waals forces*. They are named in honor of the Dutch scientist J. D. van der Waals (1837–1923) who first studied them.

Note . . .
The prefix *intra* means *within*. Forces within a molecule are described as intramolecular. The prefix *inter*, as you may know, means *between*. Forces between molecules are described as intermolecular.

van der Waals Forces

Before considering the van der Waals forces in the halogens, it will be helpful to apply them to the noble gases, particularly to helium (Z= 2) and neon (Z = 10). A neutral atom of helium can be represented by a nucleus at the center of an electron cloud. That is, the two electrons in the charge cloud are symmetrically arranged about the nucleus so that the atom is electrically neutral. However, from the kinetic theory, it is reasonable to assume that the charge cloud is not rigid, but is easily distorted. Perhaps it can vibrate back and forth about the nucleus. This could give rise to an unsymmetrical distribution of electrons with respect to the nucleus which, in turn, could cause a momentary dipole as shown in Fig. 22-3. Such an atom distorts the electron clouds of nearby atoms. For example, the positive end of the atom momentarily attracts the electron cloud of another atom as shown in Fig. 22-4. This is a weak force and moreover the atoms are in rapid motion. However, if the temperature is lowered, motion of the atoms decreases. Therefore, the attractive forces become more effective. Ultimately, when the temperature is low enough, the atoms of gas coalesce to form a liquid, and at a still lower temperature they form a solid. The con-

Deduce . . .
The fact that protons are located at the center of the atom and the electrons surround the nucleus at various energy levels can explain why the outer electrons are easily shifted. Can you deduce what the explanation might be?

Fig. 22-3 Asmmetrical charge cloud of the helium atom. Unequal distribution of electrons causes the atom to be polar.

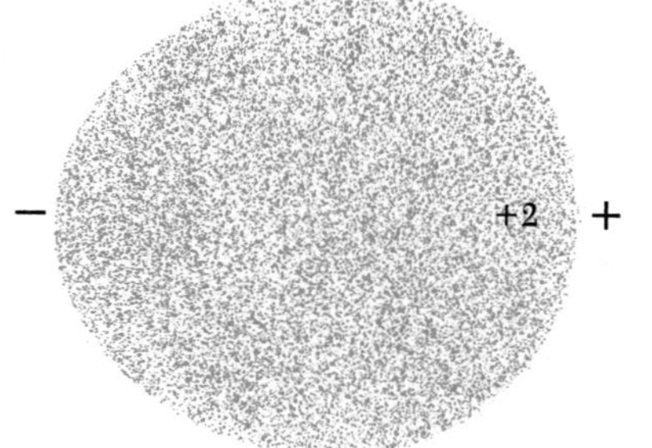

Fig. 22-4 A polar atom of helium momentarily attracting another polar atom of helium. What causes the atoms to be polar? Why are they attracted to each other?

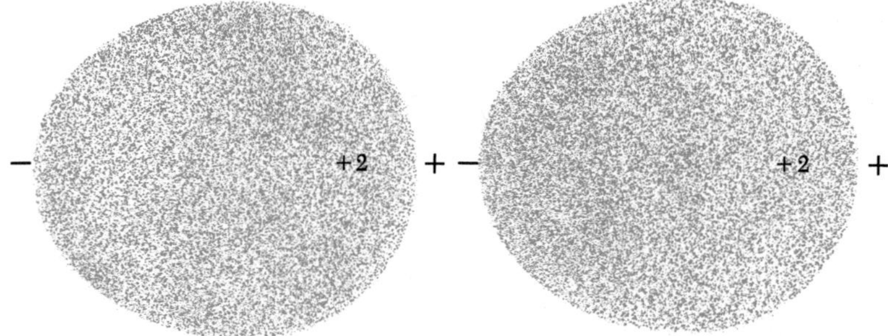

densing temperature (the boiling point) and the freezing temperature (the melting point) of helium are −269 °C and −272 °C, respectively. These low temperatures indicate that the van der Waals forces are exceedingly weak.

Define . . .
In terms of an electron cloud, define what is meant by the word *stronger*.

The charge cloud of a neon atom is larger than that of a helium atom as shown in Fig. 22-5. As a result the outer electrons of neon are shifted more easily than those of helium. In other words, the temporary dipoles of neon are stronger than those of helium and we would therefore expect its condensing and freezing temperatures to be higher. Actually, the boiling point of neon is −246 °C and its freezing point is −249 °C, which confirms our prediction.

van der Waals Forces Applied to the Halogens

As you know, halogen molecules are diatomic and their valence orbitals are filled. Therefore in this respect they have the structure of atoms of the noble gases. For example, the structure of a fluorine molecule is similar to that of a neon atom. Hence, the electron distribution in a fluorine molecule is for the most part symmetrical. But, since the electrons are in motion, the charge cloud can be momentarily displaced with respect to the two nuclei. The molecule then becomes unsymmetrical and slightly polar, and there is a weak attraction between the fluorine molecules. If the temperature is lowered to −188 °C, the attraction between the molecules is enough to cause them to condense to a liquid. And if the temperature is lowered to −220 °C, the vibrations are slowed down sufficiently so that the relative attraction between the molecules is great enough for them to form a solid.

Fig. 22-5 (*a*) A symmetrical charge cloud of the helium atom. (*b*) A symmetrical charge cloud of the neon atom. Measure the radius of each of the charge cloud diagrams, then compute the volume of each. How many times larger is the neon atom? Do some research to see if your answer is correct.

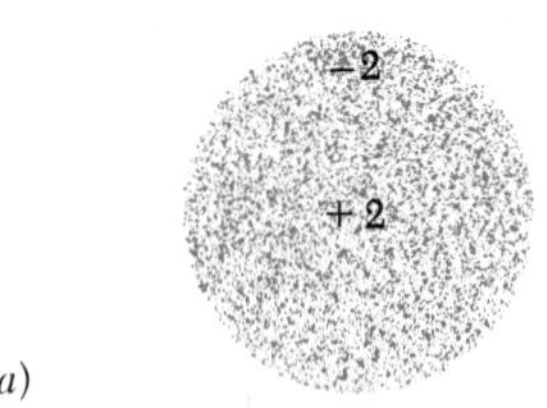

(*a*)

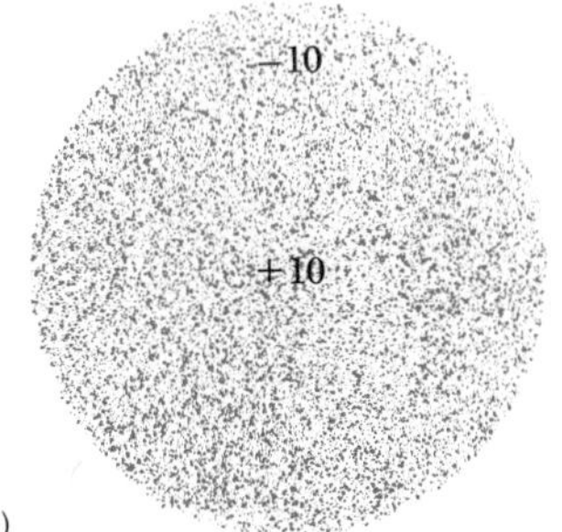

(*b*)

The same argument applies to the rest of the halogens, and the temperatures at which they change phase are shown in Table 22-2. Why is the boiling temperature of chlorine higher than that of fluorine? Why is bromine a liquid and iodine a solid at ordinary

Table 22-2 Phase-change points of selected halogens

Element	Boiling point of liquid or condensing temp. of gas, °C	Freezing point of liquid or melting temp. of solid, °C
Chlorine	−35	−101
Bromine	59	− 7
Iodine	184	114

temperatures? The answers to these questions are apparent if we remember that the greater the number of electrons in the charge cloud the less strongly are the electrons bound to the nucleus and therefore the greater are the van der Waals forces.

Some Properties of the Halogens

All the gases of the halogens are colored and the color deepens as the atomic number increases. Fluorine is pale yellow, chlorine is greenish, bromine gas is deep red, and iodine vapor is violet. Moreover, all the halogen gases are toxic; fluorine and chlorine are the most poisonous. Indeed, chlorine was the first of the poison gases to be used in World War I. Clearly, great care should be exercised when handling these gases in the laboratory.

Explain . . .
The halogens are electronegative, while the alkali metals are electropositive. Why are halogen ions larger than the ions of alkali metals? Futhermore, why is the radius of a halogen atom smaller than its ion? Explain why ionization energy decreases as atomic number increases for the halogens.

Table 22-3 Selected characteristics of the halogens

Element	Z	Radius of atom, Å	Radius of ion, Å	Ionization energy, kcal/mole
F	9	0.70	1.33	402
Cl	17	1.1	1.81	300
Br	35	1.20	1.96	273
I	53	1.36	2.20	241

Some Chemical Properties of the Halogens

All the halogens are good oxidizing agents, fluorine being the strongest and iodine the weakest. There are three types of oxidation reactions in which the oxidation number of the halogen is changed from 0 to −1.

Reactions with Metals The halogens react with most metals to form salts. A few examples are

$$4Al + 6F_2 \longrightarrow 2Al_2F_6 \quad (22\text{-}2)$$

$$2Na + Cl_2 \longrightarrow 2NaCl \quad (22\text{-}3)$$

$$Mg + Br_2 \longrightarrow MgBr_2 \quad (22\text{-}4)$$

In electron-dot notation, the chlorine reaction is

$$2Na\cdot + :\!\ddot{\underset{\times\times}{Cl}}\!:\!\ddot{\underset{\times\times}{Cl}}\!: \longrightarrow 2Na^+ + 2:\!\ddot{\underset{\times\times}{Cl}}\!:^- \quad (22\text{-}5)$$

Table 22-4 Valence-electron configurations of the halogens

Element	Atom	Ion
F	$2s^2 2p^5$	$2s^2 2p^6$
Cl	$3s^2 3p^5$	$3s^2 3p^6$
Br	$4s^2 4p^5$	$4s^2 4p^6$
I	$5s^2 5p^5$	$5s^2 5p^6$

Fig. 22-6 Copper (I) chloride and copper (II) chloride. What is the formula for each compound?

Table 22-5 Ionization energies of the alkali metals, halogens, and noble gases

Family	Element	Z	Ionization energy, kcal/mole
Halogen	Fluorine	9	402
	Chlorine	17	300
	Bromine	35	273
	Iodine	53	241
Noble gas	Neon	10	497
	Argon	18	363
	Krypton	36	323
	Xenon	54	280
Alkali metal	Sodium	11	118
	Potassium	19	100
	Rubidium	37	96
	Cesium	55	90

Notice that this reaction involves electron transfer, so that the bonding in sodium chloride is ionic. The vigor of the reaction depends upon the kind of metal. Sodium, for example, reacts with chlorine much more vigorously than does iron. Why? Binary halogen compounds are called *halides*. Thus NaF, NaCl, NaBr, and NaI are sodium halides.

Replacement Reactions Another important kind of reaction depends upon the relative electronegativities of the halogens. Fluorine is the most electronegative member of the family and iodine the least. As a result, a halogen will displace a halogen of higher atomic number from its salts. For example, chlorine will displace both bromine from bromides and iodine from iodides. And bromine will displace iodine from iodides. Typical reactions are

$$Cl_2(g) + 2Br^-(aq) \longrightarrow 2Cl^-(aq) + Br_2(l) \qquad (22\text{-}6)$$

$$Cl_2(g) + 2I^-(aq) \longrightarrow 2Cl^-(aq) + I_2(s) \qquad (22\text{-}7)$$

$$Br_2(l) + 2I^-(aq) \longrightarrow 2Br^-(aq) + I_2(s) \qquad (22\text{-}8)$$

The electron-dot equation for Eq. (22-6) is

$$:\ddot{\underset{\cdot\cdot}{Cl}}:\ddot{\underset{\cdot\cdot}{Cl}}: + 2:\ddot{\underset{\times\times}{Br}}:^- \longrightarrow 2:\ddot{\underset{\cdot\cdot}{Cl}}.^- + :\ddot{\underset{\times\times}{Br}}:\ddot{\underset{\times\times}{Br}}: \qquad (22\text{-}9)$$

Notice again that the free halogen is the oxidizer in these replacement reactions.

Fig. 22-7 Hydrogen burning in chlorine.

Hydrogen Halides

All the halogens react with hydrogen to form hydrogen halides. The hydrogen halides are hydrogen fluoride (HF), hydrogen chloride (HCl), hydrogen bromide (HBr), and hydrogen iodide (HI). All are gases at ordinary temperatures. Thus the equations for the reactions with hydrogen are

$$H_2(g) + F_2(g) \longrightarrow 2HF(g) \qquad (22\text{-}10)$$

$$H_2(g) + Cl_2(g) \longrightarrow 2HCl(g) \qquad (22\text{-}11)$$

$$H_2(g) + Br_2(g) \longrightarrow 2HBr(g) \qquad (22\text{-}12)$$

$$H_2(g) + I_2(g) \longrightarrow 2HI(g) \qquad (22\text{-}13)$$

Note . . .
When hydrogen combines with chlorine, the radiant energy in ordinary light acts as a catalyst. If the two gases are mixed in a darkened room, the reaction is so slow that it is hardly noticeable.

The gases can, of course, be liquefied by lowering the temperature sufficiently. The boiling points of the hydrogen halides are listed in Table 22-6. The boiling point of HF is clearly out of line; it is much higher than expected. If it followed the general trend, we would expect HF to boil at a temperature below the boiling point of HCl, not above it. How can this irregularity be accounted for? Do the van der Waals forces offer a clue? Since HF molecules have fewer electrons than HCl molecules, the van der Waals forces must be weaker in HF than in HCl. If these forces were the only factor, the condensing temperature of HF would follow the trend and be lower than the condensing temperature of HCl. However, the attractive forces between molecules of HF must be abnormally high to account for the exceptionally high boiling point. How can this be explained?

The polar covalent bond in HF can be shown as

$$H^+ :\ddot{\underset{\cdot\cdot}{F}}:^-$$

Since fluorine is strongly electronegative, it has a strong attraction for the hydrogen electron, making a strong dipolar bond. As a result, the hydrogen end of one molecule attracts the fluorine end

Table 22-6
Boiling points of hydrogen halides

Halide	Boiling point, °C
HF	19
HCl	−85
HBr	−66
HI	−36

of another molecule and so on to form a chain of molecules. One such molecular chain could be

$$H^+ :\ddot{F}:^- H^+ :\ddot{F}:^- H^+ :\ddot{F}:^- H^+ :\ddot{F}:^- \qquad (22\text{-}14)$$

All the hydrogen halides are very soluble in water, forming acid solutions. The equations for the reactions with water are

$$HF(g) + \text{water} \rightleftharpoons H^+(aq) + F^-(aq) \quad \text{hydrofluoric acid} \qquad (22\text{-}15)$$

$$HCl(g) + \text{water} \longrightarrow H^+(aq) + Cl^-(aq) \quad \text{hydrochloric acid} \qquad (22\text{-}16)$$

$$HBr(g) + \text{water} \longrightarrow H^+(aq) + Br^-(aq) \quad \text{hydrobromic acid} \qquad (22\text{-}17)$$

$$HI(g) + \text{water} \longrightarrow H^+(aq) + I^-(aq) \quad \text{hydriodic acid} \qquad (22\text{-}18)$$

Reactions of Halogens with Water

Fluorine, being a much stronger oxidizing agent than oxygen, reacts violently with water and displaces the oxygen,

$$2F_2 + 2H_2O \longrightarrow 4HF + O_2 \qquad (22\text{-}19)$$

Thus, fluorine is not soluble in water. However, the other halogens are soluble in water (although iodine is only very slightly soluble). Chlorine, bromine, and iodine are less powerful oxidizing agents than fluorine and they react differently with water. For example, the chlorine reaction is

$$H_2O + Cl_2 \rightleftharpoons HCl + HOCl \qquad (22\text{-}20)$$

The reaction is reversible and the mixture of all four ingredients is called *chlorine water.* Using electron-dot symbols, the reaction can be written as

$$H:\underset{\underset{H}{\cdot\cdot}}{\ddot{O}}: + :\ddot{Cl}:\ddot{Cl}: \rightleftharpoons H:\ddot{Cl}: + :\underset{\cdot\cdot}{\overset{\overset{H}{\cdot\cdot}}{O}}:\ddot{Cl}: \qquad (22\text{-}21)$$

Thus one chlorine atom per molecule forms a chloride ion

$$HCl \longrightarrow H^+ + Cl^- \qquad (22\text{-}22)$$

and the other chlorine atom forms a covalent bond with oxygen to give a so-called halogen *oxyacid.* This particular oxyacid (HOCl) is called hypochlorous acid.

Halogen Oxyacids Since the algebraic sum of oxidation numbers of atoms in a molecule is zero, the oxidation number of chlorine in hypochlorous acid must be +1,

$$\underset{H}{+1}\ \underset{Cl}{+1}\ \underset{O}{-2} = 0$$

This is unexpected since the oxidation number of chlorine in chlorides is −1. In other words, when a molecule of chlorine reacts with a molecule of water, one of the chlorine atoms is reduced and the other is oxidized. How is this possible?

The ionization energy of oxygen (313 kcal/mole) is slightly greater than that of chlorine (300 kcal/mole) and therefore oxygen is slightly more electronegative (3.5) than chlorine (3.0). We might say that in the Cl—O bond a shared pair of electrons is a little nearer the oxygen atom than the chlorine atom, and in consequence chlorine is positive with respect to oxygen; so its oxidation number is +1. A glance at the electronegativies of bromine and iodine shows that the bonding of these elements with oxygen is expected to be similar to that of chlorine; therefore in compounds such as HOBr and HOI the oxidation numbers of the halogens are +1. Moreover, the names of the compounds are similar (HOBr is hypobromous acid and HOI is hypoiodous acid).

Chlorine also forms three other oxyacids in which its oxidation numbers are +3, +5, and +7, respectively. The series of oxyacids, including their electronic formulas and chlorine oxidation numbers, is summarized in Table 22-7.

Table 22-7 Formulas of chlorine oxyacids and corresponding chlorine oxidation numbers

Acid	Symbol formula	Electron-dot formula	Oxidation number of chlorine atom
Hypochlorous	HClO	H :O: Cl:	+1
Chlorous	$HClO_2$	H :O: Cl : O:	+3
Chloric	$HClO_3$	:O: H :O: Cl : O:	+5
Perchloric	$HClO_4$	:O: H :O: Cl : O: :O:	+7

Think . . .
Rewrite the electron-dot formula of each chlorine oxyacid to indicate the proper spatial arrangement of the hydrogen atom in each molecule.

In *chlorous acid* a chlorine atom shares two pairs of electrons with two oxygen atoms. Then why is not the oxidation number of chlorine +2 rather than +3? The answer is that the chlorine atom supplies three of the four electrons that are shared with oxygen. In *chloric acid* there are three shared pairs of electrons and the chlorine atom supplies five of the six shared electrons. Therefore the oxidation number of chlorine in chloric acid is +5. It should now be apparent why chlorine in *perchloric acid* has an oxidation number of +7.

Hypochlorous acid is very weak and perchloric acid is very strong. That is, the acids become progressively stronger from acid to acid down the series. How can this fact be explained?

To provide a hydrogen ion (or a proton), the H—O bond must be broken. Since HClO is a weak acid, the H—O bond must resist cleavage. And since $HClO_2$ is stronger than HClO, it can donate a proton more readily than HOCl. In other words, the H—O bond in $HClO_2$ cleaves more easily than that in HClO. How can this be explained?

Chlorous acid ($HClO_2$) can be made from hypochlorous acid (HClO) by adding an oxygen atom to the central atom of chlorine. In the act of bonding, the additional oxygen atom draws some of the electronic charge from the chlorine atom, which in turn draws electronic charge from the H—O bond. As a result the H—O attachment to the chlorine atom is changed, making it easier for the hydrogen ion to break away. Chloric acid ($HClO_3$) is made by adding an oxygen atom to $HClO_2$. Here again the added oxygen atom draws still more electrons from the chlorine atom which in turn further weakens the H—O bond. Thus the H—O bond becomes more easily broken through the series of oxyacids and, in consequence, the acids become progressively stronger.

Salts of *hypochlorous* acid are called *hypochlorites*, salts of *chlorous* acid are called *chlorites*, and those of *perchloric* acid are *perchlorates*. The names and formulas of the sodium salts of the halogen oxyacids are listed in Table 22-8.

Which is the more stable salt, sodium chlorite or sodium chlorate?

Table 22-8 Salts of halogen oxyacids

Acid		Salt	
Formula	Name	Formula	Name
HClO	*hypo*chlor*ous*	NaClO	sodium *hypo*chlor*ite*
$HClO_2$	chlor*ous*	$NaClO_2$	sodium chlor*ite*
$HClO_3$	chlor*ic*	$NaClO_3$	sodium chlor*ate*
$HClO_4$	*per*chlor*ic*	$NaClO_4$	sodium *per*chlor*ate*

Preparation of the Halogens

The simplest way to prepare a halogen is to remove one of the outer electrons from the corresponding halide ion. Thus, if X represents a halogen atom, the general equation for the preparation of a halogen is

$$\underset{\text{ion}}{2X^-} - 2e^{-1} \longrightarrow \underset{\text{molecule}}{X_2} \qquad (22\text{-}23)$$

This is clearly an oxidation reaction and there are numerous oxidizing agents capable of removing an electron from a chloride ion, a bromide ion, or an iodide ion. As you already know, chlorine water or chlorine gas is a suitable oxidizer for bromides and iodides, as in

$$2Br^-(aq) + Cl_2 \longrightarrow 2Cl^-(aq) + Br_2 \qquad (22\text{-}24)$$

$$2I^-(aq) + Cl_2 \longrightarrow 2Cl^-(aq) + I_2 \qquad (22\text{-}25)$$

What is a suitable oxidizing agent for chloride ion? Theoretically, fluorine gas would be suitable. However, if fluorine is bubbled into a solution of a chloride, the water is decomposed and oxygen is released. The decomposition of water can be avoided by using a milder oxidizing agent such as manganese dioxide (MnO_2). In the preparation of chlorine, hydrochloric acid is the usual source of chloride ion and the equation for the reaction with manganese dioxide is

$$MnO_2 + 4HCl \longrightarrow MnCl_2 + 2H_2O + Cl_2 \qquad (22\text{-}26)$$

The simplest ionic equation for the reaction is

$$MnO_2 + 4H^+(aq) + 2Cl^- \longrightarrow Mn^{+2} + 2H_2O + Cl_2 \qquad (22\text{-}27)$$

Why is this an oxidation-reduction reaction? To answer this question, let us examine the changes in oxidation numbers that occur. The oxidation number of manganese changes from +4 in MnO_2 to +2 in Mn^{+2}, and the oxidation number of chlorine changes from −1 in Cl^- to 0 in Cl_2. (The oxidation numbers of oxygen and hydrogen remain unchanged at −2 and +1, respectively.) Thus, in terms of electron transfer the two half-reactions are

$$MnO_2 + 4H^+(aq) + 2e^{-1} \longrightarrow Mn^{+2} + 2H_2O \qquad (22\text{-}28)$$

$$2Cl^-(aq) - 2e^{-1} \longrightarrow Cl_2 \qquad (22\text{-}29)$$

Clearly the first is a reduction reaction in which MnO_2 is the oxidizing agent, and the second is an oxidation reaction in which chloride ion is the reducing agent. The industrial preparation of chlorine will be discussed in detail later.

And, finally, how is fluorine prepared? Since fluorine is the most powerful of all oxidizing agents, no other oxidizing agent is able to dislodge an electron from a fluoride ion. Therefore, the general chemical method of preparing halogens does not apply to fluorine. Instead, it is prepared by electrolysis of the *molten* salt potassium hydrogen fluoride, KHF_2. Notice the term *molten*. As you know, electrolysis experiments are usually carried out in water solution. Can you explain why a *water solution* of a fluoride cannot be used in electrolysis?

Some Uses of the Halogens

Fluorine

Fluorine, like hydrogen, has a strong attraction for carbon atoms and, in consequence, the carbon—fluorine bond, like the carbon—hydrogen bond, is very strong. Compounds in which carbon and fluorine are bonded are called *fluorocarbons*, and a wide variety of fluorocarbons have been synthesized. All the fluorocarbons are exceedingly stable. They neither burn nor corrode, and their uses reflect these properties. For instance, they are used in the preparation of corrosion-resistant materials and lubricants which are to be used at high temperatures.

Two well-known fluorocarbons are Freon® and Teflon®. Freon®, CCl_2F_2, is a derivative of methane, the four hydrogen atoms being replaced by two atoms of chlorine and two of fluorine. It is a gas at ordinary temperatures. However, it is easily liquefied and since it is chemically inert it is widely used as the liquid for transferring heat in refrigerators. Teflon® is a solid which has many uses, including coating cooking pans. This is because Teflon does not react chemically with any cooked foods and provides a surface which prevents foods from sticking to the pans.

Chlorine

Chlorine is the most versatile and the most widely used member of the halogen family. It is used as a bleaching agent on a vast scale, particularly in the bleaching of cotton and paper. The bleaching action is probably due to atomic oxygen, rather than to chlorine. A solution of chlorine contains hypochlorous acid which is unstable and slowly releases oxygen,

$$HOCl \rightleftharpoons HCl + O \qquad (22\text{-}30)$$

The atomic oxygen attacks and decomposes dye material, thereby bleaching the material.

Chlorine is also used in an antiseptic solution and in the purification of water, a process in which the oxygen released from HOCl destroys harmful bacteria.

Bromine and Iodine

The chief use of bromine is in the preparation of ethylene dibromide ($C_2H_4Br_2$), a liquid added to gasoline to remove the lead released from tetraethyllead, $Pb(C_2H_5)_4$, which has been added as an antiknock agent. Another important compound of bromine is silver bromide, which is used in the manufacture of photographic film. Silver bromide is sensitive to light and, when exposed, it decomposes to metallic silver and free bromine. In a photographic film, fine crystals of AgBr are suspended in gelatin which, in turn, adheres to a strip of transparent plastic. When light from an object passes through the lens of a camera, crystals of AgBr are decomposed

$$2AgBr \xrightarrow{\text{light}} 2Ag + Br_2 \qquad (22\text{-}31)$$

and a black silver image of the object is formed. The image is then further developed by placing the film in a solution of a suitable reducing agent, usually hydroquinone. The film is then "fixed" by immersing it in a solution of hypo (sodium thiosulfate, $Na_2S_2O_3$). In this process, the unaffected crystals of AgBr are removed, otherwise the whole film would be blackened when exposed to light. As you probably know, this process is carried out in a room illuminated only by red light, which has no marked effect upon silver bromide.

Note . . .
The term *hypo* is applied to sodium thiosulfate, because this term is a derivative of its old name, sodium hyposulfate.

The chief use of iodine is as an antiseptic. For this purpose it is frequently dissolved in ethyl alcohol which also has some antiseptic properties. This solution of iodine in alcohol is known as *tincture of iodine*. Other solutions of iodine also are used as antiseptics. Small quantities of iodine salts are also added to table salt to act as a preventive of thyroid gland diseases.

Note . . .
The *Hooker* and the *Diamond cells* account for most of the industrial production of chlorine in the United States. The *Nelson cell,* once in predominant use, is now obsolete. The mercury cell is used on a large scale to produce chlorine in Europe. This cell accounts for about 28 percent of chlorine production in the United States. Do some research to find out about the mercury cell.

The Industrial Manufacture of Chlorine

To supply the needs of many industrial processes, chlorine is manufactured on a large scale. The usual method of producing chlorine in industry is by the electrolysis of a solution of sodium chloride in the *Hooker cell* or in the *Diamond cell.*

A Hooker cell is shown in Fig. 22-8. The cell is divided into three parts: (*a*) a concrete top containing a chlorine outlet, a salt brine inlet, and a gas chamber (*b*) a concrete bottom with the graphite anode assembly (*c*) perforated steel cathodes covered by a porous asbestos diaphragm. The cathodes are "sandwiched" between (*a*) and (*b*). What happens at the anode and cathode when the current is turned on?

There are four different ions in solution—Na^+ and Cl^- in abundance and small amounts of H^+ and OH^- furnished by the water. Thus the positively charged anode attracts Cl^- and OH^- ions, while the cathode attracts Na^+ and H^+ ions. In addition, water molecules may be reduced at the cathode or oxidized at the anode. What actually happens at the electrodes depends upon the relative concentration and the stability of each of the ingredients. The electrolysis of a sodium chloride solution has been explained in Chapter 18.

Fig. 22-8 Diagram of the Hooker cell. In the top chamber (*A*), chlorine gas collects. The anode compartment is (*B*), and the cathode compartment is (*C*).

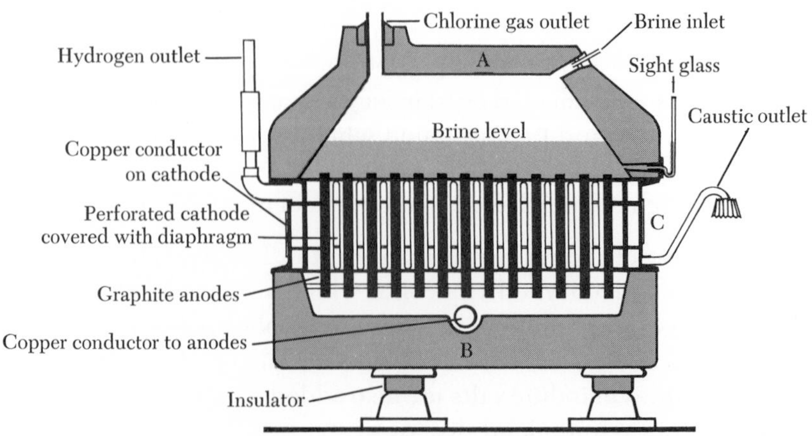

Fig. 22-9 Hooker cells connected in series.

Notice that in this method of preparing chlorine two valuable by-products, hydrogen and sodium hydroxide, are also obtained. The chlorine outlet tube is at the top of the uppermost compartment and chlorine is collected there. Similarly, hydrogen escapes through an outlet tube as shown in Fig. 22-8. The solution of sodium hydroxide seeps through the porous diaphragm and is collected. The solution is then evaporated to yield solid NaOH. Indeed, this procedure is the main source of sodium hydroxide for industrial uses.

If a Hooker cell is operated at 30,000 A, 1 ton of chlorine per day can be made. Hooker cells are connected in series, as shown in Fig. 22-9, to increase production.

Summary

The halogen family consists of fluorine, chlorine, bromine, and iodine. They were discovered over a span of 100 years. The halogens have similar electronic configurations, each with seven valence electrons. In many of their reactions with themselves, hydrogen, and metals, halogens fill their outermost *p* orbitals by adding a single electron, thus attaining the stable configuration of the noble gases.

Factual Recall

1. (*a*) What are van der Waals forces?
   (*b*) The van der Waals forces for the halogens become progressively stronger as the atomic numbers increase. Explain why.
2. The electronegativities of fluorine and iodine are 4.0 and 2.8, respectively. (*a*) What do these values mean? (*b*) What do these values indicate regarding the chemical reactivity of fluorine as compared with that of iodine?
3. Why do the halogens tend to form diatomic molecules when they are in the gas phase?
4. If chlorine gas is bubbled into a solution of sodium iodide, iodine is released as a dark-brown suspension. Explain why iodine is released.
5. The boiling point of hydrogen fluoride (20 °C), is higher than that of hydrogen chloride (−85 °C), whereas if hydrogen fluor-

ide followed the trend of the boiling points of the other hydrogen halides, its boiling point would be lower. Account for the anomaly.

6. (*a*) Write the formulas and names of the potassium salts of the halogen oxyacids.
   (*b*) Write the equation for a common preparation of oxygen from one of these salts.
   (*c*) Explain the change in the valence of chlorine that occurs in reaction (*b*).

Apply Your Knowledge!

1. Calculate the volume of Cl_2 (g) liberated at 27°C and 760 torr pressure by adding 7.5 ml of 6.0 *M* HCl solution to 0.87 g of MnO_2.

2. The HCl liberated by the reaction of 11.7 g of NaCl with concentrated H_2SO_4 is dissolved in enough water to give 100 ml of solution.
   (*a*) What mass of H_2SO_4 is consumed?
   (*b*) What volume of 0.100 *M* KOH solution is required to neutralize the HCl solution?

3. The electrolysis of a sodium halide solution is maintained for 30 min with a current of 0.50 A. Compute the volume of anode product at STP if the solution is (*a*) the fluoride, (*b*) the chloride.

Find Out!

1. Chlorine had two uses in World War I; one was deadly, the other a lifesaver. Find out about them.

2. Hydrogen fluoride is used in etching glass. Research this use in fine arts and industry.

3. What is the Diamond cell?

CHAPTER 23

ELEMENTS IN THE THIRD ROW OF THE PERIODIC TABLE

IN CHAPTERS 21 AND 22 we considered two vertical groups of elements (the alkali metals and the halogens) in the periodic table. We discovered that a vertical group constitutes a natural family of elements with a similarity in electron configurations and the same kind of chemical properties. We will now consider two horizontal rows of elements, the third in this chapter and the fourth in Chapter 24.

As we move from left to right along a row, both the number of protons in the nucleus and the number of electrons in the atom increase by one from element to element. This gradual change in atomic structure suggests a gradual change in the properties of the elements.

Let us consider the third row, which consists of the eight elements sodium (Na), magnesium (Mg), aluminum (Al), silicon (Si), phosphorus (P), sulfur (S), chlorine (Cl), and argon (Ar).

The first obvious observation is that there is a change from metals on the left (Na, Mg, and Al) to nonmetals on the right (S, Cl, and Ar).

Definition . . .
Both phosphorus and sulfur occur naturally in several forms. These are called *molecular allotropes,* which are defined as substances composed of only a single kind of atom but differing in the structural arrangement of the atoms in the molecules.

Why the change from metals to nonmetals? Let us examine the electron configurations and ionization energies of the eight elements. These are given in Table 23-1. What is the significance of the electron configurations and the ionization energies?

Table 23-1 Characteristics of elements in the third row of the periodic table

Element	Z	Melting point, °C	Electron configuration	Ionization energy, kcal/mole
Na	11	97.8	$1s^2 2s^2 2p^6 3s^1$	118
Mg	12	651	$1s^2 2s^2 2p^6 3s^2$	175
Al	13	660	$1s^2 2s^2 2p^6 3s^2 3p^1$	138
Si	14	1410	$1s^2 2s^2 2p^6 3s^2 3p^2$	188
P	15	44.1 (white)	$1s^2 2s^2 2p^6 3s^2 3p^3$	242
S	16	119(β)	$1s^2 2s^2 2p^6 3s^2 3p^4$	240
Cl	17	−101	$1s^2 2s^2 2p^6 3s^2 3p^5$	300
Ar	18	−189.2	$1s^2 2s^2 2p^6 3s^2 3p^6$	363

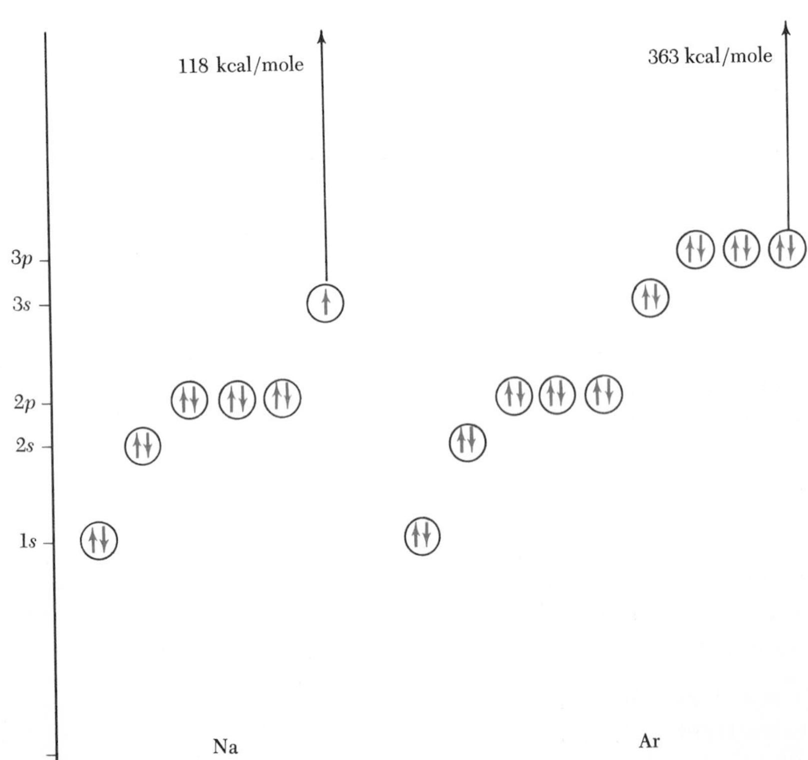

Fig. 23-1 In the third row, the 3*s* electron of the first element (Na) is most easily detached, and a 3*p* electron of the last element (Ar) is the most difficult to detach.

Electron Configurations of Elements of the Third Row

The electron configuration of sodium is $1s^2 2s^2 2p^6 3s^1$ (pronounced as one *s* two, two *s* two, two *p* six, three *s* one). As we move from left to right there is a regular increment of one electron per atom, first in the 3*s* orbital, then in the three 3*p* orbitals. Eventually, when the element argon is reached, the last available space in the 3*p* orbitals is filled.

As you learned earlier, the chemical properties of an element depend upon the ease, or difficulty, of removing electrons. The *valence* electrons (the electrons beyond the electron structure of the last noble gas) are much more easily removed than the inner electrons; they are the electrons involved in chemical reactions either by transfer or sharing. The noble gas at the end of the second row is neon, $1s^2 2s^2 2p^6$. Hence the valence electrons in the third row vary from $3s^1$ for sodium to $3s^2 3p^5$ for chlorine.

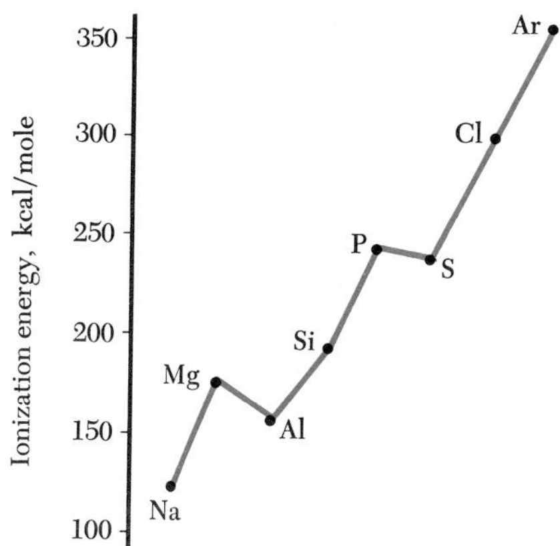

Fig. 23-2 From left to right along the third row, there is, with two exceptions, a steady increase in the ionization energies of the elements.

Ionization Energies for Elements in the Third Row

The ionization energy, you recall, is the amount of energy needed to remove the electron with the highest energy from 1 mole of atoms. Thus, as shown in Fig. 23-1, the ionization energies for sodium and argon are 118 kcal/mole and 363 kcal/mole, respectively. With two minor exceptions there is a gradual increase in ionization energy as atomic numbers (Z) increase, that is, from left to right across the row. This gradual increase is shown in Fig. 23-2.

How can this tendency be explained? The atomic radii of these elements are approximately the same, and therefore as the positive charge on the nucleus increases, more and more energy is needed to detach the outermost electron. Thus it is more difficult to detach a 3*p* electron from an atom of chlorine than from an atom of phosphorus.

Chemical Bonds of the Elements in the Third Row

As you learned in Chapters 22 and 23, sodium is a metal and a reducing agent while chlorine is a nonmetal and an oxidizing agent. It is therefore reasonable to assume that some of the elements between sodium and chlorine have both reducing and oxidizing properties. The factor that determines whether an element is a reducing or an oxidizing agent is its ability to lose or gain electrons.

Sodium Sodium is a reducing agent because a sodium atom readily releases an electron to form an ion which has the same electronic structure as a neon atom,

$$\underset{\text{atom}}{\mathrm{Na}\cdot} - e^- \longrightarrow \underset{\text{ion}}{\mathrm{Na}^+} \qquad (23\text{-}1)$$

Chlorine On the other hand, chlorine is an oxidizing agent because a chlorine atom gains an electron to form an ion with the same electronic structure as an atom of argon,

$$\underset{\text{atom}}{\cdot\ddot{\underset{\cdot\cdot}{\mathrm{Cl}}}:} + e^- \longrightarrow \underset{\text{ion}}{:\ddot{\underset{\cdot\cdot}{\mathrm{Cl}}}:^-} \qquad (23\text{-}2)$$

Magnesium The next element beyond sodium is magnesium. Magnesium has two valence electrons and so a magnesium ion is Mg^{+2}. Why does magnesium not form a +3 ion or even a +4 ion? As you learned in Chapter 9, the first ionization energy of magnesium is 176 kcal/mole, the second is 347 kcal/mole, and the third is 1850 kcal/mole. In terms of energy, it is not very difficult to remove the two 3*s* electrons. However, the removal of a third electron which would change a Mg^{+2} ion to a Mg^{+3} ion requires such a large amount of energy—almost 2 million cal/mole—that it does not take place under ordinary conditions.

Aluminum What of aluminum? Aluminum forms a +3 ion. Let us see why. Aluminum has three valence electrons (two 3*s* and one 3*p*) and the ionization energies of these electrons (in kilocalories per mole) are 138, 434, and 656. The ionization energy of the fourth electron is 2770 kcal/mole which is much too high to permit Al^{+4} ions to be formed in ordinary reactions. How can you account for this high value for an Al^{+4} ion? Notice that almost twice as much energy is needed to form Al^{+3} ions as Mg^{+2} ions. Hence aluminum shows less tendency than magnesium to form ionic bonds. On the other hand, aluminum has a greater tendency than magnesium to share electrons, that is, to form covalent bonds. An example of this is the covalent compound Al_2Cl_6.

Silicon The next element is silicon. Silicon has four valence electrons (two 3*s* and two 3*p*). If these four electrons were removed, the resulting ion, Si^{+4}, would have the same configuration as a neon atom. However, the amount of energy needed to remove the four valence electrons is so high that positive ions are not formed in ordinary reactions. If, on the other hand, a silicon atom gained four electrons, it would form an Si^{-4} ion with the same configuration as argon. But, again, negative ions are not formed because too much energy is needed to bring about this change. In short, *silicon does not form ionic bonds.* However, a silicon atom achieves the configuration of argon by sharing its four valence electrons with other atoms; that is, *silicon forms covalent bonds.* A silicon crystal is shown in Fig. 23-3.

Infer . . .
Is silicon a metal or a nonmetal? Why?

Phosphorus Next comes phosphorus with five valence electrons (two 3*s* and three 3*p*). The chance of forming a positive ion (P^{+5}) by the loss of five electrons is very remote indeed. Why? A phosphorus atom can, however, gain three electrons to form a phosphide ion, P^{-3}. However, its electronegativity is low (2.1) as compared with that of chlorine (3.0), therefore the P^{-3} ion is very rare. Usually phosphorus forms covalent bonds by sharing three of its valence electrons with other atoms in such compounds as PH_3, PCl_3, or P_4O_6. It also forms compounds such as PCl_5 in which it has an oxidation state of 5.

Sulfur The next element, sulfur, has six valence electrons (two 3*s* and four 3*p*). Its electronegativity (2.5) is reasonably near the value for chlorine and, like chlorine, it can achieve the argon configuration by either gaining or sharing electrons. If a sulfur atom gains two electrons it forms a sulfide ion (S^{-2}), and the bonding is ionic. If, on the other hand, it shares two of its valence electrons with other atoms, as in H_2S or SCl_2, its bonding is covalent.

Fig. 23-3 A crystal of silicon is made up of atoms with four covalent bonds. That is, every silicon atom is bonded to 4 other atoms of silicon. It has the same 3-dimensional structure as the diamond structure of carbon. Explain.

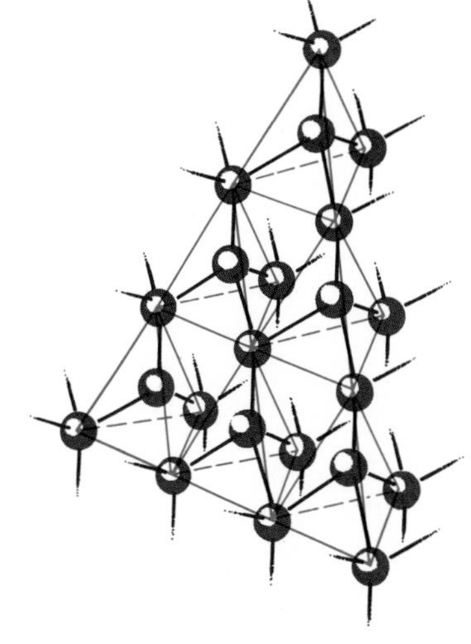

Melting Points of Elements in the Third Row

The melting points of the elements in the third row are listed in Table 23-1. You will recall that the first three elements (Na, Mg, and Al) are metals and as such they are good conductors of heat and electricity.

The Metals Notice that the melting points of the metals increase as the atomic number (Z) increases. How can this be explained? Although this is an oversimplification, melting points are often explained in terms of interatomic attractive forces. These forces between atoms depend upon the number of electrons in the charge

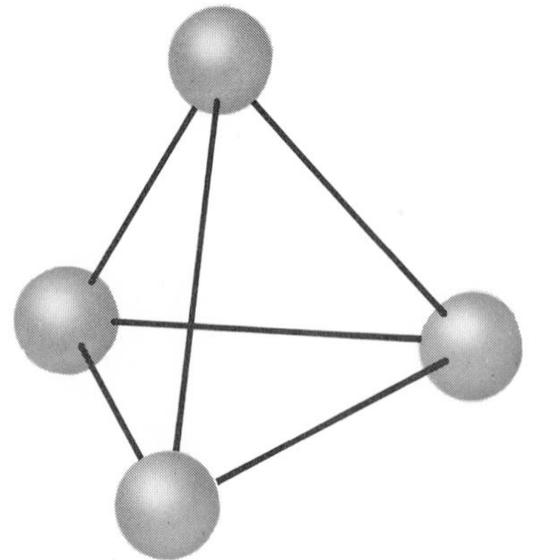

Fig. 23-4 A molecule of phosphorus consists of 4 atoms, and each atom has 3 covalent bonds which are bonded to the other 3 atoms in the molecule.

cloud—the greater the number of electrons the stronger is the force of attraction. Hence the interatomic attractive forces between atoms of Al are greater than those between atoms of Na, which explains the higher melting point of Al.

Silicon The next element, silicon, is not normally regarded as a metal, although it has a luster and looks like a metal. It is a very hard substance with a high melting point (1410 °C). Unlike aluminum, it is a poor conductor of electricity and is called a *semiconductor*. How can these facts be explained? Each silicon atom has four valence electrons, two 3*s* and two 3*p*, (as shown in Fig. 23-3), which it shares with four other silicon atoms to form covalent bonds. This process is repeated indefinitely so that a crystal of silicon is really a giant molecule made up of a network or lattice of atoms. In this respect it behaves like carbon, its next of kin in row 2. The covalent bonds in the lattice are much stronger than metallic bonding. In consequence, the bonds can be broken only at very high temperatures. Thus the melting point of silicon is very high. Covalently bonded electrons have none of the freedom of movement characteristic of the valence electrons of metals. However, if a potential is applied to a silicon crystal, a few valence electrons acquire enough energy to move to higher energy levels. These higher levels permit the electrons to move through the lattice network and so account for the feeble currents carried by the semiconductor.

Phosphorus The melting point of the next element phosphorus is 44.1 °C, much lower than that of silicon; moreover, phosphorus does not conduct electricity. In short, phosphorus is a nonmetal. How can this be explained? As you know, a phosphorus atom has three electrons in the 3*p* orbitals. In other words, its 3*p* orbitals are only half filled, and are available for bonding. Thus, each phosphorus atom has three covalent bonds which radiate like the sides of a pyramid to three other atoms to form a P_4 molecule as shown in Fig. 23-4. These P_4 molecules are held together by weak van der Waals forces, forming the soft, waxy solid called *white phosphorus*.

Note . . .

Only white phosphorus, the most common form, melts at 44.1°C. The other forms have higher melting points, each specific to a particular form.

Sulfur The next element, sulfur, has six valence electrons (two 3*s* and four 3*p*). Therefore a sulfur atom has two half-filled 3*p* orbitals which enable it to form two covalent bonds with two other atoms of sulfur. In this way, a molecule of sulfur can be built up. Actually, it can be shown that a sulfur molecule is made up of eight atoms at ordinary temperatures. What is the structure of the 8-atom molecule? First, let us suppose that the eight covalently bonded atoms could form a straight chain as in Fig. 23-5.

$$\cdot\ddot{\underset{\cdot\cdot}{S}}:\ddot{\underset{\cdot\cdot}{S}}:\ddot{\underset{\cdot\cdot}{S}}:\ddot{\underset{\cdot\cdot}{S}}:\ddot{\underset{\cdot\cdot}{S}}:\ddot{\underset{\cdot\cdot}{S}}:\ddot{\underset{\cdot\cdot}{S}}:\ddot{\underset{\cdot\cdot}{S}}\cdot$$

Fig. 23-5

Is this reasonable? Notice that there are single electrons at both ends of the chain. And since sulfur atoms at the ends of the chain would continue to share electrons with other atoms indefinitely, this arrangement as a stable molecule is unlikely. Thus we suspect that the eight atoms in a sulfur molecule do *not* form a *straight chain* of eight atoms, but rather a closed ring as shown in Fig. 23-6. The S_8 molecules are held together by van der Waals forces to form a crystalline solid. Because sulfur molecules (S_8) are larger than phosphorus molecules (P_4), the van der Waals forces are stronger in sulfur than in phosphorus. As a result, we would expect the melting point of sulfur to be higher than that of phosphorus, a prediction that is confirmed by experiment.

Chemical Properties

Aluminum

Aluminum has a low ionization energy (138 kcal/mole). Therefore its valence electrons are not strongly held and, like sodium and magnesium, aluminum is a good reducing agent. For instance, it reduces hydrogen ion in hydrochloric acid to yield hydrogen gas. The reaction is

$$2Al(s) + 6H^{+}(aq) \longrightarrow 2Al^{+3}(aq) + 3H_2(g) \qquad (23\text{-}3)$$

Aluminum has a valence of +3 in most of its compounds.

Aluminum in powdered form is a particularly good reducing agent. A mixture of powdered aluminum and a metal oxide such as iron (III) oxide reacts with great speed (and even violence) if raised to its temperature of activation by using a fuse of burning magnesium ribbon as shown in Fig. 23-7. This reaction is

$$Fe_2O_3(s) + 2Al(s) \longrightarrow Al_2O_3(s) + 2Fe(l) + \text{heat energy} \qquad \Delta H = -200 \text{ kcal} \qquad (23\text{-}4)$$

So much heat is released in this reaction that the iron melts. Indeed, a mixture of powdered aluminum and ferric oxide is called

Fig. 23-6 A sulfur molecule is a ring of eight atoms.

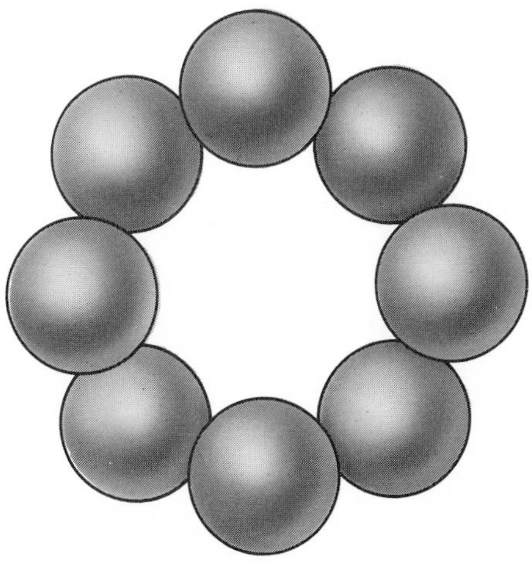

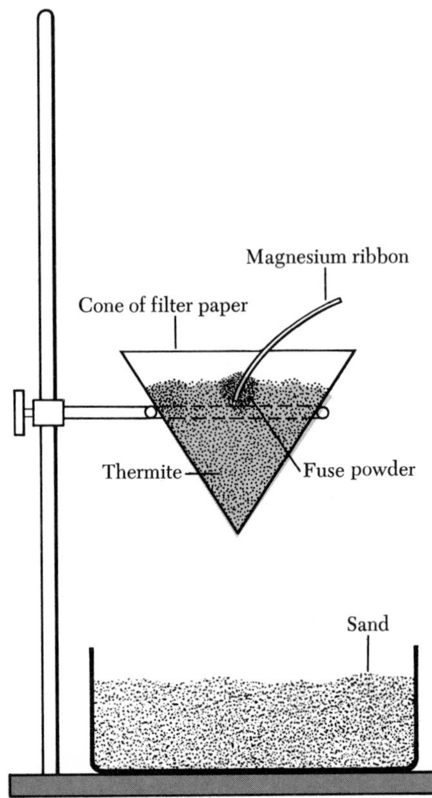

Fig. 23-7 Thermite is ignited by burning magnesium, and molten iron falls into the sand.

thermite and it is used in industry as a source of molten iron for welding cracks in structural steel such as propeller shafts or rails. For this purpose the cracked rail is packed in sand and an earthenware pot of thermite is placed over the crack. The reaction is started with a magnesium fuse and the molten iron flows through a hole in the pot and seals the crack.

Aluminum Oxide is a Stable Compound Aluminum oxide (Al_2O_3) is a very stable ionic compound and it occurs abundantly in nature as the mineral *bauxite*. Its unusual stability is the result of the small size of aluminum ions (Al^{+3}). Actually, aluminum ions are smaller than sodium and magnesium ions and, as a result, oxide ions (O^{-2}) can approach them very closely. And the nearer the ions the stronger is the electrostatic bond between them.

Aluminum Hydroxide is Amphoteric Aluminum hydroxide, $Al(OH)_3$, is a jelly-like transparent compound, almost insoluble in water. But unlike NaOH, it is a *weak* base. How can this be explained? As you have seen, the first three ionization energies of aluminum in kilocalories per mole are 138, 434, and 656, respectively. And since the second and third valence electrons are much more difficult to release than the sodium valence electron (ionization energy = 118 kcal/mole), $Al(OH)_3$ shows a good deal of covalent character. This results in very little ionization and the equilibrium

$$Al(OH)_3 \rightleftharpoons Al^{+3} + 3OH^- \qquad (23\text{-}5)$$

lies very strongly to the left. Since $Al(OH)_3$ is a base, it reacts with strong acids according to the equation:

$$3OH^- + 3H^+(aq) \longrightarrow 3H_2O \qquad (23\text{-}6)$$

That is, if dilute hydrochloric acid is added to a gelatinous precipitate of $Al(OH)_3$, the precipitate dissolves because the soluble salt, $AlCl_3$, is formed.

Aluminum hydroxide also reacts with a strong base and behaves as a weak acid. How is this possible? Hydroxide ion reacts with hydrogen ion. Hence the large concentration of OH^- ion supplied by a strong base such as NaOH breaks the O—H bond in $Al(OH)_3$.

$$OH^- + Al(OH)_3 \longrightarrow AlO_2^- + 2H_2O \qquad (23\text{-}7)$$

The AlO_2^- ion is called an aluminate ion and it probably has the formula $AlO_2 \cdot 4H_2O^{-2}$. In other words, if sodium hydroxide solution is added to $Al(OH)_3$, the gelatinous solid dissolves and soluble sodium aluminate is formed. The reaction can be written as

$$NaOH + Al(OH)_3 \longrightarrow NaAlO_2 + 2H_2O \qquad (23\text{-}8)$$

Recall . . .
What is an alloy?

In short, $Al(OH)_3$ can ionize in two different ways to give $H^+(aq)$ or OH^-; it can act either as an acid or as a base, depending upon the presence of OH^- ion or H^+ ion,

$$Al^{+3} + 3H_2O \underset{(3H^+)}{\overset{\text{In acid}}{\rightleftharpoons}} Al(OH)_3 \underset{(OH^-)}{\overset{\text{In base}}{\rightleftharpoons}} AlO_2^- + 2H_2O \qquad (23\text{-}9)$$

A substance that behaves as an acid under some conditions and as a base under others is called an *amphoteric* substance. Aluminum hydroxide is clearly amphoteric.

Aluminum Metal Pure aluminum is unsuitable as a structural metal—it is too soft and lacks toughness and strength. However, if it is alloyed with small amounts of other metals such as Cu, Mn, Mg, and Cr, it becomes hard and strong, and for many constructional purposes aluminum alloy has replaced steel. Actually, it is almost one-third as heavy as steel, and this is clearly a great advantage in the construction of aircraft. Moreover, unlike steel, it rusts only very slightly. When exposed to air, aluminum forms a thin layer of oxide which adheres to the surface so strongly that further corrosion of the metal is prevented. Indeed, a protective coat of paint, so essential for structural steel, is unnecessary.

Investigate . . .
There are two industrial processes for producing aluminum metal. They are almost identical. One was invented by the American chemist C. M. Hall. Find out about the other process. Who invented it? Compare the two processes.

Aluminum is the most abundant metal in nature and, as already stated, it occurs chiefly as an ore called bauxite. Bauxite is crude aluminum oxide which contains about 10% of rocky impurities, such as silica (SiO_2) and iron (III) oxide (Fe_2O_3). Aluminum is obtained by the electrolysis of pure molten Al_2O_3 so the first step in its manufacture is the removal of all impurities from the ore.

Aluminum oxide, or alumina as it is called in the trade, has a high melting point—over 2000°C. To provide enough electric energy to maintain such a high temperature would be exceedingly expensive, and the operating cost is reduced by using a suitable solvent. It was found that aluminum oxide would dissolve in an aluminum salt called cryolite (Na_3AlF_6) that melts at a temperature well below

1000 °C. Thus the electolytic solution is a solution of Al_2O_3 in molten Na_3AlF_6. This solution contains the four ions, Al^{+3}, O^{-2}, Na^+, and AlF_6^{-3}. Both Al^{+3} and Na^+ ions are attracted by the cathode, but only Al^{+3} ions are discharged. Let us see why. The oxidation potential (E^0) for Na is 2.71 V and for Al it is 1.67 V. Thus, a lower voltage is needed to reduce Al^{+3} ions to Al atoms than to reduce Na^+ ions to Na atoms. In other words, by selecting the right voltage, only Al^{+3} ions are discharged at the cathode. The same argument applies to the reaction at the anode. Oxide ions (O^{-2}) are more easily oxidized than AlF_6^{-3} ions so that selective oxidation is possible. Thus the two reactions in the electrolytic cell are

cathode reaction:

$$4Al^{+3} + 12e^- \longrightarrow 4Al \qquad (23\text{-}10)$$

anode reaction:

$$6O^{-2} - 12e^- \longrightarrow 3O_2 \qquad (23\text{-}11)$$

net reaction:

$$4Al^{+3} + 6O^{-2} \longrightarrow 4Al(l) + 3O_2(g) \qquad (23\text{-}12)$$

The cathode of the electrolytic cell is a steel tank lined with graphite. The anode consists of thick graphite rods suspended from a bus

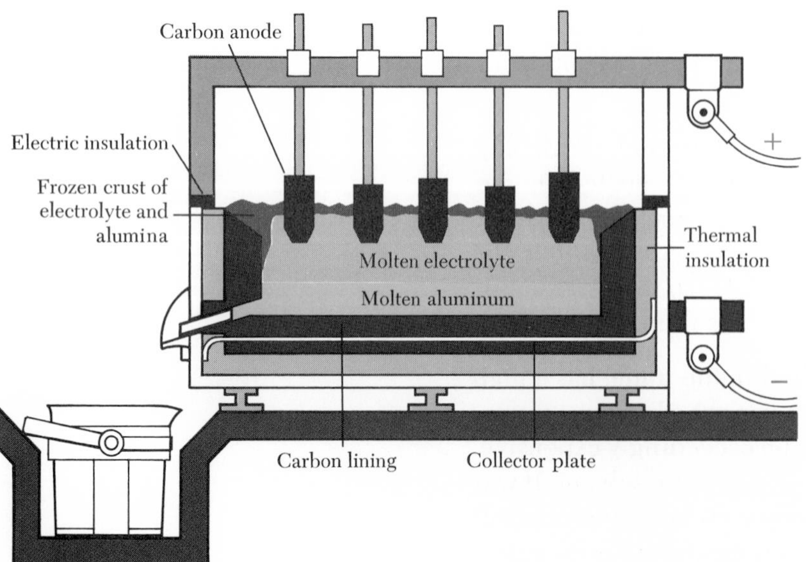

Fig. 23-8 Molten aluminum is prepared from aluminum ore in an electrolytic cell.

Fig. 23-9 Production of aluminum in a modern plant.

bar as shown in Fig. 23-8. First, cryolite is put into the tank and the current is turned on. The high resistance of the electrolyte generates enough heat to melt the cryolite. Alumina is then added to the molten cryolite and the reactions at the electrodes take place. The temperature of the molten cryolite is well above the melting point of aluminum (660 °C) so that molten aluminum is released at the cathode. The molten metal settles to the bottom of the tank and is drawn off through a tap hole from time to time (Fig. 23-9).

Sulfur

The electron configuration of sulfur is $1s^2 2s^2 2p^6 3s^2 3p^4$. Its ionization energy is high (240 kcal/mole). Therefore, it is difficult to remove a $3p$ electron from the sulfur atom. However, this atom readily gains two $3p$ electrons, thereby filling its valence orbitals and assuming the stable structure of argon. When sulfur gains electrons it behaves as an oxidizer, as illustrated by its reaction with metals such as zinc. If a mixture of powdered zinc and sulfur is heated to its activation temperature, the reaction is

$$8Zn(s) + S_8(s) \longrightarrow 8ZnS(s) \qquad (23\text{-}13)$$

Zinc sulfide contains the sulfide ion (S^{-2}); it is an ionic compound. Indeed, all the metallic sulfides are solid ionic compounds.

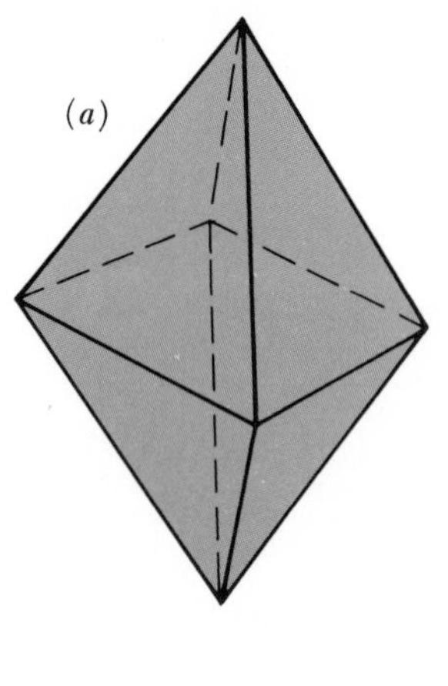

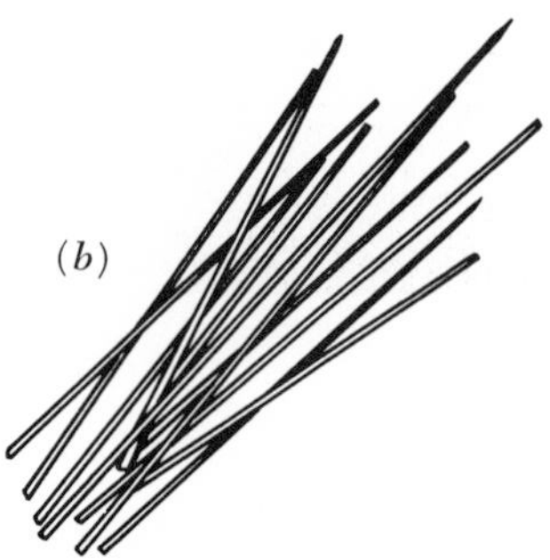

Fig. 23-10 (*a*) Rhombic (α) sulfur would form perfect octahedral crystals if there were no interference with their growth. (*b*) Crystals of monoclinic (β) sulfur.

Sulfur also reacts with the more electronegative element oxygen to form two oxides in which its oxidation numbers are +4 and +6. In these reactions sulfur is a reducing agent. Why? The first of these oxides, sulfur dioxide (SO_2), is formed when sulfur is heated in air:

$$S_8(s) + 8O_2(g) \longrightarrow 8SO_2(g) \qquad (23\text{-}14)$$

As you already know, a sulfur atom has six valence electrons (two 3*s* and four 3*p*). The 3*p* electrons are at a higher energy level than the 3*s* electrons and therefore more energetic. In this reaction, the four 3*p* electrons in a sulfur atom are shared with two oxygen atoms. Hence the oxidation numbers of sulfur and oxygen are +4 and −2, respectively.

Sulfur dioxide, which is a gas at ordinary temperatures, will combine with more oxygen in the presence of a suitable catalyst to form sulfur trioxide, which is also a gas. The equation for this reaction is

$$2SO_2(g) + O_2(g) \longrightarrow 2SO_3(g) \qquad (23\text{-}15)$$

In this compound (SO_3) the sulfur atom shares all six of its valence electrons with three oxygen atoms. Thus the oxidation number of sulfur is +6. Sulfur also forms the substance SF_6. Can you write the electron-dot formula for this substance?

Occurrence of Sulfur in Nature There are many minerals of sulfur in nature. In some it occurs as sulfide ion, that is in its reduced state. In others, it occurs as sulfate ion (SO_4^{-2}), that is in its oxidized state. Some examples of sulfur minerals are galena (PbS), iron pyrites (FeS_2), zinc blende (ZnS), Epsom salt ($MgSO_4 \cdot 7H_2O$), and gypsum ($CaSO_4 \cdot 2H_2O$). There are also large underground deposits of free sulfur (in Louisiana and Texas in the U.S.A.; also in many other parts of the world), and it is mainly from these deposits that sulfur is extracted for use in industry.

The method of mining underground sulfur (called the Frasch process) depends upon the fact that water under high pressure can be heated to a temperature well above the melting point of α-sulfur (113 °C). In the Frasch process a system of three concentric pipes is lowered into a bed of sulfur, as shown in Fig. 23-11*a*. Superheated water falls through the outer pipe and melts the nearby sulfur. Compressed air, forced through the small inner pipe, forces molten sulfur up the third pipe and into a large wooden bin where it cools and solidifies (Fig. 23-11*b*).

Infer...

Free (elementary) sulfur is found near most active volcanoes. Why do you think that sulfur was at one time called brimstone?

The Frasch process is not only a simple operation but also an ingenious one, particularly in the way that impurities in the sulfur are eliminated. The superheated water does not melt the rocky impurities and, in consequence, they are left behind. Hence the sulfur collected in the Frasch process is pure sulfur and no further purification is necessary.

The Oxyacids of Sulfur There are two common oxyacids of sulfur, sulfur*ous* acid (H_2SO_3) and sulfur*ic* acid (H_2SO_4). Sulfurous acid is formed when sulfur dioxide reacts with water:

$$H_2O + SO_2 \rightleftharpoons H_2SO_3 \quad (23\text{-}16)$$

That is, a water solution of sulfur dioxide contains some sulfurous acid. This acid is very unstable and it decomposes if the solution is heated. The sulfur dioxide then escapes into the air, leaving only water.

Sulfurous acid ionizes to form hydrogen ion and bisulfite (or acid sulfite) ion (HSO_3^-):

$$H_2SO_3(aq) \rightleftharpoons H^+(aq) + HSO_3^-(aq) \quad (23\text{-}17)$$

For this reaction (at 25 °C)

$$K_A = \frac{[H^+][HSO_3^-]}{[H_2SO_3]} = 1.7 \times 10^{-2}$$

That is, the value of the ionization constant is small, and therefore sulfurous acid is a relatively weak acid. In the second ionization step HSO_3^- ion dissociates to form sulfite ion (SO_3^{-2}).

$$HSO_3^-(aq) \rightleftharpoons H^+(aq) + SO_3^{-2}(aq) \quad (23\text{-}18)$$

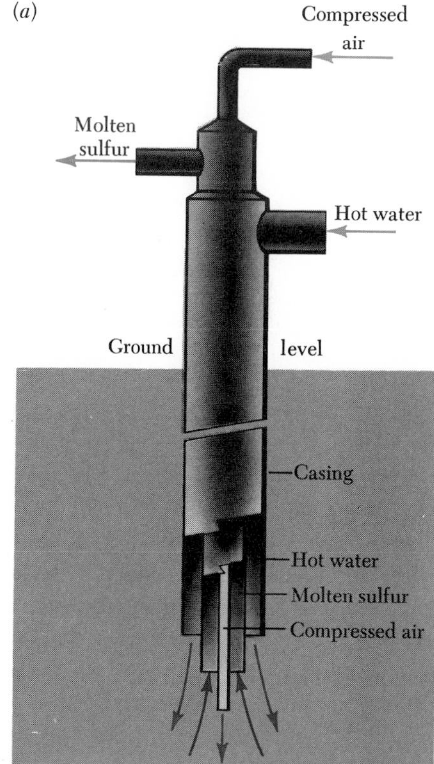

Fig. 23-11 (*a*) A system of concentric pipes is used in the Frasch process of mining sulfur. (*b*) Molten sulfur is pumped into a wooden bin, where it solidifies. The solid sulfur is blasted with dynamite and hauled away for use in industry.

The ionization constant for this reaction at 25 °C is even smaller (6.2×10^{-8}) so that HSO_3^- is a *very* weak acid.

The other common oxyacid of sulfur is sulfuric acid (H_2SO_4), and it is formed slowly when sulfur trioxide is in contact with water,

$$H_2O + SO_3 \rightleftharpoons H_2SO_4 \qquad (23\text{-}19)$$

Sulfuric acid, like sulfurous acid, ionizes in two steps:

$$H_2SO_4(aq) \rightleftharpoons H^+(aq) + HSO_4^-(aq) \qquad (23\text{-}20)$$

$$HSO_4^-(aq) \rightleftharpoons H^+(aq) + SO_4^{-2}(aq) \qquad (23\text{-}21)$$

The ionization constant (K_A) for step 1 (Eq. 23-20) is very high, since sulfuric acid is almost completely dissociated into ions. Therefore, H_2SO_4 is a strong acid. The K_A value for the second step is small at 25 °C (1.2×10^{-2}). That is, bisulfate ion (HSO_4^-) does not easily release hydrogen ion; it is a weak acid. Why is sulfuric acid so much stronger than sulfurous?

The electron-dot formulas for the two acids are shown in Figs. 23-12 and 23-13, where the electrons from sulfur are indicated by ∘, those from oxygen by ·, and those from hydrogen by ×.

```
   ..  ∘∘  ..
H ×O : S : O × H
   ..  ∘∘  ..
      :O:
       ..
```

Fig. 23-12 Sulfurous acid

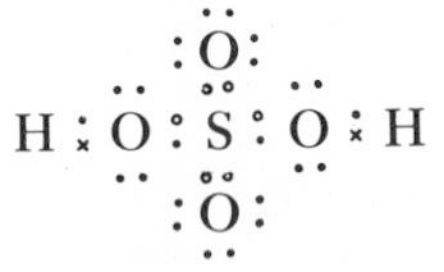

```
       ..
      :O:
   ..  ∘∘  ..
H ×O : S : O × H
   ..  ∘∘  ..
      :O:
       ..
```

Fig. 23-13 Sulfuric acid

In sulfurous acid, a sulfur atom supplies four of the six electrons it shares with three oxygen atoms. And since oxygen is more electronegative than sulfur, the oxidation number of sulfur in sulfurous acid is +4. In sulfuric acid a sulfur atom supplies six of the eight electrons it shares with four oxygen atoms. Therefore the oxidation number of sulfur in sulfuric acid is +6.

Since sulfurous acid is weak, the H—O bonds are not easily broken. As a result, hydrogen ions are released with difficulty from the H—O bonds in H_2SO_3. Why is sulfuric acid strong? Sulfuric acid is formed from sulfurous acid by the addition of an oxygen atom to the central atom of sulfur. This oxygen atom draws some of the electronic charge from the sulfur atom which, in turn, draws charge from the other oxygen atoms, thereby weakening the H—O bond. As a result, the hydrogen ion is able to break away very easily from this weak bond. Can you explain why the second H—O bond in the H_2SO_4 molecule is not as easily broken as the first?

The Manufacture of Sulfuric Acid Sulfuric acid is by far the most widely used compound of sulfur. Indeed the acid is used in so many industrial processes that it is manufactured on a large scale.

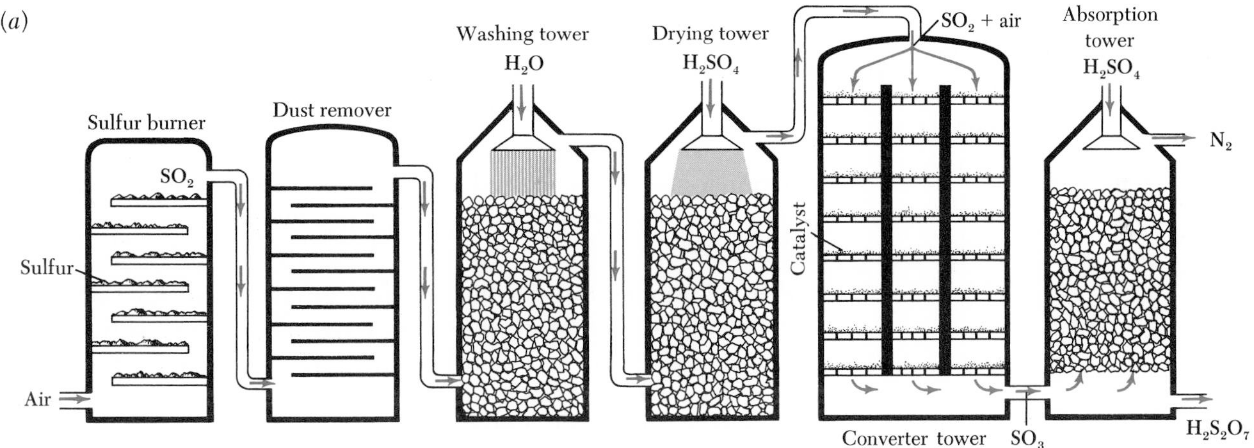

Fig. 23-14 The contact process for manufacturing sulfuric acid.

Most of the sulfuric acid in the United States is made by the *contact process*, so called because, in the principal reaction, sulfur dioxide and air (oxygen) are brought into contact in the presence of a catalyst. A diagrammatic representation of the various steps in the operation is shown in Fig. 23-4*a*. First, sulfur is burned in air and oxidized to sulfur dioxide:

$$S_8(g) + 8O_2(g) \longrightarrow 8SO_2(g) \qquad (23\text{-}22)$$

Sulfur dioxide can then be oxidized a stage further to form sulfur trioxide:

$$2SO_2(g) + O_2(g) \overset{\text{catalyst}}{\rightleftarrows} 2SO_3(g) \qquad (23\text{-}23)$$

Notice that the sulfur dioxide–oxygen reaction is reversible and, to produce the maximum amount of sulfuric acid, there must be a maximum yield of SO_3. How can this be achieved?

The SO_3 reaction is exothermic:

$$2SO_2 + O_2 \rightleftarrows 2SO_3 + \text{heat} \qquad (23\text{-}24)$$

How will the yield of SO_3 be affected if the gas mixture is heated? The heating of the gas mixture constitutes a stress and therefore by Le Châtelier's principle the reaction that opposes the stress (the reaction that absorbs heat) will be favored. Since heat is evolved (and the temperature raised) when SO_3 is formed, heat must be ab-

(*b*)

Table 23-2
Variation of yield of SO_3 with temperature

Temperature, °C	Yield of SO_3, %
400	99
600	75
800	24
1000	7

sorbed (and the temperature lowered) when SO_3 is decomposed:

$$2SO_2 + O_2 \underset{\text{heat absorbed}}{\overset{\text{heat evolved}}{\rightleftharpoons}} 2SO_3 \qquad (23\text{-}25)$$

In other words, if the temperature of the gas mixture is raised, the reaction to the left is favored and the yield of SO_3 diminished. This prediction is confirmed by experimental evidence as is shown in Table 23-2.

The ideal temperature for the reaction appears to be 400 °C. However, at this temperature the rate of reaction is very slow and it takes several hours to reach equilibrium. Fortunately, there are several catalysts that can speed up the reaction. The most effective catalyst is finely divided platinum. But platinum is very expensive and a cheaper solid catalyst, vanadium pentoxide (V_2O_5), is usually used in the contact process.

The Conversion of Sulfur Trioxide to Sulfuric Acid The final step is the conversion of SO_3 to H_2SO_4. At first sight it looks as though all that is necessary is to bubble the gas into water:

$$SO_3 + H_2O \longrightarrow H_2SO_4 \qquad (23\text{-}26)$$

However, sulfur trioxide does not dissolve readily in water, although it does dissolve in and react with concentrated sulfuric acid. Thus, SO_3 is bubbled into concentrated sulfuric acid and the following reaction takes place:

$$H_2SO_4 + SO_3 \longrightarrow H_2S_2O_7 \qquad (23\text{-}27)$$

The compound $H_2S_2O_7$ is called pyrosulfuric acid or, in the industry, *oleum*. Water is continuously added as oleum is being formed and sulfuric acid is the product of the reaction:

$$H_2S_2O_7 + H_2O \longrightarrow 2H_2SO_4 \qquad (23\text{-}28)$$

Notice that from every single molecule of H_2SO_4 added to absorb SO_3, two molecules of H_2SO_4 are produced. So, strange as it may seem, sulfuric acid is used to manufacture sulfuric acid in the contact process.

Summary

There are eight elements in the third row of the periodic classification: Na, Mg, Al, Si, P, S, Cl, and Ar. In moving from left to right in the row, there is a gradual change in both physical and chemical properties. On the left, sodium, magnesium, and aluminum are metallic solids; on the right, phosphorus, sulfur, chlorine, and argon are nonmetals. Phosphorus and sulfur occur in several forms—molecular *allotropes.* The metals form metallic bonds; silicon is a network crystal held together by strong covalent bonds; phosphorus and sulfur are molecular solids—the atoms are bonded into molecules by covalent bonds and the molecules are held together as solids by van der Waals forces. Chlorine and argon on the right are gases. Chlorine atoms combine to form diatomic molecules but argon atoms do not combine.

Sodium, magnesium, and aluminum on the left are strong reducing agents—they have low ionization energies and form predominantly ionic compounds, although aluminum does form some covalent substances. Chlorine on the right is a strong oxidizing agent; it forms chloride ions with metals and covalent compounds with nonmetals. Argon on the extreme right is chemically inert. Both chlorine and argon have very high ionization energies. The middle elements, phosphorus and sulfur, form predominantly covalent compounds and under the right conditions can react with nonmetals with higher or lower electronegativity. That is, phosphorus and sulfur can act as either oxidizing or reducing agents.

Aluminum hydroxide acts as an acid in presence of a strong base, and it acts as a base in presence of a strong acid. Such a substance is said to be *amphoteric.*

Phosphorus, sulfur, and chlorine form oxyacids. For example, H_3PO_3 (phosphorous acid) and H_3PO_4 (phosphoric acid) are oxyacids. The oxidation number of phosphorus is +3 in H_3PO_3 and +5 in H_3PO_4.

Factual Recall

1. (*a*) List, in the order of their atomic numbers, the eight elements in the third horizontal row of the periodic table.
   (*b*) List the valence electrons for each of the elements in (*a*).
2. From an examination of the valence electrons, discuss the nature of the change in chemical activity of the elements from left to right along the row.
3. There is a steady increase in the ionization energies of the elements from left to right along the third row. How do you account for this increase?

4. Explain why magnesium forms a +2 ion rather than a +1 ion or a +3 ion.
5. Which of the elements, magnesium or aluminum, forms ionic bonds more easily? Why?
6. (*a*) Explain how the bonding of silicon atoms differs from metallic bonding.
   (*b*) How does this difference in bonding in (*a*) account for the difference in electrical conductivity?
7. The melting point of silicon is very high (1410 °C). Explain.
8. Phosphorus is the element next to silicon in the third row, yet the melting point of white phosphorus is very low (44 °C). Explain why.
9. Sulfur is the element next beyond phosphorus in the third row, yet the melting point of α-sulfur (112 °C) is higher than the melting point of white phosphorus. Explain why.
10. (*a*) From the ionization energies of sodium, magnesium, and aluminum explain why these metals are all powerful reducing agents.
    (*b*) Describe a reaction in which aluminum acts as a reducing agent.
11. Aluminum hydroxide dissolves in a strong acid such as dilute hydrochloric acid. Explain why.
12. Aluminum hydroxide dissolves in dilute sodium hydroxide. Explain why.
13. What is an amphoteric substance? Give an example.
14. (*a*) Draw a diagram of an electrolytic cell used to manufacture aluminum, and label its parts.
    (*b*) Describe the reaction at the cathode of this cell.
    (*c*) What is the electrolyte in this cell and why is it used?
15. Give an example of a reaction in which sulfur behaves as an oxidizing agent, and explain why this particular reaction takes place.
16. Give an example of a reaction in which sulfur behaves as a reducing agent, and explain why this particular reaction takes place.
17. What is the Frasch process? Give details of the process and state its particular advantage as an industrial operation.

18. (*a*) Discuss the manufacture of sulfuric acid by the contact process.
    (*b*) What part does the catalyst play in this reaction?
    (*c*) The lower the temperature, the higher is the yield of sulfur trioxide in this reaction. Explain why.
19. Which is the stronger of the two acids, sulfuric or sulfurous? Why?
20. Sulfuric acid releases hydrogen ion in two steps. (*a*) What are these steps? (*b*) Which step takes place the more easily? Why?
21. The ionization constants for HSO_4^- ion and HSO_3^- ion are 1.2×10^{-2} and 6.2×10^{-8} respectively. What do these values mean?

Apply Your Knowledge!

1. A 17.6 g sample of iron (II) sulfide reacts with 6.00 *M* HCl solution. Calculate the (*a*) moles of acid used, (*b*) volume of gas product at STP, (*c*) molarity of the salt solution formed if the calculated volume of acid is used.
2. The complete combustion of H_2S gives 1.12 l of SO_2 at 273°C. (*a*) How many moles of H_2S are consumed? (*b*) What volume of air (20% oxygen) at STP is required? (*c*) What mass of water is formed?
3. Hydrogen sulfide is led into 100 ml of a 0.200 *M* $AgNO_3$ solution until precipitation is complete. Compute the (*a*) volume at STP of H_2S used, (*b*) mass of the precipitate, (*c*) molarity of the strong acid formed during the reaction, (*d*) *p*H of the final solution.
4. The H_2S liberated by adding 16.7 ml of 6.0 *M* HCl solution to 4.5 g of iron(II) sulfide is completely absorbed by 250 ml of a 0.500 *M* $Pb(NO_3)_2$ solution. What is the mass of the PbS precipitated?
5. Hydrogen sulfide is bubbled through 100 ml of a solution which is 0.100 *M* in copper (II) ion and 0.100 *M* in zinc ion. Compute the mass of precipitate if the *p*H of the solution is (*a*) zero, (*b*) 7.0.
6. A solution of H_2SO_3 is completely converted to H_2SO_4 by the absorption of 0.56 l of O_2 at STP. Calculate the volume of 0.500 *M* NaOH required to neutralize the acid.

7. (*a*) What volume of concentrated H_2SO_4 (specific gravity 1.85) must be used to react with 3.2 g of copper?
   (*b*) What volume of SO_2 at 273°C is produced in the reaction?

8. Calculate the volume of 10.0 *M* HCl solution required to react with 5.2 g of $NaHSO_3$.

9. If 100 ml of 0.100 *M* $KMnO_4$ solution are consumed in the oxidation of a solution of H_2SO_3, how many moles of SO_4^{-2} ion are formed?

10. What volume of 1.50 *M* $BaCl_2$ solution must be added to precipitate the SO_4^{-2} ion formed in Problem 9?

11. The HCl gas liberated by the reaction between 4.9 g of H_2SO_4 and NaCl is dissolved in water to give 10.0 ml of solution. Calculate the (*a*) mass in grams of NaCl consumed, (*b*) molarity of the HCl produced, (*c*) volume of 5.0 *M* KOH solution required to neutralize the HCl.

12. The addition of 0.500 *M* $BaCl_2$ solution in excess to 100 ml of a solution which contains both SO_4^{-2} ion and CO_3^{-2} ion gives 4.30 g of precipitate. After acidification with HNO_3, the mass of the precipitate is only 2.33 g. (*a*) What was the molarity of the CO_3^{-2} ion in the original solution? (*b*) What was the molarity of the SO_4^{-2} ion in the original solution? (*c*) What volume of $BaCl_2$ solution was actually needed to precipitate both anions?

13. Compute the percentage by mass of (*a*) oxygen as Al_2O_3 and (*b*) rocky impurity in a bauxite ore which contains 45% by mass of aluminum.

Find Out!

1. Research the allotropic forms of sulfur. Does each one have a distinct use?

2. Research the various forms of phosphorus. Why is only red phosphorus now used in manufacturing matches?

3. There are other methods of manufacturing sulfuric acid. Find out about at least two more.

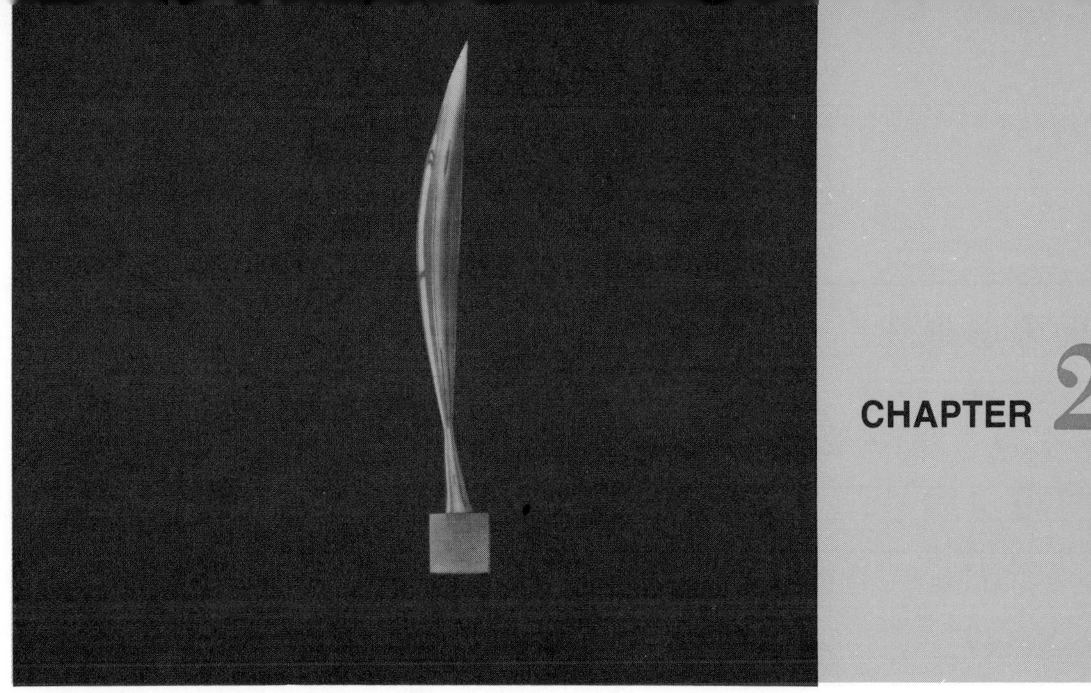

CHAPTER 24

TRANSITION ELEMENTS IN THE FOURTH ROW

WE HAVE SEEN THAT AN ELECTRON enters the orbital of lowest energy available to it. Studies of electron configurations of atoms show that electrons are added to the 4*s* orbitals before they are added to the 3*d* orbitals. After orbital 4*s* has been filled, we would normally expect the three 4*p* orbitals to be filled. However, experiments show that the energy of the 3*d* orbitals is a little higher than that of the 4*s* orbitals but a little less than that of the 4*p* as shown in Fig. 24-1. Therefore the ten available spaces in the five 3*d* orbitals are filled before electrons begin to enter the six spaces in the three 4*p* orbitals. The result of this is that the fourth row of elements consists of three groups, depending upon the orbitals being filled by the outermost electrons in their atoms. Thus, potassium and calcium atoms add electrons to the 4*s* orbital, atoms from scandium to zinc add electrons to the 3*d* orbitals, and atoms from gallium to krypton add electrons to the 4*p* orbitals. The electron configurations of the 18 fourth-row elements are given in Table 24-1.

It is apparent that in the fourth row the *s*–*p* filling sequence is interrupted by the filling of *d* orbitals whose principal quantum number

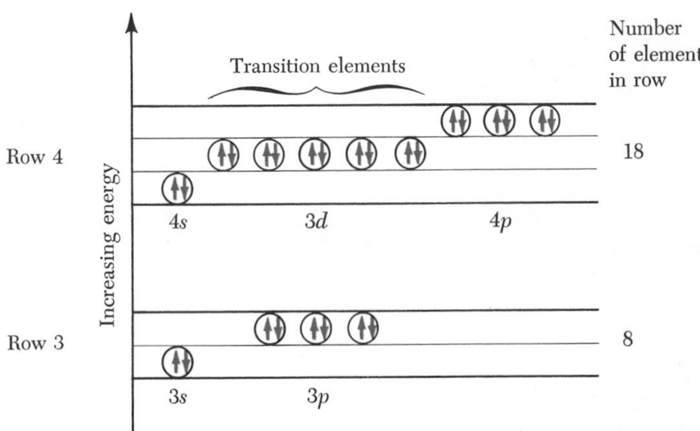

Fig. 24-1 Atomic orbitals 3*s* through 4*p* arranged in order of increasing energy.

Table 24-1 Electron configuration of elements in fourth row

Element	Symbol	Z	Electrons in orbitals beyond argon 4*s*	3*d*	4*p*
Potassium	K	19	1		
Calcium	Ca	20	2		
Scandium	Sc	21	2	1	
Titanium	Ti	22	2	2	
Vanadium	V	23	2	3	
Chromium	Cr	24	1	5	
Manganese	Mn	25	2	5	
Iron	Fe	26	2	6	
Cobalt	Co	27	2	7	
Nickel	Ni	28	2	8	
Copper	Cu	29	1	10	
Zinc	Zn	30	2	10	
Gallium	Ga	31	2	10	1
Germanium	Ge	32	2	10	2
Arsenic	As	33	2	10	3
Selenium	Se	34	2	10	4
Bromine	Br	35	2	10	5
Krypton	Kr	36	2	10	6

(3) is one less than the quantum number (4) of the *s* and *p* orbitals. The injected group of elements with the lower quantum number is called a group of *transition elements.*

The first element in the fourth row is potassium ($1s^2 2s^2 2p^6 3s^2 3p^6 4s^1$); the second is calcium ($1s^2 2s^2 2p^6 3s^2 3p^6 4s^2$).

As stated in an earlier chapter, potassium is one of the alkali metals, soft and very active chemically. Its melting point is 62 °C, its ionization energy is 100 kcal/mole and its valence is +1. Calcium is one of the alkaline-earth metals. Its ionization energy is 140 kcal/mole; that is, calcium is less active than potassium. In forming its metallic bonds every calcium atom contributes two 4*s* electrons, whereas a potassium atom contributes only one. We would therefore expect calcium to be a harder metal than potassium and its melting point higher. Actually, the melting point of calcium is 842 °C.

With the 4*s* orbital now filled, the next electron to be added goes into one of the 3*d* orbitals. Thus is formed the first of the transition elements, the element scandium.

Properties of the Transition Elements in the Fourth Row

This group of transition elements, like other groups of transition elements, has many similar properties; that is, they resemble a *family* of elements rather than a row. But this might be expected since, with few exceptions, the outer orbitals of the atoms of these elements contain the same number of electrons, and, as you recall, chemical properties are determined largely by the number of electrons in the outermost orbitals.

All the transition elements are metals and, like other metals, are good conductors of heat and electricity. Most of them have unusual magnetic properties and, in forming compounds, they show an unusual variety of oxidation states. Some of the properties of these transition elements are summarized in Table 24-2.

Electron Configurations

Except for chromium and copper, the 4*s* orbitals of these transition elements are filled with two electrons. For chromium and copper, however, the 4*s* orbital contains only one electron. Why these unexpected configurations? Or, in more specific terms, why is the configuration of chromium $3d^5 4s^1$, not the expected configuration, $3d^4 4s^2$? Why is the configuration of copper $3d^{10} 4s^1$ and not $3d^9 4s^2$? Notice that in chromium the 3*d* orbitals are just half-filled with electrons ($3d^5$) whereas in copper they are completely filled ($3d^{10}$). Apparently a chromium atom achieves a state of lower energy (and

Compare . . .
Contrast the properties of the transition metals with the properties of the alkali metals. What are the differences in terms of electron configuration and structure?

Table 24-2 Some properties of the transition elements in the fourth row

Element	Z	Melting point, °C	Ionization energy, kcal/mole	Atomic radius (Å)	Density, g/cm³	Electron configuration of outer orbitals	3d orbital configuration
Sc	21	1400	154	1.62	2.5	$3d^1 4s^2$	(↑) ○ ○ ○ ○
Ti	22	1810	157	1.47	4.5	$3d^2 4s^2$	(↑) (↑) ○ ○ ○
V	23	1730	155	1.34	6.0	$3d^3 4s^2$	(↑) (↑) (↑) ○ ○
Cr	24	1900	155	1.27	7.1	$3d^5 4s^1$	(↑) (↑) (↑) (↑) (↑)
Mn	25	1245	171	1.26	7.2	$3d^5 4s^2$	(↑) (↑) (↑) (↑) (↑)
Fe	26	1530	180	1.26	7.9	$3d^6 4s^2$	(↑↓) (↑) (↑) (↑) (↑)
Co	27	1490	180	1.25	8.9	$3d^7 4s^2$	(↑↓) (↑↓) (↑) (↑) (↑)
Ni	28	1455	175	1.24	8.9	$3d^8 4s^2$	(↑↓) (↑↓) (↑↓) (↑) (↑)
Cu	29	1085	176	1.28	8.9	$3d^{10} 4s^1$	(↑↓) (↑↓) (↑↓) (↑↓) (↑↓)
Zn	30	420	216	1.38	7.1	$3d^{10} 4s^2$	(↑↓) (↑↓) (↑↓) (↑↓) (↑↓)

therefore becomes more stable) if one of its electrons in the 4*s* orbitals migrates to a 3*d* orbital, thereby leaving both 4*s* and 3*d* orbitals half-filled. Similarly, a copper atom is in a lower energy state if one of its 4*s* electrons migrates to a 3*d* orbital and completely fills it.

High Melting Points

Except for zinc, the melting points of the transition elements are unusually high. Moreover, from scandium to chromium the melting temperatures rise, and from iron to copper they fall. How can these facts be explained? The number of unpaired electrons in the 3*d* orbitals increases from Sc to Cr, and the number decreases from Fe to Cu. Therefore, it looks as though the melting points are, in some way, related to the number of unpaired electrons.

Unpaired electrons in the 3*d* orbitals of one atom could conceivably engage in covalent bonding with the unpaired 3*d* electrons of other similar atoms. In other words, in addition to ordinary metallic bonding as explained in an earlier chapter, there is also the possibility of covalent bonding. Clearly, covalent bonding increases the attraction between atoms which, in turn, raises the melting temperatures of these elements.

The element zinc, however, is the last of the transition elements, and all its 3*d* and 4*s* orbitals are filled. Therefore there are no unpaired electrons in zinc atoms and covalent bonding is impossible. It should not therefore be surprising that the melting temperature of zinc (420 °C) is considerably lower than the melting temperatures of other transition elements.

Oxidation States

Although the transition elements have an outermost orbital that contains no more than two electrons, they form compounds, with the exception of zinc, in which the element has 2, 3, or even 4 oxidation states. Chromium, for example, has an oxidation number of +2 in chromium (II) oxide (CrO), +3 in chromium (III) oxide (Cr_2O_3), and +6 in potassium chromate (K_2CrO_4). Then again, common compounds of manganese are manganese (II) oxide (MnO), manganese (IV) oxide (MnO_2, usually called manganese dioxide), potassium manganate (K_2MnO_4), and potassium permanganate ($KMnO_4$) and the oxidation numbers of manganese in these compounds are +2, +4, +6, and +7, respectively. How can this multiplicity of oxidation states, or positive valences, be explained? As stated earlier, there is only a very small difference in energy between the 3*d* and 4*s* orbitals. Presumably then, both 4*s* and 3*d* electrons can become involved in forming compounds. Thus an atom of manganese has five electrons in its 3*d* orbitals and two in its 4*s* orbital, a total of seven electrons. Hence, the highest expected oxidation state for manganese is 7; this is observed in compounds like $KMnO_4$ where the maximum oxidation number is +7. On the other hand, scandium has two electrons in the 4*s* orbital but only one in the 3*d*, a total of three. The maximum oxidation number for scandium is +3.

Paramagnetism and Ferromagnetism

Except for zinc, all the transition elements are attracted by a magnetic field, an effect known as *paramagnetism*. How can this phenomenon be explained? We know from physics that moving charges create a magnetic field and paramagnetism is ascribed to the spins of unpaired electrons. Notice the term *unpaired* electrons. If electrons are paired, that is if there are two electrons in the same orbital, one can be imagined to spin clockwise and the other counterclockwise and, in consequence, their magnetic fields would neutralize each other.

The first five transition elements have an increasing number of unpaired electrons and, as we might expect, they show an increasing

Predict . . .
Which of the following atoms or ions would you expect to be paramagnetic in the gas phase: Sc, V, Zn, Ti^{+4}, Cr^{+2}, Fe^{+3}, CO^{+2}?

magnetic effect. Among the next five elements, the number of unpaired electrons diminishes and consequently the paramagnetic effect also diminishes.

The elements iron, cobalt, and nickel attract each other, an effect called *ferromagnetism*. Paramagnetism is dependent on the presence of an applied magnetic field, but ferromagnetism is not. The more powerful ferromagnetic effect is generally ascribed to interaction among unpaired electrons in large groups of atoms close to one another, as in a crystal. It is supposed that the atomic spacing is such that there is alignment of the magnetic fields induced by electron spin in adjacent atoms. Increasing the temperature of bringing the atoms too close together would diminish the magnetic effect due to spin and might even neutralize it altogether.

Size of Atoms: Density

The atomic diameters of the transition elements decrease slightly from left to right along the row. However, the diameters are remarkably similar. Why the similarity? Changes in atomic size are affected by changes in both the nuclear charge and the number of electrons in the $3d$ orbitals. An increase in nuclear charge would tend to pull the outer electrons closer to the nucleus, thereby reducing the size of the atom. On the other hand, an increase in the number of $3d$ electrons increases the force of repulsion between them, thereby tending to increase the size of the atom. And, since the diameters of the different atoms are almost alike, these two opposing tendencies almost counterbalance each other.

The densities of the transition elements show a steady increase in value as we move along the row. How can this be explained? Density is directly proportional to the mass and inversely proportional to the volume. The nuclear masses along the row steadily increase and the radii of the atoms slightly decrease. Therefore the densities are increased by both factors. The density of scandium (2.5 g/cm^3) is much lower than the densities of the other transition elements. But this is expected since the radius of scandium is the largest of the series.

Ionization Energies

Along the second and third rows, the elements show big differences in ionization energy. But for the transition elements the ionization energies show only slight increases—from 154 kcal/mole for scandium to 176 kcal/mole for copper. That is, 154 kcal of energy are needed to remove one of the 4*s* electrons from 1 mole of scandium atoms and only 176 kcal for the 4*s* electron in 1 mole of copper atoms. How can this very small increase be accounted for? As you may recall, ionization energy depends upon three factors: (1) the charge on the nucleus, (2) the distance between nucleus and outer electrons, and (3) the shielding effect of any electrons interposed between the nucleus and the outer electrons.

Note . . .
Scandium is chiefly produced as a by-product in the extraction of uranium from the mineral *davidite*. Scandium is the 50th most abundant element on the earth, while it is about the 23rd most abundant element in the sun.

The nuclear charge increases by one from element to element along the row. Clearly the increase in nuclear charge tends to increase the ionization energy. The distance from nucleus to outer electrons is roughly the same throughout the series, so that distance is not a significant factor in determining ionization energies of transition elements. However, the addition of 3*d* electrons shields the outer electron from the attractive force of the nucleus. That is, the shielding effect makes it easier to remove one of the 4*s* electrons, and therefore tends to reduce the ionization energy. In short, the effects of increase in nuclear charge and increase in the number of 3*d* electrons tend to neutralize each other. However, since there *is* a slight increase in ionization energy along the row, it is apparent that nuclear charge is the dominant factor.

The First Six Transition Elements in the Fourth Row

Scandium

The element scandium is next to calcium in the periodic table and, like calcium, it reacts with water, releasing hydrogen. However, unlike calcium, the 3*d* electron as well as the 4*s* electrons take part in the reaction (Fig. 24-2). The oxidation number for scandium is +3 whereas for calcium it is +2. The equations for the two reactions with water are

$$Ca + 2H_2O \longrightarrow Ca^{+2} + 2OH^- + H_2 \qquad (24\text{-}1)$$

$$2Sc + 6H_2O \longrightarrow 2Sc^{+3} + 6OH^- + 3H_2 \qquad (24\text{-}2)$$

Actually, the oxidation state of scandium is +3 in most of its compounds, so in this respect it resembles aluminum rather than calcium.

Fig. 24-2 Electron configuration of outer orbitals of scandium.

Scandium

Outer orbitals
$3d^1 \ 4s^2$

3*d* orbitals

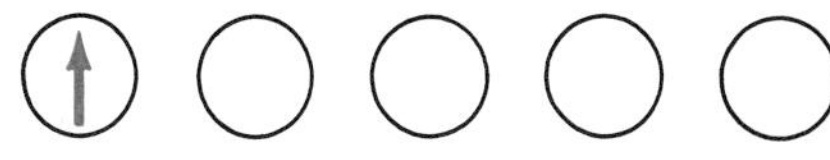

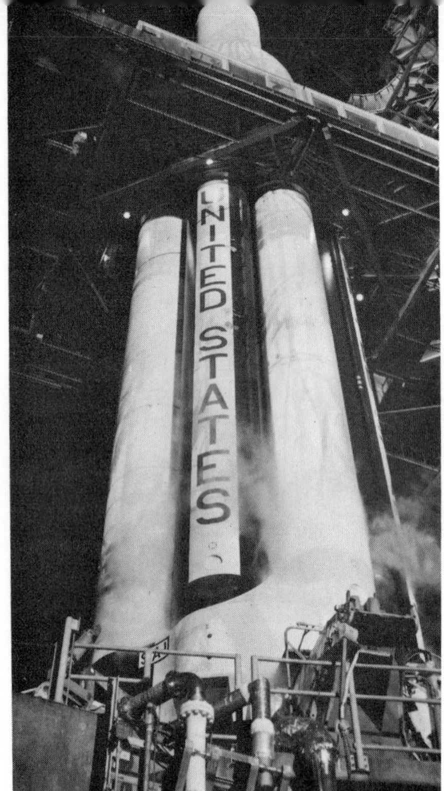

Fig. 24-3 Titanium is a light, tough metal used to build spacecraft. Why do its properties make this metal a desirable material for spacecraft construction? What is a disadvantage in its use?

3*d* orbitals

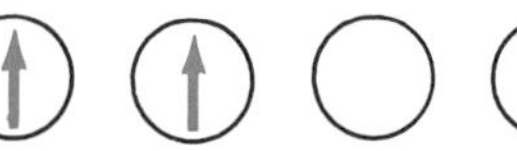

Fig. 24-4 Electron configuration of outer orbitals of titanium.

Titanium

Titanium atoms have four electrons available for bonding, two 3*d* electrons and two 4*s*. In forming compounds, the oxidation state of this element may be +2, +3, or +4, +4 being the most common. (TiO_2), a white solid, and titanium (IV) chloride ($TiCl_4$), a colorless liquid. For construction, this metal has three desirable qualities:

Speculate . . .
"Titanium white" (TiO_2) is widely used as a pigment in paint because it will not darken with time. Why?

(1) Great tensile strength. It is stronger than iron.

(2) Marked resistance to corrosion. It is much more corrosion-resistant than iron.

(3) Low density (4.5 g/cm³). It has a much lower density than iron.

But against these advantages there is a serious disadvantage. Hot titanium combines with carbon, oxygen, and even nitrogen, and the resulting compounds make the metal brittle. Clearly these reactions must be avoided in extracting titanium from its ore, *ilmenite* ($FeTiO_3$). The manufacture of titanium is a difficult and expensive process, and the uses of the metal are limited to special purposes such as the construction of spacecraft. See Fig. 24-3 and 24-4.

Note . . .
Vanadinite, $Pb_5(VO_4)_3Cl$, and *carnotite*, $K(UO_2)VO_4 \ \frac{3}{2} H_2O$ are the major ores from which vanadium is mined.

Vanadium

Vanadium atoms have five electrons available for bonding (three 3*d* and two 4*s*) and the element has oxidation states of +2, +3, +4, and +5 in its various compounds. The most common compound of vanadium is vanadium (V) oxide (or vanadium pentoxide), V_2O_5. See Fig. 24-5. As stated in Chapter 23, V_2O_5 is a catalyst in the oxidation of SO_2 to SO_3, a step in the manufacture of sulfuric acid. The way V_2O_5 accelerates the oxidation of SO_2 is probably due to the multivalence of vanadium, particularly its ability to change its oxidation number from +5 to +4, and then back to +5. One explanation of the catalytic reaction is that V_2O_5 absorbs SO_2 and in doing so transfers an atom of oxygen to SO_2, thereby changing its oxidation state from five to four:

$$V_2O_5(s) + SO_2(g) \longrightarrow V_2O_4(s) + SO_3(g) \qquad (24\text{-}3)$$

The vanadium (IV) oxide then reacts with atmospheric oxygen, thus restoring the original vanadium (V) oxide:

$$V_2O_4(s) + \tfrac{1}{2}O_2(g) \longrightarrow V_2O_5(s) \qquad (24\text{-}4)$$

Vanadium metal is used as an alloy in the manufacture of steel. Even a small percentage of vanadium makes the steel much stronger and tougher. Vanadium steel, for example, is used in the mainsprings of automobiles. (See Fig. 24-6.

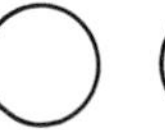

Fig. 24-5 Electron configuration of outer orbitals of vanadium.

Fig. 24-6 Vanadium alloyed with steel makes durable and strong mainsprings. Where else might vanadium be used?

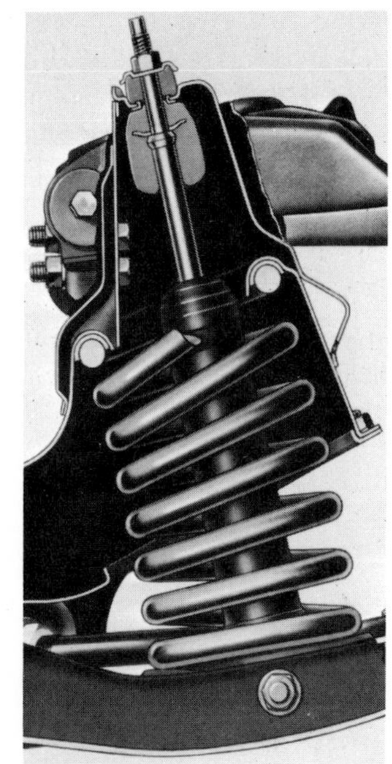

Chromium

Chromium atoms have six electrons available for bonding and the most common oxidation states are +2, +3, and +6. Typical compounds, many highly colored, are chromium (III) chloride ($CrCl_3$), a violet solid, chromium (II) chloride ($CrCl_2$), a white solid, chromium (III) oxide (Cr_2O_3), a green solid, potassium chromate (K_2CrO_4), a yellow solid, and potassium dichromate ($K_2Cr_2O_7$), an orange-colored solid. The oxidation number of chromium in chromates and dichromates is +6. All of these solids are very soluble in water and, as one might expect, chromium (II) ions (Cr^{+2}) are good reducing agents, whereas chromate ions (CrO_4^{-2}) and dichromate ions ($Cr_2O_7^{-2}$) are good oxidizing agents. (See Figs. 24-3 and 24-4.)

Chromium (II) ions are easily formed by reducing chromium (III) ion with metallic zinc:

$$\underset{\text{blue}}{2Cr^{+3}} + Zn \longrightarrow \underset{\text{colorless}}{2Cr^{+2}} + Zn^{+2} \qquad (24\text{-}5)$$

The Cr^{+2} ion is a powerful reducer and readily reverts to the +3 oxidation state by reacting with atmospheric oxygen:

$$2Cr^{+2} + \tfrac{3}{2}O_2 \longrightarrow Cr_2O_3 \qquad (24\text{-}6)$$

Outer orbitals

$3d^5$ $4s^1$

3d orbitals

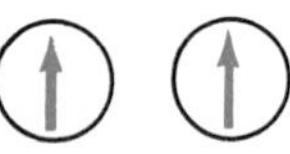

Fig. 24-7 Electron configuration of chromium.

The dichromate ion, on the other hand, readily oxidizes the iron (II) ion in acid solution with a marked change in color:

$$\underset{\text{orange}}{Cr_2O_7^{-2}} + 14H^+(aq) + 6Fe^{+2} \longrightarrow \underset{\text{blue}}{2Cr^{+3}} + 6Fe^{+3} + 7H_2O \qquad (24\text{-}7)$$

Chromium metal is very resistant to corrosion which accounts for its use in stainless steel. A thin coating of chromium also serves to protect steel against rust. A familiar example is the "chrome" plate on the bumper of an automobile. In this electrolytic process, the steel bumper forms the cathode in a cell which contains Cr^{+3} ions. What is the anode in such a cell?

Manganese

In manganese atoms there are seven electrons available for bonding. Indeed, manganese has the highest oxidation state (+7) of all the transition elements in this group. Other common valence states are +2 and +4. (See Fig. 24-8.)

The most common compound of manganese is manganese (IV) oxide (MnO_2), a black powder. This compound is usually called manganese dioxide and, you will recall, is the oxidizer of chloride ions in the common laboratory preparation of chlorine:

$$MnO_2(s) + 4H^+(aq) + 2Cl^- \longrightarrow Mn^{+2} + 2H_2O + Cl_2(g) \qquad (24\text{-}8)$$

Manganese (IV) oxide is also used as a catalyst in the preparation of oxygen:

$$2KClO_3 \xrightarrow{MnO_2} 2KCl + 3O_2 \qquad (24\text{-}9)$$

The use of MnO_2 as a catalyst is undoubtedly associated with the ability of manganese to change its oxidation state. Can you suggest a mechanism whereby the oxidation number is first changed from +4 and later restored to +4?

Fig. 24-8 Electron configuration of manganese.

Manganese

Outer orbitals

$3d^5$ $4s^2$

3d orbitals

As stated earlier, permanganate ion (MnO_4^-) is a good oxidizer. A typical oxidation reaction is the decomposition of acidified oxalic acid $(COOH)_2$ to CO_2 and H_2O.

$$\underset{\text{purple}}{2MnO_4^-} + 5(COOH)_2 + 6H^+(aq) \longrightarrow \underset{\text{colorless}}{2Mn^{+2}} + 10CO_2 + 8H_2O \qquad (24\text{-}10)$$

In this reaction there is a sharp color change from purple, the colored permangate ion, to the colorless ions of Mn^{+2}. (A concentrated solution of Mn^{+2} is pink, whereas a dilute solution appears to be colorless.)

The most abundant source of manganese is the mineral *pyrolusite* which is largely MnO_2. Manganese metal is extracted from this ore. Manganese is a scavenger of oxygen and is a constituent of all steels. That is, manganese combines with small amounts of oxygen present in molten steel. Unless manganese were used, minute bubbles of gas would be present in solid steel, and the strength of the steel would be diminished.

Iron

The most stable oxidation states of iron are +2 and +3. A mild oxidizing agent will convert iron (II) to iron (III) and, conversely, a mild reducing agent will change iron (III) to iron (II):

$$Fe^{+2} \underset{\substack{+e^- \\ \text{mild reducing agent}}}{\overset{\substack{\text{mild oxidizing agent} \\ -e^-}}{\rightleftharpoons}} Fe^{+3} \qquad (24\text{-}11)$$

For example, if hydrogen sulfide gas (H_2S) is bubbled into a solution of iron (III) chloride, the solution changes color from brown to

Iron

Outer orbitals
$3d^6$ $4s^2$

$3d$ orbitals

Fig. 24-9 Electron configuration of iron.

Fig. 24-10 This sculpture is made principally of iron.

green and sulfur is precipitated:

$$2FeCl_3(aq) + H_2S(g) \longrightarrow 2FeCl_2(aq) + 2HCl + S(s) \quad (24\text{-}12)$$

or

$$2Fe^{+3} + S^{-2} \longrightarrow 2Fe^{+2} + S^0 \quad (24\text{-}13)$$

Conversely, iron (II) hydroxide, a greenish insoluble solid, changes to iron (III) hydroxide, a brownish-red insoluble solid, on exposure to air,

$$\underset{\text{green}}{4Fe(OH)_2} + O_2 + 2H_2O \longrightarrow \underset{\text{brownish-red}}{4Fe(OH)_3} \quad (24\text{-}14)$$

Iron occurs abundantly both as *hematite* (Fe_2O_3), a reddish ore, and *magnetite* (Fe_3O_4) which is black in color. Among the metals, iron is next to aluminum in abundance. It is by far the most widely used constructional metal, and there are several reasons for this. Not only are the oxide ores abundant but they can be reduced to iron easily and cheaply. Moreover, iron, which is a transition element, can be alloyed with relatively small amounts of other transition elements to form various steels with a wide range of properties suitable for different purposes.

The Production of Iron Iron ore is converted to iron in a blast furnace, a tall tower-like structure as shown in Fig. 24-11. Iron ore, coke, and limestone are fed into the top of the furnace and a blast of hot air or oxygen is forced in through pipes near the bottom. The furnace takes its name from this steady blast of air. Hot coke reduces the iron (III) oxide in the furnace

$$3C + Fe_2O_3 \longrightarrow 3CO + 2Fe \quad (24\text{-}15)$$

But why the air and why the limestone?

The hot air (or oxygen) oxidizes coke near the bottom of the furnace. This is a highly exothermic reaction which heats up the furnace:

$$C(s) + O_2(g) \longrightarrow CO_2(g) + 94\ \text{kcal} \quad (24\text{-}16)$$

The carbon dioxide is reduced to carbon monoxide as it rises through the bed of hot coke:

$$CO_2(g) + C(s) \longrightarrow 2CO(g) \quad (24\text{-}17)$$

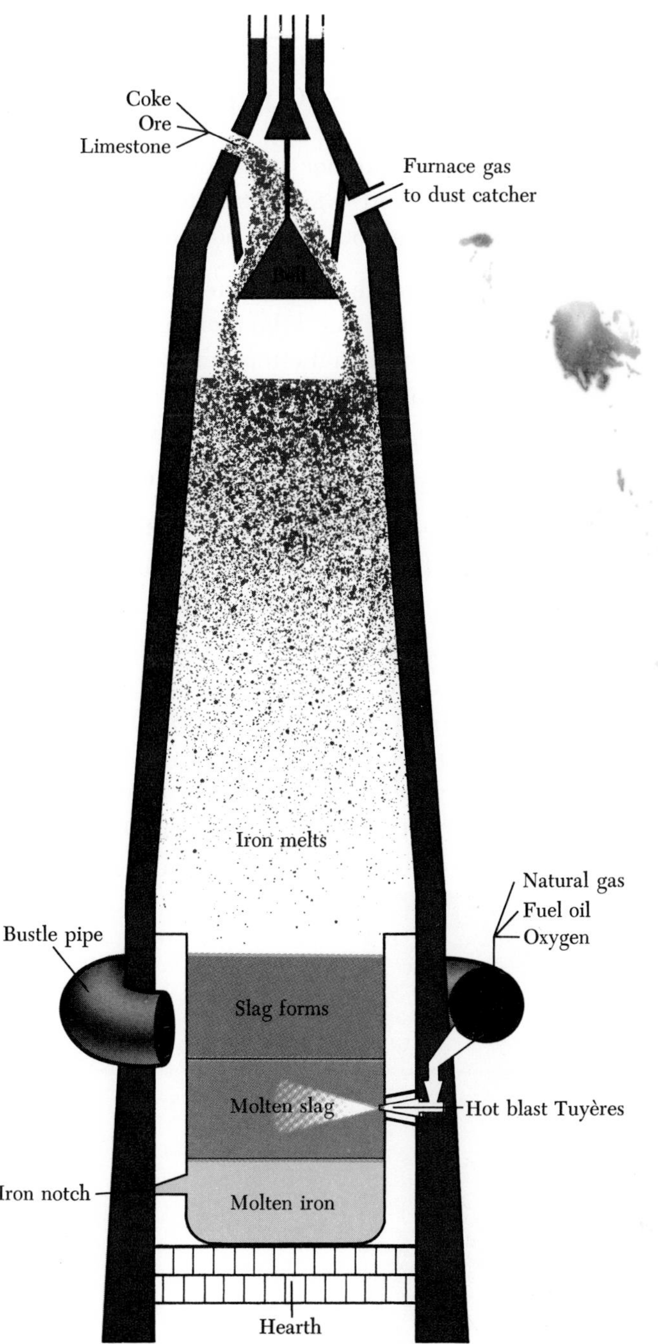

Fig. 24-11 The blast furnace. How did the name of this structure originate?

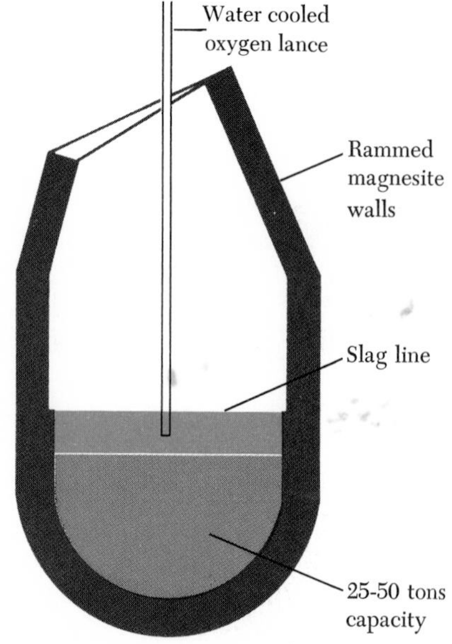

Fig. 24-12 A diagram of the basic oxygen furnace. The water-cooled lance enables impurities to be burned out quickly.

Thus there are two reducing agents, carbon monoxide and hot coke, to change the oxide to iron,

$$Fe_2O_3(s) + 3CO(g) \longrightarrow 3CO_2(g) + 2Fe(l) \quad (24\text{-}18)$$
$$Fe_2O_3(s) + 3C(s) \longrightarrow 3CO(g) + 2Fe(l) \quad (24\text{-}19)$$

The temperature of the furnace is about 1600 °C, well above the melting point of iron (1530 °C). The molten iron trickles down the furnace and collects as a pool at the bottom.

What is the function of the limestone ($CaCO_3$)? About 30% of hematite ore is *silica* (SiO_2), and the melting point of silica is about 1700 °C, which is higher than the temperature of the furnace. However, silica reacts with calcium carbonate to form calcium silicate ($CaSiO_3$), which has a melting point of about 1500 °C:

$$CaCO_3(s) + SiO_2(s) \longrightarrow CaSiO_3(l) + CO_2(g) \quad (24\text{-}20)$$

The molten silicate, called slag, falls down the furnace and, being less dense than iron, floats upon the molten iron. In this way, limestone is used to remove silica from the ore.

An average blast furnace produces about 750 tons of iron per day. However, iron produced in a blast furnace is quite impure. It contains about 4% carbon as well as smaller amounts of sulfur and phosphorus. These impurities make iron very brittle, so that blast-furnace iron (usually called pig iron or cast iron) is not satisfactory for constructional purposes. Actually, the pig iron is not even allowed to solidify. Instead, the molten pig iron is conveyed to

Fig. 24-13 Impurities being burned out in a basic oxygen furnace.

another furnace nearby called a basic-oxygen furnace. Here, the sulfur, phosphorus and most of the carbon are burned out.

Steel The furnace used in basic-oxygen steelmaking is a refractory-lined, barrel-shaped vessel which is open at the top. This furnace is shown in Fig. 24-12. A high-velocity jet of nearly pure (99.5%) gaseous oxygen is blown through a vertical, watercooled lance onto a charge of molten pig iron and steel scrap contained in the furnace. Heated lime is added as the slag-making material. Excess amounts of carbon, manganese, silicon, and phosphorus are removed by oxidation. Carbon forms carbon monoxide. The other elements form solid oxides which are taken up in the slag. Sulfur is removed by high-temperature reactions with the lime (CaO) to produce CaS, which also becomes part of the slag. Manganese and various other alloying metals such as chromium, nickel, vanadium, cobalt, and tungsten may also be added to the charge. The quantity and kind of steel are determined by the particular kind of steel desired. For example, stainless steel contains nickel, chromium, and cobalt as well as manganese. Stainless steel resists even the corrosive effects of hot acids and is therefore a suitable constructional material for chemical plants and oil refineries.

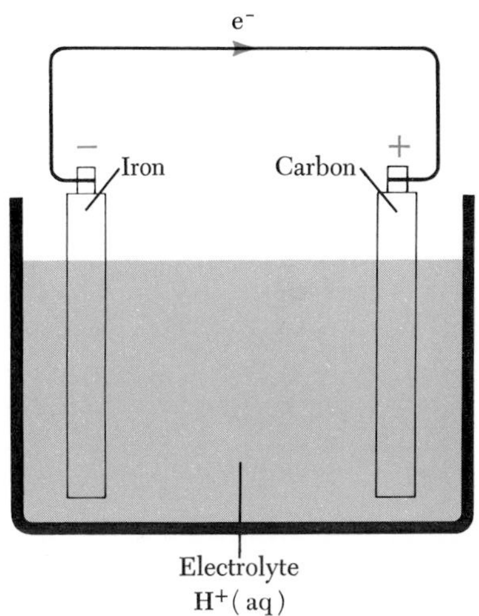

Fig. 24-14 The contact of iron and carbon in steel and the formation of an electrolyte, such as H_2CO_3 derived from water and carbon dioxide in the air, create the conditions for an electrochemical cell.

The Rusting of Iron A familiar property of iron and of most steels is its tendency to rust. Iron rust is a hydrated oxide, $Fe_2O_3 \cdot nH_2O$. How is rust formed? To rust, iron or steel must be in contact with oxygen, water, and also an electrolyte. If the electrolyte is NaCl, as in sea water, rusting proceeds at a rapid rate. But even hydrogen ions from such a weak acid as H_2CO_3 are enough to start the reaction. The actual mechanism of rusting is still somewhat obscure, but it is generally believed to be an electrolytic reaction caused by millions of minute electrolytic cells on the surface of the metal.

Fig. 24-15 Iron, when chemically pure, is almost nonreactive toward oxygen. The chemist here is investigating the properties of a bar of pure iron.

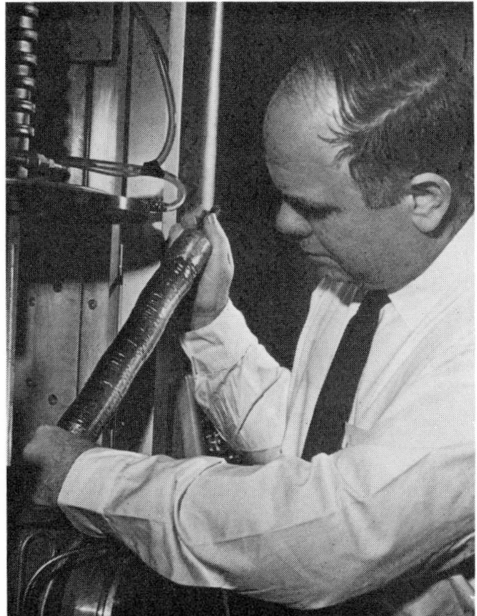

Blast-furnace iron contains about 4% carbon and all steels contain carbon in lesser amounts. Hence iron and carbon are in contact, and so probably form the electrodes of minute iron–carbon cells, as shown in Fig. 24-14. Iron is more active than carbon and therefore forms the cathode. The cathode reaction is

$$2Fe - 4e^- \longrightarrow 2Fe^{+2} \qquad (24\text{-}21)$$

and the anode reaction is

$$2H_2O + O_2 + 4e^- \longrightarrow 4OH^- \qquad (24\text{-}22)$$

Cobalt

Outer orbitals
$3d^7$ $4s^2$

3*d* orbitals

Fig. 24-16 Electron configuration of the outer orbitals of cobalt..

Since anode and cathode are in contact, Fe^{+2} will combine with OH^- to form insoluble iron (II) hydroxide:

$$Fe^{+2} + 2OH^- \longrightarrow Fe(OH)_2 \qquad (24\text{-}23)$$

Iron (II) hydroxide is then oxidized by moist air to hydrated iron (III) oxide:

$$4Fe(OH)_2(s) + O_2(g) + xH_2O(g) \longrightarrow 2Fe_2O_3 \cdot nH_2O(s) \qquad (24\text{-}24)$$

Unlike aluminum oxide, iron rust is porous and does not protect the metal underneath. The simplest way to prevent disintegration of the metal is to exclude the air by painting the surface. Another method is to plate the steel with an inert metal such as tin or chromium. "Tin" cans, for example, are made of steel covered with a thin coating of tin. The tin resists substances such as fruit juices, and so rusting is prevented. Many beverage cans are made of steel strips about 0.015 cm thick and coated with chromium. Still another way to protect iron or steel is to galvanize it with zinc, a process discussed later in the chapter.

Note . . .
Obtained chiefly by reducing the oxide with aluminum, cobalt is found in *smaltite,* $CoAs_2$, and *cobalite,* CoAsS.

The Remaining Transition Elements in the Fourth Row

Cobalt

Like iron, cobalt has oxidation states of +2 and +3. But, unlike iron, compounds in oxidation state +2 are much more stable than those in state +3. The oxide (CoO), the hydroxide [$Co(OH)_2$], and the chloride ($CoCl_2$) are common compounds in which the oxidation number of cobalt is +2. (See Fig. 24-16.)

Note . . .
There are three major ores of nickel: *nickelite,* NiAs, *millerite,* NiS, and *pentlandite,* (Ni,Fe)S.

The chief use of the metal is as an alloy in cobalt-chromium steel. This particular steel retains its temper at high temperatures; that is, it retains a cutting edge even when hot, and for this reason cobalt-chromium steel is used in the manufacture of high-speed tools.

Like iron, cobalt can be magnetized. The strongest of all magnets are made up of iron alloyed with aluminum, nickel, and cobalt. Their name, *alnico* magnets, suggests the alloying metals used in their manufacture.

Fig. 24-17 Electron configuration of the outer orbitals of nickel.

Nickel

Outer orbitals
$3d^8$ $4s^2$

3*d* orbitals

Nickel

The stable oxidation state of nickel is +2. Common compounds in which the oxidation number is +2 are NiO, $NiCl_2$, $Ni(OH)_2$, $NiSO_4$, and $Ni(NO_3)_2$.

Nickel metal is silvery in appearance and, like iron and cobalt, it can be magnetized. The metal is tough and corrosion resistant, and its most important use is in stainless steels. The metal is also used in coinage. A 5-cent piece, for example, is an alloy of nickel (25%) and copper (75%). (See Fig. 24-17.)

Copper

Copper atoms have a single electron in the outermost (4*s*) orbital. We might therefore expect copper to have chemical properties somewhat like those of the alkali metals. But far from it, copper is a relatively inactive metal. It does not release hydrogen either from dilute acids or from water. The relative inactivity of copper is due to strong metallic bonds which involve both 3*d* and 4*s* electrons.

Because of its single 4*s* electron, copper forms compounds in which the oxidation number is +1. Such compounds are copper (I) oxide (or cuprous oxide, Cu_2O) and copper (I) sulfide (or cuprous sulfide, Cu_2S). However, the energies of the 3*d* and 4*s* electrons differ only very slightly, so that one of the 3*d* electrons can easily be removed. When this happens, copper behaves as a transition element and its oxidation number is +2. (See Fig. 24-19.)

In contact with the air, copper (II) compounds are much more stable than the corresponding copper (I) compounds. For example, red copper (I) oxide is oxidized in air to form black copper (II) oxide:

$$Cu_2O(s) + \tfrac{1}{2}\,O_2(g) \longrightarrow 2CuO(s) \qquad (24\text{-}25)$$

Fig. 24-18 This is a press for stamping out nickels for the United States mint.

Copper

Outer orbitals
$3d^{10}\ \ 4s^1$

3*d* orbitals

Fig. 24-19 Electron configuration of the outer orbitals of copper.

Fig. 24-20 These electrical cables are made of copper. Why?

The most common cupric salt is hydrated copper (II) sulfate, $CuSO_4 \cdot 5H_2O$, usually called blue vitriol. Cupric salts in general are quite soluble, forming blue solutions. The blue color is due to the cupric ion which is hydrated with four molecules of water as $Cu(H_2O)_4^{+2}$.

The chief ore of copper is *chalcopyrite* ($CuS \cdot FeS$), a sulfide of copper and iron. The extraction of copper from its ore is complicated because the ore contains only a low percentage of copper (usually less than 3%) and a high percentage of iron. To remove the iron and sulfur, four different metallurgical processes are necessary, and *blister copper* is obtained. Blister copper is about 99% copper and about 1% impurities, which include small amounts of iron, zinc, silver, and gold.

Copper is used chiefly as an electrical conductor, but even traces of impurities effectively reduce its conductivity. So the copper used for this purpose must be pure. Hence the final metallurgical step is a refining process, an electrolytic process discussed in Chapter 18. You may recall that a slab of blister copper is the anode of the cell. By carefully controlling the voltage, only pure copper is deposited on the cathode.

Zinc

Zinc is the last element of this transition series and both its 4*s* and 3*d* orbitals are completely filled with electrons. Only the 4*s* electrons take part in chemical reactions, and therefore the oxidation number is +2. Since the 3*d* electrons are not involved, zinc does not exhibit variable oxidation states so that, in effect, it does not behave like a transition element.

Zinc reduces hydrogen ion to hydrogen gas in non-oxidizing acids such as HCl and dilute H_2SO_4,

$$Zn(s) + 2H^+(aq) \longrightarrow Zn^{+2} + H_2(g) \qquad (25\text{-}26)$$

As stated earlier, the melting point of zinc (420 °C) is much lower than the melting points of all other transition elements. The chief use of zinc is to protect steel from rust. If sheet steel is dipped into molten zinc, a thin coating of zinc adheres to the steel. The surface layer of zinc then slowly changes to zinc carbonate on exposure to air, thereby protecting the underlying steel. The steel is then said to be galvanized. Galvanized steel is used on a large scale for mak-

Zinc

Outer orbitals

$3d^{10}$ $4s^2$

3*d* orbitals

Fig. 24-21 Electron configuration of the outer orbitals of zinc.

ing articles that are exposed to the weather and running water, such as gutters, chains, pipes, bolts, and screws.

Summary

The transition elements in the fourth row form a block of ten metals bounded by potassium and calcium on the left, and six elements (gallium, germanium, arsenic, selenium, bromine, and krypton) on the right. Their characteristic property is the gradual filling of their 3*d* orbitals, one electron at a time, from scandium (with one 3*d* electron) to zinc (with ten 3*d* electrons).

Because the transition elements have similar configurations, they exhibit marked similarities in both physical and chemical properties. For example, they are all metals and, except for zinc, their melting points are unusually high. In the formation of compounds, most of the transition elements have at least two oxidation states. The oxidation numbers of the transition elements vary from $+1$ to $+7$, vanadium and manganese having at least four different oxidation states.

Most compounds of the transition elements are paramagnetic; that is, they are attracted by a magnetic field. The property of paramagnetism is ascribed to the unpaired electrons in the *d* orbitals.

There are also ten transition elements in the fifth row and ten in the sixth row. In the fifth row the transition elements fill the 4*d* orbitals, and in the sixth row the 5*d* orbitals are filled.

Factual Recall

1. Explain why the 3*d* orbitals belong to the fourth row of elements rather than the third.
2. (*a*) What is a transition series of elements?
   (*b*) How do elements in a transition series differ structurally from elements in a periodic family?
3. Name the transition elements in the fourth row, and write their electron configurations.
4. Compare the expected electron configuration for copper with the actual configuration. Why the difference?
5. Calcium ($Z = 20$), manganese (at. no. 25), and zinc ($Z = 30$) are all in the fourth row of the periodic table. Their melting

points are 820 °C, 1245 °C, and 420 °C, respectively.

(*a*) Why is the melting point of calcium lower than that of manganese?

(*b*) Why is the melting point of calcium higher than that of zinc?

6. (*a*) How many oxidation states of chromium would you expect to find in its various compounds? Why?

   (*b*) What is the oxidation number of chromium in the compound Na_3CrF_6?

7. (*a*) What is paramagnetism?

   (*b*) Why is paramagnetism typical of transition elements?

8. (*a*) What is ferromagnetism?

   (*b*) Name three transition elements that exhibit ferromagnetism.

Apply Your Knowledge!

1. What volume of air (20% oxygen by volume) at STP is required to convert 0.050 mole of copper (I) oxide to copper (II) oxide?

2. If 2.25 g of scandium metal react with water, compute (*a*) the moles of water consumed, (*b*) the mass in grams of metallic hydroxide formed, (*c*) the volume of gas product at 27 °C and 684 torr.

3. How many moles of titanium are required to react with 4.48 l of chlorine at 273 °C?

4. How many moles of zinc must be used to reduce 1.30 g of chromium (III) ion to chromium (II) ion?

5. An acidified solution of 0.100 *M* dichromate ion is used to convert 100 ml of 0.250 *M* iron (II) ion solution to a solution of iron (III) ion. Compute the volume of dichromate solution required.

6. 4.40 g of manganese dioxide react completely with 6.00 *M* hydrochloric acid solution. Compute (*a*) the volume of acid needed, (*b*) the molarity of the salt solution formed, (*c*) the volume of gas product at 50 °C.

7. The reaction of oxalic acid with an acidified solution of 0.100 *M* permanganate ion liberates 1.12 l of carbon dioxide at STP. Calculate (*a*) the mass in grams of oxalic acid consumed, (*b*) the volume of permanganate solution used up.

8. Hydrogen sulfide is bubbled through 10.0 ml of an acidified 0.200 *M* solution of iron (III) ion until reaction is complete. Compute (*a*) the volume of hydrogen sulfide at STP which reacts, (*b*) the moles of metallic ion produced, (*c*) the mass in grams of precipitate.

Find Out!

1. The highest oxidation state of manganese is +7. Find out why the Mn^{+7} ion cannot exist in solution. Write an equation to represent what would happen if Mn^{+7} were placed in water.
2. Find out what apparatus is used for making quantitative measurements of paramagnetism, or design one yourself showing its construction and stating how it is to be used.
3. Find out the spatial configuration for $Cr_2O_7^{-2}$ and for CrO_4^{-2}.
4. Two processes, the open-hearth process and the Bessemer converter, have been used in making steel, while since 1955 the basic oxygen process has been increasingly used. Find out about the production of steel by the Bessemer converter and the open-hearth process.

Suggested Readings

Asimov, I., *The Search for the Elements*. New York: Fawcett, 1962. (Paperback)

Asimov, I., *A Short History of Chemistry*. Garden City, N.Y.: Doubleday-Anchor, 1965. (Paperback)

Davis, H.M., *Chemical Elements*. New York: Ballantine, 1959. (Paperback)

Jaffe, B., *Crucibles: The Story of Chemistry*. New York: Fawcett, 1957. (Paperback)

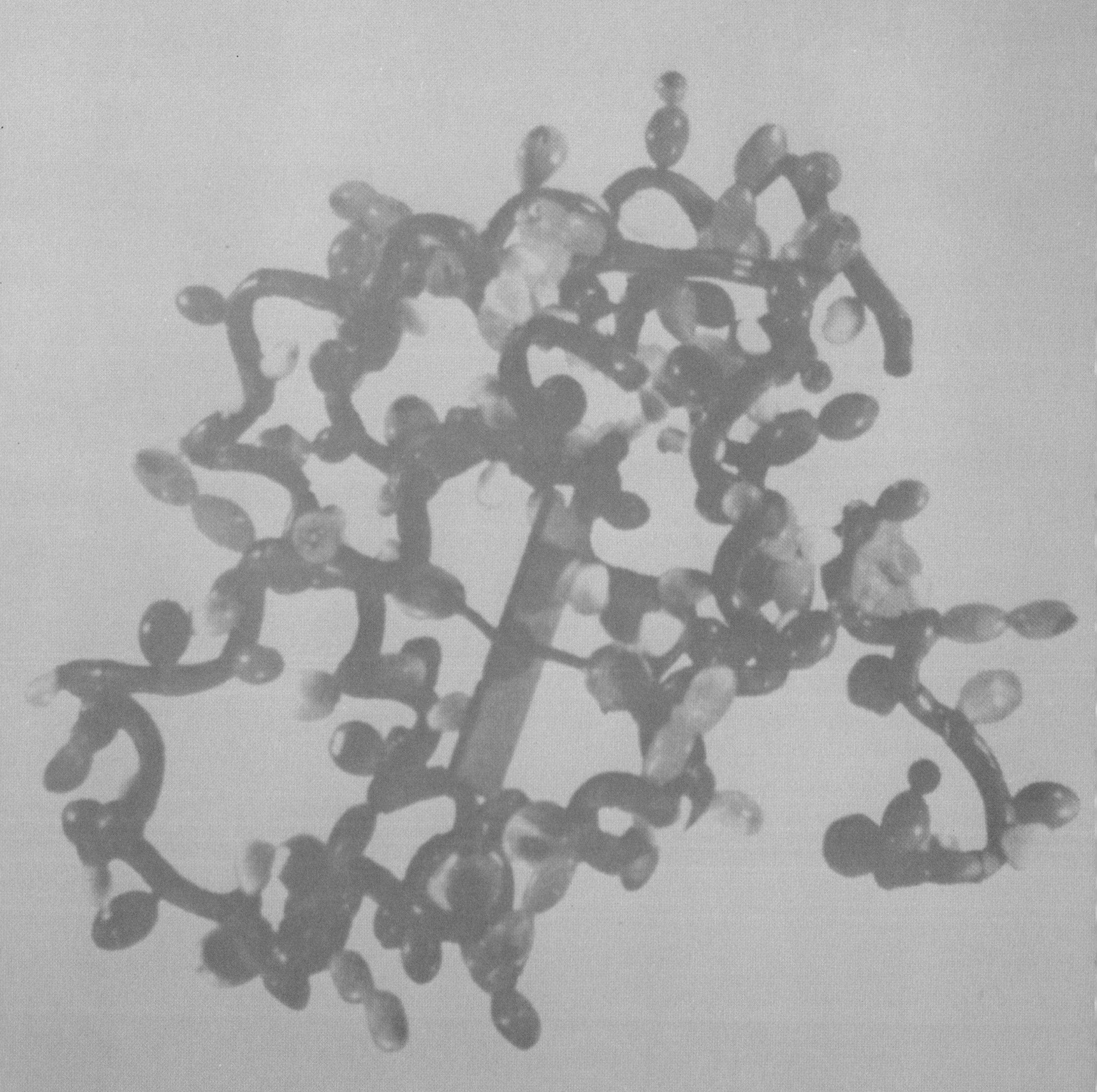

UNIT VIII

ORGANIC CHEMISTRY

THE UNIQUE STRUCTURE of carbon atoms makes it possible for them to combine with each other to form chains and rings. In addition, they also combine with atoms of hydrogen, oxygen, and other elements to form a vast array of compounds—more than two million of them. *The study of carbon compounds is the field of organic chemistry.*

Nature synthesizes many organic compounds in the photosynthesis reaction. In absorbing energy from the sun, carbon dioxide and water vapor from the air combine to form carbohydrates in living vegetation, which may ultimately be changed to coal or petroleum. When coal or petroleum is burned, the stored energy from the sun is released as heat energy.

Chemists can make carbon compounds either by *decomposition* of complex starting substances or by *synthesis* from simple starting substances. For example, the chemist can make ethanol by a decomposition process called fermentation. Indeed, this method of making alcohol by the fermentation of sugar or starch has been known for thousands of years—we even read about it in the Old Testament. On the other hand, the chemist can synthesize alcohol from ethylene which is obtained from coal or petroleum. As a matter of fact, the larger proportion of alcohol manufactured in the United States is prepared from ethylene.

HISTORICAL CHEMISTRY LABORATORY

Fredrich Wöhler was the first chemist to synthesize an organic compound from inorganic materials. These excerpts are from a translation of his original publication describing this work. It appeared in *Annalen der Physik und Chemie,* Volume 12, pp 253-256 (1828).

Friedrich Wöhler
(1800–1882)

On the Artificial Production of Urea.

In a brief earlier communication, . . . I stated that by the action of cyanogen on aqueous ammonia, besides . . . other products, there are formed oxalic acid and a crystallizable white substance which is certainly not cyanate of ammonia, but which one nevertheless always obtains when one attempts to combine cyanic acid with ammonia for instance by so-called double decomposition. The fact that in the union of these substances they appear to change their nature, and give rise to a new body, drew my attention anew to this subject, and research gave the unexpected result that by the combination of cyanic acid with ammonia, urea is formed, a fact that is the more noteworthy inasmuch as it furnishes an example of the artificial production of an organic, indeed a so-called animal substance, from inorganic materials.

. . . The above-mentioned white crystalline substance is best obtained by the decomposition of cyanate of silver with sal ammoniac solution or of cyanate of lead by aqueous ammonia. In the later way I prepared . . . the . . . amounts employed in this research. I obtained it in colorless, clear crystals often more than an inch long in the form of slender four-sided, dull-pointed prisms.

With caustic potash or chalk this substance evolved no trace of ammonia; with acids it showed none of the breakdown phenomena of cyanic acid salts, namely, evolution of carbonic acid and cyanic acid; neither would it precipitate lead and silver salts as genuine cyanic acid salts do; it could, therefore, contain neither cyanic acid nor ammonia as such. Since I found that by the last-named method of preparation no other product was formed . . . I imagined that an organic substance might arise by the union of cyanic acid with ammonia, possibly a substance like a vegetable salifiable base. I therefore made some experiments . . . on the behavior of the crystalline substance with acids. It was, however, indifferent to them, nitric acid excepted; this, when added to a concentrated solution of the substance, produced at once a precipitate of glistening scales. After these had been purified . . . they . . . gave salts of nitric acid, from which the crystallizable substance could be extracted again with alcohol, with all the characteristics it had before the addition of nitric acid. This similarity to urea in behavior induced me to carry out comparative experiments... from which it was plainly apparent that urea and this crystalline substance, or cyanate of ammonia, if one can so call it, are completely identical compounds.

CHAPTER 25

THE HYDROCARBONS: COMPOUNDS OF CARBON AND HYDROGEN

THE TOTAL NUMBER OF COMPOUNDS of sodium, of calcium, of manganese, and of many other common elements is in the hundreds. But this is not the case with carbon. Indeed, more than two million compounds of carbon are known, many of which are man-made. Why is carbon such a prolific compound former? It must be associated with some peculiarity in atomic structure that gives carbon an unusual ability to form chemical bonds.

As you recall, the atomic number of carbon is 6 and the electron configuration of a carbon atom is $1s^2 2s^2 2p^2$. The electronic structure of the carbon atom is midway between that of the noble gases helium ($1s^2$) and neon ($1s^2 2s^2 2p^6$). Carbon exhibits *no tendency to lose* its $2s$ and $2p$ electrons to form a C^{+4} ion and *shows little tendency to gain* four electrons to form a C^{-4} ion. Instead, it *shares* electrons and in the vast majority of its compounds it forms covalent bonds with little ionic character. Both the $2s$ and $2p$ electrons are involved in the bonding, so that the covalence of carbon is four; that is, carbon is tetravalent in most of its compounds.

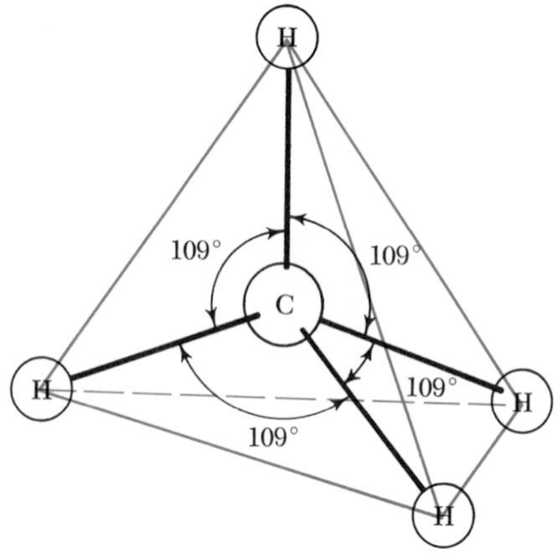

Fig. 25-1 In a methane molecule the carbon atom is at the center of a tetrahedron and the hydrogen atoms are at the corners.

Investigate . . .
With small corks and pins with colored heads, try to make models of the compounds in this chapter.

Note . . .
The rules for naming chemical compounds are established by the organization called The International Union for Pure and Applied Chemistry (I.U.P.A.C), so that uniform names will be used for compounds all over the world.

But, why such a vast number of compounds? The answer is that carbon atoms can bond with other carbon atoms. Unlike other elements they form strong covalent bonds with each other; they can link together to form long straight chains, branched chains, and closed rings. Numerous examples of these types of linkage will be given later in the chapter.

We know that the four covalent bonds of carbon are alike, so the simple compound methane (CH_4) can be represented as

```
    H
    |
H—C—H
    |
    H
```

Written in this way, the molecule appears to have a flat (two-dimensional) structure. We must remember, however, that the four pairs of valence electrons repel each other and that they will move as far from each other as is possible. It can be shown that the most stable arrangement that allows for repulsion between electrons is a tetrahedral spatial configuration. Evidence indicates that the carbon atom is at the center of a tetrahedron and the hydrogen atoms at the four corners. Such an arrangement is shown in Fig. 25-1. The angle between any two covalent bonds is 109°, which is the tetrahedral angle. This tetrahedral configuration of the four covalent bonds of a carbon atom applies to many carbon compounds.

The systematic study of each of two million carbon compounds is clearly an impossible task. Fortunately, carbon compounds can be grouped together in families, each of whose characteristic properties are similar. Such families include *hydrocarbons, alcohols, acids, esters, aldehydes, ketones, ethers, amines, amino acids, proteins, fats, and carbohydrates.* The hydrocarbons are by far the largest of these families, and they can conveniently be subdivided into smaller families which include the *alkanes* (paraffin or saturated hydrocarbons), *alkenes* (ethylenic or unsaturated hydrocarbons), *alkynes* (acetylenic or more highly unsaturated hydrocarbons), *cycloalkanes*, and *aromatic* hydrocarbons.

The Alkanes

Natural gas which is burned in furnaces is a mixture of compounds called *alkanes*. So is the principal content of gasoline used to drive

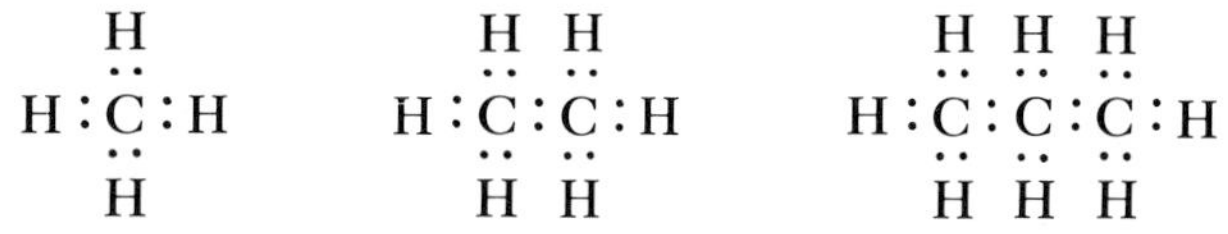

Fig. 25-2 Electron-dot formulas of methane, ethane, and propane.

```
    H            H H              H H H
    ··           ·· ··            ·· ·· ··
  H:C:H        H:C:C:H          H:C:C:C:H
    ··           ·· ··            ·· ·· ··
    H            H H              H H H
```

(*a*) methane (*b*) ethane (*c*) propane

automobiles and airplanes, and even the oil used to lubricate them. Indeed, there are thousands of alkanes in nature, most of which are present in natural gas and petroleum. These compounds differ from one another in the number of carbon and hydrogen atoms and in the spatial arrangements of these atoms in the molecules. Another name for the alkanes is *paraffin hydrocarbons*. The word *paraffin* means *inactive* or *little affinity*. But why are they called inactive when they take part in a variety of chemical reactions? The reason is that they will not react unless "attacked" by a powerful agent such as oxygen at a high temperature.

Structures and Formulas of Alkanes

The three simplest members of the alkanes are methane (CH_4), ethane (C_2H_6), and propane (C_3H_8). Notice that the name of each alk*ane* ends in *ane*. The electron-dot formulas of these compounds are shown in Fig. 25-2.

The formulas show that each bond is a shared pair of electrons (that is, a covalent bond) and that carbon atoms are linked together by shared pairs of electrons. Moreover, each linkage is a *single* shared pair of electrons. This single shared pair is characteristic of alkanes, and for this reason they are called *saturated* hydrocarbons.

It is more convenient to represent a shared pair of electrons by a line than by dots, so the formulas are often written as in Fig. 25-3. These are known as structural formulas.

We must remember, however, that the molecules are not flat; they are three-dimensional. Molecular models of methane and ethane,

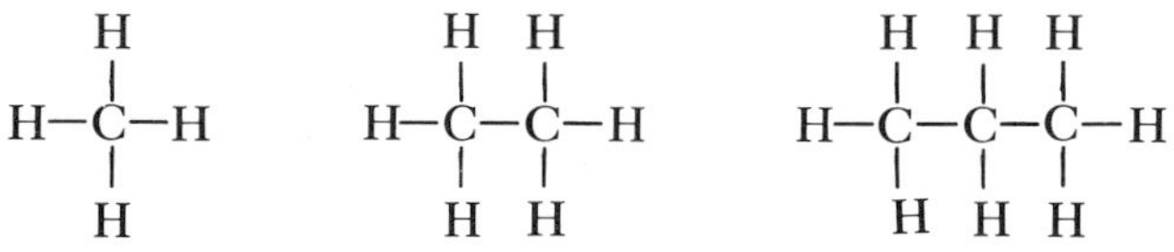

```
    H             H  H              H  H  H
    |             |  |              |  |  |
  H—C—H         H—C——C—H          H—C——C——C—H
    |             |  |              |  |  |
    H             H  H              H  H  H
```

(*a*) methane (*b*) ethane (*c*) propane

Fig. 25-3 Structural (line) formulas of methane, ethane, and propane.

Fig. 25-4 Models of the molecule of methane. The central ball represents carbon, the others represent hydrogen. Which model more clearly indicates the three dimensional nature of the molecule?

with wooden pegs representing the lines in the structural formulas, are shown in Figs. 25-4 and 25-5.

Definition . . .
Compounds composed of the same numbers of the same atoms, but differing in molecular structure and properties, are called isomers.

To repeat, the molecular formulas of these compounds are CH_4, C_2H_6, and C_3H_8. However, as we shall soon discover, these formulas are limited in their use because there are many instances where two or more carbon compounds have the same formula. For example, there are three alkanes with the formula C_5H_{12} and we must be able to identify each of them. One method of distinguishing them is to write their structural formulas. Still another way is to give them different names, names which indicate the structures.

Fig. 25-5 Model of the ethane molecule. The large balls represent carbon atoms, the small ones represent hydrogen atoms.

Let us take another look at the formulas for the first three members of the alkane series. Each compound after methane has the increment CH_2 added to the molecular formula of the preceding compound. For example

$$CH_4 + CH_2 = C_2H_6 \qquad \text{and} \quad C_2H_6 + CH_2 = C_3H_8$$

In other words, the formulas of all alkanes can be represented by the *general formula* C_nH_{2n+2}. Thus, if $n=4$, the formula of the alkane is C_4H_{8+2} or C_4H_{10}. Similarly, if $n=10$, the formula is $C_{10}H_{20+2}$ or $C_{10}H_{22}$, which represents an alkane named decane.

Physical Properties of Alkanes

As the molecular masses of the alkanes increase, their melting and boiling points rise. Thus, the C_1 to C_4 alkanes are gases, the C_5 to C_{17} compounds are liquids, and the highest members of the series are solids. The formulas, names, and melting and boiling points of some of the straight-chain alkanes are listed in Table 25-1.

Table 25-1 Some properties of representative alkanes

Name	Formula	Melting point, °C	Boiling point, °C
Methane	CH_4	−183	−162
Ethane	C_2H_6	−172	− 89
Propane	C_3H_8	−187	− 42
Butane	C_4H_{10}	−135	− 1
Pentane	C_5H_{12}	−130	37
Hexane	C_6H_{14}	− 94	69
Heptane	C_7H_{16}	− 91	98
Octane	C_8H_{18}	− 57	126
Decane	$C_{10}H_{22}$	− 30	174
Dodecane	$C_{12}H_{26}$	− 10	216
Octadecane	$C_{18}H_{38}$	28	308

Structural Isomers among the Alkanes

As you learned earlier, there are often two or more carbon compounds with the same molecular formula. These compounds may have different structures and are therefore called *structural isomers*. And, since their structures are different, the isomers have different physical and chemical properties.

There are no isomers of CH_4, C_2H_6, and C_3H_8; that is, there is only one compound corresponding to each of the formulas CH_4, C_2H_6, and C_3H_8, respectively. In fact, there is only one way in which the carbon and hydrogen atoms of these three alkanes can be arranged. But this is not true of C_4H_{10}. The four carbon atoms of C_4H_{10} can be linked to each other in what is called a straight chain:

```
    H   H   H   H
    |   |   |   |
H—C—C—C—C—H
    |   |   |   |
    H   H   H   H
```

and they can also be linked in a branched chain:

```
    H   H   H
    |   |   |
H—C—C—C—H
    |   |   |
    H   |   H
  H—C—H
      |
      H
```

These two structures are clearly different, and they represent two entirely different compounds. Since their molecular formulas are the same, they are called structural isomers. Since they are different substances, they are given different names. The straight-chain isomer is called *butane*, and the branched-chain isomer is called methylpropane or isobutane. Why the name methylpropane? Because the *longest continuous chain* of carbon atoms in the branched-chain isomer is three carbons, this isomer is considered to be a derivative of propane, which also has three carbons (C_3H_8). If one of the hydrogen atoms on the middle carbon of propane is replaced by a methyl group (CH_3— a methane molecule with one

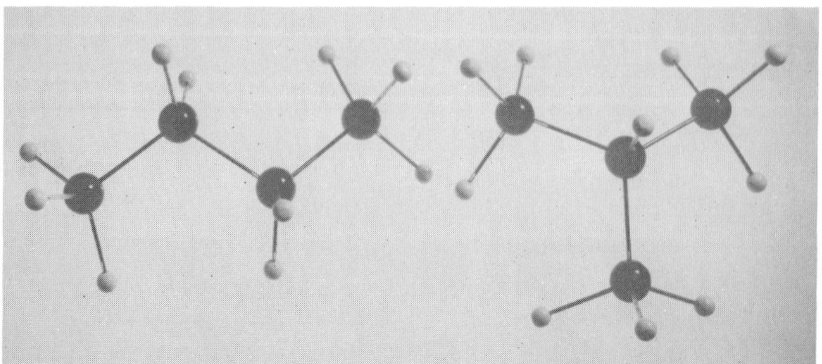

Fig. 25-6 Models of isomers of C_4H_{10}. Name them.

hydrogen atom removed, thus *methyl*), we have the branched-chain isomer of C_4H_{10}. Hence this particular name.

There are three isomers of C_5H_{12}, one straight-chain and two branched-chain; their structures are:

```
    H  H  H  H  H
    |  |  |  |  |
 H—C—C—C—C—C—H
    |  |  |  |  |
    H  H  H  H  H
(a)
```

```
    H  H  H  H
    |  |  |  |
 H—C—C—C—C—H
    |  |  |  |
    H  H  |  H
          |
       H—C—H
          |
(b)       H
```

```
          H
          |
       H—C—H
    H     |     H
    |     |     |
 H—C—————C—————C—H
    |     |     |
    H     |     H
          |
       H—C—H
          |
(c)       H
```

What are their names? The name of isomer (*a*) is *pentane* because it consists of *five* carbon atoms in a continuous chain. The name of isomer (*b*) is *methylbutane*. Can you explain why? And the name of isomer (*c*) is *dimethylpropane*. This is because the longest continuous chain is three carbon atoms long, so that this particular isomer can be considered a derivative of propane, with *two* methyl groups (hence *dimethyl*) replacing the two central hydrogen atoms of propane.

The next alkane, C_6H_{14}, has five isomers, one straight-chain and four branched-chain. Their structures are:

```
    H  H  H  H  H  H
    |  |  |  |  |  |
 H—C—C—C—C—C—C—H
    |  |  |  |  |  |
    H  H  H  H  H  H

(a)
```

```
                H
              H | H
               \|/
    H  H  H    C   H
    |  |  |    |   |
 H—C—C—C—C—C—H
    |  |  |  |  |
    H  H  H  H  H

(b)
```

```
        H H H
         \|/
  H  H   C   H  H
  |  |   |   |  |
H-C--C---C---C--C-H
  |  |   |   |  |
  H  H   H   H  H
```

(*c*)

```
        H H H H    H
         \|/   \  /
  H       C     C-H  H
   \      |     |   /
  H-C-----C-----C--C-H
    |     |     |   \
    H     H     H    H
```

(*d*)

```
        H H H
         \|/
  H  H   C   H
  |  |   |   |
H-C--C---C---C-H
  |  |   |   |
  H  H   |   H
       H-C-H
         |
         H
```

(*e*)

The name of isomer (*a*) is hexane and the molecular model of this isomer is shown in Fig. 25-7. But the naming of the branched-chain isomers is a little more complicated. We can't call isomer (*b*) methylpentane because isomer (*c*) is also methylpentane. We can, however, distinguish between these two isomers by numbering the carbon atoms of the continuous chain 1 through 5,

```
C—C—C—C—C
5 4 3 2 1
```

Fig. 25-7 Model of the hexane molecule with a chain of six carbon atoms. Note that the chain is folded; that is, the carbon atoms do not lie in a straight line. Why is this characteristic of chains of carbon atoms?

and then identifying the number of the carbon atom to which the methyl group is attached. The carbon atoms of the continuous chain are numbered from right to left so that the methyl branch in (*b*) has the smaller number. Thus, isomer (*b*) is 2-methylpentane, whereas isomer (*c*) is 3-methylpentane. Note that isomer (*b*) could have been called 4-methylpentane if the carbon atoms had been numbered from left to right.

Now, what names are given to isomers (*d*) and (*e*)? The longest continuous chain of carbon atoms in (*d*) is four atoms long, so that we can think of one methyl group replacing a hydrogen atom on carbon number 2 of the chain and of another methyl group replacing a hydrogen atom on carbon number 3 of the chain. The name of isomer (*d*) is therefore 2,3-dimethylbutane. Similarly, the longest chain of carbon atoms in isomer (*e*) is also four atoms long, so that its name is 2,2-dimethylbutane.

The number of isomers rapidly increases as the number of carbon atoms in the alkane increases. For example, there are 18 isomers of C_8H_{18}, 75 isomers of $C_{10}H_{22}$, 1858 isomers of $C_{14}H_{30}$, and an estimated 366,319 isomers of $C_{20}H_{42}$. Can you write the structures and give the names of the isomers of C_7H_{16}? You will find that there are nine isomers, and no more. Finally, note that the alkanes in Table 25-1 are all straight-chain isomers.

The Cycloalkanes

Carbon atoms can form closed rings as well as chains. If the carbon atoms in the ring are attached to each other by single pairs of electrons (that is, by single covalent bonds), the hydrocarbon is a *cycloalkane*. For example, the hydrocarbon with a ring of six carbon atoms is called cyclohexane and its structure is

```
      H    H H    H
       \  /   \  /
  H     C-----C     H
   \   /       \   /
     C           C
   /   \       /   \
  H     C-----C     H
       /  \   /  \
      H    H H    H
```

The formula of cyclohexane is C_6H_{12}, that is, it contains two hydrogen atoms less than hexane (C_6H_{14}). The *general formula* for the *cycloalkanes* is therefore C_nH_{2n}, whereas the general formula for the alkanes is C_nH_{2n+2}. Some of the rings are very large.

Later in the chapter we shall see that the cycloalkanes have the same general formula as the alkenes, but there the similarity ends.

Reactions of the Alkanes

You will recall that the alkanes are quite stable at ordinary temperatures. However, they take part in three characteristic reactions:

(1) The alkanes can be burned; that is, they combine with oxygen provided the temperature is high enough.
(2) They can be split into smaller fragments; that is, they can be *cracked* at high temperatures and high pressures.
(3) They react with the halogens in what are known as *substitution* reactions.

We will now consider each of these three types of reactions.

Combustion As you know, natural gas, gasoline, and fuel oil can be burned in the presence of oxygen (air) at high temperatures. Indeed, the combustion of these substances is one of our most important sources of energy. What are the products of combustion? To

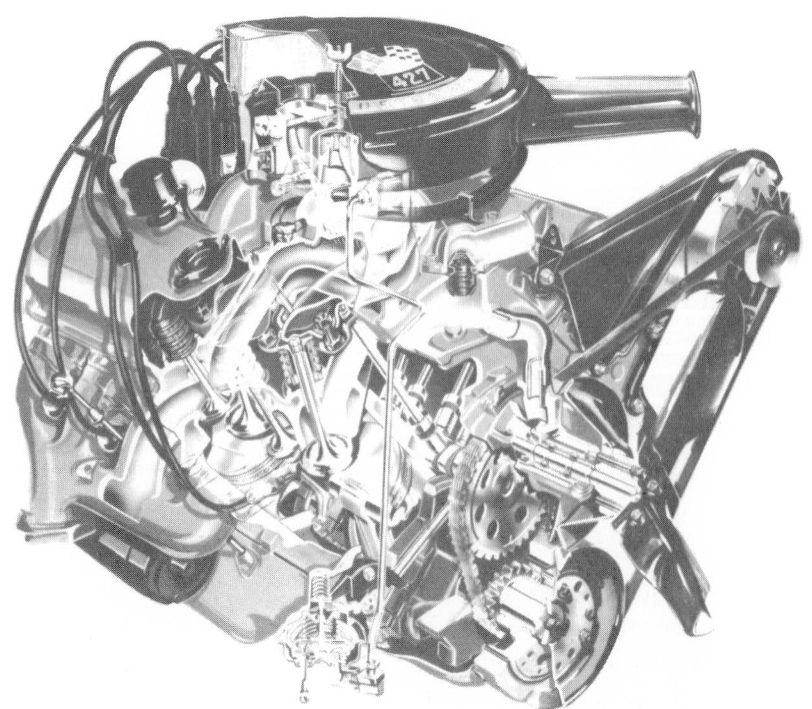

Fig. 25-8 Cutaway view of a gasoline engine.

answer this question, let us study the combustion of methane, the chief constituent of natural gas.

In the presence of an abundant supply of oxygen, methane burns with a light-blue flame to give carbon dioxide, water vapor, and heat energy:

$$CH_4 + 2O_2 \longrightarrow CO_2 + 2H_2O + \text{heat} \qquad (25\text{-}1)$$

In this reaction, the oxidation state of carbon is changed from −4 in CH_4 to +4, in CO_2, its highest value. Thus methane undergoes *complete combustion.*

If the oxygen is in short supply, methane burns with a light-blue flame to give carbon monoxide, water vapor, and heat energy:

$$2CH_4 + 3O_2 \longrightarrow 2CO + 4H_2O + \text{heat} \qquad (25\text{-}2)$$

In this case, the oxidation state of carbon is changed from −4 to +2. Thus, the methane undergoes *incomplete combustion.*

If the oxygen is in still shorter supply, methane burns with a luminous smoky flame to give carbon (soot), water vapor, and heat energy:

$$CH_4 + O_2 \longrightarrow C + 2H_2O + \text{heat} \qquad (25\text{-}3)$$

This is an even more incomplete combustion than the carbon monoxide reaction. It is worth noting that the reaction in Eq. (25-3) is the industrial method of preparing carbon black (soot) which is used as the black pigment in printer's ink and as a filler in the outer casings of automobile tires.

How do the heat quantities compare in the three reactions. If 1 mole (16 g) of methane is burned, the quantity of heat energy released in each case is shown by the value of ΔH:

$$CH_4 + 2O_2 \longrightarrow CO_2 + 2H_2O \quad \Delta H = -211 \text{ kcal} \qquad (25\text{-}4)$$
$$CH_4 + \tfrac{3}{2}O_2 \longrightarrow CO + 2H_2O \quad \Delta H = -143 \text{ kcal} \qquad (25\text{-}5)$$
$$CH_4 + O_2 \longrightarrow C + 2H_2O \quad \Delta H = -117 \text{ kcal} \qquad (25\text{-}6)$$

Clearly, the *greatest* amount of energy is released by *complete* combustion of a hydrocarbon and the smallest amount of energy is released when soot is formed. Thus, *the more complete the combustion of a fuel* such as gasoline, *the greater is the utilization of its potential chemical energy.*

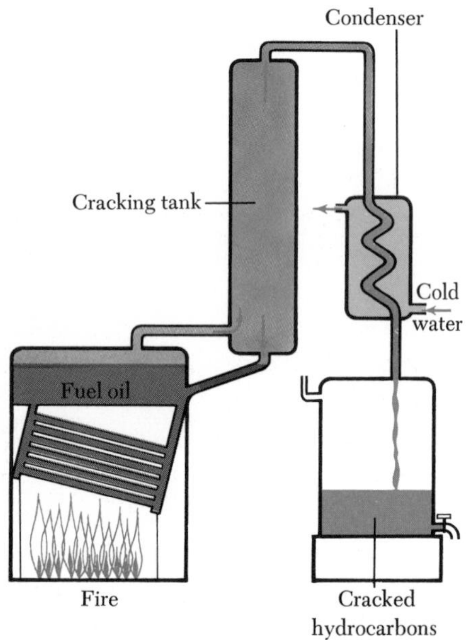

Fig. 25-9 Hot vapors from the boiler enter the cracking tower. The cracked molecules pass through the tower, and some are condensed farther along the line. Uncracked molecules of fuel oil condense in the tower and return to the boiler.

Cracking At high temperatures, the molecules of long-chain alkanes are in rapid motion and therefore there are frequent collisions between them. The higher the pressure the closer the molecules become, so that the collision rate increases. A combination of high temperature and high pressure therefore greatly increases the number of molecular collisions, and under the violence of these impacts the long carbon chains are broken. This process is called *cracking*. The simplified diagram in Fig. 25-9 illustrates the principle of the cracking operation.

Cracking involves many complex reactions and the formation of a variety of products. For simplicity, let us consider the cracking of $C_{16}H_{34}$ molecules into *two* parts. The molecules can be broken at different points along the chain, and some of the possibilities are

$$C_{16}H_{34} \longrightarrow C_8H_{18} + C_8H_{16} \tag{25-7}$$
$$C_{16}H_{34} \longrightarrow C_{12}H_{26} + C_4H_8 \tag{25-8}$$
$$C_{16}H_{34} \longrightarrow C_{14}H_{30} + C_2H_4 \tag{25-9}$$
$$C_{16}H_{34} \longrightarrow C_{10}H_{22} + C_5H_{12} + C \tag{25-10}$$

The cracking of $C_{16}H_{34}$ to give C_8H_{18} and C_8H_{16} is shown in Fig. 25-10.

Notice that the products of cracking include the *alkanes* C_8H_{18}, $C_{12}H_{26}$, $C_{14}H_{30}$, $C_{10}H_{22}$, and C_5H_{12}, and also the *alkenes* C_8H_{16}, C_4H_8, and C_2H_4. Later in the chapter you will learn that the alkenes are *unsaturated* hydrocarbons and they burn more efficiently than alkanes in an internal combustion engine. That is, alkenes improve the octane rating of a fuel such as gasoline. Cracking is therefore an important industrial process. At least 50% of the gasoline used in the United States is obtained in this way.

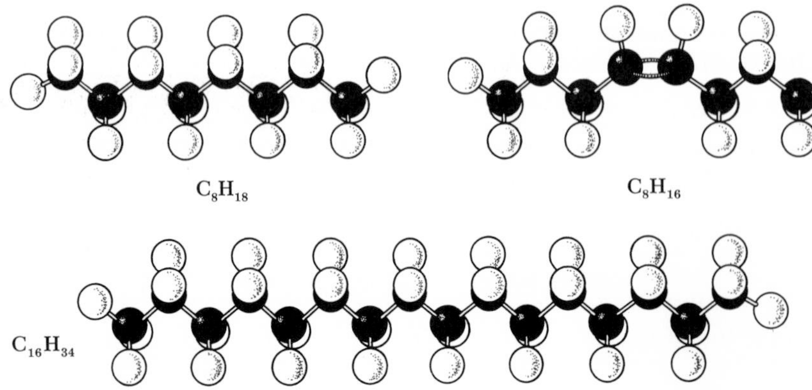

Fig. 25-10 The cracking of paraffin hydrocarbons. At the bottom is a model of the paraffin hydrocarbon $C_{16}H_{31}$. Two products which could be formed by the "cracking" of this hydrocarbon are octane C_8H_{18} (upper left), and octene-4, C_8H_{16} (model at the upper right).

Fig. 25-11 Catalytic cracking tower. This is used for a slightly different process than that in Fig. 25-9. Find out about the two processes.

Substitution You recall that all the bonds in an alkane are single covalent linkages. This means that alkanes are *saturated* hydrocarbons and therefore *addition* of atoms to an alkane molecule is impossible. However, alkanes can react by *substitution*. That is, one or more hydrogen atoms of the alkane can be replaced by another substance.

Speculate . . .
If pure 2,2,4-trimethyl pentane has an octane rating of 100 and heptane has a rating of zero, why do you think alkenes improve octane ratings?

All the halogens except iodine react with the alkanes at elevated temperatures in the presence of sunlight, giving a variety of substitution products. The reaction of methane with chlorine is typical of these reactions. The first step in the reaction of methane with chlorine is

$$CH_4 + Cl_2 \xrightarrow[\text{heat}]{\text{sunlight}} CH_3Cl + HCl \qquad (25\text{-}11)$$

One atom of chlorine atom is substituted for one hydrogen atom in a molecule of methane, and hydrogen chloride is formed. The name of the product, CH_3Cl, is *methyl chloride* or *chloromethane*. The reaction need not stop at this point, however, but may continue through three more steps, depending on conditions, until all of the hydrogen atoms in methane have been replaced by chlorine atoms.

The equations for the succeeding steps are as follows:

$$CH_3Cl + Cl_2 \longrightarrow CH_2Cl_2 + HCl \quad (25\text{-}12)$$
$$CH_2Cl_2 + Cl_2 \longrightarrow CHCl_3 + HCl \quad (25\text{-}13)$$
$$CHCl_3 + Cl_2 \longrightarrow CCl_4 + HCl \quad (25\text{-}14)$$

The name of CH_2Cl_2 is *methylene dichloride* or *dichloromethane*; $CHCl_3$ is called *chloroform* or *trichloromethane*; and CCl_4 is known as *carbon tetrachloride* or *tetrachloromethane*.

The Alkenes

Free alkenes are not ordinarily encountered by consumers, but substances derived from alkenes are very familiar to us. For example, high-octane gasoline, the rubber of an automobile tire, and plastic articles such as combs, radio cabinets, certain fibers, and films are all prepared from alkenes. The substance responsible for the yellow coloring matter in eggs, carrots, butter, and in other yellow-colored vegetables and animal products is a complex alkene known as β-carotene.

As you read earlier, many alkenes may be produced by the cracking of petroleum; that is, by the controlled decomposition of alkanes. The alkenes, like the alkanes, are hydrocarbons. However, they have less hydrogen than the alkanes and are called *unsaturated hydrocarbons*. Alkenes, with the general formula C_nH_{2n}, have *two hydrogen atoms less* per molecule than the corresponding alkanes. The first member of this series is *ethene* (C_2H_4), the second is *propene* (C_3H_6), and the third is *butene* (C_4H_8), and here again isomers are possible. Notice that the name of each alk*ene* ends in *ene* as contrasted with the ending *ane* for an alkane.

Fig. 25-12 Electron-dot formulas of ethene and propene.

```
 H  H            H   H   H
 ..  ..          ..  ..  ..
H:C::C:H       H:C::C:C:H
                         ..
                         H
```

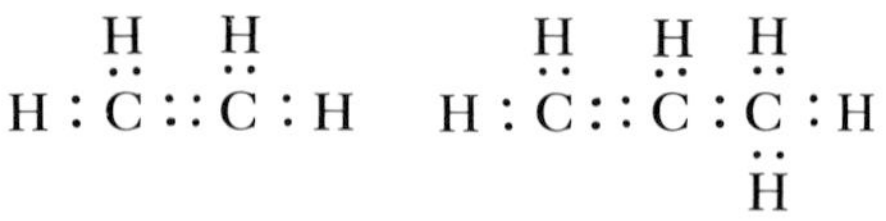

(*a*) ethene (*b*) propene

The electron-dot formulas of ethene and propene are shown in Fig. 25-12.

It is, of course, more convenient to use a line to represent a shared pair of electrons, so that the formulas are usually written as in Fig. 25-13 or even more simply as $CH_2{=}CH_2$ and $CH_2{=}CH{-}CH_3$.

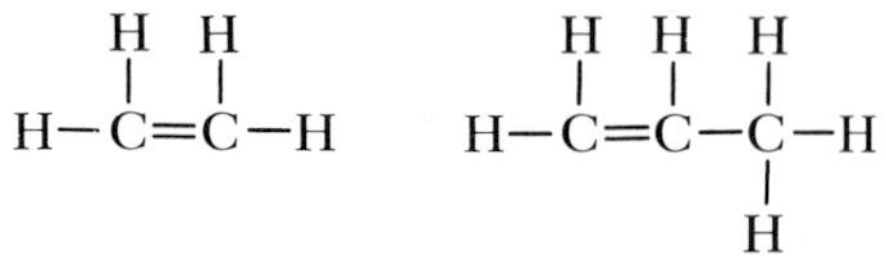

Fig. 25-13 Structural (line) formulas of ethene and propene.

```
  H H            H  H  H
  | |            |  |  |
H—C=C—H        H—C=C—C—H
                       |
                       H
```

(*a*) ethene (*b*) propene

Observe that in each structure two carbon atoms are linked by *two* shared pairs of electrons. This type of *linkage* is called a *double bond*, and it is the *identifying characteristic of the alkenes*. A double bond indicates unsaturation and therefore greater chemical activity than a single bond. It does *not* indicate greater stability as one might at first suspect. That is, a double bond is a relatively easy point to attack chemically.

There is only one compound C_2H_4 and only one C_3H_6. But there are three isomers of C_4H_8 and their structures are

$$\overset{1}{C}H_2=\overset{2}{C}H-\overset{3}{C}H_2-\overset{4}{C}H_3 \quad (1)$$

$$\overset{1}{C}H_3-\overset{2}{C}H=\overset{3}{C}H-\overset{4}{C}H_3 \quad (2)$$

$$H_3\overset{3}{C}-\overset{2}{\underset{}{C}}(CH_3)=\overset{1}{C}H_2 \quad (3)$$

How can these isomers be distinguished by name? Isomers **1** and **2** have a 4-carbon chain; they are therefore derivatives of butane. Isomer **3** has a 3-carbon chain and is a derivative of propane. In isomer **1** the double bond is at the carbon atom at the end of the chain, so that this isomer is therefore called *1-butene*. In isomer **2** the double bond links the second and third carbon atoms of the chain and this isomer is therefore called *2-butene*. The name for isomer **3** is *2-methyl-1-propene*, or just *methylpropene*. Why can the numbers 2 and 1 be omitted in naming methylpropene?

Let us now consider the names for the following three compounds:

$$\overset{1}{C}H_2=\overset{2}{C}H-\overset{3}{C}H(CH_3)-\overset{4}{C}H_3 \quad (4)$$

$$\overset{1}{C}H_3-\overset{2}{C}(CH_3)=\overset{3}{C}H-\overset{4}{C}H_2-\overset{5}{C}H_3 \quad (5)$$

$$\overset{6}{C}H_3\overset{5}{C}H_2-\overset{4}{C}(CH_3)_2-\overset{3}{C}H=\overset{2}{C}H-\overset{1}{C}H_3 \quad (6)$$

In compound 4 the longest continuous chain of carbon atoms containing the double bond consists of four atoms. Hence it is called 3-methyl-1-butene. Similarly, compound **5** has a five-carbon chain containing the double bond and is known as 2-methyl-2-pentene.

Investigate . . .
Is compound **6** correctly named by I.U.P.A.C. rules?

Compound **6** has a six-carbon chain with the double bond at the second carbon atom, and its name is 4,4-dimethyl-2-hexene.

A Second Kind of Isomerism

Carbon atoms can rotate freely about a single bond. On the other hand, two carbons atoms joined by a double bond cannot be rotated. This concept can be visualized by constructing a model of an alkene, using wooden balls and pegs to represent tetrahedral carbon atoms and pairs of electrons. The two carbon atoms joined by the double bond appear in the model as two tetrahedra joined on an edge and the four atoms or groups attached to the double-bonded carbon atoms are in a plane. This situation is shown for ethene in Fig. 25-14.

Fig. 25-14 Model of a molecule of ethene.

Suppose we construct the ball-and-peg model of 2-butene (CH_3—CH = CH—CH). When we do so, we find that there are two possible arrangements, one (*a*) with the two methyl groups on the same side of the molecule, the other (*b*) with the two methyl groups on opposite sides:

$$\begin{array}{c} H-C-CH_3 \\ \| \\ H-C-CH_3 \end{array} \qquad \begin{array}{c} H-C-CH_3 \\ \| \\ H_3C-C-H \end{array}$$

(*a*) (*b*)

Actually, these two compounds are known and they have different chemical and physical properties. Compounds like these, which have the same formula and the same bonding, are certainly not like the previously discussed structural isomers. They are called *geometrical isomers*. How can they be distinguished by name? Compound (*a*) is called the *cis* isomer of 2-butene. The prefix *cis* means *on the same side* and therefore the name indicates that similar groups are adjacent to each other. The compound on the right is called *trans* 2-butene or the *trans* isomer of 2-butene. The prefix *trans* means *across* and therefore the name indicates that similar groups are on opposite sides of the molecule. Indeed, this type of geometrical isomerism is sometimes known as *cis-trans isomerism*. See Fig. 25-15.

If we use the symbols *a* and *b* to represent atoms or groups attached to double-bonded carbon atoms, we can say that geometrical

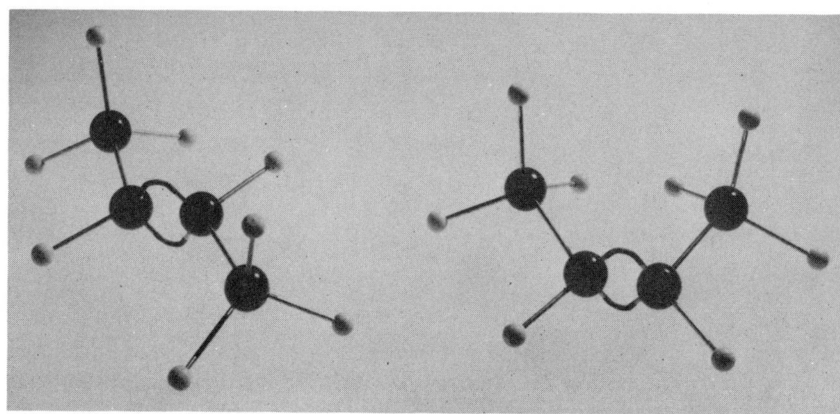

Fig. 25-15 Models of geometric isomers of 2-butene.

isomers are possible if they have the structure

$$\begin{array}{c} a-\mathrm{C}-b \\ \| \\ a-\mathrm{C}-b \end{array}$$

Geometrical isomers are also possible if all groups are different:

$$\begin{array}{c} a-\mathrm{C}-b \\ \| \\ d-\mathrm{C}-e \end{array}$$

What is the possibility of geometriacl isomerism here?

$CH_2{=}CH_2$ ethene

$CH_3{-}CH{=}CH_2$ propene

$CH_2{=}CH{-}CH_2CH_3$ 1-butene

$CH_3{-}C(CH_3){=}C(CH_3){-}CH_3$ 2,3-dimethyl-2-butene

$CH_3{-}CH{=}C(CH_3){-}CH_2CH_3$ 3-methyl-2-pentene

$Cl{-}CH{=}CH{-}Cl$ 1,2-dichloroethene

Only the last two substances, 3-methyl-2-pentene and 1,2-dichloroethene, have two dissimilar groups (or atoms) on each of the double-bonded carbon atoms. Therefore these compounds should exist as geometrical isomers. The other substances have similar groups (or atoms) on at least one of the double-bonded carbon atoms and therefore cannot exhibit geometrical isomerism.

Reactions of the Alkenes

Alkenes, like alkanes, are combustible. For example, ethene burns in oxygen (air) at high temperatures to give water vapor and a carbon product:

$$C_2H_4 + 3O_2 \longrightarrow 2CO_2 + 2H_2O + \text{heat} \qquad (25\text{-}15)$$

$$C_2H_4' + 2O_2 \longrightarrow 2CO + 2H_2O + \text{heat} \qquad (25\text{-}16)$$
(in limited supply)

$$C_2H_4 + O_2 \longrightarrow 2C + 2H_2O + \text{heat} \qquad (25\text{-}17)$$
(in very limited supply)

As you recall, the characteristic reaction of saturated hydrocarbons is *substitution*. The characteristic reaction of unsaturated compounds is *addition*. The word *addition* indicates precisely what happens, namely that something is added to the alkene. As you might expect, addition reactions usually occur more easily than substitution reactions. Indeed, some addition reactions take place about as fast as reactions between ions.

Typical Addition Reactions of the Alkenes

1.The addition of hydrogen The addition of hydrogen to an unsaturated substance is called *hydrogenation*. Hydrogenation does not occur unless a catalyst is used; in most instances the reaction does not proceed at a measurable rate unless the temperature is raised. Alkenes add hydrogen in the presence of finely divided nickel, platinum, or palladium. Ethene, for example, reacts with hydrogen to give ethane,

$$CH_2 = CH_2 + H_2 \xrightarrow[\text{heat}]{\text{catalyst}} CH_3{-}CH_3 \qquad (25\text{-}18)$$

The manufacture of edible fats such as Crisco ® and margarine is a large-scale application of the hydrogenation of unsaturated vegetable oil. Such vegetable oils such as cottonseed and corn oil are liquids whose molecules are unsaturated. However these molecules are *not* simple alkenes but unsaturated *fats* (see Chapters 26 and 27). These compounds slowly oxidize in the air and the oxidation products have an unpleasant odor. Such an undesirable reaction can be prevented by hydrogenating the oils. Hydrogenation saturates these substances, thereby preventing slow oxidation. Moreover, it also raises their melting points so that the products are (usually) low-melting solids rather than liquids. Equation (25-19) is a general word equation for the hydrogenation of an oil:

Speculate . . .
How many items in your kitchen are hydrogenated hydrocarbons or fats?

$$\text{oil} + H_2 \xrightarrow[\text{heat}]{\text{catalyst}} \text{fat} \tag{25-19}$$

2. The addition of halogens Chlorine and bromine can be added to alkenes at ordinary temperatures, so the addition reaction is not complicated by a substitution reaction at the same time. Thus, ethene reacts with bromine to give 1,2-*dibromoethane*,

$$CH_2{=}CH_2 + Br_2 \longrightarrow CH_2Br{-}CH_2Br \tag{25-20}$$

This product, also called *ethylene dibromide*, is manufactured on a large scale as an essential material in the production of "ethyl" gasoline.

3. The addition of hypochlorous and hypobromous acids The addition of hypochlorous and hypobromous acids to alkenes is almost as rapid as the addition of the halogens. For example, ethene reacts with hypochlorous acid to give ethylene chlorohydrin:

$$CH_2{=}CH_2 + HOCl \longrightarrow Cl{-}CH_2{-}CH_2OH \tag{25-21}$$

The chlorohydrin can, in turn, be easily converted into the substance *ethylene glycol* by heating the chlorohydrin with water under pressure:

$$\begin{aligned} &Cl{-}CH_2{-}CH_2{-}OH + H_2O \longrightarrow \\ &\qquad HO{-}CH_2{-}CH_2{-}OH + HCl \end{aligned} \tag{25-22}$$

Ethylene glycol (also called 1,2-dihydroxyethane) is manufactured on a large scale for use as a solvent and as a "permanent" antifreeze in automobile radiators. The term "permanent" indicates that there is only a negligible loss by evaporation. This is because the glycol has a high boiling point (197 °C).

4. The addition of sulfuric acid Unsaturated hydrocarbons react with concentrated sulfuric acid, whereas saturated hydrocarbons do not. Thus, a mixture of alkanes and alkenes can be separated by bubbling the mixture through the concentrated acid.

The reaction of unsaturated hydrocarbons with sulfuric acid results in the formation of alkylsulfuric acids. For example, when ethene reacts with sulfuric acid, ethylsulfuric acid is formed:

$$CH_2{=}CH_2 + H_2SO_4 \longrightarrow CH_3{-}CH_2{-}OSO_3H \tag{25-23}$$

Clearly, this is an addition reaction.

Ethylsulfuric acid is then easily converted to ethanol (ethyl alcohol) by the action of water,

$$CH_3CH_2{-}OSO_3H + H_2O \longrightarrow CH_3CH_2OH + H_2SO_4(aq) \tag{25-24}$$

Here, then, is a way of converting an alkene into an alcohol. Indeed, more than 50% of the ethyl alcohol manufactured in the United States is made by this method. Moreover, hitherto rare alcohols can now be manufactured on a large scale by this method. For instance, the ordinary rubbing alcohol sold in drug stores (isopropyl alcohol) is prepared in this way from propene, which in turn is obtained from the cracking of petroleum.

The Alkynes

The *alkynes* (also called acetylenic hydrocarbons) are even more highly unsaturated than the alkenes. Thus, an alkyne contains four hydrogen atoms less than the alkane molecule with the same number of carbon atoms. The general formula for the alkynes is C_nH_{2n-2} and the names of all compounds in this series end in *yne*. The simplest member of the series is ethyne (C_2H_2), and the next is propyne (C_3H_4). The common name for ethyne is *acetylene*, a name that is so firmly entrenched that the correct chemical name is seldom used.

The electron-dot formulas of ethyne and propyne are

$$H:C:::C:H$$

and

$$\begin{array}{c} H \\ \ddot{\ } \\ H:C:::C:C:H \\ \ddot{\ } \\ H \end{array}$$

These formulas are more conveniently written as $H{-}C{\equiv}C{-}H$ and $H{-}C{\equiv}C{-}CH_3$. The triple bond indicates that three pairs of electrons are shared between the two carbon atoms and is indicative of a higher degree of unsaturation than is the double bond of an alkene.

It is apparent from their structural formulas that there is only one ethyne and one propyne. But there are two isomers of butyne (C_4H_6), and their structures are

$$(a)\,H{-}C{\equiv}C{-}CH_2{-}CH_3 \quad \text{and} \quad (b)\,CH_3{-}C{\equiv}C{-}CH_3$$

Isomer (*a*) is called 1-butyne and isomer (*b*) is 2-butyne. Can you explain why?

Let us name compound **7**, which is an alkyne.

Infer . . .
Could compound **7** be numbered in any other way? Would the name be different?

$$\underset{1}{CH_3}-\underset{2}{\overset{\overset{\displaystyle CH_3}{|}}{CH}}-\underset{3}{C}\equiv\underset{4}{C}-\underset{5}{\overset{\overset{\displaystyle CH_3}{|}}{CH}}-\underset{6}{CH_3} \qquad (7)$$

The longest continuous chain of carbon atoms containing the triple bond comprises six atoms. Hence this compound is a derivative of hexane and its correct name is 2,5-dimethyl-3-hexyne.

The Spatial Orientation Around the Triple Bond

You recall that rotation about a double bond is restricted but there is *cis-trans* isomerism. Does this fact also apply to carbon atoms joined by a triple bond? If a model of ethyne is constructed from wooden balls and pegs (Fig. 25-16), it is apparent the four atoms are in a straight line; that is, the structure is linear. This is consistent with experimental evidence on the structure of the ethyne molecule, and it suggests that there is restriction of rotation about the triple bond. Moreover, because the molecule is linear, there is no possibility of geometrical isomerism associated with the triple bond.

Ethyne, the Most Important Member of the Alkyne Series

Ethyne (acetylene) is by far the most important member of the alkyne series. Moreover, ethyne occupies a unique position among carbon compounds because it can be prepared from the inorganic substances limestone, coke, and water. The reactions for this preparation are shown in Eqs. 25-25 and 25-26.

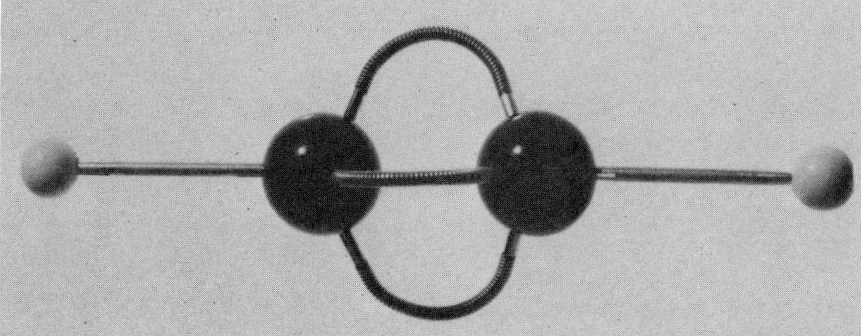

Fig. 25-16 Model of the acetylene molecule.

$$CaCO_3 + 3C \xrightarrow{\text{white heat}} CaC_2 + CO(g) + CO_2(g) \tag{25-25}$$

and

$$\underset{\text{calcium carbide}}{CaC_2} + 2H_2O \xrightarrow[\text{temperature}]{\text{room}} Ca(OH)_2 + C_2H_2(g) \tag{25-26}$$

The preparation of acetylene is an endothermic reaction, and energy is absorbed during its formation. Is it likely then that some of the energy stored in acetylene will be released when the compound reacts? The use of acetylene in oxyacetylene welding depends in large measure upon the release of this stored energy which is added to the heat of combustion when acetylene is burned:

$$C_2H_2 + \tfrac{5}{2}\,O_2 \longrightarrow 2CO_2 + H_2O \quad \Delta H = -312 \text{ kcal} \tag{25-27}$$

The heat of combustion for acetylene is higher than that of any other fuel gas.

Fig. 25-17 The flame of an oxyacetylene torch can cut through thick layers of metal. Why?

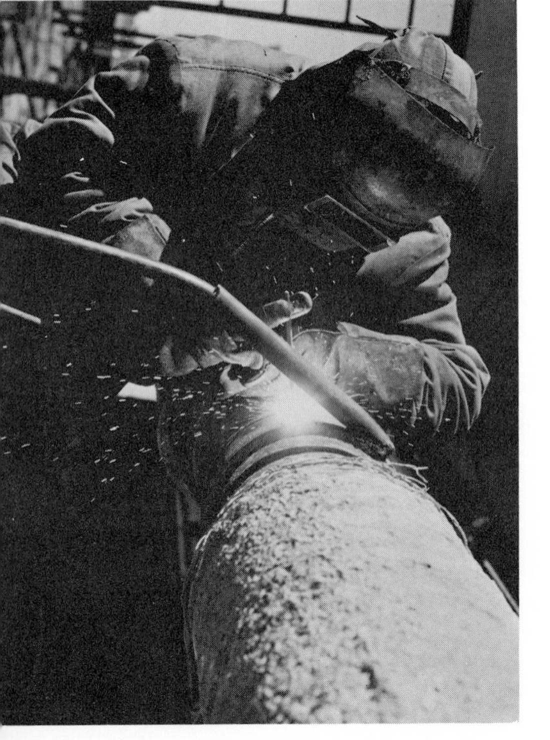

Reactions of the Alkynes

As one might expect from the activity of the triple bond, alkynes undergo a wide variety of addition reactions. Indeed, the alkynes react with the same reagents as the alkenes, but normally they absorb twice as much of each reagent as the alkenes do. For example, 2 moles of hydrogen are absorbed by 1 mole of ethyne to give ethane. This reaction may be assumed to occur in two steps, the first step giving ethene, which then absorbs a second mole of hydrogen

$$HC{\equiv}CH + H_2 \xrightarrow[\text{heat}]{\text{catalyst}} CH_2{=}CH_2 \tag{25-28}$$

$$CH_2{=}CH_2 + H_2 \xrightarrow[\text{heat}]{\text{catalyst}} CH_3{-}CH_3 \tag{25-29}$$

Another important type of reaction is the addition of acetylene molecules to each other in the presence of a suitable catalyst. Thus, two molecules of acetylene combine to give a substance known as vinylacetylene:

$$2HC{\equiv}CH \xrightarrow{\text{catalyst}} H_2C{=}CH{-}C{\equiv}CH \tag{25-30}$$

And vinylacetylene, in turn, can add a third molecule of acetylene, and so on. This process of addition of like molecules to each other is called *addition polymerization*. The manufacture of synthetic rubber, plastics, resins, and varnishes are examples of this kind of polymerization.

The Aromatic Hydrocarbons

Organic compounds are sometimes divided into two general classes, *aliphatic*, and *aromatic*. The *aliphatic* (a word that means *fatty*) compounds includes the alkanes, alkenes, and their derivatives. As you have learned, they are obtained on a large scale from petroleum and natural gas, and are, for the most part, *carbon-chain* compounds. Aromatic compounds, on the other hand, are derivatives of coal (usually coal tar). The word *aromatic* was selected because many of the compounds have a pleasant odor. But the principle characteristic of these compounds derives from a *ring* of carbon atoms, rather than the chains characteristic of the aliphatics.

Benzene—The Parent of the Aromatics

Benzene is the parent of the aromatics, just as methane is the parent of the aliphatics. This does not mean that all aromatics are derived from benzene, but rather that benzene is the simplest member of the series. Moreover, benzene is the most abundant of the coal-tar compounds.

Speculate . . .
Guess at the number of "coal-tar derivatives" known. Check your guess in an encyclopedia.

Benzene has the formula C_6H_6, and it therefore appears to be a highly unsaturated hydrocarbon. Yet it does not behave like an unsaturated substance. What, then, is the structure of benzene? This question puzzled scientists for a long time. But in 1865 a German chemist, F.A. Kekulé (1829–1886), suggested that the six carbon atoms form a closed ring with alternate single and double bonds, as shown below:

```
      H   H
      |   |
      C—C
     //    \\
H—C        C—H
     \     /
      C=C
      |   |
      H   H
```

Notice the three double bonds in this structure for benzene. If we were dealing with an aliphatic substance, the double bonds would indicate unsaturation. However, benzene has none of the typical reactions of unsaturated aliphatic compounds. Does this mean that a double bond in a ring structure behaves differently from a double bond in a chain structure? To answer this question let us consider the compound cyclohexene:

$$
\begin{array}{ccc}
 & \mathrm{H} & \\
 & | & \\
 & \mathrm{C{-}CH_2} & \\
 \mathrm{H{-}C} & & \mathrm{CH_2} \\
 & \mathrm{H_2C{-}CH_2} &
\end{array}
$$

Cyclohexene is a typical aliphatic compound yet it has the same six-carbon ring as benzene and it also has one double bond in the ring. But it acts like a typical unsaturated compound and does not behave like benzene. What, then, is the essential difference between cyclohexene and benzene?

Electron-diffraction pictures indicate that the carbon–carbon bond distances in benzene are all the same, whereas in aliphatic compounds (including cyclohexene) the carbon–carbon single bond and the carbon–carbon double bond are of different lengths. Therefore a benzene ring is symmetrical in structure, but an aliphatic ring is not. Moreover, chemists believe that the three double bonds in benzene undergo an unusual interaction known as *resonance*. Resonance results in added chemical stability. For simplicity we shall represent the benzene molecule as a regular hexagon,

with the understanding that there is a hydrogen atom as well as a carbon at each of the angles. The dashed circle inside the ring represents the resonance interaction among the bonds in the ring.

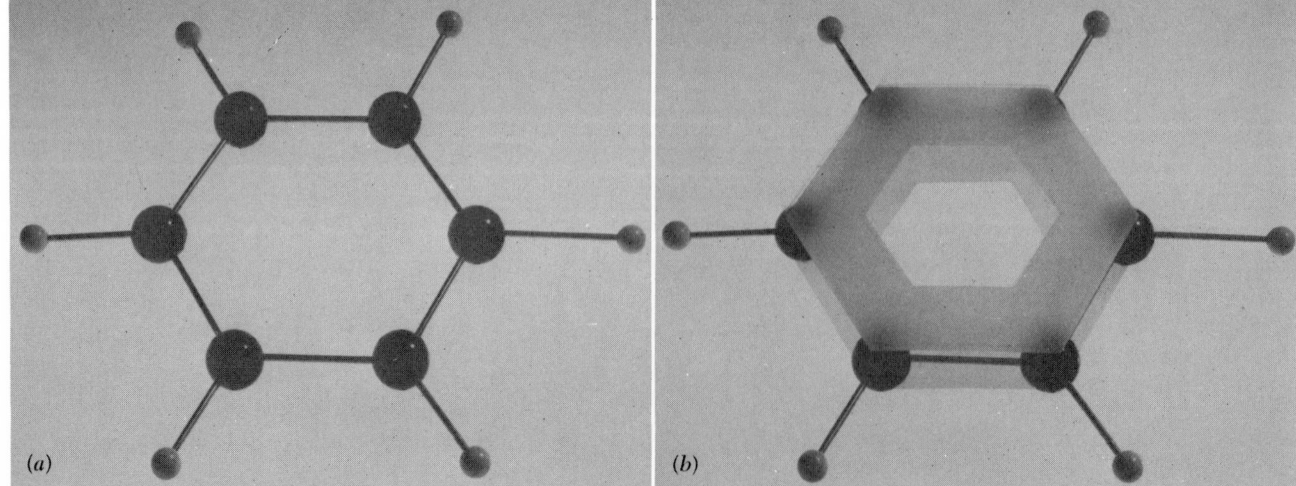

Fig. 25-18 Structural models of the benzene molecule: (*a*) bond model; (*b*) resonance model.

When the benzene formula appears with an atom or a group of atoms attached to one or more corners of the hexagon, it is implied that the hydrogen atoms in those positions have been replaced.

Definition . . .
A simple definition of resonance requires you to imagine that all the bonds in the resonance system have some double-bond character, rather than the simpler but erroneous view that some of the bonds are single and others double.

Some Reactions of Benzene As you recall, addition reactions characteristic of unsaturated hydrocarbons are not the common reactions of benzene. Instead, *substitution* reactions are the rule. Thus, benzene reacts with chlorine in the presence of iron powder as a catalyst to give substitution products such as chlorobenzene and 1,4-dichlorobenzene,

$$⌬ + Cl_2 \xrightarrow[\text{heat}]{\text{iron}} ⌬\text{—}Cl + HCl \qquad (25\text{-}31)$$

$$⌬\text{—}Cl + Cl_2 \xrightarrow[\text{heat}]{\text{iron}} Cl\text{—}⌬\text{—}Cl + HCl \qquad (25\text{-}32)$$

Notice that, as is the case with alkanes, chlorine is substituted for hydrogen and hydrogen chloride is also formed. For convenience, the carbon atoms in the ring are numbered 1 through 6. The common name for 1,4-dichlorobenzene is paradichlorobenzene (or *p*-dichlorobenzene); this is a substance frequently used in the home to protect woolens from the destructive action of moths.

Benzene also reacts with a mixture of concentrated nitric acid (HNO_3 or $HO—NO_2$) and sulfuric acid (this mixture is usually called *nitrating mixture*) to give substitution products such as nitrobenzene and 1,3,5-trinitrobenzene,

$$⌬ + HO\text{—}NO_2 \xrightarrow{H_2SO_4} ⌬\text{—}NO_2 + H_2O \qquad (25\text{-}33)$$

$$⌬ + 3HO\text{—}NO_2 \xrightarrow{H_2SO_4} (NO_2)_2⌬\text{—}NO_2 + 3H_2O \qquad (25\text{-}34)$$

These nitro derivatives of benzene can be reduced by hydrogen to yield amino compounds (substances with $-NH_2$ groups) which are used in the manufacture of dyes and photographic chemicals. Thus, nitrobenzene is reduced by hydrogen to aminobenzene:

$$⌬\text{—}NO_2 + 3H_2 \longrightarrow ⌬\text{—}NH_2 + 2H_2O \qquad (25\text{-}35)$$

Infer . . .
The common name for aminobenzene is aniline. From this, what could you say about "aniline dyes"?

Toluene and Naphthalene

Two other aromatic hydrocarbons obtained in quantity from coal tar are toluene and naphthalene.

Toluene has the formula C_7H_8 and its structure is 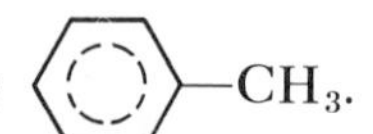

The correct name for toluene is therefore methylbenzene. The most important derivative of toluene is 2,4,6-trinitrotoluene which is prepared by the action of nitrating mixture on toluene,

$$C_6H_5\text{—}CH_3 + 3HO\text{—}NO_2 \xrightarrow{H_2SO_4} O_2N\text{—}C_6H_2(NO_2)_2\text{—}CH_3 + 3H_2O \qquad (25\text{-}36)$$

The name of this product is commonly abbreviated to trinitrotoluene or just TNT; and as you know, TNT is a powerful explosive.

Naphthalene is another aromatic compound. It has the formula $C_{10}H_8$ and its structure is shown in Fig. 25-19.

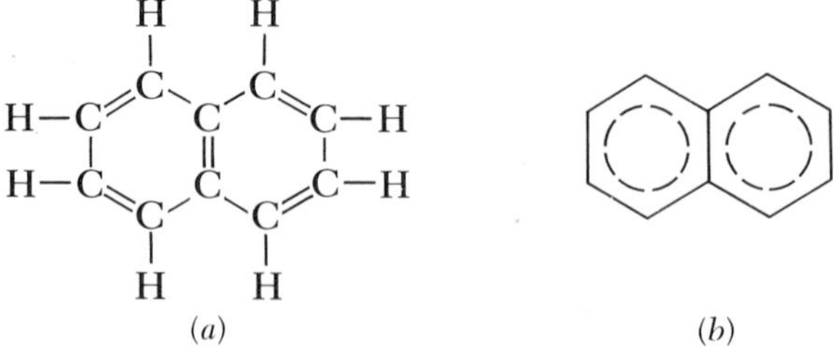

Fig. 25-19 Alternate structural formulas for naphthalene.

Notice that this aromatic hydrocarbon is constructed of two rings fused together. It is the source of many chemicals such as dyes, saccharin (a substitute for sugar), and the indicator phenolphthalein.

Summary

Hydrocarbons are compounds of hydrogen and carbon, and "families" of hydrocarbons include *alkanes*, *alkenes*, *alkynes*, and *aromatic hydrocarbons*. In the alkanes, alkenes, and alkynes the carbon atoms form a chain; in the aromatics, carbon atoms form a ring.

Alkanes have the general formula C_nH_{2n+2}, the first member of the series being *methane* (CH_4). The names of all alkanes end in *ane*. Beginning with the fourth member, butane (C_4H_{10}), the alkanes form *structural isomers* due to the branching of the carbon chain. Characteristic reactions of the alkanes are:

(1) They burn to form CO_2 and H_2O, a reaction of all hydrocarbons.
(2) They take part in substitution reactions in which an atom such as chlorine can be substituted for a hydrogen atom.
(3) They can be cracked, that is, if the carbon chain is long enough the molecule can be split into two smaller hydrocarbon molecules.

Alkenes have the general formula C_nH_{2n}. They have a double bond which indicates unsaturation. The simplest alkene is *ethene* (C_2H_4). The names of all alkenes end in *ene*. A characteristic reaction of the alkenes is addition, in which a saturated compound is formed by the addition of atoms such as hydrogen or chlorine at the double bond. If two different atoms or groups are attached to the double-bonded carbon atom, an alkene forms two geometrical (or *cis-trans*) isomers as in

$$\begin{array}{c} a-\mathrm{C}-b \\ \| \\ a-\mathrm{C}-b \end{array} \quad \text{and} \quad \begin{array}{c} a-\mathrm{C}-b \\ \| \\ b-\mathrm{C}-a \end{array}$$

Alkynes have the general formula C_nH_{2n-2}. The simplest alkyne is ethyne or acetylene (C_2H_2). The names of all alkynes end in *yne*. Alkynes have a triple bond so, like the alkenes, their characteristic reaction is addition. However, unlike the alkenes, the alkynes do not form geometrical isomers.

The simplest of the aromatic ring compounds is benzene. Its formula is C_6H_6, and its structural formula is

```
      H   H
      |   |
      C—C
     //   \\
  H—C       C—H
     \     /
      C=C
      |   |
      H   H        or
```

A characteristic reaction of the aromatics is substitution, not addition. For example, a chlorine atom can be substituted for a hydrogen atom, as in

$$C_6H_6 + Cl_2 \longrightarrow C_6H_5Cl + HCl$$

benzene chlorobenzene

Factual Recall

1. Why are there so many carbon compounds?
2. What is meant by the term *tetrahedral carbon atom*?
3. How would you represent the three-dimensional nature of methane?
4. Does freedom of rotation about a carbon—carbon single bond decrease or increase the number of possible isomers? Explain.
5. Do the carbon atoms in a straight-chain hydrocarbon lie in a straight line? Explain.
6. What is meant by the term *branched-chain hydrocarbon*? Give an example.
7. (*a*) Give the names of five alkanes. (*b*) What do these names have in common? (*c*) Is $C_{16}H_{34}$ an alkane? Why or why not?
8. A hydrocarbon has the molecular formula C_4H_{10}. (*a*) How many compounds have this molecular formula? (*b*) Write the structural formulas of these compounds.
9. (*a*) Give the names of three alkenes. (*b*) What do these names have in common? (*c*) Is $C_{14}H_{30}$ an alkene? Why or why not?
10. A hydrocarbon has the molecular formula C_4H_8. (*a*) How many compounds have this molecular formula? (*b*) Write the structural formulas of these compounds.
11. (*a*) Give the names of three alkynes. (*b*) What do these names have in common? (*c*) Is C_5H_8 an alkyne? Why or why not?
12. Distinguish between the terms *aliphatic* and *aromatic* as used in organic chemistry.

13. What structural resemblance is there between benzene, toluene, and naphthalene?

14. (*a*) What are isomers? (*b*) How do *structural isomers* differ from each other? (*c*) Write the structural formulas for three substances with the formula C_6H_{14}, and give their names.

15. (*a*) Write the structural formulas for all of the isomers of C_7H_{16}.
(*b*) Give the name for each of the isomers.

16. How do *geometrical isomers* differ from *structural isomers*?

17. Write the structural formulas for (*a*) 2-methyl propane, (*b*) 2,2,3,3-tetramethyl butane, (*c*) 2,5-dimethyl hexane.

18. Give the names for (*a*)$(CH_3)_3CH$, (*b*)$(CH_3)_3C—C(CH_3)_3$, (*c*) $(CH_3)_2CH—CH_2—CH_2—CH(CH_3)_2$

19. (*a*) Should hexene-1 exist as geometrical isomers? Explain.
(*b*) Should hexene-2 exist as geometrical isomers? Explain.
(*c*) Should hexene-3 exist as geometrical isomers? Explain.

20. By means of equations, indicate several ways in which the hydrocarbon $C_{10}H_{22}$ might decompose at high temperature.

21. Why is the gasoline obtained by "cracking" superior as a fuel to straight-run gasoline from crude petroleum?

22. Write balanced equations for (*a*) the complete combustion of propane, (*b*) the incomplete combustion of propane to give a combustible gas as one product, (*c*) the incomplete combustion of propane to give a solid fuel as one product.

23. Alkanes take part in substitution reactions but not in addition reactions. Explain this statement.

24. A mixture of alkanes and alkenes can be separated by means of concentrated sulfuric acid. Explain why this can be done.

25. Write the structural formulas for (*a*) 2-methyl-3-hexene, (*b*) 2-methyl-3-heptyne, (*c*) 3,4,5,5-tetramethyl-1-hexene, (*d*) 4-methyl-3-ethyl-1-pentyne.

26. Give the names for (*a*) $(CH_3)_3C-CH=CH-CH_2-C(CH_3)_3$,
(*b*) $HC\equiv C-CH_2-CH(CH_3)-CH_3$,
(*c*) $(CH_3)_2CH-C\equiv C-CH(CH_3)_2$,
(*d*) $CH_2=C(CH_3)—CH_2—CH_2\ CH_3$

Apply Your Knowledge!

1. By analysis, a gaseous hydrocarbon contains 80% carbon and 20% hydrogen by mass. A 1.20-g sample of the hydrocarbon occupies 950 ml at 20 °C and 770 torr pressure. (*a*) Find the simplest formula of the hydrocarbon. (*b*) Find the molecular mass of the hydrocarbon. (*c*) Find the molecular formula of the hydrocarbon. (*d*) Write the structural formula of the hydrocarbon. (*e*) To which family of hydrocarbons does this substance belong?

2. A 3.2-g sample of calcium carbide is treated with excess water. Compute the volume of *dry* gas product liberated at 40 °C and 740 torr pressure.

3. Two gaseous hydrocarbons (*A* and *B*) are analyzed; each contains 85.7% carbon and 14.3% hydrogen by mass. A 1.40-g sample of hydrocarbon *A* occupies 560 ml at STP, whereas a 2.80-g sample of hydrocarbon *B* occupies 1660 ml at 100°C and 700 torr pressure. (*a*) What is the simplest formula of each hydrocarbon? (*b*) What is the molecular formula of *A*? (*c*) What is the molecular formula of *B*? (*d*) How do you explain the answers obtained in (*b*) and (*c*)?

4. By analysis, a hydrocarbon contains 83.7% carbon and 16.3% hydrogen by mass. In the gaseous state, a 1.72-g sample of the hydrocarbon occupies 612 ml at 100 °C and standard pressure. (*a*) Find the molecular formula of the compound. (*b*) Write the structural formulas of the isomeric hydrocarbons with this molecular formula.

5. How many kilocalories of energy are liberated by the (*a*) complete combustion of 67.2 l of methane (measured at STP), (*b*) incomplete combustion of 3 moles of methane (to give a combustible gas as one product), (*c*) incomplete combustion of 48 g of methane (to give a solid as one product)?

6. One hundred moles of methane are completely chlorinated. (*a*) How many moles of chlorine are consumed? (*b*) What is the mass in kilograms of the CCl_4 product? (*c*) What is the molarity of the acid solution obtained by dissolving the hydrogen chloride product in enough water to give 100 l of acid?

7. One mole of an unsaturated hydrocarbon, known to be either ethylene or acetylene, consumes 160 g of bromine to give a sat-

urated addition product. Show by calculation whether the gas is ethylene or acetylene.

8. (*a*) Find the mass of hypochlorous acid required to convert 11.2 l of ethylene (measured at STP) to ethylene chlorohydrin.
   (*b*) How many moles of ethylene glycol can be obtained from the ethylene chlorohydrin obtained in (*a*)?

9. One hundred tons of ethanol are to be prepared industrially by the addition of sulfuric acid to ethylene, followed by hydrolysis of the addition product. (*a*) How many tons of ethylene are required? (*b*) How many tons of sulfuric acid must be used?

10. Assume that the "cracking" of dodecane is limited to the following reaction:

    $C_{12}H_{26} \longrightarrow C_6H_{14} + C_6H_{12}$

    A sample of dodecane is maintained at a temperature of 400 °C until decomposition is complete. Compute the final pressure of the mixture, if the initial pressure was 10 atm and if the volume remained constant.

11. Methane undergoes complete combustion, giving carbon dioxide and water as products. If 224 l of methane at STP are burned in this way, find (*a*) the heat in calories released, (*b*) the volume of oxygen at STP used up, (*c*) the mass in grams of water formed, (*d*) the moles of carbon dioxide produced.

12. Calculate the volume of acetylene liberated at STP when 3.20 kg of calcium carbide react with water.

13. One quart (760 g) of hexane undergoes complete combustion. Compute the volume of gas product at 546 °C.

14. Five hundred grams of ethylene dibromide are prepared by the bromination of ethylene at 1 atm pressure. (*a*) What volume of ethylene at −10 °C is consumed? (*b*) How many moles of bromine must be added?

15. One hundred ninety kilograms of fused magnesium chloride are electrolyzed, and the anode product reacts with methane to give carbon tetrachloride and hydrogen chloride. Calculate (*a*) the moles of methane required, (*b*) the mass in kilograms of CCl_4 produced, (*c*) the volume of HCl gas formed at STP, (*d*) the volume of HCl solution produced by dissolving the hydrogen chloride in water to give a 6 *M* solution.

16. By analysis, the composition by mass of a compound is 88.9% carbon and 11.1% hydrogen. A 1.32-g sample of the compound, as vapor, occupies 765 ml at 100 °C and 760 torr pressure. (*a*) Find the molecular formula of the substance. (*b*) Can you name the substance and write its structural formula? Why or why not? (*c*) One mole of the substance combines with 2 moles of bromine by addition. Can you now name the substance and write its structural formula? Why or why not? (*d*) The bromine addition product is found to contain a bromine atom on each of the carbon atoms. Can you now name the substance and write its structural formula? Explain.

Find Out!

1. The rules used for naming organic compounds are established by I.U.P.A.C. (*a*) What is this organization? (*b*) Obtain a set of these rules and copy the ones which apply to this chapter. (*c*) Why are systematic rules of this sort necessary?
2. Tetraethyl lead has been used as a gasoline additive for many years, but is now falling into disrepute. Why?
3. Wöhler's synthesis of urea was a major philosophical as well as chemical achievement. Why is this true?
4. Compare the chemistry of carbon compounds with that of the silicon compounds called *silicones*.

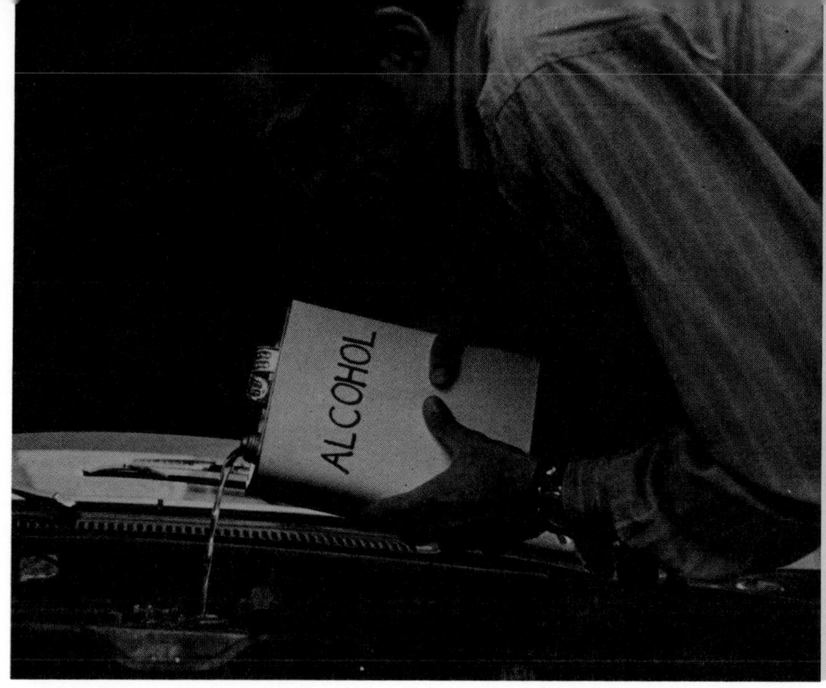

CHAPTER 26

ALCOHOLS, ACIDS, AND THEIR DERIVATIVES

IN THE LAST CHAPTER we discussed several families of hydrocarbons. However, there are thousands of carbon compounds which contain other elements instead of or in addition to hydrogen. The most frequent third element is oxygen, but a great many compounds contain nitrogen, and some contain elements such as sulfur, iron, magnesium, phosphorus, and the halogens.

In this chapter we shall study such families as *alcohols*, *acids*, *esters*, *aldehydes*, *ketones*, *amines*, *amino acids*, *proteins*, *fats*, and *carbohydrates*. The alcohols, acids, esters, aldehydes, ketones, fats, and carbohydrates contain oxygen; amines contain nitrogen, while amino acids and proteins contain both oxygen and nitrogen.

The Alcohols

The first member of the *alcohol* series (wood alcohol, methyl alcohol, or methanol) has been known for centuries. The next member (grain alcohol, ethyl alcohol, or ethanol) has been known even longer. There are numerous references to it in the Bible.

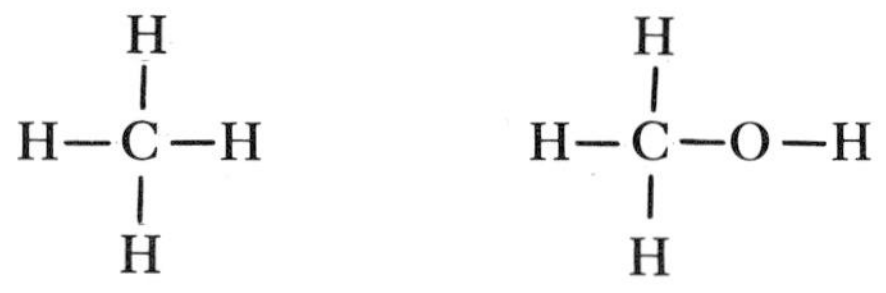

$$\begin{array}{c} H \\ | \\ H-C-H \\ | \\ H \end{array} \qquad \begin{array}{c} H \\ | \\ H-C-O-H \\ | \\ H \end{array}$$

(*a*) methane (*b*) methanol

Fig. 26-1 Structural formulas of (*a*) methane and (*b*) methanol.

All alcohols contain hydroxyl (—OH) groups; some have only one, others have two, and still others like glycerol (or glycerin) have three. The general formula for the simplest series with one hydroxyl group is $C_nH_{2n+1}OH$. We may consider these substances as derivatives of the alkanes, in which a hydrogen atom has been replaced by an —OH group. The structural relationship between an alkane and an alcohol is shown in Fig. 26-1.

In practice, the direct replacement of a hydrogen atom by a hydroxyl group is not possible so other methods of preparation must be used.

The simplest members of the alcohol series are listed in Table 26-1. Note that the names of all alcohols end in *ol*. The first part of the name indicates the parent hydrocarbon, and the ending *ol* identifies the substance as an alcohol. The hyphenated number preceding the hydrocarbon stem specifies the position of the hydroxyl group on the carbon chain. For instance, the name of the alcohol

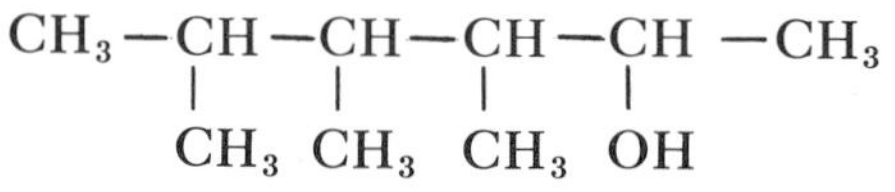

$$CH_3-\underset{CH_3}{\underset{|}{CH}}-\underset{CH_3}{\underset{|}{CH}}-\underset{CH_3}{\underset{|}{CH}}-\underset{OH}{\underset{|}{CH}}-CH_3$$

can be deduced as follows. The longest continuous chain of carbon atoms in the molecule contains six atoms, and the parent hydrocarbon is therefore considered to be hexane. The hydroxyl group is on the second carbon of the chain and there are methyl groups on carbons 3, 4, and 5. Hence, its name is 3, 4, 5-trimethyl-2-hexanol.

Table 26-1 Some properties of simple alcohols

Name	Simplified structural formula	Condensed formula	Boiling point, °C
Methanol	CH_3OH	CH_3OH	65
Ethanol	CH_3CH_2OH	C_2H_5OH	78
1-Propanol	$CH_3CH_2CH_2OH$	C_3H_7OH	98
2-Propanol	$CH_3—CHOH—CH_3$	C_3H_7OH	82
1-Butanol	$CH_3CH_2CH_2CH_2OH$	C_4H_9OH	118
2-Butanol	$CH_3CH_2—CHOH—CH_3$	C_4H_9OH	100
Methyl-1-propanol	$CH_3—CH(CH_3)—CH_2OH$	C_4H_9OH	108
Methyl-2-propanol	$(CH_3)_3—COH$	C_4H_9OH	83

Speculate . . .
What is the difference between the hydroxide ion and the hydroxyl group?

Methanol, ethanol, 1-propanol, and 2-propanol are soluble in water in all proportions, but alcohols of higher molecular weight have limited solubility in water. Indeed, some are almost insoluble. How can this be explained? The hydroxyl group constitutes an appreciable part of the molecules of the lower alcohols so that the attraction between water molecules and the hydroxyl group of the alcohol is of primary significance. On the other hand, as the number of carbon atoms increases, the effect of the hydroxyl group is overshadowed by the hydrocarbon part of the molecule. Thus, 1-hexanol is only slightly soluble in water but is very soluble in liquid alkanes.

Recall . . .
Define *solubility* as you understand it from previous chapters.

The alcohols have both odor and taste. Many are toxic and act as poisons in the body. In spite of the presence of a hydroxyl group, the alcohols and their water solutions are very poor electrical conductors. This tells us that alcohols do not ionize to give hydroxide ions in water.

Methanol (CH_3OH)

Methanol was once obtained exclusively by the destructive distillation of wood (hence the name wood alcohol). However it is now manufactured from water gas, a mixture of carbon monoxide and hydrogen (see page 326) in the presence of a catalyst. If it were not for this process, today's demands for methanol could not be met without seriously depleting our forests. As you have learned, water gas is prepared by passing steam over white-hot coke. The equation for the water-gas reaction is

$$C + H_2O \xrightarrow{\text{white heat}} \underbrace{CO + H_2}_{\text{water gas}} \qquad (26\text{-}1)$$

and the equation for the synthesis of methanol is

$$CO + 2H_2 \xrightarrow[\text{heat}]{\text{catalyst}} CH_3OH \qquad (26\text{-}2)$$

Methanol is used as a solvent for gums, resins, and shellac. Large quantities are oxidized to formaldehyde which is used in the manufacture of plastics, including those used for telephone receivers.

Ethanol (C_2H_5OH)

Ethanol is still manufactured by the fermentation of carbohydrates, a process that has been known for thousands of years. Starch is a

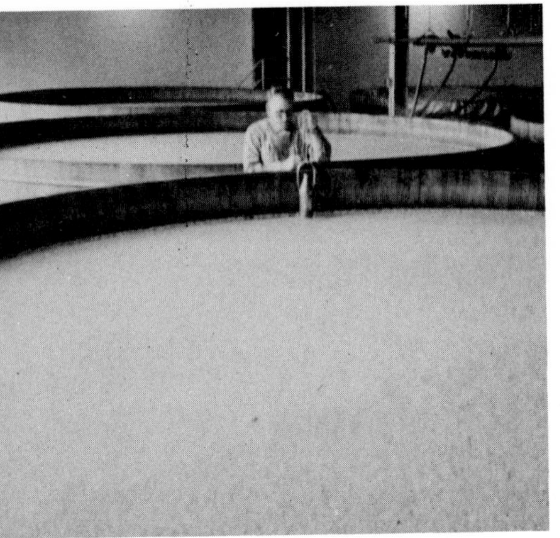

Fig. 26-2 Natural fermentation of grain to produce alcohol.

carbohydrate with the formula $(C_6H_{10}O_5)_n$ where n is a large number. It is found in potatoes, rice, corn, and other cereals. Certain biochemical catalysts called *enzymes* are able to hydrolyze the starch molecule, forming much smaller carbohydrate units called sugars, such as glucose.

$$(C_6H_{10}O_5)_n + nH_2O \xrightarrow{\text{hydrolysis}} nC_6H_{12}O_6 \qquad (26\text{-}3)$$

Glucose, in turn, can be converted into ethanol by another enzyme called *zymase*,

$$C_6H_{12}O_6 \xrightarrow{\text{zymase}} 2C_2H_5OH + 2CO_2 \qquad (26\text{-}4)$$

This process is called *fermentation* (Fig. 26-2). Fermentation is by no means the only way of preparing ethanol. Indeed, the larger proportion of ethanol manufactured in the United States is prepared from ethylene by the method described in Chapter 25.

Ethanol has many important uses. It is used as a fuel, as an antiseptic, as a solvent for drugs and perfumes, as an anti-freeze, in flavoring extracts and pharmaceutical products, and in the synthesis of the ether used in anesthesia. Ethanol is also the chief ingredient of intoxicating beverages. (See also Fig. 26-3).

Fig. 26-3 Decorative room thermometers are frequently filled with ethanol.

Glycerol

Glycerol, also known as glycerin, is a member of another series of alcohols. Its formula is $C_3H_5(OH)_3$, its structure is $CH_2OH—CHOH—CH_2OH$, so its correct name is 1, 2, 3-trihydroxypropane. Since a glycerol molecule contains three hydroxyl groups, it is classified as a *polyhydric* alcohol. Glycerol resembles the simple alcohols such as ethanol in its chemical behavior. It is the by-product of soap-making, a process discussed later in the chapter.

In industry, glycerol rivals methanol and ethanol in importance. The manufacture of nitroglycerine and dynamite are dependent upon glycerol. Enormous quantities of it are also required in the manufacture of paper, rayon, cellophane, and inks. It is used as the fluid in hydraulic systems, and as the base for many medicinal preparations and cosmetics, such as hand creams.

Primary, Secondary, and Tertiary Alcohols

The alcohols with one hydroxyl group are divided into three classes—*primary*, *secondary*, and *tertiary*. Alcohols such as ethanol and 1-propanol contain the $—CH_2OH$ group, and all alcohols which contain this group are called *primary* alcohols. On the other hand, alcohols such as 2-propanol contain the $>CHOH$ group and are called *secondary* alcohols. And, finally, alcohols such as methyl-2-propanol contain the $\geq COH$ group and are called *tertiary* alcohols.

The structural differences between primary, secondary, and tertiary, alcohols can be made clearer if we let the symbol *R* stand for an *alkyl* group. That is, *R* may be a methyl (CH_3) group, or an ethyl (C_2H_5) group, or a propyl (C_3H_7) group. The general formulas for the three types of alcohols are shown in Fig. 26-4.

It should be understood that the *R* groups may be different. Thus,

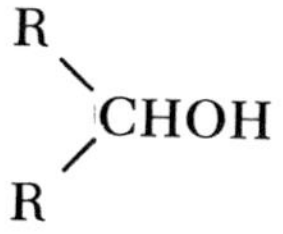

$$\begin{matrix} R \diagdown \\ \quad CHOH \\ R \diagup \end{matrix} \quad \text{could be} \quad \begin{matrix} CH_3 \diagdown \\ \quad CHOH \\ C_2H_5 \diagup \end{matrix} \quad \text{(2-butanol)}$$

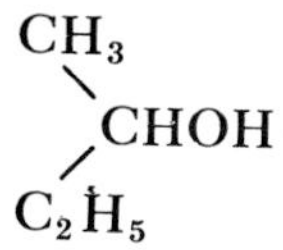

$$\text{or it could be} \quad \begin{matrix} CH_3 \diagdown \\ \quad CHOH \\ CH_3 \diagup \end{matrix} \quad \text{(2-propanol)}$$

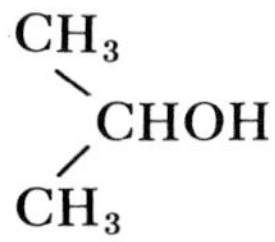

But why are alcohols classified in this way? Primary, secondary, and tertiary alcohols react quite differently with certain substances. For example, each of the three types gives its own characteristic products by controlled oxidation. A study of these products therefore enables the scientist to assign the correct structure to a given alcohol.

$$R-CH_2OH$$

(*a*) primary

$$\begin{matrix} R \diagdown \\ \quad CHOH \\ R \diagup \end{matrix}$$

(*b*) secondary

$$\begin{matrix} R \diagdown \\ R-COH \\ R \diagup \end{matrix}$$

(*c*) tertiary

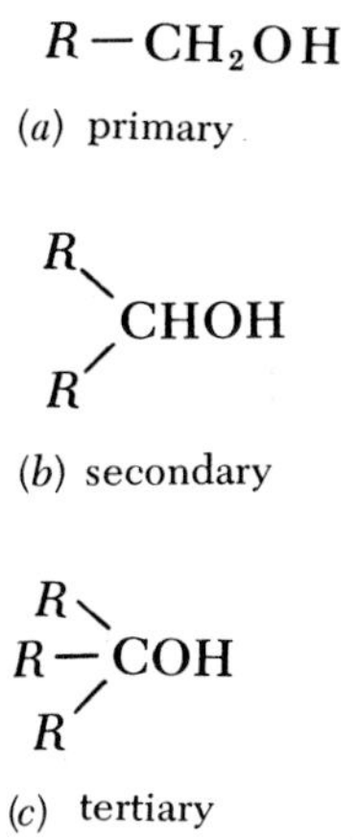

Fig. 26-4 General formulas for (*a*) primary, (*b*) secondary, and (*c*) tertiary alcohols.

The Controlled Oxidation of Alcohols

As you recall, the oxidation of an alkane cannot be controlled; that is, no matter how large or small the proportion of oxidizing agent, the carbon chain is broken. The alcohols, too, can be burned. Indeed, ethanol and methanol can be used as fuels. On the other hand, the oxidation of a primary or a secondary alcohol can be controlled so that the carbon chain is left intact. But how is this done? Oxidation can be controlled by using an oxidizing agent such as sodium dichromate and dilute sulfuric acid at a temperature below 100 °C.

Let us see what happens when an alcohol is subjected to controlled oxidation.

Infer . . .
From these examples, what is the general suffix used to denote an aldehyde?

Primary Alcohols

The first product obtained by the controlled oxidation of a primary alcohol is an *aldehyde*, a substance with the characteristic group $\overset{\displaystyle H}{\underset{}{-\overset{|}{C}=O}}$ or $-CHO$. For example, methanol gives formaldehyde (methan*al*), $H-CHO$, and ethanol gives acetaldehyde (ethan*al*), CH_3-CHO. The net equations for these two reactions are shown structurally as follows,

$$H-\underset{\underset{\displaystyle H}{|}}{\overset{\overset{\displaystyle H}{|}}{C}}-OH + [O] \longrightarrow H-\overset{\overset{\displaystyle H}{|}}{C}=O + H_2O \qquad (26\text{-}5)$$

$$CH_3-\underset{\underset{\displaystyle H}{|}}{\overset{\overset{\displaystyle H}{|}}{C}}-OH + [O] \longrightarrow CH_3-\overset{\overset{\displaystyle H}{|}}{C}=O + H_2O \qquad (26\text{-}6)$$

The source of the oxygen atom shown in brackets is the oxidizing agent (for example, the dichromate and dilute sulfuric acid mixture mentioned above). Notice that the net effect of the oxidation is the removal of two hydrogen atoms from the $-CH_2OH$ group which combine with an oxygen atom from the oxidizing agent to give a water molecule.

Aldehydes Aldehydes are useful substances. Formaldehyde is a preservative for biological specimens and is used on a large scale in the manufacture of plastics and resins by the process of *polymerization*. Acetaldehyde is the parent of many chemicals such as ethyl acetate which is a valuable industrial solvent.

Recall . . .
Define polymerization.

Care must be taken in oxidizing a primary alcohol to an aldehyde since aldehydes are easily oxidized to *acids*. Thus, methanal and ethanal are readily oxidized to the corresponding acids, methanoic acid ($HCOOH$, usually called formic acid) and ethanoic acid (CH_3COOH, usually called acetic acid).

$$H-\overset{\overset{\displaystyle H}{|}}{C}=O + [O] \longrightarrow H-O-\overset{\overset{\displaystyle H}{|}}{C}=O \qquad (26\text{-}7)$$

$$CH_3-CHO + [O] \longrightarrow CH_3-\overset{\overset{\displaystyle OH}{|}}{C}=O \qquad (26\text{-}8)$$

Acids Organic acids are not easily oxidized, so that *an acid is the end product of the controlled oxidation of a primary alcohol.* The one exception to this rule is formic acid. Formic acid has one hydrogen atom attached directly to the $-COOH$ group and it is therefore easily oxidized to carbonic acid,

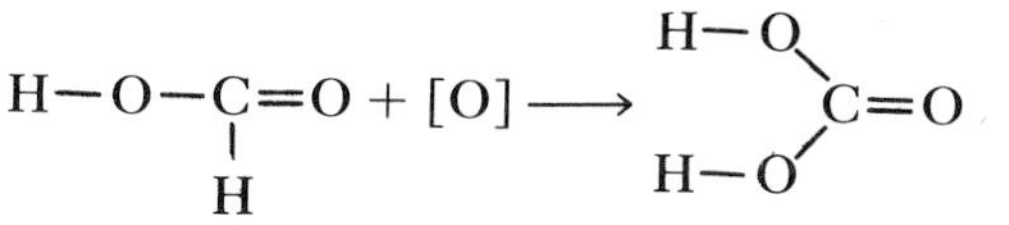

$$\underset{\displaystyle \text{H}}{\text{H}-\text{O}-\overset{}{\text{C}}}=\text{O} + [\text{O}] \longrightarrow \begin{matrix}\text{H}-\text{O}\diagdown \\ \quad \text{C}=\text{O} \\ \text{H}-\text{O}\diagup\end{matrix} \qquad (26\text{-}9)$$

The carbonic acid decomposes at once into carbon dioxide and water. The oxidation is now at an end since carbon is in its highest oxidation state of plus four.

Secondary Alcohols

The controlled oxidation of a secondary alcohol gives a *ketone*, a product which resists further oxidation. For example, the oxidation of 2-propanol gives propanone (usually called acetone), the simplest ketone,

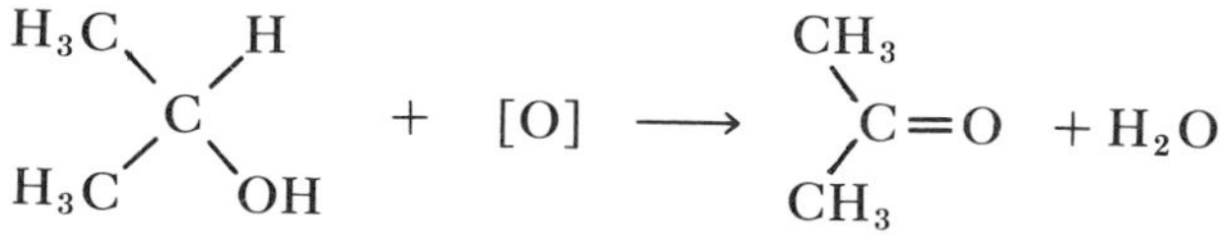

$$\begin{matrix}H_3C\diagdown & & \diagup H \\ & C & \\ H_3C\diagup & & \diagdown OH\end{matrix} + [O] \longrightarrow \begin{matrix}CH_3 \\ \diagdown \\ C=O \\ \diagup \\ CH_3\end{matrix} + H_2O \qquad (26\text{-}10)$$

$$(\text{or } CH_3COCH_3)$$

Notice that the carbon chain of the alcohol remains intact.

Observe . . . The $>C=O$ group, called the carbonyl group, is common to both aldehydes and ketones. How do they differ?

Ketones The characteristic group of a ketone is $\begin{matrix}R\diagdown \\ C=O \\ R\diagup\end{matrix}$ and the name of a ketone ends in *one*. The naming of ketones, like other substances, depends upon the length of the carbon chain. For instance, what is the name for $CH_3-\underset{\displaystyle CH_3}{\underset{|}{CH}}-CO-CH_3$? The longest continuous chain of carbon atoms contains four atoms, so that the parent hydrocarbon is butane. The name is therefore 3-methyl-2-butanone.

Tertiary Alcohols

Tertiary alcohols are not easily oxidized because there is no hydrogen atom attached to the carbon atom which holds the hydroxyl group. Indeed, the reaction of a tertiary alcohol with an oxidizing agent results in the disruption of the carbon chain, and the end products of oxidation at high temperatures are carbon dioxide and water.

The following is a summary of the controlled oxidation of alcohols:

$$\underset{\text{primary}}{R{-}CH_2OH} \xrightarrow{[O]} \underset{\text{aldehyde}}{R{-}CHO} \xrightarrow{[O]} \underset{\text{acid}}{R{-}COOH} \qquad (26\text{-}11)$$

$$\underset{\text{secondary}}{\begin{matrix} R \\ & \diagdown \\ & & CHOH \\ & \diagup \\ R \end{matrix}} \xrightarrow{[O]} \underset{\text{ketone}}{\begin{matrix} R \\ & \diagdown \\ & & C{=}O \\ & \diagup \\ R \end{matrix}} \qquad (26\text{-}12)$$

$$\underset{\text{tertiary}}{\begin{matrix} R \\ & \diagdown \\ R & - & COH \\ & \diagup \\ R \end{matrix}} \xrightarrow{[O]} \text{no reaction without disruption of the carbon chain} \qquad (26\text{-}13)$$

Organic Acids

Organic acids occur abundantly in nature. The simplest of them is formic acid (methanoic acid), first prepared by distilling red ants (Latin: *formica*, ant). Indeed, the painful sting of an ant or a bee is due to formic acid the insect injects. (Fig. 26-5). Many organic acids have a marked flavor. The sharp taste of orange juice, the sourness of lemons, the tang of vinegar, the flavor of sour milk, and the bite of ripe cheese are all due to organic acids.

Fig. 26-5 The pain of a bee's sting is caused by the formic acid in its venom.

Organic acids are characterized by the *carboxyl* group, $-\overset{\overset{\displaystyle O}{\|}}{C}-OH$ or $-COOH$, and the names of acids end in *oic* acid. Thus the name for CH_3COOH is ethan*oic* acid and for $CH_3{-}\underset{\underset{\displaystyle CH_3}{|}}{CH}{-}CH_2{-}COOH$ it is 3-methylbutan*oic* acid.

The simplest series of acids is called the *fatty* acids since some of the higher members of the series are present in fats. The general formula of the fatty acids is $C_nH_{2n+1}COOH$. Many of these compounds have strong, disagreeable odors. The odor of rancid butter, for example, is due to butanoic acid (C_3H_7COOH), while the odor of goats is largely due to hexanoic acid ($C_5H_{11}COOH$), the common name of which is *caproic* acid.

Speculate . . .
Does the word *caproic* have anything in common with the name of the Zodiac sign *Capricorn*?

Organic acids are weakly dissociated in water solution and therefore behave like weak inorganic acids. For example, ethanoic acid (acetic acid) ionizes only to the extent of about 1% in a 1 *M* solution,

$$CH_3COOH \rightleftharpoons H^+(aq) + \underset{\text{acetate ion}}{CH_3COO^-} \qquad (26\text{-}14)$$

Or, stated another way, the ionization constant value for acetic acid at 25 °C is 1.8×10^{-5}. That is,

$$\frac{[H^+][CH_3COO^-]}{[CH_3COOH]} = K_A = 1.8 \times 10^{-5}$$

The simpler organic acids are usually prepared by the oxidation of primary alcohols, a process discussed earlier in the chapter. However, the acids of high molecular weight are prepared by the hydrolysis of esters (fats) found in nature, a process described later in the chapter.

As you recall, the end product of the controlled oxidation of ethanol is a water solution of acetic acid (ethanoic acid), a product called *vinegar*. The sharp taste of vinegar is due to acetic acid, while the more subtle fruity aroma is due to traces of esters which are also formed during the oxidation.

Maleic and Fumaric Acids, Geometrical Isomers

Maleic and fumaric acids are a classical pair of *geometrical isomers*. The molecular formula of both acids is $C_4H_4O_4$ and the arrangement of atoms in both compounds is HOOC—CH=CH—COOH. They are both white solids and some of their properties are listed in Table 26-2.

Since there is restriction of rotation about the double bond, there are two possible structures, shown in Fig. 26-6.

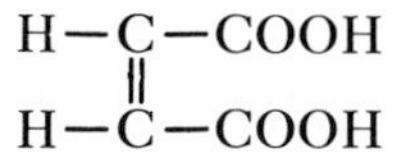

```
H—C—COOH
  ||
H—C—COOH
```

(*a*) *cis* isomer

```
     H—C—COOH
       ||
HOOC—C—H
```

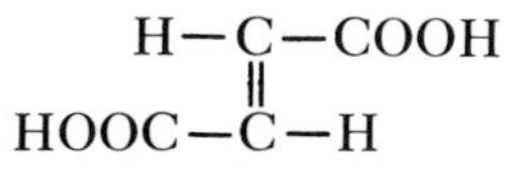

(*b*) *trans* isomer

Fig. 26-6 Geometric isomerism as demonstrated in (*a*) maleic acid (*b*) fumaric acid.

Table 26-2 Properties of maleic and fumaric acids

Acid	Melting point, °C	Solubility in water at 18°C	Heat of combustion, kcal	Dissociation of molar solution, %
Maleic	130	very soluble	327	11
Fumaric	287	0.45 g/100 g H_2O	320	3

Is maleic acid the *cis* or the *trans* isomer? The effect of heat on the two acids sheds some light on this question. Maleic acid readily loses water when heated, giving an acid anhydride:

$$\begin{array}{c}\text{CH}-\text{COOH}\\ \| \\ \text{CH}-\text{COOH}\end{array} \xrightarrow{\text{heat}} \begin{array}{c}\text{HC}-\text{C}{=}\text{O}\\ \| \quad\quad \text{O} \\ \text{HC}-\text{C}{=}\text{O}\end{array} + H_2O \qquad (26\text{-}15)$$

maleic acid — maleic anhydride

Fumaric acid, on the other hand, does not form an anhydride unless it is heated to a temperature above its melting point, when it gives a product identical with the anhydride obtained from maleic acid. Moreover, if the anhydride is treated with water (below 100 °C), the product is maleic acid:

$$\begin{array}{c}\text{HC}-\text{C}{=}\text{O}\\ \| \quad\quad \text{O} \\ \text{HC}-\text{C}{=}\text{O}\end{array} + H_2O \longrightarrow \begin{array}{c}\text{CH}-\text{COOH}\\ \| \\ \text{CH}-\text{COOH}\end{array} \qquad (26\text{-}16)$$

maleic acid

The fact that maleic acid loses water easily to form the anhydride indicates that the two carboxyl groups in maleic acid are adjacent. It is therefore apparent that maleic acid is the *cis* isomer. Hence, fumaric acid must be the *trans* isomer. This is confirmed by the fact that fumaric acid is converted to maleic anhydride only at a high temperature, which indicates that the double bond of fumaric acid is disrupted by thermal agitation. If the double bond *is* broken, the carboxyl groups would be able to swing into the position where the

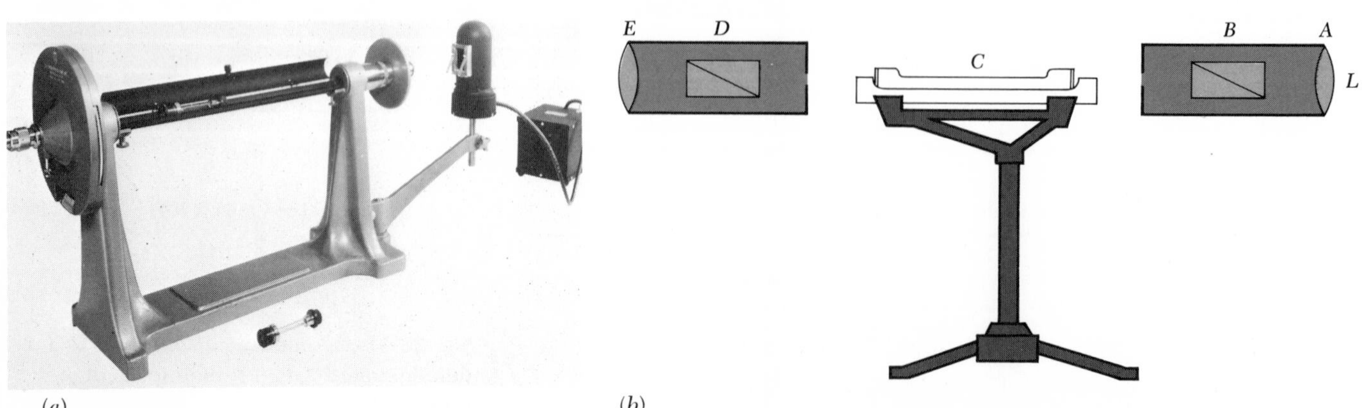

Fig. 26-7 (*a*) photograph of a laboratory polarimeter. (*b*) Diagram of a polarimeter. Light from the monochromatic source *L* is transmitted by lens *A* to the fixed (polarizer) prism *B*. Plane-polarized light is transmitted by prism *B* through the solution in tube *C* to the movable (analyzer) prism *D*. *E* is an eyepiece lens system (a telescope by which the light from *D* is viewed). When a solution of an optically active substance is placed in the tube *C*, light transmitted by *B* is rotated to a certain extent, either left orright; light reaching *E* is therefore diminished in intensity by rotating *D* to the point where the original light intensity is restored and at which *D* is aligned with the plane of light emerging from *C*. The angle of rotation is then read from the scale.

elements of water could be lost, thus giving maleic anhydride. The double bond is then re-established with the residues of the carboxyl groups on the same side of the molecule.

The changes in the structure are summarized in Eq. (26-17):

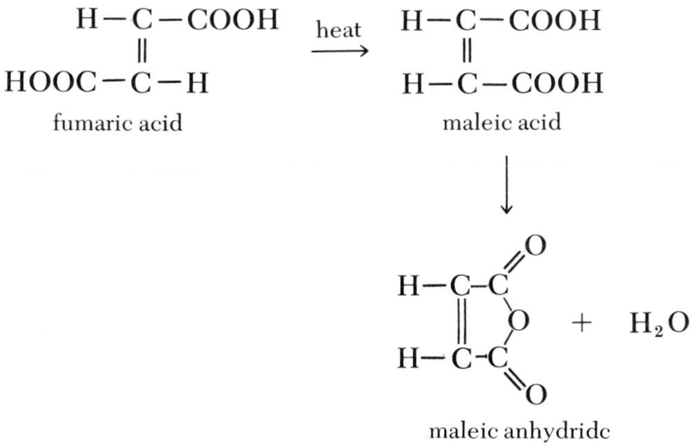

```
    H—C—COOH   heat   H—C—COOH
      ||       ---->    ||
HOOC—C—H              H—C—COOH
  fumaric acid         maleic acid
                           |
                           v
                             O
                            //
                      H—C—C
                        ||   \
                        ||    O   +   H2O     (26-17)
                        ||   /
                      H—C—C
                            \\
                             O
                      maleic anhydride
```

A Third Kind of Isomerism

We have now discussed two kinds of isomerism—structural isomerism and geometrical isomerism. There is still another kind of isomerism, called *optical isomerism*, that depends upon the way isomers affect polarized light.

Many pairs of carbon compounds have the same structure and almost identical chemical properties. Indeed, their physical properties often are the same, except that one of the substances rotates the plane of polarized light to the right (clockwise) and the other rotates the plane of polarized light to the left (counterclockwise). Such substances are said to be *optically active* and they are called *optical isomers*. The substance which rotates the plane of polarized light to the right is called the *dextrorotatory* or *dextro* isomer and the other substance is the *levorotatory* or *levo* isomer. This type of isomerism is recognized by using a polarimeter (Fig. 26-7).

Lactic Acid Exhibits Optical Isomerism

Lactic acid is one of the simplest examples of a carbon compound which exhibits optical activity. The molecular formula of lactic acid is $C_3H_6O_3$ and its structure is shown on page 470.

Note . . .
Ordinary light consists of waves vibrating in all planes containing the line of propagation of the light. When ordinary light is passed through a Nicol prism or a sheet of Polaroid, the emergent light beam consists of waves vibrating in a single plane. The emergent beam is therefore said to be plane polarized light.

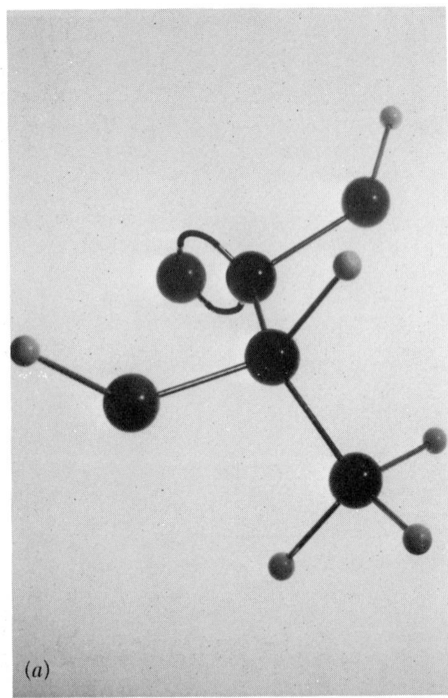

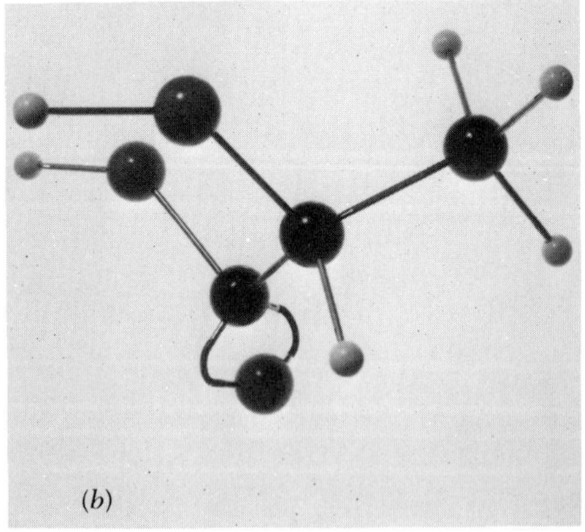

Fig. 26-8 Optical isomers: (*a*) L-lactic acid, which rotates light to the left. (*b*) D-lactic acid, which rotates light to the right.

$$CH_3-\underset{\displaystyle OH}{\overset{\displaystyle H}{\overset{|}{\underset{|}{C}}}}-COOH \qquad \text{lactic acid}$$

One lactic acid is produced in muscle tissue when the muscle does work. This particular lactic acid rotates plane polarized light to the right and is therefore the *dextro* isomer. Lactic acid is also produced by the bacterial fermentation of the sugar in milk (lactose). This lactic acid may be dextro, or levo, or a mixture of both, depending on the microorganism that promotes the fermentation. Thus there are two isomeric lactic acids, one of which rotates plane polarized light to the right and the other to the left. And this is the only difference between them; all other physical properties of the isomers are identical. Their melting points (26°C), their solubilities, their heats of combustion, their strength as acids, etc., are exactly the same. How, then, can optical isomerism be explained?

Molecular Asymmetry

The central carbon atom of lactic acid is attached to *four* different groups—carboxyl, methyl, hydroxyl, and hydrogen. These four groups are directed toward the corners of a tetrahedron. When four different atoms or groups of atoms occupy the corners of a tetrahedron, two spatial arrangements are possible, and they differ in the same way that the right hand differs from the left hand. That is, they are *mirror images* of each other and one cannot be superimposed on the other. This relationship is a consequence of the geometry of the structure only.

Molecules which are nonsuperposable mirror images of one another, are said to be dissymmetric or, in special cases, *asymmetric*. Moreover, a carbon atom to which four unlike groups are attached is called an *asymmetric carbon atom*. We can therefore say that optical activity is a property of a dissymmetric molecule.

The best way to show the configuration of the two lactic acids is to construct models of them from wooden balls and pegs. We can, however, indicate their three-dimensional configurations very crudely on paper as in Fig. 26-8.

Another way to understand the configurations of dextro and levo isomers is to hold your hands side by side with thumbs far apart and

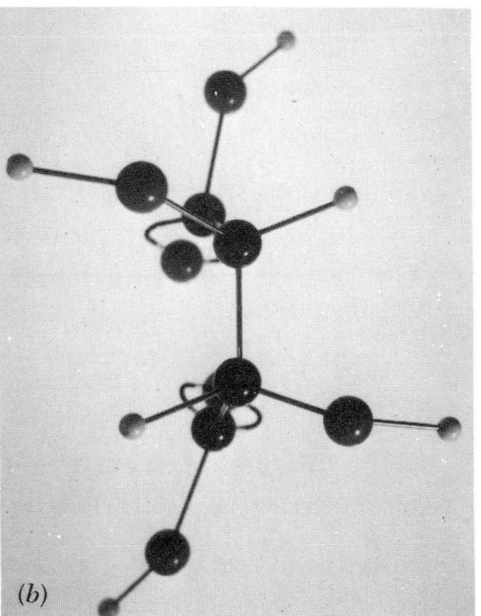

Fig. 26-9 Optical isomerism. (*a*) D-tartaric acid (*b*) L-tartaric acid (*c*) DL-tartaric acid. From its name, what can you infer about the optical activity of DL-tartaric acid?

the little fingers touching. The thumbs represent the OH groups in the diagram and the little fingers the hydrogen atoms. Now rotate your forearms so that the thumbs touch. Can you visualize bringing the OH groups together in this same way? The two lactic acid molecules are like a left hand and a right hand; they cannot be superimposed. There is no plane of symmetry in either molecule; they are dissymmetric molecules. And, because they are dissymmetric molecules, they affect plane polarized light differently. See Fig. 26-9.

Optically Active Substances are Common in Nature

Many carbon compounds found in nature are optically active.For instance, the sugars glucose and fructose are optically active substances. The glucose present in plants or formed by the hydrolysis of more complex carbohydrates is dextrorotatory. Fructose, on the other hand, is levorotatory. These facts are indicated by the common names for these substances, namely dextrose and levulose.

It is interesting to note that the biochemical behavior of dextro and levo isomers may be quite different. Thus, the optically active forms of certain drugs have been found to differ markedly in their physiological action. Indeed, the dextro form of LSD has a marked physiological action, whereas the levo form of LSD has none. As yet scientists are unable to account for this phenomenon.

Esters

An ester is formed by the reaction of an organic acid with an alcohol. For example, acetic acid reacts with ethanol to give ethyl acetate (an ester) and water:

$$CH_3COOH + HOC_2H_5 \rightleftharpoons CH_3COOC_2H_5 + H_2O \quad (26\text{-}18)$$

Or, in general:

$$\underset{\text{acid}}{R\text{—}COOH} + \underset{\text{alcohol}}{HO\text{—}R'} \rightleftharpoons \underset{\text{ester}}{R\text{—}COOR'} + H_2O \quad (26\text{-}19)$$

where the symbols R and R' represent different alkyl groups such as the methyl group (CH_3) or the ethyl group (C_2H_5).

Since the above reaction is reversible, it follows that an ester can be hydrolyzed. The hydrolysis is hastened by either hydrogen ions or hydroxide ions, and the reaction is driven to completion by a high concentration of a strong base. For example, ethyl acetate can be completely converted into sodium acetate and ethanol by the action of sodium hydroxide:

$$CH_3COOC_2H_5 + NaOH \longrightarrow CH_3COONa + C_2H_5OH \quad (26\text{-}20)$$

The hydrolysis of esters by bases is called *saponification*, a reaction used on an industrial scale in soapmaking.

The Manufacture of Soap

Fats and oils are esters of glycerol and long-chain organic acids. For example, beef fat contains the glyceryl ester of stearic acid ($C_{17}H_{35}COOH$) called *tristearin* or, more commonly, *stearin*. Its formula is

$$\begin{array}{l} C_{17}H_{35}COO-CH_2 \\ \qquad\qquad\qquad\ | \\ C_{17}H_{35}COO-CH \\ \qquad\qquad\qquad\ | \\ C_{17}H_{35}COO-CH_2 \end{array}$$

To make a soap, stearin is saponified by hot NaOH solution. The products are sodium stearate (a soap) and glycerol,

$$(C_{17}H_{35}COO)_3C_3H_5 + 3NaOH \longrightarrow 3C_{17}H_{35}COONa + C_3H_5(OH)_3 \quad (26\text{-}21)$$

A soap is the salt of a long-chain fatty acid and a base.

The Odors of Esters

Unlike organic acids, esters usually have a pleasant odor. The aroma of a ripe banana or of an orange or lemon, the smell of a peach or pineapple, the fragrance of a rose or gardenia—all these are due to esters. However, the white, greasy solid present in beef fat has no odor although it is an ester. Why not? Its molecular mass is so high that there is little evaporation. That is, we would expect a substance to have an odor only if it evaporates readily.

Some of the natural esters are listed in Table 26-3. It should be noted, however, that the odor of a particular fruit or flower may be the combined effect of a mixture of esters. An interesting fact is that although methyl butyrate has the pleasant odor of pineapple, the butyric acid from which it is derived has the very unpleasant odor of rancid butter.

Table 26-3 Naturally occurring esters

Name	Formula	Odor
Amyl acetate	$CH_3COOC_5H_{11}$	pear
Isoamyl acetate	$CH_3COOC_5H_{11}$	banana
Isobutyl acetate	$CH_3COOC_4H_9$	raspberry
Octyl acetate	$CH_3COOC_8H_{17}$	orange
Ethyl butyrate	$C_3H_7COOC_2H_5$	rum
Methyl butyrate	$C_3H_7COOCH_3$	pineapple
Butyl butyrate	$C_3H_7COOC_4H_9$	pineapple
Amyl butyrate	$C_3H_7COOC_5H_{11}$	apricot and banana
Amyl valerate	$C_4H_9COOC_5H_{11}$	apple

Amines

As stated earlier, a methyl group (CH_3) is an example of the more general alkyl group. *Amines* are the alkyl derivatives of ammonia. That is, an amine is formed if an alkyl group is substituted for one or more of the hydrogen atoms of ammonia. For example, CH_3NH_2 is an amine called methylamine, $(CH_3)_2NH$ is dimethylamine, $(CH_3)_3N$ is trimethylamine, $C_2H_5NH_2$ is ethylamine, and so on.

Infer . . .
Draw a parallel between $(CH_3)_2NH$ and $(CH_3)_2CHOH$. Would you call the nitrogen compound a secondary amine?

All the amines named are found in nature, and so are many others. Amines are formed during the putrefaction of proteins and other nitrogenous compounds. The unpleasant odor of decaying fish, for example, is due in part to the presence of amines.

The Properties of Amines

As one might expect, the simpler amines resemble ammonia; they are soluble in water and their solutions are basic. Moreover, the amines, like ammonia itself, are expelled when their solutions are boiled. Solutions of amines can be neutralized by acids to give salts similar to ammonium salts. For example, a solution of trimethylamine reacts with hydrochloric acid to give the salt trimethylammonoum chloride,

$$(CH_3)_3N + H_2O \rightleftharpoons (CH_3)_3NH^+ + OH^- \quad (26\text{-}22)$$

and

$$(CH_3)_3NH^+ + OH^- + H^+ + Cl^- \longrightarrow (CH_3)_3NH^+ + Cl^- + H_2O \quad (26\text{-}23)$$

Notice the similarity between these reactions and the corresponding reactions of ammonia,

$$NH_3 + H_2O \rightleftharpoons NH_4{}^+ + OH^- \quad (26\text{-}24)$$

and

$$NH_4{}^+ + OH^- + H^+ + Cl^- \longrightarrow NH_4{}^+ + Cl^- + H_2O \quad (26\text{-}25)$$

Amino Acids and Proteins

All living organisms, both vegetable and animal, contain complex nitrogen compounds called *proteins* which are essential to their life processes (Fig. 26-10). Proteins are built up from simple nitrogen compounds called *amino acids*.

Amino acids are derivatives of ammonia and organic acids; that is, an amino acid is both an amine and an acid. For example, the two simplest amino acids are glycine ($NH_2—CH_2—COOH$) and alanine ($CH_3—\underset{\displaystyle NH_2}{\underset{|}{CH}}—COOH$). The $—NH_2$ end of these molecules is an amine and amino acids therefore have basic properties. On the other hand, the—COOH end is an acid and the amino acids also have acid properties. Thus, an amino acid is both an acid and a base. What does this mean? It means that the basic end of one amino acid molecule can react with the acidic end of another amino acid molecule to give a new molecule of higher molecular mass than the original amino acids. Moreover, the product of this union has a free amine group at one end and a free carboxyl group at the other end so that the process of joining can continue. This kind of addition is *perhaps* the way highly complex proteins are formed from amino acids.

Fig. 26-10 All living things contain protein. How many kinds of life forms can you identify here? *Courtesy Carolina Biological Supply Co.*

The first stage of the joining process can be illustrated by the reaction of two glycine molecules to give glyclyglycine and water,

$$H_2NCH_2COOH + H_2NCH_2COOH \longrightarrow$$

$$H_2N{-}CH_2{-}\overset{\overset{\displaystyle O}{\|}}{C}{-}NH{-}CH_2{-}COOH + H_2O \qquad (26\text{-}26)$$

glycylglycine

This is, of course, an example of polymerization. Since a small unit (water) is removed during the union, the reaction of one amino acid with another is called *condensation polymerization*,

(The *combination* of one molecule of acetylene with another, a reaction mentioned in the last chapter, is an example of another type of polymerization called *addition polymerization*,

$$H{-}C{\equiv}C{-}H + H{-}C{\equiv}C{-}H \longrightarrow H_2C{=}CH{-}C{\equiv}C{-}H) \qquad (26\text{-}27)$$

There are many kinds of proteins in nature and their properties differ widely. However, in one fundamental respect all proteins are alike; they are hydrolyzed by dilute acids to give a mixture of amino acids. At least 25 amino acids have been identified among protein hydrolysis products, 10 of them are essential in the diet of man; the remaining 15 can be synthesized by the human body.

Protein molecules are large and complex. Estimated molecular mass values range from about 35,000 for simple proteins such as pepsin (an enzyme) to 20 million for the tobacco mosaic virus. The synthesis of proteins is clearly a colossal task which chemists are now learning to perform.

Carbohydrates

Carbohydrates are among the most abundant carbon compounds found in nature. They are synthesized in plants by photosynthesis, and constitute the supporting structure and tissue of plants. Carbohydrates are essential in the diet of animals, because the oxidation of carbohydrates in animal bodies provides the energy to maintain life (Fig. 26-11). It is believed that carbohydrates are the substances from which plants synthesize proteins and fats.

Fig. 26-11 Common plant sources of carbohydrates.

In all carbohydrates the elements hydrogen and oxygen are found combined in the same proportion as that found in water. The general formula $C_x(H_2O)_y$ can therefore be written for these compounds. For this reason they are called carbo*hydrates* although in a chemical sense they are *not hydrates* at all.

The carbohydrates include the *sugars*, *starch*, and *cellulose*.

The Sugars

The sugars with six carbon atoms per molecule are called *monosaccharides* (saccharide means *sugar*) or hexoses; the sugars with 12 carbon atoms, *disaccharides* (or dihexoses); and starch and cellulose, *polysaccharides*. The sugars are crystalline, soluble in water, and have a sweet taste, whereas starch and cellulose are amorphous, tasteless, and are either insoluble in water or give colloidal dispersions in it. The sugars have molecular mass values less than 400, starch a much higher value (estimates range from 10,000 to 50,000), and cellulose an estimated 300,000 to 500,000.

Glucose—the Most Common Monosaccharide

The formula for glucose is $C_6H_{12}O_6$ and its simplest structure is shown in Fig. 26-12. Notice that glucose has five hydroxyl groups and is therefore a polyhydric alcohol. The primary alcohol groups are an easy point of attack during the oxidation of glucose in the body.

Glucose is found in fruit juices, but is usually obtained by the hydrolysis of sucrose, starch, or cellulose. Thus, sucrose is hydrolyzed to give glucose and fructose:

$$\underset{\text{sucrose}}{C_{12}H_{22}O_{11}} + H_2O \longrightarrow \underset{\text{glucose}}{C_6H_{12}O_6} + \underset{\text{fructose}}{C_6H_{12}O_6} \qquad (26\text{-}28)$$

Fig. 26-12 Structural formula of glucose.

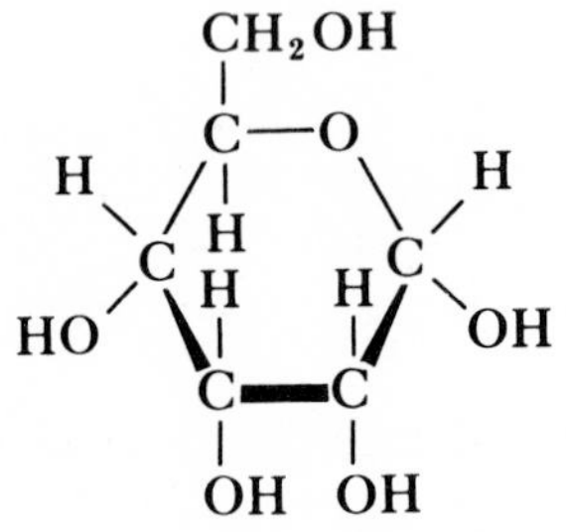

while starch and cellulose give only glucose:

$$(C_6H_{10}O_5)_n + nH_2O \longrightarrow nC_6H_{12}O_6 \qquad (26\text{-}29)$$

These results suggest that glucose is a fundamental unit in the structure of the polysaccharides and that glucose is perhaps one of the first products of photosynthesis.

Glucose is the most important energy-giving foodstuff. It is carried by the blood to the body cells where it is oxidized to carbon dioxide and water:

$$C_6H_{12}O_6 + 6O_2 \longrightarrow 6CO_2 + 6H_2O \qquad \Delta H = -674 \text{ kcal} \tag{26-30}$$

The energy evolved in this reaction is, in effect, the liberation of the sun's energy which was captured by the plant during photosynthesis of the carbohydrate.

Sucrose—the Most Abundant Disaccharide

Sucrose is produced in greater quantity than any other carbon compound, and no other substance of comparable purity is marketed so cheaply. At least 7 million tons of it are used in the United States every year. Nevertheless, the chemist has not yet been able to synthesize sucrose, and the only way to obtain it is to extract the product synthesized by the sugar cane, the sugar beet, and the sugar maple.

The formula of sucrose is $C_{12}H_{22}O_{11}$ and its structure is shown in Fig. 26-13. This is a complicated structure and this kind of structure is characteristic of the disaccharides and the polysaccharides. Notice that there are two rings joined by an oxygen "bridge." The ring at the left is six-membered (it contains five carbon atoms and one oxygen atom) and represents a glucose unit; the ring at the right is five-membered (it contains four carbon atoms and one oxygen atom) and represents a fructose unit. You will recall (Eq. 26-26) that the hydrolysis of sucrose gives glucose and fructose. Glucose and fructose are therefore isomers.

Polysaccharides

Starch is another type of carbohydrate; it is found abundantly in the kernels of grains and in such substances as potatoes and rice. For example, rice is about 75% starch, corn 50%, and potatoes 20%. When a kernel of corn germinates, the starch is converted to mal-

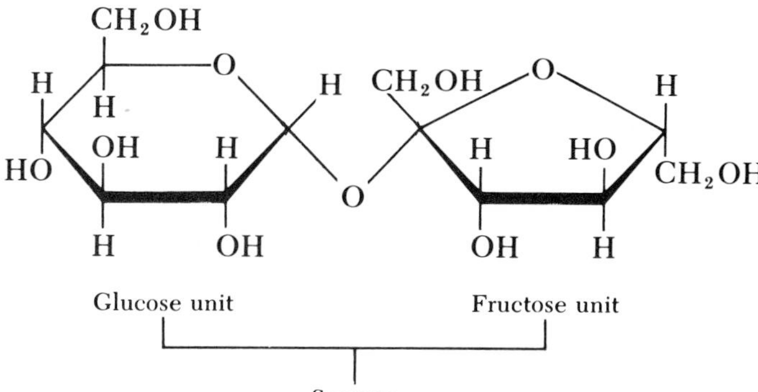

Fig. 26-13 Structural formula of sucrose.

tose (a disaccharide) and glucose which constitute the food supply of the young plant until it can establish its own root and leaf system.

Cellulose is the chief structural unit of the cell walls of plants. Cotton fiber, for instance, is more than 90% cellulose, while wood contains 40 to 50% of it. Although many useful chemical derivatives of cellulose (such as guncotton, photographic film, cellophane and rayon) are manufactured on a large scale, the cotton-textile and paper industries are by far the largest users of cellulose.

Cellulose and starch have the same simplest formula, $C_6H_{10}O_5$, but the molecular mass of cellulose is much the greater and the geometry around the oxygen bridge between glucose units is different. Moreover, you will recall that both substances give glucose upon hydrolysis. These facts suggest that the structure of cellulose and starch are similar. Indeed, the evidence indicates that the basic structure of both cellulose and starch can be represented by Fig. 26-14, where each ring represents a glucose unit. The free

```
         H   H                   H   H
       HOC—COH                 HOC—COH
        /     \                 /     \
  —O—CH   HC——————O——————CH   HC
        \     /                 \     /  \
         O—CH                    O—CH
            |                       |
          CH2OH                   CH2OH
```

Fig. 26-14

(unattached) bonds at the ends of this structure indicate that we have shown only a fragment of a cellulose or starch molecule. Indeed, a cellulose or starch molecule would contain hundreds or even thousands of these six-membered ring units. The structure in Fig. 26-14 suggests a way by which glycose units can be joined to form the long chains we associate with the polysaccharides.

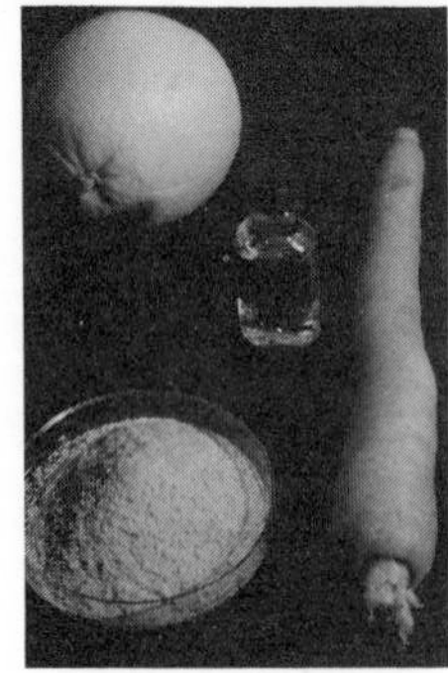

Fig. 26-15 These five photographs illustrate some of the foods which form a balanced diet. Identify the group to which each food belongs.

Foods

Foods are substances needed to build or repair the components of the body, and to provide energy for the life processes. They include such substances as *fats*, *proteins*, *carbohydrates*, *minerals*, and *vitamins*. See Fig. 26-15.

The oxidation of carbohydrates normally supplies the energy which the body needs to do work and to maintain its normal temperature. Fats are also oxidized in the body to provide energy, although they are usually stored in the tissue as a reserve source of energy. Proteins, too, may act as a source of energy but their primary function is the building and repairing of the structural parts of the body, as well as the synthesis of enzymes (the body catalysts), hormones (the regulators of body functions), and hemoglobin (the oxygen carrier in the blood).

To serve their proper purpose, the ratio of these various foodstuffs in the diet should be approximately four parts by mass of carbohydrates to one part each by mass of fat and protein. In addition to these major foodstuffs, several minerals such as calcium, phosphorus, potassium, iodine, iron, and common salt are indispensable ingredients in the diet. The amounts required are relatively small but an insufficient intake of any one of them would lead to a breakdown in the body functions. For example hemoglobin, the oxygen-carrying substance in the blood, contains combined iron. It is estimated that about 3 million red cells wear out in the body every second, so this vital element is used in the synthesis of new cells. A deficiency of hemoglobin results in a disease known as anemia. A normal diet, however, provides enough iron for cell building since liver, egg yolk, peas, spinach, and cereals are good sources of it.

Summary

Many organic compounds contain a third element in addition to carbon and hydrogen. The most common third element is oxygen, and the "family" of alcohols contains these three elements.

Alcohols contain one, two, three, or more hydroxyl groups and the general formula for alcohols with one OH group is $C_nH_{2n+1}OH$. Methanol (CH_3OH) and ethanol (C_2H_5OH) are the most common alcohols in this series. Glycerol, $C_3H_5(OH)_3$, has three hydroxyl groups.

Alcohols with one $-OH$ group are subdivided into primary ($-CH_2OH$), secondary ($>CHOH$), and tertiary ($\gtrdot COH$) alcohols. Primary alcohols can be oxidized to aldehydes and acids; secondary alcohols can be oxidized to ketones; but tertiary alcohols do not undergo controlled oxidation.

All organic acids have the characteristic carboxyl ($-COOH$) group. The general formula of the fatty acids is $C_nH_{2n+1}COOH$,

Explain . . .
Most foods are organic substances; even the minerals are usually part of a complex organic molecule. Why is salt (NaCl) exceptional in this respect?

and the first acids in the series are methanoic acid (H—COOH) and ethanoic acid (CH_3COOH), commonly called formic and acetic acids, respectively. Maleic and fumaric acids have the same formula [$(CHCOOH)_2$]. They have a double-bonded carbon atom and form a pair of geometrical isomers. Lactic acid ($CH_3CHOHCOOH$) also exists as a pair of isomers. But these isomers have the same physical and chemical properties. However, the plane of polarized light is rotated clockwise by one isomer and counterclockwise by the other. For this reason they are called optical isomers.

Esters are formed by the reaction of an organic acid with an alcohol,

$$R\text{—COOH} + R'\text{OH} \rightleftharpoons R\text{—COO}R' + \text{H}_2\text{O}$$

where R—COOR' is an ester. Esters also occur in nature, and they account for the pleasant odors emitted by flowers and fruits.

Amines contain nitrogen as the third element. They are alkyl derivatives of ammonia. For example,

$$\text{NH}_3 \longrightarrow \text{NH}_2R \longrightarrow \text{NH}R_2 \longrightarrow \text{N}R_3$$

Amino acids are derivatives of ammonia and organic acids. The simplest amino acid is NH_2—CH_2—COOH, a compound called *glycine*. One end of a glycine molecule (NH_2) is basic and the other end (COOH) is acidic. The acid end can join up with the basic end of a second molecule and the basic end can join up with the acid end of a third molecule. This process, which is called condensation polymerization, can go on indefinitely to form very large molecules. It is thought that proteins are formed by the polymerization of amino acids.

Sugars, starch, and cellulose are carbohydrates. The simplest sugars have six carbon atoms per molecule. They are called monosaccharides. Glucose ($C_6H_{12}O_6$) is a monosaccharide. Sugars with twelve carbon atoms per molecule are disaccharides. Sucrose ($C_{12}H_{22}O_{11}$) is a disaccharide. Starch and cellulose are polysaccharides. They have the same simplest formula, $C_6H_{10}O_5$. The molecular formulas of starch and cellulose can be written as $(C_6H_{10}O_5)_x$ and $(C_6H_{10}O_5)_y$ respectively, where x and y are very large numbers and y is larger than x.

Factual Recall

1. (*a*) Name three families of carbon compounds which contain carbon and hydrogen only. (*b*) Name three families of carbon compounds which contain carbon, hydrogen, and oxygen. (*c*) Name two families of carbon compounds which contain carbon, hydrogen, oxygen, and nitrogen. (*d*) Name a family of carbon compounds which contains carbon, hydrogen, and nitrogen.
2. (*a*) How does the general formula of an alcohol differ from that of a paraffin hydrocarbon? (*b*) Write the structural formulas of a paraffin and the corresponding alcohol.
3. Write the structural formulas for (*a*) 1-propanol, (*b*) 2-propanol, (*c*) 1-pentanol, (*d*) 2-pentanol, (*e*) 3-pentanol.
4. Give the chemical names for (*a*) $CH_3CH_2CH_2OH$ (*b*) $CH_3CHOHCH_2CH_3$ (*c*) $CH_3CH_2CHOHCH_2CH_3$ (*d*) $CH_3CH_2CH_2CH_2CHOHCH_3$.
5. Give the name of each of the following: (*a*) $CH_3CH{=}CHCH_3$ (*b*) $(CH_3)_2CHCH_2CH_2OH$ (*c*) $CH_3CH_2{-}C{\equiv}CH$ (*d*) $(CH_3)_2CH{-}CH{=}CH{-}CH_3$ (*e*) $(CH_3)_4C$ (*f*) CH_3COOH (*g*) CH_3COOCH_3 (*h*) CH_3CH_2OH (*i*) CH_2ClCH_2Cl (*j*) $CH_3CHClCH_2CH_2Cl$ (*k*) $(CH_3)_3COH$ (*l*) CH_3NH_2 (*m*) $C_{12}H_{22}O_{11}$ (*n*) $CHBr{=}CHBr$
6. (*a*) How does the general formula of an organic acid differ from that of a paraffin hydrocarbon? (*b*) Write the structural formulas of a paraffin and the corresponding acid.
7. How are esters prepared?
8. (*a*) What is meant by the term *saponification*? (*b*) What important industry is based on the saponification process? (*c*) Write the equation for a reaction that occurs in the industrial saponification process.

Apply Your Knowledge!

1. Find the percentage by mass of oxygen in (*a*) 2-butanol, (*b*) 1-butanol, (*c*) glycerol.
2. Compute (*a*) the volume (at STP) of carbon monoxide and (*b*) the moles of hydrogen needed to synthesize 1,000 kg of methanol.

3. Ninety kilograms of glucose are fermented.
   (*a*) How many moles of ethanol are formed?
   (*b*) What volume of gas is liberated at 30 °C and 760 torr pressure?
4. If 10 moles of ethanol are oxidized to give acetic acid, calculate (*a*) the mass in grams of acid formed, and (*b*) the volume in liters of air (20% oxygen by volume) required at STP.
5. A sample of vinegar, 50.0 ml in volume, neutralizes 67.0 ml of 0.500 *M* NaOH solution. Calculate the percentage by mass of acetic acid in the vinegar, assuming that the only acidic substance in vinegar is acetic acid and that the specific gravity of the vinegar is 1.02.
6. A soap, sodium stearate, is manufactured by saponifying 10.0 tons of tristearin.
   (*a*) How many kilograms of soap are produced?
   (*b*) How many moles of glycerol are obtained?
7. What volume of 6.00 *M* hydrochloric acid solution would be needed to react with 0.500 mole of trimethylamine?
8. If 100 ml of a 3.00 *M* trimethylammonium chloride solution is warmed with excess sodium hydroxide, calculate the volume of trimethylamine liberated at 60 °C and 760 torr pressure.
9. How many moles of glucose are obtained by the hydrolysis of 100 kg of starch?
10. How many moles of glucose must be oxidized in the body to provide 4,000 kcal of energy?

Find Out!

1. Sulfur is frequently found in organic compounds. Find one property that all organic sulfur compounds have in common.
2. What is the chemical reason for the effect of ethanol on the nervous system?
3. Follow the steps from sucrose to ethanol in the yeast fermentation of sucrose.

CHAPTER 27

SOME CHEMISTRY OF LIFE PROCESSES

BIOCHEMISTRY IS THE STUDY of the chemical processes in living things. Today the major research effort in this area is the study of the chemical reactions taking place in living cells. While the chemistry of the cell is especially complicated, the underlying principles are easily understood: The chemical reactions of the cell are thought to be controlled by large template molecules called enzymes which adsorb the reacting substances on their surfaces, catalyze the reactions, and release the products to the cell. Energy conversion and utilization center around one molecule which absorbs energy in its formation and releases energy when it dissociates. Reproduction and heredity revolve around large thread-like molecules which carry the genetic information along the thread in the form of a four-letter code composed of specific chemical structures.

The essential organic constituents of living cells include carbohydrates, lipids, and proteins. These substances also make up the three major types of foods of animals. In order to understand the functioning of the living cell, it is necessary to visualize the structure and chemical makeup of these three types of substances.

Carbohydrates

Carbohydrates include simple sugars, starches, and celluloses. Simple sugars such as sucrose (table sugar), glucose, and fructose are constituents of many fruits and vegetables, and of many candies and confections. Starches are essentially long chains of chemically bound glucose molecules which serve as the energy-reserve (or stored) carbohydrate in plants. Starch makes up large fractions of cereals, potatoes, and rice. Glycogen—which is similar to starch in that it consists of long chains of glucose molecules—is the energy-reserve carbohydrate of animals found mainly in muscles and liver. Cellulose—also made of glucose chains—is the structural material of plants and trees, the principal component of cell walls, the chief constituent of cotton fiber (90%), wood (50%), and paper. About 75% of the solid matter of plants consists of carbohydrates.

Carbohydrates play an important role in all organisms, serving as an essential source of energy for the cells and as a storage bank for food and energy. Specific carbohydrates are found in the components of the cell responsible for growth and reproductivity.

The empirical formula for glucose is $C_6H_{12}O_6$ but there are numerous compounds having this formula. The structural formula for glucose is

```
   H CH₂OH                                          CH₂OH
     \|                                               |
  H   C—O   H                                    H    |‾‾‾‾‾‾‾‾‾O    H
   \ /     \ /                                   |   H          \   |
    C OH    C        sometimes simplified to     |/              \  |
   / \|    / \                                   |\   OH      H   / |
 HO   C—C    OH                                 HO \  |       |  /  OH
      |  |\                                         |‾‾‾‾‾‾‾‾‾‾|
      H  O H                                        H          OH
         H
```

Glucose is formed in plants by photosynthesis from carbon dioxide and water. About 0.1% of normal human blood is glucose but the blood glucose level varies, increasing immediately after eating and decreasing between meals. In the presence of certain enzymes (biochemical catalysts), glucose will ferment to form ethyl alcohol:

$$C_6H_{12}O_6 \xrightarrow{\text{enzyme}} 2C_2H_5OH + 2CO_2 \tag{27-1}$$

Fructose is another simple sugar which occurs with glucose in fruits and honey. Sucrose is a compound containing one glucose and one fructose molecule which combine with the loss of a water molecule. It is obtained from cane sugar, sugar beets, and maple syrup and is used principally for food.

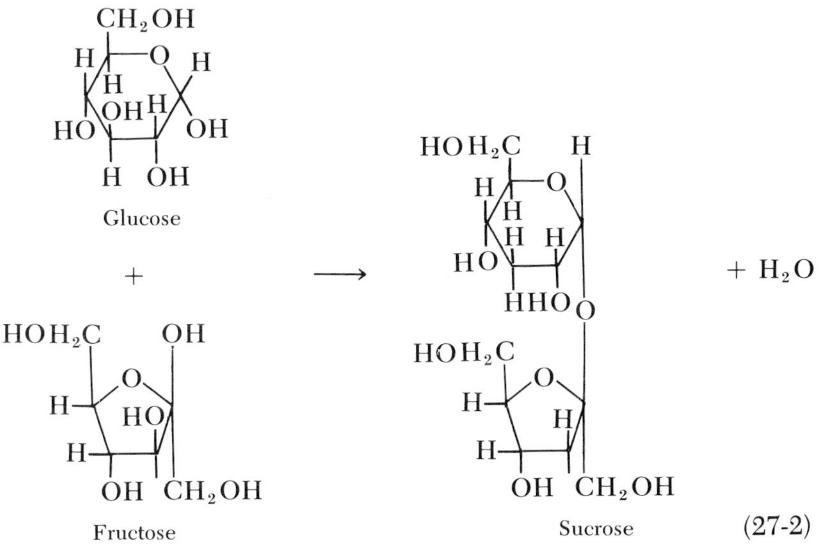

Glucose + Fructose ⟶ Sucrose + H_2O (27-2)

Because it contains the major fragments of two simple sugars, sucrose is called a disaccharide. Other important disaccharides containing glucose are lactose, which is the principal sugar in milk, and maltose, a sugar present in germinating grains. Human saliva contains an enzyme, known as amylase, which catalyzes the hydrolysis of starch to maltose. Thus, as we chew starch-containing products, some of the starch is being converted to maltose in our mouths. Maltose is then hydrolyzed to glucose in the small intestine.

As indicated, starch and cellulose are large molecules containing from 300 to as many as 10,000 glucose units per molecule. Portions of chains of glucose units in starch and cellulose are in Fig. 27-1.

Fig. 27-1 Portions of the glucose chains in (*a*) starch, (*b*) cellulose. Note the different orientations of the glucose units in the two structures. The starch chain often contains considerable branching and is helical in structure. The cellulose chains usually are longer than those in starch and they have no branching. As a result of these structural differences, starch is a fluffy, more soluble material of lower density, while cellulose shows the long, rod-like, carefully packed arrangement expected of a structural material.

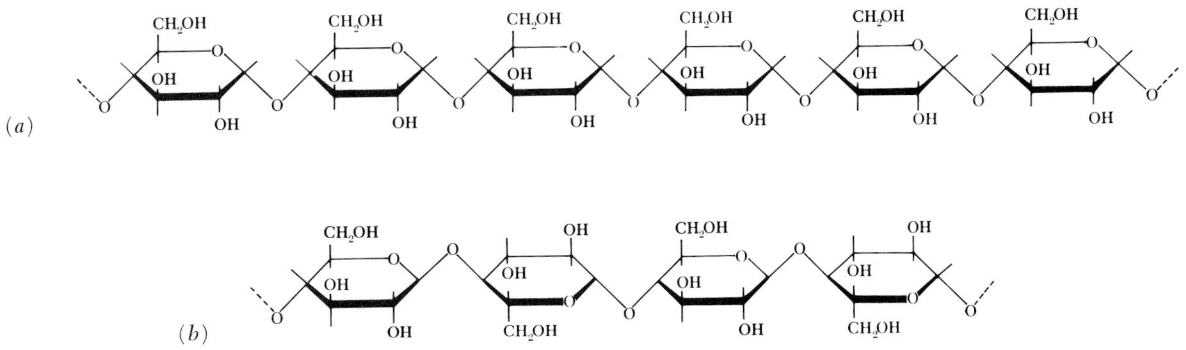

(*a*)

(*b*)

Lipids

Fats and oils found in living organisms compose a class of organic substances known as lipids. Lipids are essential constituents of virtually all living cells. In the human body, they are concentrated in fat depots such as under the skin, in cell membranes, and in brain and nerve tissue. Two types of lipids will be described here.

Fats

The first type of lipids, known as fats, has the general formula

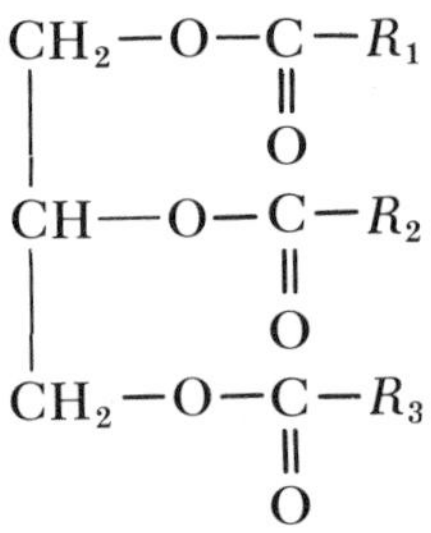

$$\begin{array}{l} CH_2{-}O{-}\underset{\underset{O}{\|}}{C}{-}R_1 \\ | \\ CH{-}O{-}\underset{\underset{O}{\|}}{C}{-}R_2 \\ | \\ CH_2{-}O{-}\underset{\underset{O}{\|}}{C}{-}R_3 \end{array}$$

they are said to be esters of glycerin (glycerol) and long-chain carboxylic acids which might be imagined to result from a reaction such as (27-3)

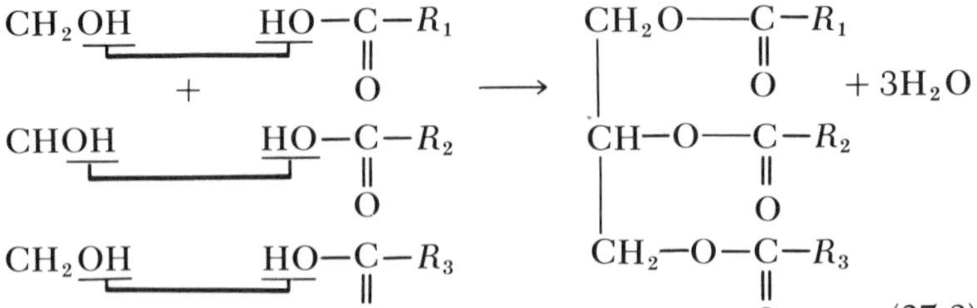

$$\begin{array}{l} CH_2OH \\ CHOH \\ CH_2OH \end{array} + \begin{array}{l} HO{-}\underset{\underset{O}{\|}}{C}{-}R_1 \\ HO{-}\underset{\underset{O}{\|}}{C}{-}R_2 \\ HO{-}\underset{\underset{O}{\|}}{C}{-}R_3 \end{array} \longrightarrow \begin{array}{l} CH_2O{-}\underset{\underset{O}{\|}}{C}{-}R_1 \\ | \\ CH{-}O{-}\underset{\underset{O}{\|}}{C}{-}R_2 \\ | \\ CH_2{-}O{-}\underset{\underset{O}{\|}}{C}{-}R_3 \end{array} + 3H_2O \qquad (27\text{-}3)$$

The R groups found in fats vary widely depending on the species of plant or animal. However the most common R groups found contain 15 or 17 carbon atoms. Not only are the three R groups in a given fat molecule likely to be different (e.g., a C_{17}, a C_{15}, and a C_9), but an assembly of fat molecules from a single source will contain a variety of R groups. An analysis of a sample of human fat is given in Table 27-1. Hydrolysis of fats with bases produces soaps and glycerine. Most soaps are sodium or potassium salts of long-chain carboxylic acids found in fats.

Table 27-1 Analysis of human fat

R Group	%	*R* Group	%
$CH_3(CH_2)_{15}—CH_2—$	8.4	$C_{17}H_{33}$	45.9
$CH_3(CH_2)_{13}—CH_2—$	25.0	$C_{15}H_{29}$	6.2
$CH_3(CH_2)_{11}—CH_2—$	3.3	$C_{13}H_{25}$	0.4
$CH_3(CH_2)_9—CH_2—$	0.5	$C_{17}H_{31}$	9.8

In the human body, stored fat represents a rich source of energy since the energy value of fats is more than twice that of carbohydrates or of protein. The body obtains most of its required energy from the oxidation of carbohydrates or fats. In normal adults, little or no digestion of fat occurs as the food passes through the mouth and stomach. In the duodenum, fats encounter bile acids and bile salts; these emulsify the fats, preparing them for digestion by enzymes secreted for this purpose by the pancreas. Digestion consists in hydrolyzing the fats to glycerine, soaps, and fatty acids. These products pass through the intestinal mucosa and are reconverted to fats (triglycerides). The reconstituted fats then enter the lymph circulation. Low concentrations of fat are present in the blood stream. These substances may be removed from the blood stream and stored in the various fat depots of the body. Considerable quantities of fat may be stored around organs such as the heart, lungs, and kidneys, thereby helping to protect them from injury.

Steroids

A second important class of lipids are the steroids. These are compounds containing the structural unit

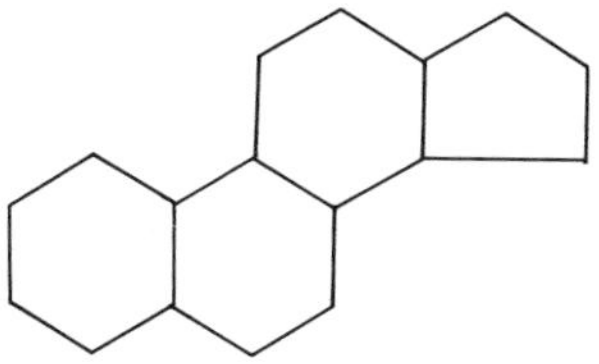

where each line junction represents a carbon atom bonded to an appropriate number of hydrogen atoms. Steroids are widely distributed among plants and animals and are essential constituents of bile and sex hormones, as well as brain, spinal tissue, and other parts of the nervous system.

An especially important steroid is cholesterol

$$\text{Cholesterol: steroid ring system with HO group, two angular } CH_3 \text{ groups, and side chain } CH(CH_3)-CH_2-CH_2-CH_2-CH(CH_3)_2$$

Investigate . . .
Look up the meaning of *in vivo* and *in vitro.*

This substance, which can be synthesized in the cells of animals starting with acetic acid, is itself the key compound in the *in vivo* synthesis of other essential steroids such as bile acids, six hormones, and vitamin D. Cholesterol excreted in bile can give rise to gallstones. If the cholesterol level in the blood remains at an abnormally high level, deposition of cholesterol plaques may occur in the arteries, including the aorta. Such accumulations often result in circulatory or heart failure. Much medical research is directed toward methods of controlling cholesterol blood levels in the hope of reducing this form of circulatory disease.

Proteins

Proteins are essential constituents of all cells and body tissues, and are present in all body fluids except bile and urine. They also are essential constituents of the diet, being required for the synthesis of body tissues, certain hormones, enzymes, and blood and liver components. In plants, proteins are made by a complex process which starts with photosynthesis. Animals synthesize only a small amount of their protein from inorganic sources. They synthesize most of their protein from the material resulting from digestion of dietary protein obtained from plant and animal sources. Proteins are used in the body for growth of new tissues and maintenance of existing tissues; they also appear in the form of enzymes, as the catalysts which control virtually all the chemical processes of the cells.

Speculate . . .
Among the commonly known proteins of the body are hemoglobin and insulin. Insulin is a hormone that facilitates the change of water-soluble glucose to insoluble glycogen that can be stored in the liver. Hemoglobin can reversibly combine with oxygen, picking up that element in the lungs and releasing it in the tissues. Hemoglobin then picks up CO_2 from the tissues and releases it in the lungs. When CO is present in the air, hemoglobin also combines with CO. Which chemical bond do you think is stronger: hemoglobin-CO_2 or hemoglobin-CO?

Proteins are composed mainly of carbon, hydrogen, oxygen, and nitrogen. They are very large molecules having molecular masses varying from 34,000 to 50 million. Compare this with the mass of a water molecule which is approximately 18.

Upon hydrolysis with acids or bases, proteins yield smaller molecules known as amino acids. For this reason, proteins sometimes are said to be polymers of α-amino acids. The general formula for an α-amino acid is

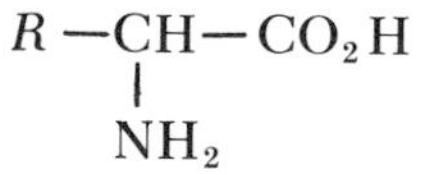

$$\begin{array}{l} R-\underset{\displaystyle NH_2}{\underset{|}{CH}}-CO_2H \end{array}$$

The amino acids are bonded in the protein molecule by what is known as a peptide link. This link results when water is eliminated between the NH_2 group of one amino acid and the OH group of a second acid, with the resulting linking together of the remaining portions of the amino acids:

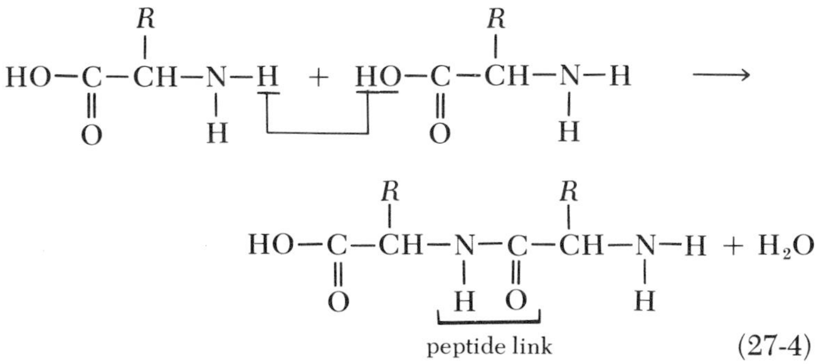

$$HO-\underset{\displaystyle O}{\underset{\|}{C}}-\overset{\displaystyle R}{\overset{|}{CH}}-\underset{\displaystyle H}{\underset{|}{N}}-H + HO-\underset{\displaystyle O}{\underset{\|}{C}}-\overset{\displaystyle R}{\overset{|}{CH}}-\underset{\displaystyle H}{\underset{|}{N}}-H \longrightarrow$$

$$HO-\underset{\displaystyle O}{\underset{\|}{C}}-\overset{\displaystyle R}{\overset{|}{CH}}-\underbrace{\underset{\displaystyle H}{\underset{|}{N}}-\underset{\displaystyle O}{\underset{\|}{C}}}_{\text{peptide link}}-\overset{\displaystyle R}{\overset{|}{CH}}-\underset{\displaystyle H}{\underset{|}{N}}-H + H_2O \qquad (27\text{-}4)$$

Such peptide links, when formed between large numbers of amino acids, give rise to the protein molecule. A portion of such a molecule is represented by the formula in Fig. 27-2.

A protein molecule consists of one or more such chains which are often coiled and bonded to one another in a variety of ways. This coiling and bonding confers a definite shape on the protein molecule. This shape is related to the size and shape of the various R groups along the polypeptide chain and is largely responsible for the highly specific catalytic behavior of one important group of proteins—the enzymes.

When proteins are hydrolyzed, approximately 20 different amino acids are found. These differ in the chemical structure of the R

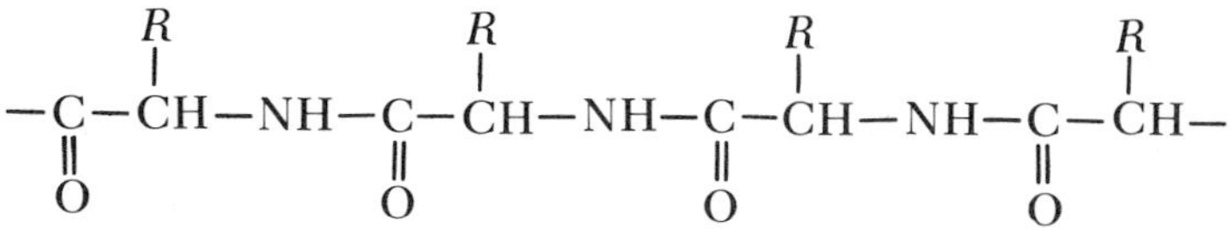

$$-\underset{\displaystyle O}{\underset{\|}{C}}-\overset{\displaystyle R}{\overset{|}{CH}}-NH-\underset{\displaystyle O}{\underset{\|}{C}}-\overset{\displaystyle R}{\overset{|}{CH}}-NH-\underset{\displaystyle O}{\underset{\|}{C}}-\overset{\displaystyle R}{\overset{|}{CH}}-NH-\underset{\displaystyle O}{\underset{\|}{C}}-\overset{\displaystyle R}{\overset{|}{CH}}-$$

Fig. 27-2 Portion of a protein molecule (a polypeptide).

group in the formula given in Fig. 27-2. Examples of several amino acids found in proteins are given in Table 27-2.

Table 27-2

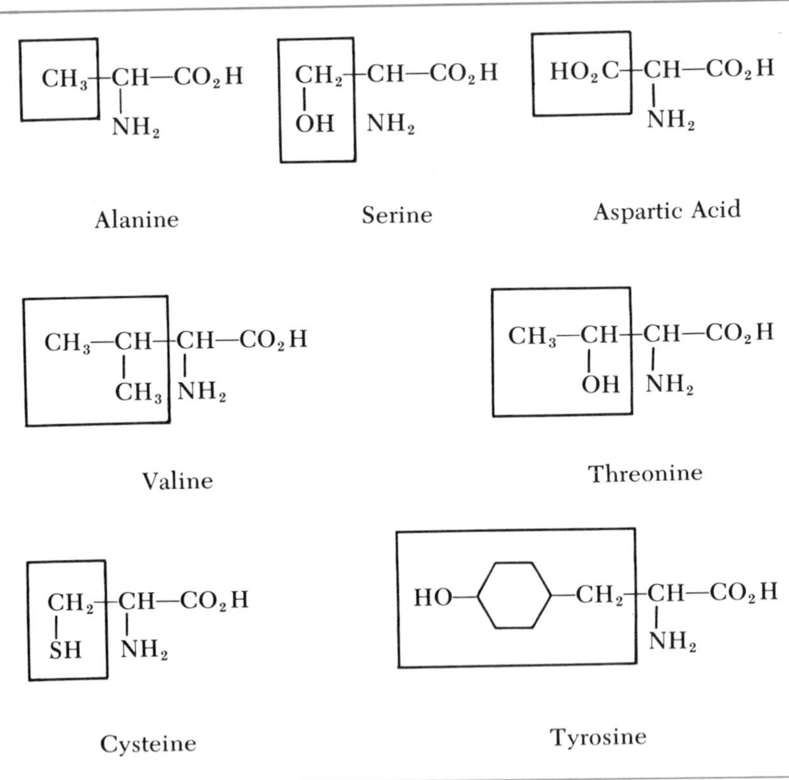

Since most proteins contain 20 or more amino acids, the exact sequence of amino acids in the protein chain is especially important, for it determines the final shape and many of the properties of the protein molecule. This sequence is illustrated in the polypeptide structure in Fig. 27-3 where the sequence is alanine-serine-aspartic acid-cysteine:

Research . . .
Myoglobin is a protein similar to hemoglobin, but it has only one polypeptide chain. What is its molecular mass?

$$-\underset{\underset{\text{O}}{\|}}{\text{C}}-\overset{\overset{\text{CH}_3}{|}}{\text{CH}}-\text{NH}\,\vdots\,-\underset{\underset{\text{O}}{\|}}{\text{C}}-\overset{\overset{\text{CH}_2\text{OH}}{|}}{\text{CH}}-\text{NH}\,\vdots\,-\underset{\underset{\text{O}}{\|}}{\text{C}}-\overset{\overset{\text{CO}_2\text{H}}{|}}{\text{CH}}-\text{NH}\,\vdots\,-\underset{\underset{\text{O}}{\|}}{\text{C}}-\overset{\overset{\text{CH}_2\text{SH}}{|}}{\text{CH}}-\text{NH}-$$

Alanine Serine Aspartic acid Cysteine

Fig. 27-3 A polypeptide.

The amino acid composition of several important proteins is given in Table 27-3.

Table 27-3 Amino acid composition of three proteins (Numbers represent residues of amino acids per protein molecule.)

Amino acid	Protein: Human serum albumin	Pepsin, an enzyme	Horse hemoglobin
Alanine	—	—	54
Glycine	15	29	48
Valine	45	21	50
Leucine	58	27	75
Proline	31	15	22
Phenylalanine	33	13	30
Tyrosine	18	16	11
Serine	22	40	35
Threonine	27	28	24
Cystine/2	32	4	2.5
Arginine	25	2	14
Histidine	16	2	36
Lysine	58	2	38
Aspartic acid	46	41	51
Glutamic acid	80	28	38
Amide N	44	32	36

The number of ways in which 20 or so amino acids found in proteins can be arranged in a molecule is extremely large—for example, consider a few of the many possible arrangements for only 4 amino acids designated as acids A, B, C, and D. These might be arranged in the order

—A—B—C—D—A—B—C—D— etc. or
—A—C—B—D—A—C—B—D— etc. or
—A—A—B—C—D—A—A—B—C—D— etc. or
—A—A—A—A—B—B—B—B—C—C—C—C etc.

How many other arrangements can you imagine for the four amino acids? No wonder there are so many different proteins.

Once formed, the protein chain may acquire a helix structure made stable by a large number of hydrogen bonds formed between

Note . . .
Mirror-image isomers exist for every amino acid except glycine. In plant and animal life, there exists—for a reason no one knows—only one of the two isomers of the 23 amino acids. That isomer is the L-amino acid.

portions of the same huge molecule, or it may form sheets or fibers if the hydrogen bonds are formed between parallel planes. Hydrogen bonding between protein chains is illustrated in Fig. 27-4. Other attractive forces such as van der Waals forces, ion-dipole forces, and even covalent bonds in the form of S—S—bridges also contribute to the stabilization of the shape of the protein molecule. Figure 27-5 shows the helical structure of a protein chain and a model of the myoglobin molecule worked out from X-ray analysis.

Some Chemistry of Living Cells

Under the microscope, cells appear to be drops of viscous liquid surrounded by a membrane, Inside the membrane is the cytoplasm—mostly water but containing various heterogeneous regions identified as mitochondria, ribosomes, lysosomes, and others. Near the center of the cell is the nucleus where the genetic information is retained. In terms of chemical processes, the cell is seen by biochemists as a highly organized chemical factory, capable of carrying out a host of very specific chemical reactions rapidly and efficiently. The cell is able to control these reactions to meet its needs and those of the organism, and it is so skillful in regulating its energy requirements that it utilizes 60% of the energy of its fuel—an accomplishment only a few man-made machines have achieved.

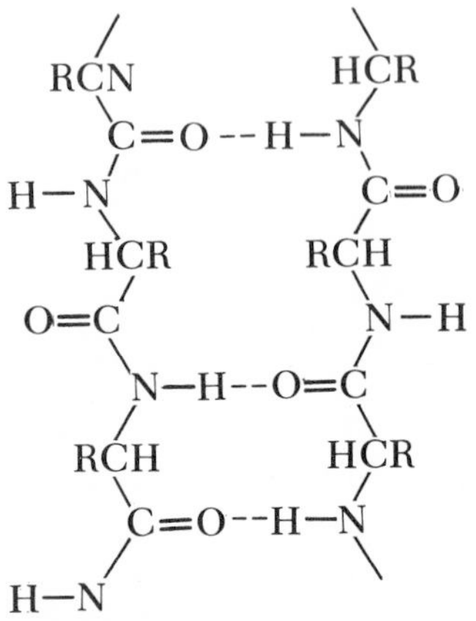

Several of the most vital questions concerning this complex proficient chemical factory follow:

1. How is it possible for the cell to carry out only certain chemical process when the materials needed for carrying out so many other processes are present?
2. What is the chemical explanation for the efficient energy utilization of the cell?
3. How is the information specifying which chemical reactions are to be carried out passed on to the newly formed cells of the organism?

We shall use these questions as the basis for our brief study of the cell.

Enzymes, The Reaction Regulators

Nearly every chemical reaction in the cell proceeds readily only

Fig. 27-4 Illustrating hydrogen bond formation between protein chains or between portions of the same chain. Thousands of hydrogen bonds are believed to exist along the chains of proteins. These give structural stability to fibrous proteins such as hair and prevent other proteins from being jelly-like masses.

```
     /               \
  RCN               HCR
     \              /
      C=O--H-N
     /               \
H-N                 C=O
    \               /
    HCR          RCH
    /               \
O=C                 N-H
    \               /
     N-H--O=C
    /               \
  RCH               HCR
    \               /
     C=O--H-N
    /               \
H-N
```

in the presence of a specific enzyme. Without the appropriate enzyme, most reactions would proceed so slowly that the cell could not live. Enzymes are proteins with molecular masses in the 50,000 range, although some are larger than this. Most enzymes will speed up one chemical reaction but not another even though the second reaction may be quite similar to the first. For example, the enzyme *sucrase* will catalyze the hydrolysis of sucrose into glucose and fructose, but it will not catalyze the chemically similar hydrolysis of maltose into two glucose molecules. Because enzymes are so specific and because most uncatalyzed biochemical processes are so slow, the cell can carry out only those reactions for which an appropriate enzyme is present and very few others. To be viable, the cell must contain a very large number of different types of enzymes. It is estimated that cells contain as many as 1000 different kinds of enzymes.

Most cellular reactions proceed through a series of steps, each of which usually requires a specific enzyme. For example, in the oxidation of glucose to carbon dioxide and water—a reaction nearly all students have attempted using a test tube and burner—the cell uses 17 steps and 17 enzymes. Eleven of these steps take place in the cytoplasm of the cell; the remainder occur in the mitochondria.

What is there about the structure of enzymes that enables them to be so specific? Many biochemists believe that the shape of a given enzyme is such that only those molecules involved in the reaction will fit at an active site on the enzyme surface. One could imagine, for example, that the enzyme *maltase* might have a crater on its surface into which only a maltose molecule might fit.

Adjacent to this maltose "crater site" might be a second site into which only a water molecule could fit. When maltose and water are adsorbed on the enzyme surface, they are in the correct orientation for reaction to occur. The enzyme can then catalyze the reaction, release the reaction products to the cell, proceed to adsorb new reactants, and so on. This process could be repeated until the

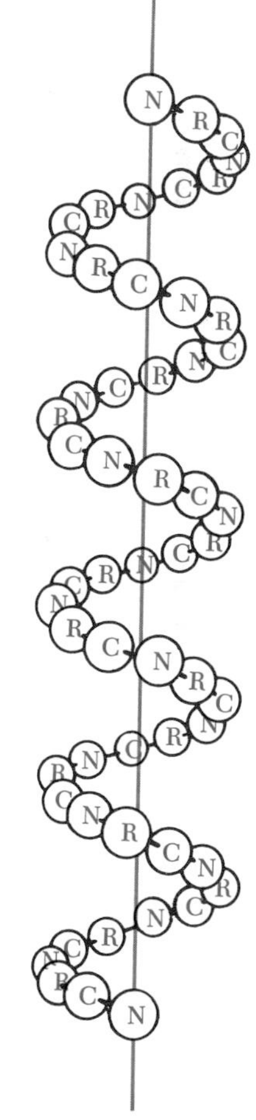

(*a*)

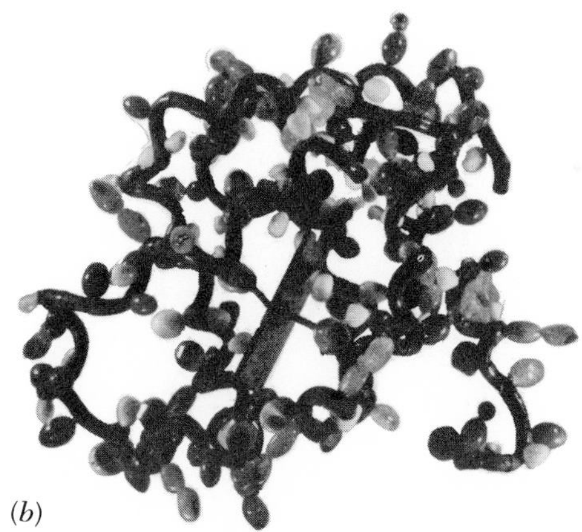

(*b*)

Figure 27-5 (*a*) Representation of the α-helix arrangement of a protein chain. (*b*) Model of a protein molecule reconstructed from X-ray diffraction data. This protein is myoglobin found in muscle extracts from the sperm whale. It consists of a single chain of 153 amino acid residues and one heme group. Hemoglobin, the oxygen-carrying protein of blood, also contains the heme group.

Table 27-4 Some enzymes and the reactions they catalyze

Enzyme	Reaction catalyzed
Amylase	Starch to the disaccharide maltose
Maltase	Maltose to glucose
Pepsin	Hydrolysis of protein chain at phenylalanine or tyrosine residues
Trypsin	Hydrolysis of protein chain at lysine or arginine residues
Lipase	Hydrolysis of fats to glycerol and fatty acids

cell has acquired a sufficient quantity of the reaction products to meet its immediate needs, at which time the products may remain on the enzyme surface, temporarily inactivating it. Experiments show that a given enzyme can transform from 10,000 to 5 million reactant molecules to product molecules in one minute under optimum conditions. Examples of enzymes present in the human body and the reactions they control are given in Table 27-4.

In the body, many enzymes are secreted from glands such as the pancreas. However to prevent these enzymes from acting on the tissues and other components of the very glands that produce them, the enzymes are released from the gland in an inactive form. Activation of the enzymes is accomplished in various ways, including a change in pH, the addition of inorganic ions—such as manganese (II) or magnesium ions—or the addition of organic materials, principally the vitamins or derivatives of vitamins. The additional inorganic or organic materials needed to activate enzymes are called coenzymes. Since the body is unable to synthesize most vitamins, and because these substances are needed to activate certain enzymes, vitamins are an essential part of the human diet. However, the amounts of vitamins needed are not large, since their role is in the catalyst system which functions with very small concentrations of active components.

Energy Utilization and Control

Relatively large quantities of fuel are required to sustain the operation of the cell because a large fraction of the reactions are both endothermic and nonspontaneous. This is proved by the spontaneous decomposition of cellular chemicals upon death. The fuels of cells are glucose and the decomposition products from fats and proteins. Oxidation of glucose to carbon dioxide and water can supply an adequate quantity of energy; however, the cell cannot always use this energy at the time it is produced. Neither can the cell allow too much energy to be released to the surroundings. If even a portion of the energy of oxidizing glucose were released to the surroundings, the temperature of the cell would rise so high that all the enzymes would be inactivated. For these reasons, the cell needs a mechanism for capturing and storing the energy from its fuel and another mechanism for supplying energy when and where it is needed.

The mechanisms employed by the cell are actually very simple. They are based on two elementary chemical principles. The first is the concept of carrying out the oxidation of glucose in a series of steps (17 in all) with the possibility that energy can be extracted in small amounts in several steps. This might avoid both inefficient trapping of the energy released and overheating of the cell. If, as these small amounts of energy are released, much of it could be captured and stored for later use, then considerable efficiency in the conversion of fuel to usable energy could be attained. This is where the second elementary chemical principle is used. Stated simply this principle is: When a compound *A* is converted to compound *B* energy may be released or absorbed, and when compound *B* is converted back to compound *A*, the reverse will be true. Now suppose that, as glucose oxidation proceeds, the energy released in the various steps is used to convert compound *A* to compound *B*. All along the oxidation sequence, compound *B* molecules are being formed and energy is captured and stored in this compound. Later when the cell needs energy to aid in carrying out other important reactions, can it not obtain this stored energy in small amounts by converting compound *B* back to compound *A*?

This is essentially the energy conversion mechanism of the cell. The molecules *A* and *B* are adenosine diphosphate (ADP) and adenosine triphosphate (ATP), respectively, although several other pairs of compounds can serve the same function. The formulas for these two compounds are given in Fig. 27-6. Despite their complicated formulas, the energy conversion capability lies in the addition or removal of *the third phosphate group* in the molecule.

The critical reaction is

$$\mathrm{ATP} + \mathrm{H_2O} \rightleftarrows \mathrm{ADP} + \mathrm{H_2PO_4^-} + \text{energy} \qquad (27\text{-}5)$$

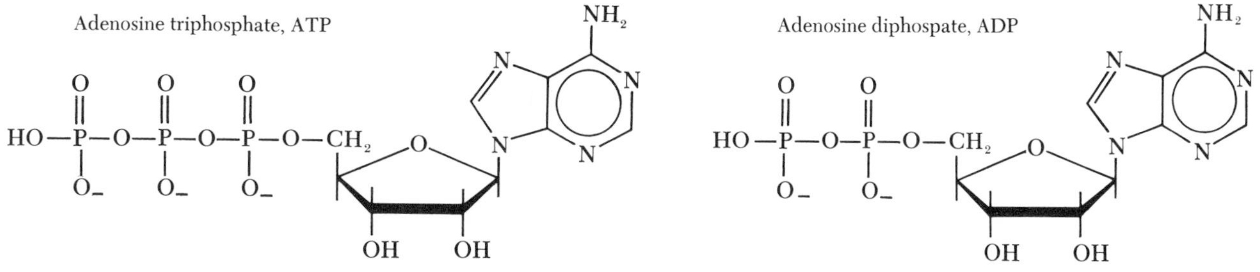

Fig. 27-6 Structural formulas for adenosine diphosphate, (ADP), and adenosine triphosphate, (ATP). When ADP is converted to ATP, energy is absorbed and when ATP is converted to ADP, energy is released. In the cell, the fuel glucose is oxidized to carbon dioxide and water in a series of 17 steps. In several of these steps energy is released, but immediately captured and stored by converting ADP to ATP. Later, when small amounts of energy are needed ATP molecules can be reconverted to ADP molecules releasing energy.

Adenosine triphosphate, ATP

Adenosine diphospate, ADP

Thus energy utilization in the cell centers around ATP and ADP. When the cell needs energy, it converts some ATP to ADP, and when the supply of ATP becomes low, it oxidizes glucose to produce more ATP. In the human body the blood sugar content, high immediately after eating, drops as glucose oxidation occurs and as ATP molecules capture much of the energy released. Should the glucose level in the blood become too low because of greater bodily needs for energy than the fuel supplied by food intake, glucose can be released to the blood from the liver where it is stored as the reserve carbohydrate *glycogen*, a substance similar to starch, which was described earlier in this chapter.

The Destiny of Food

Food entering an organism must be transformed into useful form. In our bodies the fats, starches, and proteins all must be broken down into smaller molecules such as glycerine and fatty acids in the case of fats, into glucose and other simple sugars in the case of carbohydrates, and into amino acids in the case of proteins. Most of these reactions occur in the alimentary tract under the influence of digestive enzymes secreted into various regions of the tract by digestive glands.

If the food is to be used as fuel, it will be oxidized as described above. However, much of the food material entering the cell is used to build new cell material either as replacements for worn-out parts or components for new cells. Since much of this material is protein, the cell must first assemble the needed amino acids, making some where necessary, and synthesize the very complicated proteins, being sure to arrange the amino acids in the correct sequence to give the exact protein needed.

Protein Synthesis

The most demanding task of the cell is to see to it that each protein synthesized has the correct sequence of amino acids, for unless the amino acid sequence is correct, the shape of the protein cannot be correct. If the protein shape is not correct, it cannot perform its function in the cell. For enzymes this means they cannot catalyze the reactions needed to keep the cell alive and healthy. To illustrate just how critical it is that the sequence of amino acids be correct in a protein, it is known that if *one* amino acid residue in the 574 that are present in a hemoglobin is incorrectly placed, the individual becomes ill.

For these reasons, the cell needs an unfailing mechanism for precisely directing the synthesis of proteins. This mechanism must be one that transmits the information of the exact amino acid sequence for each protein needed by the cell and assures that when the protein is synthesized, this sequence is unmistakably reproduced.

Protein Synthesis Templates The substances responsible for ordering the amino acids during protein synthesis are known as ribonucleic acids, RNA. They appear to be long, chain- or thread-like molecules with hundreds of small molecules hanging from the thread at regular intervals. The thread consists of an alternating sequence of residues of phosphate and the simple sugar ribose. The small molecules hanging from the thread are four different organic nitrogen compounds—two are known as purines and two as pyrimidines. The structure of a portion of an RNA molecule can be represented as follows:

```
Ribose — Phosphate — Ribose — Phosphate — Ribose — Phosphate — Ribose — Phosphate
  |                    |                    |                    |
Nitrogen             Nitrogen             Nitrogen             Nitrogen
Compound             Compound             Compound             Compound
```

There are many different kinds of RNA molecules; the differences between them lie in the order or sequence of the four different nitrogen compounds along the RNA chain. This order or sequence is analogous in many ways to the sequence of amino acids in proteins. If the four nitrogen compounds are designated as A, B, C, and D, respectively, we can readily imagine a great many possible arrangements of these compounds along the RNA chain. For example, Fig. 27-7 shows three possibilities:

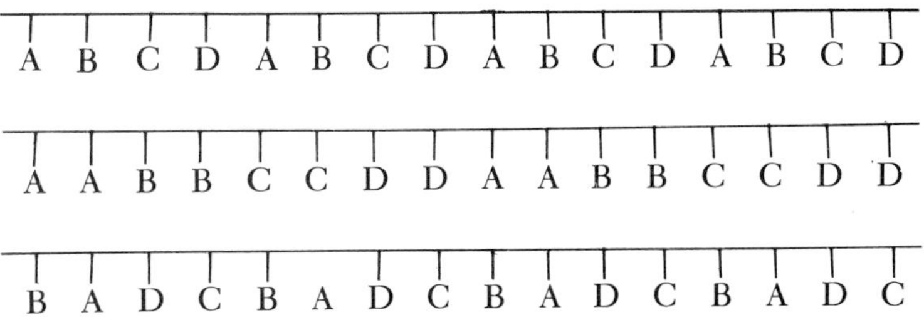

Fig. 27-7 Possible RNA arrangements.

In the cell there are two varieties of RNA. The first, known as *messenger RNA*, carries all the information needed for arranging the amino acids in the proper sequence during protein synthesis. There are at least as many messenger RNA molecules as there are different proteins in the cell. The second variety of RNA is known as *transfer RNA*. These RNA molecules appear to pick up amino acids and bring them to the messenger RNA molecule. There are at least as many transfer RNA molecules as there are amino acids.

In essence then, the messenger RNA molecules serve as templates for the synthesis of proteins while the transfer RNA molecules serve to place the amino acids in the correct order on the template. Reaction of the amino acids with their neighbors on the template is facilitated by appropriate enzymes. A more detailed explanation of this mechanism of protein synthesis is given in Fig. 27-8..

The Gene: Template for RNA, Thread of Life

The synthesis of messenger RNA is thought to take place in the nucleus of the cell in a manner analogous to the protein synthesis previously described. In RNA synthesis however, it is the *gene* which is the template. Chemically, the gene is similar to RNA. It too is a thread-like structure with hundreds of small molecules suspended from the thread at regular intervals. Like RNA, the gene has residues of phosphate and a simple sugar in an alternating sequence along the thread and only four different organic nitrogen compounds—again two purines and two pyrimidines—make up the structures hanging from the thread. The simple sugar in the gene is deoxyribose. For this reason the gene is known as a deoxyribonucleic acid, DNA. Three of the four pendant nitrogen compounds are the same as those in RNA; the fourth is closely related to the corresponding compound in RNA. Apparently, a DNA molecule is able to line up appropriate segments of RNA along its chain, perhaps somewhat as illustrated in Fig. 27-9. Once in position, the segments are linked together chemically with the aid of enzymes. After synthesis, the RNA molecule leaves the nucleus and moves to the ribosomes of the cell where it supervises the synthesis of proteins.

(*a*)

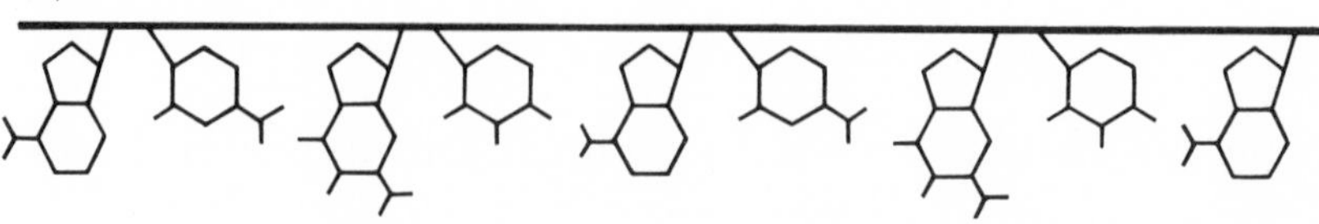

(*b*)

(*i*)

(*ii*)

(*iii*)

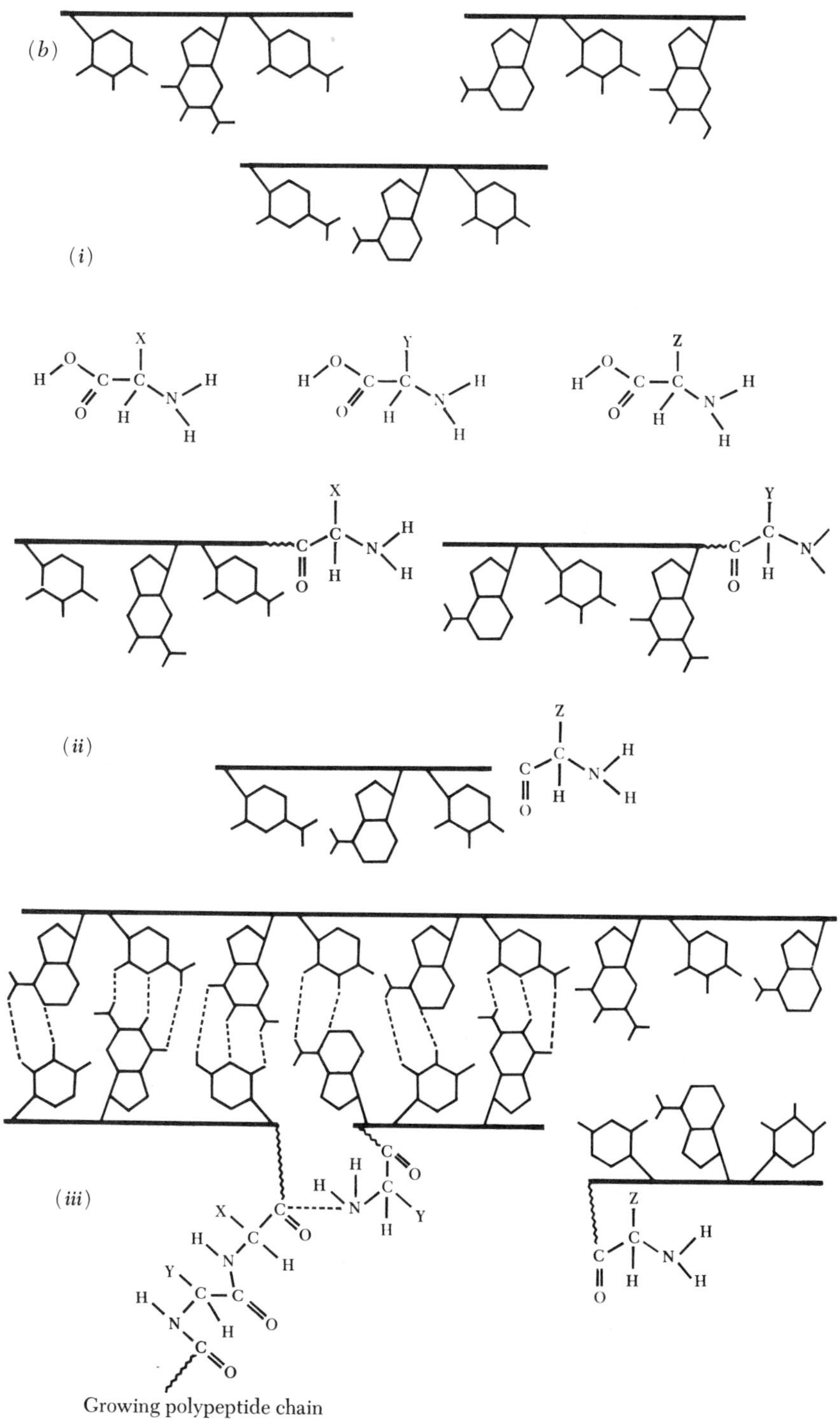

Growing polypeptide chain

Fig. 27-8 (*a*) This diagram (p. 498) represents messenger-RNA. The four nitrogen bases are indicated by line formulas. (*b*) These drawings represent three kinds of transfer-RNA. (*c*) There is a complementary relation between pairs of the nitrogen bases. This is brought about by hydrogen bonding. In RNA, the complementary pairs are adenine and uracil, guanine and cytosine, as shown here. The matching pairs of nitrogen bases in RNA demonstrate alignment through hydrogen bonding.

(*c*)

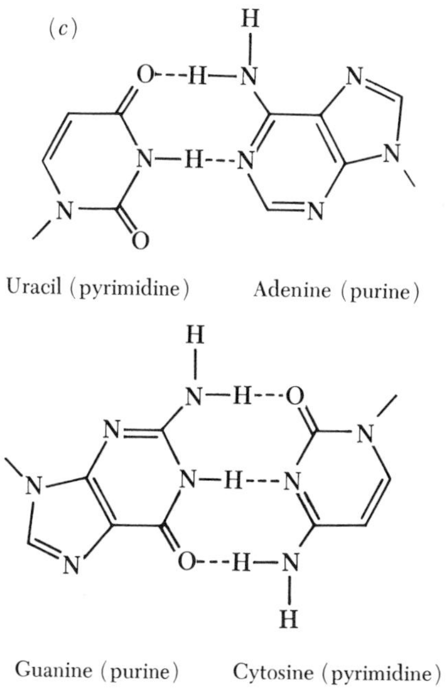

Uracil (pyrimidine) Adenine (purine)

Guanine (purine) Cytosine (pyrimidine)

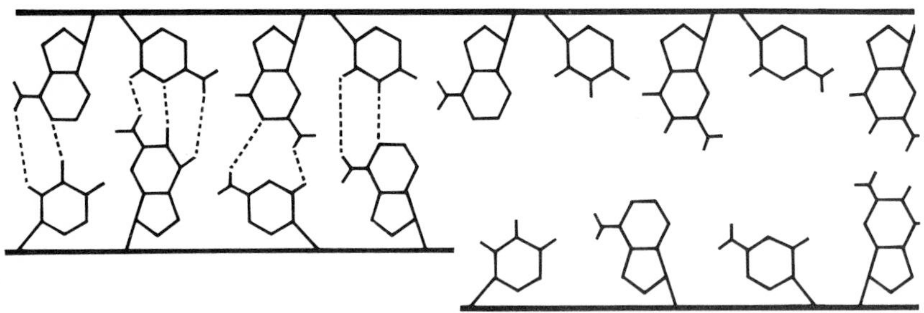

Fig. 27-9 Illustrating RNA synthesis with DNA serving as template. Note the complementary nature of the pendant nitrogen structures between the template and the entering segments. These complementary structures are the key to RNA synthesis and to heredity.

DNA molecules not only carry the chemical code needed to direct the manufacture of proteins which sustain the cell, but they also have the ability to split into two parts. From a pool of food and other components of the cell, each part can make exact copies of its complementary part and in this way each DNA unit has the ability to reproduce not only two identical DNA molecules but, because RNA is synthesized from DNA and proteins from RNA, it can assure the reproduction of all the essential reaction controlling molecules of the cell. In essence this means that the DNA molecules are the molecules of life. They define the life processes in the cell; they have the ability to produce new cells that are exact replicas of the parent cell. The DNA double helix is well-known to biology students. It is represented in Fig. 27-10.

DNA molecules are present in the nucleus of every cell, well protected from potential dangers and shock. The molecular mass of DNA is about 6 million. One molecule of DNA may contain several genes; i.e., several coded sequences, each able to direct the synthesis of a different RNA molecule.

The fertilized human egg weighs about 6×10^{-12} g. It contains all the genetic information (DNA) needed to make a full-grown adult. In fact, every cell in the body contains all the genetic information in the fertilized egg. One of the great problems of modern biochemistry is: Why are the cells in a complex organism so different if they all contain the same genes?

The genetic characteristics of a human being, such as the color of his hair, skin, and eyes, his facial characteristics, the shape of his

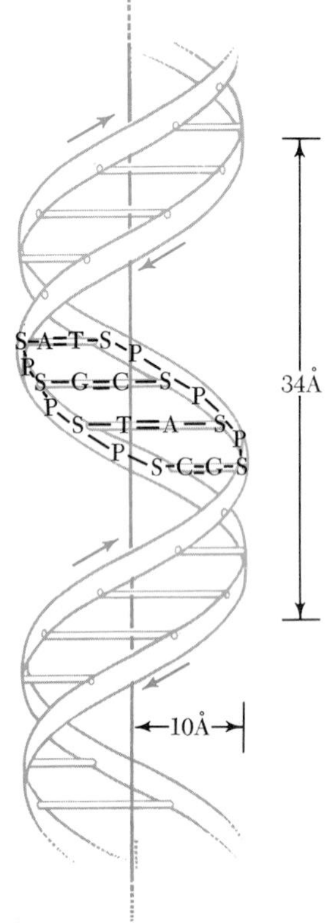

Fig. 27-10 Representation of the double helix of DNA. Here, P represents a phosphate and S a deoxyribose (sugar) residue, and the A=T, G=C symbols represent the pairing of the complementary pairs of organic nitrogen compounds along the chain. When the strands separate and each strand directs the synthesis of its complement, exact replication is assured by the pairing of complements since two and only two complementary pairs are possible.

body, his susceptibility to certain diseases, and so on are all determined by the DNA molecules in his cells and by the number and kind of RNA molecules they manufacture. The color of hair, skin, and eyes is determined by the amount of a pigment called melanin (black) present in the hair, skin, or pupil of the eye. Melanin is formed from the amino acid tyrosine in a series of steps, each of which requires a different enzyme. The enzymes are produced from RNA molecules which in turn are made on the appropriate DNA molecules in the nucleus of the cell. Evidently all humans (except albinos) have the genes that govern color, but since the amount of melanin varies widely among humans, color-producing genes must be more active in producing the RNA in some individuals than in others. Thus, another major critical problem of modern biochemistry is the discovery of mechanisms that control the activity of the gene. Understanding these mechanisms might lead to a cure for cancer and other genetic malfunctions, and to a better appreciation of the processes of aging and of memory improvement.

Summary

The major constituents of living cells are proteins, carbohydrates, and lipids. These substances also make up the three major types of foods of animals. Carbohydrates serve as an essential source of energy for the cell and as a bank for storing food and energy. In plants, the carbohydrate cellulose is the principal structural material. Lipids are found in the human body in cell membranes, in brain and nerve tissue and in fat deposits such as under the skin. Cholesterol, a lipid, is the key compound in the *in vivo* synthesis of such important body materials as bile acids, sex hormones, and vitamin D. In large amounts, cholesterol in food may constitute a threat to the circulatory system.

Proteins are components of much body tissue, of certain hormones, all enzymes, and of important blood and liver components. They are huge molecules made from α-amino acids. The particular amino acids present in a protein and their exact sequence in the protein chain determine the shape of the protein and its function in the cell.

The living cell can be viewed as a complex chemical factory capable of carrying out a variety of reactions rapidly and with unusually efficient utilization of energy. Nearly all cellular reactions require specific enzymes, protein molecules, to act as catalysts and to control the amount of reaction products produced. The specificity of enzymes is related to their shape and to the availability on their surfaces of active sites, where the reactant molecules can be adsorbed and from which the products are released to the cell.

Energy utilization in the cell revolves about two molecules. Energy is absorbed when ADP is converted to ATP and released when ATP is reconverted to ADP. Glucose is oxidized to carbon dioxide and water in 17 steps in the cell. Small amounts of energy released in several of these steps are absorbed and stored by converting ADP molecules to ATP molecules. When the cell needs energy to carry out other reactions, it acquires this energy by converting ATP to ADP.

Enzymes appear to be synthesized in the cell under the direction of messenger RNA molecules which carry the information needed to place the amino acids in the correct sequence to give the desired protein. This information is carried by RNA in a code generated by the ordering of four kinds of simple organic nitrogen compounds along the RNA chain. Messenger RNA acts as a template for protein synthesis. Transfer RNA molecules seem to place the amino acids in the correct positions along the template.

RNA molecules apparently are synthesized in the nucleus under the direction of the gene or DNA molecule. In addition to directing the synthesis of RNA, the DNA—which exists as a double helix—can divide into two parts. Each part can reproduce its complement from small molecules present in the cell. Since DNA can reproduce itself and since it also directs the synthesis of RNA molecules which in turn direct the synthesis of enzymes, which catalyze the reactions that keep the cell alive and healthy, DNA has the ability to replicate the entire cell, provided sufficient starting materials are present. Thus, DNA is the molecule of life. Much is still to be learned about how and why DNA functions or fails to function in the cell.

Factual Recall

1. What is biochemistry? How does it differ from biology?
2. Name several common carbohydrates and give their formulas.

3. How are starch and cellulose related to glucose?
4. What is glycogen? Where is it to be found in your body?
5. What important role do carbohydrates play in all organisms? Name one additional role that carbohydrates play in plants.
6. How much glucose is present in human blood? Does this remain constant? Why or why not?
7. List several chemical features that sucrose, lactose and maltose have in common.
8. What are lipids? Where are they found in your body?
9. Give the general formula for a soap. How is soap made from fats?
10. What use can the human body make of its stored fat?
11. Describe the digestion of fats in the human.
12. How is cholesterol used by the human body? In what way can this substance be harmful?
13. Where are proteins found in the human body?
14. How are proteins used in the body?
15. How do animals get the proteins they need? How do plants get the protein they need?
16. What are the building blocks of proteins?
17. How are these building blocks linked together in a protein?
18. (*a*) What chemical features do all amino acids have in common? (*b*) How do they differ?
19. The membrane, cytoplasm, and nucleus are important components of all living cells. Describe a living cell in terms of these three components.
20. What is an enzyme? What function do enzymes perform?
21. (*a*) How is glucose oxidized in living cells? (*b*) Why is it oxidized?
22. Why does the living cell need energy?
23. Why must this energy be supplied in only small amounts?
24. How does the body transform food into useful form in the digestion process?
25. What are the roles of RNA and DNA in the cell?

26. How is it chemically possible for a single cell to produce two identical daughter cells in cell division?

Apply Your Knowledge!

1. Study the structural formulas for the carbohydrates given in this chapter and describe one or more structural features which all carbohydrates have in common.
2. What structural features do starch and cellulose have in common? In what ways do their structures differ? How are these differences manifested in the appearance of starch-containing and cellulose-containing portions of plants?
3. Is human fat a single chemical substance? Explain your answer using the information in Table 27-1.
4. Write chemical equations, using structural formulas, for the reactions of fats in the duodenum. What happens to the products of these reactions?
5. Using a biochemistry or organic chemistry text write the structural formulas for the male and female sex hormones, vitamin D, and a bile acid. Compare these formulas with that of cholesterol. What features do all these structures have in common?
6. Write structural formulas for polypeptides having the following arrangements of amino acids:

   --alanine--serine-- aspartic acid--valine--threonine--

   --tyrosine--cysteine--threonine--serine--tyrosine--serine--
7. Can the human body synthesize all the amino acids it needs to make proteins? If not where does it get the amino acids it cannot synthesize?
8. Describe how enzymes acquire and maintain their shapes.
9. How is the shape of an enzyme molecule related to its role in the living cell?
10. Are reactions involving enzymes normally fast or slow? Cite evidence to support your answer.
11. What are coenzymes? What role do they play? How are they related to vitamins?
12. Describe the principal role of ATP and ADP in the cell. Illustrate this role by chemical equations whenever possible.

13. Describe how ATP molecules are formed in the *in vivo* oxidation of glucose.
14. Distinguish between *messenger* and *transfer* RNA.
15. Describe the important structural features of DNA molecules. How are these molecules able to reproduce their kind?
16. Why are the cells in a complex organism so different if they all contain the same genes?

Find Out!

1. In a balanced diet, certain amino acids are required by man. Man also requires vitamins and certain inorganic substances. Find out what vitamins and inorganic substances are required for a balanced diet.
2. Each of the following names represent a step forward in man's fight with disease. By no means is the list exhaustive. Select one or two names and find out what their contribution to medical science was: Paul Ehrlich (1845–1915), G. Domagk (1895–1964), Alexander Fleming (1881–1955).

Suggested Readings

Asimov, I., *World of Carbon.* New York: Collier, 1962. (Paperback)

Benfey, O., *From Vital Force to Structural Formulas.* New York: Houghton-Mifflin, 1964. (Paperback)

Herz, W., *Shape of Carbon Compounds: An Introduction to Organic Chemistry.* New York: W.A. Benjamin, 1963. (Paperback)

NSTA, *Chemistry of Life* (Vistas of Science Series #471–14100) Englewood Cliffs, N.J.: Scholastic Book Service. (Paperback)

Rochow, E., *Organometallic Chemistry.* New York: Reinhold, 1964. (Paperback)

-----, *Bio-Organic Chemistry*-Readings from SCIENTIFIC AMERICAN. San Francisco: Freeman, (Paperback)

-----, *The Cell.* (Life Science Library) Morristown, N.J.: Silver-Burdett, 1964.

UNIT IX

Chapter 28 Radioactivity
Chapter 29 Nuclear Energy

NUCLEAR REACTIONS

CHEMICAL REACTIONS ARE concerned with electrons outside the nucleus. However, protons and neutrons *within* a nucleus may be disturbed, causing a nuclear reaction to occur. Normally, the nucleus of an atom is stable. But this condition does not apply if the nucleus is unusually large (that is if it contains about 90 protons), and it reacts by ejecting particles. This kind of nuclear reaction is called *radioactivity*. One kind of particle emitted in a radioactive charge is called an alpha (α) particle. It is made up of 2 protons and 2 neutrons which consitiute an exceptionally stable combination. Whan a α particle is emitted, the resulting nucleus is the nucleus of an atom of lower atomic mass. In other words, the emission of a an α particle constitutes a nuclear reaction.

Radioactive changes are spontaneous nuclear reactions and they usually proceed at a slow rate. However, some nuclear reactions take place at such a high speed as to be almost instantaneous, and they can be "sparked" by neutrons. If a single neutron enters the nucleus of an atom of U-235, the atom is split into two parts and at the same time a vast amount of energy is released. This kind of nuclear reaction is called *fission*.

In fission reactions the amount of heat released is millions of times greater than the energy released in chemical reactions, because a small fraction of the mass of the nucleus is converted into energy. Einstein concluded from his theory of relativity that mass and energy are equivalent. The sum of the masses of the fission products is a little bit less than the total mass of the starting substances, since some mass has been transformed from the mass form of energy to the heat form of energy.

This extract from the works of Marie Curie announces her important discoveries of radium and polonium.

Pierre Curie (1859–1906) Marie S. Curie (1867–1934)

I will define, in conclusion, the part I have personally taken in the researches upon radio-active bodies.

I have investigated the radio-activity of uranium compounds. I have examined other bodies for the existence of radioactivity, and found the property to be possessed by thorium compounds. I have made clear the atomic character of the radio-activity of the compounds of uranium and thorium.

I have conducted a research upon radio-active substances other than uranium and thorium. To this end I investigated a large number of substances by an accurate electrometric method, and I discovered that certain minerals possess activity which is not to be accounted for by their content of uranium and thorium.

From this I concluded that these minerals must contain a radio-active body different from uranium and thorium, and more strongly radio-active than the latter metals.

In conjunction with M. Curie, and subsequently MM. Curie and Bemont, I was able to extract from pitchblende two strongly radio-active bodies--polonium and radium.

I have been continuously engaged upon the chemical examination and preparation of these substances. I effected the fractionations necessary to the concentration of radium and I succeeded in isolating pure radium chloride. Concurrently with this work, I made several atomic weight determinations with a very small quantity of material, and was finally able to determine the atomic weight of radium with a very fair degree of accuracy. The work has proved that radium is a new chemical element. Thus the new method of investigating new chemical elements, established by M. Curie and myself, based upon radio-activity, is fully justified.

I have investigated the law of absorption of polonium rays, and of the absorbable rays of radium, and have demonstrated that this law of absorption is peculiar and different from the known laws of other radiations.

I have investigated the variation of activity of radium salts, the effect of solution and of heating, and the renewal of activity with time, after solution or after heating.

In conjuction with M. Curie, I have examined different effects produced by the new radio-active substances (electric, photographic, fluorescent, luminous colourations, &c.).

In conjunction with M. Curie, I have established the fact that radium gives rise to rays charged with negative electricity.

CHAPTER 28

RADIOACTIVITY

IN 1896 A FRENCH PHYSICIST named Henri Becquerel (1852–1908) noticed that some photographic plates became fogged even though they were wrapped in black paper and stored in a drawer. The effect was the same as if the plates had been exposed to sunlight. What had caused the fogging? He traced the cause to a piece of *pitchblende*, an ore of uranium, which he had inadvertently placed upon the wrapped photographic plates. He concluded that the ore contained an element which emitted penetrating radiations, and he coined the word *radioactivity* to describe this new phenomenon.

What was the substance in uranium ore that produced these radiations? Marie Curie (1867–1934), one of Becquerel's students, sought the answer to this question as a research project. Indeed, Marie Curie and her husband, Pierre (1859-1906), worked on this problem for four years (from 1898 to 1902). Starting with several tons of uranium ore, they eventually separated two small fractions, both of which exhibited intense radioactivity. From one fraction they isolated a minute amount of a new element which they called

Note . . .
A testament to the Curies' persistence and painstaking care in their research is the fact that reliable estimates indicate that 1000 kg of the uranium ore with which these scientists worked contained about 0.05 mg of polonium. How many tons of uranium ore—assuming a perfect analytical technique—would it take to produce 0.5 g of polonium?

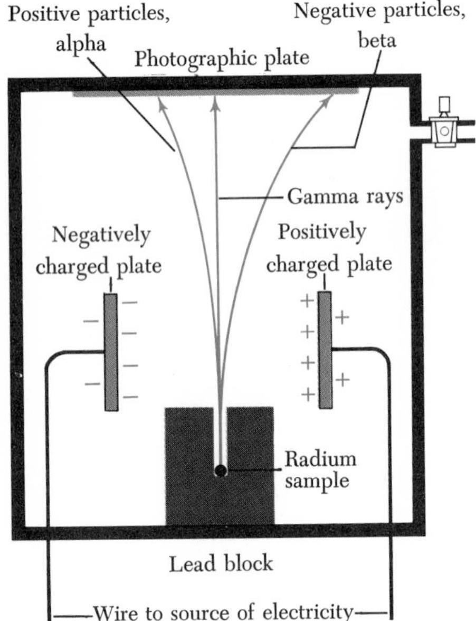

Fig. 28-1 A representation of the apparatus used by Rutherford to study the radiations emitted by radium.

polonium, named after Marie Curie's native country Poland. And from another fraction they isolated a minute quantity of an even more radioactive element. This element they called *radium*. The radioactive rays emitted by radium were found to be at least a million times more powerful than those of uranium.

What is the nature of the radiations emitted by radium? The mystery of the Becquerel radiations was solved by the British scientist Rutherford who proved that the radiations consist of three entirely different kinds of rays.

Radiations Emitted by a Sample of Radium

In an experiment, carried out in a darkened room, Rutherford dropped a minute sample of radium into a hole bored in a block of lead. The radium emitted radiations in all directions but only the upward radiations escaped through the hole. The rest were stopped and absorbed by the lead. The block of lead was placed in a light-tight box and a photographic plate was attached to the top of the box. The box also contained a pair of metal plates arranged as shown in Fig. 28-1. The air was first removed from the box and the two plates were electrically charged, one positively and the other negatively. The photographic plate was exposed for some time and, when developed, it showed three dark spots. One spot was immediately above the hole, another was slightly deflected towards the negatively charged plate, and a third was strongly deflected towards the positively charged plate.

From the position of the spots, Rutherford concluded that three kinds of rays were emitted by the radium, one positively charged, another negatively charged, and the third uncharged. Using the first three letters of the Greek alphabet he called them alpha (α), beta (β), gamma (γ) rays, names that are still used to this day. What is the nature of these rays?

Alpha Rays

Rutherford proved experimentally that an α ray is the nucleus of a helium atom that has lost its two orbital electrons. In other words, it is really not a ray at all but rather a particle that consists of two protons and two neutrons. Thus an α particle is really a helium ion, and it can be written as He^{+2}.

Alpha particles are shot out of the nuclei of atoms with speeds that vary from one-tenth to one-hundredth of the velocity of light, depending upon the particular radioactive element that emits them. They can knock electrons off nearby gas molecules and ionize them; that is, they are powerful ionizing agents. However, they have very little penetrating power and can be stopped even by a sheet of paper. In air they collide with molecules of oxygen and nitrogen and these collisions limit the range of the α particle to about 5 cm. That is why the Rutherford experiment was performed in a vacuum. In traveling through air (or through any gas) α particles pick up electrons they have dislodged from the gas molecules and, in the process, become ordinary atoms of helium,

$$\mathrm{He}^{+2} + 2\mathrm{e}^- \longrightarrow \mathrm{He} \qquad (28\text{-}1)$$

Beta Rays

Beta rays are particles which have the same e/m value as electrons. Indeed they are electrons, and they travel much faster than α particles. Because of their higher speed and smaller charge, they are about 100 times more penetrating than α particles. However, they are much lighter than α particles, so that in spite of their high speed they can be stopped by a thin sheet of metal.

Like α particles, they collide with gas molecules and ionize them. But since their penetrating power is about 100 times greater than α particles, their ionizing power is about 100 times less. Can you explain why?

Since β particles are associated with radioactive changes, they must originate in the nuclei of atoms, not in the orbital electrons. But how is this possible since a nucleus contains only protons and neutrons? It is believed that this kind of emission is due to the spontaneous splitting of a neutron into a proton and an electron, or

$$\text{neutron} \longrightarrow \text{proton} + \beta \text{ particle} \qquad (28\text{-}2)$$

The liberated proton remains in the nucleus but the electron is ejected from the nucleus at high speed.

Gamma Rays

Gamma rays are not deflected by either magnetic or electrostatic fields. Therefore, unlike α and β particles, they are not electrically charged. Indeed, γ rays, like visible light and X rays, are a form of electromagnetic energy, and they are best described in terms of wavelength and frequency. Actually, γ rays have shorter wavelengths than X rays and are therefore more penetrating. Gamma rays can penetrate several inches of lead, a foot of steel, and several feet of concrete. If they penetrate human tissue, they may cause serious physiological damage. Thus, in working with radioactive material, it is essential to shield the body against these rays. This is one reason the radium sample was, except for the opening, surrounded by lead in the Rutherford experiment.

Where do γ rays come from? How are they propagated? As we shall read later, an α or β particle is emitted from a nucleus because the nucleus is in an excited or highly energetic state. Thus, in nuclear reactions, as in chemical reactions, the products are less energetic and more stable than the original nuclear particle. However, even after an α or β particle has been ejected, the resulting nucleus is still in an excited state although it may lack enough energy to eject another particle. In such a case, it emits the excess energy as a quantum of γ energy and the nucleus then settles down to a normal state. In short, γ radiation usually accompanies the ejection of an α or β particle from the nucleus of a radioactive atom.

Radioactive Disintegration

If an atom of radium (Ra) emits an α particle it changes into another element, radon (Rn)

$$\mathrm{Ra} \longrightarrow \mathrm{Rn} + \alpha \qquad (28\text{-}3)$$

This process is called radioactive disintegration or decay. The atomic number (the number of protons) of radium is 88 and the atomic number of an α particle is 2. Therefore, by difference, the atomic number of radon is 86. This change can be written as

$$_{88}\mathrm{Ra} \longrightarrow {}_{2}\mathrm{He} + {}_{86}\mathrm{Rn} \qquad (28\text{-}4)$$

where *atomic numbers* are written as *subscripts* on the *left side* of the *symbols*.

The *mass number* (the *sum of the protons and neutrons*) of radium is 226 (88 + 138) and the mass number of an α particle is 4 (2 + 2).

Therefore the mass number of radon is 222 (86 + 136). This change can be written as

$$^{226}\text{Ra} \longrightarrow {}^{4}\text{He} + {}^{222}\text{Rn} \qquad (28\text{-}5)$$

where *mass numbers* are written as *superscripts* on the left side of the *symbols*. The changes in both atomic numbers and mass numbers of this reaction are combined in a nuclear equation and written

$$^{226}_{88}\text{Ra} \longrightarrow {}^{4}_{2}\text{He} + {}^{222}_{86}\text{Rn} \qquad (28\text{-}6)$$

Notice that in a nuclear equation both the total number of protons (the atomic number) and the total number of neutrons are conserved. In contrast to a chemical equation, the total number of atoms is not conserved.

Let us now consider a nuclear change that involves the emission of a β particle. The element thorium (Th) is present in uranium ore. It emits a β particle to form the element protactinium (Pa). What is the nuclear equation for this reaction?

The nucleus of a thorium atom contains 234 nucleons (90 protons plus 144 neutrons). Therefore its symbol is $^{234}_{90}\text{Th}$. In this nuclear reaction a neutron changes to a proton and a β particle is ejected. Hence the atomic number of protactinium is one greater than that of thorium but the mass number of thorium remains the same. The nuclear equation for this radioactive change is

$$^{234}_{90}\text{Th} \longrightarrow {}^{234}_{91}\text{Pa} + {}^{0}_{-1}\text{e} \qquad (28\text{-}7)$$

The symbol for an electron ($^{0}_{-1}\text{e}$) shows that its mass number is 0 and that its charge is -1. Notice that, by this device, atomic numbers, as well as the number of nucleons, are conserved.

In summary, the emission of both α and β particles results in the formation of new elements. If an α particle is emitted, the atomic number is decreased by two; if a β particle is emitted, the atomic number is increased by one.

The Half-life of a Radioactive Element

As the disintegration of a lump of radium proceeds, fewer and fewer atoms of radium remain in the original piece and, as a result, the rate of disintegration steadily decreases. Experiments prove that the rate of disintegration is proportional to the number of atoms of the radioactive element present at that particular moment. Therefore, *the fraction of atoms which disintegrate per second remains constant.*

Suppose, for example, that 1.00 g of radioactive material disintegrates to 0.5 g in 1 hour. Clearly, after 1 hour, 0.5 g of radioactive material would remain. During the next hour the same fraction of atoms present will disintegrate; that is, 0.5×0.5 g or 0.25 g will disintegrate. Thus, after 2 hours 0.25 g (1.0 g − 0.75 g) of the original amount will remain intact. During the third hour 0.5×0.25 g or 0.125 g will disintegrate and 0.125 g will remain intact. During the fourth hour 0.5×0.125 g or 0.0625 g will disintegrate and 0.0625 g will remain intact. The rate of disintegration or decay is shown graphically in Fig. 28-2. This graph is typical of the decay curves of all radioactive elements. It shows that the rate of decay becomes slower and slower as time passes. Moreover, the curve approaches the time ordinate but never quite touches it. Therefore the full life span of all radioactive atoms is infinity. Hence the term *life span* would not differentiate between different elements and so is not meaningful. However, the term *half-life* is meaningful. A *half-life is the time required for one-half of the radioactive atoms to disintegrate.* The graph in Fig. 28-2 includes six half-lives. From the slope of the curve it is apparent that the rate of disintegration is most rapid during the first half-life.

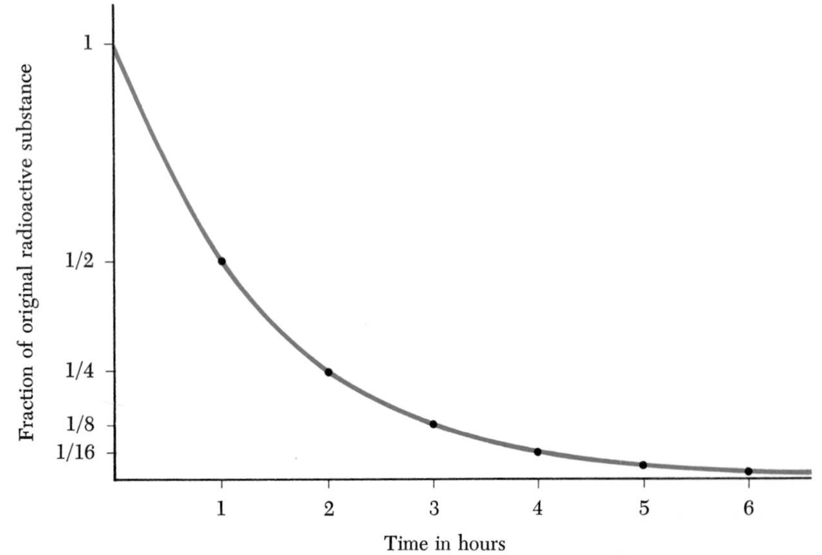

Fig. 28-2 Rate of decay of a radioactive substance.

The half-lives of radioactive elements vary a great deal. For example, the half-life of radium is 1620 years, for radon it is only 3.82 days. Uranium (U-238) has one of the longest half-lives (4.5 billion years), and one of the isotopes of polonium has one of the shortest (1.5×10^{-4} second).

One final point concerning half-lives. As stated earlier, the shorter the half-life of an element, the more intense is its radioactivity. The Curies, you recall, were surprised when they discovered that pitchblende, an ore of uranium, was more radioactive than uranium itself. The reason is now apparent. Pitchblende contains radium and polonium, both of whose half-lives are much shorter than the half-life of uranium.

The Uranium Disintegration Series ($^{238}_{92}U \longrightarrow {}^{206}_{82}Pb$)

Starting with uranium-238, a series of nuclear reactions occurs until, finally, a stable nucleus is formed and then all radioactivity stops. This last stable element is Pb-206. (Lead-206 is one of the rarer isotopes of lead, the most common being Pb-207.)

Uranium-238 ($^{238}_{92}U$) emits an α particle and forms the element of mass number 234 and atomic number 90. This element is called thorium. The half-life of $^{238}_{92}U$ is 4.49×10^9 years. Thorium-234 emits a β particle and forms an isotope of a new element called protactinium (Pa). The atomic number of Pa is 91 and its mass number is the same as thorium's. The half-life of thorium-234 is 24.5 days. Protactinium-234 ($^{234}_{91}Pa$) is also a β emitter and forms an element of atomic number 92. This new element has the same atomic number as that of the starting substance U-238. It is therefore an isotope of uranium and its symbol is $^{234}_{92}U$. The half-life of Pa-234 is 1.14 minutes.

Uranium-234 emits an α particle (its half-life is 2.67×10^5 years) to form an element of atomic number 90. This is clearly an isotope of thorium and its symbol is $^{230}_{90}Th$. Thorium-230 emits an α particle (its half-life is 8.3×10^4 years) to form radium, $^{226}_{88}Ra$. Radium-226 (half-life 1620 years) also emits an α particle and forms radon, $^{222}_{86}Rn$. Radon-222 (half-life 3.82 days) is also an α emitter and it changes to polonium, $^{218}_{84}Po$. The disintegration of uranium-238 to polonium-218 is shown as a graph in Fig. 28-3, where mass

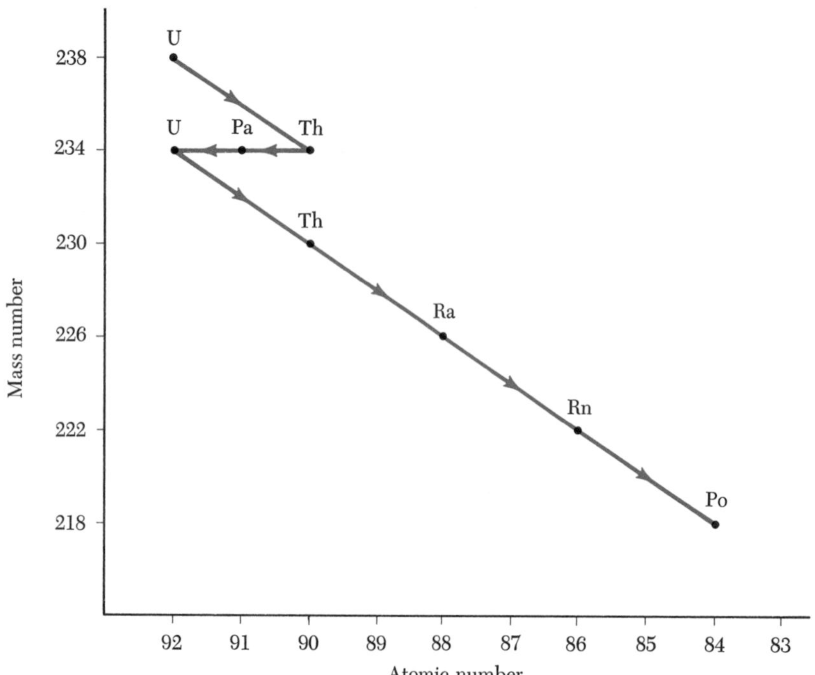

Fig. 28-3 The disintegration of U-238 to Po-218.

numbers are plotted against atomic numbers. However, as stated earlier, radioactivity does not stop at polonium. There are in all 14 nuclear eruptions and these, together with the half-lives, are shown in Fig. 28-4.

Observe that in this series there are two isotopes of uranium, two isotopes of thorium, three of polonium, two of bismuth, and three of lead. This is not the only radioactive disintegration series. There are two others: in one, $^{235}_{92}U$ disintegrates into $^{207}_{82}Pb$, and in the other $^{232}_{90}Th$ disintegrates into $^{208}_{82}Pb$.

Recall that radium has a half-life of 1620 years, but some radium atoms disintegrate instantly. The lives of *individual* atoms cannot be predicted. The statistical average is 1620 years but some atoms have half-lives much shorter than 1620 years and others much longer. Thus, some atoms of radium begin to change to atoms of radon as soon as they are formed.

Finally, you recall that in Rutherford's experiment α and β particles were emitted as well as γ rays. Why are α and β particles emitted when radium itself emits only α particles?

Radon is an α emitter but its half-life is only 3.82 days. The next element polonium-218 is also an α emitter with a half-life of only

Fig. 28-4 The disintegration of U-238 to Pb-206; y=year; d=day; m=minute; s=second.

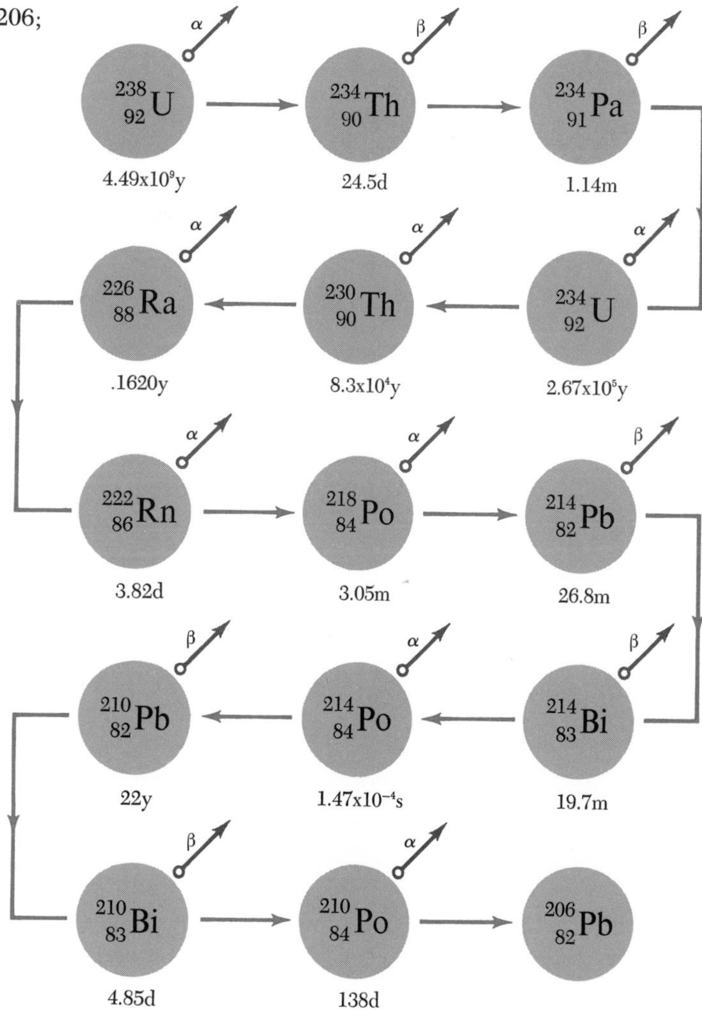

3.05 minutes. Next, there are two short-lived β emitters, lead-214 and lead-210. In other words, the β particles in Rutherford's experiment are due to the decay of β emitters which, in turn, result from the decay of radon and polonium-218.

Transmutations of Nonradioactive Elements

The next question raised by scientists was: Could the nuclei of stable or nonradioactive atoms also be split? Rutherford's approach to this question was both simple and ingenious. The only reasonable way to attempt to split a stable nucleus was by bombardment, and the α particles emitted by radium or polonium could be used for this purpose. However, the nuclei of all atoms

Research . . .
Trace the concept of transmutation from the alchemists to Rutherford's experiment with radium and nitrogen.

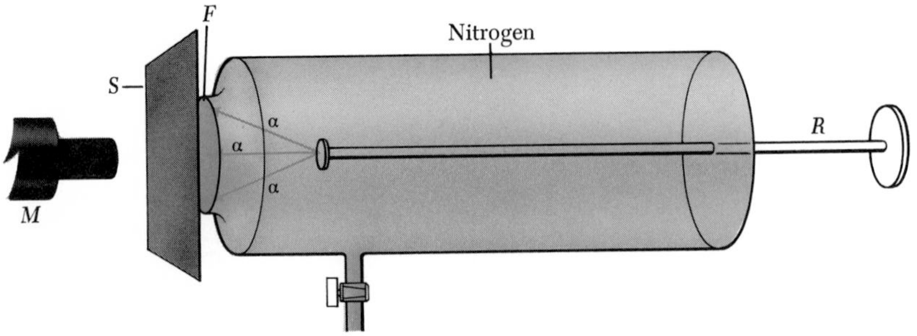

Fig. 28-5 Rutherford's apparatus used to observe collisions between alpha particles and atoms of nitrogen.

are positively charged and so are α particles. Thus, before an α particle could penetrate a nucleus it would have to overcome the electrostatic force of repulsion between the nucleus and itself. But, by using light elements rather than heavy ones, the force of repulsion would be reduced. Indeed, Rutherford selected nitrogen as the element to be bombarded.

Fig. 28-6 Tracks of α particles seen in a cloud chamber in the transmutation of nitrogen to oxygen.

A diagram of Rutherford's apparatus is shown in Fig. 28-5. He attached a minute amount of polonium to the end of a rod which was then inserted in a box. A thin sheet of silver foil (F) covered the far end of the box. A screen (S) coated with zinc sulfide was placed just beyond the silver foil. The air was then removed from the box and nitrogen gas admitted. When the screen was examined through a microscope (M), scintillations were seen on the screen even though the distance from polonium to screen was increased to 30 or even 40 cm. What caused the scintillations?

At first sight it looked as though the scintillations were caused by the bombardment of the screen by α particles emitted by the polonium. But this could not be the explanation, since α particles have a range of only about 7 cm in a gas such as nitrogen or air. Rutherford examined the particles and from their e/m value, he concluded they were protons. The only possible source of these protons was nitrogen atoms. Alpha particles must have knocked protons out of the nuclei of nitrogen atoms. Let us examine this reaction more closely.

Since the number of protons in the reactants equals the number in the products, we can say the atomic number of nitrogen (7) plus the atomic number of an α particle (2) equals the atomic number of a proton (1) plus the atomic number of substance formed (x). Hence, $7 + 2 = 1 + x$, or $x = 8$. The element whose atomic number is 8 is oxygen. In other words, Rutherford had transmuted nitrogen to oxygen. Oxygen atoms were identified in the mixture. This was the first case of artificial transmutation; it occurred in 1919.

The mass numbers of nitrogen and an α particle are 14 and 4; the mass number of a proton is 1. Therefore, by difference, the mass number of oxygen is 17. This is one of the rare isotopes of oxygen, the mass number of the common isotope being 16. Thus, the nuclear equation for this transmutation reaction is

$$^{14}_{7}N + ^{4}_{2}He \longrightarrow ^{17}_{8}O + ^{1}_{1}H \quad (28\text{-}8)$$

Notice that the symbol for a proton in a nuclear equation is $^{1}_{1}H$, the same as the symbol for a hydrogen ion.

Research . . .
How has the definition of the word *element* changed since the discovery of radium and polonium? The Curies' discovery brought about one change, and Rutherford's experiment with nitrogen brought about further change.

Bombardment of Stable Nuclei with High-speed Particles

Rutherford found that nearly all light elements emitted protons when bombarded with α particles. Indeed, this was the first direct evidence that protons are present in the nuclei of all atoms. And, you may recall, it was Rutherford who gave the name *proton* to these positively charged particles.

When α particles were used to bombard heavy elements (elements heavier than potassium), they failed to penetrate the nuclei, but instead they were deflected or scattered as shown in Fig. 28-7. Why was this? The larger the atomic number of an element, the greater is the number of protons in the nucleus and therefore the greater is the force of repulsion between an α particle and the nucleus. So, to split a heavy nucleus a bombarding particle had to be made more penetrating. One way to do this was to use bombarding particles with a smaller positive charge than α particles, for example hydrogen ions, H^+ (protons) or deuterium ions, D^+ (deuterons, $^{2}_{1}H$). A proton or a deuteron is repelled by a nucleus with only half the force with which it repels an α particle. Why is this? Moreover, the bombarding effect would be further increased by increasing the speed of the particles. Both protons and deuterons can be accelerated to almost the speed of light in a device called a cyclotron, shown in Fig. 28-8. Lithium was one of the first elements to be bombarded by deuterons in a cyclotron. Lithium is a light element (its atomic number is 3) and so the forces of repulsion between deuterons and lithium nuclei are relatively small

Note . . .
To accelerate elements as heavy as uranium, much larger "atom smashers" are being built by the United States and by Russia. Machines such as the heavy ion linear accelerator (HILAC) at the University of California at Berkeley will permit the study of nuclear theories concerning the synthesis of superheavy elements. Undoubtedly, such giant machines will shed new light on the nature of matter and energy.

Fig. 28-7 Alpha particles are deflected by nuclei of heavy elements like zinc.

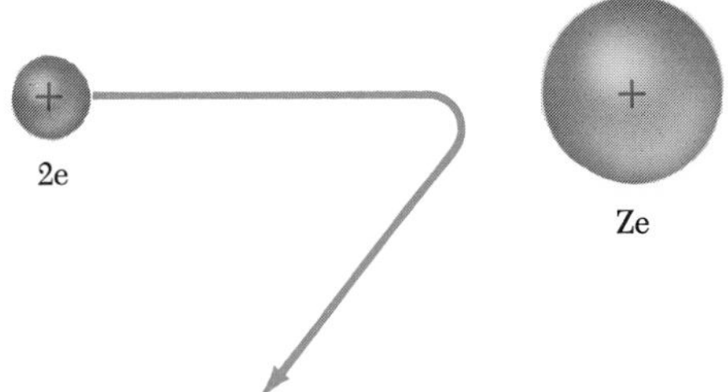

Fig. 28-8 A cyclotron at the University of California.

and, as expected, a nuclear reaction took place. Actually, the element beryllium ($^{8}_{4}Be$) was formed and a beam of neutrons was emitted. The equation for this nuclear reaction is

$$^{7}_{3}Li + ^{2}_{1}H \longrightarrow ^{8}_{4}Be + ^{1}_{0}n \tag{28-9}$$

Notice that the symbol for a neutron, ($^{1}_{0}n$) shows that its mass number is 1 and its atomic number is 0.

Neutrons released in this way are excellent particles for bombarding nuclei. Actually, they are more penetrating than either protons or deuterons. Let us see why.

Neutrons

In practice, it is very difficult to hit the nuclei of atoms with positively charged particles such as protons, or deuterons, or even α particles. There are two reasons for this. First, every nucleus is surrounded by orbital electrons which tend to attract the charged particles and deflect them from the nucleus. But even if this electron screen is penetrated, there remains an even more formidable barrier, namely the repulsive force of the positively charged nucleus. Neutrons, on the other hand, are not electrically charged and, in consequence, they are neither attracted by orbital electrons nor repelled by protons in the nucleus, as illustrated in Fig. 28-10. As a result, neutrons are ideal projectiles for bombarding nuclei. Indeed, it was the ease with which they penetrate nuclei that led to their discovery.

In 1930, after Rutherford's transmutation of nitrogen to oxygen,

Fig. 28-9 A view near the input end of the heavy ion linear accelerator at the University of California.

Walther Bothe (1891-1957), a German scientist, found that radiations of great penetrating power were emitted when some powdered beryllium was mixed with a minute quantity of a radium salt. What were these radiations? A British scientist named James Chadwick (1891-) proved that they were uncharged particles with a mass slightly greater than the mass of protons. And, as you know, he called them *neutrons*.

The nuclear equation for the Bothe reaction is

$$^{9}_{4}\text{Be} + ^{4}_{2}\text{He} \longrightarrow ^{13}_{6}\text{C} \longrightarrow ^{12}_{6}\text{C} + ^{1}_{0}\text{n} \qquad (28\text{-}10)$$

That is, if an α particle penetrates the nucleus of a beryllium atom, a highly unstable isotope of carbon ($^{13}_{6}$C) is formed. To achieve stability, carbon-13 emits a neutron, thereby forming the stable isotope $^{12}_{6}$C. The Bothe reaction with its neutron source led to an important type of nuclear reaction known as *neutron capture*.

Fig. 28-10 Protons are deflected and may be completely stopped by the electronic force of attraction. Neutrons penetrate atoms without hindrance unless they collide directly with a nucleus.

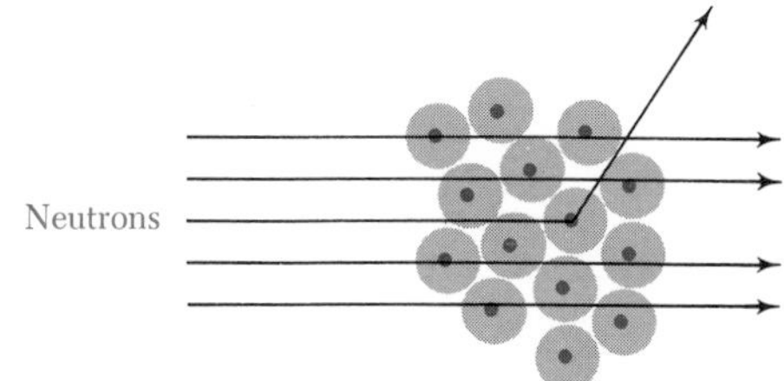

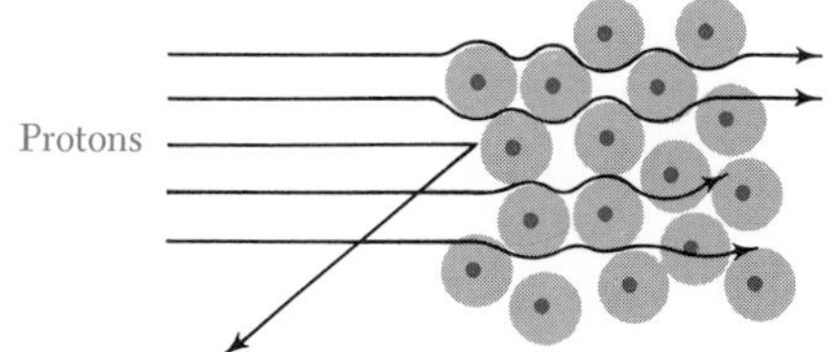

Artificial Radioactivity

In neutron capture a nucleus absorbs a neutron to form an isotope of higher mass number. Isotopes formed in this way are usually radioactive so that neutron capture opened up an important new field of *artificial radioactivity*. Suppose for example that common salt is bombarded with deuterons in the presence of a lithium salt. As stated earlier, deuterons react with lithium nuclei releasing neutrons. The released neutrons are then available to react with nuclei of sodium atoms.

If a neutron enters the nucleus of an atom of Na-23, the isotope Na-24 is formed,

$$^{23}_{11}\text{Na} + ^{1}_{0}\text{n} \longrightarrow ^{24}_{11}\text{Na} \tag{28-11}$$

However, $^{24}_{11}$Na is unstable (its half-life is only 15 hours) and it emits a β particle, thereby being transmuted into magnesium-24 which is stable. Or, in symbols

$$^{24}_{11}\text{Na} \longrightarrow ^{24}_{12}\text{Mg} + ^{0}_{-1}\text{e} \tag{28-12}$$

Combining the two nuclear reactions, the transformation of Na-23 to Mg-24 can be shown as

$$^{23}_{11}\text{Na} + ^{1}_{0}\text{n} \longrightarrow \underset{\text{radioactive}}{^{24}_{11}\text{Na}} \longrightarrow ^{24}_{12}\text{Mg} + ^{0}_{-1}\text{e} \tag{28-13}$$

Radioisotopes

Many of the lighter elements were transformed into artificial radioactive isotopes (usually called radioisotopes) in the cyclotron. However, as explained in the next chapter, an atomic reactor is also an excellent source of neutrons and today most of the useful radioisotopes are made in this way.

Artificial radioisotopes are used on a large scale in such fields as medicine, agriculture, and industry. All are β emitters and, in general, their half-lives are very short. Indeed, many of them lose a high proportion of their activity within a few hours. Moreover, they are safer to handle than radium and other naturally occurring radioactive substances. Some of the artificial isotopes in common use are listed in Table 28-1.

Table 28-1 Half-lives of common radioisotopes

Radioisotope	Half-life
carbon-14	5700 years
calcium-45	160 days
cobalt-60	5.2 years
iodine-131	8.1 days
iron-59	45 days
phosphorus-32	14.5 days
sodium-24	15 hours
sulfur-35	87 days

Nuclear emanations can easily be detected by a device called a Geiger-Mueller (G-M) counter. As shown in Fig. 28-11, a G-M counter consists of a sealed glass tube that contains a central wire as the anode and a metal cylinder surrounding the wire as the cathode. The tube contains argon gas. If β particles enter the tube, they ionize by bombardment a large number of argon atoms and a corresponding number of electrons is released.

Or,

$$n\text{Ar} \longrightarrow n\text{Ar}^{+} + ne^{-} \tag{28-14}$$

Argon ions are attracted to the cathode and electrons to the anode. There is a short burst of current and the tube is discharged. Each discharge is amplified so that it gives an electrical signal, either causing a loudspeaker to click or producing a flashing light in a small light bulb.

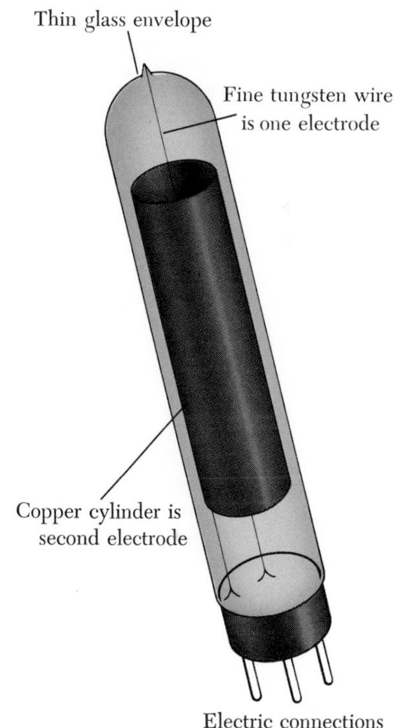

Fig. 28-11 A Geiger-Mueller counter tube. What gas is in the tube? Why is the gas ionized?

Radioisotopes in Medicine

Radioisotopes are used to treat a variety of diseases. Goiter, an abnormality of the thyroid gland, can be controlled by iodine-131 which emits beta particles

$$^{131}_{53}I \longrightarrow {}^{131}_{54}Xe + {}^{0}_{-1}e \qquad (28\text{-}15)$$

The patient swallows I-131 as sodium iodide and the radioiodide ion emitting β particles is carried in the blood stream to the thyroid gland. The effect of the radioiodine is to reduce the amount of thyroxin formed.

Then again, if ordinary cobalt (Co-59) is irradiated by neutrons in a reactor, it is changed to cobalt-60

$$^{59}_{27}Co + {}^{1}_{0}n \longrightarrow {}^{60}_{27}Co \qquad (28\text{-}16)$$

Cobalt-60 is highly radioactive, emitting both β particles and γ-rays

$$^{60}_{27}Co \longrightarrow {}^{60}_{28}Ni + {}^{0}_{-1}e + \gamma \qquad (28\text{-}17)$$

The γ rays from radiocobalt are widely used in the treatment of cancerous tissue.

Radioisotopes are also used as tracer elements. For example, sodium-24, which is a β emitter, is used to locate obstructions in blood vessels. In cases of normal circulation, a minute quantity of Na-24 as a chloride injected in the forearm would be detected by a G-M counter held near the foot in only a few seconds. But an obstruction in a blood vessel would prolong the time interval of the blood traveling from arm to foot. By moving the counter in the direction of the forearm, the position of the obstruction could be located.

Radioisotopes in Industry

Radioisotopes are also used for many purposes in chemical industry. For example, when a metal is cast in a mold, internal cracks may develop in the casting as it cools. Cracks impair the strength of a casting and it is important to detect them before the casting is put into service. Gamma rays from radioisotopes pass

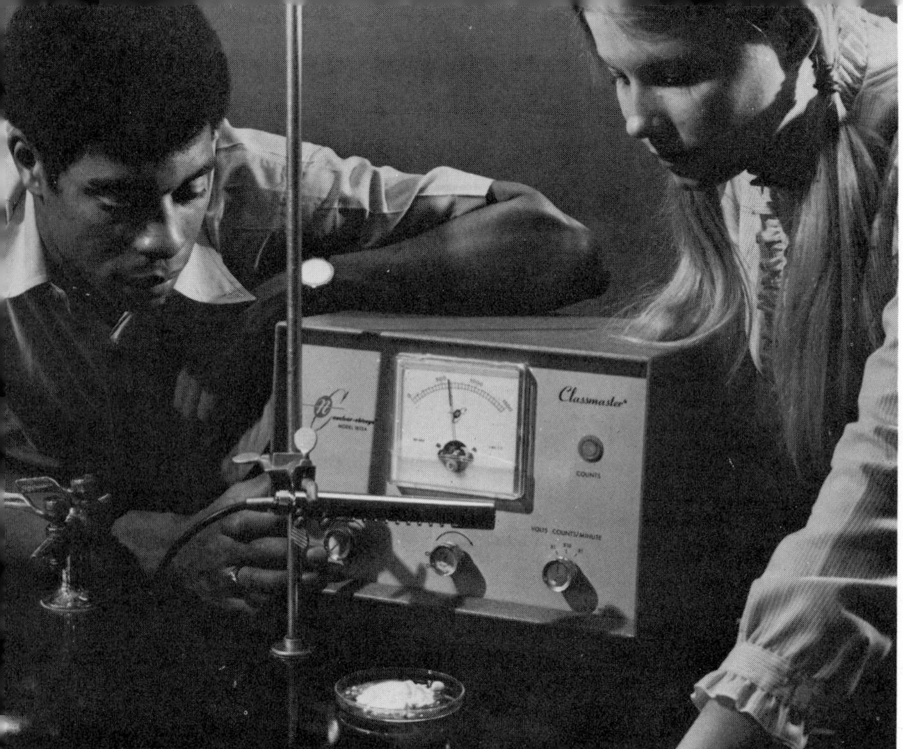

Fig. 28-12 This device indicates both visually and aurally the detection of nuclear particles emitted from a radioactive sample. Though the sample the students are using is safe, prolonged contact is to be avoided.

right through castings and can be used to photograph the internal structure of the casting. A crack in a casting would be seen as a flaw in the developed photographic plate. In such a case the casting would then have to be remelted and recast.

Note . . .
While Russian scientists claim the synthesis of element 104, scientists at the University of California (Berkeley) approached the synthesis by a different technique and, consequently, challenged the authenticity of the Russian findings. This conflict is dramatized by the fact that, while the Russians propose the name *kurchatovium* for element 104 and the scientists at Berkeley propose the name *rutherfordium*, neither name has been accepted by the International Union for Pure and Applied Chemistry. Naming new elements is traditionally the perogative of the discoverer. We may expect such conflicts to reoccur in the fast-changing field of nuclear studies.

Transuranium Elements

Uranium (atomic number 92) is the heaviest of the natural elements, and until 1940 it was the last element in the periodic table. In that year it occurred to some scientists that elements of atomic number higher than 92 might be created by neutron capture. Indeed, their ideas were well founded.

When natural uranium-238 is bombarded with neutrons, a new isotope of uranium ($^{239}_{92}U$) is formed,

$$^{238}_{92}U + ^{1}_{0}n \longrightarrow ^{239}_{92}U \qquad (28\text{-}18)$$

Uranium-239 is highly radioactive (its half-life is only 23 minutes) and it emits a β particle to form an element of atomic number 93. This new element is called neptunium (Np),

$$^{239}_{92}U \longrightarrow ^{239}_{93}Np + ^{0}_{-1}e \qquad (28\text{-}19)$$

Neptunium-239 is also radioactive (its half-life is 2.3 days) and it too emits a β particle, forming an element of atomic number 94 called plutonium (Pu),

$$^{239}_{93}Np \longrightarrow ^{239}_{94}Pu + ^{0}_{-1}e \qquad (28\text{-}20)$$

Plutonium-239 unlike neptunium-239, is an emitter of α particles. Unlike neptunium, this isotope of plutonium has a long half-life of 24,000 years. Therefore plutonium-239 disintegrates very slowly and has little radioactivity. As we shall read in the next chapter, plutonium is an important source of nuclear energy.

The elements beyond uranium are called *transuranium* elements. In addition to neptunium and plutonium, 11 others have been synthesized. They are americium (Am, 95), curium (Cm, 96), berkelium (Bk, 97), californium (Cf, 98), einsteinium (En, 99), fermium (Fm, 100), mendelevium (Md, 101), nobelium (No, 102), lawrencium (Lr, 103), element 104, and element 105.

All the transuranium elements beyond plutonium have very short half-lives. They have been synthesized by bombarding either uranium-238 or even heavier nuclei with various positive ions. For example, if uranium-238 is bombarded with carbon ions (with a charge of + 4) californium is formed, and if U-238 is bombarded with oxygen ions (with a charge of + 6), fermium is formed. The equations for these two nuclear reactions are

$$^{238}_{92}U + ^{12}_{6}C \longrightarrow ^{246}_{98}Cf + 4^{1}_{0}n \qquad (28\text{-}21)$$

$$^{238}_{92}U + ^{16}_{8}O \longrightarrow ^{250}_{100}Fm + 4^{1}_{0}n \qquad (28\text{-}22)$$

Two isotopes of the as-yet unnamed element 104 have been made by the reactions:

$$^{249}_{98}Cf + ^{12}_{6}C \longrightarrow ^{257}_{104}? + 4^{1}_{0}n \qquad (28\text{-}23)$$

$$^{249}_{98}Cf + ^{13}_{6}C \longrightarrow ^{259}_{104}? + 3\,^{1}_{0}n \qquad (28\text{-}24)$$

These isotopes have half-lives of about 4 seconds. A third isotope with a half-life of about 1 minute has been made by the process

$$^{248}_{96}Am + ^{18}_{8}O \longrightarrow ^{261}_{104}? + 5^{1}_{0}n \qquad (28\text{-}25)$$

Theoretical considerations led to the prediction that element 114, if synthesized, might have a half-life as long as a year or more. However, the synthesis would require bombardment with heavier atoms than have been used in the past. For example,

$$^{244}_{94}Pu + ^{48}_{20}Ca \longrightarrow ^{288}_{114}? + 4^{1}_{0}n \qquad (28\text{-}26)$$

$$^{238}_{92}U + ^{136}_{54}Xe \longrightarrow ^{298}_{114}? + ^{72}_{32}Ge + 4^{1}_{0}n \qquad (28\text{-}27)$$

Note . . .
The synthesis of element 105 by scientists at the University of California (Berkeley) was publicly announced on April 28, 1970. It is to be placed in the family of vanadium, niobium, and tantalum. Synthesized by bombarding californium-249 with high-energy nitrogen-15 ions, the new element has a half-life of 1.6 seconds. The name hahnium, after the German physicist Otto Hahn, has been proposed.

have been suggested as possibilities and work in this direction is proceeding.

Summary

The heavy elements in the seventh row of the periodic table are unstable. They tend to achieve stability by spontaneously releasing α or β particles and radiant energy from the nuclei of the atoms. These radiations, which accompany nuclear changes, constitute the phenomenon of *radioactivity*.

An α particle consists of two protons and two neutrons—it is essentially the nucleus of a helium atom. A β particle is an electron.

Radioactivity is a random but statistically predictable process. One-half of any sample of the same radioactive isotope always disintegrates in the same period of time. This constant time period is called the *half-life* for that particular radioactive isotope.

Radioactive isotopes are formed when most light elements (elements with an atomic number less than 19) are bombarded with protons or deuterons in a cyclotron. Neutrons are more penetrating particles than protons or deuterons, and radioactive isotopes of both light and heavy elements are formed by the neutron bombardment of nuclei in a reactor.

Thirteen transuranium elements have been synthesized. All transuranium elements are radioactive but by far the most stable of them (that is, the one with the longest half-life) is plutonium.

Factual Recall

1. Discuss the contributions of (*a*) Becquerel and (*b*) the Curies in the field of radioactivity.
2. Describe Rutherford's experiment by which he discovered the three kinds of rays emitted by radium.
3. What is the source of β particles in radioactive emission?
4. What are γ rays and how are they produced?
5. (*a*) What is meant by the term *half-life*?
   (*b*) Draw a graph to show the change of radioactivity of polonium-210 through a period of two years. (The half-life of polonium-210 is 138 days.)

6. (*a*) Describe Rutherford's experiment by which he transmuted nitrogen to oxygen.
   (*b*) Write the nuclear equation for the Rutherford transmutation reaction.
7. Alpha particles from a radioactive source are able to penetrate the nuclei of light elements but not the nuclei of heavy elements. Explain why.
8. What is the advantage of bombarding nuclei with neutrons rather than protons?
9. What is meant by neutron capture? Give an example.
10. Five nuclear reactions occur as $^{238}_{92}U$ disintegrates to $^{226}_{88}Ra$.
    (*a*) What is the total change in atomic mass?
    (*b*) What is the total change in atomic number?
    (*c*) What number of each kind of particle must be emitted to account for these changes?
11. What are artificial radioisotopes, and what are they used for?
12. What is a G-M counter, and how does it operate?
13. (*a*) What are transuranium elements?
    (*b*) Name six transuranium elements.

Apply Your Knowledge!

1. Polonium (atomic number 84, atomic mass 218) emits an α particle to form an isotope of lead. What are the atomic number and the atomic mass of this isotope of lead? Give a reason for each selection.
2. Bismuth (atomic number 83, atomic mass 210) emits a β particle to form an isotope of polonium. What are the atomic number and the atomic mass of this isotope of polonium? Give a reason for each of your selections.
3. (*a*) Write nuclear equations for the nuclear reactions in Questions 1 and 2.
   (*b*) In each of the above reactions are (*i*) protons, (*ii*) neutrons, (*iii*) nucleons, (*iv*) atomic numbers conserved?
   (*c*) Give a reason for your answer in (*b*) if it happens to be "No."
4. $^{238}_{92}U$ emits an alpha particle to form radioactive atom A_1; A_1 emits a β particle to form A_2; A_2 emits a β particle to form

atom A_3; A_3 emits an α particle to form atom A_4. Draw a graph, plotting mass numbers against atomic numbers for the atoms $^{238}_{92}U$, A_1, A_2, A_3, A_4.

5. Write the nuclear equations to show (*a*) how neptunium is formed from $^{238}_{92}U$, and (*b*) how plutonium is formed from neptunium.
6. Add the missing item to balance the following nuclear equations:

(*a*) $^{238}_{92}U \longrightarrow {}^{234}_{90}Th + \_\_\_$
(*b*) $^{14}_{7}N + {}^{4}_{2}He \longrightarrow {}^{17}_{8}O + \_\_\_$
(*c*) $^{24}_{11}Na \longrightarrow \_\_\_ + {}^{0}_{-1}e$
(*d*) $^{23}_{11}Na + \_\_\_ \longrightarrow {}^{24}_{12}Mg + {}^{1}_{1}H + {}^{0}_{-1}e$
(*e*) $^{9}_{4}Be + {}^{4}_{2}He \longrightarrow {}^{12}_{6}C + \_\_\_$

Find Out!

1. Discover by research one of the ways by which the stability of nonradioactive nuclei is measured.
2. Radiocarbon dating is a process by which the age of archeological fragments is measured. It is an extremely accurate process. Find out how it works.

CHAPTER 29

NUCLEAR ENERGY

AS STATED IN CHAPTER 28, transuranium elements are formed if uranium is bombarded with neutrons. While working with uranium and the products formed by bombardment, Otto Hahn (1879–1967), a German chemist, made an unexpected but important discovery. He found a trace of the element barium among the reaction products, and in the same reaction a vast amount of heat energy was released—far more than in any other known chemical reaction. Hahn published these facts in 1939. Where did the barium come from? And, what was the source of the abnormal amount of heat energy?

The atomic numbers of uranium and barium are 92 and 56 respectively. So it looked as though a nucleus of uranium had been split into two parts. If the atomic number of one part is 56 then, by difference, the atomic number of the other part is 36. However, 36 is the atomic number of the element kypton and a spectroscopic examination proved that krypton was one of the products of the nuclear reaction. Thus, according to Hahn the nuclear reaction was

$$\text{uranium} \longrightarrow \text{barium} + \text{krypton} + \text{much energy}$$

Note . . .
While uranium is the rarest metal of the chromium group, its abundance in the earth's crust is about the same as that of lead. In addition to being found in *pitchblende*, U_3O_8, uranium is also found in its second most common ore, *carnotite*, $K_2U_2V_2 \cdot 3H_2O$.

This was an entirely new kind of reaction, a reaction in which a heavy nucleus is split into two approximately equal parts. It was called a *fission* reaction.

Fission of U-235

It was soon discovered that the fission reaction was due to the splitting of atoms of U-235, not atoms of U-238. Ordinary uranium is essentially a mixture of U-235 and U-238. Uranium-235 is the rare isotope and constitutes only 0.7% of the mixture.

One way U-235 can split is shown by the equation,

$$^{235}_{92}\mathrm{U} + ^{1}_{0}\mathrm{n} \longrightarrow ^{140}_{56}\mathrm{Ba} + ^{93}_{36}\mathrm{Kr} + 3^{1}_{0}\mathrm{n} + \text{heat energy} \qquad (29\text{-}1)$$

Notice that in this reaction one neutron is used up and three neutrons are released. This increase in the number of neutrons has important implications as we shall read later. Then again, the elements created in reaction (29-1) are unstable isotopes of barium and krypton (the stable isotopes are $^{137}_{56}\mathrm{Ba}$ and $^{84}_{36}\mathrm{Kr}$) and, in consequence, they are highly radioactive. Computation shows that the amount of heat energy released in this nuclear reaction is about 4.5×10^9 kcal per mole of uranium. Let us compare this value with the heat evolved in a chemical reaction such as the combustion of carbon. In Chapter 19 it was stated that $\Delta H = -94$ kcal in the reaction,

$$\mathrm{C} + \mathrm{O_2} \longrightarrow \mathrm{CO_2} \qquad (29\text{-}2)$$

That is, 94 kcal are released per mole of carbon burned. Thus,

$$\frac{\text{heat per mole of uranium fissioned}}{\text{heat per mole of carbon burned}} = \frac{4.5 \times 10^9 \text{ kcal}}{94 \text{ kcal}} \approx 4.8 \times 10^7$$

In other words, more than 10 million times as much heat is generated in the nuclear reaction as in the chemical reaction. What is the source of the vast amount of heat released in a nuclear reaction? To answer this question we must consider the mass-energy relationship as expressed in the Einstein equation.

Fig. 29-1 If this lump of coal were 90 per cent carbon and had a mass of 640 grams, how much heat would it produce if burned with sufficient oxygen? How much heat would 640 grams of fissionable uranium produce?

The Equivalence of Mass and Energy

Even as early as 1905 Einstein had expressed the mass-energy relationship as a simple equation, $E = mc^2$, where E stands for energy, m is mass expressed in grams, and c is the velocity of light in centimeters per second (3×10^{10} cm/sec). What are the units of energy?

According to the Einstein equation, the energy produced by the conversion of 1 g of mass is

$$\begin{aligned} E &= mc^2 \\ &= 1 \text{ g} \times (3 \times 10^{10} \text{ cm/sec})^2 \\ &= 9 \times 10^{20} \text{ g-cm}^2/\text{sec}^2 \end{aligned}$$

The units of g-cm^2/sec^2 are, for convenience, called *ergs*. Therefore *a mass of 1 g is equivalent to 9×10^{20} ergs of energy.* In terms of heat units, 1 erg of energy is equal to 2.4×10^{-8} calorie. Therefore the energy equivalent to a mass of 1 g is

$$\begin{aligned} 9 \times 10^{20} \text{ ergs} \times 2.4 \times 10^{-8} \text{ cal/erg} &= 21.6 \times 10^{12} \text{ cal} \\ &= 21.6 \times 10^{9} \text{ kcal} \end{aligned}$$

This is a vast amount of energy. A simple computation shows that the energy equivalent of 1 g of mass is enough to melt about 300,000 tons of ice.

Fig. 29-2 A nuclear power plant. What is not present in this photograph that might be seen near a conventional power plant?

The Law of Mass–Energy

Since heat is evolved when carbon burns in air, there is, according to the Einstein equation, a loss of mass in this reaction, and the loss of mass can be computed:

$$1 \text{ g converted to energy} = 21.6 \times 10^{9} \text{ kcal}$$

and $$9.4 \times 10^{1} \text{ kcal} = \text{heat liberated for each mole of carbon burned}$$

Therefore,

$$\begin{aligned} \frac{9.4 \times 10^{1} \text{ kcal} \times 1.00 \text{ g}}{21.6 \times 10^{9} \text{ kcal}} &= 0.435 \times 10^{-8} \text{ g converted to energy} \\ &= 4.35 \times 10^{-9} \text{ g converted to energy} \end{aligned}$$

That is, if 12.00 g of carbon are completely burned, the mass of the product (carbon dioxide) is less than the mass of the reactants by 0.00000000435 g. Clearly this quantity is much too small to be registered on even the most sensitive balance. Nonetheless this leads us to suspect that the law of conservation of mass is not strictly true. Instead, it is the conservation of mass and energy that is valid, and the law of mass-energy states: *In any reaction (chemical or nuclear) the mass–energy of the reactants equals the mass-energy of the products.* For all chemical reactions the mass difference between reactants and products is so small that the law of conservation of mass is valid within the limits of the experimental conditions. However, in nuclear reactions the mass–energy conversion is much larger than in chemical reactions, and the mass difference between reactants and products cannot be disregarded.

Nuclear Forces

How is mass converted to energy? Is matter completely destroyed when it is changed to energy? Before answering these questions we must consider the forces that bind protons and neutrons together in a nucleus.

As stated earlier, α particles can be used as projectiles to bombard nuclei of other atoms. It is apparent that the nucleons of α particles must be held together by exceedingly strong forces, otherwise they would break apart when used as bombarding particles. These strong attractive forces are exerted between neutron and neutron, neutron and proton, and even between proton and proton. They are called *nuclear forces.* The nuclear forces in an α particle (or the nucleus of a helium atom) are shown diagrammatically in Fig. 29-3.

Fig. 29-3 The arrangement of forces in the nucleus of a helium atom. The helium nucleus contains two protons and two neutrons. At what corners of this diagram could an n or a p be placed to indicate the stability of this nucleus? Assume each side of the square is 10^{-12} cm long. Why can the protons *not* occupy the ends of the same diagonal? Why do nuclear particles at opposite ends of the same diagonal repel each other?

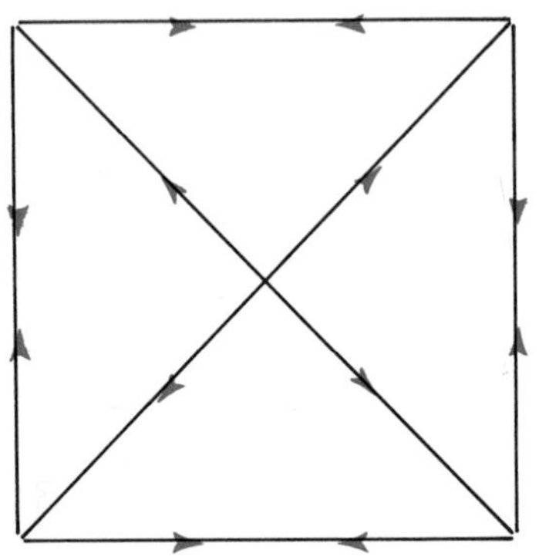

Nuclear forces are effective only through exceedingly short distances. Indeed, their maximum range is not more than 10^{-12} cm, which is roughly the diameter of the nucleus of an atom. Electrical forces are of course also exerted between protons but, at distances of 10^{-12} cm or less, nuclear forces are much stronger than electrical forces. Therefore within this short range, the nuclear force of attraction between protons is greater than the electrical force of repulsion. Moreover, if any bombarding particle gets as near as 10^{-12} centimeter to a nucleus, it is pulled into the nucleus and a reaction takes place.

Neutron/Proton Ratio and Nuclear Stability

There is an interesting relationship between the stability of an element and the ratio of neutrons to protons in its nucleus. In Table 29-1 the neutron/proton ratio is given for a few elements.

Table 29-1 Neutron/proton ratio for selected elements

Element	p	n	n/p *ratio*
He	2	2	1.00
C	6	6	1.00
O	8	8	1.00
Mg	12	12	1.00
Ca	20	20	1.00
Fe	26	30	1.15
Ag	47	61	1.30
Pb	82	126	1.54
Ra	88	138	1.57
U	92	146	1.59

(Letter p represents the number of protons in the nucleus and letter n the number of neutrons.)

For elements of low mass (that is, up to atomic number 20) the number of neutrons in a nucleus is approximately the same as the number of protons so that the n/p ratio is approximately 1.00. As the atomic number increases, the force of repulsion between the protons also increases. To counteract this increasing force of repulsion, the number of neutrons must increase at a faster rate than protons, otherwise the nucleus would become unstable. That is, beyond atomic number 20 the ratio of neutrons to protons steadily increases up to a maximum value of 1.54 for the heaviest of the stable elements namely Pb-82. However, there is a limit to the compensating effect of extra neutrons. Indeed, as stated in Chapter 28, if the atomic number of an element is greater than 82, the attractive forces of the extra neutrons are unable to counterbalance the electrostatic repulsive forces between "distant" protons, and the element becomes radioactive.

Thus, the n/p ratio for thorium-232 ($^{232}_{90}Th$) is 142/90 or 1.58. This value is outside the zone of stability, and to achieve stability a series of transformations takes place in which α and β particles are emitted.

The emission of α particles from heavy nuclei increases the n/p ratio of the product and therefore does not stabilize a nucleus. But the ejection of β particles always tends to stabilize a nucleus. Let us see why.

The emission of a β particle indicates that a neutron has been changed to a proton and an electron. Thus the value of n is decreased by one and the value of p is increased by one. Therefore, the ratio n/p is decreased.

Now let us compare the n/p values of the two isotopes of carbon, C-12 and C-14. The n/p value for C-12 ($^{12}_{6}C$) is 1.00. It is therefore a stable isotope. The n/p value for C-14 ($^{14}_{6}C$) is 1.33, and C-14 is therefore an unstable isotope. To achieve stability, a C-14 nucleus emits a β particle and in doing so forms a nitrogen nucleus with an n/p ratio of 1.00

$$^{14}_{6}C - {}^{0}_{-1}e \longrightarrow {}^{14}_{7}N \qquad (29\text{-}3)$$

Similarly, the n/p ratio for iodine-127 is 74/53 or 1.39. Another isotope of iodine is I-131 and its n/p ratio is 78/53 or 1.47. We would therefore predict that I-127 is stable and that I-131 is radioactive and is a β emitter, which is actually the case.

Mass Defect and Binding Energy

Let us now consider the simple hypothetical nuclear reaction in which 2 protons and 2 neutrons combine to form an α particle. Or,

$$2\,{}^{1}_{1}H + 2\,{}^{1}_{0}n \longrightarrow {}^{4}_{2}He \qquad (29\text{-}4)$$

The atomic masses of all these particles are known. They are:

mass of 2 protons	$= (2 \times 1.0078)$ amu	$= 2.0156$ amu
mass of 2 neutrons	$= (2 \times 1.0087)$ amu	$= 2.0174$ amu
total mass of reacting particles		$= 4.0330$ amu
mass of α particle as determined by a mass spectrograph		$= 4.0026$ amu
loss of mass in forming nucleus		$= 0.0304$ amu

That is, in this reaction there is a loss of mass of 0.0304 g/mole of helium nuclei formed. The loss of mass in a nuclear reaction is usually called *mass defect* and, according to the Einstein equation, the mass defect is released as energy.

$$\begin{aligned} E &= mc^2 \\ &= 0.0304 \text{ g/mole} \times 9 \times 10^{20} \text{ cm}^2/\text{sec}^2 \\ &= 0.274 \times 10^{20} \text{ ergs/mole} \times 2.4 \times 10^{-8} \text{ cal/erg} \\ &= 6.6 \times 10^{11} \text{ cal/mole} \quad \text{or} \quad 6.6 \times 10^{8} \text{ kcal/mole} \end{aligned}$$

Or, expressed in words, if 2 moles of protons combine with 2 moles of neutrons to form 1 mole of helium nuclei, 660 million kcal of heat energy are released. This is about the same as the amount of heat energy released when 100 tons of coal are burned.

It is important to observe that the *number* of nuclear particles is the same after the reaction as it was before. Therefore loss of mass is not due to a destruction of matter, but rather to a change in the energy of the particles. Thus, when two protons and two neutrons combine to form a helium nucleus they revert to a lower energy state. And, to separate 1 mole of helium nuclei into their constituent nucleons, 6.6×10^8 kcal would have to be supplied from an outside source.

The energy released when a nucleus is formed from its constituent particles is called *binding energy*. Binding energy is therefore a measure of the energy needed to break up a nucleus into its constituent particles. Or, expressed another way, it is a measure of the tremendous forces of attraction between nucleons in a nucleus.

Binding Energy/Nucleon in Nuclei of Different Elements

If the binding energy for helium is divided by the number of nucleons in the nucleus, the binding energy *per nucleon* can be computed for one mole of nuclei.

$$\begin{aligned}\text{Binding energy per nucleon of helium} &= \frac{6.6 \times 10^8}{4} \text{ kcal} \\ &= 1.65 \times 10^8 \text{ kcal} \\ &= 165 \text{ million} \\ &\qquad \text{kcal per mole}\end{aligned}$$

That is, 165 million kcal of energy are needed to remove one nucleon from every nucleus in one mole of helium nuclei.

Computations show that binding energies for different stable nuclei vary a great deal. If binding energy per particle is plotted against mass number, a curve like that shown in Fig. 29-4 is obtained.

Elements at the peak of the curve have mass numbers in the region of 56 to 60. On the left of the peak the slope of the curve

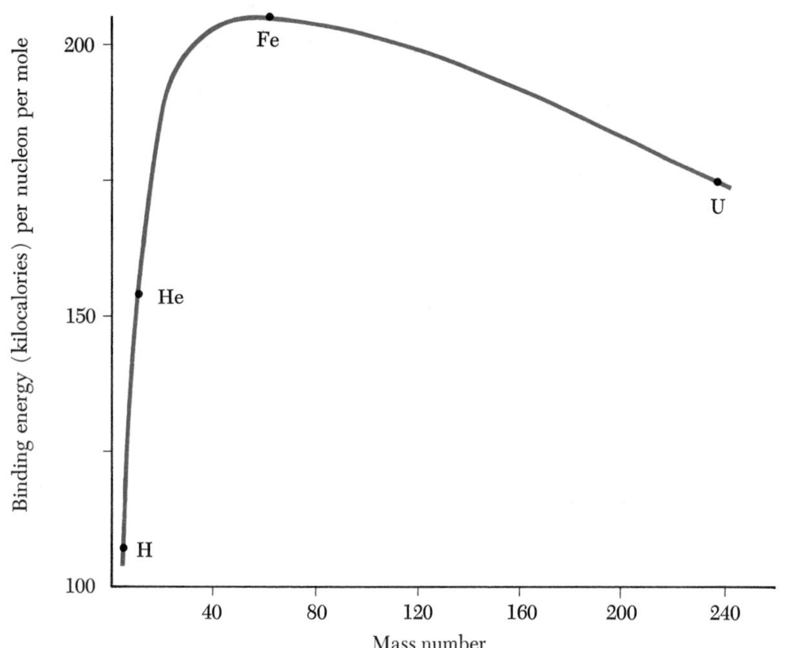

Fig. 29-4 A graph of nuclear binding energy plotted against mass number.

is steep, but on the right the slope is gentle. How can such a curve be interpreted?

For the lighter elements the binding energy per nucleon increases as the mass number increases. For the heavier elements the binding energy increases as the mass number decreases. Elements with the greatest binding energy per nucleon are those near the peak of the curve. These are therefore the most stable elements. Let us now consider uranium on the extreme right of the curve. If a uranium nucleus is split into two approximately equal fragments, the curve shows that the binding energy of each of the fragments is greater than the binding energy of uranium itself. That is, the fragments (or products) are more stable than uranium. Hence the products are in a lower energy state than uranium, and therefore energy must be released in the process. But this is what we expect because we are discussing the process of fission.

On the other hand, if nucleons are added to a hydrogen nucleus so that it is transformed into helium, the slope of the binding energy curve is much steeper than the fission slope. The transformation of hydrogen to helium is called *fusion* and, by comparing the two slopes, we conclude that much more energy is released in fusion than in fission. The actual amounts of energy released in these two processes are discussed later in the chapter.

Energy Released in Fission

Barium and krypton are by no means the only pair of elements formed when uranium is split by neutron bombardment. Actually, the fission of U-235 yields a wide range of products, and the pair found in greatest abundance is lanthanum ($^{139}_{57}La$) and molybdenum ($^{95}_{42}Mo$). Let us compute the mass loss and the energy released in this fission reaction. In words, the reaction is uranium-235 + neutron = lanthanum + molybdenum. The mass numbers of the reactants are 235 + 1 or 236, and of the products 139 + 95 or 234. The difference of two must be made up by the release of two neutrons in the fission process. Therefore, the equation for the nuclear reaction is

$$^{235}_{92}U + ^{1}_{0}n \longrightarrow ^{139}_{57}La + ^{95}_{42}Mo + 2^{1}_{0}n \qquad (29\text{-}5)$$

The proton count is

$$92 + 0 \longrightarrow 57 + 42 + 0 \qquad \text{or} \qquad 92 \longrightarrow 99 \qquad (29\text{-}6)$$

A gain of 7 is indicated. The neutron count is

$$143 + 1 \longrightarrow 82 + 53 + 2 \qquad \text{or} \qquad 144 \longrightarrow 137 \qquad (29\text{-}7)$$

A loss of 7 is indicated. It is therefore apparent that 7 neutrons in the reactants have been converted to 7 protons and 7 β particles in the products. (This information appears in Table 29-2.) Therefore, the complete equation for the nuclear reaction is

$$^{235}_{92}U + ^{1}_{0}n \longrightarrow ^{139}_{57}La + ^{95}_{42}Mo + 2^{1}_{0}n + 7\,^{0}_{-1}e \qquad (29\text{-}8)$$

Table 29-2 Summary of atomic reaction $^{235}_{92}U \longrightarrow ^{139}_{57}La + ^{95}_{42}Mo$

Particles	Reactants	Products	Change
Neutrons	144	137	−7
Electrons		+7	+7
Protons	92	99	+7

The sum of the exact atomic masses of the reactants is 235.124 amu + 1.009 amu = 236.133 amu. The sum of the atomic masses of the products is 138.955 amu + 94.945 amu + 2(1.009) amu + 7(0.0005) amu = 235.922 amu. Therefore, the loss of mass is 0.211 amu.

Notice again that there is no destruction of matter in this nuclear reaction. Notice also that the mass loss is approximately 0.1% of

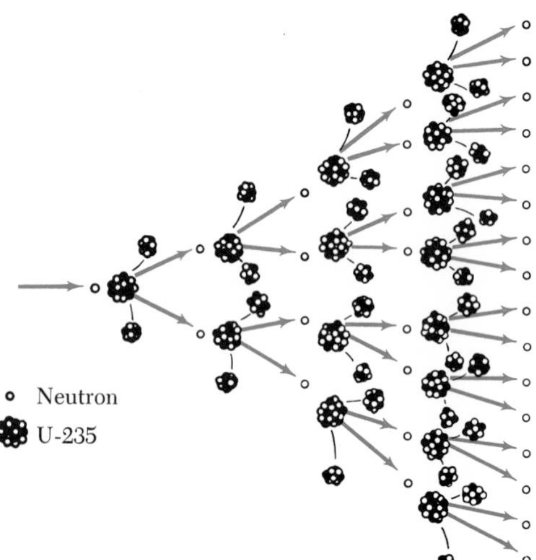

Fig. 29-5 A chain reaction is almost instantaneous. In this diagram it is assumed that only two neutrons are released in each fission.

the mass of uranium. Indeed, the conversion of approximately 0.1% of mass to energy is true of all fission reactions. How much heat energy is released in this fission reaction?

The mass loss from one mole of U-235 is 0.211 gram. Converting mass in grams to kilocalories of heat energy

$$0.211 \text{ g} \times 21.6 \times 10^9 \text{ kcal/g} = 4.62 \times 10^9 \text{ kcal}$$

Or, expressed in other terms, the energy released by the fission of one mole of U-235 is approximately the same as the heat energy produced by burning about 1000 tons of coal.

A Chain Reaction

It is characteristic of a fission reaction that the nucleus first absorbs one neutron and then ejects two or three or even more neutrons. And, if the released neutrons collide with other nuclei, the reaction becomes self-propagating. A self-propagating or *chain reaction*, as it is usually called, is illustrated diagrammatically in Fig. 29-5. Here a single neutron enters a nucleus of U-235 and two effective neutrons are released per fission. The two neutrons released in the first fission attack two nuclei and release four neutrons. The four neutrons then attack four nuclei and release eight neutrons, and so on. Actually, the fissions increase at a fantastically rapid rate, spreading throughout the mass of uranium in a fraction of a second, and causing a violent explosion. That is what happens in an atomic bomb.

Compare . . .
Can the discovery of controlled fission of atomic nuclei and the controlled release of atomic energy be fairly compared to primitive man's controlled use of fire? Some scientists think so. What do you think?

To use the released energy for peaceful purposes it is apparent that the fission reaction must be controlled. How can this be done? The fission of uranium is slowed down and controlled in a device called a *reactor*. One way to slow down the reaction rate is to use natural uranium instead of U-235. Another is to place substances in a reactor such as cadmium or boron whose nuclei readily absorb neutrons. In practice, control rods of cadmium or boron are inserted through the walls of a reactor to act as dampers to the reaction. Indeed, they can stop it altogether if necessary.

A Nuclear Power Reactor

An atomic reactor may be used primarily to produce radioisotopes or to generate electric power. But, whatever its use or design, all reactors have the same five essential parts, namely (1) the fuel,

Fig. 29-6 Fuel elements for a power reactor.

(2) a moderator, (3) control rods, (4) a coolant, and (5) a protective shield. We shall consider the kind of reactor used as a power plant, where the intense heat of the interior is transferred to a turbo-generator and changed to electrical energy.

The reactor fuel is usually natural uranium enriched with U-235. The neutrons emitted by U-235 in the fission process are ejected at very high speeds, speeds too high to penetrate other nuclei effectively. For this reason a *moderator* is used to slow down the neutrons to speeds just enough to keep the reaction going. But although the nuclei of a moderator slows down neutrons, it must not absorb them, otherwise the fission reaction would stop altogether. One of the most common moderators is highly purified graphite. The uranium fuel, usually in aluminum containers, is surrounded by blocks of graphite. Fast neutrons ejected in the fission reaction collide with and rebound from the carbon atoms. As a result, the neutrons lose kinetic energy and their speeds are reduced. As stated earlier, cadmium and boron rods also control the reaction rate. If the rods are lowered into the reactor, the rate of reaction is slowed down; if the rods are withdrawn, the reaction rate speeds up.

A neutron released in a fission reaction could do one of three things after being slowed down by a moderator. It could cause the

Define . . .

Ordinary uranium contains about 99.3% U-238 and 0.7% U-235. U-235 readily undergoes fission when a neutron strikes an atom of this isotope. Why is U-238 enriched with U-235 in a reactor?

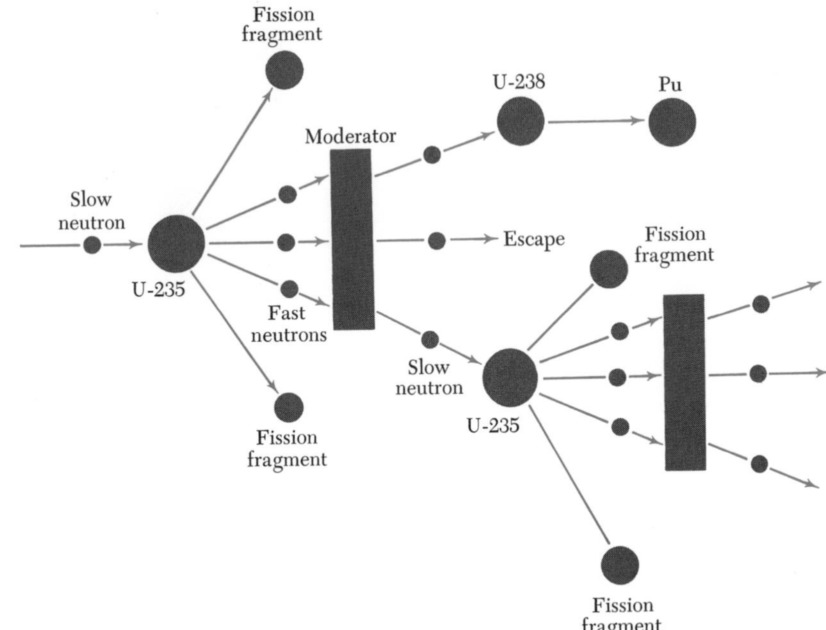

Fig. 29-7 The main "reactions" in a reactor.

fission of a nucleus of U-235 and so maintain the chain reaction. Or it could be captured by a nucleus of U-238, and thereby form plutonium. Or it might miss nuclei altogether, in which case it would stay in the reactor where the free neutrons accumulate. All three of these possibilities are shown in Fig. 29-7.

A liquid coolant, which may be a mixture of molten sodium and potassium (or it may even be water), carries heat out of the reactor. After circulating through tubes in the reactor, the heated coolant flows out of the reactor and through the inner pipes of a heat-exchanger. The outer pipes of the heat exchanger contain water and are connected to a turbine. The hot coolant vaporizes the water in the pipes and the steam rotates the turbine which, in turn, operates an electric generator. A diagram of a power reactor is shown in Fig. 29-8. Finally, as a safety measure, all reactors must be covered by an impervious shield, usually of concrete, thick enough to absorb the intense and dangerous radiations.

Power reactors not only supply electric energy to many cities, but they are also a source of power for ships, particularly for submarines. The great advantage of reactors on ships is that storage space for fuel oil is eliminated. Moreover, reactor-driven ships can operate for many months without the need of refueling.

Note . . .
The significance of uranium was not appreciated before 1939, the year in which it was realized this element could be used as a source of nuclear energy. Before 1939, it was commonly used to color glass and glazes a greenish-yellow. Uranium glasses were used in stained glass windows in European cathedrals.

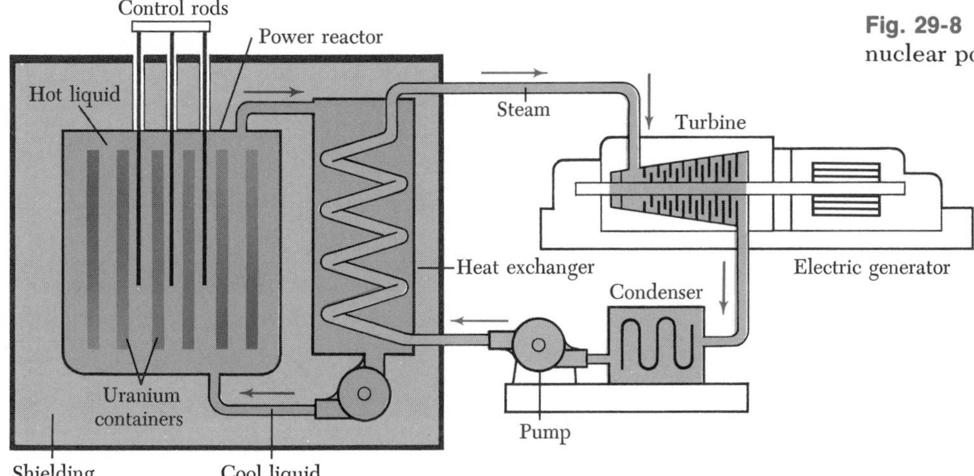

Fig. 29-8 A schematic diagram of a nuclear power plant.

Nuclear Fusion

The steep slope of the curve in Fig. 29-4 indicates that more heat energy would be released by transforming hydrogen to helium than in the fission of uranium. Indeed, it is believed that the heat energy produced in the sun and other stars is due to the transformation of hydrogen to helium.

The combination of light particles to form a heavier nucleus is called *fusion;* it is the reverse of the fission process. The solar fusion reaction assumed to occur is the combination of four hydrogen atoms to form a helium atom and 2 positrons. Or,

Recall . . .
A positron is an elementary particle equal in mass to the electron but opposite in charge.

$$4\,{}^1_1\text{H} \longrightarrow {}^4_2\text{He} + 2\,{}^{\;0}_{+1}\text{e} \tag{29-9}$$

Let us compute the mass loss in this reaction.

mass of 4 protons = 4 × 1.0078 = 4.0312 amu
mass of electrons = 2 × 0.0005 = 0.0010 amu
mass of reacting particles = 4.0322 amu
mass of alpha particle = 4.0026 amu
mass loss = 0.0296 amu

The percentage loss in mass is $\dfrac{0.0296}{4.0322} = 0.0074 \times 100$ which is approximately 0.7%. In other words, seven times more energy is released in this fusion reaction than in the fission of uranium.

However, while a fission reaction occurs readily at ordinary temperatures, a fusion reaction takes place only at exceedingly high temperatures. Why is this? All nuclei are positively charged and to make them combine they must move at speeds high enough to overcome the forces of electrostatic repulsion, Indeed, the hydrogen to helium reaction in the sun occurs at a temperature of about 20,000,000 °C. The only way to attain such a high temperature on earth is to explode an atomic bomb. That is, a fission bomb explosion is needed to trigger a fusion reaction.

Fig. 29-9 This is the South West Experimental Fast Oxide Reactor (SEFOR), located near Fayetteville, Ark. It is a fast-spectrum, experimental reactor designed and being operated by General Electric Breeder Reactor Development Operation (BRDO) for the Southwest Atomic Energy Associates, a group of 17 investor-owned utilities. This Pu-U oxide fuel reactor was issued a full power license by the AEC in Jan., 1970 and is in the second phase of a planned 3-year experimental program.

It is known that nuclei of the heavier isotopes of hydrogen, deuterium (^2_1H) and tritium (^3_1H), fuse more readily than protons and at lower temperatures. Such a reaction is

$$^2_1H + ^3_1H \longrightarrow ^4_2He + ^1_0n + \text{energy} \qquad (29\text{-}10)$$

Once the fusion reaction has started, it generates enough heat to be self-sustaining. As you know, hydrogen bombs have been exploded. And, as stated above, such an explosion is due to the fusing of heavy isotopes of hydrogen triggered by a uranium or plutonium bomb. A bomb explosion is of course an uncontrolled reaction, but so far scientists have not been able to achieve a controlled fusion reaction.There is enough deuterium in the oceans to supply deuterium fuel in almost unlimited amounts. If deuterons could be fused under controlled conditions, enough energy would be available for all purposes for all mankind for thousands of years. This is the problem that poses one of the greatest challenges to scientists in the Twentieth Century, and scientists are hard at work upon it.

Summary

Nuclear fission consists of splitting an atom of high atomic mass into two fragments by a neutron that enters the nucleus of the heavy atom. In addition to the two fragments (which are atoms of lower atomic mass than the original atom), several neutrons are released along with a great deal of energy. The energy released in a nuclear reaction is due to the conversion of mass into energy. The mass-energy relation is expressed in Einstein's equation, $E = mc^2$, where E represents energy in ergs, m stands for mass in grams, and c represents the velocity of light in centimeters per second. Although there is a loss of mass, there is no destruction or annihilation of particles of matter.

All exothermic chemical reactions can be said to result in a loss of mass. However, in chemical reactions there is a change in the bonding energy among the different atoms. but the binding energy in the nuclei is not normally affected. Energy released in nuclear reactions is at least a million times as much as in chemical reactions. Mass-energy changes in chemical reactions are too small to be measured by instruments, but the larger mass-energy changes in nuclear reactions are easily measurable.

In a nuclear reactor both neutrons and energy are produced under controlled conditions. The released neutrons can be used to produce radioactive isotopes, and the released energy can be converted into electric energy.

Factual Recall

1. (*a*) Write the Einstein equation for the mass–energy relationship, and state the meaning of the symbols in the equation.
   (*b*) What is the significance of this equation?
2. (*a*) State the law of mass–energy.
   (*b*) Why is this law of significance in nuclear reactions but not in chemical reactions?
3. (*a*) What are nuclear forces?
   (*b*) Compare the nuclear forces in a helium atom with the forces outside the nucleus of the same atom.
4. (*a*) What conclusion would you draw concerning the stability of an element if the value of its n/p ratio is 1.60? Why?
   (*b*) How does the emission of (*i*) an α particle and (*ii*) a β particle affect the stability of a nucleus?
5. (*a*) What is meant by the term *binding energy*?
   (*b*) What is the significance of binding energy?
6. (*a*) What is meant by the term *fission*?
   (*b*) How many neutrons are released in the reaction

$$^{235}_{92}U + ^{1}_{0}n \longrightarrow ^{137}_{56}Ba + ^{84}_{36}Kr$$

7. What is the source of the energy released in a fission reaction? Explain.
8. Briefly describe the function of the various essential components in an atomic reactor.
9. Explain how a reactor (*a*) produces radioisotopes, (*b*) generates electricity.

Apply Your Knowledge!

1. The equation for the reaction in the oxyacetylene flame is

   $$2C_2H_2 + 5O_2 \longrightarrow 4CO_2 + 2H_2O$$

   and $\Delta H = -312$ kcal/mole

   (*a*) Compute the loss of mass in this reaction, assuming that $2.16 + 10^{10}$ kcal is the energy equivalent of a mass of 1 g.

2. One of the fission reactions is the splitting of uranium ($^{235}_{92}U$) into promethium ($^{151}_{61}Pm$) and bromine ($^{82}_{35}Br$). Write a balanced nuclear equation for this reaction.

Find Out!

Look up the so-called "nuclear zoo." Information is available in *Secrets of the Nucleus* by J.S. Levenger, published by Scholastic Book Services, New York, 1967.

Suggested Readings

Bethe, H.A., *What Holds the Nucleus Together* (SCIENTIFIC AMERICAN Offprint #201). San Francisco: Freeman.

Hill, R.D., *Tracking Down Particles.* New York: W.A. Benjamin, 1963. (Paperback)

Hughes, D.J., *The Neutron Story.* Garden City, N.Y.: Doubleday-Anchor, 1959. (Paperback)

Hurley, P.M., *Radioactivity and Time* (SCIENTIFIC AMERICAN Offprint #220). San Francisco, Freeman.

Overman, R.T., *Basic Concepts of Nuclear Chemistry.* New York: Reinhold, 1963. (Paperback)

Seaborg, G.T., *Man-Made Transuranium Elements.* Englewood Cliffs, N.J.: Prentice-Hall, 1963. (Paperback)

APPENDIX

SUPPLEMENT

MEASUREMENT

Since science is based upon experimentation, measurement is vital to its study.

The Metric System

A system of measurement must have fixed, convenient, and reproducible standards for length, mass, and time. The metric system meets these requirements, and this system is especially convenient because it is based on powers of 10.

Length In the metric system, the standard unit of length is the *meter*. How long is a meter? The meter was first defined as one ten-millionth of the distance between the North Pole and the equator. Later the meter was defined as the distance between two scratches on a platinum-iridium bar preserved at the International Bureau of Weights and Measures (Paris). To provide an indestructible standard, however, in 1960 the International Conference on Weights and Measures redefined the meter as 1,650,763.73 times the wavelength of the orange-red spectral line of krypton-86. The meter is equal to 39.37 in. or a little more than a yard.

Prefixes are used to indicate multiples and submultiples of the meter. Thus, a distance of 1000 meters (m) is 1 *kilometer* (km), 1/100 of a meter is 1 *centimeter* (cm), and 1/1000 of a meter is 1 *millimeter* (mm).

Look at a meter stick. Notice that it is divided into 100 units. Each of these units is a centimeter. Moreover, each centimeter is divided into 10 units. Each of these units is a millimeter.

Volume In the metric system the standard unit of volume is the cubic meter (m^3). To measure fluid volume, the liter (l) is used. The liter is equal to 10^{-3} cubic meter; that is, it is equal to 1 cubic decimeter (dm^3). The volume of a cubic decimeter is equal to 1000 cubic centimeters (cm^3). One cm^3 is therefore equal to 1/1000 of a liter. Since the prefixes applying to the meter also apply to the liter, what would 1/1000 of a liter be called?

Mass The standard unit of mass in the metric system is the *gram* (g). The standard for the gram is defined as 1/1000 of the mass of the standard kilogram preserved at the International Bureau of Weights and Measures in Paris. The prefixes applied to the meter and the liter also apply to the gram. How many centigrams equal 1 g?

Time The standard unit of time is the second (sec). In 1964 the Twelfth General Conference on Weights and Measures defined the second in terms of the spin characteristics of the valence electron of cesium-133.

Summary The units of the metric system are listed in Table 1 of the Appendix. All units of the system can be derived from the three basic units of length, mass, and time. Their equivalents in the English system are listed in Table 2.

Limitations in Measurement

If measurement is the way a scientist describes things, he must be able to estimate how closely a measurement describes a length, area, volume, mass, or elapsed time.

The scientist must consider two different concepts in order to express the limitation of a measurement. These concepts are *accuracy* and *precision*. Although most people use these words interchangeably, a scientist uses each word to express a specific idea.

Accuracy is the comparison of a measurement with the accepted value of the measurement. For example, the instrument used to measure the distance traveled by a car is an odometer. The accuracy of the odometer can be checked by comparing its reading with that of a known distance, such as a measured mile. To be accurate, the odometer must indicate 1 mile. If the odometer gives another reading, such as 0.9 mile or 1.1 miles, the odometer is inaccurate.

What is precision? Let us assume that the odometer is tested repeatedly over a mile course, and that for each test the odometer records a distance of 0.9 mile. Since the odometer readings are the same, the odometer is precise but inaccurate. Precision, therefore, refers to reproducibility or how well two or more measurements agree with each other.

Significant Figures

A platform balance is a common laboratory instrument used to measure mass, and it is usually precise to 0.1 g. Let us assume that the mass of an object weighed on a platform balance is 56.3 g. Since the balance is precise to ± 0.1 g, the last digit of 56.3 g is uncertain. Significant digits in a number are all the digits in that number known with certainty in addition to the first digit which is uncertain.

A zero, however, is significant only under certain conditions. If it is used to locate a decimal point, it is not a significant figure. The measurement 0.0065 g, for example, has only two significant figures. A zero to the left of an understood decimal point and to the right of a nonzero digit is not significant unless a bar is placed above it. For example 6500 km has two sigificant figures. However, 65$\bar{0}$0 km has three significant figures. If a zero appears between nonzero digits, the zero is significant. Thus the measurement 106 g has three significant figures. If a zero appears after a nonzero digit which follows a decimal point, the zero is significant. For example, 0.08040 g has four significant figures. Notice the zero to the right of the decimal point. It is not a significant digit.

Arithmetic and Significant Figures The result of any computation can be no more precise than the least precise figure used.

Addition and Subtraction Examine the addition of the following numbers:

$$\begin{array}{r@{\,}l} 18.093 & \text{g} \\ 6.7 & \text{g} \\ 4.78 & \text{g} \\ \hline 29.573 & \text{g} \end{array}$$

The sum of the three numbers can contain no more significant figures than the number with the fewest significant digits, which in this case is 6.7. Thus, the sum of 29.573 g can only contain three significant figures. To reduce the number to its significant digits, round off 29.573 g. The rule to be applied is (*a*) if the doubtful significant figure is even, increase it by one if the following digit is 6, 7, 8, or 9, and (*b*) if the doubtful figure is odd, increase it by one if the following digit is 5, 6, 7, 8, or 9. In the above example, 29.573 g is therefore rounded off to 29.6 g.

Multiplication and Division The principle for arriving at significant figures in a quotient or a product is: the quoteint or product of any number and a doubtful number is uncertain. Thus, if the dimensions of a rectangle are 10.3 cm and 12.1 cm, the area of the rectangle, as calculated by longhand, is 124.63 cm^2. However, the product can only contain three significant figures, and therefore the product must be rounded off to 125 cm^2.

Exponential Notation

The number of atoms in 12 g of carbon is 602,000,000,000, 000,000,000,000,000. To be handled easily in computation, this number can be expressed by exponential notation. The expression of exponential notation is $M \times 10^n$, where M is a number comprised of only significant digits. M is equal to or greater than one but less than 10 and n is a positive or negative exponent of 10.

How would 602,000,000,000,000,000,000,000,000 be expressed exponentially? The significant figures in the number are 602. The zeros after 2 are not significant. Why? Since M must be less than 10, we must place a decimal point after the first digit (6). M would then be 6.02. The number of places to the right of the decimal point determines how many times M would have to be multiplied by 10 to be equal to 602,000,000,000,000,000,000, 000. The number of places after the decimal point is 23. Therefore, 6.02 multiplied by 10^{23} is equal to our large number. The exponential expression for this large number is 6.02×10^{23}.

The hydrogen atom's mass is 0.000000000000000000000 0017 g. M is 1.7. Try to state why M is 1.7. The number of places to the *left* of the decimal point of 1.7 is the number of times 1.7 must be divided by 10 to be equal to our very small number. The number of places to the left of the decimal point of 1.7 is 24. Therefore, 1.7×10^{-24} g is the exponential notation for the exceedingly small mass of the hydrogen atom. Exponential notation is a convenience in chemistry and science in general. How would you exponentially express the distance between the sun and the planet Pluto (3,700,000,000 miles)?

The Slide Rule

Slide rules are made in various types and sizes. Some are circular, but probably the most convenient for classwork is a straight 10-inch rule.

Examine your slide rule. Notice the numerous scales on both sides of it and notice also that there is a fixed and a movable part. We shall concentrate on scales C and D, since these will be used for multiplication and division. Scale D is on the lower fixed part of the slide rule; scale C is on the movable part, usually called the *slide*. A movable glass or plastic section is called the *cursor*. The fine line (called a *hairline*) that crosses the cursor is used to mark scale readings. The slide rule is shown in Fig. SR-1.

On what principle does the slide rule work? To multiply numbers using the slide rule, we in fact *add* distances by moving the slide. To divide, we subtract distances. The question, therefore, is: how is it possible to multiply or divide by adding or subtracting? The answer is that numbers are multiplied when their logarithms are added. The logarithm of 2 (that is, the *mantissa* and not the *characteristic*) is, therefore, assigned a distance on the C and D scales. Try multiply 2×2 using the slide rule and remember that you are multiplying by adding "logarithmic distances". Move the slide so that mark 1 on the C scale coincides with mark 2 on the D scale. Move the cursor so that the hairline coincides with mark 2 on the C scale. With what mark does the hairline coincide on the D scale? Is it 4? The characteristic of a logarithm is excluded from the slide rules because, to use the slide rule, you must determine by yourself by what power of ten your number must be multiplied to arrive at the correct answer. To multiply 20×20, the slide rule is operated as if you were multiplying 2×2; but you must multiply mark 4 on the D scale by 10^2 or 100 to arrive at the correct answer which is 400.

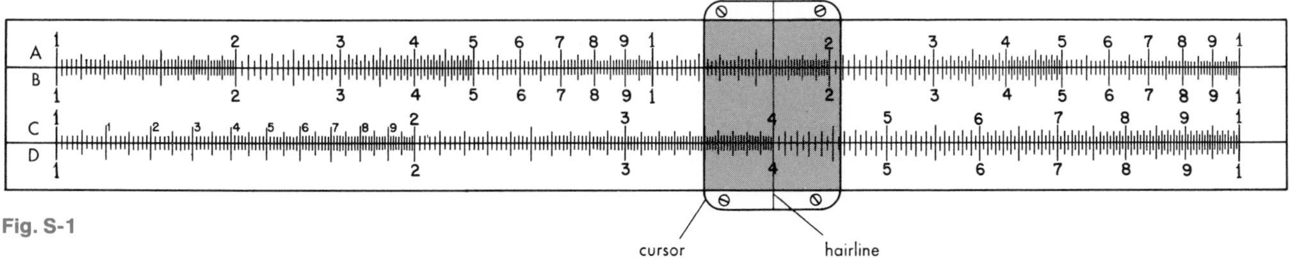

Fig. S-1

Examination of C and D Scales

Move the slide so that mark 1 on the C scale coincides with mark 1 on the D scale. Notice that the two scales are identical—the divisions on scale C coincide exactly with those on scale D. Notice also that the divisions are not equal—the distances from one mark to the next become shorter as we go from left to right. Place the hairline on mark 1 and then move the cursor to the right until the hairline is over mark 2, a distance of about 3 inches. Now move the cursor until the hairline is over mark 3, a distance of about 1 3/4 inches. Continue to move the cursor to the right so that the hairline passes in turn through marks 4, 5, 6, 7, 8, 9, 1 (observe that both end points on C and D scales are labelled 1, not 1 and 10 as we might expect). The distance between marks 9 and 1 is less than half an inch.

Next, notice that the distance between marks 1 and 2 is divided into 10 parts of unequal length which are indicated by small numerals. These parts are subdivided into 10 still smaller parts. The distance between marks 2 and 3 is also divided into 10 parts, each of which is subdivided into 5 smaller parts. The same is true of the distance between marks 3 and 4. All the distances between marks 4 and 5, 5 and 6, 6 and 7, 7 and 8, 8 and 9, 9 and 1, are divided into 10 parts but each of these parts is subdivided into only 2 smaller parts.

We can now read the scales. For convenience, we will refer to the scale readings shown in Fig. S-2, and then locate them on the slide rule. (These readings on both scales C and D are 11, 125, 1755, 1925, 24, 274, 314, 545, 705, 86, 995.)

Notice that the first digit of the number indicates the section of the scale to be used. For example, the number 545 is between marks 5 and 6 (and not between the subdivisions 5 and 6 on the section between marks 1 and 2).

Multiplication by Slide Rule

Example 1 To multiply 2 by 4, move the slide, placing mark 1 on scale C opposite mark 2 on scale D. Now move the cursor so that the hairline is over 4 on scale C. The reading under the hairline on scale D indicates the answer which is 8. With the same setting of the slide rule and by simply moving the cursor, we can show that $2 \times 2 = 4$, $2 \times 3 = 6$, $2 \times 5 = 10$.

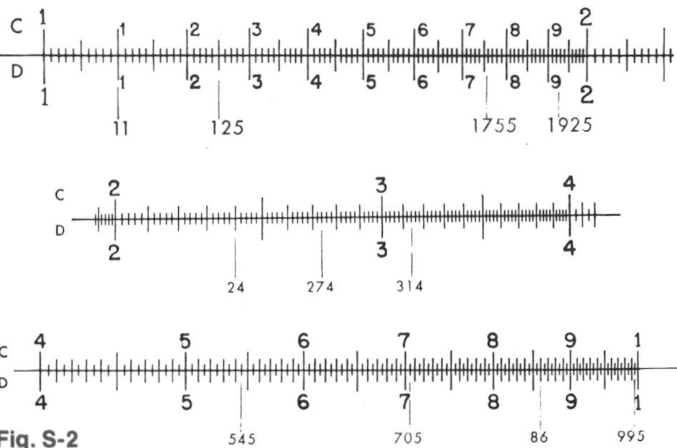

Fig. S-2

Division by Slide Rule

Division is the reverse of multiplication and to divide, using the slide rule, "logarithmic distances" are subtracted.

Example 2. To divide 6 by 3, let us recall Example 1, 2×4. Set up your slide rule again to multiply 2×4 and read the answer 8 on the D scale. In this position the slide rule is also set up for the division of 6 by 3. To do this, simply move the hairline to mark 1 on the C scale and read the answer on the D scale. The answer is 2.

ENTHALPY, ENTROPY, AND FREE ENERGY

Enthalpy

The energy content in a substance is called *enthalpy*, and changes in enthalpy can be computed from experimental data. Let us first consider the change in enthalpy (ΔH) in the reaction

$$2H_2(g) + O_2(g) \longrightarrow 2H_2O(l) \qquad (1)$$

$$\Delta H = \text{enthalpy of product} - \text{enthalpy of reactants}$$

$$= -136.6 \text{ kcal}$$

ΔH has a negative sign because the enthalpy of the system has diminished; that is, heat energy is given off and the reaction is exothermic.

In reaction (1) the final state of the system is liquid water. However, steam could also be selected as the final state. In such a case, the reaction would be

$$2H_2(g) + O_2(g) \longrightarrow 2H_2O(g) \qquad (2)$$

and the change in enthalpy is 115.6 kcal, or $\Delta H = -115.6$ kcal. The enthalpy difference between the liquid phase and the gas phase is 21.0 kcal per 2 moles of water formed, or 10.5 kcal per mole of water. This difference is called the *heat of vaporization* or the enthalpy of vaporization of water. In symbols

$$H_2O(1) \longrightarrow H_2O(g) \qquad \Delta H = 10.5\ \text{kcal} \tag{3}$$

That is, to convert 1 mole of liquid water to gas (or vapor) at the same temperature, 10.5 kcal of heat must be put into the system. Conversely,

$$H_2O(g) \longrightarrow H_2O(1) \quad \Delta H = -10.5\ \text{kcal} \tag{4}$$

That is, if 1 mole of water vapor is condensed to liquid water, 10.5 kcal of heat are evolved.

Let us now compute the enthalpy of water gas, a fuel once used on a large scale in industry in the United States. Water gas is essentially a mixture of carbon monoxide and hydrogen. The gas is manufactured by forcing steam over white-hot coke. The reaction is

$$C + H_2O \longrightarrow CO + H_2 - \text{heat} \tag{5}$$

That is, the reaction is endothermic and the temperature drops.

When water gas is burned, heat is evolved and the reaction is

$$CO + H_2 + O_2 \longrightarrow CO_2 + H_2O + \text{heat} \tag{6}$$

If these two equations are combined (or the reactions added), as in

$$\begin{aligned} &C + \cancel{H_2O} + \cancel{CO} + \cancel{H_2} + O_2 \longrightarrow \\ &\cancel{CO} + \cancel{H_2} + CO_2 + \cancel{H_2O} \end{aligned} \tag{7}$$

the net reaction is

$$C + O_2 \longrightarrow CO_2 \tag{8}$$

The enthalpy of this reaction is found by experiment to be -94.1 kcal per mole of carbon burned. This can also be computed by adding the heats of reaction of the separate reactions. For example,

$$\begin{aligned} &C(s) + H_2O(g) \longrightarrow CO(g) + H_2(g) \\ &\Delta H_1 = +31.4\ \text{kcal} \end{aligned} \tag{9}$$

$$\begin{aligned} &CO(g) + \tfrac{1}{2}O_2\,(g) \longrightarrow CO_2\,(g) \\ &\Delta H_2 = -67.7\ \text{kcal} \end{aligned} \tag{10}$$

$$\begin{aligned} &H_2(g) + \tfrac{1}{2}O_2\,(g) \longrightarrow H_2O\,(g) \\ &\Delta H_3 = -57.8\ \text{kcal} \end{aligned} \tag{11}$$

By addition,

$$\begin{aligned} \Delta H &= \Delta H_1 + \Delta H_2 + \Delta H_3 \\ &= (31.4) + (-67.7) + (-57.8)\ \text{kcal} \\ &= -94.1\ \text{kcal/mole of C burned} \end{aligned}$$

Entropy

Suppose two flasks A and B are connected by a stopcock as shown in the diagram. Suppose further that flask A is

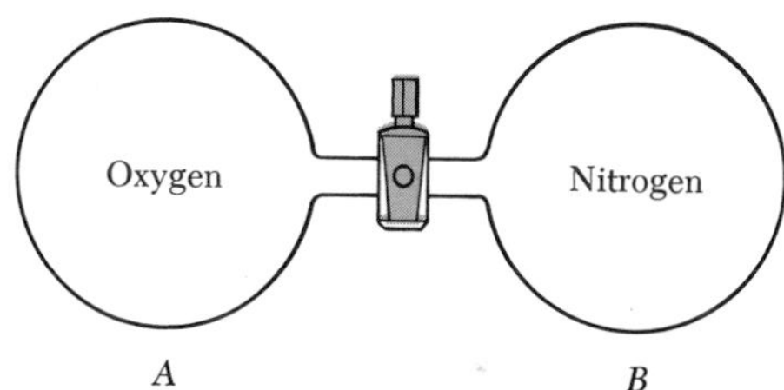

filled with oxygen and that flask B is filled with nitrogen at the same pressure. If the stopcock is opened, oxygen flows from A to B and nitrogen flows from B to A until the gases are evenly distributed between the two flasks. The mixing of the two gases is a spontaneous change; it has involved neither a change in energy nor temperature. Clearly there is no tendency to reverse the process. Indeed, to separate the gases, work would have to be done on the system. For example, the gases could be liquefied and then separated because of a difference in their boiling points.

The reverse process is not a spontaneous change. Hence there is a natural tendency for the gases to proceed from the unmixed condition to the mixed condition. But the unmixed condition is a state of order whereas the mixed condition is a state of disorder. We therefore conclude that in spontaneous processes there is a decrease in order, or an increase in randomness. The tendency to move towards a condition of maximum randomness or disorder is a natural process. The degree of randomness or disorder is called *entropy*, and it is usually represented by the symbol S. Thus if ΔS is the difference in entropy between the initial and final states, we can say

$$\Delta S = S_{final} - S_{initial} \tag{12}$$

Let us consider the change in entropy involved in the evaporation of water which is a spontaneous process,

$$\text{liquid water} \xrightarrow{\text{heat absorbed}} \text{water vapor} \tag{13}$$

The vapor molecules are in a more disordered state than the molecules of liquid water. Expressed in other terms, the vaporization process tends to proceed to a more disordered state. However, it should be observed that vaporization is an endothermic process in which the faster moving water molecules escape as vapor. As a result, the temperature of the water drops, and to maintain a constant temperature, heat of vaporization must be supplied from an outside source. A drop in temperature would slow down the rate of evaporation. That is, in the process of vaporization the natural energy effect opposes entropy (or the natural tendency towards random distribution). Indeed that is why the process is endothermic.

In summary, we can say that the state of equilibrium in any reaction is determined by two factors: (1) entropy (or disorder) and (2) energy. These factors tend to oppose each other. The condition of an equilibrium is favored both by the degree of disorder and also by the state of lower energy. Since both these factors cannot operate fully at the same time, the actual state of equilibrium must be a compromise between the state of maximum disorder and the state of minimum energy.

Free Energy

The energy released in most chemical reactions can be determined either as electrical energy or heat energy.

For example, the reaction in a Daniell cell is

$$Zn(s) + Cu^{+2}\,(1\,M) \longrightarrow Zn^{+2}(1\,M) + Cu(s) \qquad (14)$$

The voltage of this cell is 1.10 V. The electron exchange is

$$\begin{aligned} &Zn(s) \longrightarrow Zn^{+2} + 2e^- \\ &Cu^{+2} + 2e^- \longrightarrow Cu(s) \end{aligned} \qquad (15)$$

If 1 mole of zinc reacts with 1 mole of copper (II) ion, 2 faradays (**F**) of electrical charge are transferred. It can be shown that if the potential of a cell is 1.00 V, the amount of energy transferred from one electrode to the other amounts to 23.05 kcal/**F**. Hence, the energy transferred between the electrodes of a Daniell cell is

$$2\ \mathbf{F} \times 1.10\,\text{V}/1.00\,\text{V} \times 23.05\,\text{kcal}/\mathbf{F} = 50.7\,\text{kcal}$$

This electrical energy is the *maximum* energy available from this system and it is called *free energy.*

If Zn and Cu^+ react by contact in a beaker or calorimeter, heat energy is released. The reaction is

$$\begin{aligned} &Zn(s) + Cu^{+2}(aq) \longrightarrow Zn^{+2}(aq) + Cu(s) \\ &\Delta H = -52.1\ \text{kcal/mole} \end{aligned} \qquad (16)$$

Notice that there is a difference between the electrical energy and the heat energy in the same system. In this case the difference is 1.4 kcal. Sometimes the free energy is greater than ΔH as in the above reaction, and sometimes it is less. How can this difference be explained?

In every chemical reaction there is a change in entropy. Since 1.4 kcal of energy have apparently disappeared in the above reaction, we assume that it was used to bring about more orderliness (or less randomness) in the products, Zn^{+2} and Cu. During the changes, $Zn \longrightarrow Zn^{+2}$ and $Cu^{+2} \longrightarrow Cu$, bonds are broken and reformed with a more orderly result. The total energy of reorganization is $T\Delta S$, where T is the absolute temperature and ΔS is the change in entropy. The change in free energy for the chemical reaction is represented by the symbol ΔG. It is the difference between the two energy factors, enthalpy (or ΔH) and organization energy (or $T\Delta S$). Hence, $\Delta G = \Delta H - T\Delta S$. Thus ΔG represents the energy that drives a reaction in its own particular direction and reaction (16) reflects the effect of changes in enthalpy and entropy upon ΔG.

THE PHASE RULE

Liquid water has only one set of chemical and physical properties and is, therefore, said to be *homogeneous.* A system with a uniform set of properties is called a one-phase system. A mixture of ice and water has two sets of properties and is said to be *heterogeneous.* It is called a two-phase system. Similarly, a system that includes water, ice, and water vapor is a three-phase system.

Phase changes are physical changes and appear in many chemical reactions. For example, in the decomposition of calcium carbonate by heat

$$CaCO_3(s) \rightleftharpoons CaO\,(s) + CO_2(g) \qquad (1)$$

there is one gas phase (CO_2) and there are two solid phases (CaO and $CaCO_3$).

In 1876 Professor Willard Gibbs (1839–1903) of Yale University discovered an important generalization that applies to heterogeneous systems in equilibrium. It is called the *phase rule*. The phase rule states that *a system will be in equilibrium when the number of degrees of freedom (F) equals the number of components (C) minus the number of phases (P) plus two*. This rule, expressed in a formula, is

$$F = C - P + 2$$

The phase rule is a way of classifying states of equilibrium and it applies to both physical and chemical changes.

The word *phase* describes a homogeneous substance with the same physical and chemical properties; it can be a solid, a liquid, or a gas. The number of *components* is the smallest number of constituents needed to determine the composition of each phase. For example, in the system of reaction (P-1) there are three chemical substances but only two constituents. That is, if the two components CaO and CO_2 are selected, the percentage by mass of $CaCO_3$ can be computed. Similarly, if $CaCO_3$ and CaO are chosen, the composition of the CO_2 phase can be found by difference between the constituents $CaCO_3$ and CaO. The number of *degrees of freedom* is the smallest number of variables, such as temperature, pressure, and concentration (or density), which must be specified in order to define a particular system.

Let us apply the phase rule to the equilibrium system

$$\text{liquid water} \rightleftharpoons \text{water vapor} \qquad (2)$$

Therefore, if $C = 1$ and $P = 2$,

$$\begin{aligned} F &= C - P + 2 \\ &= 1 - 2 + 2 \\ &= 1 \end{aligned}$$

That is, to define the state of equilibrium only one variable, such as temperature, needs to be fixed. Expressed another way, the pressure is determined by the temperature.

Consider the case where water, ice, and vapor are in equilibrium. That is,

$$\text{ice} \rightleftharpoons \text{water} \rightleftharpoons \text{vapor} \qquad (3)$$

Here, $C = 1$, $P = 3$, and

$$\begin{aligned} F &= C - P + 2 \\ F &= 1 - 3 + 2 \\ &= 0 \end{aligned}$$

None of the variables can be changed without causing one phase in the system to disappear altogether. In Table P-1 the values of C, P, and F are given for four familiar examples of equilibrium.

Table P-1 Four phase systems of water in equilibrium

Reaction	C	P	F
$H_2O(l) \rightleftharpoons H_2O(g)$	1	2	1
$H_2O(l) \rightleftharpoons H_2O(s)$	1	2	1
$H_2O(s) \rightleftharpoons H_2O(g)$	1	2	1
$H_2O(l) \rightleftharpoons H_2O(s) \rightleftharpoons H_2O(g)$	1	3	0

A phase diagram of the water—ice—vapor system is given here (Fig. P-1) in which pressure is plotted along the ordinate and temperature along the abscissa.

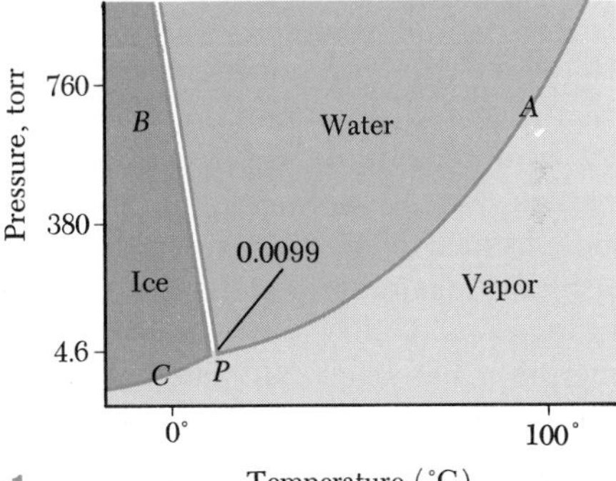

Fig. P-1

If warm water is slowly cooled, its vapor pressure falls as shown in curve A. Ultimately, point P is reached when both temperature and vapor pressure remain constant even though the liquid is still being cooled. However, at this point ice begins to separate and continues to do so until all the water is frozen. Curve B shows the effect of pressure on the melting point of ice. When all the water has frozen, and the cooling continues, both temperature and vapor pressure begin to fall again, as shown by curve C. In other words, curve C is the vapor pressure curve for ice.

Thus the three curves (A, B, and C) indicate the conditions of equilibrium of each of the two-phase systems: water—vapor, water—ice, ice—vapor. The three curves meet at a point P called the *triple point*. At the triple point all three phases are in equilibrium. Therefore, all three phases can be in equilibrium at only one particular temperature and pressure. Thus there are zero degrees of freedom and if either the temperature or pressure is changed (no matter how small the change), either the ice phase or the water phase will disappear and a two-phase system (water—vapor or ice—vapor) will result.

CAN THE PERIODIC TABLE BE EXTENDED?

What determines an element's position in the periodic table? The answer, as discussed in Chapter 6, is the electron configuration of the element. Since the electron configuration of the recently-made element 104 is like that of hafnium, element 104 is placed under hafnium (Z = 72). Similarly, the electron configuration of element 105 places this element under tantalum (Z = 73). Is there something significant about the positions of elements 104 and 105? Is something important suggested?

A number of scientists, such as Dr. Glenn Seaborg, have calculated that the periodic table might be extended to element 168. These new elements would have the positions shown in the sample of the periodic table. Elements 104 through 118 would complete Period 7. Elements 119-121, 154-168 would represent Period 8. Like element 118, element 168 would show an inert gas configuration. Element 122 would begin a "super-actinide" series of elements, which would show very closely related chemical and physical properties, since these elements fill "inner orbitals" as do those elements of the actinide and lanthanide series. Unlike the actinide series, which has 14 elements, it has been calculated that the super-actinide series would contain 32 elements. Element 153 would be the last member of this row.

However, might any of these elements be stable? Present machines are being modified and new ones are being built to make some of these new elements. Basing their ideas on empirical evidence, calculation, and theories about the structure of the nucleus proposed about 20 years ago, scientists believe that elements 110–114 may show a half-life on the order of 10^8 years. The magnitude of such a half-life is similar to that of U-235. Element 110 would be placed in the family of platinum and element 114 would be placed in the family of lead. Scientists using Mendeleev's terminology describe element 110 as eka-platinum and element 114 as eka-lead.

Since a half-life of 10^8 years has been proposed for these elements, scientists have attempted to discover the presence of these elements in nature, but without success. It is presumed that eka-platinum and eka-lead exist only in trace amounts. However, American scientists at the Lawrence Radiation Laboratory (Berkeley, California) and Russian scientists (Dubna) are building very large devices which are capable of accelerating heavy ions at extremely high speeds. Therefore, bombarding the nucleus of U-238 with another nucleus of U-238 might yield element 114.

$$^{238}_{92}\text{U} + ^{238}_{92}\text{U} \longrightarrow {}^{298}114 + ^{170}_{70}\text{Yb} + 8n^{1}_{0}$$

Another proposed synthesis of super-heavy element 114 is

$$^{238}_{92}\text{U} + ^{136}_{54}\text{Xe} \longrightarrow {}^{298}114 + ^{72}_{32}\text{Ge} + 4n^{1}_{0}$$

The production of these super-heavy elements will tell us more about the nature of the nucleus, confirming or denying calculations and hypotheses made about it.

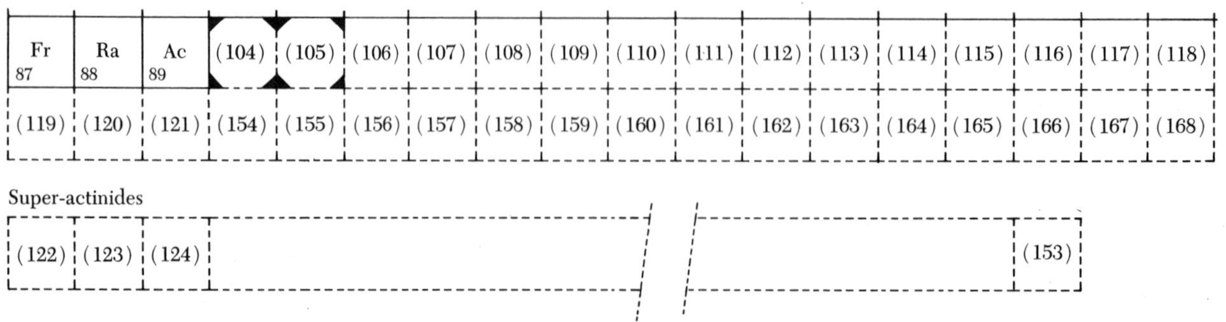

APPENDIX

TABLES

Table 1 The metric system

Length		
10 millimeters (mm)	=	1 centimeter
10 centimeters (cm)	=	1 decimeter
10 decimeters (dm)	=	1 meter
1000 meters (m)	=	1 kilometer (km)
Mass		
10 milligrams (mg)	=	1 centigram
10 centigrams (cg)	=	1 decigram
10 decigrams (dg)	=	1 gram
1000 grams (g)	=	1 kilogram (kg)
Fluid Volume		
1 liter (1)	=	1000 milliliters (m1)

Table 2 English-metric equivalents

1 centimeter (cm)	=	0.394 inch
1 meter (m)	=	39.37 inches
1 kilometer (km)	=	0.621 mile
1 kilogram (kg)	=	2.20 pounds (mass)
1 liter (1)	=	1.06 quarts
1 inch (in.)	=	2.54 centimeters
1 foot (ft)	=	30.5 centimeters
1 mile (mi)	=	1.61 kilometers
1 pound (lb) (mass)	=	454 grams
1 quart (qt)	=	943 milliliters

Table 3 Atomic mass values

Name of element	*Symbol*	*Atomic mass*
Actinium	Ac	(227)
Aluminum	Al	26.9815
Americium	Am	(243)
Antimony	Sb	121.75
Argon	Ar	39.948
Arsenic	As	74.9216
Astatine	At	(210)
Barium	Ba	137.34
Berkelium	Bk	(247)
Beryllium	Be	9.0122
Bismuth	Bi	208.980
Boron	B	10.811
Bromine	Br	79.904
Cadmium	Cd	112.40
Calcium	Ca	40.08
Californium	Cf	(254)
Carbon	C	12.01115
Cerium	Ce	140.12
Cesium	Cs	132.905
Chlorine	Cl	35.453
Chromium	Cr	51.996
Cobalt	Co	58.9332
Copper	Cu	63.546
Curium	Cm	(247)
Dysprosium	Dy	162.50
Einsteinium	Es	(254)
Erbium	Er	167.26
Europium	Eu	151.96
Fermium	Fm	(257)
Fluorine	F	18.9984
Francium	Fr	(223)
Gadolinium	Gd	157.25
Gallium	Ga	69.72
Germanium	Ge	72.59
Gold	Au	196.967
Hafnium	Hf	178.49
Helium	He	4.0026
Holmium	Ho	164.930
Hydrogen	H	1.00797
Indium	In	114.82
Iodine	I	126.9044
Iridium	Ir	192.2
Iron	Fe	55.847
Krypton	Kr	83.80
Kurchatovium°	Ku	
Lanthanum	La	138.91
Lawrencium	Lr	(257)
Lead	Pb	207.19
Lithium	Li	6.939
Lutetium	Lu	174.97
Magnesium	Mg	24.312
Manganese	Mn	54.9380
Mendelevium	Md	(256)
Mercury	Hg	200.59
Molybdenum	Mo	95.94
Neodymium	Nd	144.24
Neon	Ne	20.183
Neptunium	Np	(237)
Nickel	Ni	58.71
Niobium	Nb	92.906
Nitrogen	N	14.0067
Nobelium	No	(254)
Osmium	Os	190.2
Oxygen	O	15.9994
Palladium	Pd	106.4[1]
Phosphorus	P	30.9738
Platinum	Pt	195.09
Plutonium	Pu	(244)
Polonium	Po	(209)
Potassium	K	39.102
Praseodymium	Pr	140.907
Promethium	Pm	(145)
Protactinium	Pa	(231)
Radium	Ra	(226)
Radon	Rn	(222)
Rhenium	Re	186.2
Rhodium	Rh	102.905
Rubidium	Rb	85.47
Ruthenium	Ru	101.07
Samarium	Sm	150.35
Scandium	Sc	44.956
Selenium	Se	78.96
Silicon	Si	28.086
Silver	Ag	107.868
Sodium	Na	22.9898
Strontium	Sr	87.62
Sulfur	S	32.064
Tantalum	Ta	180.948
Technetium	Tc	(97)
Tellurium	Te	127.60
Terbium	Tb	158.924
Thallium	Tl	204.37
Thorium	Th	232.038
Thulium	Tm	168.934
Tin	Sn	118.69
Titanium	Ti	47.90
Tungsten	W	183.85
Uranium	U	238.03
Vanadium	V	50.942
Xenon	Xe	131.30
Ytterbium	Yb	173.04
Yttrium	Y	88.905
Zinc	Zn	65.37
Zirconium	Zr	91.22

All known elements are included in the list. The value in parentheses in the atomic mass column is, in each case, the mass of the most stable isotope, based on 0 = 16.000. All other atomic masses are based on C = 12.000.

°This name is not accepted in the U.S., where the name proposed is rutherfordium.

Table 4 The natural isotopes of elements 1-94

Z	Symbol	Mass number (A) of isotopes, amu
1	H	1, 2
2	He	4, 3
3	Li	7, 6
4	Be	9
5	B	11, 10
6	C	12, 13
7	N	14, 15
8	O	16, 18, 17
9	F	19
10	Ne	20, 22, 21
11	Na	23
12	Mg	24, 25, 26
13	Al	27
14	Si	28, 29, 30
15	P	31
16	S	32, 34, 33, 36
17	Cl	35, 37
18	Ar	40, 36, 38
19	K	39, 41, 40
20	Ca	40, 44, 42, 48, 43 46,
26	Fe	56, 54, 57, 58
27	Co	59
28	Ni	58, 60, 62, 61, 64
29	Cu	63, 65
30	Zn	64, 66, 68, 67, 70
35	Br	79, 81
36	Kr	84, 86, 82, 83, 80, 78
37	Rb	85, 87
38	Sr	88, 86, 87, 84
47	Ag	107, 109
53	I	127
54	Xe	132, 129, 131, 134, 136, 130, 128, 124, 126
55	Cs	133
56	Ba	138, 137, 136, 135, 134, 130, 132
79	Au	197
80	Hg	202, 200, 199, 201, 198, 204, 196
82	Pb	208, 206, 207, 204, 210, 211, 212, 214
85	At	218, 215
86	Rn	222, 220, 219
87	Fr	223
88	Ra	223, 224, 226, 228
92	U	238, 235, 234
94	Pu	239

(The isotopes of each element are listed in order of abundance.)

Table 5 Properties of common elements

Element	*Specific gravity*		*Melting point, °C*	Boiling point, °C	*Common oxidation numbers*
	(*Water std.*)	(*Air std.*)			
Aluminum	2.70		660.2	2467	+3
Antimony	6.69		630.5	1380	+3, +5
Argon		1.380	−189.2	−185.7	0
Arsenic	5.73		(sublimes)	(sublimes)	+3, +5
Barium	3.5		725	1140	+2
Beryllium	1.848		1278	2970	+2
Bismuth	9.75		271.3	1560	+3
Boron	2.34		2300	2550 (sublimes)	+3
Bromine	3.12		−7.2	58.8	−1, +5
Calcium	1.55		842	1487	+2
Carbon	1.7–3.5		(sublimes above 3500°C)	4827	+2, +4
Chlorine		2.486	−101.0	−34.6	−1, +5, +7
Chromium	7.18		1890	2482	+2, +3, +6
Cobalt	8.9		1495	2900	+2, +3
Copper	8.96		1083.0	2595	+1, +2
Fluorine		1.312	−219.6	−188.1	−1
Gold	19.32		1063.0	2966	+1, +3
Helium		0.1380	−272.2 (26 atm)	−268.6	0
Hydrogen		0.0695	−259.1	−252.5	−1, +1
Iodine	4.93		113.5	184.4	−1, +5
Iron	7.87		1535	3000	+2, +3
Lead	11.35		327.5	1744	+2, +4
Lithium	0.534		179	1317	+1
Magnesium	1.74		651	1107	+2
Manganese	7.3		1244	2097	+2, +4, +7
Mercury	13.55		−38.9	356.6	+1, +2
Neon		0.6960	−248.67	−245.92	0
Nickel	8.90		1453	2732	+2
Nitrogen		0.968	−209.9	−195.8	−3, +3, +5
Oxygen		1.105	−218.4	−183.0	−2
Phosphorus	1.8–2.7		44.1	280	+3, +5
Platinum	21.45		1769	3800	+2, +4
Potassium	0.86		63.6	774	+1
Radium	5(?)		700	<1737	+2
Silicon	2.33		1410	2355	+4
Silver	10.50		960.8	2212	+1
Sodium	0.97		97.8	892	+1
Strontium	2.54		769	1384	+2
Sulfur	2.0		114.5	444.6	−2, +4, +6
Tin	7.31		231.9	2270	+2, +4
Titanium	4.54		1675	3260	+3, +4
Tungsten	19.3		3410	5927	+6
Uranium	19.05		1132.3	3818	+4, +6
Zinc	7.13		419.4	907	+2

Table 6 Common complex ions

Name	*Formula*
Acetate	CH_3COO^-
Ammonium	NH_4^+
Carbonate	CO_3^{-2}
Bicarbonate	HCO_3^-
Chlorate	ClO_3^-
Chlorite	ClO_2^-
Chromate	CrO_4^{-2}
Dichromate	$Cr_2O_7^{-2}$
Hydroxide	OH^-
Hypochlorite	ClO^-
Nitrate	NO_3^-
Nitrite	NO_2^-
Perchlorate	ClO_4^-
Permanganate	MnO_4^-
Phosphate	PO_4^{-3}
Monohydrogen phosphate	HPO_4^{-2}
Dihydrogen phosphate	$H_2PO_4^-$
Sulfate	SO_4^{-2}
Bisulfate	HSO_4^-
Bisulfide	HS^-
Sulfite	SO_3^{-2}
Bisulfite	HSO_3^-

Table 7 Electrochemical equivalents of metals (grams deposited by 1 coulomb)

Aluminum	0.00009
Copper	0.00033
Gold	0.00068
Hydrogen	0.00001
Iron	0.00029
Lead	0.00107
Nickel	0.00030
Oxygen	0.00008
Platinum	0.00051
Silver	0.00112
Zinc	0.00034

Table 8 Dissociation of acids in water at room temperature

Acid	*Reaction in water*	K_A
Perchloric acid	$HClO_4 \rightleftharpoons H^+ + ClO_4^-$	>1
Hydriodic acid	$HI \rightleftharpoons H^+ + I^-$	>1
Hydrobromic acid	$HBr \rightleftharpoons H^+ + Br^-$	>1
Hydrochloric acid	$HCl \rightleftharpoons H^+ + Cl^-$	>1
Nitric acid	$HNO_3 \rightleftharpoons H^+ + NO_3^-$	>1
Sulfuric acid	$H_2SO_4 \rightleftharpoons H^+ + HSO_4^-$	>1
Sulfurous acid	$H_2SO_3 \rightleftharpoons H^+ + HSO_3^-$	1.7×10^{-2}
Hydrogen sulfate ion	$HSO_4^- \rightleftharpoons H^+ + SO_4^{-2}$	1.3×10^{-2}
Phosphoric acid	$H_3PO_4 \rightleftharpoons H^+ + H_2PO_4^-$	7.1×10^{-3}
Hydrofluoric acid	$HF \rightleftharpoons H^+ + F^-$	6.7×10^{-4}
Acetic acid	$CH_3COOH \rightleftharpoons H^+ + CH_3COO^-$	1.8×10^{-5}
Carbonic acid	$H_2CO_3 \rightleftharpoons H^+ + HCO_3^-$	4.4×10^{-7}
Hydrosulfuric acid	$H_2S \rightleftharpoons H^+ + HS^-$	1.0×10^{-7}
Dihydrogen phosphate ion	$H_2PO_4^- \rightleftharpoons H^+ + HPO_4^{-2}$	6.3×10^{-8}
Hydrogen sulfite ion	$HSO_3^- \rightleftharpoons H^+ + SO_3^{-2}$	6.2×10^{-8}
Hydrogen carbonate ion	$HCO_3^- \rightleftharpoons H^+ + CO_3^{-2}$	4.7×10^{-11}
Hydrogen peroxide	$H_2O_2 \rightleftharpoons H^+ + HO_2^-$	2.4×10^{-12}
Monohydrogen phosphate ion	$HPO_4^{-2} \rightleftharpoons H^+ + PO_4^{-3}$	4.4×10^{-13}
Hydrogen sulfide ion	$HS^- \rightleftharpoons H^+ + S^{-2}$	1.2×10^{-15}

The equilibrium expression for the dissociation of an acid is $HB(aq) \rightleftharpoons H^+(aq) + B^-(aq)$

All particles in water solution are hydrated (aquated) so that the (aq) notation may be assumed. The ionization constant (K_A) expression can therefore be written $K_A = \frac{[H^+][B^-]}{[HB]}$

Table 9 Table of solubilities (s: soluble in water; sl: slightly soluble in water; sa: insoluble in water, soluble in acids;

	Acetate $C_2H_3O_2^{-1}$	*Bromide,* Br^{-1}	*Carbonate,* CO_3^{-2}	*Chlorate,* ClO_3^{-1}	*Chloride,* Cl^{-1}	*Chromate,* CrO_4^{-2}	*Hydroxide,* OH^{-1}	*Iodide* I^{-1}	*Nitrate* NO_3^-	*Oxide* O^{-2}	*Phosphate* PO_4^{-3}
Aluminum	s	s	—	s	s	—	sa	s	s	sa	sa
Ammonium	s	s	s	s	s	s	s	s	s	—	s
Barium	s	s	sa	s	s	sa	s	s	s	s	sa
Calcium	s	s	sa	s	s	sa	sl	s	s	sl	sa
Copper (II)	s	s	sa	s	s	sa	sa	s	s	sa	sa
Iron (I)	s	s	sa	—	s	—	sa	s	s	sa	sa
Iron (II)	sa	s	—	—	s	—	sa	s	s	sa	sa
Lead	s	sl	sa	s	sl	sa	sa	sl	s	sa	sa
Magnesium	s	s	sa	s	s	s	sa	s	s	sa	sa
Mercury (I)	sa	ia	sa	s	ia	sl	—	ia	s	—	—
Mercury (II)	s	s	sa	s	s	sl	—	sl	s	sa	sa
Potassium	s	s	s	s	s	s	s	s	s	s	s
Silver	sl	ia	sa	s	ia	sa	—	ia	s	sa	sa
Sodium	s	s	s	s	s	s	s	s	s	s	s
Zinc	s	s	sa	s	s	sa	sa	s	s	sa	sa

ia: insoluble in water and acids)

Sulfate SO_4^{-2}	Sulfide S^{-2}	Sulfite SO_3^{-2}
s	—	—
s	s	s
ia	—	sa
sl	—	sa
s	ia	—
s	sa	sa
s	—	—
ia	ia	sa
s	—	sl
sa	sa	—
sa	ia	—
s	s	s
sa	ia	sa
s	s	s
s	sa	sa

Table 10 Approximate solubility product values at room temperature

Compound	K_{sp}
Aluminum hydroxide	10^{-15}
Barium carbonate	10^{-8}
Barium chromate	10^{-10}
Barium fluoride	10^{-6}
Barium hydroxide	10^{-2}
Barium sulfate	10^{-10}
Barium sulfite	10^{-7}
Cadmium sulfide	10^{-29}
Calcium carbonate	10^{-8}
Calcium chromate	10^{-2}
Calcium fluoride	10^{-11}
Calcium hydroxide	10^{-4}
Calcium sulfate	10^{-4}
Calcium sulfite	10^{-8}
Copper (II) sulfide	10^{-42}
Iron (I) sulfide	10^{-19}
Lead bromide	10^{-5}
Lead carbonate	10^{-14}
Lead chloride	10^{-4}
Lead chromate	10^{-14}
Lead fluoride	10^{-8}
Lead hydroxide	10^{-10}
Lead iodide	10^{-8}
Lead sulfate	10^{-8}
Lead sulfide	10^{-28}
Magnesium carbonate	10^{-5}
Magnesium hydroxide	10^{-11}
Magnesium sulfite	10^{-3}
Mercury (I) bromide	10^{-21}
Mercury (I) chloride	10^{-18}
Mercury (I) iodide	10^{-28}
Mercury (I) sulfide	10^{-47}
Silver bromide	10^{-13}
Silver chloride	10^{-10}
Silver chromate	10^{-12}
Silver iodide	10^{-16}
Silver sulfide	10^{-49}
Zinc sulfide	10^{-23}

Table 11 Standard oxidation potentials at 25°C

Half-reaction		E^0*(volts)*
Li(s)	$\longrightarrow Li^+ + e^-$	+3.05
K(s)	$\longrightarrow K^+ + e^-$	2.93
Rb(s)	$\longrightarrow Rb^+ + e^-$	2.93
Cs(s)	$\longrightarrow Cs^+ + e^-$	2.92
Ba(s)	$\longrightarrow Ba^{+2} + 2e^-$	2.90
Sr(s)	$\longrightarrow Sr^{+2} + 2e^-$	2.89
Ca(s)	$\longrightarrow Ca^{+2} + 2e^-$	2.87
Na(s)	$\longrightarrow Na^+ + e^-$	2.71
Mg(s)	$\longrightarrow Mg^{+2} + 2e^-$	2.37
Al(s)	$\longrightarrow Al^{+3} + 3e^-$	1.66
Mn(s)	$\longrightarrow Mn^{+2} + 2e^-$	1.18
Zn(s)	$\longrightarrow Zn^{+2} + 2e^-$	0.76
Fe(s)	$\longrightarrow Fe^{+2} + 2e^-$	0.44
Cd(s)	$\longrightarrow Cd^{+2} + 2e^-$	0.40
Co(s)	$\longrightarrow Co^{+2} + 2e^-$	0.28
Ni(s)	$\longrightarrow Ni^{+2} + 2e^-$	0.25
Sn(s)	$\longrightarrow Sn^{+2} + 2e^-$	0.14
Pb(s)	$\longrightarrow Pb^{+2} + 2e^-$	0.13
H_2(g), 1 atm	$\longrightarrow 2H^+(aq) + 2e^-$	0.00
Sn^{+2}	$\longrightarrow Sn^{+4} + 2e^-$	−0.15
Cu^+	$\longrightarrow Cu^{+2} + e^-$	0.15
Cu(s)	$\longrightarrow Cu^{+2} + 2e^-$	0.34
$2I^-$	$\longrightarrow I_2(s) + 2e^-$	0.54
Fe^{+2}	$\longrightarrow Fe^{+3} + e^-$	0.77
2Hg(1)	$\longrightarrow Hg^{+2} + 2e^-$	0.79
Ag(s)	$\longrightarrow Ag^{+2} + e^-$	0.80
$2Br^-$	$\longrightarrow Br_2(l) + 2e^-$	1.09
$2Cl^-$	$\longrightarrow Cl_2(g) + 2e^-$	1.36
$Pb^{+2} + 2H_2O$	$\longrightarrow PbO_2(s) + 4H^+(aq) + 2e^-$	1.46
Au(s)	$\longrightarrow Au^{+3} + 3e^-$	1.50
$2F^-$	$\longrightarrow F_2 + 2e^-$	2.87

Table 12 Vapor pressure values for water

Temperature, °C	*Pressure,* *torr*	*Temperature,* °C	*Pressure,* *torr*
−10	2.2	24	22.4
0	4.6	25	23.8
5	6.5	26	25.2
10	9.2	27	26.7
11	9.8	28	28.4
12	10.5	29	30.0
13	11.2	30	31.8
14	12.0	40	55.3
15	12.8	50	92.5
16	13.6	60	149.4
17	14.5	70	233.7
18	15.5	80	355.1
19	16.5	90	525.8
20	17.5	100	760.0
21	18.7	110	1074.6
22	19.8	120	1489.1
23	21.1		

GLOSSARY

Absolute scale. A temperature scale with $-273°C$ as zero.

Absolute zero. The temperature at which the motions of gas molecules theoretically would cease.

Acid. A substance whose water solution has a hydrogen-ion concentration greater than 10^{-7} mole per liter; a donor of protons.

Acid anhydride. The oxide component of an acid which remains when water is removed, or which combines with water to form the acid.

Acid oxide. An oxide that dissolves in water to form an acid. The oxide of a nonmetal.

Acid salt. The substance formed if only part of the hydrogen of an acid is replaced by a metal.

Actinide series. A series of heavy, rare earth, radioactive metals in the seventh period following radium in the periodic table.

Active metal. A metal which yields electrons to the ions of a less active metal.

Addition. The characteristic reaction of unsaturated compounds.

Adsorption. A surface effect of a solid by which it adsorbs gases.

Alcohols. Organic compounds which contain OH (hydroxyl) groups.

Aldehyde. A compound which contains the group $\begin{matrix}-C=O \\ | \\ H\end{matrix}$. Formed by the oxidation of a primary alcohol.

Aliphatic compounds. The alkanes and their derivatives.

Alkali. A strong base.

Alkane. A saturated hydrocarbon with a straight or branched chain in which the carbon atoms are joined by single covalent bonds. General formula: C_nH_{2n+2}.

Alkene. A hydrocarbon with a straight or branched chain in which [some of] the carbon atoms are joined by double bonds.

Alkyl group. A group formed when an alkane is deprived of an atom of hydrogen; often written *R*—.

Alkyne. A hydrocarbon with a straight or branched chain, in which carbon atoms are joined by a triple covalent bond.

Allotropes. Different forms of the same element.

Allotropy. The ability of an element to exist in more than one form.

Alloy. A solid solution made up of two or more metals.

Alpha (α) particle. The nucleus of a helium atom; a helium ion.

Amine. Any of a variety of compounds derived from ammonia (NH_3) where one or all of the hydrogen atoms have been replaced by an alkyl group.

Ampere (A). Amount of current introduced into a silver nitrate solution which will deposit 0.001118 g of silver per second; the practical unit of current strength.

Ammeter. A device for measuring an electric current.

Amphiprotic. Able to react chemically as either a base or an acid.

Amphoteric. Another term with the same meaning as *amphiprotic.*

Analysis. The determination of the composition of a substance by separation and examination of its components.

Angstrom. One angstrom (Å) equals 10^{-8} centimeter.

Anhydrous salt. A salt without water of hydration.

Anions. Negatively charged ions that flow toward the anode.

Anode. An electrode at which oxidation takes place.

Aromatic compounds. Benzene and its derivatives.

Atmospheric pressure (standard). Equivalent to a 760-torr column of mercury.

Atom. A positively charged nucleus with a balancing array of electrons outside the nucleus.

Atomic mass unit. A unit of atomic mass which is one-twelfth of the mass of a carbon atom of atomic weight 12.000.

Atomic number. The number of protons in the nucleus of an atom.

Atomic mass. The mass of an atom of an element compared with the mass of an atom of the isotope of carbon taken as 12.000.

Avogadro's number. The number of atoms of carbon-12 in 12 g of the substance; equal to 6.02252×10^{23}.

Avogadro's law. Equal volumes of different gases, under the same conditions of temperature and pressure contain the same number of molecules.

Base. A substance whose water solution has a hydrogen-ion concentration less than 10^{-7} mole per liter; an acceptor of protons.

Basic oxide. An oxide that dissolves in water to form a base. A metallic oxide.

Basic oxygen process. A method of producing steel which employs a basic furnace lining and oxygen to reduce the impurities.

Bauxite. An aluminum ore.

Beta (β) particle. An electron.

Binary acid. An acid made up of a hydrogen ion and an ion of another element.

Binary compound. A compound made up of atoms of two elements.

Binding energy. The energy needed to split a nucleus into its constituent nucleons.

Blast furnace. A furnace that converts iron ore into iron.

Blister copper. A highly pure crude copper converted in a reverberatory furnace.

Boiling point. The temperature at which the vapor pressure of a liquid equals the pressure of the atmosphere.

Bond angle. Angle between the bonds in a covalent molecule.

Boyle's law. The volume of a given mass of gas, at constant temperature, varies inversely as its pressure.

Brownian movement. The random motion of microscopic particles suspended in a fluid medium. It results from collisions with the molecules of the fluid.

Calorie. The amount of heat needed to raise the temperature of one gram of water through one Celsius degree.

Carbohydrate. A substance with the general formula $C_x(H_2O)_y$.

Catalyst. A substance that changes the speed of a chemical reaction.

Cathode. An electrode at which reduction takes place.

Cathode rays. A stream of electrons emitted from the cathode of a discharge tube.

Cations. Positively charged ions that flow toward the cathode.

Celsius (or centigrade) scale. A temperature scale with melting ice as 0° and boiling water as 100°.

Chain reaction. A self-sustaining reaction. Usually refers to the decomposition of a mass of U-235 by a neutron.

Charge cloud. The region occupied by an electron.

Charles' law. The volume of a confined gas, at constant pressure, varies as its absolute temperature; the pressure of a confined gas, at constant volume, varies as its absolute temperature.

Combustion. A rapid chemical process that produces measurable heat and light.

Common-ion effect. A change in equilibrium occurring when a given volume of one substance is added to a given solution of another substance with which it has an ion in common.

Complex ion. A charged particle composed of a group of atoms.

Compound. A distinct substance composed of two or more simpler ingredients and capable of being chemically decomposed.

Concentrated. A term describing a solution with a proportionally high concentration of solute.

Constant. An amount that is invariable as to value.

Constant, equilibrium. The value of the ratio in a reversible reaction of the concentration of one product with its reactant; a numerical value usually expressed as K.

Constant, ionization. A constant value that causes ionization in a reversible reaction.

Contact process. The method of manufacturing sulfuric acid.

Continuous spectrum. The complete spectrum from red to violet.

Cosmic rays. Streams of ultrafast atomic nuclei from outer space which bombard atoms in the earth's atmosphere, producing nuclear particles.

Coulomb (C). A unit of electrical quantity equal to 6.29×10^{18} electrons.

Covalent bond. A chemical bond formed by the sharing of electrons between two atoms, or the bond produced by the overlapping of electron clouds.

Cracking. The splitting of molecules by a combination of high temperature and high pressure; also mediated by catalysts.

Critical potential. The applied potential required to excite an atom.

Critical volume. The volume occupied by one mole of a gas at critical temperature and pressure.

Crystal. A body formed by plane surfaces intersecting each other at regular angles, forming a geometric pattern.

Crystal, ionic. A crystal composed of geometrically arranged ions.

Crystal lattice. The point pattern in a crystal that determines the arrangement of its particles.

Crystal, molecular. A crystal composed of geometrically arranged molecules.

Cycle. A single vibration, or one of a number of periodic movements back and forth.

Cyclotron. A device for accelerating charged particles used in bombarding nuclei.

Density. The mass of unit volume of a substance.

Destructive distillation. Decomposition of a complex substance by heat out of contact with air and the condensation of at least part of the gaseous products.

Deuterium. An isotope of hydrogen with one neutron and one proton in the nucleus.

Dibasic acid. An acid with two replaceable hydrogen atoms per molecule.

Dilute. A term describing a solution with a relatively lower amount of solute.

Dipole moment. The product of one of the charges in a molecule and the distance between the charges.

Diprotic. Term used for an acid which can donate two protons for each molecule.

Disaccharide. A sugar which upon hydrolysis yields two monosaccharide molecules.

Discharge tube. A glass tube which contains two electrodes and which can be evacuated and used to examine electrical discharges.

Distillation. The evaporation of a liquid followed by the condensation of its vapor.

Downs cell. An apparatus used for the electrolysis of sodium from fused sodium chloride.

Dynamic equilibrium. Equilibrium between particles in motion.

Einstein equation. $E = mc^2$, where E represents energy, m mass, and c the velocity of light.

Eka-. A term joined to the name of a known element designating another element assumed to stand beyond it in the same family of the Periodic Table and not yet discovered or very recently discovered.

Electrical field. A region of mechanical force which surrounds an electric charge or moving magnet.

Electrochemical cell. A device that permits an electrochemical reaction to produce electricity.

Electrochemical equivalent. The mass of a substance liberated at an electrode if 1 coulomb passes through the solution of an electrolyte.

Electrode. An electrically charged conductor immersed in a solution of an electrolyte.

Electrolysis. The decomposition of a compound by electricity. A discharge of ions by passing a current through an electrolyte.

Electrolyte. A substance whose water solution conducts a current.

Electrolytic cell. A cell containing two electrodes in a solution of an electrolyte, and operated by a direct current.

Electromagnetic spectrum. The complete spectrum of radiated energy.

Electromotive (emf) series. A list of metals and their half-cell electrode potentials, indicating the relative tendencies of metals to react chemically.

Electron. The unit negative charge of electricity.

Electron affinity. The energy released when an electron enters the outermost orbital of an atom.

Electron cloud. That spatial region surrounding a nucleus in which electrons are generally located; an orbital.

Electronegativity. A measure of the attraction of a nucleus of a particular atom for nearby electrons.

Electron-volt. The energy needed to move an electron through a potential difference of one volt.

Element. A distinct substance that resists decomposition by ordinary chemical methods.

End point. The point in a titration at which the indicator changes color.

Endothermic reaction. A reaction which absorbs energy.

Energy. The capacity to do work.

Energy, activation. That energy which causes collision between reactant molecules, causing a reshuffling of bonds and creation of new molecules.

Energy, binding. That energy released by particles forming a nucleus.

Energy, bond. The amount of energy needed to disrupt a chemical bond.

Energy, ionization. The amount of energy needed to attract a single electron from its atom.

Energy level. A region (shell) of energy surrounding the nucleus of an atom in which a specified number of electrons move.

Enthalpy. The amount of heat held by a system under constant pressure.

Entropy. A term describing the randomness and disorder of particles and hence energy in a given system, such as in the intermixing of two gases.

Equation mass. Equal to the product of the formula mass and the coefficient of the formula in an equation.

Equilibrium. A state in which two reactions absolutely balance each other as to time and rate.

Equivalent mass. That mass of an element which combines with (or replaces) one part by mass of hydrogen or eight parts by mass of oxygen.

Eudiometer. A tube for the measurement of gases.

Evaporation. The change from liquid to vapor.

Exothermic reaction. A reaction which releases energy.

Exponential notation. A method using a power (exponent) to indicate how many times the base number must be multiplied by itself to equal the number so symbolized.

Faraday (F). The quantity of electricity (96,500 C) required to liberate one gram equivalent weight of any element at an electrode.

Faraday's first law of electrolysis. The mass of a substance liberated at (or deposited on) an electrode is proportional to the quantity of electricity which passes through a solution of the electrolyte.

Faraday's second law of electrolysis. The masses of different elements liberated at the electrodes by the same quantity of electricity are proportional to the equivalent weights of the elements.

Fat. An inorganic compound (ester) of various long-chain fatty acids and glycerol; insoluble in water.

Fermentation. The slow decomposition of organic compounds due to the action of enzymes.

Fission. The splitting of a nucleus into two approximately equal parts.

Fixation of nitrogen. A reaction in which free nitrogen is made to combine with another element.

Flame test. A test in which the color of a flame applied to a compound identifies the elements that compose it.

Flotation. A method of concentrating ores which depends on differential wetting.

Formula. The representation of a molecule by chemical symbols.

Formula mass. The sum of the atomic masses in the formula of a substance.

Fractional distillation. The separation of two or more liquids with different boiling points.

Free-energy change. The amount of energy available in a reaction system; the difference between the change in heat content and energy loss.

Freezing. The physical reaction that occurs when a liquid is transformed to a solid.

Freezing-point constant, molal. A constant value representing the amount of depression of the freezing point in a 1-molal solution by a molecular solid.

Frequency. The number of waves that pass a given point per second.

Fusion (nuclear). The combining of the nuclei of light elements with the release of energy.

Gamma (γ) rays. Electromagnetic radiations (of higher frequency and shorter wave length than X rays) emitted in nuclear reactions.

Gas. A substance which retains neither shape nor volume.

Gas law equation. $\frac{P_1V_1}{T_1} = \frac{P_2V_2}{T_2}$

Gas pressure. The effect of the bombardment of a surface by gas molecules.

Gay-Lussac's law. The volumes of gases that combine with each other (measured under the same conditions of temperature and pressure) are in the ratio of small whole numbers.

Geiger counter. A device for counting α or β particles released during disintegration of a radioactive element.

Geometrical isomers. Isomers with identical structures but with different properties.

Gram-atom (or gram-atomic mass). The atomic mass of an element expressed in grams.

Gram-equivalent mass. The equivalent mass of substance expressed in grams.

Half-cell. A strip of metal in a solution of the metallic ion.

Half-life. The time required for the radioactivity of a radioactive element to drop to one-half of its original value.

Halides. Binary compounds of the halogens.

Halogenation. The introduction of halogen atoms by the reaction of a halogen with a compound.

Halogens. A family comprising the elements fluorine, chlorine, bromine, iodine, and astatine.

Heat exchanger. A device permitting transfer of heat from one liquid to another while preventing their actual mixture.

Heat of neutralization. The heat liberated when one gram-equivalent mass of an acid is added to one gram-equivalent mass of a base (equal to about 13,500 cal).

Heavy-ion linear accelerator (HILAC). A particle accelerator for the nuclear study of the synthesis of superheavy elements.

Heisenberg's uncertainty principle. If one variable is known (for example, the velocity of an electron), other variables (for example, the position of the electron) cannot be predicted with precision.

Hematite. An ore of iron.

Hertz (Hz). Unit of frequency equal to one cycle per second in a recurrent process.

Homologous series. A group of compounds with similar structures and which exhibit similar properties.

Hooker cell. Device with graphite anodes and wire-screen cathodes with asbestos diaphragms; used in the electrolysis of sodium chloride to produce sodium hydroxide and chlorine.

Hydrate. A crystalline salt with water of hydration as an essential part of its composition.

Hydrocarbons. Compounds of hydrogen and carbon.

Hydrogenation. The addition of hydrogen to a substance.

Hydrolysis. A reaction between a salt and water.

Hydronium ion. A hydrated hydrogen ion, H_3O^+.

Hygroscopic substance. A substance that absorbs water vapor from the air.

Indicator. A dye whose color changes as the *p*H of the solution changes.

Induced charge. A charge induced upon an uncharged body by a nearby charged body.

Infrared light. Light radiation of too long a wave length to affect the retina (that is, to be seen).

Ingot. A mold for casting metal, and the metal so cast.

Inversion of sugar. The hydrolysis of sucrose to give glucose and fructose.

Ion. An electrically charged particle.

Ionic bond. An electrostatic force between oppositely charged ions.

Ionization energy. The energy needed to detach completely an electron from an atom.

Ionization potential. The potential or voltage needed to dislodge an electron from its outer orbital.

Isomers. Two or more compounds having the same molecular formula, but with dissimilar structures.

Isotopes. Two or more forms of atoms of the same element having the same atomic number but different atomic masses.

Ketone. A compound which contains the group $>C{=}O$. Formed by the oxidation of a secondary alcohol.

Kinetic energy. Energy due to motion.

Kinetic theory. The theory which states that molecules are in a state of motion.

Lanthanide series. A group of rare earth elements, forming part of the sixth period beyond barium, in which filling of the 5*d* sublevel is interrupted by inner building in the 4*f* orbitals.

Latent heat of vaporization. The amount of heat needed to change one gram of liquid to vapor.

Law of Conservation of Energy. Energy can be neither created nor destroyed, under ordinary circumstances.

Law of Conservation of Mass. Matter cannot be created or destroyed, under ordinary circumstances.

Law of Constant Proportions. A given compound always contains the same elements in the same fixed proportion by weight.

Law of Mass-Energy. In any reaction the mass-energy of the reactants is the same as the mass-energy of the products.

Law of Simple Multiple Proportions. Of two elements combine to form more than one compound, there exists a simple ratio between the different masses of one of these elements which combine with a fixed mass of the other.

Le Châtelier's Principle. If a stress is applied to a system in equilibrium, a change takes place to relieve the stress.

Lime, slaked. The commercial name for calcium hydroxide, $Ca(OH)_2$.

Line spectrum. A series of bright lines characteristic of a particular gas.

Liquid. A substance which retains its volume but not its shape.

Liter. A metric unit of volume equivalent to 1.06 quarts.

Litmus. A coloring matter prepared from lichen plants and used as an acid-base indicator, having the property at *p*H 7 of color transition (acid, pink to base, blue).

Magnetic field. A region of magnetic force surrounding a magnet or a moving electric charge.

Mass. The quantity of matter possessed by a body, or a measure of its inertia.

Mass defect. The difference between the mass of a nucleus and the sum of the masses of the constituent nucleons.

Mass number. The number of nucleons in the nucleus of an atom.

Mass spectrograph. An instrument for determining the presence and relative abundance of isotopes of an element.

Matter. Something that occupies space and possesses mass.

Metallic bond. A lattice of positively charged cores bound by valence electrons which are free to move throughout the lattice.

Metalloid. An element commonly classed as a nonmetal but which has some of the properties typical of a metal; also, an alloy of a metal and nonmetal.

Metallurgy. The science of extracting metals from their ores.

Metric system. A decimal system of units; the centimeter-gram-second system, or the CGS system.

Molality. The concentration of a solution expressed in moles of solute per kilogram of solvent.

Molarity. The concentration of a solution expressed in moles of solute per liter of solution.

Molar volume (gram-molecular volume). The volume occupied by one mole of a gas at STP; 22.4 liters.

Mole. The molecular mass of a substance expressed in grams.

Molecule. A molecule of a gas or liquid is the smallest particle of that substance capable of independent motion.

Molecular mass. The mass of a molecule of a substance compared with the weight of a carbon atom taken as 12.000.

Monoprotic. Term used for an acid which can lend one proton for each molecule.

Neutralization. A reaction between the hydrogen ion of an acid with the hydroxide ion of a base to form water.

Neutron. A neutral elementary particle, a constituent of all nuclei except the nucleus of ordinary hydrogen.

Neutron capture. The capture of a neutron by a nucleus.

Nitrogen cycle. A cycle of transformations in nature in which atmospheric nitrogen is repeatedly fixed and released.

Nonmetal. Any of a class of electronegative elements that are poor conductors of both heat and electricity.

Normality. The concentration of a solution expressed in gram-equivalent weights of solute per liter of solution.

Normal salt. The substance formed if all the hydrogen of an acid is replaced by a metal.

Nuclear equation. A type of equation dealing with changes within the nucleus of the atom.

Nuclear forces. Strong, short-range forces between nucleons in a nucleus.

Nuclear reactor. A device for controlling the rate of a nuclear chain reaction.

Nucleon. A nuclear particle—proton or neutron.

Nucleus. The central positively charged part of an atom.

Nuclide. A species of atom typified by the number of neutrons and protons and the energy content of its nucleus.

Nuclide, parent. In a radioactive decay series, the most complex natural nuclide.

Open-hearth furnace. A furnace used to convert iron into steel.

Optical isomers. Isomers which differ only in their action on plane-polarized light.

Orbital. That volume of space about a nucleus that is statistically most likely to be occupied by an electron; electron cloud.

Ore. A mineral from which a metal can be profitable extracted.

Organic acids. Compounds which contain a carboxyl (—COOH) group.

Ostwald process. A method of manufacturing nitric acid.

Oxidation. A process involving a loss of electrons.

Oxidation number. The charge on the ion of a particular element.

Oxidation potential. (or electrode potential). The tendency of a metal to gain (or lose) electrons; measured in volts relative to hydrogen, to which a value of zero volt has been arbitrarily assigned.

Oxidation-reduction reaction. A reaction that involves an exchange of electrons.

Oxide. A compound of oxygen and another element.

Oxidizing agent. A substance that gains electrons and decreases its oxidation number.

Oxyacids. Acids whose molecules include covalent bonded oxygen.

Pauli's exclusion principle. Only two electrons may occupy the same orbital.

Periodic law. The properties of the elements are a periodic function of their atomic numbers.

Periodic table. An arrangement of the elements in order of their atomic numbers which reveals periodic properties of families of elements.

***p*H.** An index of the hydronium-ion concentration: the common logarithm of the reciprocal of the hydronium-hydronium-ion concentration.

Phases of matter. Those forms in which a substance can exist: solid, liquid, gas, or plasma.

Phenolphthalein. A yellowish-white crystalline compound used as an indicator, it turns from colorless (acidic) to magenta (basic) at *p*H 9.

Photoelectric effect. The ejection of electrons from a metal surface by means of light.

Photosynthesis. The formation of carbohydrates from carbon dioxide and water vapor, activated by the energy of light and a catalyst.

Photon. A quantum emitted or absorbed as light energy.

Plasma. An ionized gas with about equal numbers of positive ions and electrons; one of the phases of matter.

Polarimeter. A device for measuring the angle of rotation of polarized light.

Polar molecule (or dipole). A molecule which has different centers of positive and negative charge.

Polymer. A large molecule formed from small molecules.

Polymerization. The formation of a large molecule from small molecules.

Polysaccharide. A sugar which upon hydrolysis yields many monosaccharide molecules.

Positron. A particle of positive charge with the same mass and magnitude of charge as the electron.

Potential energy. The energy stored in a body because of its position or condition.

Precipitate. A substance, commonly a solid, separated from a solution or a suspension by chemical or physical means.

Precipitation. The production of a precipitate from a solution or suspension.

Pressure. Force per unit area.

Primary alcohol. An alcohol which contains the $—CH_2OH$ group.

Product. Any substance resulting from a chemical reaction.

Principal quantum numbers. The main energy levels of an electron of an atom.

Protein. Any of many natural, complex organic substances composed of amino acids and containing carbon, hydrogen, oxygen, nitrogen, and traces of other elements.

Proton. The unit positive charge of electricity, present in the nuclei of all atoms.

Quantum. A packet of energy emitted or absorbed by an atom.

Radioactive decay. A spontaneous nuclear breakdown in which particles are ejected and the atom is transmuted.

Radioactivity. The emission of alpha and beta particles and gamma rays from the nuclei of atoms.

Radio waves. Electromagnetic radiation of greater wavelength than infrared light.

Raoult's law. The depression of the freezing point of a solution varies directly as the molecular concentration of the solute.

Redox reaction. An oxidation-reduction process involving a transfer of electrons.

Reducing agent. A substance that loses electrons and increases its oxidation number.

Reduction. A process involving a gain of electrons.

Refraction. The change in the direction of light as it passes from one medium into another.

Replacement reaction. A process in which one substance is chemically displaced from a compound by another substance.

Resonance. A property of a molecule (or ion) whereby it can be assigned two or more structures which differ only as to bonding and the configuration of electrons.

Reversible reaction. A reaction that proceeds in both directions at the same time.

Saccharide. A simple sugar.

Salt. A substance that consists of the positive ion of a metal and the negative ion of an acid.

Saponification. The hydrolysis of an ester by a base.

Saturated hydrocarbon. A hydrocarbon in which each carbon-carbon linkage is a single pair of electrons.

Saturated solution. A solution in which dissolved particles and undissolved particles are in equilibrium with each other.

Secondary alcohol. An alcohol which contains the >CHOH group.

Significant figures. Reliable figures in a number.

Solid. A substance which retains both its shape and volume.

Solubility. The number of grams of substance per 100 g of water in a saturated solution of the substance at a given temperature.

Solubility product. The product of the concentrations of the dissolved ions of a slightly soluble substance in a saturated solution. For example for copper (II) sulfide is $[Cu^{+2}] \times [S^{-2}] = 8.4 \times 10^{-43}$.

Solute. The dissolved substance in a solution.

Solution. A homogeneous mixture of solute and solvent.

Solvay process. A method of manufacturing sodium bicarbonate and sodium carbonate.

Solvent. The part of a solution used for dissolving the solute.

Specific gravity. The ratio of the density of a substance to the density of water.

Specific heat. The number of calories needed to raise the temperature of one gram of a body through one celsius degree.

Speed of light. 186,000 miles second (or 3.0×10^{10} cm sec) in a vacuum; symbolized *c*.

Stable electron arrangement. A 2-electron structure or an 8-electron structure in the outer energy levels of an atom.

Standard solution. A solution of known concentration.

Stoichiometry. The mass relationship of reactants and products in a chemical equation.

Storage cell. A cell capable of operating either as a voltaic cell or as an electrolytic cell.

STP. An abbreviation meaning standard temperature (0°C) and pressure (760 torr).

Strong acid. An acid whose water solution contains a high proportion of hydrogen ions.

Strong base. A substance whose water solution contains a high proportion of hydroxide ions.

Strong electrolyte. A substance whose water solution contains a high ratio of ions to molecules.

Subscript. An inferior number adjoined to a chemical symbol for an element; written at the left it represents the atomic number ($_{88}Ra$), and at the right, the number of atoms in the molecule (H_2).

Substance. A quantity of matter of particular or definite and uniform chemical composition.

Substitution. Replacement of one kind of atom (or group) by another.

Superheavy transuranium elements. Non-natural elements assigned to the periodic table beyond uranium; they must be synthesized.

Supersaturated. Term used for a solution to which has been added an amount of solute beyond the usual saturation quantity.

Superscript. A superior number adjoined to a chemical symbol and representing the mass number if to the left (^{226}Ra) and valence if to the right (Cu^{+2}).

Synthesis. The joining of more fundamental substances into a higher or more complex type; commonly, making an artificial substance from several natural ones.

Temperature. A relative measure of heat as between two systems, the heat representing the kinetic energy of the molecules within a system.

Ternary acid. An acid made up of hydrogen ions and a complex ion containing two elements.

Ternary compound. A compound made up of atoms of three elements.

Tertiary alcohol. An alcohol which contains the ⋛COH group.

Theory. An explanation of a phenomenon of nature according to scientifically plausible general principles.

Thermonuclear reactions. Fusion reactions.

Titration. The addition of an acid (or base) to an equivalent quantity of base (or acid) in presence of an indicator.

Torr. A unit of barometric pressure approximately equal to one millimeter of mercury at 0°C. [Named for E. Torricelli (1608–1647).]

Transition elements. Elements formed by the addition of electrons to an inner orbital after the outer orbital has been filled.

Transmutation. The conversion of one element into another.

Transverse wave. A form of wave motion in which the direction of wave motion is at right angles to the wave front.

Ultraviolet light. Light radiation of too short a wavevelength to be visible.
Unit cell. In the crystal lattice, the simplest polyhedron that embodies all the characteristics of the whole structure.
Unsaturated hydrocarbon. A hydrocarbon in which a carbon–carbon bond consists of two (or three) shared pairs of electrons.

Valence. The number of atoms of hydrogen that combine with, or replace, one atom of the particular element.
van der Waals' forces. Weak attractive forces between neutral atoms and molecules; due to the number and arrangement of electrons in each.
Vapor pressure. The pressure exerted by a vapor when liquid and vapor are in equilibrium with each other.
Vib/sec. Abbreviation meaning vibrations per second (also vps).
Volt (V). The unit of electromotive force; the difference of potential that will produce a current of 1 A when applied against a resistance of 1 ohm.
Voltaic cell. A device that changes chemical energy to electrical energy.

Water of hydration. Water that combines chemically with salts as they crystallize from solution.
Wave equation. Speed = frequency × wavelength or $c = \nu \times \lambda$.
Wavelength. The distance between corresponding points of successive waves.
Weak acid. An acid whose water solution contains a low proportion of hydrogen ions.
Weak electrolyte. A substance whose water solution contains a low ratio of ions to molecules.
Whole-number rule. All atomic masses are close to whole numbers, and any deviations from whole numbers are due to isotopes.
Work. The product of a force and the distance through which the force acts.

X rays Electromagnetic radiatons of shorter wavelength than ultraviolet light.

INDEX

Periodic Table of the Elements

	I	II	Transition elements							
1	1 1.00797 H Hydrogen									
2	3 6.939 Li Lithium	4 9.0122 Be Beryllium								
3	11 22.9898 Na Sodium	12 24.312 Mg Magnesium								
4	19 39.102 K Potassium	20 40.08 Ca Calcium	21 44.956 Sc Scandium	22 47.90 Ti Titanium	23 50.942 V Vanadium	24 51.996 Cr Chromium	25 54.9380 Mn Manganese	26 55.847 Fe Iron	27 58.9332 Co Cobalt	28 58.71 Ni Nickel
5	37 85.47 Rb Rubidium	38 87.62 Sr Strontium	39 88.905 Y Yttrium	40 91.22 Zr Zirconium	41 92.906 Nb Niobium	42 95.94 Mo Molybdenum	43 (99) Tc Technetium	44 101.07 Ru Ruthenium	45 102.905 Rh Rhodium	46 106.4 Pd Palladium
6	55 132.905 Cs Cesium	56 137.34 Ba Barium	57-71 Series of lanthanide elements	72 178.49 Hf Hafnium	73 180.948 Ta Tantalum	74 183.85 W Tungsten	75 186.2 Re Rhenium	76 190.2 Os Osmium	77 192.2 Ir Iridium	78 195.09 Pt Platinum
7	87 (223) Fr Francium	88 (226) Ra Radium	89-103 Series of actinide elements	104 Kurchatovium (?)	105 Hahnium (?)					

Series of lanthanide elements	57 138.91 La Lanthanum	58 140.12 Ce Cerium	59 140.907 Pr Praseodymium	60 144.24 Nd Neodymium	61 (145) Pm Promethium	62 150.35 Sm Samarium	63 151.96 Eu Europium
Series of actinide elements	89 (227) Ac Actinium	90 232.038 Th Thorium	91 (231) Pa Protactinium	92 238.03 U Uranium	93 (237) Np Neptunium	94 (242) Pu Plutonium	95 (243) Am Americium